ENCYCLOPEDIA OF
Agricultural Science

Volume 4   S–W, Index

EDITORIAL ADVISORY BOARD

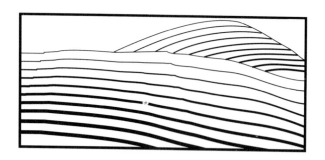

Perry Adkisson★
Department of Entomology, Texas A&M
University, College Station, Texas

Norman Borlaug★, ★★
CIMMYT, Lisboa, Mexico

Ricardo Bressani★
Division of Agricultural and Food Science,
Institute of Nutrition of Central America
and Panama, Guatemala City, Guatemala

Martin J. Bukovac★
Department of Horticulture, Michigan
State University, East Lansing, Michigan

Donald Duvick
Iowa State University, Johnston, Iowa

Donald M. Edwards
Institute of Agriculture and Natural
Resources, University of Nebraska,
Lincoln, Nebraska

Neal First★
Department of Animal Science, University
of Wisconsin—Madison, Madison,
Wisconsin

Richard Flavell
John Innes Centre, Colney, Norwich,
England

Wilford Gardner★
College of Natural Resources, University
of California, Berkeley, California

Ray A. Goldberg
Harvard University, Boston,
Massachusetts

Major M. Goodman★
Department of Crop Science, North
Carolina State University, Raleigh,
North Carolina

James Peacock
Division of Plant Industry, CSIRO,
Canberra, Australia

Gary C. Smith
Department of Animal Sciences, Colorado
State University, Fort Collins, Colorado

M.S. Swaminathan
Madras, India

Stan Tixier
Society for Range Management,
Eden, Utah

★ Member of United States National Academy of Sciences.
★★ Nobel Laureate.

ENCYCLOPEDIA OF

Agricultural Science

Volume 4   S–W, Index

Editor-in-Chief

Charles J. Arntzen

Institute of Biosciences and Technology
Texas A&M University
Houston, Texas

Associate Editor

Ellen M. Ritter

Department of Agricultural
Communications
Texas A&M University
College Station, Texas

86094

Academic Press

San Diego   New York   Boston   London   Sydney   Tokyo   Toronto

This book is printed on acid-free paper. ∞

Copyright © 1994 by ACADEMIC PRESS, INC.
All Rights Reserved.
No part of this publication may be reproduced or transmitted in any form or by any
means, electronic or mechanical, including photocopy, recording, or any information
storage and retrieval system, without permission in writing from the publisher.

Academic Press, Inc.
A Division of Harcourt Brace & Company
525 B Street, Suite 1900, San Diego, California 92101-4495

United Kingdom Edition published by
Academic Press Limited
24-28 Oval Road, London NW1 7DX

Library of Congress Cataloging-in-Publication Data

Encyclopedia of agricultural science / edited by Charles J. Arntzen,
    Ellen M. Ritter.
        p.   cm.
    Includes index.
     ISBN 0-12-226670-6 (set) -- ISBN 0-12-226671-4 (v. 1)
     ISBN 0-12-226672-2 (v. 2) -- ISBN 0-12-226673-0 (v. 3)
     ISBN 0-12-226674-9 (v. 4)
     1. Agriculture--Encyclopedias.   I. Arntzen, Charles J.
    II. Ritter, Ellen M.
    S411.E713   1994
    630'.3--dc20   94-3143
                                                      CIP

PRINTED IN THE UNITED STATES OF AMERICA
94 95 96 97 98 99 QW 9 8 7 6 5 4 3 2 1

94-3143

R
630.3
AR66E
V.4

CONTENTS OF VOLUME 4

86094

CONTENTS OF OTHER VOLUMES

CONTENTS OF VOLUME 2

CONTENTS OF VOLUME 3

HOW TO USE THE ENCYCLOPEDIA

The *Encyclopedia of Agricultural Science* is intended for use by both students and research professionals. Articles have been chosen to reflect major disciplines in the study of agricultural science, common topics of research by professionals in this realm, areas of public interest and concern, and areas of economics and policy. Each article thus serves as a comprehensive overview of a given area, providing both breadth of coverage for students and depth of coverage for research professionals. We have designed the *Encyclopedia* with the following features for maximum accessibility for all readers.

Articles in the *Encyclopedia* are arranged alphabetically by subject. A complete table of contents appears in each volume. Here, one will find broad discipline-related titles such as "Agroforestry" and "Plant Pathology," research topics such as "Transgenic Animals" and "Photosynthesis," areas of public interest and concern such as "Plant Biotechnology: Food Safety and Environmental Issues" and "World Hunger and Food Security," and areas of economics and policy such as "Macroeconomics of World Agriculture" and "Consultative Group on International Agricultural Research."

Each article contains an outline, a glossary, cross references, and a bibliography. The outline allows a quick scan of the major areas discussed within each article. The glossary contains terms that may be unfamiliar to the reader, with each term defined in the context of its use in that article. Thus, a term may appear in the glossary for another article defined in a slightly different manner or with a subtle nuance specific to that article. For clarity, we have allowed these differences in definition to remain so that the terms are defined relative to the context of each article.

Each article has been cross referenced to other articles in the *Encyclopedia*. Cross references are found at the end of the paragraph containing the first mention of a subject area covered elsewhere in the *Encyclopedia*. We encourage readers to use the cross references to locate other encyclopedia articles that will provide more detailed information about a subject. These cross references are also identified in the Index of Related Titles, which appears in Volume 4.

The bibliography lists recent secondary sources to aid the reader in locating more detailed or technical information. Review articles and research articles that are considered of primary importance to the understanding of a given subject area are also listed. Bibliographies are not intended to provide a full reference listing of all material covered in the context of a given article, but are provided as guides to further reading.

Two appendices appear in Volume 4. Appendix A lists United States colleges and universities granting degrees in agriculture. Appendix B lists United Nations organizations concerned with agriculture and related issues. Both appendices provide address and telephone information for each institution listed.

The Subject Index is located in Volume 4. Because the reader's topic of interest may be listed under a broader article title, we encourage use of the index for access to a subject area. Entries appear with the source volume number in boldface followed by a colon and the page number in that volume where the information occurs.

Silk Production and Processing

TETSUO ASAKURA, *Tokyo University of Agriculture and Technology*

DAVID L. KAPLAN, *U.S. Army Natick Research and Development Center*

Glossary

Fibroin Structural peptide in silk that forms a highly crystalline β sheet and imparts mechanical strength to the fiber
Sericin A family of gummy peptides in silk that bind the fibroin chains together to form the silk fiber
Silk Spun fibrous protein polymer secretions produced by biological systems which usually form an external structure (e.g., cocoon, web)

Silks are generally defined as spun fibrous protein polymer secretions produced by biological systems. Silks are synthesized by a variety of organisms including silkworms (and most other Lepidoptera larvae), spiders, scorpions, mites, and flies. The structure and function of silk fibers depend on the organism producing the silk. Silkworm silks have been the most intensively studied and are synthesized in specialized sets of modified salivary glands and extruded from spinnerets located in the head of the larva. The majority of silks are spun into air, although some aquatic insects produce silks with differing compositions that are spun under water.

I. General Characteristics of Silk

The most well-characterized silk is that produced by the domesticated silkworm, *Bombyx mori*. Sericulture

is the agricultural practice of growing mulberry (primary food for the silkworms), raising silkworms for silk production, harvesting silk from cocoons, and processing of the cocoon silk into useful textile fibers. The practice of sericulture originated in China nearly 5000 years ago and since that time silk has been used in textiles. Silkworm silk is produced primarily at one stage in the life cycle, during the fifth larval instar just before molt to the pupa. Smaller quantities of silk are produced at all larval stages except during molts. The silkworm cocoon is composed of silk fibroin, the structural fibers of the silk, and sericins, a family of gummy proteins that bind the fibers together. The cocoon is essentially a composite structure of fibroin fibers embedded in a sericin matrix to provide the insect with a protective sheath from the environment. The silk from each cocoon comprises a single thread ranging between 10 and 25 μm in diameter and between 300 and 1200 m in length. Silks are of interest in textiles and other material applications due to their visual appearance, their texture (or "feel"), their environmental stability, and their unique mechanical properties.

II. Silk Production in Silkworm

A. Life Cycle

The life cycle of *B. mori* is summarized in Fig. 1. The silkworm is a holometabolous insect. In about 50 days it completes its life cycle of four different metamorphosing phases; egg or embryo, larva, pupa, and adult (moth). When over-wintered eggs are kept at natural temperatures, the larvae hatch in April or May in response to an increase in temperature. Of the life cycle, about half is the larval stage, the only stage at which they consume food, mulberry leaves. Although silk protein is produced throughout the larval stages, except during molting, large amounts are syn-

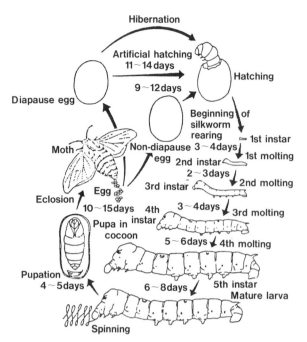

FIGURE 1 Life cycle of *Bombyx mori*.[Reprint with permission from Asakura, T. *JEOL News* **23A** (2), 1987.]

thesized in fifth instar larval stage. Pupation occurs at the end of spinning (or cocoon formation); the latter takes 3–4 days. This spinning stage is characterized by the extrusion of silk from spinnerets located in the head and drawing of the fiber by a characteristic figure-eight head movement. Inside the cocoon, the larva pupates. The moth emerges after a 10- to 15-day period of adult development. Mating occurs soon after emergence and 300–600 eggs are laid immediately afterward.

The duration of the developmental stages can be controlled throughout the life cycle by regulating environmental conditions, mainly temperature and nutrition. The developmental character of the early embryo, either diapausing or nondiapausing, can also be controlled by conditioning the female with temperature and photoperiod cycling during the egg incubation period and early larval stages. Furthermore, even the date of hatching can be scheduled by applying artificial hatching treatments in combination with cold storage. [*See* INSECT PHYSIOLOGY.]

B. Synthesis of Silk Protein

After the fourth larval molt or ecdysis, the silk gland of the silkworm develops rapidly for active fibroin production, and in the fifth instar larva it is the second largest organ following the alimentary canal. The

gland in which the silk of *B. mori* is secreted is shown in Fig.2. This consists of three relatively distinct regions. Fibroin, the main component of silk proteins, is exclusively synthesized in the posterior region of the silk gland and is transferred by peristalsis into the middle region of the gland in which it is stored as a very viscous aqueous solution until required for spinning. In the walls of the middle region of the gland, another silk protein, sericin is produced which coats the silk fibroin, acting as an adhesive; both proteins have unique and easily distinguishable amino acid compositions (Table I). The two glands join together immediately before the spinnerets through the anterior region and the fiber is spun into air. In the extruded thread, the two fibroin cores remain distinct. The silk gland is considered to be an ideal model system for producing large amounts of specialized proteins. Recently, an *in vitro* silk fibroin production system has been developed by the culture of the posterior region of the silk gland from *B. mori*.

C. Silkworm Nutrition

B. mori feeds almost exclusively on mulberry leaves (or close botanical relatives) because of the need for chemo-attractants and feeding stimulants, as well as essential nutrients found in the leaves. Approximately 12 g of dry mulberry leaves must be ingested for the production of 1 g of dry cocoon shell (efficiency,

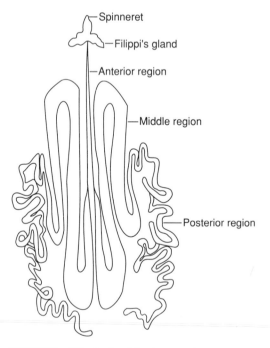

FIGURE 2 Silk glands of *Bombyx mori* larva.

TABLE I

Amino Acid Compositions of the Silk Fibroins from *B.mori, P.c.ricini, A.pernyi* and *A.yamamai*, and of the Silk Sericin from *B.mori* (mol%)

Amino acids	B.mori fibroin	B.mori sericin	P.c.ricini fibroin	A.pernyi fibroin	A.yamamai fibroin
Gly	42.9	13.5	33.2	26.7	26.1
Ala	30.0	5.8	48.4	48.1	48.1
Ser	12.2	34.0	5.5	9.1	9.0
Tyr	4.8	3.6	4.5	4.1	3.9
Asp	1.9	14.6	2.7	4.2	4.5
Arg	0.5	3.1	1.7	2.9	3.5
His	0.2	1.4	1.0	0.8	0.8
Glu	1.4	6.2	0.7	0.8	0.7
Lys	0.4	3.5	0.2	0.2	0.1
Val	2.5	2.9	0.4	0.7	0.7
Leu	0.6	0.7	0.3	0.3	0.3
Ile	0.6	0.7	0.4	0.4	0.4
Phe	0.7	0.4	0.2	0.3	0.2
Pro	0.5	0.6	0.4	0.3	0.4
Thr	0.9	8.8	0.5	0.5	0.6
Met	0.1	0.1	Trace	Trace	Trace
Cys	Trace	0.1	Trace	Trace	Trace
Trp	—	—	0.3	0.6	0.7

TABLE II

Composition of Artificial Diets Containing Mulberry Leaf Powder

Substance	Diets for first–fourth instars (g)	Diets for fifth instar (g)
Mulberry leaf powder	25.0	25.0
Soybean oil	1.5	3.0
Defatted soybean meal	36.0	45.0
Cholesterol	0.2	0.2
Citric Acid	4.0	4.0
Ascorbic acid	2.0	2.0
Sorbic acid	0.2	0.2
Agar	7.5	5.0
Salt mixture	3.0	3.0
Glucose	8.0	10.0
Potato starch	7.5	15.0
Cellulose powder	20.8	—
Vitamin B mixture	Added	Added
Antiseptic	Added	Added
(Total)	(115.7)	(112.4)
Water	300 ml	220 ml

8.26%). The weight of the silk glands of the fifth instar larvae increases approximately 100-fold during only 8 days prior to the spinning period. This abrupt increase is attributed to the active synthesis and accumulation of fibroin in the silk glands. This protein is specifically rich in glycine, alanine, and serine , which account for 85% of total amino acids (Table I). These three amino acids must be supplied not only by free amino acids contained in the mulberry leaves, but also by interconversion of other ingested amino acids. Approximately 70% of these amino acids are synthesized *de novo* in late fifth instar larvae.

Efforts have been made to manufacture artificial diets for silkworms for industrial purposes, and fairly satisfactory compositions have been developed. Two examples of artificial diets containing mulberry leaf powder are shown in Table II and are used for practical rearing. Recent development of polyphagous silkworm strains in Japan can be reared to maturity on diet.

The carbon skeleton of *B. mori* silk fibroin is formed mainly from sucrose in mulberry leaves. This disaccharide is decomposed to two hexoses and then metabolized to 3-triphosphoglycerate and pyruvate through the glycolytic pathway and to 2-oxoglutarate in the tricarboxylic acid, TCA, cycle (Fig. 3). Then serine, glycine and alanine are synthesized from these glycolytic intermediates. The nitrogen source for the synthesis of these amino acids may be derived from ammonium split from the degradation of other ingested amino acids and proteins. Ammonium is utilized for the formation of glutamate from 2-oxoglutarate by glutamate dehydrogenase.

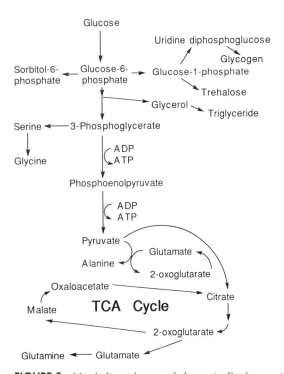

FIGURE 3 Metabolic pathways of glucose in *Bombyx mori* silkworm related to the formation of silk fibroin through glycolysis and carbohydrate reserves. ADP (adenosine diphosphate), ATP (adenosine triphosphate).

III. Silk Structure

A. Primary Structure

The silk fibroin from *B. mori* comprises high-molecular-weight polypeptides containing a predominance of the amino acids glycine, alanine, and serine (Table I). Acid side-chain groups predominate by 2.3-fold over basic side-chain groups. Sericin, which comprises 30% of the cocoon weight, has an amino acid composition that is significantly different from that of fibroin, with a high percentage of serine, aspartic acid, glycine, and threonine residues, which total over 65%. Acid side-chain groups also predominate by 2.6-fold over basic side-chain groups. The hydrophilic nature of sericin permits its separation and removal from the fibroin during the processing of silkworm cocoons in boiling water. Traces of lipid, pigment, and carbohydrate have been reported in *B. mori* cocoons.

B. mori silk fibroin consists of two primary peptides, one approximately 325,000 Da (heavy chain) and the other 25,000 Da (light chain). Silkworm silk can be described as a block copolymer containing crystalline domains (regions of the polypeptide containing the short side-chain amino acids), interrupted with amorphous domains consisting of the bulkier side-chain amino acids. Approximately 70% of the fibroin (sum of the heavy chain and light chain) is the amino acid sequence, Ser–Gly–Ala–Gly–Ala–Gly. A more extended sequence has been reported for the crystalline fraction precipitated after chymotrypsin hydrolysis, as Gly–Ala–Gly–Ala–Gly–Ser–Gly–Ala–Ala–Gly–[Ser–Gly–(Ala–Gly)$_n$]8–Tyr, where n is usually 2. This sequence accounts for 55% of fibroin. Other characteristics of the primary structure of fibroin are the absence of the sequence Gly–Gly and the presence of the sequences, Gly–Tyr–Gly and Gly–Val–Gly (tyrosine (Tyr) and valine (Val)). Thus, *B. mori* fibroin is regarded as an alternate copolymer of Gly. There have been no detailed reports on the amino acid sequence of sericin.

B. Secondary Structure

Different types of silk can exhibit a variety of characteristic protein secondary structures, including β-sheets, cross-β sheets, α helices, and random coils. *B. mori* cocoon silk is characterized by the β-sheet secondary structure wherein the protein polymer chains run antiparallel to each other interact and interact through hydrogen bonds (Fig. 4). The polymer chains run parallel to the fiber axis. Overlying sheets in the secondary structure interact by hydrophobic attractions to further stabilize the structure. The tight packing density of the overlying sheets is due to the high percentage of short side-chain amino acids consisting of approximately 85% (glycine + alanine + serine in a $3:2:1$ ratio).

Two key crystalline structures have been identified for silkworm silk, silk I and silk II. The silk I conformation represents the water-soluble form present when silk is first synthesized in the posterior region of the silk gland. The silk II form represents the water-insoluble conformation present in the spun silk fiber. The unit cell dimensions for both crystalline structures of native silk are shown in Table III ; the silk I dimensions are based on predictions from conformational energy calculations with glycine–alanine repeats, while the silk II data are based on X-ray diffraction studies. The change in unit cell dimensions during the transition from silk I to silk II during fiber spinning is most dramatic in the intersheet plane, with a decrease of 18.3% between three overlying sheets, which excludes water and reduces solubility. The silk II form is more energetically stable, and though the energy barrier from silk I to silk II is relatively low, the transition is generally considered irreversible. The transition occurs in the silk-producing gland of the silkworm from shear during the spinning process. Artificially, the same transition can be induced by mechanical shear or drawing, heat, use of polar solvents such as methanol and acetone, and under the influence of electric fields.

IV. Silk Properties

A. General Characteristics

Silkworm silk is insoluble in water, dilute acids and alkali, and most organic solvents. In addition, silks are resistant to most proteolytic enzymes. Silk fibers are hygroscopic, with a moisture regain of 10 to 15%. Other physical properties include a characteristic translucence with high lustre or sheen, abrasion resistance, ability to bind dyes, resistance to environmental degradation because of their resistance to proteolytic enzymes, and susceptibility of the undyed fiber to sunlight. The specific gravity for silkworm silk is 1.25.

B. Mechanical Properties

Silk fibers combine strength and toughness. For example, silkworm silk exhibits up to 35% elongation

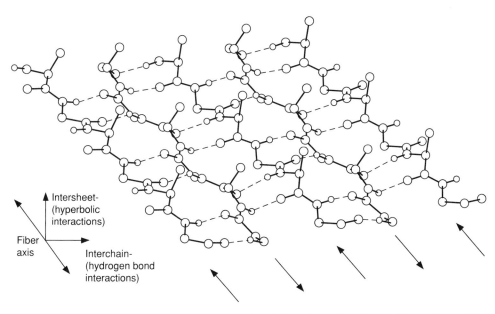

FIGURE 4 Generalized picture of the anti-parallel β-sheet structure (single sheet shown) for the crystalline regions of silk. Note: polymer chains run according to the arrows, thicker lines indicate covalent linkages, while the dotted lines represent hydrogen bonding between neighboring chains (carbonyl groups on one chain and amine groups on the neighboring chain). The methyl side chains from the alanine amino acids all project upward on the same side of the sheet structure shown. Overlying sheets (not shown) would interact through hydrophobic interactions.

with tensile strengths approaching those of high strength synthetic fibers. The tensile strength for silkworm silks is approximately $6 \times 10^8 \, N/m^2$, the modulus is approximately $5 \times 10^9 \, N/m^2$, and the energy to break is approximately $7 \times 10^4 \, J/kg$. This is particularly impressive when considering that natural silk fibers undergo minimal draw to enhance molecular orientation, which improves mechanical properties. Unlike most fibers, increased rates of loading of silk fibers result in increased strength and modulus as well as elongation; this increases the amount of work to rupture. The mechanical properties of silkworm silks have been shown to correlate in part with the ratio of long side-chain amino acids to short side-chain

TABLE III

Unit Cell Dimensions for Silk I and Silk II

Dimension	Silk II	Silk I
a axis (intersheet distance)[a]	0.920 nm	1.126 nm
b axis (interchain distance)	0.944 nm	0.894 nm
c axis (fiber axis)	0.697 nm	0.646 nm

Note. The silk II values are based on X-ray diffraction data and the silk I values are based on predictions from conformational energy calculations.

[a] intersheet distance between three overlying sheets (p.530 and 0.390 nm silk II, 0.565 nm for silk I)

amino acids in the fibroin, high ratios correlating with higher elongation and lower tenacity.

V. Silk Processing

A. Solution

It is very important to be able to obtain an aqueous solution of silk fibroin in order to use it in biomaterials as described below. It is possible to get a solution of fibroin directly from the glands, where the concentration is 12–15% in the posterior silk gland and approximately 20–30% in the middle silk gland. An aqueous solution of silk fibroin can also be obtained from raw silks or cocoons indirectly. A degumming process, desericinization with boiling soap solution or boiling dilute Na_2CO_3 solution, is used to obtain only silk fibroin fiber. Such a fibroin is soluble in certain concentrated aqueous salts; dialysis removes these salts and leaves the fibroin in aqueous solution. Salts that have been extensively used in this way are LiBr, LiSCN, and $CaCl_2$.

It has been established that in dilute aqueous solution, *B. mori* silk fibroin exists in a random coil structure. However, with slow concentration at room temperature, the side-by-side chain aggregation of the fibroin molecules occurs and as a result, fluctuations around the backbone bonds decrease, generating a silk I conformation . The content of silk I of the silk fibroin stored in the middle silk gland is about 40%.

B. Films

Films of *B. mori* fibroin are prepared by air-drying an aqueous solution cast on a film of poly(vinylidene chloride) or acrylic resin plates. The conformation of these films usually consists of silk I and random coil. The fresh films are usually water-soluble. Hydration by placing the films in a closed chamber of about 100% relative humidity for 24 hr stabilizes the silk I form and the membrane becomes water-insoluble. By immersing water-soluble films into polar hydrophilic solvents such as methanol and acetone, the conformational transition to the silk II form occurs at the surface of the films which become water-insoluble. However, fibroin molecules in inner parts of the films are still in random coils and the backbone chains are mobile in water, that is, the films become heterogeneous in structure. The water-insoluble films are also obtained by the stretching treatment of the water-soluble films. In addition, preparation of a porous fibroin film is possible by adding polyethylene glycol to an aqueous solution of fibroin. This causes a conformational transition to silk II and the dried film becomes water-insoluble. After immersing the films into water, porous fibroin films are obtained by the removal of polyethylene glycol.

C. Fibers

In sericulture silkworm cocoons are harvested and immersed in a hot soapy water bath to solubilize and remove the sericin in a degumming operation. The remaining silk fiber in the cocoon is then reeled by either hand or machine and subsequently dyed or chemically treated (e.g., to reduce wrinkling, improve washability) depending on the intended application for the fibers. The reeled fibers are usually woven into textiles.

Rheology studies with soluble silk indicate that the degree of crystallinity of the silk fiber correlates with shear rate and draw rate, and that a critical extrusion rate of slightly under 1-cm/sec is necessary to induce a conformational shift to the silk II secondary structure and for the appearance of birefringence. In the natural spinning process, the silk polypeptides in the posterior region of the gland are water-soluble and optically featureless and exhibit a range of secondary structures including random coil. This region of the gland is less than a millimeter in diameter and the shear rate is low. In the middle region or storage area of the gland, the diameter is 1.2 to 2.5 mm and the shear rate is also very low. In the anterior region of the gland the diameter is very narrow, 0.05 to 0.3 mm, the shear rate is very high, there is active water transport out of the gland, there is a decrease in pH, and there is ion exchange particularly with potassium, sodium and phosphates. It is assumed that at this stage the silk begins to take on the predominant β-sheet secondary structure. The diameter of the fiber can vary depending on the rate of spinning and the diameter of the silk fiber changes in the different layers of the cocoon. The total length of the fiber is presumably determined by the rate and duration of protein synthesis.

The viscosity of the protein solution in the anterior region of the gland decreases due to the formation of a lyotropic liquid crystalline phase. This phase apparently helps to avoid premature clogging of the spinning apparatus by aiding the flow of the material and reducing the processing energy requirements by the organism. An added benefit for this process is the high degree of molecular orientation and alignment achieved with the combination of the liquid crystalline phase and the spinning process itself. This orientation is achieved with minimal draw and imparts to the fibers their unusual mechanical properties. A nematic liquid crystalline phase has been demonstrated by isolating the protein solution from the silk gland and allowing it to gradually dry on a shear stage of an optical microscope. This phase is characterized by axial alignment and interaction of polymer chains in various stages of registry with each other while remaining soluble in the aqueous medium. The role of sericin during fiber formation, aside from serving as the matrix to hold the two fibroin fibers together, may be to aid the passage of the silk polypeptides through the spinneret, to serve as a reservoir of divalent cations, and to act as a receptor for water coming from the fibroin.

VI. Gene Structure and Function of Silk

A. Gene Structure

Silks are encoded by highly repetitive structural genes that are under tight regulatory control in the cell. The repetitive domains influence the higher-order conformation and result in fibers with unusual functional properties. The structure of the fibroin gene has been partially described. The gene encoding the fibroin heavy chain is reported to be on the order of 16 kb and to contain, in order, a 5′ adenine/thymine-rich flanking region, a 970-bp intron, a short nonrepetitive coding region (414 bp), a core repetitive region of approximately 15 kb containing 10 crystalline domains of 1 to 2 kb each interspersed with amorphous domains containing about 220 bp, and an untranslated flanking region at the 3′ end. Restriction maps of the fibroin gene have been generated. Due to the guanine/cytosine-rich content of the crystalline domains of the gene many restriction enzymes do not cut or cut rarely in the core repetitive region of the gene which makes internal mapping difficult. Only a small fraction of the total gene has been sequenced. The gene encoding the fibroin light chain has also been sequenced. The synthesis of the heavy and light fibroin chains is jointly regulated such that equimolar amounts of the two polypeptides are formed; however, the two genes are located on different chromosomes. Joint synthesis and secretion of the fibroin heavy and light chains is dependent on covalent crosslinking between the two chains which occurs post-translationally through a disulfide link. Sericins are encoded by at least two genes, with different gene splicing events giving rise to different sericin mRNAs ranging in size from 2.8 to 10.5 kb.

B. Gene Regulation

The high level of protein production within a specific stage in the life cycle of the silkworm has prompted strong interest in understanding the regulation of the system, as well as for the potential use of *B. mori* as a host system to express genetically engineered proteins once suitable gene transfer systems are developed. Genetically engineered viruses have been used to infect fifth instar larvae of *B. mori* to produce non-silk proteins (pharmaceuticals) such as interferon and interleukin. Expression of the fibroin gene is localized to the epithelial cells lining the posterior region of the silk gland, similarly, expression of sericin is limited to the middle region of the gland. Tight transcriptional controls exist in the cell for both types of genes. For example, activation of fibroin gene transcription starts from the anterior part of the posterior silk gland at the beginning of the fifth instar and spreads toward the posterior end of the gland. Although only a single copy of the fibroin gene exists per haploid genome, the mRNA formed is very stable with a half life of several days. This enables the gradual accumulation

of large amounts of the message which accounts for the high rates of fibroin synthesis at the end of the fifth instar. Strong translational controls are also required to permit the high level of production of protein in this system. Silk gland-specific tRNAs and tRNA synthetases are required to support the high levels of glycine, serine, and alanine amino acids for both fibroin and sericin synthesis. The expression *in vitro* of at least tRNAala is under the control of tissue-specific transcription factors which bind both upstream and internal to the gene. There is also a requirement for a class of transcriptional regulatory RNA (TFIIIR) described for the first time in this system. In a cell-free system supplemented with insect tRNAs (particularly those for glycine, alanine, and serine), as well as in silk gland maintained in culture, discontinuous translation patterns were noted, with increasing sizes of peptide chains up to full length. The discontinuous nature of the translation (which results in a series or ladder of polypeptide chains of increasing size) corresponds to the different times required for ribosomal recognition-binding at each codon and may be due to suboptimal concentrations of specific tRNAs due to the preponderance of glycine, alanine, and serine (approximately 85%) in the peptide. This relates to the repetitive nature of the gene and the encoded protein.

The compartmentalization of the silk gland, with sericins produced in the middle region and fibroins in the posterior, provides a significant level of control over silk expression and processing. In both cases, primary transcription is controlled by the presence of specific DNA binding proteins (transcription factors) which interact with the flanking or control regions associated with each class of genes to form active transcription complexes. The specialization of the posterior silk gland for high levels of fibroin protein synthesis appears to be primarily controlled by the expression and high stability of its mRNA, which is synthesized continuously in the posterior silk gland except at molts, and thus accumulates to very high levels by the middle of the fifth instar.

VII. New Applications of Silk

A. Textile (hybrid silk)

A hybrid silk composed of fine silk at the surface of a synthetic fiber core was recently commercialized. It is produced by extruding silk and nylon together through an air jet nozzle with a nylon filament placed at the center and five raw silk filaments (2 denier each) twined around the nylon core. The hybrid fiber retains excellent handling and a good silk luster as well as having the fiber strength of nylon. When stockings made from this hybrid silk are degummed to remove surface sericin, they show a metallic-silver luster. The fibroin threads also increase in thickness because of thermal shrinkage of the nylon core. This product is, therefore, a genuine hybrid of silk and nylon, and yields quite different characteristics from those of a conventional blended yarn of the two fibers.

B. Biocosmetics

Fatty deposits on the skin surface can be removed by washing with soap. Protein deposits from skin, however, cannot readily be removed unless they are first hydrolyzed with a proteinase. Some conventional cosmetics contain proteinase, but its hydrolysis activity deteriorates rapidly with time, particularly when left with surfactant in the wet state. Many attempts have been made to stabilize the proteinase activity in cosmetics. Proteinase immobilized in fibroin powder is stable to heat and its hydrolysis activity lasts for a considerable period of time, since fibroin protects the enzyme against heat and moisture. Thus, granules of mixed proteinase-encapsulated fibroin powder and detergent have been successfully developed for this purpose.

C. Biosensors

As a support for enzyme immobilization, silk fibroin has certain, several inherent advantages. First, in the preparation of an enzyme-immobilized film with fibroin, simultaneous insolubilization of the water-soluble film and immobilization of the enzyme in the film is possible without any chemical reagents for crosslinking. This is based on the fact that conformational transition of the silk fibroin chain is induced easily by various treatments, such as drawing, compression, and immersion in alcohol, or hydration under high humidity. The sensor was prepared with a glucose oxidase (GOD)-immobilized silk fibroin film attached on an oxygen electrode surface and assembled in the apparatus shown in Fig. 5. Moreover, a fourfold increase in sensitivity was observed when the glucose sensor was made with the GOD immobilized on nonwoven silk fabrics compared with a GOD-immobilized silk fibroin film. The membrane potential of the GOD-immobilized silk fibroin film is induced by an enzymatic reaction after the addition

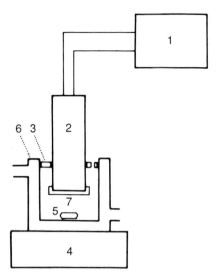

FIGURE 5 Apparatus for determination of immobilized GOD activity: (1) recorder; (2) oxygen electrode with Teflon film; (3) silicone ring; (4) magnetic stirrer; (5) stirring bar; (6) reaction cuvette; (7) GOD-immobilized film. (This film was attached when apparatus was used as a glucose sensor.)

of the substrate glucose. An application for the process has shown by the preparation of a new type of glucose sensor, which functions without an oxygen electrode. Biophotosensors have also been made, using fibroin films with immobilized peroxidase.

VIII. Wild Silkworm Silks

A. Silk Structure

Many kinds of wild silkworms produce silk. The classification of common silkworms is shown Fig. 6. Those which are reared for cocoon production are *Antheraea yamamai*, *A. pernyi*, *A. mylitta*, and *Philosamia cynthia ricini*. The characteristics of these cocoons, including those of *B. mori*, are summarized in Table IV. The cocoons of the wild silkworms also mainly consist of silk fibroin and sericin, but the content of sericin is relatively low as is expected from the fact that the size of middle region of the silk gland is more slender than that of posterior region of the gland. In addition, the content of lipid, pigment, and carbohydrate is relatively high compared with that of *B.mori* cocoons.

Table I shows the amino acid compositions of silk fibroins of *P. cynthia ricini*, *A. pernyi* and *A. yamamai*. The major amino acid residues of these wild silkworm fibroins are alanine and glycine; as with *B.mori*, the sum of these two amino acid residues comprises

TABLE IV
Characteristics of cocoons

	Cocoon color	Thickness and stiffness of cocoon shell	Size of cocoon (width × length, cm)
Bombyx mori	White	Thick, hard	2.5 × 3.5
Antheraea yamamai	Greenish-yellow	Thin, hard	2.3 × 4.5
Antheraea pernyi	Brown	Thin, hard	2.3 × 4.5
Antheraea mylitta	Brown	Thick, hard	(2.3–3.5) × (3.5–6.5)
Philosamia cynthia ricini	Pale brown	Flossy	1.5 × 4.5

74–82% of the silk fibroin (Table I). However, the relative content of alanine is larger than that of glycine, in contrast to the case of *B.mori* fibroin, where the reverse is the case. As a result, the most striking conformational characteristic of these silk fibroins in the silk gland or in aqueous solution is the presence of α-helical domains consisting of only alanine residues. The average number of alanine residues in such an α-helical domains has been reported to be 22 for *P.c.ricini*. With increasing temperature, a conformational transition from α helix to random coil occurs and the helix content of whole silk fibroin decreases from 26% (0°C) to 15% (25°C). Such a conformational transition from an α helix to random coil is also observed directly in living silkworm. After spinning, the conformation of the silk fibroin changes from α helix and random coil to mainly anti-parallel β-sheet structure (silk II). The amino acid compositions of the sericins of these wild silkworms are similar to those of *B.mori*.

B. Silk Properties and Processing

The characteristics of wild silkworm fibroin fibers are considerably different from those of *B. mori* silk fibroin fibers, producing woven goods with different physical and mechanical properties. For example, the values of the modulus of *A. pernyi* and *A. yamamai* silk fibers are smaller than that of *B. mori* silk fiber. In addition, the load increases more slowly with increasing extension in the load-extension plots of *A. pernyi* and *A. yamamai* fibers compared to *B. mori* fiber. Other differences include a lower hygroscopic property and different dying characteristics compared with *B. mori* fiber.

An aqueous solution of *P.c.ricini* silk fibroin with α-helical domains can be obtained from the posterior region of the silk gland and a cast film of fibroin can be prepared by a preparation similar to that described

for *B. mori* fibroin . A water-insoluble film is obtained by drawing or immersing it in methanol causing a conformational transition from α helix or random coil to β forms to occur. This film can be also used for the immobilization of GOD and applied to a glucose sensor. It is of special interest that the thermal stability of *P.c.ricini* films is higher than that of *B. mori* film.

IX. Spider Silk

A. Silk Structure

Over 35,000 species of spiders have been identified, representing some of the most diverse and abundant organisms in nature. Web building spiders produce silks for the purpose of catching prey; however, unlike the silkworm, the silk production and collection processes from spiders have never been domesticated. Spiders can produce a variety of different silks, some of which are formed throughout their life cycle. Techniques for the controlled silking of spiders have been developed and under such conditions, *Nephila clavipes,* the golden orb weaver, can produce up to 200 g of silk protein fiber in a single silking session. Females are primarily responsible for orb-web construction and webs are often recycled by the spider. Aside from functioning in prey capture, the different spider silks are used in reproduction, adhesion, dispersing of young by the wind, and as vibration receptors for prey detection. Visual displays on webs, such as the zigzag stabilimenta pattern characteristic of certain orb webs, may function to stabilize or strengthen the web, disguise the spider, warn off birds from damaging the web, or absorb water. Some spiders produce only one type of silk, while others may produce up to 10 or more different kinds of silk, each for a different function. The different silks are produced in different sets of specialized glands in the

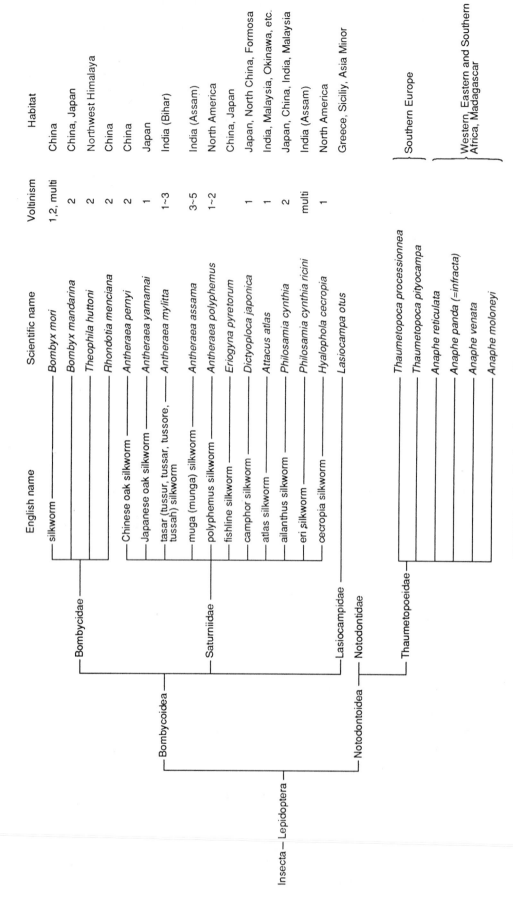

FIGURE 6 Classification of common silkworms.

TABLE V

Examples of the Different Types of Spider Silk Protein Polymers and Their Functions

Gland	Type of silk	Function
Major ampullate	Dragline, orb frame, radii	Saftey line, mechanical strength
Minor ampullate	Orb frame, dragline	Support fibers—frame and dragline
Flagelliform	Viscid	Prey capture
Aggregate	Gluelike	Prey capture and retention
Cylindrical	Cocoon	Reproduction
Aciniform	Wrapping	Captured prey
Piriform	Attachment	Coupling to environmental substrates

abdomen of the spider (Table V). Each of these silks has a different amino acid composition and presumably a different amino acid sequence, giving rise to the differing functional properties and roles in the lifecycle of the spider. Generally, spider silk orb web fibers are smaller in diameter than silkworm fibers, usually ranging from 1 to 5 m. Soluble organic chemicals, salts, and water on the surface of web fibers appear to play a role in species identification and in maintaining the mechanical properties of the fibers. Dragline silk is the strongest of the spider silks, and unlike the cocoon silk of the silkworm, does not appear to contain sericin gluelike proteins. In addition, only one polypeptide has been reported to date in the dragline silk, with a molecular weight in excess of 300,000 Da. The amino acid composition of spider dragline silk from *N. clavipes* indicates a lower percentage of short side-chain amino acids (glycine, alanine, serine) than the silkworm cocoon silk, totalling 63 vs 85%, respectively. Spider dragline silk exhibits a lower degree of crystallinity than silkworm silk.

B. Silk Properties and Processing

Spider dragline silk generally exhibits almost an order of magnitude enhancement in mechanical strength when compared with silkworm silk. Therefore, there is a great deal of interest in a variety of high-strengh fiber applications for these proteins. The mechanical properties of spider silks correlate to their function in absorbing the impact of flying insects without breaking. The orb-web dissipates energy over a broad area by balancing stiffness, strength, and extensibility. The majority of the energy of impact is lost as heat through viscoelastic processes in the web. This avoids an elastic recoil which could potentially eject the insect back out of the web. Unrestrained spider silk fibers from the web (major ampullate gland) are reported to supercontract to almost half their original length upon exposure to water. The minor ampullate gland silks do not exhibit this behavior, nor do silkworm silks. A lyotropic liquid crystalline phase has also been demonstrated with a number of different spider silks.

Bibliography

Fraser, R. D. B. and MacRae, T. P. (1973). Silks. *In* "Conformation in Fibrous Proteins." Academic Press, New York.

Ito, T. (1978). Silkworm Nutrition. *In* "The Silkworm." (Y. Tazima, ed.). Kodansha, Tokyo.

Kaplan, D. L., Lombardi, S. J., Muller, W. S. and Fossey, S. A. (1991). 1 Silks. *In* "Biomaterials: Novel Materials from Biological Sources" (D. Byrom, ed.). Stockton, New York.

Livengood, C. D. (1990). Silk. *In* "Polymers—Fibers and Textiles: A Compendium" (J. I. Kroschowitz, ed.), Encyclopedia Reprint Series, pp.789–797. Wiley, New York.

Silviculture

DAVID M. SMITH, *Yale University*

Glossary

Advanced regeneration Trees that appear spontaneously or are induced to appear beneath existing stands

Forest stand Aggregation of trees with sufficient uniformity of species composition, age(s), spatial arrangement, or condition as to be distinguishable from adjacent aggregations and large enough to be treated separately for purposes of forest management

Regeneration or **reproduction** Act of renewing aggregations of trees either naturally or artificially or the small trees resulting from the renewal

Regeneration or **reproduction methods** Tree removal treatments made to create conditions favorable for establishment of regeneration

Microenvironment Small space throughout which the physical, chemical, and biotic environmental factors are uniform in their ecological effect

Rotation Period of years elapsing between the initiation of a new crop of trees and its final harvest

Silvicultural system Program of silvicultural treatment of a stand that extends throughout the life of the stand

Tending or **intermediate cutting** Treatments carried out during the life of a stand in order to improve it, regulate its growth, or obtain early financial returns but not to regenerate it

Silviculture is the theory and practice of controlling the establishment, species composition, structure, and growth of forests. It is to forestry as agronomy is to agriculture. Almost all the natural and social sciences are applied to the design of silvicultural solutions to the wide variety of problems, objectives, and circumstances encountered at each stand and site.

I. Purposes of Silviculture

Silviculture can be applied to cause forest stands to yield such benefits as wood, water, wildlife, forage, recreation, and aesthetics in settings varying from urban to wilderness. Ordinarily two or more uses are pursued simultaneously in the same stands. The combinations depend on the priorities and limitations imposed by the objectives of owners and of public land-use policies. These vary widely but it is very difficult to formulate silvicultural systems for particular stands unless the priorities attached to each kind of use are clearly defined.

Some uses are well-nigh universal. In most forests precipitation exceeds evapotranspiration during some season so surpluses of water flow to streams or groundwater. Therefore, water supply becomes a matter of public policy regardless of whether the landowner uses the water. Likewise, all forests have wildlife which is often treated as a kind of public property; it may be a benefit used by people or a source of damage to the vegetation; in any event, silviculture can play a key role in the construction and management of wildlife habitats.

II. Silviculture as Simulation of Natural Processes

Silviculture is a low-intensity form of plant culture in which one intervenes in natural processes only at infrequent crucial stages and more often guides rather than alters their progress. It is applied forest ecology (see below) in which the natural processes of stand development and the lethal disturbances that initiate new stands are imitated. [*See* FOREST ECOLOGY.]

In most silvicultural treatments vacancies are created in the total growing space to make room for new plants or to give existing plants more space in which to expand. The vacancies are normally created by killing trees, often but not always in the act of harvesting them. The *growing space* is the combination of the stratum of soil that can be occupied by plant roots and the stratum above ground into which tree crowns can reach. Vegetation tends to refill such vacancies. Because of their ability to grow tall, forest trees can fill growing space more completely than other plants.

Fire, one of the the most common kinds of natural lethal disturbance, is more likely to kill small trees than large ones. The small new trees that follow fire germinate or resprout after fire. Other kinds of lethal disturbance, such as wind and pests, usually kill from the top of the old stand downward rather than from the bottom up. The species that are adapted to take advantage of such disturbances are often ones that start as preestablished *advanced regeneration* before the disturbances that release them to grow. Usually they are tolerant of partial shade and root competition from the older trees.

However, if fire burns the large amounts of dry fuel left by windstorms, pest outbreaks, or similar events all preexisting vegetation is likely to be completely killed although true soil generally remains. Some so-called pioneer species such as jack and lodgepole pine can recolonize from seed after such fires but artificial planting is the common silvicultural simulation of this lethal combination. Fire can also cause some species to resprout from basal sprouts or roots. Some pioneer species are adapted to germinate on bare mineral soil exposed by natural agencies other than fire, such as animals or the uprooting of trees by wind.

Natural events such as landslides or volcanic eruptions that expose raw parent material rather than true soil constitute the most severe natural disturbances. These are seldom deliberately simulated in silvicultural practice, although the reforestation of deeply eroded areas and mine spoil banks is an unplanned simulation.

Nature is not imitated slavishly or precisely. It is instead a case of knowing which natural processes to simulate and which to prevent, redirect, or modify.

III. Kinds of Forest Stands

Stands of trees vary as to the number of age classes and species that comprise their structure (Fig. 1). The simplest kind is *even-aged* (with one age class) and *pure* (composed of a single species). *Uneven-aged stands* have three or more age classes. A *balanced uneven-aged stand* would have all age classes evenly spaced as to age, from very young to mature, with each class covering an equal area; these are really theoretical constructs that are almost impossible to create. Stands with two age classes are maintained mainly where one category of trees is allowed to live much longer than another. The different kinds of age-class structure are most easily recognized in pure stands.

Pure stands are often found in nature because the combination of dry soils and fire commonly favors one species over all others. They are also often created artificially either because of simplicity of management or because some single species is deemed ideal.

The development of mixed stands is complicated and less predictable. They are most common where favorable soil moisture conditions make it possible for many species, or at least more than one, to grow. Since different species seldom grow at exactly the same rate in height the species tend to sort themselves out into different strata. Species that can endure shade are in fact often adapted to exist in the lower levels of such *stratified mixtures* (Fig. 2); these combinations of species generally utilize light more completely than is possible for one alone. Some species may share the same stratum but not necessarily throughout the life of a stand. The different strata are designated sequentially by letters with A denoting the uppermost even if it consists only of isolated *emergents* that project higher than their neighbors.

The structure of mixed stands can be further complicated by inclusion of different age classes. As is true of age classes in general these can usually be identified by differences in the height of the top of the crown canopy. Total height is the best indicator of ages of free-growing trees, except that it is modified by the ability of the soil to supply water and nutrients; the better the soil the faster the trees grow in height. The effect of age on tree diameter is so variable that it is a poor indicator of age. This is why the distributions of diameter in relation to age shown in Fig. 1 for even-aged stands are normal distribution curves

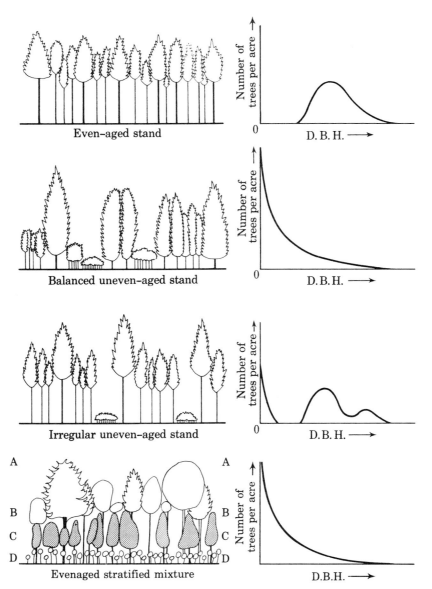

FIGURE 1 Four kinds of forest stand structure with their corresponding curves of distribution of tree diameters. The trees of the first three stands are all of the same species but the fourth consists of several species all of the same age. The four horizontal strata of the stratified mixture are lettered A, B, C, and D. [D.B.H., diameter at breast height (4.5 ft)] [Reprinted with permission from Smith, D. M. (1986). "The Practice of Silviculture," Fig. 1-3, p. 17. Copyright © 1986 by John Wiley & Sons, Inc., New York.]

(truncated at the low end because of competition-induced mortality of small trees).

IV. Regeneration

A. Ecology of Germination and Establishment

Forests are renewed by creation of vacancies in growing space suitable for the initiation and survival of new plants. The natural vegetation of any locality generally includes species adapted to colonize any habitable vacancy that has been created in nature. Knowledge of the adaptability of desired species is the key to knowing what kinds of vacancies to create. These vacancies are best thought of as microenvironments because the most crucial stages of life of new seedlings are passed in the space of a few centimeters.

These microenvironments are regulated mainly by adjusting the light and moisture conditions of each

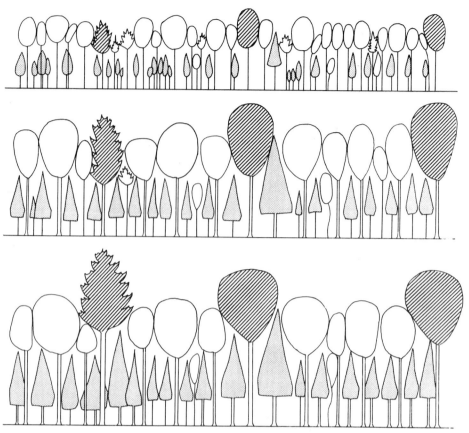

FIGURE 2 Stages in the natural development of a stratified mixture in an even-aged stand of eastern hemlock, hardwoods, and eastern white pine. The upper sketch shows the stand at 40 years with the hemlock *(gray crowns)* in the lowest stratum beneath an undifferentiated upper stratum. By the 70th year *(middle sketch)* the emergents of the A stratum *(hatched crowns)* have ascended above the rest of the main canopy (B stratum), except that the white pine *(jagged crown)* has only started to emerge. The lower sketch shows the stand at age 120 with the ultimate degree of stratification with the hemlock in the lowest C stratum. [Reprinted with permission from Smith, D. M. (1986). "The Practice of Silviculture," Fig. 17-3, p. 495. Copyright © 1986 by John Wiley & Sons, Inc., New York.]

spot by shading, reduction of preexisting vegetation, and physical treatment of the soil surface. Some pioneer species germinate in full light on bare soil like many agricultural annuals. Most tree species, however, require some protection from the extremes of temperature that occur on soil surfaces exposed to direct sun and open sky. Water losses from direct evaporation can make exposed surfaces too dry for most seeds to germinate.

Sometimes ideal conditions exist in side-shade where there is no direct solar radiation except for sunflecks but plenty of diffuse sky light. Some species are so tolerant of shade that they can start in very small vacancies beneath nearly closed stands of overhead trees. In other words, the species composition can be partly governed by determining whether establishment of new trees is sought in (a) the open, (b) along stand edges, or (c) beneath canopy shade.

Figure 3 shows how cutting patterns can be altered to create these different conditions. New trees that are adapted to start underneath other trees usually grow slowly in height at first but remain capable of initiating rapid growth when the trees above are removed. Many species require less and less shade as they go from the germination stage, to that of establishment, and then to a subsequent one of vigorous height growth.

Small-seeded species usually germinate best at or very close to the surface of bare mineral soil or some other medium that provides close contact with a steady supply of water. Large seeds, on the other hand, usually need to be buried beneath litter or soil; in nature, this is often done by rodents. Species with large seeds have abundant food reserves so their seedlings are more able to survive at low light intensity than those with very small seeds.

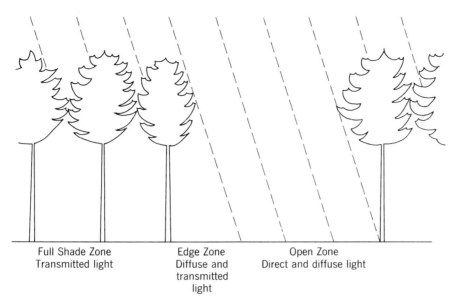

Full Shade Zone
Transmitted light

Edge Zone
Diffuse and
transmitted
light

Open Zone
Direct and diffuse light

FIGURE 3 Zonation of solar radiation across an opening cut in a stand showing the zones of incidence of the slanting rays of direct sunlight, the diffuse light that comes most abundantly from the sky straight above, and the transmitted light (including sun flecks) that come through the leaves of the trees. [Reprinted with permission from Smith, D. M. (1986). "The Practice of Silviculture," Fig. 7-4, p. 206. Copyright © 1986 by John Wiley & Sons, Inc., New York.]

B. Sources of Regeneration

The simplest source of forest tree regeneration is the kind of seed which falls from the parent tree, germinates, and produces a seedling that promptly initiates rapid height growth. However, regeneration can also arise from vegetative sprouts produced by the parents and there are also ways in which seeds or slow-growing seedlings are stored on the site.

The seeds of some species, usually fire-followers such as lodgepole and jack pines or eucalypts, can be stored for many years in cones or fruits that open during fires. Some hard-coated seeds remain stored in the soil until conditions of heat, moisture, or light favor germination.

Many species are adapted to becoming established as advanced regeneration which starts beneath old stands, grows slowly and persists until it is released from overhead competition. This kind of regeneration can sometimes be induced by reducing the amount of shade gradually in series of partial cuttings called shelterwood cuttings.

Some species are adapted to grow slowly in height during the early years until they have developed root systems extensive enough to provide water sufficient for more rapid growth. Longleaf and some subtropical pines may, for example, not grow at all in height until large root systems have formed.

Many species can be regenerated by vegetative sprouting which can be induced by cutting the parent trees and thus simulating natural tree killing by fire or animal browsing. Sprouting is common in angiosperms but only a few gymnosperms commonly regenerate from sprouts.

The sprouts usually arise from *dormant buds* that started as normal leaf buds but failed to develop. Instead they grow outward just under the bark, often for many years, and burst only when the crown of the tree is severed or becomes debilitated. *Stump sprouts* grow in rings around severed stumps.

In some species, such as aspen poplar and sweet gum, more uniformly spaced *root-suckers* arise from all parts of the root systems of the parents after they are cut or damaged. A few species can regenerate vegetatively from natural *layers* that are the rooted ends of branches that drooped down to the ground and were buried by litter or mosses.

Artificial regeneration can be accomplished by sowing seeds in the field or, much more commonly, by the planting of nursery-grown seedlings or cuttings.

C. Preparation of Sites for Regeneration

Treatments of soil or vegetation can sometimes facilitate the establishment of both artificial and natural regeneration. The treatments may involve use of fire, various kinds of plows and scarifiers, or herbicides. However, such site preparation is not always necessary for regeneration and can destroy advanced regeneration.

The most common purpose is reduction of preexisting competing vegetation. This requires killing the roots of the unwanted plants. Mechanical action pulls them bodily out of the soil. Fire kills woody plants by heat-girdling which interrupts movement of sugar through the phloem to the roots. Herbicides kill either by similar girdling action or by translocation to roots. Flooding kills the roots by excluding oxygen from them.

Poorly drained soils can be aerated by plowing up ridges or *beds* on which seedlings can be established. Where hardpans impede internal drainage deep plowing can be used to break the pans. Sometimes wet areas with peat deposits are drained by use of elaborate canal systems.

At the other extreme shallow trenches may be created to collect water and improve survival of young trees planted in them. Irrigation of forest trees is possible but uncommon.

Sometimes exposure of mineral soil by scarification or burning of the litter layer is enough to improve germination of seed and survival of seedlings. Removal of organic litter improves upward and downward conductivity of the soil thus reducing damage from high temperatures or frost. Sometimes the litter of some species is *allelopathic* (i. e., chemically antagonistic) even to seedlings of the same species. Especially for small-seeded species, improved contact between the seed and denser water-supplying media is vital to germination.

Site preparation with machinery can harm the soil by excessive scraping, gouging, or packing. Much of the nutrient capital of the site is often in the litter. Therefore, any scraping action that moves litter more than a few feet to the side can impair soil fertility. Anything that impairs the porosity of the surface soil on slopes may cause accelerated erosion and stream siltation.

Fire is far less harmful because it leaves much more of the nutrient capital in place; some nitrogen and sulfur compounds may, however, be lost by volatilization. Oftentimes the burning of logging debris and the continuous blanket of fuel represented by leaf litter is important in reducing the hazard of fire in regions with long dry seasons.

Fertilization is one kind of soil treatment that is usually not necessary for the establishment of regeneration. Often it enhances the growth of weeds more than it does that of young trees. However, it may be necessary in the very early stages in cases with comparatively unusual nutrient deficiencies, especially those of phosphorus on poorly drained soils.

The greatest benefits from fertilizing forest trees come after trees have become large enough to be laying down high-quality wood in the outer portions of their stems. In those circumstances and most others nitrogen compounds are the nutrients most likely to be deficient.

D. Artificial Regeneration

Artificial regeneration is usually accomplished by planting nursery-grown seedlings. *Direct seeding*, the sowing of seed directly in the forest, is successful only where seed predation by rodents and birds is avoided. It also requires rains frequent enough to keep the seeds wet. It is seldom feasible to apply the stupendous quantities of seeds that nature uses to overwhelm the appetites of the predators. Sometimes direct seeding works with species that have seeds so small that the predators ignore them. Otherwise direct seeding waits upon the invention of environmentally acceptable repellents of predators.

Planting evades many of the microenvironmental problems to which newly germinated seedlings are exposed in the field. The roots are put in contact with soil at depths from which water is not lost to direct evaporation. The top of the seedling also projects above the thin layer of air close to the surface that is subject to wide extremes of temperature. Enough environmental restrictions are evaded that it becomes possible to establish species or subspecies of trees in places where they could not become established in nature. This can be advantageous but also enables choices that can come to be mistakes.

The nursery practices used for forest trees are much like those employed for horticultural woody plants. They often involve techniques of forest tree genetic improvement (see below). [*See* FOREST TREE, GENETIC IMPROVEMENT.]

Nursery-grown trees that are moved only once are called *seedlings*; those that are replanted one or more times in the nursery are *transplants*. The purpose of transplanting is to confine a large amount of root surface into a small volume and allow the top to grow larger before the plant goes to the field. The same purpose can be achieved by drawing knives beneath or beside the seedlings to prune the roots in place. The chief advantage of planting large stock is that the taller seedlings are more likely to overtop competing vegetation. There is, however, the risk that the roots, which are inevitably reduced in extent during planting, may not provide enough water for the leaves.

Nursery stock is sometimes grown from rooted vegetative cuttings. Cuttings of some species, mostly ones such as cottonwood poplars that normally grow along moist river banks, can be planted as unrooted cuttings directly in the field.

Nursery stock is planted either as *bare-rooted* or *containerized* plants. The bare-rooted ones are separated from the soil when lifted from the nursery beds; the containerized ones are planted with roots attached to the medium in which they grew.

It is easy to transport large numbers of bare-rooted seedlings to planting sites but success depends on meeting some restrictive requirements. The most important is the need for the seedling to reestablish contact between the root and the soil. Some of this can be accomplished initially by packing soil around the roots; however, it is more important that the planting be done just before or during a period in which the roots grow rapidly. Such periods usually occur at the beginning of the growing season and before leaf buds burst. Therefore, it is best to lift and move the seedlings late in their dormant season.

The roots will not grow unless the soil is moist. Sometimes there is a second period of root growth after that in which leaves and stems grow. However, success from planting then depends on getting enough root growth to supply the water that will be lost even during the dormant season.

Dormant bare-rooted plants can be kept in cold storage (above freezing). This may postpone the time of maximum root growth and extend the planting season. If there is no dormant season, as in species of tropical rain forest, bare-rooted plants survive only if planted within hours of lifting. The roots of any bare-rooted stock must be kept visibly moist at all times; freezing or air-drying before planting will kill them. The period during which this kind of planting can be done is often limited to a few frantic weeks.

Ordinarily the plants should be reestablished with their root-collars level with the soil surface as they were in the nursery, but better too deep than too shallow. The roots should extend downward vertically as deeply as possible and not be bent upward into shapes like the letters J or L. Despite all these limitations, bare-rooted planting is the most common mode of artificial regeneration.

Containerized planting is expensive but more dependable. The main advantage is that contact between the roots and the medium in which they grew is not broken. This means that the planting can be done whenever the soil is moist and unfrozen. It has always been the standard method of tree planting in the moist tropics where there is no dormant period and in arid regions where survival after planting is poor. The same is true of planting trees more than about a meter tall.

One problem with containers is that they can cause the roots to spiral around inside the container walls. In this "root-bound" condition root systems do not resume their normal radial growth. Therefore, seedlings cannot be left to grow very long in the containers and it best that the containers either be removed or ruptured severely before the plants are put into the soil. This problem can be avoided if the container is a block of some organic material and has no walls.

V. Tending of Established Stands

After stands of trees are well established it may be desirable to apply various treatments, sometimes called *intermediate cuttings*, to improve the crop but not to replace it. Usually they involve eliminating some trees to create vacancies in growing space into which favored trees can expand.

A. Releasing Operations

The species composition of new stands can seldom be perfectly controlled during the regeneration phase. It may be necessary to adjust this by eliminating plants that overtop the desirable ones or threaten to do so. This can be done by cutting the undesirable, although this may have to be repeated if the unwanted plants resprout. It is also possible to kill them by *girdling* in which the bark is removed or severed; this kills the roots by starving them of carbohydrates from the crowns.

Herbicides are usually more effective although they may have to be injected through the bark or specially formulated to penetrate the waxy coverings of leaves or bark. Foliage spraying, which can be done from the air, may be used to release narrow-leaved species, such as most conifers, from overtopping broadleaves, but the timing of such operations is crucial and variable. With foliage spraying it is necessary that the herbicide penetrate the leaves and then move to the rest of the plant, especially the roots. There are some herbicides sufficiently phytotoxic that they can leach down to the roots and kill them after applications to the soil surface.

Tending operations are *cleanings* if the desirables and undesirables are of equal age and *liberation operations* if the undesirables are older.

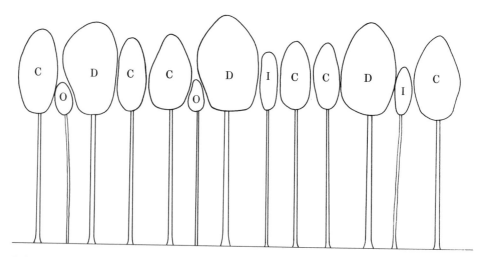

FIGURE 4 Relative positions of trees of different crown classes in a pure, even-aged stand. The letters, D, C, I, and O, stand for dominant, codominant, intermediate, and overtopped crown classes. [Reprinted with permission from Smith, D. M. (1986). "The Practice of Silviculture," Fig. 2-3, p. 47. Copyright © 1986 by John Wiley & Sons, Inc., New York.]

B. Prescribed Burning

Where the desirable trees have thick enough bark fires may periodically be set to burn the leaf litter and other fuels beneath the stands. The purposes may be (a) reduction of fuels in which wildfires might burn, (b) improvement of forage production for wild or domestic animals, (c) killing of small undesirable woody plants, (d) pest control, or (e) exposure of bare mineral soil to prepare for regeneration. Fire is most commonly prescribed where conditions are dry enough, at least seasonally, that fires often run under the stands in nature.

The weather and fuel-moisture conditions must be carefully chosen; the areas to be burned must be surrounded by plowed fire-lines or other belts from which the fuels have been removed at least temporarily. *Back-fires*, which are caused to burn against the wind move slowly but cause heat to be concentrated near the ground. *Head-fires* burn with the wind; much of their heat is wafted aloft where it may scorch some foliage but is less likely to scar the bases of the trees. Only *surface fires* which burn only the material on the forest floor are used. *Ground fires* which burn fuels underground and *crown fires* which burn both foliage on the trees *and* surface fuels are avoided because they are too difficult to control and too harmful.

C. Thinning

Forest stands start with many trees and then the numbers dwindle as the crowns of the more vigorous trees expand and shade out the losers. During this process the trees of a pure, even-aged stand differentiate into the *crown classes* depicted in Fig. 4. The leading trees or *dominants* have crowns free on all four sides.

Codominants are free on one to three sides. Trees that receive light only at their tops are of the *intermediate* crown class and are fast dropping out of the race for the sky. *Overtopped* trees are completely closed over and, at least if competing with the same species, doomed to early death. Figure 5 shows the process of differentiation into crown classes and the suppression of the laggards.

The diameters of the stems are closely correlated with those of the crowns and with the crown classes. The volume, value, and utility of the stem wood vary directly with the square of the diameter so small increases in diameter growth can be valuable. If the natural decline in numbers of trees is speeded by thinning both the tree crowns and the stems increase faster in diameter.

The diminution of numbers also means that some of the wood that has been produced will be lost to decay unless the doomed trees are harvested in thinnings. In this way the yield of wood from the stand is increased even though the total production of biomass is not. In fact, any temporary vacancies in the upper crown space created by thinning result in reductions of total biomass production. However, this sacrifice is deliberately made because the utilizable yield of wood in the larger stem sizes is increased.

The choices of trees cut and left in thinning also enables removal of poor or unhealthy trees to favor

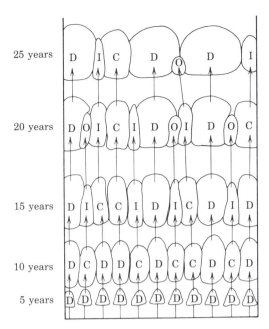

FIGURE 5 Changes in relative position in the crown canopy at successive ages as trees that all start as dominants race for the sky and some drop out. The letters refer to crown classes as in Fig. 4. [Reprinted with permission from Smith, D. M. (1986). "The Practice of Silviculture," Fig. 2-4, p. 48. Copyright © 1986 by John Wiley & Sons, Inc., New York.]

the growth of those of best quality or species. The increases in diameter growth caused by thinning are greatest at the base of the stem. This ultimately increases resistance to wind damage but requires several years of growth; until then thinning has the temporary effect of increasing vulnerability to wind.

The *methods of thinning*, which are patterns of choices of trees to cut and leave, vary with the objectives and the characteristics of the stands. Figure 6 illustrates how the different methods alter the distribution of classes of stem diameter.

Low thinning imitates and accelerates the natural decline in numbers of trees by removing the small ones that have crowns submerged in the lower levels of the crown canopy. It provides the best way of salvaging prospective mortality caused by competition. It does not enhance diameter growth of residual trees very much unless the removals are heavy enough to make some gaps at the top of the foliar canopy.

Crown thinning concentrates on removing those trees of the top of the canopy that are the most serious competitors of chosen trees for the final harvest. These chosen *crop trees* are usually from among the dominants; the ones that are removed come from the codominants, except that a few good

codominants may be promoted to crop-tree status if they are of better quality than some dominants. The intermediate and overtopped trees are left; usually they are too small to be utilized but it is sometimes hoped that some will respond to the release and grow large enough later. Leaving small trees and lesser vegetation beneath the larger trees decreases the growth of the larger ones where soil moisture is a limiting factor.

Selection thinning or *thinning of dominants* involves removing the tallest and largest trees and the hope that the shorter ones will respond with good growth. Sometimes this is done when the dominant trees are misshapen or otherwise less desirable than some codominants. Sometimes it is nothing more than *"high-grading"* in which the biggest and best trees are cut leaving the stand stocked with poorer ones. If the residual trees are of shade-enduring species and are of good form this pattern of removals can give acceptable results.

Geometric or *mechanical thinning* involves removal of trees in rows, strips or patterns that leave trees at fixed spacing intervals without much attention to choices of individual trees to leave.

Free thinning is that which is not limited to any one of these methods but varies from spot to spot. It is commonly applied to mixtures of species but can be used in irregular pure stands.

Commercial thinning involves any one of the foregoing methods in which the wood is extracted from the stand and utilized. In *precommercial thinning* the trees that are eliminated are left to rot in the stand. It is often geometric thinning and frequently involves killing individual trees with injected herbicides.

The severity of removals of trees in thinnings is usually regulated by determining the amount of crown cover to be left. Since that is difficult to measure the *basal area per acre* is often used as a surrogate parameter. The basal area of a tree is its cross-sectional area at breast height (4.5 feet) and is well correlated with the crown diameter. The number of trees per acre is not a good parameter, except for precommerical thinning in young stands, because it has nothing to do with tree sizes.

It should be noted that these methods of thinning and the terminology of crown classes were devised for even-aged stands composed of only one species; they do not fit most mixtures of species. Sometimes each stratum of a stratified mixture can be regarded and thinned as if it were a separate stand, although each stratum is retarded in growth by any that are

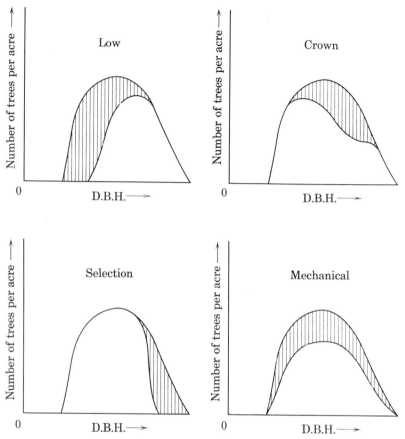

FIGURE 6 Diameter distributions for the same, pure, even-aged stand showing, by shading, the parts that would be removed in four different thinning methods. It is assumed that diameter at breast height (D.B.H.) is closely correlated with the crown classes. [Reprinted with permission from Smith, D. M. (1986). "The Practice of Silviculture," Fig. 4-11, p. 109. Copyright © 1986 by John Wiley & Sons, Inc., New York.]

above it. The difference is that the species of the lower strata are adapted to survive there.

D. Pruning

Trees cannot grow without branches but the branches may be detrimental after they die or even if they survive too low on the tree. Knots in boards are the remains of branches; they reduce the strength, utility and value of the lumber. Dead branches can also be infection courts for fungi or merely be unattractive. In growing trees for many purposes it is desirable to strike some desirable balance between the length of stem that is clothed with living branches and that which is free of branches. Knots left by dead branches are especially undesirable because they are apt to fall out when the lumber dries. The greater the proportion that is living the faster is the diameter growth of the stem.

A moderate amount of crowding in the early stages causes the lower branches to die when they are small. With many species small dead branches are attacked by wood-rotting fungi that cause the branches to fall off soon; fortunately these particular fungi are not the ones that can cause the heart of the tree to rot. However, this sort of *natural pruning* does not always take place. Furthermore, it is sometimes desirable to speed up the process by cutting off some living branches.

The most common purpose is to increase the proportion of knot-free lumber. It is often desirable to follow the pruning with heavy thinning so that the pruning wounds will heal swiftly and the trees will lay down knot-free wood rapidly. If too many live branches are removed, dormant buds along the pruned portion of the stem are likely to sprout and form new branches that defeat the purpose of the pruning.

VI. Silvicultural Planning

The growing of forest stands requires continuity of purpose and of treatment extending over many decades. The programs that are formulated to assure such continuity are *silvicultural systems*. They set forth the schedules of treatment planned for whole rotations. Usually one important part of the long-term plan is that it be reviewed and improved about once each decade. It is always necessary to keep looking at least one rotation ahead but to respond to changes in what is seen. The many considerations that enter into the plan generally conflict with each other so that each solution is a compromise.

A. Ownership Objectives

The natural conditions of each stand and forest govern the options available to the silviculturist but the objectives and characteristics of ownership come next in line. Helping ownership decide upon its objectives is often a major part of the formulation of a silvicultural system. This is especially true of public ownership where conflicts between groups seeking different kinds of benefits often keep the objectives confused and uncertain.

Such things as the choice of species to be grown depend heavily on how much of each kind of benefit is sought. The intensity of practice and degree of control of the vegetation depend on the capacity and willingness of ownership to make long-term investments in silvicultural treatment. The question of how long rotations should be partly depends upon ownership objectives. The result is that the optimum silvicultural program will not necessarily be the same for two different owners who have adjacent holdings of exactly the same kind of forest. For individuals the life expectancy is often a factor. Most important, however, is the relative importance attached to timber production, wildlife, watershed management, recreation and similar uses. Even then there is almost as much variation within categories as there is between them.

B. Control of Damaging Agencies

Trees must live through all seasons for many years in environments where it is not possible to afford them much protection. Control measures are *indirect* and *direct*. The general purpose is not to eliminate the sources of damage but to manage them in ways that make the damage tolerable or even advantageous for some purposes.

The indirect measure that is the first line of attack is silvicultural control which is maintaining stands with species, age classes, and overall structure that are not susceptible to damage. Much damage can be avoided simply by refraining from putting particular species on sites to which they are not adapted.

Sometimes the generalization is made that mixed, uneven-aged, stands of natural origin with vigorous fast-growing trees are most resistant to damage. While the various parts of this statement are singly more often true than not, exceptions are very numerous; the statement as a whole is probably more often false than true. The prospective damaging process must be analyzed and almost every general case treated differently.

Most of the control of fungus pests and abiotic agencies is silvicultural. Fungus spores are so omnipresent that fungicide use is usually confined to nurseries. Wind damage is best reduced by avoiding actions which create horizontal or vertical constrictions in the path of storm winds. That from frozen precipitation can be reduced by developing trees with symmetrical crowns and strong stems free of weak crotches.

Biological control, as in agriculture, involves use of the pests of pests. In forestry the most important application has been in the introduction of organisms that are enemies of introduced insects. The most effective predators of mammalian herbivore pests are hunters; fencing is feasible but very expensive. [*See* PEST MANAGEMENT, BIOLOGICAL CONTROL.]

Direct control with insecticides is applied mainly for control of outbreaks of defoliating insects and ordinarily involves aerial spraying.

Uncontrolled forest fires are incompatible with forestry; the section on Forest Fire Management deals with their control.

The final line of defense against sources of damage is the salvage of dead or dying trees, a purpose for which roads are very necessary. However, consideration must often be given to the role that dead trees, standing or fallen, play in wildlife management.

C. Sustained Yield

Forest production is one of the most truly sustainable of all human uses of resources. The fundamental basis of sustainability lies in maintaining the desirable physical and chemical properties of the soil. Where there is vegetative cover the large amounts of organic mat-

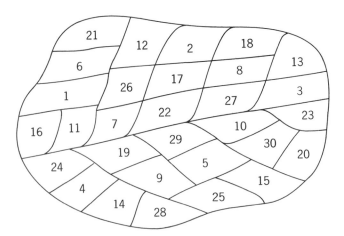

FIGURE 7 Schematic map of a forest divided into 30 equally productive stands arranged so that the replacement of one stand each year would provide a perpetual sustained yield of wood. Numbers denote stand ages, each of which is harvested at age 30. [Reprinted with permission from Smith, D. M. (1986). "The Practice of Silviculture," Fig. 12-2, p. 346. Copyright © 1986 by John Wiley & Sons, Inc., New York.]

ter that fall from the trees feed the soil organisms that keep the soil porous and resistant to surface erosion. The chief threat to forest soils is poor management of roads and trails; the actual cutting of trees and even fires have little effect.

The next consideration for sustainability is ensuring that stands are regenerated after timber harvests or similar disturbance.

The most difficult part of sustained yield is developing and maintaining some semblance of a steady flow of timber and other benefits from forests. The ideal in this respect is a *balanced distribution of age classes*, in which every age class from 1-year-old seedlings to that deemed mature is represented by an equally productive area of forest land (Fig. 7).

If the mature age class is replaced with seedlings each year, there is theoretically an even flow of benefits that goes on forever. This kind of age class distribution is almost never created within single uneven-aged stands. The smallest administrative units for which it can be developed are whole forests consisting of thousands of acres. Even then the proper distribution is built through the course of many decades from even-aged stands. It is almost always necessary to have some age classes that have saleable timber but are not yet mature. True sustained yield depends on resisting all the temptations that exist to harvest such age classes prematurely.

It is very difficult to develop an appropriate range of age classes mainly because in most forest regions almost all of the stands are of essentially the same age when management starts. Sometimes most are beyond rotation age. In those cases it is necessary to replace a small area each year while most stands are kept to get even older and more decrepit. If the forests of a locality were all cut or destroyed at once there is often the problem that readjusting the age class distribution means cutting some stands when they are too young and leaving more to get too old.

Maintaining diversity of forest wildlife also depends on having a full range of age classes of stands. The actual ages need not be as precise but it may be desirable that some trees and stands be carried beyond the ages at which they would be regarded as mature from the timber standpoint. The kinds of species composition would also be more varied than those desired for timber production.

D. Optimizing Use of Capital and Growing Stock

The question of how long trees should be allowed to grow can be answered in part by assessing the compound interest return from two different kinds of investments made in the trees. The first is the return that trees earn on their own value and the second the return on the money invested in growing them.

In the first kind of analysis the value of the tree at the beginning of a given period of years is treated as an investment. The interest return on the investment is determined from the change in value of the tree that results from increase in size or quality. If the rate of return falls below that demanded by the owner–investor the tree is harvested. The same test applied collectively to all the trees of a stand may help determine rotation length. This mode of analysis often guides the choice of trees to harvest in thinning or other kinds of partial cutting. It also helps determine how heavy thinnings have to be to make trees grow fast enough to justify keeping them. With this method the rate of return earned by a tree is infinitely high on the first day it attains a positive financial value; it declines rapidly after that but can be made to increase again if the tree is made to grow fast and into sizes of high product value.

The second kind of analysis involves the rate of return on money actually invested in growing the tree. This method is chiefly useful for comparing different programs for growing stands of trees. The analysis is usually done by discounting estimates of all future costs and returns to the beginning of the rotation at the demanded rate of compound interest. The difference between the prospective costs and returns is the *present net value*. If it is positive this means that the proposed silvicultural system would earn the demanded rate; the present net value is what one could now afford to pay for the land under the trees.

These two financial tests are alternative methods; their interest rates are not additive. No analytical test of any sort takes everything into account. These financial tests are hard to apply to values other than timber. However, they can be very useful in formulating silvicultural systems.

E. Arrangement of Operations in Time and Space

Forests both as natural and administrative units spread over large areas of terrain. The pattern of their arrangement heavily depends on how the transportation network is arranged and maintained. This network is not limited to roads but may have to include the corridors along which some animal populations move. Some forest roads are kept open all the time and are used for many different purposes. Others are used temporarily and then best left closed and well drained until needed for the next operational entry.

Greatest operational efficiency usually results from maximum concentration of activity in space and time. At the extreme this would be achieved if all the trees of a large stand were cut and replaced during a single year and then left entirely alone until the next harvest at the end of the rotation. The other extreme would involve the intricate intermingling of trees of different ages and species with frequent silvicultural operations.

The most common compromise is keeping most stands essentially even-aged so that most treatments can be applied uniformly over the whole stand. Other considerations require that such stands not be unduly large. Among the logical criteria of stand size are (a) the operating radius of the equipment that first moves logs from the stand and (b) the extent of areas with the same kind of soil. It is also desirable to restrict the area covered by the activities of each year so as to limit the total length of road surface being disturbed at any one time.

VII. Silvicultural Systems and Their Application

The design of silvicultural systems for particular kinds of stands must be based on analysis of the foregoing considerations in the light of their relationship to given situations. It is fallacious in terms of economics, politics, and ecological science to accept the notion that any one universal system should prevail or that all are equally valid everywhere. Furthermore, there is much variation in the details of each category of systems. In fact the variable details are so important that none of the systems can be successfully applied as unvarying cookbook recipes followed without analysis of the particular cases at hand.

The regeneration step of a rotation-long silvicultural system is so crucial that the name of the *method of regeneration* is usually given to the whole system. These methods really describe the patterns of arrangement of cutting areas in space and time and only secondarily the sources of the regeneration. No system or method can be understood from the name alone; there must be further description of other details.

The methods (and systems) are initially categorized according to whether the regeneration comes primarily from (a) seeds or (b) vegetative sprouts. Within each category they are further subdivided as to whether the stands are even- or uneven-aged. There is terminology to indicate whether the cuttings are arranged (a) uniformly in space or are done in (b) strips or (c) groups and patches. An additional dimension is added for stratified mixtures of species in which individual species or groups thereof become segregated into different horizontal strata without necessarily being of different age.

There are three even-aged cutting methods in which reliance is placed on regeneration from seed: clearcutting, seed-tree cutting, and shelterwood cutting.

Clear-cutting, in the narrow silvicultural sense of the term, involves nearly complete removal of preexisting vegetation and reestablishment of a new one from planted seedlings or newly germinated seeds. It is most commonly carried out by heavy cutting, thorough site preparation, and planting of nursery-grown seedlings. The resulting plantations are usually pure but can also be of intermingled mixed species. With some species adapted to reseed areas after severe fires, the clear-cutting method can be made to work with natural or artificial seeding. The natural supplies of seeds that germinate after cutting may be stored in the soil or be dispersed by wind from adjacent stands. The term "clear-cutting" is often loosely used to refer to any form of heavy cutting regardless of whether or how a new stand is established.

Seed-tree cutting is the same as clear-cutting with thorough site preparation, except that trees left on the cutting area are the source of seeds. As is the case with other methods of cutting the pattern of application can leave trees in strips, groups, or as scattered individuals. The distances of effective dissemination are seldom more than three times the height of the seed trees.

In *shelterwood cutting* the renewal of the stand depends on advanced regeneration. Usually this is induced by a series or two or more partial cuttings in which enough trees are left on the site to provide seeds or partial shade. Emphasis is placed on creating vacancies in the growing space beneath the stand and admitting some sunlight to the forest floor. The trees that are reserved are generally the largest and fastest-growing of those in the stand; getting them to grow faster as a result of the heavy thinning effect is often part of the purpose of the treatment.

With the simplest form of shelterwood cutting the overstory trees are removed as soon as the new crop is well established. This creates the even-aged condition. However, in *irregular shelterwood cutting* the final removal cuttings may be postponed for many years or some of the smaller trees in the stand may be released and induced to resume rapid growth. This approach is best adapted to mixed stands in which different species do not grow at the same rate; new stands created by this approach are not perfectly even-aged. In cases where adequate advanced regeneration has already become established naturally it may be possible to create new stands with a single final-removal cutting of the old stand in "one-cut shelterwood cutting." While shelterwood cutting carries little risk of regeneration failure, there is no reason

why the natural regeneration cannot be supplemented by artificial seeding or planting.

Uneven-aged stands are created and maintained by the *selection method of cutting* in which new age classes are established by removing trees in small patches or groups on three or more occasions during a rotation. Theoretically the same effect can be achieved by removing single large trees; however, the openings thus created are almost always so small that they are closed over by adjacent trees before any new trees can reach the top of the crown canopy. On the other hand the openings can be made large enough that it is possible to have uneven-aged stands that consist of groups of shade-bearing and even of sun-loving species.

The selection method is most commonly applied in stands that are already definitely uneven-aged and some trees would have to be harvested prematurely to make them even-aged. It also is applied in stands where it is desirable that there always be some large trees for such purposes as aesthetics, wildlife management, or protection against landslides and avalanches.

Theoretically the selection method can be applied in ways that mold each stand into a self-contained sustained-yield unit with the proper arrangement of age classes for that purpose. This is a goal that can be approached only very imperfectly. Sometimes there is the illusion of doing so in mixed stands in which tree diameter is taken as a good indicator of tree age, which it is not.

Unfortunately many sins are committed in the names of the selection method of regeneration and uneven-aged management, especially in mixed stands. It frequently degenerates into "high-grading" in which the biggest and best trees are removed from a stand often without actually making gaps large enough for truly new age classes to become established. It is often fallacious to assume that one can cut the big trees and expect the smaller ones to grow to replace them. The nontechnical term, "selective cutting," which denotes almost any kind of partial cutting, is sometimes a euphemism for high-grading.

The existence of two age classes in a stand is ordinarily a temporary condition. However, it can be a continuing one when there is reason to allow some trees of a stand to grow on rotation lengths at least twice as long as those of others. Usually this involves different species of differing longevity.

The *coppice* methods and systems depend on vegetative regeneration. The *simple coppice method* is the same as clearcutting except that the regeneration comes from sprouts, the surest mode of regeneration of all. It is by far the most ancient silvicultural method and has been used for millenia in Eurasia as a means of producing fuelwood and small poles. Cuttings at intervals of a few years repeated for centuries often induce clumps of sprouts so dense that the new trees are too feeble to stand straight or grow tall. This gave the coppice method a bad reputation. Much more recent experience in America has shown that trees of vegetative origin can be of good form if very short rotations are avoided. In fact, sprout regeneration is very important and useful in most forests of broad-leaved species, including tropical rain forests.

One ancient variant of the coppice method is the *coppice-with-standards method* in which the basic coppice stand is regenerated frequently but scattered larger trees are carried for two or more coppice rotations. The purpose of this was usually to grow the small trees for fuelwood and the larger ones for construction material.

The methods of cutting applied in stratified mixtures usually involve thinking of each stratum separately. Each stratum can be thinned or otherwise treated as if it were a stand by itself. It is also possible by judicious removals in the upper strata to release trees of some (but not all) lower-stratum species to ascend into the top stratum. Regeneration is usually started as advanced regeneration by heavy removals of some of the lowermost strata in shelterwood cut-tings. If it is later thoroughly released by removal of the upper strata the various species of the new stand gradually rearrange themselves into their respective strata.

Bibliography

Barrett, J. W. (ed.) (1980). "Regional Silviculture of the United States," 2nd Ed. Wiley, New York.

Daniel, T. W., Helms, J. S., and Baker, F. S. (1979). "Principles of Silviculture," 2nd Ed. McGraw–Hill, New York.

Kimmins, J. P. (1987). "Forest Ecology." Macmillan, New York.

Matthews, J. D. (1989). "Silvicultural Systems." Clarendon, Oxford.

Oliver, C. D., and Larson, B. C. (1990). "Forest Stand Dynamics." McGraw–Hill, New York.

Shepherd, K. R. (1986). "Plantation Silviculture." Martinus Nijhoff, Boston.

Smith, D. M. (1986). "The Practice of Silviculture." 8th Ed. Wiley, New York.

Spurr, S. H., and Barnes, B. V. (1980). "Forest Ecology," 3rd Ed. Wiley, New York.

U.S. Forest Service (1983). "Silvicultural Systems for the Major Forest Types of the United States." USDA Agriculture Handbook 445. Government Printing Office, Washington, DC.

Soil, Acid

JAMES L. AHLRICHS, WILLIAM W. MCFEE, *Purdue University*

Glossary

Buffered Buffered systems are able to resist change; soils are buffered against pH change by their ability to adsorb and desorb cations (+) including H^+ and Al^{3+}, at anionic (−) sites on their particle surfaces; buffered chemical solutions are also used in standardizing pH meters and estimating lime requirement of acid soils

Cation exchange Ability of soil to adsorb and desorb positively charged ions at negative sites on its particle surfaces; the capacity to adsorb cations is expressed in centimoles of charge that can be attracted per kilogram of soil

Cycle Carbon, nitrogen, and sulfur compounds each undergo modifications in nature that circulate them through various chemical states; carbon (e.g., as atmospheric CO_2) is reduced to -CHx forms in plants by photosynthesis; later it is returned to the atmosphere as organisms complete the cycle by oxidizing the plant residues back to CO_2

Nernst equation Equation relating the potential (voltage) produced by a specific ion electrode to the activity of the ion in solution; H^+ sensitive glass electrode of a pH meter produces 0.059 V change for each 1 unit pH change

Soil profile Vertical cross-section of the soil exhibiting the soil horizons (layers) which differ in physical or chemical properties

Indiana Agricultural Experiment Station, Purdue Journal no. 13768.

Soil taxonomy System of classifying soils derived for international use. It is analogous to the botanical classification of plants; soil order is the highest level of classification; all soils, based on chemical and physical properties, are assignable to 1 of the 11 soil orders (see the bibliography reference to Fanning and Fanning for more detail)

Acid soil has a pH of less than 7 on the 0–14 scale used to define acidity (pH < 7) and alkalinity (pH > 7). Acid soils have an excess of protons (H^+) over hydroxyls (OH^-) in their solution phase. This acidity produces increased solubility of metal compounds of iron (Fe), manganese (Mn), zinc (Zn), copper (Cu), and aluminum (Al), with Al and Mn sometimes reaching levels that are phytotoxic. The proton and metal cation competition increases leaching of potassium (K), magnesium (Mg), and calcium (Ca) which may result in K and Mg deficiency and, in extreme cases, Ca deficiency. The cations which leach during acidification are accompanied by anions and thus acid soil may also be deficient in sulfur, boron, molybdenum, and phosphorus. For many plant species a slightly acid soil is the most desirable, but at a pH below about pH 5.5 many species begin to show adverse effects from the acid condition.

In this article the distribution and causes of soil acidity are followed by the soil chemistry of acidity, the nutritional and toxicity effects on plant growth, and the approaches to ameliorating and managing acid soils.

I. Location of Acid Soils

A. Geography and Climate

A major factor in production of acid soils is the naturally acidic rain which leaches the soil of salts, dis-

Encyclopedia of Agricultural Science, Volume 4   Copyright © 1994 by Academic Press, Inc.   All rights of reproduction in any form reserved.

29

solves the weatherable minerals, and removes alkali metal and alkaline earth cations from the soil. The replacement of the basic cations by protons from the rain then initiates the "acid soil" condition. Thus, acid soils occur in climatic zones where precipitation exceeds evapotranspiration for at least part of the year. High rainfall areas in the temperate, subtropical, and equatorial tropic zones have many regions of acid soils. The pH may be equally low in these three zones; however, subtropical and tropical soils are often more highly weathered due to higher temperatures, and thus show more auxillary or secondary effects of soil acidity. Strong acidity occurs in cool humid mountain ranges in most regions of the world. Significant acidity also exists where precipitation occurs as a short rainy season which exceeds the seasonal evaporative losses and causes leaching such as observed in Sahelian Africa. If regions where acidity exists, but is not severe enough to require amelioration, are included, then one notes that agricultural land of the earth is dominated by acid soils.

B. Taxonomic Classification

Soil taxonomy classifies all soils into 1 of 11 soil orders. Strong acidity occurs in the taxonomic orders of Spodosols, Ultisols, Oxisols, and Andisols. Most Histisols also are markedly acid but high pH seepage water from surrounding uplands causes some peat and muck soils to be near neutral as occurs where the uplands are formed from recent calcareous glacial till. Alfisols typically are acid but less severely so; this soil order requires >35% saturation of the exchange sites by basic cations in the diagnostic horizon. The developmental conditions necessary for Mollisols, Vertisols, and Aridisols generally exclude acidic soils from these orders. Finally, acidity in the soil orders of Entisols and Inceptisols is primarily dependent on the parent material pH and thus these soils can be either acid or alkaline. [See SOIL GENESIS, MORPHOLOGY, AND CLASSIFICATION.]

C. Within the Soil Profile

Acidity is not uniformly distributed vertically in the soil profile. Since acidity mainly enters soil at the surface from rainfall and other processes, one would expect the surface layer (A horizon) of a soil to be the most acid and lower horizons progressively less acid. This situation exists in some acid soils; however, many soils have a distinctive pH profile with the A horizon only slightly acid, the subsequent E and/or

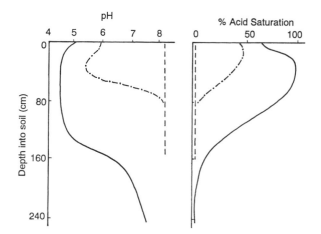

FIGURE 1 pH and percentage acid saturation in soils derived from unconsolidated calcareous parent material: young (Entisol), mature (Alfisol) and old (Ultisol) soils. ----, Entisol; —·—·—, Alfisol; _____, Ultisol.

B horizon(s) moderately to strongly acid, and finally the deeper C horizon has the pH of the parent material. Nutrient recycling by plants and liming by man are mainly responsible for the less acid surface. Plant roots take large quantities of basic cations (Ca^{2+}, Mg^{2+}, K^+, Na^+) from various depths within the soil profile and translocate them to the stem and leaf tissue. Roots absorbing these basic cations release an equivalent quantity of protons which acidify the root zone. Finally, with senescense or death, the stem and leaf tissue decomposes at the soil surface, releases the basic cations, and effectively relimes the surface. Figure 1 illustrates the effect of these processes in a profile view of unconsolidated calcareous parent material in a young, a mature (15,000 yr) and an old (>150,000 yr) soil, each receiving about 1 m of annual rainfall. As the acidification progresses, pH decreases and the percentage saturation of the cation exchange sites with acid increases. This process is even more extreme in very old, highly weathered soils (e.g., the Ultisols and Oxisols of high rainfall subtropical and tropical areas) where plant nutrition is often almost totally dependent on the recycled nutrients in the A horizon. Very little nutrition is retrievable from the acid subsoil, and the parent material is too deep for roots to benefit from basic cations in it. [See SOIL FERTILITY.]

II. Source of Acidity

Four atmospheric gases, carbon dioxide (CO_2), nitrogen (N_2), nitrogen oxides (NO_x), and sulfur dioxide (SO_2), via hydrolysis and/or redox reactions, are the primary sources of soil acidity. Atmospheric CO_2 and N_2 are major natural sinks for carbon and nitrogen. The CO_2, NO_x, and SO_2 all occur naturally, but are also industrial pollutants. [*See* SOIL CHEMISTRY; SOIL POLLUTION.]

CO_2, NO_x and SO_2 produce carbonic, nitric, and sulfuric acid (H_2CO_3, HNO_3 and H_2SO_4) upon further oxidation and/or reaction with water. In addition, living plants convert CO_2 and N_2 to the reduced forms of carbon and nitrogen (-CH_x, -NH_x) which predominate in living tissue. Subsequent oxidation of the plant residue introduces organic acids into the soil from the carbon and nitric acid from the nitrogen. The formation of reduced compounds typically results in proton consumption while oxidation releases protons. Reactions involving C, N, S, as well as Fe and Mn are major factors in acidification.

A. CO₂ and the Carbon Cycle

Rainwater in equilibrium with atmospheric CO_2, at its typical 30 Paschals partial pressure, has a pH near 5.6. However, the carbonic acid produced is a weak acid so the pH of the rainwater does not reflect the large quantity of undissociated carbonic acid that is also present. The magnitude of the acidifying effect is indicated by the calculation that 1 meter of annual rain at pH 5.6 should be able to dissolve 400–500 kg of $CaCO_3$ from a hectare of soil. A clear example of this is acidification in the eastern section of the glacial till plains of northcentral United States. The original coarse loamy till was 20 to 50% ground limestone rock and received an annual rainfall of about 1 m. These soils are leached of carbonates and acidified to a depth of nearly 1 m. About 5000 to 13,000 metric tons of carbonates per hectare have dissolved and leached over the 15,000 years since glaciation; an annual loss in the range of 350 to 880 kg ha^{-1}.

Some of the acidification by carbon is from the organic acids produced during decomposition of plant residue. If the decomposition occurs in somewhat anaerobic conditions, as exist in wet soils, then abundant simple organic acids are formed. The later stages of decomposition produce the rather stable black humus compounds common in surface soils. The main humus components are complex high-molecular-weight humic and slightly lower molecular weight fulvic acid. These all are carboxylic acids. The final oxidation of the carbon in soil organic matter produces carbonic acid at a high concentration in the soil solution because of the high partial pressure of CO_2 (5 to 20 times atmospheric) produced by this decomposition and by root and microbial respiration within the soil pores.

B. NOx and the Nitrogen Cycle

Acidification by nitrogen differs from that of carbon in that most plants do not directly use N_2 from the atmosphere. Thus, the main acidification by nitrogen is associated either with legume/*Rhizobium* symbiosis or with use of ammonium forms of nitrogen fertilizers [NH_3, $(NH_2)_2CO$, $(NH_4)_2SO_4$, NH_4NO_3]. [*See* NITROGEN CYCLING.]

In the legume/*Rhizobium* symbiosis the *Rhizobium* bacteria convert atmospheric N_2 to an $-NH$ or $-NH_2$ form that the host plant can use in protein synthesis. On death of the plant the decomposing tissue releases NH_4^+ which can nitrify and release protons to the soil.

$$NH_4^+ + 2\,O_2 \rightarrow NO_3^- + 2\,H^+ + H_2O.$$

Ammonium forms of nitrogen fertilizer undergo the same nitrifying process. This nitrification is actually a two-stage microbial oxidation from NH_4^+ to NO_2^- by *Nitrosomonas* species and on to NO_3^- by *Nitrobacter* species, but the two protons per NH_4^+ are released in the first stage.

Nitrogen fertilizer additions of up to several hundred kg ha^{-1} are often used on nonleguminous crops to provide the nutritional needs for nitrogen. This is the single most acidifying factor in many agricultural soils. Not all added NH_4^+ produce the theoretical two protons per ion since some NH_4^+ ions are taken up by plants before oxidation and secondary reactions may lessen the impact of others. Yet, the Association of Official Analytical Chemists (AOAC) procedure for neutralization of the acid produced by ammonium-type fertilizers recommends 1.8 kg $CaCO_3$ for each kilogram N added as ammonia or urea and 5.35 kg $CaCO_3$ per kilogram of N added as ammonium sulfate which is, respectively, 0.5 and 1.5 mol$_c$ as $CaCO_3$ per mol N.

The contribution of atmospheric NO_x pollution to soil acidity is small. The nitric acid formed typically produces considerably less than 1 kg of H^+ per hectare per year. Since a hectare of soil 15 cm deep weighs about 2,000,000 kg, less than 0.5 ppm H^+ is being added annually to the tilled portion of the soil. The N added is useful as a nutrient, but it too is not very significant, generally less than 10 kg ha^{-1} year^{-1}.

C. SO₂ and the Sulfur Cycle

Elemental sulfur (S), protein sulfur (R-SH), and iron sulfides (FeS, Fe_3S_4 or FeS_2) are all reduced forms of sulfur. In each the sulfur will oxidize to sulfate and in the process release several hydrogen ions. Elemental sulfur is used to acidify soil especially when growing certain ornamental and crop species that are favored by more acid soil.

The reduced sulfur in plant and animal residues is mainly in two amino acids, cystine and methionine. The quantities of sulfur are small, usually about 0.3% in most tissue and thus contribute very little acidity during oxidation in the soil.

The major acidifying effect of sulfur occurs in isolated locations where iron sulfides have formed under special reducing conditions until large amounts have accumulated. When the environment then suddenly changes from reducing to oxidizing, sulfuric acid forms and a large amount of acidity is released. This oxidation occurs when certain coastal marshlands are drained, and where coal mine spoil or harbor dredgings are exposed to aeration. Some metal ores also exist as sulfides and mine spoil from the ore processing reacts like iron sulfide.

The iron sulfides form mainly in tidal marshes and ocean harbors. The marshes and harbors provide (1) a supply of sulfate and iron ions in the seawater, (2) adequate metabolizable organic matter as food both for the sulfate-reducing organisms and to maintain an anerobic system, plus (3) the flushing action of the tides to remove bicarbonates and to give partial oxidation, all of which combine to produce the correct environment. Sulfate then is reduced to sulfide and reacts with iron to form precipitates of FeS, Fe_3S_4 or FeS_2. These are black precipitates intermixed in the sediments of tidal marshes and harbors. Over geologic time iron sulfides have accumulated in coal, lignite, and sedimentary rocks and have often grown into larger, golden crystals of pyrite (fool's gold). The iron sulfides maintained under reducing conditions will not be acidic. Harbor dredgings often are black sediment with pH near 7. However, exposure to air rapidly produces sulfuric acid plus the sulfate and hydroxides of iron. The initial reaction of pyrite (FeS_2),

$$FeS_2 + 3\tfrac{1}{2} O_2 + H_2O \rightarrow FeSO_4 + H_2SO_4,$$

shows a mole of acid formed for each mole of pyrite. This can produce extreme acidity; the pH may be as low as 2. Extreme acidity in turn produces rapid weathering and many secondary reactions including formation of several ferrous and ferric iron minerals. The iron eventually becomes a ferric hydroxide precipitate, and a second mole of sulfuric acid is obtained from this hydrolysis of $FeSO_4$ to $Fe(OH)_3$.

In the atmosphere, SO_2 gas reacts with water and oxygen to give H_2SO_4. Like the HNO_3 produced from NO_x in the air, the SO_2, will produce a typical annual deposition of less than 1 kg H^+ per hectare. On a regional basis, in an industrialized country, the annual atmospheric acid deposition could be 1 kg of H^+ of which about one-third would be from NO_x and two-thirds from SO_2 reactions. In industrialized countries the sulfur in rainfall can easily equal 10 kg ha^{-1} $year^{-1}$ which fills a significant portion of the nutritional needs of plants for this nutrient.

III. Chemistry of Acid Soil

A. Clay and Humus as Acids and Acidic Soils

Soil acid is composed of an anion($-$) and a cation ($+$). Typically, the anion is a mineral particle, one of the well-defined clay minerals, and may have from near zero to over 100 cmol of negative charge per kilogram of solid ($cmol_c$ kg^{-1}). Partially decomposed organic tissue, humus, also is high in negative charge, up to 200 $cmol_c$ kg^{-1}. These clay or humus anions are thus analogous to the immobile anion in a cation exchange resin. With H^+ as the exchangeable cation these immobile anions are true acids. Acid soil partially dissociates its H^+ to give an acidic solution. If, however, Al^{3+} is the cation on the clay or humus, it behaves as an acidic salt releasing Al^{3+} which reacts with H_2O (hydrolysis) to produce H^+ which acidifies the solution.

It is appropriate to note here that soil pH is a measure of the activity of the H^+ in solution (an intensity factor) and gives no quantitative indication of the amount of undissociated hydrogen or aluminum on the cation exchange sites of the soil (the quantity factor).

It is also important to realize that acidification requires leaching of the basic cations out of the soil upon displacement from the exchange sites by H^+ or Al^{3+}. The bases leach away, when rainfall is adequate, accompanied by the anions (e.g., HCO_3^- or NO_3^-) which were originally associated with the incoming acid.

Acid saturation differs between organic and mineral soils. Organic soils have carboxylate groups as the primary anion sites and the acid saturation can come from either Al or H, although H may predominate in the more purely organic soil. However, mineral soils most commonly have Al as their exchangeable acid cation on both their mineral and organic colloids.

The study of acid mineral soils thus is primarily a study of Al soils.

B. Acidity from Aluminum

Al^{3+} is a small ion with a high charge. This high-charge density gives Al a strong attraction for the oxygen of water molecules. Space around the Al ion permits coordination by the oxygens of six water molecules. The protons of water are repulsed by the close proximity to the trivalent Al and dissociate readily producing free protons (acidity) plus a series of hydrated Al–hydroxy compounds.

$$[Al(H_2O)_6]^{3+} \rightarrow [Al(H_2O)_5(OH)]^{2+} + H^+$$
$$\rightarrow [Al(H_2O)_4(OH)_2]^+ + H^+$$
$$\rightarrow [Al(H_2O)_3(OH)_3]^o + H^+$$
$$\rightarrow [Al(H_2O)_2(OH)_4]^- + H^+.$$

As pH rises, the hydrated aluminum ion $[Al(H_2O)_6]^{+3}$ gives stepwise release of protons until Al finally appears as the anionic aluminate when pH is above 6.5. Figure 2 shows the pH effect on the general distribution of these ion forms (shown more simply without their hydrating water). In addition, $Al(H_2O)_5(OH)^{+2}$ ion can polymerize with others of its kind by sharing hydroxyl groups and thus produce Al species which are large, high-charge, polymeric cations. The Al–hydroxy compounds formed during hydrolysis are all quite stable (dissociate very little) and thus are very weak bases while the protons produced give a strongly acidic character to the system.

The Al ions come from dissolution of soil minerals. Aluminum is the third most abundant element in the earth's crust. It is present in many minerals where it is found surrounded by oxygen or hydroxyl in six-fold, and occasionally fourfold, coordination. Hydrogen entering the soil mineral dissolves Al by reacting with its coordinating oxygen or hydroxyl. The Al becomes $Al(H_2O)_6^{+3}$ or one of its soluble hydroxy ions upon dissolution while the proton becomes H_2O (a reverse of the type of reaction depicted in the equation above).

C. Acid Soil, a Buffered System

Measuring soil pH gives only the hydrogen ion activity in the soil solution phase. Most acidity is stored on the colloid surfaces as exchangeable H^+ and as Al cations which hydrolize to produce H^+. The quantity of exchangeable acidity is commonly three to four orders of magnitude (1000 to 10,000×) greater than that in solution. When H^+ ion concentration in solution is reduced by addition of a base (e.g., liming), then either H^+ dissociates from the exchange sites to re-establish H ion concentration in the solution or more Al hydrolysis occurs to release additional H^+. In reverse, adding acid to a soil causes only small decreases in pH because most of the added protons react with the ion-exchange surface of the colloids and do not stay in solution. With a higher surface charge (higher cation exchange capacity) the soil has a greater buffering against pH change.

The greatest buffering occurs from the large permanent negative charge on most 2:1 lattice clays and from the variable (pH dependent) negative charge of carboxylate groups on soil humus. Some pH buffering also occurs in highly weathered soils low in 2:1 clays and organic humus. This buffering comes primarily from the ability of surface oxides and hydroxides of iron and aluminum to gain or lose protons (H^+) or hydroxyls (OH^-) as the H^+ activity in the solution phase increases or decreases. These oxide and hydroxide surfaces represent a type of variable charge surface. At the isoelectric point the surface absorbs equal amounts of H^+ and OH^- and has no net charge. If the pH of the isoelectric point is high, e.g., above 7, the surface will have a greater affinity for H^+ than for OH^- and vice versus. Thus, these surfaces develop a + or − charge which provides some pH buffering character.

Another type of buffering, long-term buffering, against acidification exists in soils which form from parent materials high in weatherable minerals: i.e., minerals which are relatively unstable in a humid climate. Weatherable minerals include carbonates, most

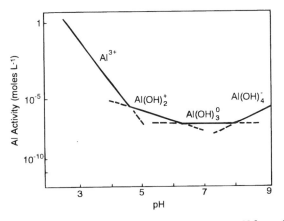

FIGURE 2 Activity of dominant Al species versus pH from gibbsite, $Al(OH)_3^0$, in equilibrium with water. [Adapted with permission from Lindsay, W. L. (1979). "Chemical Equilibria in Soils," Fig. 3.3, p. 40. Copyright © 1979 by John Wiley & Sons, Inc.]

2:1 lattice clays, and such primary minerals as feldspars, feldspathoids, ferromagnesian minerals, and micas. Mg, Ca, K, and Na are significant components of such minerals. The H^+ in soil solution reacts with the carbonate, oxygen, and hydroxyl coordinating these basic ions, thus deactivating the H^+ and releasing the basic ions. This slows the soil acidification; however, eventually, the more weatherable minerals are depleted as in the Oxisols of the tropics. The soils then increasingly consist of the less weatherable 1:1 lattice clays, silica and iron, and aluminum oxides or oxyhydroxides and lose their large cation exchange capacity and most of the buffering associated with it.

As a result of the buffering, soils change pH very slowly. Thus, one would expect little or no measureable change in pH from an annual increment of acid rain, unless the soils had very low cation exchange capacities. Even high rates of acid-producing ammonical fertilizer should normally give only small annual pH changes in well buffered soils. The buffered character of soil, likewise, is active against attempts to raise soil pH. Liming an acid soil, if the soil is highly buffered, requires many tons of lime [$CaMg(CO_3)_2$] per hectare, and even on a poorly buffered soil a ton or two is required to significantly increase soil pH.

IV. Measuring Soil Acidity

Soil acidity is determined in two fundamentally different ways, a measure either of the H^+ in the soil solution or of the total (solution plus exchangeable) acidity in the system. The acidity in the soil solution controls the solubility of nutrient and nonnutrient ions and represents the acidity in which the plant roots and other soil organisms must live. It is often referred to as the "intensity" of the acidity. The total acidity, in contrast, represents that which must be considered in altering the acidity of the soil solution and is the "quantity" factor. [*See* SOIL TESTING FOR PLANT GROWTH AND SOIL FERTILITY.]

A. pH of Soil Solution

Soil solution acidity is measured in units of moles of H^+ per liter of solution. For convenience, these units are expressed as pH which is the negative log of the activity; thus, pH 5 is 10^{-5} mol liter^{-1} while pH 6 is 10^{-6} mol liter^{-1}. Each change of one pH unit represents a 10-fold change in H^+, e.g., a pH of 5 is 10 times more acid than pH 6.

pH is a measure of H^+ "activity," rather than "concentration"; however, activity and concentration are essentially equal when concentrations are low as they are in soil solution. As ionic strength of a solution increases, the H^+ activity will be somewhat less than concentration by an amount calculable by the Debye-Hueckel equation. In any case, the H^+ activity which the pH electrodes measure is the preferred information because activity, rather than concentration, determines the reactions in soil.

Soil solution pH is usually measured potentiometricaly with a glass electrode which is specific for H^+. As the H^+ activity in the soil suspension differs from the constant H^+ activity within the electrode, a potential is produced across the thin glass membrane. The potential is compared by the pH meter to a constant potential produced in a reference electrode which is also immersed in the soil suspension to complete the circuit, as shown in Fig. 3. The glass electrode responds according to the Nernst equation, which dictates that each 10-fold change in hydrogen ion activity should give a 59 mV change in potential. For use, the meter is standardized against solutions of known pH. The meter scale is labeled in pH units with one pH unit higher or lower for each 10-fold change in H^+ activity.

Soil solution consists of films of water adsorbed on soil particle surfaces and in the finer capillary pores. This is inadequate solution to give good contact with pH electrodes. Thus, solution pH is typically measured by adding distilled water, or a 0.01 M $CaCl_2$ solution to give a suspension of either a 1:1 or 2.5:1 solution to soil ratio. Adding distilled water dilutes the natural salts in the soil solution and tends to give an artificially higher pH rather than the true solution pH of an acid soil. The $CaCl_2$ solution attempts to maintain a salt content in the solution near that found in the original undiluted soil solution and thus gives

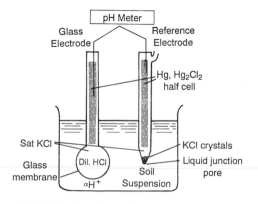

FIGURE 3 Glass electrode system for measurement of pH.

a slightly more valid pH. However, pH fluctuates within a field soil as salt and water content change with mineralization, evaporation, and rainfall; thus, either way of measuring pH can be valid for assessing soil solution acidity.

The pH can also be measured by equilibrating soil with solutions of certain organic acid indicators which change color as they go from associated to dissociated forms. Dilute solutions of the indicators are added to a small amount of soil in a spot plate and observed for indicator color change. Each indicator usually functions over a short range of less than 1 pH unit above and below its pKa. Commonly used indicators are Brom Cresol Green (pKa 4.6), Chlor Phenol Red (pKa 6.0), Brom Thymol Blue (pKa 6.6), and Brom Cresol Purple (pKa 6.0)

B. Total Soil Acidity

Total soil acidity is measured by displacement of cations from the soil with a salt solution and titration of the amount of acid present. Displacement by 1 M KCl gives the acidity that can be removed at the pH of the system because KCl is an unbuffered salt that immediately adjusts to the soil pH. Titration of the displaced acidity with a standard base then converts H^+ to H_2O and Al^{3+} to $Al(OH)_3$ and the hydroxyls consumed equal the total salt-exchangable acidity. Subsequent addition of a fluoride salt (KF) to the titrated solution causes F^- to displace the OH^- from the $Al(OH)_3$. The OH^- can then be titrated with standard acid (HCl) to determine how much of the acidity is attributable to Al.

A method of displacement with a solution of $BaCl_2$ buffered at pH 8.2 with triethanolamine is used to obtain total "potential" acidity. Buffering at pH 8.2 assures removal of acidity from weakly dissociating soil acids. This determination approximates the acidity that $CaCO_3$ in limestone can neutralize since saturated $CaCO_3$ solution has a pH near 8.2. It measures considerably more acidity than the KCl extraction, especially in acid soils that contain large amounts of humus and/or amorphous alumino-silicate material.

V. Acid Soil and Plant Nutrition

A. Direct Effects of Hydrogen

The effects of acid soil on plant growth are mostly secondary effects of the acid condition on the solubility of nutrient and nonnutrient ions and their availability to plants. The direct influence of the H^+ on plants is minor unless the pH is very low: pH 4 or less. It has been difficult to separate the hydrogen ion effect from the secondary effects associated with low pH.

B. Transition Metal Solubility

Increased solubility of the transition metals, Fe, Mn, Zn, and Cu, is generally a positive effect of an acid soil. In nonacid (alkaline or calcareous) soils deficiencies of these elements often occur because of the low solubility of their carbonate, hydroxide, and oxide forms.

C. Microorganism Activity

Acid soils reduce activity of most soil bacteria and actinomycetes. Thus, soil acidity can be used to control pH-sensitive disease organisms such as the potato scab organism which is controlled by keeping pH low. However, low pH also reduces microbial decomposition of plant residue. Since much of the N, P, and S needed by plants must be recycled from previous plant tissue, acid soil decreases the available N, P, and S supply. Also, some species of the symbiotic nitrogen-fixing organisms on legume roots (*Rhizobium* spp.) are sensitive enough to acidity (Al, H, low Ca) to result in nitrogen-deficient legumes on acid soils. [*See* SOIL MICROBIOLOGY.]

D. Phosphorus Solubility

Soil acidity can depress phosphorus availability in the natural situation because phosphorus forms low solubility salts with Fe, Mn, and Al. These three metal ions are much more abundant in acid soil solution than the meager supply of P, and therefore depress the quantity of P in solution. However, recent research indicates that soils that have had P added as fertilizer actually show greater P solubility in more acid soils.

E. Cation and Anion Leaching

Ions which leach are often in low supply in acid soil because acidity is mainly an artifact of long-term leaching. Thus K^+, Mg^{2+}, and Ca^{2+} can be reduced to deficiency levels by such leaching, augmented by their displacement from exchange sites by H^+ and Al^{3+}. Such deficiency occurs commonly in humid regions for K^+, less commonly for Mg^{2+}, and seldom for Ca^{2+}: in this order because of natural abundance and/or relative order of resistance to leaching. Leaching of Mn^{2+}, Zn^{2+}, and Cu^{2+} during soil acidification can cause deficiencies especially if followed by liming which decreases solubility of the small amounts of these three micronutrient metals remaining in the depleted soil. [See SOIL, CHEMICALS: MOVEMENT AND RETENTION.]

The anions (NO_3^-, SO_4^{2-}, and MoO_4^{2-}) leach readily because soils generally have little anion-exchange capacity. Boron, as H_3BO_3, has no charge and also leaches. Thus, acidic soils often are low in these nutrients. Interestingly, liming to raise the pH increases the MoO_4^{2-} in the solution often eliminating Mo deficiency; however, liming decreases solution H_3BO_3, accentuating B deficiency.

VI. Acid Soil Toxicity to Plants

Al and Mn, metal ions, reach toxic levels in some acid soils. Aluminum, a nonnutrient ion, has been most studied. Estimates of soil limitations to plant growth in the "developing" world show an average of 23% of the soil use is constrained by Al toxicity and another 16% limited by acidity without Al toxicity. Al toxicity is primarily due to the Al^{3+} ion species. Al^{3+} toxicity damages roots of sensitive species, an effect which occurs at concentrations below 2 μM liter^{-1} in solution culture. Yet soil solutions containing Al up to several hundred μM liter^{-1} may be either toxic or nontoxic. This ambiguity occurs because solution Al in soils occurs in many forms which are either nontoxic or less toxic than the Al^{3+} ion (e.g., $Al(OH)_2^+$, $Al(OH)^{2+}$, $Al(SO_4)^+$, and organic complexes of Al). Al toxicity is not expected in soils above pH 5.5 and seldom occurs until pH declines to <5.

Thus, without accurate speciation, it is difficult to know whether an acid soil will produce phytotoxicity from Al. Since accurate speciation is very difficult, a short-term bioassay with an aluminum-sensitive plant species gives the most efficient indicator of the toxicity. Roots in a toxic soil observed as soon as 2 to 3 days after germination are generally lacking in root hairs, much shorter, and may show spatulated root tips and necrotic tissue in comparison to those grown in a nontoxic check soil.

Toxicity of Mn is less common because Mn levels in soil are lower. Mn toxicity may be induced by a combination of high Mn content in the soil with low pH and/or reducing conditions which increase the solution concentration of Mn^{2+}, accompanied by an abundant supply of a nutrient anion like NO_3^- to stimulate cation uptake.

VII. Managing Acid Soils

A. Ameliorating the Soils

Soil acidity can be decreased or increased. Finely crushed limestone and marl are the most common products used to decrease acidity. Limestone and marl are available in most parts of the world and are easy to crush, thus making them inexpensive. Their primary ingredients are calcium and magnesium carbonate, two basic salts. Reacted with the soil solution they produce $Ca(OH)_2$ and $Mg(OH)_2$ which neutralize the acidity. Because of low solubility, the limestone must be finely crushed to expose a large surface area to the soil solution. The fine powder produced also provides adequate particles to permit good distribution, and thus uniform neutralization of acidity throughout the surface soil. Either calcium oxide or hydroxide (CaO or $Ca(OH)_2$) are occasionally used. Because they are manufactured from limestone they are more expensive; however, they have 179 and 136%, respectively, of the acid neutralizing value of calcium carbonate per unit weight. Other bases or basic salts also decrease acidity but generally are less available, less suitable, or more expensive. [See SOIL MANAGEMENT.]

Conversely, where a more acid soil is desired, elemental sulfur, an inexpensive yellow powder, can be added. It slowly oxidizes and hydrolyzes to sulfuric acid. A more expensive alternative which gives rapid acidification is the addition of the acid salts, ferrous sulfate ($FeSO_4$) or aluminum sulfate [$Al_2(SO_4)_3$], which form sulfuric acid upon hydrolysis. If one wishes to maintain or slowly increase acidity in soil, ammonium sulfate used as the nitrogen source for plants will accomplish this.

Liming an acid soil typically requires from 1 to as much as 20 tons of limestone per hectare. Prediction of the amount needed is based on determination of the acidity present by laboratory titration of the acidity of a sample of the soil: a slow process. More commonly, the amount needed is approximated by adding a measured sample of the soil to a standard solution which has been buffered at a rather high pH, e.g., 7.5 in the commonly used Shoemaker-McLean-Pratt (SMP) buffer solution. The acid soil decreases the pH of the buffer solution and this decrease has been calibrated to give the approximate lime needed to obtain the

TABLE I
Lime Required to Bring Soils to Desired pH as Determined by Equilibrium pH of SMP Buffer (pH 7.5) with Acid Soil

pH of soil–buffer mix	Desired soil pH[a]		
	7.0	6.5	6.0
6.8	2.5	2.0	1.8
6.7	4.0	3.6	3.0
6.6	5.4	4.5	3.8
6.5	7.0	5.8	4.7
6.4	9.0	7.6	6.3
6.3	10.5	9.0	7.4
6.2	12.1	10.3	8.3
6.1	13.4	11.2	9.2
6.0	15.2	12.8	10.5
5.9	17.2	14.6	11.9
5.8	18.6	15.7	12.8
5.7	20.2	17.0	13.9

[a] Values are tons pure $CaCO_3$/hectare to a depth of 20 cm. Adjust actual rate for quality of lime and depth of tillage.

desired soil pH as shown in Table I. The effect on soil acidity of adding limestone occurs over a period of a few months but should not need repeating for some years unless the soil has a very low cation-exchange capacity and large amounts of ammoniacal nitrogen fertilizer are being used.

Lime has little effect below the depth to which it is mixed. Thus, the subsoil will continue to be acid after liming. If the acidity inhibits deep and thorough root penetration, there will be inefficient use of soil water. Much of the drought stress observed in the southeastern United States and similar areas is probably induced by the adverse effect of subsoil acidity on root development.

B. Selecting Tolerant Species

Plant species differ in sensitivity to the elevated levels of aluminum, hydrogen, and manganese ions in acid soils. Pearl millet (*Pennisetum glaucum*) cowpea (*Vigna sinensis*), and cassava (*Manihot esculenta*) are examples of food species with great tolerance to acidity. In contrast, many edible beans (*Phaseolus vulgaris*), soybeans (*Glycine max*), and alfalfa (*Medicago sativa*) are examples of sensitive species. Variability in acid-soil tolerance within individual species also exists, and an acid tolerant variety or genotype will often grow well in a low pH soil where another variety of the same species does poorly. Plant breeders working especially with sorghum, forage legumes and grasses, wheat, and maize are evaluating their genetic material for acid/Al tolerance for use in producing varieties adapted to acid soil situations.

Thus, one can ameliorate a bad growth situation produced by acid soil by either amending the soil or selecting tolerant plant species or varieties. However, using plants with acid/Al tolerant roots will be important when liming materials are not available or too expensive and where acid subsoils are causing poor root development and drought stress.

Bibliography

Adams, F. (1984). "Soil Acidity and Liming" (F. Adams, ed.), 2nd ed. American Society of Agronomy, Madison, WI.

Bohn, H. L., McNeal, B. L., and O'Connor, G. A. (1985). "Soil Chemistry," 2nd ed. Wiley, New York.

Fanning, D. S., and Fanning, M. C. B. (1989). "Soil: Morphology, Genesis and Classification." Wiley, New York.

Robson, A. D. (1989). "Soil Acidity and Plant Growth." (A. D. Robson, ed.). Academic Press, New York.

Sposito, G. (1989). "The Chemistry of Soils." Oxford Univ. Press, New York.

Ulrich, B., and Sumner, M. E. (1991). "Soil Acidity" (Ulrich and Sumner, eds.). Springer-Verlag, Berlin.

Wright, R. J., Baligar, V. C., and Murrmann, R. P. (1991). "Plant–Soil Interactions at Low pH." Kluwer Academic, Dordrecht.

Soil and Land Use Surveys

M. A. MULDERS, *Agricultural University, The Netherlands*

Glossary

Land Soil is one aspect of land; land concerns the complex of soil, vegetation, hydrology, climate, and infrastructure; much land is used by man for various purposes.
Land use Major kind of land use is a major subdivision of rural land use, such as rainfed agriculture, grassland, forestry or recreation; land utilization type is a kind of land use described or defined in a degree of greater detail than land use; it consists of a set of technical specifications in a given physical, economic, and social setting; terms multiple or compound land utilization types refer to situations in which more than one kind of land use is practiced within an area: a land use system.
Soil Collection of natural bodies on the earth's surface, in places modified or even made by man of earthy materials, containing mineral and living matter and supporting or capable of supporting plants out of doors; soils are classified according to systems such as the Soil Map of the World, the U. S. Soil Taxonomy and the French Soil Taxonomy.

Soil and land use surveys involve activities, which are intended to construct maps providing for the regional distribution of soils and land use. Different techniques are used for this purpose: (1) Field description and laboratory analysis of soils; (2) Land cover description and inquiries on land use; (3) Processing and interpretation of remote sensing imagery including aerial photography; and (4) Application of Geographic Information Systems (GIS).

I. Introduction

Soil maps are still needed in many countries. Many countries possess maps at a scale of 1:500,000 with information too broad to enable adequate planning of land use. For this a 1:100,000 soil map is a minimum requirement. After a first selection of promising areas, maps at larger scale (e.g., 1:25,000) provide definite lay out of parcels, drainage, and irrigation systems.

While soil may be regarded as a more or less stable feature with regard to the build up of the profile, the processes active in soil fauna, the distribution of salts and moisture, and the formation of soil structure are highly dynamic. One has to be aware of the fact that a soil map is not the final task of the soil survey. The same applies for land use: a highly dynamic feature. The mapping of land use may be done at a regular time basis. It is often aimed to characterize the process and indicate the causes for a change in land use, which can be socioeconomic or related to land degradation.

II. Soil Survey

Soils are surveyed in accordance to the physiography of the land. The latter may help in exploring the history of the land in a geological way (several millions of years) or in a human historical way (several hundreds and thousands of years). Both ways are important in defining "natural soil bodies" or cultural soil bodies, the latter entirely made up by human activity, e.g., soils with a plaggen epipedon produced by long and continued manuring. Different systems may be used in soil survey ranging from a grid system to a landscape-guided physiographic approach and the survey of key areas. In the latter, interpretation of aerial photographs and satellite imagery make it possible to extrapolate the results of well-defined soil surveys in relatively small areas.

The system used for physiographic interpretation of aerial photographs and other remote sensing imagery is illustrated in Fig. 1.

The resulting interpretation maps are used as an entry to plan the field survey, that is to locate the points, transects, and key areas to be surveyed. Field observations on soils, vegetation, land use, and relief provide the information required for locating boundaries between soil units, which can be checked for accuracy in a later stage. Grid surveys, or detailed observations in transects at relatively short distances, are generally used in detailed surveys at scales of 1:5000, where remote sensing imagery does not offer any key to soil distribution, where the soil landscapes are monotonous, or where statistical approaches to detect soil variability are intended.

Soil analyses are carried out for different purposes:

• To support the soil survey. That is, of different horizons in soil profile pits, a normal set of analyses involves the determination of soil texture, C, N, P, K, cation exchange capacity, exchangeable cations, base

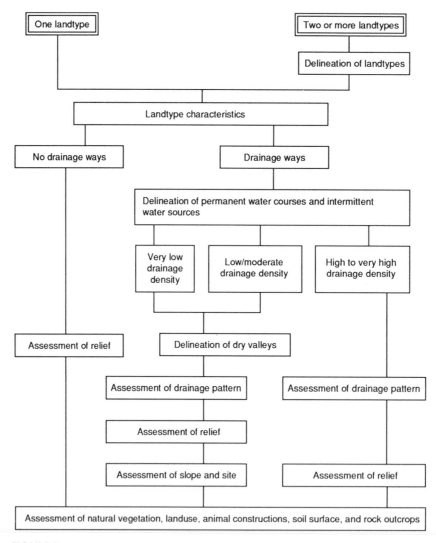

FIGURE 1 Physiographic interpretation for soil survey. [From Mulders, M. A. (1987). Remote sensing in soil science. *Dev. Soil Sci.* **15**, 379. Copyright Elsevier Science, Amsterdam.]

saturation, pH KCl, pH H$_2$O, and other data needed to characterize materials or soil horizons for soil classification.
- Samples at regular intervals to estimate salinity, that is by electrical conductivity and types of salts.
- To estimate soil fertility, that is besides N, P, and K, the exchangeable cations and trace elements (Cu, Zn, Mb, etc.).
- Physical measurements to estimate soil permeability and soil moisture availability.

Soils may be grouped in a number of sets according to the Soil Map of the World:

- organic soils or Histosols;
- mineral soils in which soil formation is conditioned by human influences—Anthrosols;
- mineral soils in which soil formation is conditioned by parent material—Andosols in volcanic material, Arenosols in residual and shifting sands, Vertisols in expanding clays;
- mineral soils in which soil formation is conditioned by physiography—Fluvisols and Gleysols in lowlands with flat to undulating relief, Leptosols and Regosols in elevated regions;
- mineral soils in which soil formation is conditioned by limited age—Cambisols;
- mineral soils in which soil formation is conditioned by climate and climate induced vegetation
  - Plintosols, Ferralsols, Nitisols, Acrisols, Alisols, and Lixisols in tropical and subtropical regions
  - Solonchaks, Solonetz, Gypsisols, and Calcisols in arid and semi-arid regions
  - Kastanozems, Chernozems, Phaeozems, and Greyzems in steppes and steppic regions
  - Luvisols, Podzoluvisols, Planosols, and Podzols in sub-humid forest and grassland regions

[See SOIL GENESIS, MORPHOLOGY, AND CLASSIFICATION; SOIL TESTING.]

III. Land Use Survey

A land use survey involves interpretation of aerial photographs and satellite imagery as well as terrain observations and inquiries on management and socio-economics. The definition of a land utilization type may involve management practices, crop types, and capital and labor inputs. A summary of the main land use systems is given below.

- Settlement/industries: residential use, industrial use, transport, recreational, and excavations
- Agriculture: annual field cropping, perennial field cropping, tree, and shrub cropping
- Animal husbandry: extensive grazing and intensive grazing

- Forestry: exploitation of natural forest and woodland, plantation forestry
- Mixed farming: agroforestry and agropastoralism
- Extraction/collecting: exploitation of natural vegetation, hunting, and fishing
- Nature protection: nature and game preservation, degradation control

Land use is often of a complex nature, for example: forestry and recreation in the same area or different agricultural activities on the same land. In Burkina Faso, sylvopastoral areas do not have clear-cut boundaries. These boundaries are vague, with sylvopastoral land only gradually changing into agricultural land. Furthermore, the use of the agricultural land is of a complex nature since sylvopastoral activities usually take place on these fields after harvesting. [See LAND USE PLANNING IN AGRICULTURE.]

IV. Application of Remote Sensing in Soil and Land Use Surveys

The information required for a soil survey involves a number of landscape attributes, such as relief, drainage system, natural vegetation, and land use (Fig. 1). The usual tool to gather this information is the stereoscopic interpretation of aerial photographs but other remote sensing techniques may be very helpful. These are:

- SLAR or side-looking airborne radar for small-scale analysis of vegetation, drainage systems, and relief
- MSS or multispectral scanning with Landsat MSS (80 m ground resolution), Landsat-TM (thematic mapper with 30 m ground resolution), and SPOT (*système probatoire d'observation de la terre* with multispectral and stereomode of 20 m ground resolution and a panchromatic mode of 10 m ground resolution). Apart from multispectral characterization of the land surface as used in medium- and small-scale mapping, these systems allow multitemporal observation of the land surface to study dynamic aspects: the relation with crop growth, development of natural vegetation, and soil moisture conditions is evident
- IRLS or (thermal) infrared line-scanning data are used for estimations on evapotranspiration and thus are valuable for waterbalance studies
- Multispectral aerial photographs at large-scale and different acquisitions throughout the growing season allow the accurate identification of crop types and the detection of growth differences within and between agricultural fields, thus serving studies on soil variability and fertility

Normally aerial photographs are used for survey purposes in combination with satellite data, the latter of most recent acquisition dates or spread out over a certain period of time to study changes of the land surface. Land surface properties are of equal interest to soil surveys and the survey of land use. The dynamics of the surface have to be translated into land use, using data such as provided for by crop calendars. The aerial photographs at large or medium scale generally provide those details, which help understanding of the small-scale information of the multispectral remote sensing tools.

Land cover describes the natural, vegetational, and man-made resources covering the land surface. It forms the basic output of the application of remote sensing for soil surveys and land use.

Three stages can be distinguished in land cover mapping using single-date Landsat thematic mapper data (TM):

1. Image processing in the prefieldwork stage focused on the overall variation of the scene
2. Small-scale reconnaissance fieldwork and processing thereafter, directed toward the production of thematic imagery
3. Medium-scale reconnaissance fieldwork and classification

These stages involve analyzing the digital data-structure of the remote sensing data (here: TM) as well as a structured method of field data sampling (Fig. 2).

As a first step in analyzing the digital structure, the digital numbers, the values assigned to the different TM wavelength bands, are processed according to selection criteria based on standard deviations and correlation coefficients. A three-band combination with the lowest correlation is composed. To indicate the variation of bands other than those selected by the former criteria, combinations of two or three principal components, expressing most of the variation contained in the TM bands (PC 1-2 or PC 1-2-3), are used.

In the field, the land cover types are identified and described, first sampled at small scale, and later on at medium scale, this latter after the inclusion of highly informative imagery showing variation within land cover class.

The final classification normally involves the inclusion of aerial photographic data besides TM data and training data (a combination of field data and classification results). Most of the land cover identification names have already sufficient detail to include them into land use systems; others have to be translated into land use terms using knowledge of the actual land use systems practiced in the area under consideration.

The scale and the physiognomy of the land use systems, the presence of parcel boundaries, etc., are important for the degree of detail. Figure 3 presents a TM image of an area in Costa Rica. The large parcels are identified without difficulty: banana in light grey; bamboo in grey.

Black and dark grey comprise natural forest while the irregular grey tone pattern mainly represents grassland.

Figures 4a and 4b are aerial photographs originally acquired at a scale of 1:50,000 (size 23 × 23 cm). Figure 4a represents an area with low annual rainfall in Burkina Faso (600 mm), where light-grey tones near valley bottoms and adjacent colluvial slopes indicate agricultural use (millet, sorghum, and peanuts); this in contrast to light-grey tones at the footslopes of ironcaps which have another meaning (discussed later). Parcel boundaries are absent or vague due to changing boundaries and the lack of permanent transport ways.

Figure 4b represents agricultural use in the same country but in an area with higher annual rainfall (900 mm) and ongoing agricultural development projects. Much of the area is occupied by a permanent lay out of parcels (with millet, sorghum, peanuts, cotton, and rice).

V. Matching Soil and Land Use

Experimental fields on which a specific land utilization type is practiced on a specific soil or soil association provide for quantitative data on technical and on economic aspects valid for that particular situation. The experiments can be used to define requirements of the land use, land qualities, and land suitability for that use. The method, which matches land and land use, is called land evaluation.

Most often, there are no experimental data available and information has to be collected by inquiries among farmers and interpretation of soil and climatic data.

Alternatives on this qualitative land evaluation are quantitative procedures, using a.o. simulation of the soil water regime to estimate the moisture supply capacity and estimates on the consumptive use of water by plants.

The latter is taken as an example for the soil and climatic data needed in quantitative land evaluation.

STAGE	INPUT SAMPLING	SCHEME	ACTIVITIES	SELECTION CRITERIA	OUTPUT
I. PREFIELDWORK STAGE AUTOMATED PROCESSING FOR PRODUCTION OF IMAGERY DIRECTED BY OVERALL VARIANCE	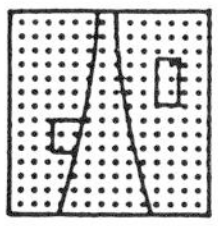	FIXED GRID 512*512 PIXELS SKIP FACTOR: 3	STATISTICS PER BAND MAXIMUM-MINIMUM FOR LINEAR STRETCHING STANDARD DEVIATIONS	HIGHEST VALUES	3-BAND IMAGERY USED FOR SELECTION OF TRAINING FIELDS
		TRAINING FIELD 40*250 PIXELS	CORRELATION COEFFICIENTS BETWEEN BANDS	BANDS WITH LOWEST CORRELATION	3-BAND IMAGERY HIGH INFORMATION POTENTIAL
			AND		AND
	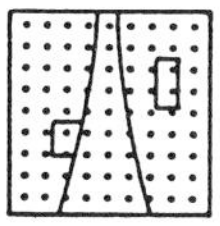	FIXED GRID 512*512 PIXELS SKIP FACTOR: 5	PRINCIPAL COMPONENT TRANSFORMATION	SUM OF VARIANCE	PC 1-2 OR 1-2-3 IMAGE
II. RECONNAISSANCE FIELDWORK SMALL SCALE 1:200,000 AND PRODUCTION OF IMAGERY WHICH IS OBJECT AND FEATURE DIRECTED	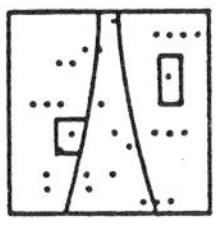 SAMPLE SPOTS	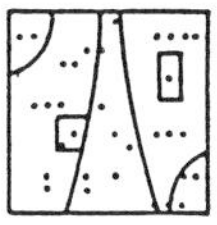	FIELDWORK: IDENTIFICATION AND DESCRIPTION LAND COVER TYPES	VARIATION BETWEEN AND WITHIN LAND COVER TYPES	MAJOR LAND COVER CLASSES FOR FURTHER PROCESSING
	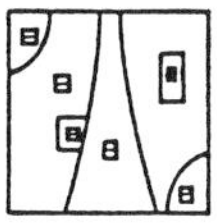	TRAINING FIELDS	AUTOMATED PROCESSING MAJOR LAND COVER CLASSES: MEAN VALUES AND STANDARD DEVIATIONS	SPECTRAL DISCRIMINATION BETWEEN CLASSES	3-BAND IMAGERY RATIO IMAGERY WITH HIGH CONTRAST BETWEEN CLASSES
			AND		AND
			WITHIN CLASS: PCT AND LINEAR STRETCH	IMAGE CONTRAST	IMAGERY WITH CONTRAST WITHIN CLASS
III. RECONNAISSANCE FIELDWORK MEDIUM SCALE 1:50,000 OR 1:100,000 AND CLASSIFICATION	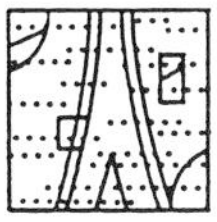	SAMPLE SPOTS DIRECTED BY IMAGE DETAIL	FIELDWORK: ESTIMATION OF CAUSES OF DIFFERENCES BETWEEN AND WITHIN CLASSES	LAND COVER TYPES AND FEATURES OF INTEREST	LANDCOVER CLASSES AND RELEVANT FEATURES
			AUTOMATED PROCESSING SPECTRAL SIGNATURE FILES OF CLASSES AND FEATURES	MINIMUM DISTANCE MAXIMUM LIKELIHOOD, ETC.	CLASSIFIED LAND COVER CLASSES AND FEATURE IMAGE ACCURACY OF CLASSIFICATION
	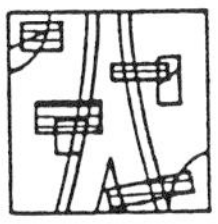	SAMPLE AREAS	FIELDWORK: CHECK ON MEANING AND BOUNDARIES OF CLASSES SUPERVISED CLASSIFICATION	FIELD AND COMPUTER ACCURACY OF CLASSIFICATION	IMAGE AND LEGEND FINAL CLASSIFICATION

FIGURE 2 A structured approach in land cover mapping using single date Landsat Thematic Mapper data. [From Mulders, M. A., De Bruin, S., and Schuiling, B. P. (1992). *Int. J. Remote Sensing* **13**(16), 3019–3036.]

FIGURE 3 PC 1-2-3 combination of TM acquisition of 6 February 1986; Guapiles area in Costa Rica.

The maximum amount of available moisture that can be stored in the rooting zone can be defined by:

$$TASM = (SMFC - SMPWP) \times RD, \quad (1)$$

where TASM is the maximum possible amount of available moisture (cm)

SMFC is the volume fraction of moisture in soil at field capacity ($cm^3 \ cm^{-3}$)

SMPWP is volume fraction of moisture at permanent wilting point ($cm^3 \ cm^{-3}$)

RD is equivalent depth of a homogeneously rooted surface layer (cm).

The amount of moisture actually available for uptake at any moment (AASM) is defined by:

$$AASM = (SMPSI - SMPWP) \times RD, \quad (2)$$

where AASM is actual amount of available moisture (cm)

SMPSI is actual volume fraction of moisture in the root zone ($cm^3 \ cm^{-3}$); Eq. (2) is valid if SMSPI is greater than SMPWP.

The compounded losses of water vapor from the rooted surface soil can be described for three ranges of soil moisture:

- if SMPSI ≥ SMCR (where SMCR is critical volume fraction of moisture in soil $cm^3 \ cm^{-3}$, at which stomata start to close), water is consumed at the maximum rate (ETm = maximum rate of evapotranspiration cm d^{-1})

- if SMPSI drops to a value ≤ SMPWP, transpiration ceases; loss of water from the root zone is set at 0.05 × ETO (where ETO is potential rate of evapotranspiration cm d^{-1})

- if SMPWP < SMPSI < SMCR, the rate of loss of water from the rooted surface soil decreases proportionally to the decrease in moisture content, i.e., from ETm to 0.05 ETO.

This schematized ET-SMPSI relation is shown in Fig. 5.

The condition where SMPWP<SMPSI<SMCR is described by Eq. (3):

$$ET = (SMPSI - SMPWP) \times (ETm - 0.05 \times ETO)/(SMCR - SMPWP) + 0.05 \times ETO, \quad (3)$$

where ET is actual rate of evapotranspiration (cm d^{-1}).

For a dynamic analysis of land use systems, the following data are important:

- volume fractions of moisture in soil at field capacity and at pF = 4.2
- rates of precipitation and of potential evapotranspiration
- early mid-season stage of crop, duration of growing cycle, maximum rooting depth and the crop coefficient (relating the potential evapotranspiration with the maximum rate of evapotranspiration)
- initial volume fraction of moisture in soil, initial rooting depth and planting or sowing date.

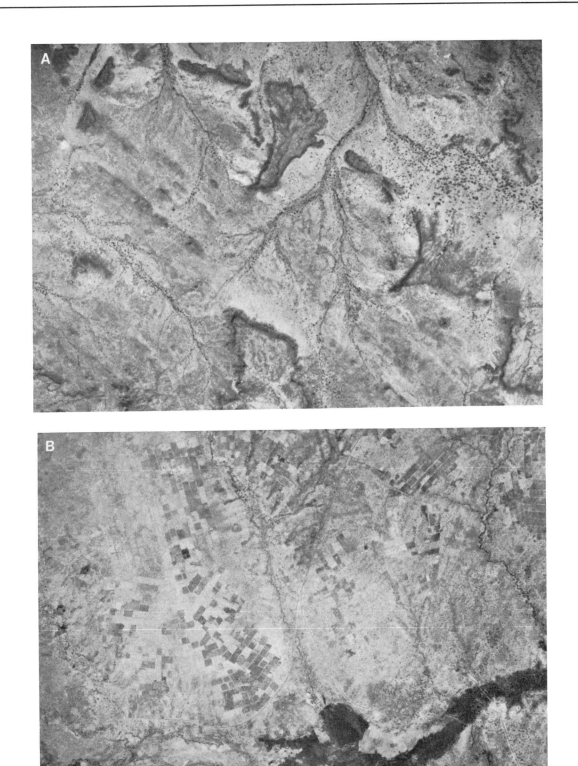

FIGURE 4 Aerial photographs of Burkina Faso. (a) Zablou area near Kaya; January 1982. (b) Kaibo area near Manga; January 1985.

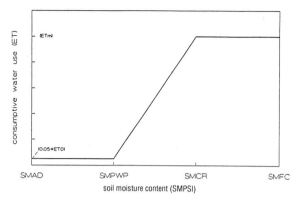

FIGURE 5 Approximate relation of ET to SMPSI. Abbreviations: see text. SMAD, volume fraction of moisture in soil at air dry condition (cm^3 cm^3). [From Driessen, P. M., and Konijn, N. T. (1992). "Land Use Systems Analysis." Wageningen Agricultural University, The Netherlands.]

VI. Land Degradation

Land evaluation is important for the selection of the most appropriate land use on particular land. If the land use is not in balance with the carrying capacity of soil or with that of natural vegetation, for example in case of natural grazing ground, it leads to land degradation. This can take place in many ways, for example, deterioration of soil structure (e.g., crusting and compaction), high soil salinity due to mismanagement in irrigation, truncation of soil profiles due to rain erosion and wind erosion, or the opposite namely accumulation of colluvial material, water transported materials and wind-blown sands.

Land degradation may be caused by remote activities, such as

- deforestation of watersheds causing problems in lowlands
- agricultural activities in areas with climatic drought leading to increased wind erosion and deposition in far away areas
- excess of gaseous waste in industries and of manure on agricultural lands causing sedimentation from polluted rain, which leads to an excess in soil nitrogen.

Some examples of land degradation are given below.

Figure 3 (Costa Rica) presents an example of replacement of tropical rainforest by banana, bamboo, and extensively used pasture. The economic value of the latter replacement is questionable and proceeds in a rapid and uncontrolled way.

Figure 4a is an example of degraded savanna in Burkina Faso.

The remaining trees are concentrated in the valley bottoms and where possible, agriculture is practiced. Lands exclusively used for pasture are the badlands with steep slopes (elongated hills) and ironcaps (dark grey features) as well as their stony footslopes. The scarce vegetation on the latter gives rise to accumulation of wind-blown sands and formation of low dunes (as apparent by white tones). Both Figures 4a and 4b show signs of accelerated water erosion. [See SOIL AND WATER MANAGEMENT AND CONSERVATION.]

VII. Geographic Information Systems (GIS)

GIS combines geographic data with the aid of computers. Different maps of terrain features may be constructed and combined to evaluate the coincidence or the absence of coincidence of boundaries.

Dbase is a computer program, which by sorting and comparing field data, evaluates the physiographic unit as a soil mapping unit and detects inaccuracies in the basic data.

Most of the aspects connected with soils and land use, such as land use requirements, land qualities for the intended use, and land degradation, have a complex nature. For example, to estimate land qualities, a number of relevant land characteristics are combined and weighted for this purpose. Such complex evaluations are served by the application of data bases and GIS.

As stated above, remote sensing data may be used to study dynamic aspects of the land surface. Figure 6 represents combinations of the TM bands 4, 5, and 3 at two dates of acquisition of the Kaibo area near Manga in Burkina Faso: 26 October 1989 (Fig. 6a) and 3 March 1987 (Fig. 6b).

October (Fig. 6a) marks the end of the rainy season; the dry period has started. Locally on the plateaux, crops still are green as evident by their medium grey-tones in the image. It indicates among others irrigated cotton. Furthermore, the agricultural areas with dry weeds and bare soil are visible in the image by white grey tones.

Figure 6b represents an image of March with in black the areas where burning of the savanna has been practiced.

The phytomass in this period is reduced considerably being limited to grass and shrubland on the plateaux and trees in the valley bottoms.

Such information on temporal changes in land surface features can serve land use and soil studies in an

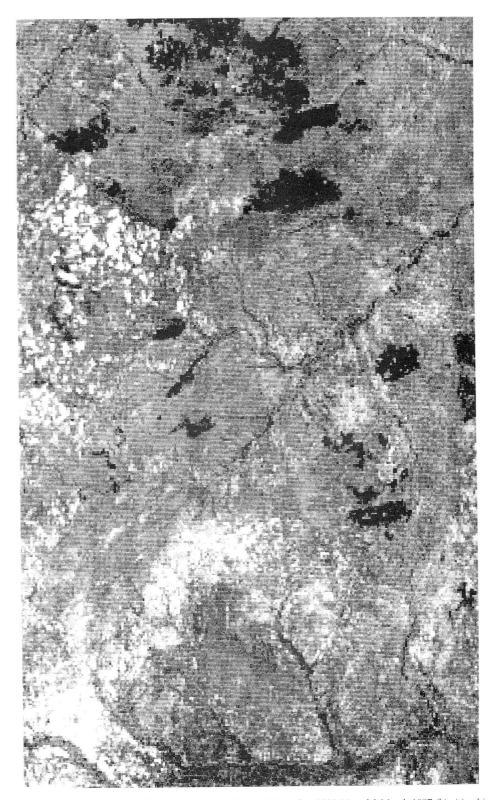

FIGURE 6 TM imagery of Burkina Faso (Kaibo area). Acquisitions: 26 October 1989 (a) and 3 March 1987 (b). (a) white, bare soil and dry grass + weeds; light grey, dry grass, shrubs, and trees; grey, shrubs and trees with dry grass; dark grey, crops and abundant trees + shrubs; black, burned savanna area. (b) white, bare soil and dry grass + weeds; light grey, dry grass, shrubs, and trees; grey, shrubs and trees with dry grass; dark grey, abundant green trees in valley bottoms; black, burned savanna area.

FIGURE 6 Continued

important way since it may be used to define the land surface dynamics. GIS is suitable for data handling and processing of products for interpretation.

The type of the basic data, which have to be collected for environmental studies considering the impact of man and biosphere, may be directed by those used in GLASSOD (Global Assessment of Soil Degradation). This project aims with SOTER (world Soils and Terrain digital data base) to define the input needed for calculating erosion factors and to evaluate erosion hazard on a regional and global base. Environmental data, such as climatic data, slope, soil, and crop coverage (as a protection factor), are regarded in this system and may also be applied at larger scales than originally intended.

Bibliography

Bouma, J. (1989). Using soil survey data for quantitative land evaluation. *Adv. Soil Sci.* **9,** 177–213.

Driessen, P. M., and Dudal, R. (eds.) (1991). "The Major Soils of the World. Lecture Notes on their Geography, Formation, Properties and Use," p. 310. Wageningen Agricultural University, Department of Soil Science and Geology, The Netherlands.

Driessen, P. M., and Konijn, N. T. (1992). "Land Use Systems Analysis," p. 230. Wageningen Agricultural University, Department of Soil Science and Geology, The Netherlands.

FAO-UNESCO (1988). "Soil Map of the World," revised legend, p. 109. Food and Agriculture Organization of the United Nations, Rome, Italy.

Mulders, M. A. (1987). Remote sensing in soil science. *Dev. Soil Sci.* **15,** 379.

Mulders, M. A., De Bruin, S., and Schuiling, B. P. (1992). Structured approach to land-cover mapping of the Atlantic zone of Costa Rica using single date TM data. *Int. J. Remote Sensing,* **13**(16), 3019–3036.

Soil Survey Staff (1990). "Keys to Soil Taxonomy," p. 422. SMSS Technical Monograph No. 19, Virginia Polytechnic Institute and State University.

Van Engelen, V. W. P., and Pulles, J. H. M. (1991). "The SOTER Manual. Procedures for Small Scale Digital Map and Database Compilation of Soil and Terrain Conditions," p. 91. International Soil Reference and Information Centre, Wageningen, The Netherlands.

Soil and Water Management and Conservation

RATTAN LAL, *The Ohio State University*

Glossary

Anaerobiosis Excessive soil wetness due to poor or impeded drainage
Conservation tillage Methods of seed bed preparation designed to protect soil against erosion
Drought Inadequate water supply to plant roots
Infiltration capacity Rate of water entry into the soil
Mulch farming Soil management based on retention of crop residues and other biomass on soil surface
Runoff Overland flow caused by excessive precipitation
Salinization Buildup of salts in the root zone at concentrations toxic to plant growth
Soil conservation Protecting soil against agents of erosion
Soil erosion Soil displacement by water, wind, ice, or gravity
Terraces Channels constructed with earthen dikes down slope to intercept runoff

Soil, three dimensional upper surface of the earth crust in dynamic equilibrium with its environment and capable of supporting plant growth, needs to be managed on the basis of science-based inputs for enhanced and sustained agricultural production. Fresh water resources of the earth are also finite and limited. Adequate water availability is a major constraint for an intensive land use and increased agricultural production especially in semiarid and arid eco-regions.

Therefore, soil and water management means judicious manipulation of soil and water resources to maintain and enhance their productive capacity and environmental regulatory functions. Principal among environmental regulatory functions are filtering pollutants from water, detoxification of industrial wastes, and regulation of gaseous concentrations in the atmosphere.

Conservation is a generic term. In a broad sense, it means preserving the resource base. In the context of soil, the term conservation means minimization of losses of soil due to accelerated erosion by water, wind, and other erosive agents. Conservation also implies enhancement of soil quality and productivity. In the context of water on agricultural land, conservation implies decreasing losses from the root zone due to surface runoff, deep seepage or evaporation. Conservation of soil and water resources is necessary for maintaining or enhancing their capacity to produce goods and services of economic, cultural, and aesthetic interests to humans.

I. Introduction

Soil resources of the world are finite, nonrenewable, and fragile. They are finite because potentially cultivable land resources are limited and unevenly distributed. Until about the 1970s, a considerable proportion of increase in food production was achieved by bringing new land under cultivation. However, reserves of potentially arable land are rapidly shrinking, especially in densely populated regions of the world. Furthermore, potentially arable land is either inaccessible, located in ecologically sensitive regions, or located in countries with robust economies. Densely populated regions of Asia and Europe have few additional lands to bring under cultivation. The per capita arable land area of the world has decreased from 0.32 ha in 1975

TABLE I

Per Capita Arable Land Area[a]

Region	Per capita arable land (ha)			
	1975	1980	1985	1990
Africa	0.368 (0.023)	0.326 (0.021)	0.288 (0.019)	0.254 (0.018)
America				
North Central	0.756 (0.066)	0.714 (0.074)	0.668 (0.069)	0.624 (0.062)
South	0.353 (0.029)	0.351 (0.030)	0.333 (0.029)	0.330 (0.030)
Asia	0.178 (0.052)	0.163 (0.051)	0.149 (0.050)	0.135 (0.048)
Europe	0.269 (0.027)	0.262 (0.030)	0.256 (0.033)	0.249 (0.034)
Oceania	2.046 (0.076)	1.949 (0.074)	1.920 (0.080)	1.834 (0.081)
USSR (Former)	0.895 (0.057)	0.857 (0.066)	0.822 (0.072)	0.779 (0.073)
World	0.321 (0.046)	0.298 (0.047)	0.276 (0.0465)	0.255 (0.0448)
Developed countries	0.574 (0.045)	0.556 (0.051)	0.540 (0.052)	0.519 (0.051)
Developing countries	0.223 (0.047)	0.206 (0.046)	0.189 (0.045)	0.173 (0.043)

[a] Calculated from population, arable land, and irrigated land statistics in FAO (1991). "Production Yearbok." Rome, Italy. Figures in parentheses are per capita irrigated land area.

to 0.25 ha in 1990 (Table I). In Asia, the per capita land area is only 0.14 ha with some countries having less than 0.1 ha. Average per capita irrigated land area is 0.07 ha in the world and that in Asia has steadily declined from 0.052 ha in 1975 to 0.048 ha in 1990 (Table I).

Soil resources are also nonrenewable at the human time scale. Under normal conditions, new soil is formed at the rate of about 2.5 cm in 150 to 1000 years. An exception to this rule may be the formation of soils in the flood plains or on the parent material of volcanic origin. Soils are also fragile to severe perturbations in harsh environments. Although most soils have built-in resilience, constant misuse and mismanagement can accentuate sensitivity to degradative processes. Soil degradation is a severe global problem especially in semi-arid and arid climates. As much as 38% of the arable land of the world is affected by some form of degradation (Table II). The per capita arable land area affected by degradation is about 0.1 ha out of the total per capita arable land of about 0.25 ha. At present 5 to 7 million ha of arable land (0.3–0.5%) is supposedly lost every year to soil degradation. The projected loss by the year 2000 is 10 million ha or 0.7% of the currently cultivated area. [See SOIL MANAGEMENT; SOIL POLLUTION.]

Despite these limitations of soil resources, the global agricultural production must be increased. An important strategy toward achieving this goal is proper use and science-based management of soil and water resources. In this regard, soil and water conservation and management play a crucial role in sustainable use of soil and water resources, decreasing degradation, restoring productivity of degraded resources, and maintaining or enhancing environmental quality.

The objective of this report is to describe basic principles of and technological options for soil and water management and conservation. The major emphasis is on addressing these problems on arable land with regards to water management, salinity control, and erosion management. These technological options are discussed in view of the global extent of the problems related to degradation of soil and water resources.

II. Water Management

Total global precipitation is estimated at 1130 mm/yr of which 233 mm or 20.6% falls on the land. Of the precipitation received on the land, 141 mm/yr accounts for evaporation or evapotranspiration and

TABLE II

Global Extent of Soil Degradation of Arable Land

Region	Degraded land		Per capita degraded land in 1990 (ha)
	Total (10^6 ha)[a]	% of arable land	
Africa	121	64.7	0.188
America			
Central	28	37.0	0.445
North	63	26.7	0.172
South	64	45.1	0.215
Asia	206	38.4	0.066
Europe	72	25.1	0.143
Oceania	8	16.3	0.296
World	562	38.1	0.106

[a] Source: Oldeman, L. R. (1992–1993). "Global Extent of Soil Degradation." Bi-Annual Report, ISRIC, Wageningen, The Netherlands.

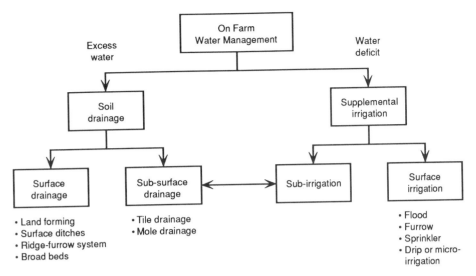

FIGURE 1 Technological options for on-farm water management involving drainage and supplementary irrigation.

the remaining 92 mm is returned to the ocean as surface runoff. Only 2.5% of the world's water is freshwater, and is an extremely scarce resource indeed. On-farm water management, crucial to sustained productivity and favorable environmental quality, involves drainage and irrigation (Fig. 1). Irrigation has played a major role in increasing world's food production since the 1940s. The world's irrigated land area has increased from 8 million ha in 1800 to 237 million in 1991 (Table III). In the United States irrigated land area was 8.3 million ha in 1944, 11.96 million ha in 1954, 14.98 million ha in 1964, 16.70 million ha in 1974, 20.38 million ha in 1978, and about 20 million ha in the 1980s. On a global scale, irrigated land accounts for only 16% of the cropland but produces 33% of the world's food. Management of irrigated land and water resources is, therefore, crucial to sustaining agricultural production. [*See* WATER: CONTROL AND USE; WATER RESOURCES.]

A. Improving Drainage and Reclaiming Salt-Affected Soils

Salt buildup in the surface layer is a natural phenomenon in soils of arid and semiarid regions with restricted drainage. In addition, mismanagement of irri-

TABLE III
Global Extent of Irrigated Land Area

Region/continent	Irrigated land (10^6 ha)			
	1975	1980	1985	1990
Africa	9.5	10.0 (5.3)	10.7 (7.0)	11.3 (5.6)
America				
North Central	22.9	27.7 (21.0)	27.6 (−0.4)	26.6 (−0.4)
South	6.3	7.2 (14.3)	7.9 (8.9)	8.8 (11.4)
Asia	121.7	132.4 (8.8)	141.2 (6.6)	150.2 (6.4)
Europe	12.7	14.5 (14.2)	16.0 (10.3)	17.1 (5.6)
Oceania	1.6	1.7 (6.3)	2.0 (17.6)	2.2 (10.0)
USSR (Former)	14.5	17.5 (20.7)	20.0 (14.3)	21.2 (6.0)
World	189.2	211.0 (11.5)	225.4 (6.8)	237.4 (5.3)
Developed countries	50.4	59.2 (17.5)	62.8 (6.1)	64.3 (2.4)
Developing countries	138.8	151.8 (9.4)	162.6 (7.1)	173.1 (6.5)

Source: Recalculated from FAO (1991); "Production Yearbook." Rome, Italy.
Note: Figures in parentheses refer to percentage increase over the past 5-year period.

gated water and misuse of irrigated lands can lead to two problems, e.g., salt buildup and poor drainage, soil wetness or anaerobiosis. Soils with toxic concentrations of soluble salts are widely distributed in arid and semi-arid regions and cover about 1 billion ha worldwide (Table IV). Total cropland and pasture land affected by salt buildup in the root zone in the United States is estimated at 225 million ha or about 9% of the total land in these categories. Unless properly managed, many irrigated lands are prone to salt buildup. Poor quality irrigation water is a major factor responsible for salt buildup. In addition to toxic concentrations of soils, an adverse consequence of high concentration of sodic salts in the root zone is the adverse effect on soil structure leading to restricted drainage and poor aeration. Rise in water table and poor drainage of the root zone are also caused by excessive seepage losses from unlined canals and delivery channels and low water use efficiency. Installation of artifical drainage can be expensive. It is estimated that about 44 million ha or 20% of the cropland in the United States required some drainage system by 1985 because of excessive wetness during early spring that delayed sowing operations. [See SOIL DRAINAGE; SOIL-WATER RELATIONSHIPS.]

B. Technological Options for Drainage

Provisions for drainage to remove excess water may preferably be made prior to planning for supplementary irrigation. Field drainage or farm drainage involves installation of techniques to remove excess wa-

TABLE IV
Global Extent of Salt-Affected Soils

Region	Area (10^6 ha)	Irrigated land: Salt-affected soils (1990)
Africa	80.44	0.141
America		
Central and Mexico	1.97	
North	15.76	1.50
South	129.16	0.068
Asia		
North and Central	211.69	
South	85.11	
Southeast	19.98	0.474
Europe	50.80	0.337
Oceania	357.33	0.006
World	952.3	0.249

Source: Gupta, R. K., and Abrol, I. P. (1990). Salt-affected soils: Their reclamation and management for crop production. *Adv. Soil Sci.* **11**, 223–288.

ter from a farm unit or part of the farm with localized problem of excess water. In contrast, land drainage involves installation of drainage network on a large scale to drain excess water from a large area. Drainage techniques described below refer to the field or farm drainage: Farm drainage is required for several reasons.

- Better drainage improves crop growth and yield. Increase in crop yield may be 5 to 20% depending on crop, soil, climate, and management.
- Improved drainage enhances nutrient use efficiency. Poor drainage conditions restrict availibility and uptake of several plant nutrients, e.g., N, P, K, Zn, Cu, B, etc.
- Drained soil has more favorable soil tilth and better soil physical properties than poorly drained soil.
- Trafficability is greatly enhanced with farm drainage and soil becomes accessible early in the season.
- Depending on the antecedent soil moisture content and microclimate, improved drainage may also warm up more quickly in the spring.
- Drained soils may also emit less greenhouse gases into the atmosphere than poorly drained soils, e.g., N_2O (Lal *et al.*, 1994).
- Drainage facilitates removal of excess salt from the root zone and is necessary to reclaim salt-affected soils.

Installing a drainage system, however, is a major capital investment. Furthermore, aging drainage systems are no longer effective and need replacement every 20 to 25 years.

There are two types of drainage systems (Fig. 1). Surface drainage, installed by a combination of land forming and open ditches, facilitates removal of surface water by land leveling and providing a gentle grade to speed-up the water movement. Surface drainage can also be provided through ridge-furrow system and by broad bed techniques of seedbed preparation. Open ditches are constructed to remove surplus water from the farm unit to the drainage way installed for the large area.

Heavy-textured soils require more than just the surface drainage to improve aeration conditions in the slowly permeable subsoil. Subsurface drainage is designed to regulate the groundwater table and consists of installing tube drains at about 50 cm depth. Spacing between the drain pipes depends on soil permeability, water table depth, and many other factors. Tube drains may be made of ceramic (tiles) or plastic. The gap between the two adjacent tiles or plastic drains, adjusted to facilitate free movement of water, is covered with a protective permeable fill or backfill.

One of the principal benefits of installing a drainage system is removal of excess salts from the root zone of salt affected soils by repeated leaching with the drainage water. Leaching is often facilitated by application of farm yard manure, compost, green manure, gypsum, and other amendments. The problem of salt buildup and need for reclamation are particularly severe in irrigated regions of China, India, Pakistan, and the Middle East. Restoration of productivity of irrigated lands in these regions depends on provisions for proper drainage so that salts can be leached and kept out of the root zone.

C. Irrigation Techniques

Irrigation is the reverse of drainage because it implies application of water to the root zone to alleviate soil water deficit. Irrigation is used for several purposes but mainly to:

- Increase plant-available water reserves and decrease the risks of drought.
- Extend the growing season in regions with abrupt cessation of rains.
- Leach soluble salts out of the root zone in salt-affected soils.
- Regulate soil temperature especially for protecting sensitive plants from frost damage.
- Regulate nutrient supply to the root zone.

However, misuse of irrigation water can also lead to secondary problems with severe economic and ecological consequences. These problems include waterlogging and elevation of groundwater table, salt buildup in the root zone, decline in soil structure leading to crusting and slaking, and erosion of top soil especially in the furrow irrigation system. Adverse effects of irrigation on soil structure are related to water quality and composition of dissolved salts, e.g., Na, Ca, Mg, K, and the ratio of Na to other cations. Susceptibility to waterlogging and salinization in arid and semiarid regions also depend on the quantity and frequency of irrigation. Excessive application of water must be avoided, and irrigation water must be applied just enough to meet the crop water requirement. Crop water requirement depends on several factors including crop and soil types, climate, topography, etc.

On the basis of method of water application, there are two types of irrigation, e.g., subirrigation and surface irrigation (Fig. 1). The subirrigation method applies water to the root zone below the soil surface. In this method, the drainage system installed to remove surplus water is plugged and irrigation is applied through the same system. This is a cost-effective method with high water use efficiency and low evaporative losses. [See IRRIGATION ENGINEERING: FARM PRACTICES, METHODS, AND SYSTEMS.]

There are several methods of surface irrigation, the most common among these is the flood irrigation. This is the simplest method with least expenditure on equipment and storage. Surface irrigation is a natural system for semiaquatic crops (e.g., rice) and for large-scale reclamation of salt-affected soils by leaching. However, surface irrigation is an inefficient method with large losses due to evaporation. It also requires land forming and construction of several delivery channels. Efficiency of surface irrigation methods can be enhanced by using furrow rather than flood irrigation. A semi-permanent ridge-furrow system is a useful method for drainage in spring and for irrigation in summer. The ridge-furrow method of seed bed preparation is also useful for growing crops on salt-affected soils. While salt rises by evaporation to the ridge top, crops can be grown in the furrow or halfway up on the ridge to avoid salt injury.

Sprinkler irrigation system is the most capital-intensive but an efficient method in terms of water use. Principal advantages of sprinkler method include:

- Use on undulating terrain without prior land forming.
- Efficient water use because of low losses by seepage and poor delivery.
- Controlled application in terms of amount, and frequency.
- Flexibility in equipment use.

In addition to large capital investment, the timing of sprinkler application is affected by wind velocity. Structurally unstable soils can develop crust and surface seal due to impacting water drops.

Drip irrigation or microirrigation system is used to apply water at very low rates. The water is applied directly to the root zone of individual plants through a porous tube or especially designed emitters. Salt buildup is not a severe problem with drip irrigation. This system is extremely efficient because evaporative losses are reduced to the minimum. The system is also very effective in applying fertilizers and other chemicals directly to the root zone. However, the system requires a high capital investment and is feasible only for high value cash crops.

III. *In Situ* Conservation of Soil Water

In situ conservation of soil water, for minimization of losses due to runoff and evaporation, is extremely important to enhance productivity in rainfed agriculture.

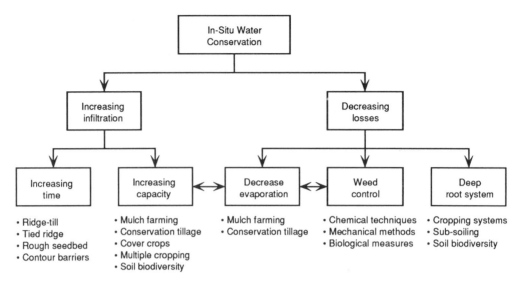

FIGURE 2 Strategies and techniques to improve *in situ* soil–water conservation.

Risks of drastic yield reductions due to drought in arid and semi-arid regions can be minimized through conservation of precipitation in the root zone. Techniques for *in situ* conservation of soil water are outlined in Fig. 2 and can be classified under two principal categories: (1) techniques to increase infiltration and reduce runoff losses, and (2) methods to decrease evaporation losses.

Losses due to surface runoff can be reduced by increasing the amount of precipitation infiltrating into the soil. The proportion of rain entering the soil can be enhanced by increasing the time for water to infiltrate or increasing soil's infiltration capacity. Increasing the time for water to infiltrate into the soil involves enhancing surface detention capacity through soil surface management or land forming. Commonly used techniques include rough seed bed, ridge-furrow system, and tied ridges (Fig. 2). Some of these techniques are described in the following section dealing with soil surface management. Contour barriers (e.g., bunds, vegetative hedges, etc.) are also used to contain runoff and allow it to infiltrate into the soil. Contour bunds create large storage to impound all the surface runoff and hold it for slow infiltration.

Evaporation losses are reduced by mulch farming and conservation tillage techniques. Mulches regulate the soil temperatures and decrease evaporation losses. These techniques are also described in the following section dealing with soil conservation.

IV. Soil Conservation

Accelerated soil erosion is a severe global problem, especially in ecologically sensitive ecoregions includ-ing the Himalayan–Tibetan ecosystem, the Andean region, the Caribbean, East African highlands, the loess region of China, and other steep lands in harsh climates. Wind erosion is severe in arid and semiarid climates. The data in Table V show that globally land area affected is about 56% by water erosion and 28% by wind erosion. Water erosion is severe in steep lands. Global distribution of steep lands include 3.3 billion ha with slopes ranging from 0 to 8%, 2.1 billion ha with slope of 8 to 30%, and 1.0 billion ha with slopes in excess of 30%. The largest areas affected by water and wind erosion are in Asia followed by that in Africa.

Accelerated soil erosion is also a serious problem in the United States. Land area affected is estimated

TABLE V
Global Extent of Water and Wind Erosion

Region	Water erosion		Wind erosion	
	Total (10^6 ha)	% of soils affected	Total (10^6 ha)	% of soils affected
Africa	227	46	186	38
America				
Central	46	74	5	7
North	60	63	35	36
South	123	51	42	17
Asia	441	59	222	30
Europe	114	52	42	19
Oceania	83	81	16	16
World	1094	56	548	28

Source: Modified from Oldeman, L. R. (1992–1993). "Global Extent of Soil Degradation." Bi-Annual Report, ISRIC, Wageningen, The Netherlands.

TABLE VI
Soil Erosion Hazard in the United States

Land use	Total area	Erosion hazard (10^6 ha)		
		$<T^a$	Sheet and rill	Wind
Crop land	170.4	100.4	42.9	27.1
Pasture land	54.3	49.4	4.5	0.4
Range land	162.7	134.0	20.6	8.1
Forest land	159.5	149.8	9.3	0.4
Minor land	24.2	20.2	3.2	0.8
Total nonfederal rural land	571.1	453.8	80.5	36.8

Source: Modified from USDA (1989). "The Second RCA Appraisal: Soil, Water, and Related Resources on Non-federal Land in the United States, Analysis of Conditions and Trends," Washington, DC.
[a] T, tolerable level of soil erosion.

at about 81 million ha by sheet and rill erosion, and 37 million ha by wind erosion (Table VI). Some regions are affected by both water and wind erosion.

Principles of erosion control are well understood. However, techniques for erosion management are locale specific and vary with climate, terrain, land use, soil type, and other socio-economic and cultural factors. Erosion management techniques can be broadly grouped into three categories: (a) soil surface management, (b) slope management, and (c) runoff management. Basic principles of these techniques are briefly outlined below.

A. Soil Surface Management

Tillage and crop residue management are the principal tools of soil surface management for seed bed preparation, water conservation, and erosion control. In addition to seed bed preparation, an objective of soil surface management is to reduce or minimize risks of soil erosion by decreasing the aggressivity of agents of erosion, e.g., raindrop, overland flow, wind velocity. Basic principles of soil surface management through tillage are outlined in Fig. 3. In comparison with traditional (local methods) and conventional tillage (plow-based methods involving soil inversion), conservation tillage systems are designed to minimize soil erosion risks by decreasing exposure of the soil surface to climatic elements, through retention of crop residue mulch, and reduction in soil disturbance. Different types of conservation tillage systems are briefly discussed below. [*See* TILLAGE SYSTEMS.]

1. Conservation Tillage

It refers to some form of noninversion tillage with at least 30% of the soil surface covered with crop residue mulch. There are three principal types of conservation tillage: mulch tillage, reduced tillage and ridge tillage system. A classification scheme of conservation tillage is shown in Fig. 3.

a. Mulch Tillage Mulch tillage is any tillage system that retains a high percentage of crop residue on the soil surface. This system is also called stubble mulch tillage, mulch farming, trash farming, subsurface tillage, and plowless farming. There are two additional variants of mulch tillage. Sod seeding refers to the tillage system where crop is seeded directly in unplowed soil with chemically killed sod, weeds, cover crops, or previous crop residue. Contact or systemic herbicides (e.g., Paraquat or glyphosate) are used to replace plowing to kill vegetative growth. Sometimes a cover crop, usually a legume, is specifically grown to procure mulch, improve soil fertility, and enhance soil structure. This system is also called planted fallow or eco-fallow. In contrast, a cropless and weed-free fallow is used in arid climates to conserve water in the root zone. When a food crop is grown through the low-growing cover crop, the system is called live mulch. A live mulch system is based on the principle of mixed cropping in which a fast-growing and aggressive legume is established to smother weeds and then grow a seasonal food crop through it. It is usual to mechanically open a small strip, with or without herbicides, to establish the food crop. The live mulch system is effective only if the cover crop is a low-growing, nonclimber, and has a shallow root system.

b. Reduced Tillage Reduced tillage is a generic term which refers to reduction in intensity and/or

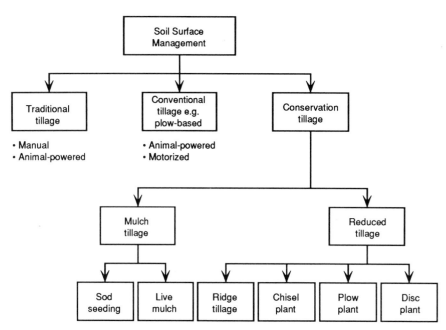

FIGURE 3 Soil surface management techniques for soil and water conservation.

frequency of mechanical or plow-based tillage systems. The most widely practiced form of reduced tillage is the no-tillage system in which all preplanting seed bed preparation is eliminated. This system is also called direct drilling or zero-tillage. In this system, all crop residue is left on the soil surface. Other commonly used variants of reduced tillage include chisel plant, plow plant, or disk plant depending on the equipment used to prepare seed bed prior to seeding.

2. Ridge Tillage

Ridge tillage involves heaping up the surface soil in a series of raised beds at regular intervals. Ridge tillage is a very versatile form of reduced tillage system. Ridges are made on the contour to contain runoff on soils of low permeability, up and down the slope on poorly drained soils to improve surface drainage, widely spaced and large to increase rooting depth on shallow soils, and to concentrate soil fertility by heaping up the nutrient-rich top soil in the root zone in subsistence farming or low-input systems. Ridges can be made every season, every other season, or with cross-ties (tied ridge system) to create a series of basins to increase water storage capacity.

3. Soil Guide for Tillage Methods

Tillage methods are soil, crop, and climate specific. It is difficult to recommend any single tillage system for all soils and to address all soil-related constraints to

crop production. Furthermore, tillage requirements vary according to the antecedent soil conditions, e.g., compaction, residue cover, etc. It is, therefore, useful to develop a soil guide to identify tillage methods in relation to soil constraints and crop requirements. The author developed a rating system to assess tillage requirements to alleviate specific soil properties. The schematic in Fig. 4 is a soil guide to tillage needs in relation to texture and soil moisture regimes. In general, no-till system is a suitable method of seed bed preparation for coarse-textured soils with good internal drainage. Heavy-textured soils with poor internal drainage do not respond favorably to a no-till system. Structurally inert soils prone to compaction and crusting also require mechanical loosening and plow-based tillage methods for water conservation and adequate root growth. In general, biostructurally active soils on undulating terrain and harsh climate should be managed with mulch tillage, no-tillage, or other reduced-tillage systems.

B. Runoff Management

Runoff management is important for soil erosion control and for efficient and sustainable use of water resources. There are at least three strategies for runoff management (Fig. 5) which include (1) decrease runoff amount, (2) reduce runoff velocity, and (3) store runoff for water recycling and future use.

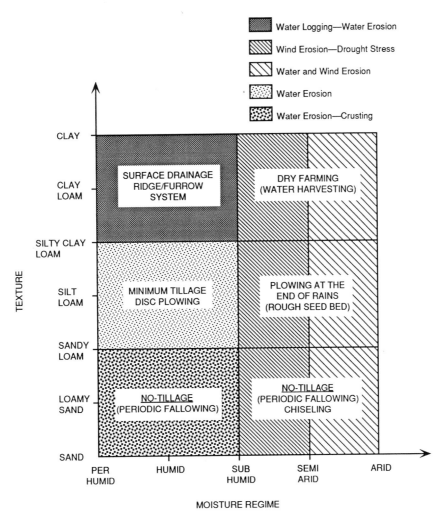

Legend:
- Water Logging—Water Erosion
- Wind Erosion—Drought Stress
- Water and Wind Erosion
- Water Erosion
- Water Erosion—Crusting

TEXTURE (vertical axis): CLAY, CLAY LOAM, SILTY CLAY LOAM, SILT LOAM, SANDY LOAM, LOAMY SAND, SAND

MOISTURE REGIME (horizontal axis): PER HUMID, HUMID, SUB HUMID, SEMI ARID, ARID

SURFACE DRAINAGE RIDGE/FURROW SYSTEM

DRY FARMING (WATER HARVESTING)

MINIMUM TILLAGE DISC PLOWING

PLOWING AT THE END OF RAINS (ROUGH SEED BED)

NO-TILLAGE (PERIODIC FALLOWING)

NO-TILLAGE (PERIODIC FALLOWING) CHISELING

FIGURE 4 Conservation tillage systems in relation to moisture regime and soil texture. (Lal, 1985).

1. Decreasing Runoff Amount

Strategies for decreasing runoff amount involve contour farming and installing barriers on the contour.

a. Contour Farming Contouring or contour farming implies performing all farm operations on the contour rather than up and down the slope. Plowing on the contour, establishing ridge-furrow system on the contour, planting crop rows on the contour, and applying fertilizers and other chemicals on the contour increase surface detention capacity, increase time for water to infiltrate, and decrease runoff amount. Contour farming is, however, effective on gentle slopes of up to 5%. Steeper slopes require slope management techniques outlined in Fig. 5. Contour farming can be sometimes inconvenient because it possibly involves frequent turning of farm vehicles and loss of area which has to be put into buffer strips.

b. Strip Cropping Another aspect of contour farming is strip cropping or growing crops into long narrow strips established on the contour. In this system, open row crops (e.g., corn) are grown in alternate strips with close canopy crops (e.g., soybeans, alfalfa, etc.). The close canopy crop is often grown in a contour strip down slope from the open row crop. It is also important to establish buffer strips on the contour. There are various types of strip cropping. On the basis of objectives, vegetative materials used, and field design adopted, buffer strips are called contour strip cropping, buffer strip cropping, barrier strips, border strips, or field strips. In addition to reducing runoff amount, establishing strips against

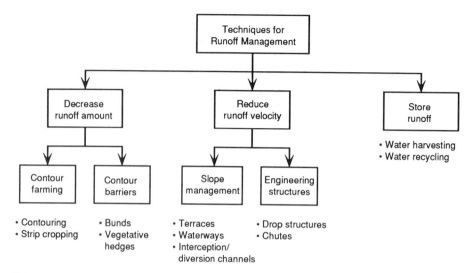

FIGURE 5 Techniques for decreasing runoff amount and velocity through engineering structures.

the prevailing wind direction also decreases wind erosion.

c. Contour Barriers Runoff amount can also be decreased by establishing contour bunds, which are embankments or earthen dikes established on the contour. These bunds are protected by establishing appropriate vegetation cover, and are particularly effective in semi-arid climates for water conservation on slowly permeable soils. Draw backs of contour bunds include extra costs, and some land area taken out of production.

d. Vegetative Hedges Rather than earthen embankments, vegetative hedges are established on the contour to create a barrier and increase time for water to soak into the soil. Vegetative hedges are mostly established from bench-type grasses. A widely adapted grass for tropical ecoregions for vegetative hedges is Vetiver (*Vetiveria zizanioides*) or khus grass. Vetiver is densely tufted bunch grass which can be easily established. In addition to grasses, vegetative hedges can also be established from woody perennials, e.g., *Leucaena leucocephala, Gliricidia sepium,* etc. Properly established and adequately maintained, vegetative hedges decrease runoff velocity, encourage sedimentation, and reduce runoff and soil erosion. However, closely spaced and narrow strips of grass or woody perennials are likely to be more effective in reducing runoff and soil erosion than narrow or single-row hedges.

2. Reducing Runoff Velocity

There are two general strategies for reducing runoff velocity: (a) slope management, and (b) special engineering structures.

a. Slope Management It involves breaking a long slope into short segments for decreasing overall slope gradient, and is an important and a widely practiced strategy for management of steep lands. Terracing is a practice of installing earthen dikes on the contour and preferably at right angle to the steepest slope for intercepting surface runoff originating from within the farm land. A terrace consists of two parts: an excavated channel and a bank or ridge on the down slope side. There are different types of terraces based on the size, shape, gradient, location, and protective material used for the channel vis-a-vis the ridge. Commonly used terms are graded channel terraces, stone terraces, broad-based terraces, etc. Terrace nomenclature is also based on the objective or use, e.g., orchard terraces, convertible terraces, individual basins, etc. Parameters for terrace design include shape, size, and gradient for channel; vertical/horizontal interval between terraces; and protective system to stabilize dikes and embankment. The design also includes expected runoff volume on the basis of 10-, 50-, or 100-year storm. While overdesigning is expensive, underdesigning can cause overflow and breach in terrace leading to severe gullying.

b. Waterways Installing waterways, another aspect of reducing runoff velocity, involves broad-based natural or artificial channels conveniently installed for safe disposal of surplus runoff originating from terraces and within the field. Waterways are called grass waterways, sod waterways, or meadow strips on the basis of the nature of protective material used in stabilizing them. Similar to terraces, capacity of the waterways is also designed on the basis of expected runoff from 10-, 50-, or 100-year storm.

c. Diversion Channels Diversion channels or ditches are installed to prevent run-on from surrounding hills or adjacent land. These ditches are also called storm water diversion drains. The primary objective is to prevent flood water from entering the farm. Design criteria and guidelines for construction and installation of diversion channels also based on soil type, terrain, and expected runoff.

d. Engineering Structures Permanent mechanical structures are needed for safe disposal of concentrated runoff on steep slopes. The objective is to dissipate the kinetic energy of flow through permanent structures made of concrete and other resistant materials. There are several types of engineering structures used for this purpose. Drop structures, small dams with water storage capacity, constructed in pairs at the steepest segment of the slope, are designed to stabilize steep waterways, diversion channels, or interception ditches. The longitudinal wall of the structure is constructed across the channel and anchored onto the bank on both sides. The notch or box inlet in the wall serves as a spillway. The spilling basin is below the spillway and is designed to absorb the energy. These structures are constructed from poured concrete, cement blocks, timber, corrugated metal, etc.

Chutes are specially designed spillways constructed to transmit concentrated runoff from the highest point of the waterway to the lowest. Chutes are made of poured in concrete, and the chute outlet is usually protected with brought in stones or stone rip rap.

There are also several types of check dams constructed at strategic locations to stabilize waterways and trap sediments. Check dams may be made of concrete with a notch/box spillway or they may be made of porous materials, e.g., stones held together by a wind net. Such porous structures are also called gabions which comprise prefabricated baskets of heavy-duty wire netting and are filled with stone. Gabions are flexible in dimensions, but several baskets can be placed in series or on top of one another.

3. Water Harvesting and Recycling

It involves collecting excess runoff, natural or induced, in surface reservoir for agricultural use. Water thus harvested can be stored in surface reservoirs or ponds or in soil. Appropriate water harvesting strategies depend on soil type, terrain, and rainfall characteristics. The strategy may involve microcatchment for individual trees, ridge catchment for harvesting water from a raised bed into the furrow where crops are grown, strip catchment where alternate strips are left uncropped and deliberately treated to accentuate runoff, and large catchment where large areas are set aside to harvest water and store in above-ground or below-ground reservoirs for supplementary irrigation.

V. Conclusions

Soil and water resources of the world are finite and require careful appraisal and science-based management. Mismanagement and misuse can lead to severe problems of degradation of soil and water resources, e.g., accelerated erosion, salt buildup in the root zone, soil wetness, and anaerobiosis. Limited extent of prime agricultural land, high rates of soil degradation, and rapid increase in population are responsible for decrease in global per capita land area to 0.25 ha for arable land and 0.07 ha for irrigated land.

There are several technological options for water management including drainage for improving aeration and leaching salt out of the root zone, and supplemental irrigation for alleviating drought and prolonging the growing season.

Soil conservation involves soil surface management based on conservation tillage techniques, runoff management based on slope modification and engineering structures, and water harvesting techniques.

Basic principles of these technological options are well known. Locale-specific adaptations are needed to address specific constraints to soil type, terrain, landuse, climate, and socio-economic factors.

Implementation of soil and water management and conservation techniques is essential for sustainable use of soil and water resources and for enhancement of environmental quality.

Bibliography

FAO (1991). "Production Yearbook." Rome, Italy.
Gupta, R. K., and Abrol, I. P. (1990). Salt-affected Soils:

Their reclamation and management for crop production. *Adv. Soil Sci.* **11**, 223–288.

Hall, C. W. (1989). Mechanization and food availability. *In* "Food and Natural Resources" (D. Pimentel and C. W. Hall, eds.). Academic Press, San Diego, CA.

Hoffman, G. J., Howell, T. A., and Solomon, K. H. (eds.) (1990). "Management of Farm Irrigation System." American Society of Agricultural Engineers. St. Joseph, MI.

Lal, R. (1985). A soil suitability guide for different tillage systems in the tropics. *Soil Tillage Res.* **5.**

Lal, R. (1990). "Soil Erosion in the Tropics: Principles and Management." McGraw-Hill, New York.

Lal, R. (1992). "Sustainable Land use Systems and Soil Resilience." Proceedings of the International Symposium on Soil Resilience and Sustainable Land Use, 28 Sept.–2 October, 1992, Budapest, Hungary.

Moldenhauer, W. C., Huson, N. W., Sheng, T. C., and San-Wei Lee (eds.) (1991). "Development of Conservation Farming on Hillslopes." Soil and Water Conservation Society, Ankeny, IA.

Moldenhauer, W. C., and Hudson, N. W. (eds.) (1988). "Conservation Farming on Steep Lands." Soil and Water Conservation Society, Ankeny, IA.

NRC (1993). "Vetiver Grass: A Thin Green Line Against Erosion." National Academy Press, Washington, DC.

Oldeman, L. R. (1992–1993). "Global Extent of Soil Degradation." Bi-Annual Report, ISRIC, Wageningen, The Netherlands.

Schwab, G. O., Fangmeier, D. D., Elliot, W. J., and Frevert, R. K. (1993). "Soil and Water Conservation Engineering." Wiley, New York.

Stewart, B. A., and Nielson, D. R. (1990). "Irrigation of Agricultural Crops." ASA Monograph 30, Madison, WI.

USDA (1989). "The Second RCA Appraisal: Soil, Water, and Related Resources on Non-federal Land in the United States, Analysis of Conditions and Trends." USDA, Washington, DC.

World Resources Institute (WRI) (1992–1993). "Towards Sustainable Development: A Guide to Global Environment." WRI, Washington, DC.

Soil, Chemicals: Movement and Retention

H. M. SELIM, *Louisiana State University*

Glossary

Adsorption and ion exchange Adsorption is a process whereby solutes bind to surfaces of soil particles to form outer or inner-sphere solute–surface site complexes, whereas ion exchange is the process whereby charged solutes replace ions on soil particle surfaces

Desorption Solute release from the soil matrix to the soil solution phase when the mechanisms are not known

Dispersion A primary process of solute spreading which occurs during water flow in soils or porous media. Often referred to as mechanical or hydrodynamic dispersion, it is due to nonuniform flow distribution due to nonuniform sizes of the conducting soil pore space, fluctuation of the flow path due to tortuosity effect, and the variation in velocity from the center of a pore (maximum value) to zero at the solid surface interface

Equilibrium retention models Mathematical formulations describing the amount of solute retained from solution when solute reactions in the soil system occur instantaneously

Hysteresis A phenomenon associated with adsorption/desorption isotherms where for a given solute concentration in solution, the amount retained by the soil is lower during adsorption in comparison to desorption

Physical/chemical nonequilibrium retention models Mathematical formulations describing the amount of solute retained from solution when reac-

tions in the soil system are time-dependent due to physical processes (pore geometry and accessibility to retention sites) or chemical processes (chemically controlled heterogeneous reactions)

Retention/release of solutes Reactions which occur between solutes present in the soil solution and the soil matrix which may include precipitation/dissolution, ion exchange, and adsorption/desorption

Sorption Solute removal (or retention) from solution by soil when the mechanisms are not known, unlike the term adsorption which describes the formation of solute–surface site complexes

The movement of chemicals and their retention in the soil profile play a significant role in their leaching losses beyond the rootzone, availability to uptake by plants, and the potential contamination of groundwater supplies. We present commonly used approaches for predicting retention behavior of chemicals in soils. First we discuss mechanisms governing the transport of dissolved chemicals in water-saturated and water-unsaturated soils and boundary conditions commonly encountered under field conditions. Major features of single retention approaches of the reversible and irreversible kinetic type are then presented. Furthermore, general purpose models of the multiple reaction type including the two-site equilibrium-kinetic, the concurrent and consecutive multireaction, and the competitive ion exchange. Physical and chemical nonequilibrium approaches such as the two-region (mobile–immobile) and second-order kinetic models are also discussed. Illustrative examples of modeling of the fate of nitrogen, potassium, and other ions interactions are given.

I. Overview

Minimizing the use of agricultural chemicals for groundwater quality and farm profitability is of major

Encyclopedia of Agricultural Science, Volume 4   Copyright © 1994 by Academic Press, Inc.   All rights of reproduction in any form reserved.

concern nationally and within the agricultural community. Health concerns for drinking water quality must be balanced with maintaining economically viable agriculture. Central to the issue of agricultural chemical management is best management practices which maximize profit with minimum potential contamination of surface and subsurface waters. Agricultural chemicals applied to soils in large amounts are fertilizers which contain major plant nutrients namely N, P, K, and S which are applied in different forms including granular, pellets, or as a liquid. In contrast, micronutrient (e.g., B, Mo, Cu, among others) are applied sparingly and only when necessary to modify diagnosed deficiencies in the soil composition. Pesticides and insecticides are commonly applied to the soils or as foliar applications on agricultural crops and ornamental for weed and pest control. Other applied chemicals include gypsum and lime as soil amendments for the primary purposes including alteration of soil acidity/alkalinity (pH) and Al toxicity. Moreover, soils are often used as a resource for land treatment of disposal of animal and municipal wastes. Occasionally, soils receive industrial and toxic or hazardous wastes which often include organic chemicals and heavy metals, among others. [See FERTILIZER MANAGEMENT AND TECHNOLOGY; GROUND WATER; PEST MANAGEMENT, CHEMICAL CONTROL; SOIL, ACID; SOIL POLLUTION.]

The fate of fertilizers, pesticides, and waste chemicals applied to the soil depends on physical, chemical, and biological processes in the soil. Many of these processes are not yet well understood, however. Physical processes include solute transport according to mass flow or convection and transport due to diffusion and hydrodynamic dispersion. Physical processes are influenced by water flux density, bulk density, pore geometry or tortuosity, and the occurrence of regions within the pore space which do not contribute to solute convection (i.e., mobile–immobile regions). Chemical and biological processes in the soil environment can often involve a series of complex interactions including biological transformations or degradation, oxidation and reduction, volatilization, precipitation/dissolution, complex formation, and cation or anion exchange. Knowledge of the reactions is essential for the purpose of predicting the retention reactions of solute in soils and their potential mobility to within the soil profile. The ability to predict the mobility of applied chemicals in the soil is a prerequisite in any program aimed at achieving optimum farm

profitability while protecting groundwater quality. [See SOIL CHEMISTRY; SOIL MICROBIOLOGY.]

In this article, the principles governing the transport of solutes in soils are presented. The equation of mass conservation of solutes is given and the convection–dispersion equations for nonreactive and reactive solutes in soils are formulated. The general form of the convection–dispersion transport equation for water-unsaturated and transient water flux is derived. Major features of mechanistic models which describe the extent of adsorption/desorption or retention of solutes in soils are presented. Single reaction models of the equilibrium and kinetic types are discussed. Retention reactions of fully reversible and irreversible types are incorporated into the transport equation. Models of the multisite or multiple reaction type including the two-site equilibrium-kinetic models, the concurrent and consecutive multireaction models, and the second-order approach are presented. This is followed by multicomponent or competitive type models where ion exchange is considered the dominant retention mechanism. Incorporation of the role of specific sorption as a mechanistic approach for adsorption of ions on high-affinity sites is discussed. Moreover, selected experimental data sets are described for the purpose of model evaluation and validation. Finally, the two-region approach is described to introduce physical nonequilibrium behavior during transport in soils.

II. Transport

To describe the general equation dealing with the transport of dissolved agricultural chemicals present in the soil solution, a number of definitions must be given. For a given bulk volume within the soil, the total amount of solute χ (μg cm^{-3}) for a species i may be written as

$$\chi_i = \Theta C_i + \rho S_i, \tag{1}$$

where S is the amount of solute retained by the soil (μg g^{-1} soil), C is the solute concentration in solution (μg ml^{-1}), Θ is the soil moisture content (cm^3 cm^{-3}), and ρ is the soil bulk density (g cm^{-3}). The rate of change of χ for the ith species with time is subject to the law of mass conservation such that (omitting the subscript i)

$$\frac{\partial(\Theta C + \rho S)}{\partial t} = - \operatorname{div} J - Q \tag{2}$$

or

$$\frac{\partial(\Theta C + \rho S)}{\partial t} = -\left(\frac{\partial J_x}{\partial x} + \frac{\partial J_y}{\partial y} + \frac{\partial J_z}{\partial z}\right) - Q, \quad (3)$$

where t is time (hr) and J_x, J_y, and J_z represent the flux or rate of movement of solute species i in the x, y, and z directions ($\mu g\ cm^{-2}\ hr^{-1}$), respectively. The term Q represents a sink (Q positive) or source which accounts for the rate of solute removal (or addition) irreversibly from the bulk solution ($\mu g\ cm^{-3}\ hr^{-1}$). The irreversible term Q can also be considered as a root uptake term for the extraction of ions from the soil solution. For one-dimensional flow in the z-direction, the flux J_z in the soil may be given by

$$J_z = -\Theta(D_m + D_L)\frac{\partial C}{\partial z} + qC, \quad (4)$$

where D_m is the molecular diffusion coefficient ($cm^2\ hr^{-1}$), D_L is the longitudinal dispersion coefficient ($cm^2\ hr^{-1}$), and q is Darcy's flux ($cm\ hr^{-1}$). Therefore, the primary mechanisms for solute movement are due to diffusion plus dispersion and by mass flow or convection with water as the water moves through the soil. The molecular diffusion mechanism is due to the random thermal motion of molecules in solution and is an active process regardless of whether there is net water flow in the soil. A well-known description of the diffusion process is Fick's law of diffusion where the flux is proportional to the concentration gradient. The longitudinal dispersion term of Eq. (4) is due to the mechanical or hydrodynamic dispersion phenomenon which is due to the nonuniform flow velocity distribution during fluid flow in porous media. Nonuniform velocity distribution through the soil pores is a result of variations in pore diameters along the flow path, fluctuation of the flow path due to tortuosity effect, and the variation in velocity from the center of a pore (maximum value) to zero at the solid surface interface (Poiseuille's law). The effect of dispersion is that of solute spreading which is a tendency opposite to that of piston flow. Dispersion is effective only during fluid flow, so that for a static water condition or when water flow is near zero, molecular diffusion is the dominant process for solute transport in soils. For multidimensional flow, longitudinal dispersion coefficient (D_L) and transverse dispersion coefficients (D_T) are needed to describe the dispersion mechanism. Longitudinal dispersion refers to that in the direction of water flow and that for the transverse directions for dispersion perpendicular to the direction of flow. Based on ex-

perimental values of D_L determined by various scientists, a unique relationship exists between (D_L/D_m) and the Peclet number P ($= vd/D_m$), where d is the average diameter of the soil particles (cm) and v is referred to as the pore-water velocity and is given by (q/Θ). Based on these findings a generalized relation for D_L may be written as

$$D_L = \lambda v, \quad (5)$$

where λ is a characteristic property of the porous media known as the dispersivity (cm). Apparent dispersion D is often introduced to simplify the flux Eq. (4) such that

$$J_z = -\Theta D\frac{\partial C}{\partial z} + qC, \quad (6)$$

where D ($= D_m + D_L$) refers to the combined influence of diffusion and hydrodynamic dispersion for dissolved chemicals in porous media. Unless the water flow velocity is extremely slow, D is dominated by longitudinal dispersion D_L. Moreover, since D_m is difficult to quantify, direct methods are often used to determine the apparent dispersion coefficient D of Eq. (6). Miscible displacement results for a tracer (e.g., Br, ^3H_2O or ^{36}Cl) in soil columns are the required data set. Determination of D is obtained through either regression or trial and error by curve fitting of effluent data to analytical solution of the transport equation for nonreactive solutes. [See SOIL–WATER RELATIONSHIPS.]

Incorporation of flux Eq. (6) into the conservation of mass Eq. (3) yields the following generalized form for solute transport in soils in one-dimension,

$$\frac{\partial \Theta C}{\partial t} + \rho\frac{\partial S}{\partial t} = \frac{\partial}{\partial z}\left[\Theta D\frac{\partial C}{\partial z}\right] - \frac{\partial qC}{\partial z} - Q. \quad (7)$$

The above equation is commonly known as the convective–dispersive equation for solute transport which is valid for soils under transient and unsaturated soil–water flow conditions. In order to describe the fate of solutes in unsaturated soil profiles under transient flow conditions, Richards' equation for water flow (in one-dimension) must also be considered,

$$\frac{\partial \Theta}{\partial t} = \frac{\partial}{\partial z}\left[K(h)\frac{\partial h}{\partial z}\right] - \frac{\partial K(h)}{\partial z} - A(z,t), \quad (8)$$

where h is the soil–water pressure head (cm) and $K(h)$ is the soil hydraulic conductivity ($cm\ hr^{-1}$). The above equation is known as the h-form of the water flow equation. Knowledge of the functional relation of K versus pressure head h and the moisture characteristic relation (Θ versus h) are prerequisites for solving Richards' flow equation. In addition, Eq. (8) includes a root uptake term $A(z,t)$, for water extraction as a function of depth and time (cm^3 cm^{-3} hr^{-1}). This term is analogous to the irreversible source/sink term Q for solutes in Eq. (7). Upon solution of Eq. (8) subject to the appropriate initial and boundary conditions, one can obtain the water content Θ and Darcy flux q for any depth (z) and time (t). Both $\Theta(z,t)$ and $q(z,t)$ are needed in order to obtain a solution for solute transport in the convection–dispersion equation.

For conditions where steady water flow is dominant, q and Θ are constants, i.e., for uniform Θ in the soil, we have the simplified form of the convection-dispersion equation as

$$\frac{\partial C}{\partial t} + \frac{\rho}{\Theta} \frac{\partial S}{\partial t} = D \frac{\partial^2 C}{\partial z^2} - \nu \frac{\partial C}{\partial z} - \frac{Q}{\Theta}. \qquad (9)$$

Solutions of the above convection–dispersion Eq. (7) or (9) yield the concentration distribution of the amount of solute in soil solution C and that retained by the soil matrix S with time and depth in the soil profile. In order to arrive at such a solution, the appropriate initial and boundary conditions must be specified. Several boundary conditions are identified with the problem of solute transport in porous media. First-order type boundary conditions for a solute pulse input may be described as

$$C = C_s, \qquad z = 0, \qquad t < T, \qquad (10)$$

$$C = 0, \qquad z = 0, \qquad t \geq T, \qquad (11)$$

where C_s (μg cm^{-3}) is the concentration of the solute species in the input pulse. The input pulse application is for a duration T which is then followed by a pulse input which is free of such a solute. Third-type boundary conditions are commonly used and account for advection plus dispersion across the interface. For a continuous input at the soil surface we have

$$\nu C_s = - D \frac{\partial C}{\partial z} + \nu C, \qquad z = 0, \qquad t > 0. \quad (12)$$

For a flux type pulse-input we have

$$\nu C_s = - D \frac{\partial C}{\partial z} + \nu C, \qquad z = 0, \qquad t < T. \quad (13)$$

The boundary conditions at some depth L in the soil profile are often expressed as

$$0 = - D \frac{\partial C}{\partial z} + \nu C, \qquad z = 0, \qquad t \geq T \quad (14)$$

$$\frac{\partial C}{\partial z} = 0, \qquad z = L, \qquad t \geq 0, \qquad (15)$$

which is used to deal with solute effluent from soils having finite depths. However, it is often convenient to solve the dispersion–convection equation where a semi-infinite rather than a finite length (L) of the soil is assumed. Under such circumstances, the appropriate condition for a semi-infinite medium is

$$\frac{\partial C}{\partial z} = 0, \qquad z \rightarrow \infty, \qquad t \geq 0. \qquad (16)$$

Analytical solutions to the convection–dispersion equation subject to the appropriate boundary and initial conditions are available for a limited number of situations whereas the majority of the solute transport problems must be solved using numerical approximation methods. In general, whenever the form of the retention reaction is linear, a closed-form solution is obtainable. A number of closed-form solutions are available in the literature. However, most retention mechanisms are nonlinear and time-dependent in nature and analytical solutions are not available. As a result a number of numerical models using finite-difference or finite element approximations have been utilized to solve nonlinear retention problems of multireaction and multicomponent solute transport for one- and two-dimensional geometries.

III. Single Retention Models

The reversible term ($\partial S/\partial t$) and the irreversible term Q of Eqs. (7) and (9) must be identified in order to predict the fate of reactive solutes in the soil. The reversible term is often used to describe the rate of sorption or exchange reactions with the solid matrix. Sorption or exchange has been described by either instantaneous equilibrium or a kinetic reaction where C and S vary with time. Linear, Freundlich, and one- and two-site Langmuir equations are perhaps the most commonly used to describe equilibrium reactions. Ion exchange is often considered instantaneous in nature and governs the retention of cations such as Ca, Mg, and Na in soils. In contrast, retention for several solutes has been observed to be strongly time-dependent (e.g., phosphorus, several heavy metals, and organics). Selected examples of kinetic retention for P are given in Fig. 1. The influence of kinetic reactions on the shape of sorption isotherms of P for an Oldsmar fine sand (from south Florida) is clearly illustrated in Fig. 1. The amount of P removed from solution increased with P concentration and time. Several approaches have been proposed to describe kinetic retention behavior such as that shown in Fig. 1. First-order kinetic is perhaps the earliest single form of reaction used to describe sorption versus time for several solutes in soils,

$$\rho \frac{\partial S}{\partial t} = k_f \Theta C - k_b \rho S. \qquad (17)$$

The reaction is reversible with k_f and k_b representing the forward and backward rate coefficients (hr^{-1}). Integration of Eq. (17) subject to initial conditions of $C = C_i$, and $S = 0$ at $t = 0$, yields a system of linear sorption isotherms. That is, following any reaction

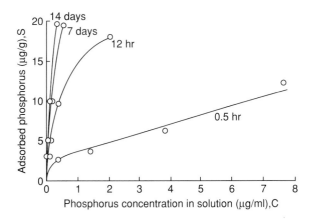

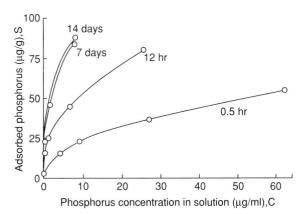

FIGURE 1 Relationship of P sorbed versus solution concentration with time in shallow tilled (top) and deep-tilled (bottom) Oldsmar fine sand. [Reprinted with permission from Fiskell, J. G., A., Mansell, R. S., Selim, H. M., and Martin, G. G. (1979). Kinetic behavior of phosphate sorption by acid sandy soil. *J. Environ. Qual.* **8**, 579–584.]

time t, a linear relation between S and C is obtained. However, linear isotherms are not often encountered except for selected cations, heavy metals, and pesticides at low concentrations. In contrast, nonlinear retention behavior is commonly observed for several solutes as depicted by the nonlinear isotherms for P shown in Fig. 1. As a result, the single reaction given by Eq. (17) has been extended to include the nonlinear kinetic form,

$$\rho \frac{\partial S}{\partial t} = k_f \Theta C^m - k_b \rho S, \qquad (18)$$

where m is a dimensionless parameter commonly less than unity and represents the order of the nonlinear reaction. For both single kinetic forms (Eqs. 17 and 18), the magnitude of the rate coefficients dictates the extent of the kinetic behavior of the reaction. For small values of k_f and k_b, the rate of retention is slow and strong kinetic dependence is anticipated. In contrast, for large values of k_f and k_b, the retention reaction is rapid and should approach quasi-equilibrium in a relatively short time. In fact, at large times ($t \rightarrow \infty$) equilibrium is attained and the rate of retention ($\partial S / \partial t$) approaches zero and Eq. (18) yields,

$$S = K_d C^m,$$

where

$$K_d = \left(\frac{\Theta}{\rho}\right) \frac{k_f}{k_b}, \qquad (19)$$

which is analogous to the Freundlich equilibrium equation where K_d is the distribution coefficient ($cm^3 \, g^{-1}$). For Freundlich or linear isotherms ($m = 1$), one may regard K_d as the ratio of the forward rate coefficient for sorption to that for desorption or release (backward reaction). An alternative to the first- or nth order models is that of the second-order kinetic approach. This approach is commonly referred to as the Langmuir kinetic and has been used for P retention and sorption of heavy metals by high-affinity or specific sites. According to second-order formulation, the rate of retention is a function of solution concentration and the amount of available retention sites on matrix surfaces such that

$$\rho \frac{\partial S}{\partial t} = k_f \Theta \phi C - k_b \rho S \qquad (20)$$

or

$$\rho \frac{\partial S}{\partial t} = k_f \Theta (S_T - S) C - k_b \rho S, \qquad (21)$$

where ϕ is the amount of available or vacant sites

and S_T is the total amount of sorption sites (μg g^{-1}). Available or vacant specific sites are not strictly vacant. They are assumed occupied by hydrogen, hydroxyl, or other specifically sorbed species. At $t \rightarrow \infty$, when the reaction achieves local equilibrium, the second-order Eq. (20) obeys the widely recognized Langmuir sorption isotherm equation

$$\frac{S}{S_T} = \frac{\omega C}{1 + \omega C}, \quad (22)$$

where ω ($= \Theta k_f/\rho k_b$) is the (equilibrium) Langmuir coefficient. Sorption/desorption studies showed that highly specific sorption mechanisms are responsible for solute retention at low concentrations. The general view is that metal ions have a high affinity for sorption sites of oxide minerals surfaces in soils.

Adsorption–desorption hysteretic behavior has been observed by several scientists. Examples of hysteretic behavior for atrazine adsorption–desorption isotherms for a Sharkey clay soil from Louisiana are given in Fig. 2. Atrazine desorption shows significant hysteresis or nonsingularity behavior which becomes apparent with increasing incubation time. The adsorption and desorption isotherms are nearly identical for the case where no incubation time was allowed and desorption for six consecutive steps were followed. If adsorption and desorption isotherms are identical and follow the same path, i.e., nonhysteretic behavior, the retention is regarded as fully reversible where local equilibrium is dominant. Based on the hysteresis behavior for several initial concentrations (not shown), desorption results suggest that part of the adsorbed atrazine is not easily desorbed or becomes nondesorbable by forming strong complexes or due to degradation to more strongly adsorbed hydroxyatrazine or other metabolites. It has been shown theoretically that hysteresis results from failure to achieve equilibrium during adsorption or desorption. If adsorption and desorption are carried out for times sufficient for equilibrium to be attained, or the kinetic rate coefficients are sufficiently large, such hysteretic behavior is minimized.

IV. Transport and Ion Exchange

Modeling cation retention and transport in the soil profile requires knowledge of several chemical and physical properties of the soil matrix, including the cation exchange capacity and the distribution of exchangeable cations between solution and sorbed phases. Only recently, competitive ion exchange of cations in the soil solution during transport in soils was considered. The simplest model is that for a binary system based on the convective–dispersive equation with cation retention during steady water flow in soils. Reversible ion exchange is considered to govern the retention of cations present in the soil. In addition, the ion-exchange reactions are assumed to be rapid or instantaneous which implies that local equilibrium conditions are dominant. A set of recursion equations is needed to describe multispecies, heterovalent cation exchange, however. Examples of predictions of breakthrough curves (BTCs) using ion-exchange models compared to experimental data for pulses of Mg plus Na leached by Ca in a Sharkey clay soil column is shown in Fig. 3. Breakthrough of Na was early and well described by the model. The retardation of Ca and Mg peaks were accurately described; however, peak heights were not well estimated. Nev-

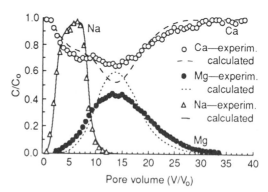

FIGURE 3 Breakthrough results, pore volume (V/V_o) and relative concentration (C/C_o) for a ternary (Na–Ca–Mg) system in a sharkey soil. Solid curves are predictions using equilibrium ion exchange transport model. [Reprinted with permission from Gaston, L. A., and Selim, H. M. (1990). Transport of exchangeable cations in an aggregated clay soil. *Soil Sci. Soc. Am. J.* **54**, 31–38.]

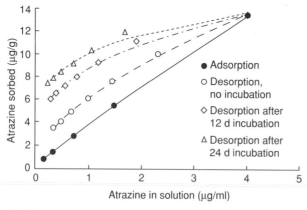

FIGURE 2 Atrazine adsorption-desorption hysteresis isotherms for a Sharkey clays soil.

ertheless these predictions are surprising achievements for simple transport models based on ion exchange.

Predicting cation transport in soils as shown in Fig. 3 requires knowledge of several chemical and physical properties of the exchange medium including, at a minimum, the cation exchange capacity (CEC), exchange selectivity coefficients, bulk density, and the dispersion coefficient. The CEC and the physical properties are fairly readily determined. Estimation of cation exchange selectivities, however, typically requires development of exchange isotherms. The experimental methods are laborious. If exchange selectivities for reference materials could be used to obtain fairly accurate predictions of cation movement in field soils then it might be feasible to broaden the data base of land management decisions for agricultural production or waste disposal to include such predictions. The applicability of selectivity parameters of a common type of soil mineral for prediction of cation mobilities in soils having mineralogies dominated by a similar mineral was recently investigated. To achieve this goal, the determination of a data base for pure clays such as that shown in Fig. 4 was essential. Transport model predictions based on selectivity coefficients on pure montmorillonite, as obtained from Fig. 4, adequately described cation leaching in columns of bulk samples of a predominantly montmorillonitic Sharkey soil. Experimental and predicted effluent results of Na and Mg applied to a Ca-saturated Sharkey soil are shown in Fig. 5. In addition, comparison of predictions of binary (Ca–Mg) or ternary (Ca–Mg–Na) transport using selectivity coefficients on pure montmorillonite to transport in columns of Olivier series (fine silty, mixed, thermic, Aquic Fragi-

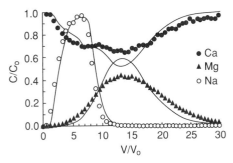

FIGURE 5 Breakthrough results, pore volume (V/V_o) and relative concentration (C/C_o) for a ternary (Na–Ca–Mg) system in a sharkey soil. Predictions are based on exchange isotherm data for bentonite clay. [Reprinted with permission from Gaston, L. A., and Selim, H. M. (1990). Predictions of cation mobility in montmorillonitic media based on exchange selectivities of montmorillonite. *Soil Sci. Soc. Am. J.* **54**, 1525–1530.]

udalf) and Yolo series (fine silty, mixed, nonacid, thermic, Typic Xerorthent) revealed generally good agreement. These results for one common clay mineral are encouraging. However, the applicability of exchange data for pure clays to description of cation transport in soils is not possible until the transport or exchange behavior in several such soils is examined.

Several studies showed that ion exchange is a kinetic process in which local equilibrium was not reached instantaneously. In fact, an extensive list of cations (and anions) exhibited kinetic ion exchange behavior in soils (e.g., aluminum, ammonium, potassium, and several heavy metal cations). The extent of the kinetics of potassium retention on kaolinite, montmorillonite, and vermiculite is illustrated in Fig. 6. A single first-

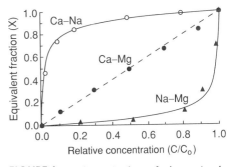

FIGURE 4 Exchange isotherm for bentonite clay in 0.05 M ClO$_4$ background solution. Solid curves are predictions based on average selectivities. [Reprinted with permission from Gaston, L. A., and Selim, H. M. (1990). Predictions of cation mobility in montmorillonitic media based on exchanged selectivities of montmorillonite. *Soil Sci. Soc. Am. J.* **54**, 1525–1530.]

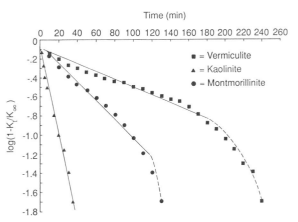

FIGURE 6 First-order plots of potassium adsorption on clay minerals where K_t is quantity adsorbed at time t and K_∞ is quantity adsorbed at equilibrium. [Reprinted with permission from Jardine, P. M., and Sparks, D. L. (1984). Potassium–calcium exchange in a multireactive soil system, I. Kinetics. *Soil Sci. Soc. Am. J.* **48**, 39–45.]

order decay type reaction described the data adequately for kaolinite and montmorillonite whereas two first-order reactions were necessary to describe potassium retention on vermiculite. Deviations from first-order kinetics for longer reaction time is likely due to the fact that potassium retention is not an irreversible but rather a reversible mechanism. At large times, the contribution of the reverse or backward retention process becomes significant and thus should not be ignored. Kinetic ion-exchange behavior in soils is probably due to mass transfer (or diffusion) and chemical kinetic processes. For chemical sorption to occur, ions must be transported to active (fixed) sites of the soil particles. The film of water adhering to and surrounding the particles and water within the interlayer spaces of the particles are both zones of low concentrations due to depletion by adsorption of ions onto the exchange sites. The decrease in concentration in these two interface zones may be compensated by diffusion of ions from the bulk solution. Therefore, a kinetic ion-exchange model formulation was recently developed analogous to mass transfer or diffusion between the solid and solution phase such that,

$$\frac{\partial S}{\partial t} = \gamma \, (S^\star - S), \qquad (23)$$

where S is the amount sorbed on exchange surfaces, $S^\star$ is the equilibrium sorbed amount (at time t), and γ is an apparent rate coefficient (h^{r-1}). Here, the sorbed amount was calculated using the respective sorption equilibrium condition based on laws of mass action governing ion exchange processes. Expressions similar to the above have been used to describe chemical kinetics as well as mass transfer between mobile and immobile water.

V. Multiple Reaction Models

Several studies showed that sorption–desorption of dissolved chemicals on several soils was not adequately described by use of a single reaction of the equilibrium or kinetic types. Failure of single reactions is not surprising since they only describe the behavior of one species with no consideration to the simultaneous reactions of others in the soil system. Multisite or multireaction models deal with the multiple interactions of one species in the soil environment. Such models are empirical in nature and are based on the assumption that retention sites are not homogeneous in nature, rather the sites are heterogeneous

and thus have different affinities to individual solute species. One of the earliest multireaction models is the two-site model which was developed in order to describe observed batch results which showed rapid initial retention followed by slower type reactions. It was also developed to describe observed excessive tailing of BTCs from pulse inputs in miscible displacement experiments. The two-site model is based on several simplifying assumptions. First it is assumed that a fraction of the total sites (referred to as type I sites) reacts rapidly with the solute in soil solution. In contrast, type II sites are highly kinetic in nature and react slowly with the soil solution. The retention reactions for both types of sites were based on the nonlinear (or mth order) reversible kinetic approach discussed earlier.

The two-site approach was also adapted for the case when type I sites were assumed to be in equilibrium with the soil solution whereas type II sites were considered of the kinetic type. The two-site model provided improved pesticide predictions of the excessive tailing of the desorption or leaching side and the sharp rise of the sorption side of the BTCs in comparison to predictions with single reaction equilibrium or kinetic models. The model proved successful in describing the retention and transport of several dissolved chemicals including aluminum, 2,4-D, atrazine, phosphorus, potassium, cadmium, chromium, and methyl bromide. However, there are several inherent disadvantages of the two-site model. The reaction mechanisms are restricted to those which are fully reversible. Moreover, the model does not account for possible consecutive type solute interactions in the soil system.

Due to the limitations of the single reaction approach, several multireaction models which account for multiple reactions (reversible and irreversible) of solutes during transport in soils have been proposed. An example is a phosphorus multireaction and transport model which includes different sorption sites for P reactions in soils shown in Fig. 7. It is assumed that applied P in a dissolved form is subject to six reversible-kinetic reactions that are assumed to control the transfer of applied P between solution, adsorbed, immobilized, and precipitated phases within the soil. Sinks are shown for irreversible removal of P from the soil solution by plant uptake and leaching. Model formulation is based on the observed slow reaction of P in soils which may represent chemisorption or diffusion into the micropore space of soil aggregates. Moreover, kinetic P behavior may be physically controlled by the geometry of the soil pore space as well as the accessibility of retention sites to P in

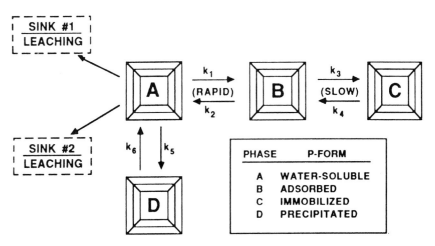

FIGURE 7 A schematic representation of six reversible-kinetic reactions that are assumed to control the transfer of applied phosphate (P) between solution, adsorbed, immobilized (chemisorbed), and precipitated phases within the soil. Sinks are shown for irreversible removal of P from the soil solution by plant uptake and leaching. [Reprinted with permission from Mansell, R. S., Selim, H. M., and Fiskell, J. G. A. (1977). Simulated transformations and transport of phosphorus in soils. *Soil Sci.* **124,** 102–109.]

the bulk solution. The presence of inaccessible sites is proposed as a controlling mechanism of the slow decline of P in the soil solution with time. Such a slow process may be caused by solid diffusion of surface phosphate within soil particles. It may also be due to differences in rates of reactions which occur between P and different reaction sites of the soil matrix.

A schematic representation of the reactions of K in soils is illustrated in Fig. 8. This empirical multireaction approach considers kinetic reactions to govern transformation between solution, exchangeable, non-exchangeable (secondary minerals), and primary mineral phases of K in soils. The first two compartments account for K uptake by plant roots and transport of K due to mass flow and dispersion. The subsequent compartments deal with reversible reactions of adsorption/desorption between the solution and exchangeable phases. The transformations of exchangeable, nonexchangeable (secondary minerals), and primary mineral phases are considered time-dependent and dictated by extremely slow rates of reactions.

One should recognize that a multireaction model cannot account for all possible interactions occurring with the soil system. For example, characterization of chemical, biological, and physical interactions of nitrogen within the soil environment is a prerequisite in the formulation of a multireaction nitrogen model. One major point is how strongly such factors affect nitrogen behavior and distribution within soil systems. Among these factors are: the effect of soil texture and structure on oxygen diffusion; distribution

of plant residues (vertically and horizontally) which affects infiltration rates, leaching, and biological transformations including plant uptake, mineralization, and denitrification; as well as cultural practices, such as tillage and fertilizer distribution which affect nitrogen distribution vertically and horizontally. Since nitrate is a highly mobile nitrogen form that can leach through the soil profile and eventually into groundwater, the goal of any nitrogen management plan must include minimizing nitrate leaching from agricultural activities into groundwater. Nevertheless, description of N dynamics in the soil is often simplified. To illustrate this, one needs to examine the N dynamics in soils as described in the simplified approach shown in Fig. 9. The model accounts for nitrification, denitrification, immobilization, mineralization, and ion exchange of ammonium as a reversible first-order kinetic process. To utilize such a model, despite its simplicity, requires several independent parameters (rate coefficients) many of which are not easily available. As a result, simplified versions (or submodels) of the model shown in Fig. 9 are commonly utilized for management decisions. [*See* NITROGEN CYCLING.]

VI. Two-Region Models

A number of experimental studies demonstrated early breakthrough results and tailing with nonsymmetrical concentration distributions of BTCs. Discrepancies from symmetrical or ideal behavior for several solutes led to the concept of solute transfer between mobile

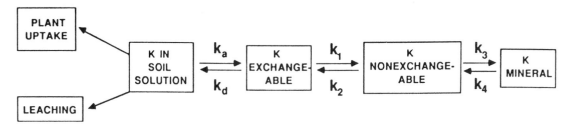

FIGURE 8 A schematic representation of the reactions of potassium (K) in solution, exchangeable, nonexchangeable (secondary minerals), and primary mineral phases in soil. [Reprinted with permission from Selim, H. M., Mansell, R. S., and Zelazny, L. W. (1976). Modeling reactions and transport of potassium in soils. *Soil Sci.* **122,** 77–84.]

and immobile waters. It was postulated that tailing under unsaturated conditions was perhaps due to the fact that larger pores are eliminated for transport and the proportion of the water that does not readily move within the soil increased. This fraction of water was referred to as stagnant or immobile water. A decrease in water content increases the fraction of air-filled macropores resulting in the creation of additional dead end pores which depend on diffusion processes to attain equilibrium with a displacing solution. However, the conceptual approach of mobile–immobile or two-region behavior is perhaps more intuitively applicable for well-structured or aggregated soils under either saturated or unsaturated flow. Here one can assume that within soil aggregates, where micropores are dominant, diffusion is the primary process. In contrast, convection and dispersion are the dominant processes in the macro (or intra-aggregate) pore space which occur between large aggregates or structural units.

The equations describing the movement for a non-reactive solute through a porous media having mobile and immobile water fractions are

$$\Theta_m \frac{\partial C_m}{\partial t} + \Theta_{im} \frac{\partial C_{im}}{\partial t} = \Theta_m D_m \frac{\partial^2 C_m}{\partial z^2} - v_m \Theta_m \frac{\partial C_m}{\partial z} \tag{24}$$

and

$$\Theta_{im} \frac{\partial C_{im}}{\partial t} = \alpha \, (C_m - C_{im}), \tag{25}$$

where D_m is the hydrodynamic dispersion coefficient in the mobile water region, Θ_m and Θ_{im} are mobile and immobile water fractions, respectively (cm³ cm⁻³), C_m and C_{im} are the concentrations in the mobile and immobile water (μg cm⁻³), and ν_m is the average pore-water velocity in the mobile region. We also assume that the immobile water (Θ_{im}) is located inside aggregate pores (inter-aggregate) where the solute transfer occurs by diffusion only. In Eq. (24), α is a mass transfer coefficient (hr⁻¹) which governs the transfer of solutes between the mobile- and immobile-water phases in an analogous manner to a diffusion process. Incorporation of reversible and irreversible retention for reactive solutes in Eqs. (24) and (25) yields

$$\Theta_m \frac{\partial C^m}{\partial t} + \rho f \frac{\partial S_m}{\partial t} + \Theta_{im} \frac{\partial C_{im}}{\partial t} + \rho \, (1 - f) \frac{\partial S_{im}}{\partial t}$$
$$= \Theta_m D \frac{\partial^2 C_m}{\partial z^2} - v_m \, \theta_m \frac{\partial C}{\partial z} - Q_m \tag{26}$$

and

$$\Theta_{im} \frac{\partial C_{im}}{\partial t} + \rho \, (1 - f) \frac{\partial S_{im}}{\partial t}$$
$$= \alpha \, (C_m - C_{im}) - Q_{im}. \tag{27}$$

Here the soil matrix is divided into two regions (or sites) where a fraction f is a dynamic or easily accessible region and the remaining fraction is a stagnant or

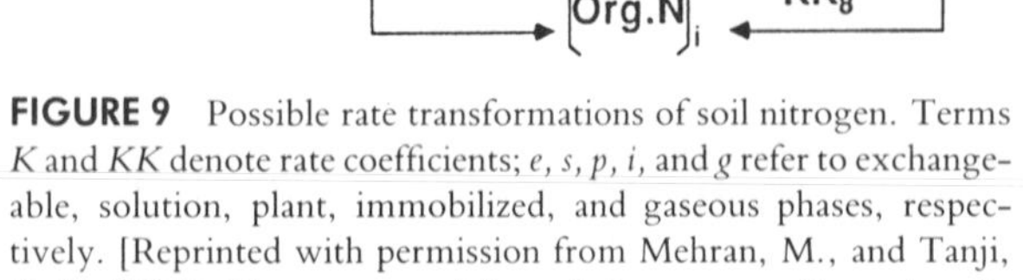

$$\left(NH_4 \right)_p \quad \left(NO_2 \right)_p \quad \left(N_2O + N_2 \right)_g \quad \left(NO_3 \right)_p$$

$$\left(NH_4 \right)_e \underset{K_{se}}{\overset{K_{es}}{\rightleftharpoons}} \left(NH_4 \right)_s \xrightarrow{K_1} \left(NO_2 \right)_s \underset{KK_2}{\overset{K_2}{\rightleftharpoons}} \left(NO_3 \right)_s$$

$$KK_6 \quad K_6 \qquad \qquad KK_7 \qquad \qquad KK_8$$

$$\left(Org.N \right)_i$$

FIGURE 9 Possible rate transformations of soil nitrogen. Terms K and KK denote rate coefficients; e, s, p, i, and g refer to exchangeable, solution, plant, immobilized, and gaseous phases, respectively. [Reprinted with permission from Mehran, M., and Tanji, K. K. (1974). Computer modeling of nitrogen transformations in soils. *J. Environ. Qual.* **3,** 391–395.]

less accessible region (see Fig. 10). The dynamic region is located close to the mobile phase whereas the stagnant region is in contact with the immobile phase. Moreover, S_m and S_{im} are the amounts of solutes sorbed in the dynamic and stagnant regions ($\mu g\ g^{-1}$ soil), respectively. Also Q_m and Q_{im} are sink (or source) terms associated with the mobile and immobile water regions, respectively. The two-region approach was successful in describing the fate of several pesticides in soils when linear and Freundlich reversible reactions were considered. However, it is often necessary to include a kinetic rather than an equilibrium reaction to account for the degradation of pesticides in soils. The two-region approach was successfully used to describe heavy metal transport in soils when adsorption was considered as a Langmuir kinetic along with a first-order irreversible reaction as the sink term. This approach received only limited success when extended to describe the transport and ion-exchange of ions in soils for binary (Ca–Mg) and ternary (Ca–Mg–Na) systems

The two-region (mobile–immobile) is often regarded as a mechanistic approach where physical nonequilibrium is the controlling mechanism. In contrast, in the two-site (equilibrium/kinetic) approach is utilized when chemically controlled, heterogeneous reactions are the governing mechanisms. However, one can show that the two models are analogous mathematically. Therefore, analysis of data sets of effluent results from miscible displacement experiments alone could not be used to differentiate between physical and chemical processes that caused an apparent nonequilibrium situation in a soil. The similarity of the two transport models also means that the two formulations can be used in macroscopic and semi-empirical manner without having to delineate the exact physical and chemical processes on the microscopic level.

Although the two-region model concept has been shown to successfully describe the appearance of lack of equilibrium behavior and tailing for a wide range of conditions, this approach has several drawbacks. First, the value of α is difficult to determine for soils because of the irregular geometric distribution of immobile water pockets. In addition, the fraction of mobile and immobile water within the system can only be estimated. Thus, two parameters are needed (for nonreacting solute) and they can only be found by curve fitting of the flow equations to effluent data. Another drawback of the mobile–immobile approach is the inability to identify unique retention reactions associated with the dynamic and stagnant soil regions separately. Due to this difficulty, a general assumption implicitly made is that similar processes and associated parameters occur within both regions. Thus, a common set of model parameters are utilized for both regions. Such an assumption has been made for equilibrium (linear, nonlinear, and ion exchange) as well as kinetic reversible and irreversible reactions. Therefore, this model disregards the heterogeneous nature of various types of sites on matrix surfaces. This is not surprising, since soils are not homogeneous systems but are complex mixtures of clay minerals, several oxides/hydroxides, and organic matter with varying surface properties. [*See* SOIL GENESIS, MORPHOLOGY, AND CLASSIFICATION.]

Bibliography

Cheng, H. H. (ed.) (1990). Pesticides in the soil environment: Processes, impacts, and modeling. *Soil Sci. Soc. Am.*

Follett, R. F., Keeney, D. R., and Cruse, R. M. (eds.) (1991). Managing nitrogen for water quality and farm profitability. *Soil Sci. Soc. Am.*

Jury, W. L., Gardner, W. R., and Gardner, W. H. (1992). "Soil Physics," 5th ed. Wiley, New York.

Sawhney, B. L., and Brown, K. (1989). Reactions and movement of organic chemicals in soils. *Soil Sci. Soc. Am.*

A

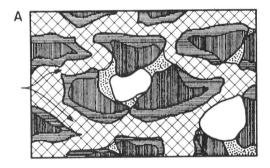

B

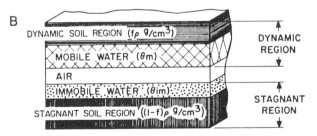

FIGURE 10 A schematic diagram of unsaturated aggregated porous medium. (A) Actual model. (B) Simplified model. The shading in A and B represent the same region. [Reprinted with permission from van Genuchten, M. Th., and Wierenga, P. J. (1976). Mass transfer studies sorbing porous media I. Analytical solutions. *Soil Sci. Soc. Am. J.* **40**, 473–480.]

Selim, H. M., Amacher, M. C., and Iskandar, I. K. (1990). "Modeling the Transport of Heavy Metals in Soils." CRREL-Monograph 90-2, US Army Corps of Engineers.

Sparks, D. L. (1989). "Kinetics of Chemical Processes in Soils." Academic Press, San Diego, CA.

Sparks, D. L., and Suarez, D. L. (ed.) (1991). Rates of soil chemical processes. *Soil Sci. Soc. Am.*

Soil Chemistry

DONALD L. SPARKS, *University of Delaware*

Glossary

Adsorption Net accumulation of matter at the interface between a solid phase and an aqueous solution phase

Chemical kinetics Study of chemical reaction rates and molecular processes where transport is not limiting

Clay mineral Any crystalline inorganic substance of clay size, i.e., $<2 \mu m$ equivalent spherical diameter

Kinetics General term referring to time-dependent phenomena

Soil chemistry Branch of soil science that deals with the chemical composition, chemical properties, and chemical reactions of soils

Transport phenomena Includes displacement of solutes and sorbates in the liquid phase, in the solid phase (soil), and at the solid/liquid interfaces

Soil chemistry is the branch of soil science that deals with the chemical composition, chemical properties, and chemical reactions of soils. Soils are heterogeneous mixtures of both inorganic and organic solids, air, water, and microorganisms. Soil chemistry is concerned with reactions involving these phases. For example, air and water weather the solids and reactions of the solids with the soil solution affect water quality. Soil chemistry has both an inorganic and organic branch; however, there is overlap between the branches. It is closely allied to various aspects of surface chemistry, geochemistry, and environmental chemistry.

I. Historical Perspective

Soil chemistry, as a subdiscipline of soil science, originated in the early 1850s in the celebrated research of J. Thomas Way, a consulting chemist to the Royal Agricultural Society in England. Way, who is considered the father of soil chemistry, carried out a remarkable group of experiments on the ability of soils to exchange ions. He found that soils could adsorb both cations and anions that could be exchanged with other ions. He noted that ion exchange was rapid, that clay was most important in the adsorption of cations, and that heating or acid treatment decreased the ability of soils to adsorb ions. The vast majority of Way's findings were correct, and he laid the groundwork for many seminal studies on ion exchange and ion sorption that were later conducted by soil chemists.

The progenitor of soil chemistry in the United States was Edmund Ruffin, a philosopher, rebel, politician, and farmer from Virginia. Ruffin fired the first Confederate cannon at Fort Sumter. He committed suicide after Appomattox because he did not wish to live under the "perfidious Yankee race." Ruffin was attempting to farm near Petersburg, Virginia, on soil that was rather unproductive. He astutely applied oyster shells to his land for the proper reason—to correct or ameliorate soil acidity. He also described zinc deficiencies quite well in his journals.

Much of the research in soil chemistry between 1850 and 1900 was an extension of Way's work. During the early decades of the 20th century classic ion exchange studies by Gedroiz in Russia, Hissink in

Holland, and Kelley and Vanselow in California extended the pioneering investigations and conclusions of Way. Numerous ion exchange equations were developed to explain and predict binary reactions on clay minerals and soils. These were named after the scientists that developed them and included the Kerr, Vanselow, Gapon, Schofield, Krishnamoorthy and Overstreet, Donnan, and Gaines and Thomas equations. These equations enable one to determine ion selectivity coefficients to predict preferences of ions on soils. Some of these selectivity coefficients were also equated to an exchange equilibrium constant. However, it would be 1951 before a rigorous thermodynamic treatment of ion exchange by Argersinger and co-workers would provide an approach for the calculation of exchange equilibrium constants (K_{eq}) and adsorbed phase activity coefficients.

In the 1930s a major discovery was made by Hendricks and co-workers and Kelley and co-workers who found that clay minerals in soils were crystalline. Shortly thereafter, X-ray studies were conducted to identify clay minerals and to determine their structures. Immediately, studies were carried out to investigate the retention of inorganic and organic species in clays, oxides, and soils and the mechanisms of retention were proposed. Particularly noteworthy were early studies conducted by Schofield and Mehlich who validated some of Sante Mattson's earlier theories on sorption phenomena. These studies were the forerunners of one of the hallmarks of soil chemistry research—surface chemistry of soils.

One of the most interesting and important bodies of research in soil chemistry has been that of the chemistry of soil acidity. As Hans Jenny so eloquently wrote, investigations on soil acidity were like a merry-go-round. Fierce arguments ensued about whether acidity was primarily attributed to hydrogen or aluminum and were the basis for many studies during this century. The work of Samuel Johnson, F. P. Vietch, C. G. Hopkins, Emil Truog, Jenny, R. Bradfield, C. E. Marshall, V. A. Chernov, H. Paver, P. F. Low, Michael Peech, N. T. Coleman, M. E. Harward, and C. I. Rich were particularly elegant and important. It was Coleman and Rich who concluded that aluminum, trivalent, monomeric, and polymeric hydroxy, was the primary culprit in soil acidity. [See SOIL, ACID.]

Another important historical debate in soil chemistry involved the heated, and often caustic, arguments over the cause of the suspension effect, the observation that soil pH is usually lower in the paste than in the supernatant of a soil and water mixture. Marshall in Missouri and M. Peech at Cornell attributed the suspension effect to a Donnan membrane phenomenon, while Jenny and his co-workers, particularly Coleman, ascribed the suspension effect to a liquid junction potential. Jenny and co-workers reasoned that when the salt bridge electrode was placed in contact with the soil, the mobilities of potassium and chloride ions were no longer similar, as they would be in aqueous solution. This alteration in mobilities was ascribed to the attraction of the potassium ions to the charged soil surface. Thus, a junction potential was created resulting in a lower pH reading. This debate, while never definitively resolved, involved some of the most outstanding soil chemists of modern times.

Studies on soil acidity, ion exchange, the suspension effect, and sorption of ions by soils and soil components such as clay minerals and hydrous oxides were major research themes of soil chemists for many decades. Without question, for over 100 years, the major emphasis in soil chemistry was the effects of soil chemical reactions on plant growth and plant nutrition.

Beginning in the 1970s, and certainly in the 1990s, the emphasis in soil chemistry and the research endeavors of soil chemists have shifted heavily to studies on environmental quality. In fact, many soil chemists are referring to themselves as environmental soil chemists and there are increasing interactions between soil chemists and environmental engineers, chemical engineers, agricultural engineers, geochemists, chemists, and material scientists. Most likely, the major emphasis of soil chemistry over the next few decades, and perhaps beyond, will be on environmental soil chemistry.

Throughout the world, concerns have been expressed about a number of soil and water contaminants. These include nitrates and phosphates, heavy metals such as arsenic, cadmium, chromium, copper, lead, mercury, and nickel, radionuclides, pesticides, industrial chemicals, and pollutants in municipal sludges and animal wastes. At present, studies on the following environmental soil chemistry topics are prevalent throughout the world: rates and mechanisms of heavy metal, radionuclide, pesticide, and industrial pollutant interactions with soils and soil components; the environmental chemistry of aluminum in soils, particularly acid rain effects on soil chemical processes; oxidation–reduction phenomena involving soils and soil components and inorganic and organic contaminants; and chemical interactions of sludges, manures, and industrial byproducts and coproducts with soils. [See SOIL POLLUTION.]

To make major advances in the above areas, it is no longer enough to conduct only macroscopic, equilibrium-based investigations. We must increasingly study the kinetics of soil chemical phenomena and employ modern, surface spectroscopic and microscopic techniques to elucidate mechanisms of pollutant interactions in soils. Such studies will help us to speciate contaminants in soils, to understand interactions of metals and organics with soils and assist in developing strategies for mitigating pollutant mobility into surface and groundwaters, and to develop effective and economically feasible approaches for remediating polluted soils.

Before discussing some of the themes in modern soil chemistry, it would be instructive to discuss characteristics of soil minerals. The chemical properties and the types of chemical reactions that occur in soils are dramatically affected by the types of inorganic and organic components found in a given soil.

II. Soil Minerals

A. Inorganic Minerals

Inorganic minerals in soils can be divided into primary and secondary minerals. Primary minerals are less weathered than secondary minerals and are formed from parent material. The secondary minerals form as weathering products of primary minerals. [See SOIL GENESIS, MORPHOLOGY, AND CLASSIFICATION.]

Among the primary minerals, micas and feldspars are very common in soils, and their weathering rates play important roles in soil formation, in soil fertility and plant nutrition, and in soil chemistry and soil mineralogy.

Micas are basically 2 : 1 structures—they consist of two sheets of silica tetrahedra ($Si_2O_5^{-2}$ repeating unit) bound to each planar side of an octahedral sheet that is usually made up of ions such as Al, Mg, and Fe that are coordinated to O^{2-} and OH^{-1}. These 2 : 1 layers are bound together by large interlayer cations. In K-bearing micas such as muscovite, the interlayer cation is mainly K. Micas are more prevalent in fine-grained sediments and sedimentary rocks (clays, shales) than in coarser textured sedimentary rocks (sandstones).

Some of the more important feldspars in soils are K-bearing (e.g., sanidine, orthoclase, microcline, and adularia). The K feldspar polymorphs are a three-dimensional framework of SiO_4 and AlO_4 tetrahedra,

with enough space in the framework to hold K to maintain electroneutrality. The K-feldspar polymorphs comprise about 16% of the total earth's crust, and when they are considered along with alkali feldspars that contain K, the total K-bearing feldspars make up about 31% of the total earth's crust.

Feldspars are usually present in the silt and sand fractions of young to moderately developed soils, representing a number of types of soil-parent material and soil-forming conditions. Alkali feldspars occur in the clay fraction of soils formed under moderate weathering.

Among the secondary minerals, the clay minerals, which are aluminosilicates and which are common in the clay fraction of soils, are most important in affecting the chemistry of soils. A list of some representative clay minerals found in soils, along with some of their important characteristics, is given in Table I.

Clay minerals are composed of silica tetrahedral sheets ($Si_2O_5^{2-}$ repeating unit) bound to octahedral sheets that are made up of ions such as Al, Mg, and Fe that are coordinated to O^{2-} and OH^{-1}. Clay minerals can be classified as either 1 : 1 or 2 : 1, depending on how the tetrahedral or octahedral sheets are arranged.

For example, kaolinite, a 1 : 1 clay mineral, consists of a silica tetrahedral sheet bound to an octahedral sheet. In 2:1 clay minerals like vermiculite, there are two sheets of silica tetrahedra bound to each planar side of an octahedral sheet. Other examples of 2 : 1 clay minerals are montmorillonite, and illite (Table I).

The solid inorganic components discussed previously are crystalline. However, there are amorphous materials in soils. Allophane and imogolite are two amorphous inorganic components of an Al-Si framework. They are found in the clay fraction of soils derived from volcanic parent materials.

Intergrade clay minerals are also found in soils. In acid soils, they are characterized by having hydroxy-aluminum interlayered material.

Other important secondary minerals include oxides and hydroxides such as goethite, gibbsite, and birnessite. Goethite is an Fe-oxide, gibbsite is an Al-oxide, and birnessite is a Mn-oxide. The metal oxides and hydroxides arise by weathering of primary silicate weathering or by hydrolysis and desilication of secondary clay minerals such as kaolinite.

Carbonates and sulfates are also significant solid components in soils and are particularly prevalent in soils of arid regions. In acid soils, sulfates can react with Al and Fe to form minerals such as jarosite, alunite, basaluminite, and jurbanite.

TABLE I

Important Characteristics of Secondary Clay Minerals

Mineral	Type	Chemical formula	Layer charge	Cation exchange capacity (cmol kg^{-1})	Surface area (m^{2}g^{-1})	Permanent charge	Variable charge
Kaolinite	1:1	$[Si_4]Al_4O_{10}(OH)_8 \; nH_2O(n = O \text{ or } 4)$	<0.01	1–2	10–20	No	Yes
Montmorillonite	2:1	$M_x[Si_8]Al_{3.2}Fe_{0.2}Mg_{0.6}O_{20}(OH)_4$	0.5–1.2	80–120	600–800	Yes	No
Vermiculite	2:1	$M_x[Si_7Al]Al_3Fe_{0.5}Mg_{0.5}O_{20}(OH)_4$	1.2–1.8	120–150	600–800	Yes	No
Mica	2:1	$K_2Al_2O_5[Si_2O_5]_3Al_4(OH)_4$	1.0	20–40	70–120	Yes	No
Chlorite	2:1	$(Al(OH)_{2.55})_4[Si_{6.8}Al_{1.2}]$	variable	20–40	70–150	Yes	Yes
With hydroxide Interlayer		$Al_{3.4}Mg_{0.6}O_{20}(OH)_4$					
Allophane	—	$Si_3Al_4O_{12} \cdot nH_2O$	—	10–150	70–300	No	Yes

Source. Reprinted by permission of John Wiley & Sons, Inc. from Bohn, H. L., McNeal, B. L., and O'Conner, G. A. (1985). "Soil Chemistry," 2nd ed. Copyright © 1985 John Wiley and Sons, New York.

B. Organic Components

Important organic components in soils are humic substances. They are naturally occurring, heterogeneous substances that are important in mineral weathering, mobilization and transport of metal ions, sorption of pesticides and other organic chemicals, formation of stable aggregates, and the overall cation exchange capacity of soils. Humic substances can generally be classified as humic acid (not soluble in acid), fulvic acid (soluble in acid), and humin (insoluble in base). The average composition of humic acid is $C_{187}H_{186}O_{89}N_9S$ and of fulvic acid is $C_{135}H_{182}O_{95}N_5S_2$.

III. Soil Mineral Charge

Inorganic and organic soil components can exhibit both permanent and variable charge. Permanent charge arises primarily from ionic substitution when an ion substitutes for another of similar size in a crystal structure. For example, if Al^{3+} substitutes for Si^{4+} in the tetrahedral layer of a phyllosilicate or if Mg^{2+} substitutes for Al^{3+} in the octahedral layer, a net negative charge exists on the mineral. Permanent charge is invariant with pH and is created during the crystallization of aluminosilicates. Smectite and vermiculite are permanent charge minerals.

With variable charged surfaces, such as kaolinite, goethite, gibbsite, and humic substances, the net charge changes with pH and is positive at lower pH and negative at higher pH. The principal source of variable charge on soils is the protonation and deprotonation of functional groups on colloidal surfaces such as hydroxyl (OH^{-1}), carboxyl (-COOH), phenolic (-C_6H_4OH), and amine (-NH_2). In most soils, there is a combination of both permanent and variable charged surfaces and soil chemical reactions are occurring on both types of surfaces.

IV. Important Soil Chemical Reactions

Many types of reactions take place in soils. Ion association reactions include ion pairing, inner- and outer-sphere complexation, and chelation in solution. Gas–water reactions involve gaseous exchange across the air/liquid interface. Ion-exchange reactions occur when cations and anions are adsorbed and desorbed from soil surfaces by electrostatic attractive forces. Ion exchange is an outer-sphere complexation reaction which is reversible and stoichiometric. Sorption reactions can involve physical binding, outer-sphere complexation, inner-sphere complexation, and surface precipitation. Inner-sphere reactions are those in which a species is bonded directly to a solid without the presence of a water molecule. Such a complex occurs when a metal such as selenite is adsorbed on the surface of a soil mineral such as goethite by exchanging with an OH^{-1} ion or H_2O molecule. This is referred to as ligand exchange. Ligand exchange reactions are considered specific and nonelectrostatic. Outer-sphere complexation reactions are reversible, physical, and electrostatic interactions in which the solid remains hydrated and is thus separated from the surface by a water molecule. An example of such a complex is Na^+ adsorption on vermiculite. Mineral–solution reactions include precipitation/dissolution of minerals, and coprecipitation reactions whereby minute constituents become a part of mineral structures.

It should be realized that all of these reactions can occur concurrently and consecutively in soils. Thus, an understanding of soil chemical phenomena in such a system is indeed complex.

V. Modern Soil Chemistry

A plethora of soil chemical studies have been conducted on sorption/desorption processes, ion-exchange reactions, precipitation and dissolution phenomena, oxidation/reduction reactions and other soil chemical reactions. Many of these investigations have been studied strictly from an equilibrium standpoint invoking solubility product principles and empirical, semi-empirical, surface complexation, and ion-exchange models. These approaches have been employed to ascertain a number of parameters including: partition coefficients, binding coefficients, maximum sorption values, intrinsic equilibrium constants, solubility products, and selectivity coefficients.

While these parameters often provide useful information, they are often not applicable to reactions in the field, since soils are seldom, if ever, at equilibrium. Consequently, no rate or kinetic data are derived that would be useful in predicting the fate of metal and organic contaminants in heterogeneous soils with time. Moreover, no definitive mechanistic conclusions can be made. To provide direct molecular information on soil chemical processes, one must employ surface spectroscopic and microscopic techniques.

Accordingly, I will briefly discuss some aspects of what I consider will be extremely important and pioneering areas in soil chemistry for the rest of this century and into the 21st century. My focus is on the kinetics of soil chemical processes and the application of surface and microscopic techniques to the elucidation of reaction mechanisms in soils.

VI. Kinetics of Soil Chemical Processes

One of the most exciting and active fields in soil chemistry today and arguably in the future will be the kinetics of soil chemical processes. The study of chemical kinetics is arduous, even in homogeneous solutions. When one attempts to apply chemical ki-

netics to heterogeneous soils that comprise an array of inorganic and organic components that are reacting with one another, the complexities are magnified.

Chemical kinetics refers to the study of chemical reaction rates and molecular processes where transport is not limiting. Transport processes refer to the movement of solutes and sorptives in the soil solution, at the soil/soil component interface, and in the solid phase. It is very difficult to eliminate transport in most laboratory experiments, and in the field, transport phenomena often predominate. Thus, they commonly are rate-limiting, i.e., they are usually slower than the actual chemical reaction at a soil surface. Accordingly, in most soil chemistry investigations, one is studying time-dependent phenomena, or the *kinetics* of reactions. [*See* SOIL, CHEMICALS: MOVEMENT AND RETENTION.]

Soil chemical reactions transpire over a range of time scales, occurring from microseconds to millennia. These are illustrated in Fig. 1. The kinetics of soil chemical reactions are greatly affected by the inorganic and organic composition of the soil. The types and amounts of clay minerals, primary minerals, and humic substances substantially affect the rates and mechanisms of soil chemical reactions. Thus, in any kinetic study, one should carefully assess and characterize the physicochemical and mineralogical aspects of the soil or soil component.

Another important aspect of any kinetic study is the type of method that one employs. Several kinds of techniques are used and these can broadly be classified as batch, flow (e.g., stirred-flow and stopped-flow), and relaxation. None of these methods is a panacea for kinetic analyses.

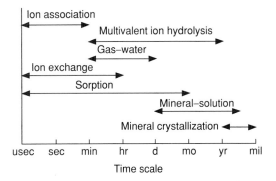

FIGURE 1 Time ranges required to attain equilibrium by different types of reactions in soil environments. [Reprinted with permission from Amacher, M. C. (1991). Methods of obtaining and analyzing kinetic data. *In* "Rates of Soil Chemical Processes" (D. L. Sparks and D. L. Suarez, eds.), pp. 19–59. SSSA Spec. Publ. 27. Copyright © 1991 Soil Science Society of America, Inc.]

Batch and flow methods can be used to measure reaction time scales of seconds or greater. As one can see in Table I, many important soil chemical reactions occur on time scales faster than this. These methods are also often plagued by problems of mixing and thus, physical phenomena are occurring simultaneously with chemical reactions. Thus, the rate parameters that are measured are apparent and dependent on mixing rates.

Relaxation methods can be used to measure reactions on time scales of microseconds and milliseconds. These include such techniques as pressure-jump, temperature-jump, concentration-jump and electric field pulse methods. All of these techniques are based on the principle that a chemical equilibrium can be perturbed by a change in some external parameter such as pressure, temperature, concentration, or electric field and the equilibrium will be slightly perturbed. One can then follow the time that it takes for the system to relax to the new equilibrium state (relaxation time) via a particular detection method such as conductivity. The perturbation is small and thus, the final equilibrium is close to the initial equilibrium. Rate expressions are reduced to first-order equations regardless of reaction order or molecularity and the rate equations are linearized, greatly simplifying determination of complex reaction mechanisms. From the linearized rate expressions, one can plot experimental data and if a linear relation exists, the forward and backward rate constants can be calculated from the slope and intercept of the line, respectively.

In soil chemistry, the pressure-jump relaxation method has successfully been used in our laboratories and in others to study metal sorption/desorption reactions on aluminum and iron oxides and cation exchange kinetics on clay minerals.

In the past decade some important contributions have been made in the following areas of kinetics of soil chemical processes. These include: the development and utilization of kinetic methodologies that enable one to measure soil chemical reactions involving ion-exchange and sorption/desorption on time scales ranging from microseconds to days; elucidation of rate-limiting phenomena for various soil chemical processes; the development of models to describe rates of reactions in heterogeneous systems where chemical reaction and mass transfer kinetics are occurring simultaneously; a greater understanding of metal oxidation kinetics on soil components; and studies on the kinetics of soil weathering reactions.

However, despite advances in the above areas, there are many research needs that must be addressed in the decades ahead to aid in solving environmental soil chemical problems. These are: improvement of kinetic methodologies for elucidating soil chemical reactions over a range of time scales; more sophisticated kinetic analyses of heterogeneous, soil chemical processes; definitive elucidation of interactions of inorganic and organic chemicals with soils by combining kinetic and spectroscopic/microscopic approaches; detailed studies on the kinetics of pesticide, industrial pollutant, and organic waste reactions in soils with particular emphasis on long-term studies; reaction dynamics of humic substances with inorganic and organic contaminants; incorporation of experimentally determined rate parameters into transport models (many of which now assume local equilibrium); effect of macropores on the kinetics of preferential flow of pollutants in soils; effect of mobile humics and other colloids on the kinetics of contaminant reactions in soils; more definitive studies on the oxidation kinetics of metals with soils and soil components; and the kinetics of surfactant-modified clay interactions with organic chemicals.

VII. Use of Surface Spectroscopies and Microscopies

The only way to glean direct information about the molecular and mechanistic aspects of soil chemical reactions is to use surface microscopies and spectroscopies. These techniques can be employed to elucidate surface reaction mechanisms and solid-state species. For example, they can be used to identify the type of interaction that exists or results between soil surfaces and sorbates, e.g., an inner- or outer-sphere complex, surface precipitate, etc., and to assist in speciating contaminants in soils. Thus, their potential use in developing remediation strategies to decontaminate soils and in modeling pollutant interactions so as to minimize pollution of soils and waters is immense.

There are a number of exciting developments in using surface microscopic and spectroscopic techniques to investigate soil chemical processes. However, some of the surface probing techniques are invasive, and they can cause alterations in the surfaces being studied due to the need to: dessicate the sample, place it under high vacuum, heat the sample or bombard the particles. Such treatments can cause experimental artifacts or even prevent experimental analysis. Fortunately, a number of recent advances in surface spectroscopic/microscopic techniques allow an experimentalist to obtain information *in situ*, without subjecting the sample to conditions of drying, high vacuums, etc. Additionally, more extensive structural and chemical information can be obtained with these techniques.

Magnetic and vibrational spectroscopies e.g., electron paramagnetic resonance (EPR), nuclear magnetic resonance (NMR), infrared (IR), and Raman spectroscopies have been used for some time and can provide surface and solid state information under *in situ* conditions. Atomic force (AFM) and scanning tunneling microscopies (STM) have recently been developed and offer innovative ways to investigate soil chemical reactions.

One of the most powerful and useful ways to study reactions on soil components and soils at the atomic scale is to employ X-ray absorption fine structure spectroscopy (XAFS). The energy dependence of X-ray absorption by a material provides information as to the valence and chemical state of the X-ray absorbing species and structural information about its environment, including coordination environments, and in some cases, near neighbor distances. Recently, XAFS has been applied to study metal reactions on metal oxides and clay minerals by geochemists and soil chemists. In our own laboratories, we have used XAFS to elucidate the mechanism for Cr(III) sorption on SiO_2 and to speciate lead contaminants in soils. Without question, the use of this spectroscopic tool, as well as those spectroscopic and microscopic tech-

niques mentioned earlier, will become one of the hallmarks of soil chemistry research.

VIII. Conclusions

An attempt has been made to discuss various historical aspects of soil chemistry, characteristics of soil minerals, development of charge on soil minerals, and important soil chemical reactions. A better understanding of environmentally important soil chemical reactions will be the major thrust in soil chemistry for decades to come. To elucidate the mechanisms of these reactions and to better predict the fate of pollutants in soils will require an increasing application of chemical kinetics and sophisticated surface microscopic and spectroscopic techniques.

Bibliography

Bohn, H. L., McNeal, B. L., and O'Connor, G. A. (1985). "Soil Chemistry." Wiley, New York.

Sparks, D. L. (ed.) (1986). "Soil Physical Chemistry." CRC Press, Boca Raton, FL.

Sparks, D. L. (1989). "Kinetics of Soil Chemical Processes." Academic Press, New York.

Sposito, G. (1989). "The Chemistry of Soils." Oxford Univ. Press, New York.

Thomas, G. W. (1977). "Historical Developments in Soil Chemistry: Ion Exchange." *Soil Sci. Soc. Am. J.* **41**, 230–238.

Soil Drainage

A. AMOOZEGAR, *North Carolina State University*

Glossary

Artificial drainage Removal of water from land surface by land forming and open ditches and removal of groundwater by buried or open drains installed below the water table

Drainable porosity Amount of water that can be removed from a unit area of the soil when the groundwater level is lowered a distance equal to unity

Hydraulic conductivity Index of the ability of soil to transmit water

Impermeable layer Layer with very low hydraulic conductivity which impedes vertical movement of water

Leaching requirement Fraction of irrigation water that must percolate below the root zone to maintain soil salinity below a tolerance level for the crop under consideration

Saturated zone Volume of soil where all pores are filled with water and soil water pressure head is ≥ 0

Unsaturated (vadose) zone Volume of soil where pores are filled with both water and air and soil water pressure head is < 0

Water table Upper surface of the groundwater or the upper boundary of the saturated zone where the water is at atmospheric pressure

Soil drainage refers to the removal of water from soil and its replacement by air. Soil drainage is a natural and dynamic process, and it is an integral part of the hydrologic cycle that includes precipitation and evapotranspiration. In soils that do not naturally drain adequately or as rapidly as desired, artificial drainage may be employed to carry excess water out of the soil. In general, soil drainage is a function of many factors including soil properties, climate, and land management.

Soils are considered a three-phase system composed of solids, liquids (water), and gases (air). The water and air phases occupy the pore spaces between the solid particles, and for nonswelling soils their proportions are inversely related to one another. The proportion of water occupying the soil pore spaces can range from near zero in an oven-dried soil to almost 100% in a saturated soil. Water that occupies the pore spaces in the soil is subject to many fates such as evaporation, plant uptake, and drainage. Soil drainage encompasses the downward movement of water to underlying aquifers as well as the lateral flow of groundwater to streams and other surface outlets including springs that may appear on the landscape. In many cases, natural drainage may be adequate to provide a suitable environment for the intended land use. In other cases, removal of water from soil may be enhanced by artificial drainage for land management purposes. [*See* SOIL-WATER RELATIONSHIPS; WATER: CONTROL AND USE; WATER RESOURCES.]

I. Purpose of Drainage

The main purpose of artificial drainage is to provide a better soil environment for the intended land use. In agriculture, drainage is used for enhancing soil conditions for crop production and improving the profitability of farming the land. In addition, drainage may be employed to provide suitable conditions for other land uses such as wastewater application on land, disposal of solid wastes in sanitary landfills, or construction of buildings, highways, and other man-made structures. Surface drainage is also used to elimi-

Encyclopedia of Agricultural Science, Volume 4   Copyright © 1994 by Academic Press, Inc.   All rights of reproduction in any form reserved.

nate the environment where mosquitoes and other insects can breed.

In humid regions the goals of drainage by lowering the water content to less than saturation in the upper soil layers are: (1) to facilitate movement of air into the soil and transport of CO_2 and other gases produced by crop roots, microorganisms, and chemical reactions into the atmosphere; (2) to lower the heat capacity of the soil so that the soil warms faster in the spring, improving seed germination; and (3) to improve the trafficability of the soil for timely completion of agricultural operations. The need for artificial drainage depends on the time and amount of precipitation as well as on the rate of natural drainage (i.e., movement of groundwater into natural outlets or deeper aquifers). The need for artificial drainage in areas with high rainfall and good natural drainage may be substantially greater than in areas with low rainfall and relatively poor natural drainage.

In areas where natural drainage is inadequate, irrigation of agricultural lands may result in saturation of the soil (often called waterlogging). In arid and semi-arid regions, where irrigation is essential for agriculture, artificial drainage may also be required for the management of soil salinity. The sources of salts that may accumulate in the root zone are irrigation water, soil minerals (parent material), shallow groundwater with a high level of salt content, and fertilizers or amendments applied to the soil. Accumulation of salts as a result of irrigation in many parts of the world has resulted in the formation of saline and sodic soils. Many fertile agricultural lands have been abandoned due to salt accumulation or waterlogging following irrigation. Concentration of soluble salts in the soil solution increases when irrigation water that is applied to the root zone is removed from the soil by plants and/or evaporation from the soil surface. The result is the eventual build up of salts in the entire soil profile and specifically in the root zone of agricultural crops. To alleviate the problem of soluble salts in the soil, excess irrigation water must be applied to leach the salts below the root zone. If natural drainage is not adequate, water applied for leaching purposes will accumulate in the soil resulting in groundwater (i.e., saturated zone) with a high concentration of solutes. In these soils artificial drainage is needed to remove the excess water and allow leaching of the salts from the root zone. Because of the salinity of groundwater under irrigated areas, the water table (i.e., the top of groundwater) must be kept well below the root zone, therefore requiring deeper artificial drains compared to the humid regions. Proper management of irrigation with artificial drainage can sustain the productivity of many arid lands for agricultural production. [*See* IRRIGATION ENGINEERING: FARM PRACTICES, METHODS, AND SYSTEMS; SOIL FERTILITY.]

II. Surface and Subsurface Drainage

Both natural and artificial drainage can be divided into surface and subsurface drainage. Surface drainage is used to remove water that is standing (or can potentially stand) on the soil surface. Standing water can be due to low permeability of the soil, presence of an impermeable layer at or near the soil surface, and/or a flat topography with surface depressions. Low permeability of the surface horizon or subsurface layers near the soil surface prevents water (mainly from rainfall) from moving into the soil. A flat landscape with or without surface depressions impedes the natural overland flow of rainfall. In some cases, there may not be adequate natural drainage channels (e.g., streams, gullies) to carry the amount of rain falling in an area.

Subsurface drainage is primarily used in areas where excess water can penetrate into and through the root zone, and then move laterally toward a drainage outlet (e.g., a drainage pipe, open ditch). For the reasons mentioned earlier (e.g., low hydraulic conductivity, presence of an impermeable layer, gentle slope), water infiltrating the soil from rainfall or irrigation may not seep into lower aquifers or move laterally to a natural drainage outlet. When excessive water is accumulated in the soil, agricultural operations may be halted and/or plants may suffer from excessive water or lack of air exchange between soil and atmosphere. Subsurface artificial drainage is then needed to remove excess water from the soil. A drainage system may be used to lower the water table over an area or it may be employed to intercept the lateral subsurface flow from adjacent areas.

III. Soil Water Regime and Water Flow

A. Soil Water Content and Soil Water Potential

Soil drainage can only affect a portion of the soil water content and not the entire body of water in a soil system. In soil drainage both the total porosity and the distribution of pore sizes are of interest. The total porosity F (dimensions of volume per volume, $L^3 L^{-3}$) in the soil is derived from

$$F = 1 - \rho_b/\rho_p, \qquad (1)$$

where ρ_b and ρ_p are bulk density and particle density of the soil (dimensions of mass per volume, ML^{-3}), respectively. In general, fine-textured soils (e.g., clayey soils) have a higher porosity than coarse-textured soils. The pores in coarse-textured soils, on the other hand, are generally larger and their distribution narrower than finer-textured soils. In theory, all the pores in a soil are filled with water at saturation. Practically, however, complete saturation may not be achieved due to the presence of entrapped air and variations in pore geometry (e.g., pores not being interconnected). Soil pore size distribution is generally obtained from the relationship between the soil matric potential (pressure head) and volumetric water content. This relationship is called the soil water characteristic or soil water retention curve. The soil water characteristic is not a unique relationship between soil water content and soil water potential because it depends on whether the soil is wetting (i.e., adsorption) or draining (i.e., desorption). This phenomenon is referred to as hysteresis and represents a series of relationships that can be obtained depending on whether sorption (wetting) or desorption (draining) is taking place. Because of the hysteresis and entrapped air, the amount of rise in the water table level when a unit quantity of water enters the water table is higher than the amount of drop in water level when a unit volume of water is drained from the soil.

Soil drainage depends on the energy status of soil water at every point within the soil system. The energy level of water in the soil is generally described by soil water potential. Soil water potential is defined as the amount of work necessary to transfer a unit quantity of water from a reference state to the situation of interest in the soil. Factors that affect the amount of work necessary to make the appropriate transfer are elevation with respect to the reference level, attraction of soil particles and small pores for water (i.e., matric effects), liquid and gas pressures, solute in soil solution, temperature, and overburden pressure. Grouping the pressure and matric potentials together, and assuming isothermal conditions with no solute effect (osmotic potential = 0), the hydraulic head H (i.e., the total soil water potential expressed per unit weight, dimensions of length, L) is given by

$$H = z + h, \qquad (2)$$

where z (L) is the elevation above a specified reference level and h (L) is the soil water pressure head. For most field conditions the soil water pressure head (h) is zero or positive for saturated soils, whereas for unsaturated soils h is negative.

B. Soil Water Movement

Water is expected to move from a region of high potential to a region of lower potential in the soil. The rate of water movement is directly related to the hydraulic conductivity of the soil. Hydraulic conductivity is an index of the ability of soil to transmit water, and is perhaps the most important parameter affecting soil drainage. Under saturated conditions almost all the pores in a soil are filled with water, the soil water pressure head (h) is ≥ 0, and hydraulic conductivity, referred to as the saturated hydraulic conductivity (K_{sat}), is assumed to be a constant. Under unsaturated conditions, where h is negative, hydraulic conductivity (K_{unsat}) is a function of soil water content (θ) or soil water pressure head (i.e., $K(\theta)$ or $K(h)$). Both saturated and unsaturated hydraulic conductivities can be measured *in situ* using the soil in its natural state, or be determined in the laboratory using intact or repacked soil columns.

Water movement in soils is governed by Darcy's law

$$v = - K\ grad\ H, \qquad (3)$$

where v is the flux density (dimensions of length over time, LT^{-1}), K is the soil hydraulic conductivity (LT^{-1}), and *grad H* is the hydraulic gradient (LL^{-1}). The hydraulic gradient is the difference between the hydraulic head at two points (or regions) under consideration divided by the distance between the two points, and it determines the direction that water will flow.

Water entering the soil surface increases the water content of the upper layers of the soil before being redistributed through the profile. (Note that the presence of macropores such as cracks and root channels that are open to the soil surface may result in rapid movement of water to lower layers or to a shallow water table in that soil.) The process of soil drainage begins with redistribution of water in the profile. Assuming evaporation is negligible (i.e., no upward flux of water) and plant water uptake is zero, the water movement in the unsaturated (vadose) zone would be primarily vertical (i.e., one dimensional). After infiltration of water into soil ceases, water movement within the soil, and hence drainage, continues. Initially, the rate of drainage in the upper soil layers is high. However, as drainage continues, the decrease in water content of the surface layers and the eventual decrease in the amount and size of the pores filled with water result in a substantial drop in the unsaturated hydraulic conductivity. Subsequently, the rate of drainage decreases with time as the soil water content gradually decreases. For example, the rate of drainage in the first few hours after infiltration may be an order of magnitude (i.e., 10 times) larger than the rate of drainage during the second day after infiltration.

To demonstrate the rate of drainage, let us assume that for a deep water table water under no evaporation and no plant uptake moves vertically downward under a unit hydraulic gradient. In this case, the gradient in Eq. (3) is equal to one (i.e., unit hydraulic gradient) through the depth of interest Z^* (L), and the rate of drainage q, i.e., flux at the depth of interest $(L\,T^{-1})$, is equal to the K_{unsat}. Assuming an empirical functional relationship for unsaturated hydraulic conductivity of the form

$$K_{unsat} = K_{sat}\exp[\alpha(\theta_v - \theta_s)], \qquad (4)$$

where θ_v is the volumetric water content, θ_s is the saturated volumetric water content, and α is an empirical constant, the simple model

$$q = K_{sat}/[1 + (\alpha K_{sat}t/Z^*)] \qquad (5)$$

can be obtained to describe the rate of vertical drainage past the depth Z^*. Equation (5) is based on conservation of mass, and although simple, it describes the decrease in the drainage rate with time.

C. Soil Water Profile and Drainable Porosity

The patterns of volumetric water content (θ_v) distribution above a deep water table and above shallow water tables in a homogeneous and a layered soil are shown in Fig. 1. For a deep water table, the rate of drainage decreases with time, but drainage to greater depths may continue indefinitely (Fig. 1A). For a shallow water table (at depth Z_0), on the other hand, the drainage ceases when the pressure head and consequently soil water content in the vadose zone reach an equilibrium with the water table (Fig. 1B). For homogeneous soils, soil water distribution in the profile above a shallow water table can be obtained from the distance above the water table and the respective soil water characteristic curve. For a layered soil, the soil water pressure head distribution above the water table will be the same as the one for a homogeneous soil profile. Because of the differences in the soil water characteristic of each layer, however, water content distribution with depth may change abruptly at the

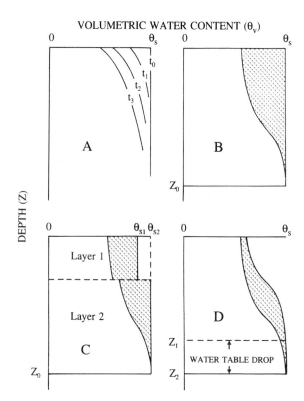

FIGURE 1 Volumetric water content (θ_v) distribution with depth (Z) for (A) a homogeneous profile with deep water table at various times (t_i), (B) a homogeneous profile with a shallow water table (depth Z_0) at equilibrium, (C) a two-layered soil with shallow water table at equilibrium, and (D) two different water table positions (Z_1 and Z_2) at equilibrium. The shaded areas in (B) and (C) represent the total volume of pores that can be drained above the water table, and the shaded area in (D) (the difference between the two water content profiles) is related to the drainable porosity.

boundary between the layers as shown schematically in Fig. 1C. Figure 1C depicts a coarse-textured soil with saturated water content θ_{s1} overlying a finer-textured soil with saturated water content θ_{s2} ($\theta_{s1} < \theta_{s2}$). At the boundary shown in this figure, the soil water pressure heads for the two layers are equal, but the amount of pores filled with water in the upper layer is less than the amount of water-filled pores in the lower layer (i.e., water content of the upper layer is less than the water content of the lower layer).

The portion of the water that cannot be held in a soil against the force of gravity, i.e., the difference between volumetric water content at saturation and the volumetric water content after the soil has drained, is referred to as drainable pore space (Fig. 1D). Drainable porosity is equated to the specific yield in groundwater hydrology and is defined as the amount of water removed from a unit area of the soil when the groundwater level is lowered a distance equal to unity (i.e., a unit volume of the soil). Drainable porosity can be obtained by plotting the volumetric water contents versus depth for two different water table positions Z_1 and Z_2 (Fig. 1D), and dividing the area between the two curves (shaded area) by the distance between the two water table positions (i.e., $Z_2 - Z_1$). The amount of water held in the soils against the force of gravity may be called field capacity. Because of a number of factors (such as rainfall, evaporation, water uptake by plants, and variation in soil hydraulic properties) equilibrium in water content above a water table may never be achieved in practice.

IV. Water Table

Soil drainage may be impeded when water moving downward through a layer with a relatively high permeability or hydraulic conductivity encounters a layer with substantially lower hydraulic conductivity. Subsequently, water accumulates above the layer of lower hydraulic conductivity resulting in the formation of a saturated zone. From a drainage standpoint, a layer is considered restrictive (frequently referred to as impermeable) when its hydraulic conductivity is an order of magnitude smaller than the conductivity of the overlying horizons.

Hydraulically restrictive layers are caused by many conditions in the soil. The most impermeable ones are high in clay (small pores) or are very dense (low porosity, see Eq. (1)). In some areas relatively thin layers of clay materials may be found within a highly permeable sandy soil. In some other areas, an impermeable layer may be very dense soil that was compressed by overburden pressure during the soil formation. If an impermeable layer extends horizontally over a large area, a permanent saturated zone (commonly called groundwater) may be formed on top of it. For shallow impermeable layers, the water table may readily respond to precipitation and evapotranspiration resulting in fluctuations in the thickness of the vadose zone. Although individual rainfall events may influence the water table, fluctuations are generally noticed over seasons rather than individual events. Thus, the term seasonal high water table indicates a fluctuating water table with high water levels during the rainy season with low evapotranspiration, and low water table levels when evapotranspiration is high and/or rainfall is low. If the horizontal extension of the impermeable layer is limited, then a temporary saturated zone, often called a perched water table, may be formed above that layer. Although a perched

water table may not last for an extended period of time (e.g., a season), the presence of an impermeable lens may result in local saturation that may interfere with the intended land use. Also, because the pore sizes in the impermeable lens are much smaller than the pores in the materials above or below it, the lens itself may remain saturated (or near saturated) due to the discontinuity of pore sizes between the lens and the soil above or below it. [See GROUND WATER.]

V. Natural Drainage

The geomorphology and landscape position greatly affect the natural drainage and formation of saturated zone or the position of water tables in soils. In areas where the landscape is generally flat with long distances between streams (wide interfluves), the streams act as the natural outlet for most of the precipitation that infiltrates the soils lying between them. If the soils in these areas contain a less permeable (low hydraulic conductivity) layer below relatively permeable (high hydraulic conductivity) materials, deep percolation (i.e., drainage flux in the vertical direction) will be negligible. For these areas, the depth to water table and the degree of water table fluctuation are primarily a function of distance from the streams (or other free surface water bodies such as rivers, lakes or sea) (Fig. 2A). Due to the relatively small slope and large distance to the stream outlets, the horizontal hydraulic gradient is rather small, and drainage flux in horizontal direction will be very low. As a result, the amount of water flowing laterally to streams is limited and soils farther away from the streams have poor drainage conditions. Near the streams, however, the hydraulic gradient is high and water table fluctuations are pronounced with relatively long strips of well-drained soils along the streams.

In areas with rolling landscapes and narrow stream divides soil drainage is substantial at distances away from the streams and lakes (Fig. 2B). Unlike flat areas, the soils near the streams or lakes may have poor drainage while at the top of the landscape position depth to groundwater may exceed a few meters. In general, these conditions are formed due to the slope of the land from the stream to the interfluve. Although hydraulic conductivity may be low to moderate in these soils, a high gradient and shorter distances between the streams allow the water table to remain a substantial distance below the soil surface in most of the landscape positions.

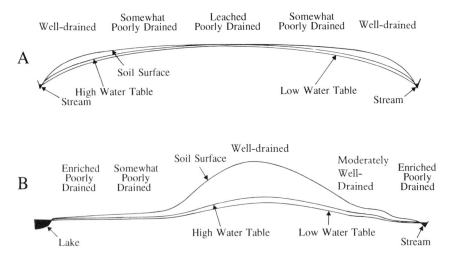

FIGURE 2 Relationships between soil drainage (water table) and landscape position for (A) an area with relatively flat topography and long distance between streams, and (B) an area with rolling topography and relatively short distance between the interfluve and stream. The positions of well-drained to poorly drained soils as well as the leached and enriched areas are shown. [Adapted from *Soil Genesis and Classification*, 3rd ed., by Buol, S. W., Hole, F. D., and McCracken, R. J. © 1989 by Iowa State University Press, Ames, IA.]

Drainage conditions also have a great impact on soil formation. Poorly drained soils are formed in areas where water stands in the soil for a substantial part of the year. In flat areas, poorly drained soils are generally found near the middle of the interfluves, whereas well-drained soils occur near the streams. As indicated in Fig. 2A, the poorly drained soils in the middle of the landscape are generally leached of materials. Conversely, in areas where well-drained soils are formed at the interfluves, enriched poorly drained soils are found near the streams as shown in Fig. 2B.

VI. Artificial Drainage

Whether for controlling the soil wetness in humid regions, or minimizing the impact of salts by leaching them through the soil profile in irrigated arid and semi-arid areas, artificial drainage is used to manage the water table. Both surface and subsurface drainage systems are employed to control excessive water in poorly drained soils.

For areas with insufficient surface drainage, construction of open channels and/or land forming to provide adequate slope for overland flow and elimination of depressions may be required. In general, areas with surface drainage problems have many depressions of varying sizes and shapes. Land forming to remove the high spots and filling the low areas can eliminate surface impoundment in shallow depression areas. The larger depression areas, however, may require direct connection to an open ditch. The types

of drainage ditch systems include random or natural pattern, parallel, and cross slope or interception drainage.

As discussed earlier, poorly drained soils are generally underlain by an impermeable layer at a relatively small distance below the surface. They may also be located in flat areas where surface drainage is inadequate. When precipitation (or irrigation water) reaches the ground surface, infiltration begins at a rate that is generally greater than the saturated hydraulic conductivity of the soil. As rainfall enters the soil, the water content of the profile increases, and water may start to accumulate above the impermeable layer resulting in a rise in the water table. Depending on the antecedent soil water content, the rate of infiltration decreases with time reaching a final value that is operationally equivalent to the saturated hydraulic conductivity. If the rainfall intensity is greater than the final infiltration rate of the soil, water accumulates at the soil surface. In areas where adequate surface drainage is naturally or artificially available, the excess water moves as runoff away from the area. Otherwise, water remains at the soil surface until infiltration, runoff, and/or evaporation depletes it. If surface drainage is not adequate, water in the depressional areas at the soil surface continues to infiltrate into the soil causing higher soil water content, and in some areas, a rise in the water table level.

To control the water table level the excess water entering the soil must be removed via evapotranspiration, vertical and lateral natural drainage, or an artificial drainage system consisting of tile drains, ditches, and/or wells. In general, an artificial drainage system is composed of various size drains ranging from laterals serving individual fields to main drain lines which carry the drainage water to an outlet. Artificial drainage is accomplished by maintaining the water level in lateral drains that are installed below the water table. The drain tubes (or open ditches) are generally installed at a predetermined depth to allow the water table at the mid-point between two adjacent drain tubes to be lowered a desired distance below the soil surface. This distance is usually selected based on the intended land use. A schematic diagram of the cross-sectional area for a tile drain system in a poorly drained soil showing the positions of the water table for drainage during high rainfall and/or low evapotranspiration and for subirrigation to raise the water level for crop production during low rainfall and/or high evapotranspiration is given in Fig. 3.

Water that is removed by artificial drainage must be eventually disposed of away from the drained area. The final drainage outlet for a field can be a natural body of water or may be channels constructed to facilitate transport of drainage water away from the area. Depending on the topography and land elevation above the final drainage outlet, gravity or pump outlets may be employed to transfer water from drains into the drainage channels or final outlet.

In arid and semi-arid regions irrigation has caused (or may cause) toxic levels of salts (or specific ions such as sodium or chloride) to accumulate in the root zone. Irrigation water generally contains some salt which can accumulate in the soil when water is re-

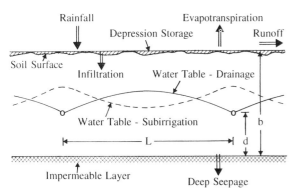

FIGURE 3 Schematic diagram of the cross-sectional area of a tile drainage and subirrigation system depicting the components of the hydrologic cycle and the water table positions for drainage and subirrigation. The depth to an impermeable layer, the height of the tile drain above the impermeable layer, and the distance between the tile drains are shown as b, d, and L, respectively. [Published with permission from Professor R. W. Skaggs (1993). North Carolina State University, Raleigh.]

moved from the root zone by plants or surface evaporation. Depending on the salinity of the irrigation water and the amount of irrigation necessary for an economical crop production, the amount of soluble salts applied annually with irrigation water may range from less than a ton to over 50 tons per hectare. Basically, for every 1 g salt/liter in irrigation water the amount of salts added to each hectare is 100 kg for each centimeter of irrigation water. In general, little of the salt added to the soil can be extracted by plants. To maintain the required salt balance for the cropping system under consideration, the excess salt must be removed from the root zone through leaching. If natural drainage is not adequate, the soil solution containing a high level of soluble salts must be removed by artificial drainage to prevent a build up of salty groundwater reaching the root zone. For salinity control purposes, the depth to water table must be lowered sufficiently to prevent an upward flux of salty water by capillary action into the root zone.

To remove the added salts not used by plants, irrigation water in excess of the crop needs must be applied. The fraction of irrigation water that passes through the root zone is referred to as the "leaching fraction" and is given by

$$LF = D_{dw}/D_{iw}, \qquad (6)$$

where D_{dw} and D_{iw} are the amounts of drainage and irrigation waters (commonly expressed as depth of water), respectively. Maintaining the soil water salinity at a constant level and assuming (i) uniform application of irrigation water with no rainfall, (ii) no salt precipitation or plant uptake, and (iii) no salt release from soil minerals or salt transport from shallow water tables under the capillary action, the leaching fraction can also be equated to the ratio of salinity in the irrigation and drainage waters as expressed by the electrical conductivities of the irrigation (EC_{iw}) and drainage water (EC_{dw})

$$LF = D_{dw}/D_{iw} = EC_{iw}/EC_{dw}. \qquad (7)$$

Based on the above equation, the concentration of salts in drainage water, and hence the level of salts in the root zone can be controlled at some desirable level (between EC_{iw} and EC_{dw}) by varying LF. The leaching requirement (LR) is defined as the fraction of irrigation water that must be applied in excess of the evapotranspiration needs of the crop under consideration to maintain soil salinity below the tolerance level for that crop. Various models are available to determine the LR based on the salt tolerance of the crop and EC_{iw}. Salt tolerance levels and tolerance levels for certain ions are also available.

A. Types of Drains

Open drains, used in some areas for lateral to main drains, may be considered the most economical means of controlling both surface and subsurface drainage problems. They can be constructed by a wide variety of machinery or be hand-dug, and are capable of transporting a large quantity of water. The open ditches, however, are not efficient for controlling the water table in agricultural fields because of their rather large width and interference with agricultural operations. In addition, the maintenance cost of this type of drainage in areas with high labor cost may prohibit its use. Open drain lines (ditches) may be employed for urban developments in areas with a high water table to control both surface and subsurface waters. An open ditch should have stable side slopes and sufficient flow capacity to remove water at a rate not to cause sedimentation or scouring. The side slope of a drainage ditch depends on the soil texture, and in general, a more flat side slope is required for coarse-textured soils compared to a fine-textured soil with a more stable structure.

Buried drain lines do not generally interfere with agricultural operations and may require considerably less maintenance than open drains. A wide variety of materials and techniques are available for installing buried subsurface drains. The materials include short clay pipes, concrete pipes, perforated plastic or other types of tubings. To prevent inflow of soil particles into the drains (which may result in their clogging) and/or to increase the effective diameter of the drain lines, filter or envelop materials such as gravel may be placed around the drain pipes.

B. Drainage Layout and Drain Slope

The outlet pattern of the lateral drains and their associated main drain(s) depends primarily on the topography of the area to be drained. If waterlogging is confined to a few large depression areas in the field, a random or natural pattern (Fig. 4) in which lateral drains are installed systematically within the depression (wet) areas may be the most effective way of providing drainage. Because of the required number of laterals and their associated collector drains the random or natural drainage pattern becomes less efficient as the size of the depressions decreases and their number increases. When the depressions are scattered

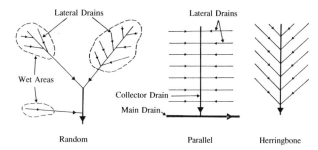

FIGURE 4 Schematic diagram of the plan view of three types of drainage collection system.

throughout the field, or where water table is uniformly high in a large area, a regular pattern such as parallel or herringbone layout (see Fig. 4) becomes more practical.

The slope of the drain lines should be sufficient to prevent sedimentation in the pipe (provide nonsilting velocity), but should not be too high (causing turbulence) to reduce the efficiency of the system or damage the drains. For lateral drains, and where siltation is not a problem, a slope of 0.05 to 0.10% has been recommended for different size pipes. A higher slope may be used in sloping areas or where siltation is a problem. For sloping areas, the lateral drains may be installed at a slight angle to the contour lines of the land. For flat sites, the desired slope for the laterals must be obtained by adjusting the depth of the drain with respect to the depths of the sub and main drains, and pumping may be required for transferring the drainage water to an outlet.

C. Depth and Spacing of Lateral Drains

The depth and spacing of drain lines depend on many factors including the soil hydraulic properties, the desired distance between soil surface and the water table, depth to impermeable layer, land topography, the amount of water entering the soil via irrigation and/or precipitation, and lateral and upward flow of groundwater. Many mathematical models have been developed to describe water flow into open and tile drains and for determining drainage spacing and depth. The depths at which the laterals and the associated collector drains can be installed are limited by the availability of equipment for installing the lines, the depth of the main drain and outlet, and the topography of the area. In general, the spacings between lateral drain lines can be increased by increasing the depth of the drain lines. Spacing and depth for the lateral drains are generally obtained through an iterative process to calculate the most efficient and yet economical drainage spacing.

D. Subsurface Irrigation

In some soils the subsurface drainage systems can be used for irrigation when soil water content drops below the crop needs. This method of irrigation, also referred to as subirrigation, involves raising the water table above the drains and maintaining it at an appropriate position for providing water to the roots of the growing crops. This is accomplished by damming the open drainage outlet (controlling drainage) and raising the water level above the lateral drains as depicted by the dashed line in Fig. 3. Improvements in the design and operation of subsurface irrigation systems in recent years have increased their use in many areas. To use a subsurface drainage system for subirrigation purposes, certain natural conditions must be present. These requirements include the presence of an impermeable layer or relatively shallow permanent groundwater table within a few meters of the surface, relatively flat land, a moderate to high hydraulic conductivity, and a readily available source of water. Many areas in the humid regions of the United States meet the above requirements.

Perhaps the greatest advantage of the subirrigation/drainage system is the increased ability to manage the water table for crop production. Because both irrigation and drainage are provided through one system, substantial cost reduction can be achieved in areas where seasonal irrigation may be required to maximize yield. Because of the possibility of salt build up, subsurface irrigation is not recommend for arid and semi-arid regions. For humid areas, combining irrigation and drainage into one system requires a careful prediction of the performance of the system through computer simulations.

E. Drainage Models

Various theoretical models based on steady-state and transient water flow conditions are available for drainage design purposes. In general, these models relate tile drain depth and spacing to rainfall and/or irrigation, as well as various soil and site characteristics. Using the models, the drainage rate and the rate of fall of the water table can be determined for an area based on measured and estimated soil and site properties. Simulation models enable the designer of a drainage system to evaluate the future performance of the system under consideration based on several years of climatological data. This will allow optimization of the design parameters to achieve the objectives of the drainage system. For agricultural purposes, drainage designs can be based on the crop(s), soil types, and locations.

Available theoretical models include those with rigorous approaches for modeling soil water movement based on saturated and unsaturated flow in two or three dimensions. Although these models can provide valuable information about soil water with time and space, water table position, drainage, and subsurface irrigation, they are generally complicated and may require numerical evaluations. The complexity of solving the problem numerically, and the difficulties associated with determining the required soil input parameters for unsaturated flow conditions limit the use of complicated models. To overcome the problems associated with analytical and numerical models, a number of user friendly simulation models have been developed. One of the less complex approaches has been the development of the DRAINMOD model that is based on water balance in the soil profile. This simulation model includes methods to simulate surface and subsurface drainage, surface irrigation and subirrigation, and controlled drainage. The data required for this model include soil properties, crop parameters, climatological information, and drainage and irrigation system criteria. This model can be used to simulate the performance of both drainage and irrigation systems over an extended period of time according to known climatological data. The major advantages of this model are the ease of use and the relatively minimal computational requirements as compared to other approaches. The model has been tested for a wide range of soils, crops, and climatological conditions with good results.

F. Water Quality

Drainage waters may carry agricultural chemicals and other solutes present in soil solution to surface waters resulting in undesirable water quality. Enhancing run-off to improve surface drainage may result in transportation of suspended soil particles and soluble chemicals to surface waters making them undesirable for drinking water, fishery, or recreational purposes. In this regard, transport of chemicals attached to soil particles is of great concern. In subsurface drainage to control soil salinity, the quality of drainage water may not be suitable for discharge to a body of water or reuse as irrigation water. In humid areas, the nutrient loading of the drainage water may result in degradation of water quality in streams and lakes. For example, it has been shown that phosphorous from agricultural fields travels mainly by surface drainage while the main transport mechanism for nitrogen is subsurface drainage water. To minimize the impact of agricultural water management on the quality and quantity of ground and surface waters, consideration of the soil drainage must be an integral part of any agricultural operation.

Bibliography

Buol, S. W., Hole, F. D., and McCracken, R. J. (1989). "Soil Genesis and Classification," 3rd ed. Iowa State Univ. Press, Ames, IA.

Gilliam, J. W., and Skaggs, R. W. (1986). Controlled agricultural drainage to maintain water quality. *J. Irrigation Drainage Eng. ASCE* **112,** 254–263.

Skaggs, R. W., and Murugaboopathi, C. (1994). Drainage and subsurface water management. *In* "Management of Water Use in Agriculture" (K. K. Tanji and B. Yaron, eds.), pp. 104–125. Springer-Verlag, New York.

Stewart, B. A., and Nielsen, D. R. (eds.) (1990). "Irrigation of Agricultural Crops," Agronomy Monograph 30. ASA, CSSA, SSSA, Madison, WI.

USDA-SCS (1973). "Drainage of Agricultural Land—A Practical Handbook for the Planning, Design, Construction, and Maintenance of Agricultural Drainage Systems." Water Information Center, Port Washington, NY.

van Schilfgaarde, J. (ed.) (1974). "Drainage for Agriculture," Agronomy Monograph 17. ASA, Madison, WI.

Vos, J. (ed.) (1987). Proceedings, Symposium 25th International Course on Land Drainage—Twenty-Five Years of Drainage Experience. International Institute for Land Reclamation and Improvement/ILRI and International Agricultural Centre/IAC. Wageningen, The Netherlands.

Soil Fertility

W. R. RAUN, S. L. TAYLOR, G. V. JOHNSON, *Oklahoma State University*

Glossary

Mineralization Process by which organic materials are decomposed and inorganic ions are released

No-tillage Management practice in crop production whereby all residues (excluding grain) are left on the soil surface without incorporation

Nutrient sufficiency Degree to which the nutrient supply approaches 100% of the plant requirement

Volatilization Release of gaseous forms into the atmosphere generally referring to ammonia losses from urea and anhydrous ammonia nitrogen fertilizers

The science of soil fertility examines the availability of essential plant nutrients in soils and their effect on growth, composition, and yield of plants. Scientists in this field develop fertilizer application technologies that make prudent use of natural resources and that protect the environment.

I. History of Soil Fertility

Ever since Justus von Leibig (1803–1873) stated the mineral theory of plant nutrition, scientists have been interested in whether elements were essential, the nature of their available forms in soil, and the relationships between the amounts of these available forms and plant growth. The development of the science of soil fertility has depended heavily on this knowledge. Thousands of scientists have contributed to our understanding of how soils should be managed and how organic and inorganic fertilizers should be used to maximize yields and limit environmental contamination. Two thousand years ago, Virgil (70–19 B.C.) encouraged the use of legumes in crop rotations, and he also understood soil acidity as it relates to crop production. Pietro de Crescenzi (1230–1307) is considered by some to be the founder of modern agronomy via his work that encouraged increased use of manures. Since that time, numerous scientists have added to our knowledge of soil fertility via the discovery of essential elements, chemical sources of these elements, and appropriate methods of application.

The development of soil science got off to a slower start in America than it did in Europe, partly because of the abundance of land that could be exploited for its native fertility. Because of the vast areas available, the need was less urgent for maintaining the fertility and productivity of the soil. It was easier to move West. Bradfield stated that

> A worker in the field of soil fertility must have a good understanding of the general principles of soil physics, chemistry, microbiology and pedology. I like to think of soil fertility as the highest development of science. It must be built upon the information supplied by these other fields. None of the others are concerned primarily with the growing of plants. Because of the very nature of our subject, we are primarily concerned with integration and synthesis of these other fields.

As the science of soil fertility has progressed, we have come to appreciate how much has been accomplished and how important this knowledge is to feeding our increasing world population. [*See* SOIL, CHEMICALS: MOVEMENT AND RETENTION; SOIL CHEMISTRY; SOIL GENESIS, MORPHOLOGY, AND CLASSIFICATION; SOIL MICROBIOLOGY.]

II. Soil–Plant Relationships

Justus von Leibig was probably the first scientist to explain the nature of soil fertility. He stated that the nutrient present in the least relative amount is the limiting nutrient for plant growth. This law implied that all the other nutrients were present in excess until the deficient or limiting nutrient was in adequate supply, whereupon the one present in the next least relative amount became the deficient nutrient and so on.

Work by E. A. Mitscherlich established that plant growth follows a diminishing increment type of curve now known as the yield curve. In his work it is assumed that every plant species has a finite growth possibility when all nutrients and growth factors are adequate but not in harmful excess. Baule concluded that when more than one nutrient was deficient, the final percentage sufficiency is the product of the individual sufficiencies. Supposing that soil potassium is adequate for 90% of a yield and phosphorus for 80%, then the final yield is 72% of the yield obtainable when both nutrients were adequate (100%). The sufficiency level of available nutrients (SLAN) concept is based on a general mathematical expression of the law of diminishing returns where increases in yield of a crop per unit of available nutrient decreases as the level of available nutrient approaches sufficiency. The concept implies that (1) levels of available nutrients range in a group of soils from insufficient to sufficient for optimum plant growth, (2) amounts of nutrients removed by suitable extractants will be inversely proportional to yield increases from added nutrients, and (3) calibrations have been made for changing the levels of available nutrients in the soil by adding fertilizer (or lime).

Work by Bray identified two distinct types of sorption zones for plants. One is the large volume of soil occupied by the major part of the plant root system (root system sorption zone) from which mobile nutrients are taken up by plants. The other sorption zone is a relatively thin layer of soil adjacent to each root surface (root surface sorption zone) from which immobile nutrients can be removed by the plant (Fig. 1). This concept has assisted many researchers in the development of appropriate methods of applying fertilizers depending on whether the nutrient elements are relatively mobile or immobile in soils.

III. Essential Plant Nutrients

More than 100 chemical elements are known today. However, only 16 have proven to be essential for plant growth. Early work by Arnon and Stout noted that there were three criteria which had to be satisfied in order for an element to be classified as essential for plant growth: (1) the plant cannot complete its life cycle without it; (2) no other element can take its place; and (3) the element must be directly involved in the plant's nutrition and not indirectly through correction of some other unfavorable condition in the soil or release of some other essential element.

The essential plant nutrients, chemical symbols, mobility in the soil and plant and general deficiency symptoms are listed in Table I. Three of the essential elements (carbon, hydrogen, and oxygen) are used in relatively large amounts by plants and are considered nonmineral since they are supplied to plants by carbon dioxide and water. The other 13 essential elements are mineral elements and must be supplied by the soil and/or fertilizers. The essential plant nutrients can be grouped into three categories which are as follows: (1) Primary nutrients, nitrogen (N), phosphorus (P), and potassium (K). (2) Secondary nutrients, calcium (Ca), magnesium (Mg), and sulfur (S). (3) Micronutrients, iron (Fe), manganese (Mn), zinc (Zn), copper (Cu), boron (B), molybdenum (Mo), and chlorine (Cl). Nutrient deficiencies tend to express varied symptoms in the plant and therefore should be used with caution, especially if more than one element is limiting. In general, mobile nutrients in the plant tend to induce chlorosis in the older leaves. Alternatively, immobile nutrients in the plant cause the deficiency symptom to appear in newer leaves (Table I).

IV. The Nitrogen Cycle

Because nitrogen deficiencies have historically been more common, this nutrient has also received more attention in research. A thorough understanding of the nitrogen cycle is essential for those involved in soil fertility work. Following Leibig's law of the minimum, if this nutrient is deficient, all others will be adversely affected. Nitrogen is an integral component of amino acids which are the building blocks for proteins. Proteins are in turn present in the plant as enzymes that are responsible for metabolic reactions in the plant. Noting the complexity of nitrogen in soils, Allison stated the following:

> Many things can happen to nitrogen in the soil. There are so many possible transformations that can lead to gaseous products, or to the formation of soluble forms of nitrogen that are subject to leaching, that it is little wonder that recoveries in the crop may sometimes be

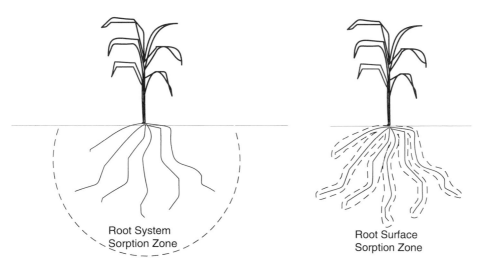

Root System
Sorption Zone

Root Surface
Sorption Zone

FIGURE 1 Root system and root surface sorption zones identified by R. H. Bray to explain the areas where mobile and immobile nutrients will be taken up by plants, respectively.

low. But it is well not to overemphasize these possible losses for, fortunately, under conditions of good management most of the worst possibilities can usually be avoided. [*See* NITROGEN CYCLING.]

Most of the nitrogen in continuously cultivated soils is present as organic nitrogen in the soil organic matter (Fig. 2). In temperate climate soils, there is approximately 2000 kg of N for every 1% of organic matter in the surface horizon (0–30 cm). Soils in many of the northern parts of the United States and southern Canada contain in excess of 4% organic matter and

can have over 8000 kg N/ha stored in organic pools. Not surprisingly, the supplying power of this soil organic N pool must be considered in making N recommendations in crop production systems. Under frequent cultivation, approximately 2% of the total nitrogen in soil organic matter will be mineralized each year. Cultivation alone unleashed a radical change in soil N dynamics and in organic matter composition of soils. Various long-term experiments that have been conducted for more than 100 years have documented the decrease in soil organic matter which

TABLE I

Essential Plant Nutrients, Chemical Symbols, Mobility of Elements in the Soil and Plant, and Chemical Form Taken up by Plants

Deficiency symptom	Element	Mobility in the soil	Mobility in the plant	Form taken up by plants
Overall chlorosis seen first on lower leaves	N (Nitrogen)	Yes	Yes	NO_3^-, NO_2^-, NH_4^+
Purple leaf margins	P (Phosphorus)	No	Yes	HPO_4^{-2}, $H_2PO_4^-$, H_3PO_4
Chlorotic leaf margins	K (Potassium)	No	Yes	K^+
Uniform chlorosis, stunting (younger leaves)	S (Sulfur)	Yes	Yes	SO_4^{-2}, SO_2^{a}
Stunting—no root elongation	Ca (Calcium)	No	No	Ca^{2+}
Interveinal chlorosis, veins remain green	Fe (Iron)	No (ls)	No	Fe^{3+}, Fe^{2+}
Interveinal chlorosis	Mg (Magnesium)	No (ls)	Yes/No	Mg^{2+}
Reduced terminal growth = chlorotic tips	B (Boron) (NM)	Yes	No	$H_3BO_3^{\circ}$
Interveinal chlorosis	Mn (Manganese)	No	No	Mn^{2+}, Mn^{3+}
Wilting, chlorosis, reduced root growth	Cl (Chlorine)	Yes	Yes	Cl^-
Young leaves, yellow & stunted	Cu (Copper)	No (ls)	No	Cu^{2+}
Interveinal chlorosis in young leaves	Zn (Zinc)	No (ls)	No	Zn^{2+}
Interveinal chlorosis, stunting	Mo (Molybdenum)	Yes/No (ls)	No	MoO_4^{-2}
Dark green color	Na (Sodium)	No (ls)	Yes	Na^+
	C (Carbon)			CO_2
	H (Hydrogen)			H_2O
	O (Oxygen)			H_2O

Note: NM, nonmetal; ls, low solubility. Mo availability increases with soil pH, other micronutrients show the opposite of this.
[a] Absorbed through plant leaves.

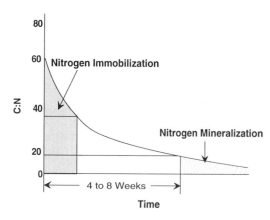

FIGURE 2 Narrowing of carbon to nitrogen ratio as organic matter decays until mineral nitrogen finally becomes available via mineralization.

has been the direct result of continuous cultivation. Unfortunately, many research institutions have discontinued some of their long-term continuous corn and wheat experiments which over time have provided accurate estimates of sustainable production systems.

Because nitrogen release from organic matter is dependent upon decay by microorganisms, which themselves require mineral nitrogen, the amount of mineral nitrogen available for a crop is in constant flux. Nitrogen availability depends upon the relative amount of carbon and nitrogen in the organic matter, its resistance to decay, and environmental conditions to support microbial activity. Figure 2 illustrates how nitrogen becomes more concentrated as soil organic matter decays with time. Nitrogen is not released during the first stages of decay because it is immediately consumed by active microorganisms. With time, remaining organic material becomes more resistant to decay, microorganisms die off, and there is more mineral nitrogen present than can be consumed by the few active microorganisms.

Prior to the time when the native prairie soils in North America were cultivated, N proceeded through the same cycle that is understood today. However, many of these processes took place at much slower rates. Mineralization (combined process of releasing inorganic N from organic N pools), ammonium fixation (ammonium ions bound within clay fractions of the soil), organic immobilization (ammonium and nitrate consumed by microbial organisms), plant volatilization (loss of N as ammonia gas from the leaves of plants), denitrification (microbial transformation of nitrate to gaseous N forms), and leaching (movement of nitrate and or other mobile compounds

through the soil profile) all took place for thousands of years before these soils were cultivated. Background levels of nitrate in soils are therefore not uncommon but rather the result of a natural time consuming process.

Nitrogen is added to the N cycle when fixed from gaseous N in the atmosphere by lightning and various symbiotic and free-living microorganisms and additions of inorganic and organic fertilizers. The major sources of plant available nitrogen loss within the N cycle include: (1) volatilization, (2) immobilization, (3) gaseous plant loss, (4) denitrification, and (5) leaching. Immobilization does not result in a net loss but is used in this discussion to reflect removal of inorganic N from plant available forms. It is important to note that nitrate leaching in most crop production systems can only take place once inorganic N has bypassed each of the first four categories (Fig. 4).

1. Additions of fertilizer N can initially be lost by volatilization. Losses of fertilizer N as ammonia (NH_3) generally occur on high pH soils. Applications of fertilizer N (especially urea) on the surface without incorporation on soils where surface residues are present will magnify ammonia volatilization losses.

2. Immobilization of fertilizer N will take place in virtually all soils by both microbial consumption and formation of highly stable lignin–N compounds. Microorganisms will not multiply and organic matter will not be decomposed unless nitrogen is assimilated into microbial protoplasm, and assimilation will take place as long as there is microbial activity. A common phrase used among soil microbiologists is that "the microbial pool eats at the first table." In other words, the demands of soil microflora are met prior to the time crop N uptake occurs. This is important since the majority of all microbial activity takes place in the surface soil horizon (0–15 cm) where plant root volumes are greatest.

3. Once the plant consumes inorganic N, gaseous N losses from the plant as NH_3 are known to take place.

4. When excess N is neither consumed by the aerobic microbial pool and/or the crop, facultative anaerobes (generally present below 30 cm) are involved in the denitrification of inorganic N (Fig. 4).

5. Finally once inorganic N is not volatilized, fixed by the soil, immobilized in organic pools, consumed by the plant, or denitrified by facultative anaerobes, leaching of N as nitrate can take place (Figs. 3 and 4). Many comprehensive N cycles fail to illustrate this point since they show microbial immobilization as taking place simultaneously with leaching (Fig. 3). In the absence of the first four nitrogen sinks, it is likely that groundwater

Nitrogen Cycle

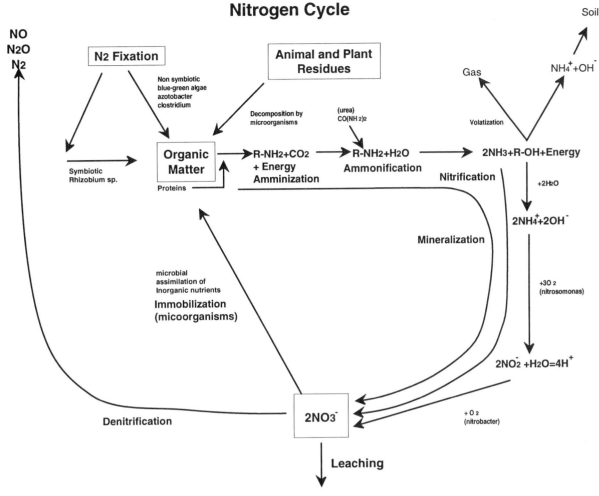

FIGURE 3 Comprehensive nitrogen cycle for plant–soil relationships.

levels of NO_3-N would be considerably higher than found today.

V. Soil Organic Matter, a Key to Nutrient Management

One hundred years ago, most of the native prairie soils in temperate climates had soil organic matter levels in excess of 4%. Today, following 100 years of continuous cultivation, these soils now have organic matter levels less than 2%. Under annual, frequent cultivation, decomposition of soil organic matter exceeds its formation. This continuous cultivation of soils greatly affects the organic matter nutrient supplying power, which in return has an important bearing on both the physical and chemical characteristics and response in crop yields. Organic matter

influences structure, and affects aeration, drainage, water-holding capacity, and erosion.

When our forefathers first tilled these soils, there were no fertilizer needs because of the nutrient supplying power that had been stored within the organic matter fraction and the small demands of low yield potential crops. However, today, inorganic and organic fertilizers are needed to supply the nutrients required for economically sustainable crop yields. Excluding nitrogen, phosphorus, and potassium, even the depleted soil organic matter pool present today continues to provide adequate supplies of micronutrients for continuous corn and wheat for the vast majority of soils in the grain belt. [See FERTILIZER MANAGEMENT AND TECHNOLOGY.]

Although this resource has been mined, it is seldom understood that organic matter contents in soils can be increased by various management practices. Increased

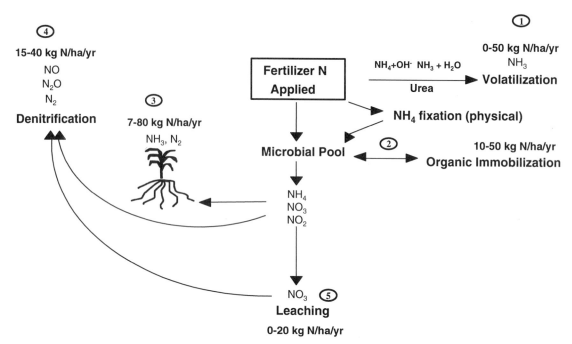

FIGURE 4 Fate of inorganic nitrogen in soils describing losses that can exist in crop production prior to nitrate leaching and general amounts lost from each sink in continuous crop production systems.

use of no-tillage management practices can increase soil organic matter. Soil scientists have demonstrated that the long-term use of no-tillage in continuous crop production systems results in increased surface soil organic matter levels. Similarly, nitrogen fertilizer applied at rates in excess of that needed for maximum yields can also result in increased soil organic matter levels via increased total biomass production. Crop management systems that include rotations with high residue-producing crops and maintenance of surface residue cover with reduced tillage also can result in greater soil organic matter, increased total soil N, and improved soil productivity.

VI. Soil Testing

Soil testing is considered to have started with Justus von Leibig's work in 1840. The aims in soil testing are to assess the relative adequacies of available nutrients (and lime requirements) and to provide guidance on amounts of fertilizers (or lime) required to obtain optimum growth conditions for plants. These objectives are dependent upon obtaining representative soil samples, analyzing them using the appropriate methods, and calibrating the effects on crop response (or increased soil test values) of added units of fertilizer

(or lime) to soils at various initial levels of available nutrients. The inclusion of lime in this discussion points to the importance of soil pH in all soil testing procedures and ultimate nutrient recommendations. Soil pH is generally determined from a 1 : 1 soil : water mixture whereby hydrogen ion concentrations (activities) are inversely related to the resultant pH value. In general terms, measured pH reflects the acidity or basicity of a soil which in turn can affect crop production. [*See* SOIL TESTING FOR PLANT GROWTH AND SOIL FERTILITY.]

Total soil analysis (determining the entire amount of a nutrient in soils) for soil testing purposes has been almost completely abandoned except to confirm the absence or very low total reserves of an element. However, total soil N is still used to some extent for predicting availability. In the 1920s and early 1930s, soil scientists' attention turned to displacement of the soil solution with organic solvents, water, and compressed air. Such studies showed that the soil solution did not contain enough N, P, K, and other elements to sustain plants very long, and so the mineral and organic phases must be important in continually replacing the solution phase. This development led chemists and soil scientists to use weak solvents such as CO_2-saturated water and dilute acids in an attempt to imitate what the plant might be able to extract from a given soil. The total amounts in soil could not reflect when and where a deficiency could occur because much of this was bound (in the clay fraction or within organic matter pools) in unavailable forms.

Various extracting solutions have been developed over time that quantitatively assessed the nutrient supplying power of soils for a particular element. Major modifications of how these extractants are used for specific soils have improved our ability to predict when and where nutrient deficiencies will take place. Soil testing is an all-encompassing program that can be divided into four stages: collecting soil samples, extracting and determining the index of soil fertility, interpreting the analytical results (indexes), and making the fertilizer recommendations. First, a population of samples is needed to establish the given nutrient deficiency with corresponding yield data. Second, the program must then establish field trials at respective locations where nutrient levels are considered deficient, moderately deficient, and not deficient. At these sites, fertilizer rates are applied and crop response determined for a given soil test level. Once enough data have been collected optimum fertilizer rates can be determined (recommendation) for a particular soil test level (index) using the defined extracting procedure. While much of the research in soil testing has focused on developing chemical procedures for evaluating the levels of available soil nutrients, techniques for relating soil test results to crop yield response have been equally important.

An example of soil analysis and resultant percentage yield is illustrated in Fig. 5. Percentage yield for this example would be the yield obtainable at a given soil test P level when all other nutrients were present

in adequate amounts. In this example, two distinct statistical methods are listed that are commonly used to detect the critical level (point at which an increase in soil analysis no longer results in an increase in yield). The critical level determined using quadratic and linear-plateau methods was 92 and 52, respectively. Given these large differences, it becomes apparent that not only is the soil analysis method important in determining critical levels, but also the statistical method applied to identify the critical test level of the research data. If a soil sample from a farmers field were taken, the correlation response data in Fig. 5 would be used to decide whether P was deficient in the soil. A fertilizer rate recommendation (assuming the P level was deficient) would then be generated from field data where grain yield response to applied P had been previously determined.

Almost without question, improved soil testing procedures for phosphorus and potassium have contributed more toward the efficient use of these elements. This has been largely due to the common need for P and K fertilizers and also because more research has been conducted on these elemental deficiencies.

VII. Fertilizer Sources and Methods of Application

Over the years, soil scientists have conducted thousands of experiments evaluating various methods of applying nutrients to soils. Historically, most fertilizers have been sold in granular forms and have been broadcast and incorporated prior to planting. However, in the interest of efficiency and economy improved methods of fertilization have been developed. Phosphorus, which is an extremely immobile nutrient in soils should be band applied (localized placement) when soil test levels are low and when economics dictate the application of low rates. This method of application is also recommended for soils which have high phosphorus fixation capacities. Soils derived from volcanic ash have extremely high phosphorus fixation capacities, and therefore, band applications improve effectiveness by limiting the surface area of the fertilizer in contact with the soil. Research has demonstrated that broadcast applications (uniformly applied on the surface with or without incorporation) of phosphorus decreased the efficiency of this fertilizer on soils where fixation capacities were high. Improved methods of application and fertilizer sources

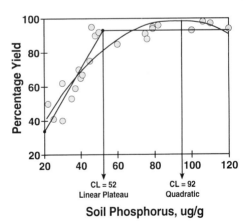

FIGURE 5 Critical soil analysis levels determined using linear-plateau and quadratic functions. CL = critical soil test level below which applied phosphorus fertilizer would be recommended to achieve maximum yields.

for correcting iron deficiencies in plants have also been developed. Because this element is immobile in the soil and most fertilizer materials quickly react in the soil and become unavailable, foliar applications of iron sulfate solutions continue to provide the best results when iron deficiencies are present.

With the development of liquid fertilizer sources, altered methods of application have become necessary. The most common nitrogen source used today is anhydrous ammonia, which is a gas, but is sold as a liquid under pressure. This source, which contains 82% nitrogen must be injected beneath the surface of the soil in order to limit gaseous losses. Today, it is common for other liquid sources to be applied jointly with anhydrous ammonia within the same band. Most recently, soil scientists have developed techniques to fertilize specific portions of an entire field based on differences in soil test indices (variable rate technology). In the past, farmers applied a given fertilizer rate based on the average nutrient deficiency for an entire field; however, variable rate technology allows the farmer to apply more fertilizer where it is needed and less where nutrient deficiencies are small. As has been the case in other scientific fields, improved fertilizer use efficiency has come as the result of hundreds of research years dedicated to improving methods, and the development and evaluation of improved sources.

VIII. Future Needs

Many developing countries have traditionally used various kinds of organic materials to maintain or improve the productivity, tilth, and fertility of their agricultural soils. However, several decades ago organic recycling practices were replaced with chemical fertilizers applied to high-yielding cereal grains that responded well to high levels of fertilizers and adequate moisture. Along with the failure to implement effective soil conservation practices, the agricultural soils in many developing countries have seriously degraded and declined in productivity because of excessive soil erosion and nutrient runoff and the decrease in stable soil organic matter levels. Soil scien-

tists are continually developing agronomic solutions to these problems while constantly evaluating alternative production systems that are economically sustainable.

Although organic farming research (crop production without the use of commercial fertilizers) has been instrumental in decreasing inputs, it cannot sustain present world population food needs nor is it a viable alternative for the future. It has been estimated that an overnight switch from the use of commercial fertilizers to organic farming (use of manures, compost, etc.) would result in net food production levels of one-fourth that required for man today. Technologies are present today that will ensure environmentally safe and economically sustainable crop yields for future generations; however, these technologies require commercial fertilizer inputs. As the world population grows, the science of soil fertility will be challenged with improving nutrient management and fertilizer use efficiency on a total world land area that is continually shrinking. Production areas in the developed world cannot sustain future world populations without the continued development of appropriate sustainable technologies for developing nation lands.

Bibliography

Allison, F. E. (1966). The fate of nitrogen applied to soils. *Adv. Agron.* **18,** 219–258.

Arnon, D. I., and Stout, P. R. (1939). Molybdenum as an essential element for higher plants. *Plant Physiol.* **14,** 559–602.

Baule, B. (1918). Zu Mitscherlichs Gesetz der physiologischen Beziehungen. *Landwirtsch. Jahrb.* **51,** 363–385.

Bradfield, R. (1961). A quarter century of soil fertility research and a glimpse into the future. *Soil Sci. Soc. Am. Proc.* **25,** 439–442.

Bray, R. H. (1954). A nutrient mobility concept of soil–plant relationships. *Soil Sci.* **104,** 9–22.

Mitscherlich, E. A. (1913). "Bodenkunde fur land und forstwitre." Paul Parey, Berlag., Berlin.

Tisdale, S. L., Nelson, W. L., Beaton, J. D., and Havlin, J. L. (1993). "Soil Fertility and Fertilizers," 5th ed. Macmillan, New York.

Troeh, F. R., and Thompson, L. M. (1993). "Soils and Soil Fertility," 5th ed. Oxford Univ. Press, New York.

Soil Genesis, Morphology, and Classification

S. W. BUOL, *North Carolina State University*

I. Soil Genesis
II. Soil Morphology
III. Soil Classification

Glossary

Clay Solid particles less than 0.002 mm in diameter
Pedology Collective term more frequently used in Europe than in the United States referring to the science of the ground
Sand Solid particles 0.05 to 2 mm in diameter
Silt Solid particles 0.002 to 0.05 mm in diameter

Soil genesis, morphology and classification are subdivisions of pedology. Soil genesis deals with the factors and processes that are responsible for the formation of soils at the earth's surface. Soil morphology encompasses the measurement of soil properties such as color, structure, and chemical and mineralogical composition. Soil classification is the categorization of soils into groups according to systems devised by people and reflecting their understanding of soil morphology and/or presumed genesis. Numerous soil classification systems are in use. Each system reflects the specific objectives of originators of the system to organize the continuum of soil properties naturally present for specific practical uses of soil, or more universally, to aid in remembering properties and communicating these properties from individual to individual and preserving them in the scientific literature. A closely related subject, not included in the article, is soil survey. Soil survey is an integrated activity of classifying soils and representing the spacial distribution of different soils at a reduced scale on a map. [*See* SOIL AND LAND USE SURVEYS.]

I. Soil Genesis

The thin, usually less than 2- or 3-m-thick layer of the earth's surface not covered by water is nature's meeting place of organic and inorganic chemistry. It is also the meeting place of solids, the mineral components of the earth's crust, and the gases of the earth's atmosphere. In addition, this thin layer interacts with all of the precipitation falling upon it causing that precipitation to run off over its surface, be filtered through that layer to the underlying groundwater, or be temporarily retained to be extracted by the roots of vegetation. [*See* SOIL DRAINAGE.]

A. Factors in Soil Genesis

The degree to which each of these factors affects the thin near surface layer of the earth's surface, henceforth called soil, is best presented in the following state factor equation:

$$S = F(P, C, O, R, T).$$

In this often used expression, S is the resulting soil properties; F is an integrating function of P, the initial solid minerals of the geologic material; C includes all the climatic conditions primarily temperature and precipitation; O represents all organisms that live in and on the soil; R is the relief or topographic factor mainly including the slope of the soil surface; T is the time within which the other factors are able to alter the morphology of the soil.

Although the state factor concept of soil genesis is academically valuable in conceptualizing why soil morphology differs from one place to another, it provides little insight into how soils form. A more complete understanding of soil genesis can be obtained by examining the processes that can take place within the soil during its formation and use.

B. Processes of Soil Genesis

Conceptualizing soil as an open system within which changes take place and where matter and energy are

Encyclopedia of Agricultural Science, Volume 4   Copyright © 1994 by Academic Press, Inc.   All rights of reproduction in any form reserved.

both entering and leaving can be done in Fig. 1. Here a volume of soil is portrayed with its surface interfacing with the air, its lower boundary is at an undetermined depth but below the deepest extension of plant roots, and it is bounded on either side by other soils.

1. Energy Exchange

Except for minor amounts of heat coming from the internal mass of the earth, soils heat and cool from the surface. Heating and cooling have a daily cycle in most soils that extends to a depth of about 50 cm. Annual temperature changes take place to depths of several meters.

2. Water Exchange

In most soils water enters through the surface. Water also is lost from the surface by evaporation if the soil is not covered by vegetation but more often through transpiration from growing plants. The exchange of water, although represented as cyclic, is sporadic with entry during rainfall and loss at other times. Some entry may take place under deep snow packs when the soil is not frozen and in some soils with little rainfall exchange is minimal for long peri-ods during the year. In some soils water also enters the soil by lateral groundwater flow from adjacent soils. [See SOIL–WATER RELATIONSHIPS.]

3. Biocycling

Vegetation growing on soil is a key factor in defining soil from geologic material. During the life cycle of vegetation, it captures inorganic forms of plant-essential elements through its roots and transports them to its aboveground parts. Upon the death of the aboveground parts, these same elements are deposited upon the surface. Animals may enter this picture by eating some of the vegetation but the ultimate fate is the same, except that animals, especially humans, often transport the elements to another site, thus breaking the cycle portrayed. Plants and some of their associated microorganisms also obtain carbon, in the form of carbon dioxide, from the air and thus add it to the soil to be lost again as a gas or in solution as the organic compounds decompose.

4. Erosion and Deposition

In response to the energy available from the force of falling raindrops, the solid mineral particles at the soil surface may be suspended and be moved to another location. That other location very often is another soil. Thus, erosion or removal of soil material from one soil results in deposition on another soil. Of course, some soil material is totally removed to the oceans or deeply buried in lakes. Erosion and deposition are key processes in understanding soil genesis because their actions clearly point out that the surface of the soil is not stable throughout time. During the long time spans within which soils form, the proverbial firm foundation is either going up or going down. The amount of time involved is highly variable and often sporadic as in flood or landslide events.

5. Intrasoil Translocations and Transformations

An analysis of the water exchange process reveals that in most soils, in a reasonably warm climate and actively supporting vegetation, most of the rainfall is lost by transpiration. Soluble and suspendable materials move rapidly downward during the rainfall. Between rainfalls much of the water stored in the soil is taken up by the plant roots. Plant roots are selective membranes and ingest only those dissolved elements the plant needs for its life cycle. Particles such as clay or organic particles, suspended near the soil surface during a rain event, are left to accumulate in the sub-

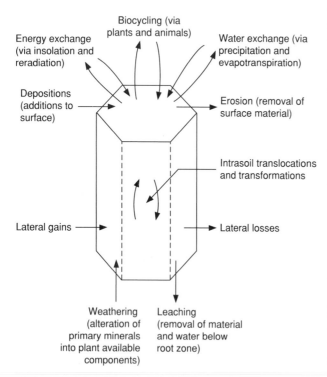

FIGURE 1 Schematic representation of soil as an open system. [Reprinted with permission from Buol, S. W., Hole, F. D., and McCracken, R. J. (1989). "Soil Genesis and Classification," 3rd ed. Copyright © Iowa State Univ. Press, Ames.]

soil. As the subsoil dries during the rainless periods, mostly by plants transpiration, clay and other water-translocated materials excluded by the plant roots form coating on larger mineral grains or root channels or precipitate as rather insoluble forms. Thus, many but not all soils have greater contents of clay, iron, carbonate, and other mobile compounds in the subsoil than in the surface. Organic compounds go through a multitude of transformations during this downward trek, thereby loosing identity with the organic forms deposited on the soil surface from decaying organisms.

Not all the activity represented in the open system figure forms layers in the soil. Roots, insects, burrowing animals, and volumetric shrinking and swelling of some soil particles as they wet and dry physically mix materials within the soil. The magnitude and type of intrasoil transformations and translocations differ greatly from soil to soil. A detailed discussion of these processes is beyond the scope of this article.

6. Lateral Gains and Losses

No soil exists as a single entity. Each soil has other soils surrounding it and materials can flow from one soil to another. This is most evident on hillsides where the lower part of the soil is less permeable than the upper part of the soil. When this situation exists, infiltrating water flows from one soil to another carrying with it suspended solids and more commonly soluble salts.

7. Leaching

In the context of soil genesis, leaching refers to the removal of material to such a depth that it cannot be gathered by the plant roots and cycled via biocycling. In most respects, this represents material originating in or passing through the soil and entering the regional groundwater. Although there is possible reentry into another soil, perhaps as seepage at the base of a slope, leaching is strictly a loss from the soil. In arid regions leaching may be a sporadic event or never occur. In such regions subsoils accumulate even the most soluble materials at the maximum depth of water penetration. [*See* SOIL, CHEMICALS: MOVEMENT AND RETENTION.]

8. Weathering

The inorganic minerals that now find themselves near the earth's surface (i.e., in the soil) almost all formed at higher temperature and pressure within the cooling magma of the earth's crust. Thus, many of them are quite unstable and soluble in the soil water. As they decompose, many of their elements become ions in the soil solution and in this form are available for uptake by plant roots. Essentially all the elements required for plant growth, except nitrogen, carbon, hydrogen, and oxygen, come from the weathering of minerals. Some soils are forming in materials relatively rich in plant-essential nutrients, such as glacial deposits and volcanic ash, whereas many soils form from quartz sandstones or iron oxides that contain almost no plant nutrients. In the latter case, the resulting soil has very limited mineral reserves from which to derive plant-essential elements. Although Fig. 1 represents weathering as entering the soil volume from the bottom, in some cases aerosolic dust or flood depositions can input weatherable minerals at the surface. Also, human activity of adding mineral fertilizer, which in some soils has been taking place for several hundred years, can be conceived of as a mechanism for contributing weatherable minerals to a soil.

II. Soil Morphology

What we see, feel, and measure within a soil is included in morphology. What we see should not be limited to the resolution of the naked eye and considerable literature exists on the subject of micromorphology, a branch of soil morphology that employs optical and electron microscopes to observe the association of clay particles, bacteria, and other microscopic features in the soil.

A. Soil Horizons

As has been discussed in the factors and processes of soil genesis, soil is a relatively thin layer separating the geologic and atmospheric components of the earth. Thus, it is natural that although being only a couple meters thick, soil like other "skin tissues," is organized into discrete layers. These layers within a soil are called horizons.

The surface, or uppermost layer of a soil, is where most of the organic residue from biocycling is placed. It therefore usually has the highest concentration of organic compounds and a black or darker color than layers deeper in the soil. Also, all of the water that infiltrates into the soil passes through the surface, so small particles of clay size tend to be removed from this surface horizon. The darker color is simply organic compounds in various stages of decomposition.

By convention surface horizons are referred to as A horizons if the organic carbon content is less than 12% or 0 horizons if they contain more than that amount of organic carbon. A popular term, but having no adequate scientific definition for such horizons, is topsoil.

In many, but not all soils, there is a lighter colored horizon immediately under the A horizon. This results mostly in forested soils where almost all of the clay and iron oxide have been removed by percolating water. Because almost all the organic matter additions have been on the surface by leaves from the vegetation, this horizon contains little organic matter. This horizon is conventionally called the E horizon to connote eluviation.

Under the A and E horizon, where present, is what is commonly referred to as the subsoil. By convention subsoils are referred to as B horizons. There are numerous kinds of B horizons and they have only one of two genetic interpretations in common. The most simple of B horizons are identified because they have evidence of more mineral weathering than the underlying parent material. This is usually identified by some red or yellow colors indicative of iron oxide released when primary minerals in the parent material weathered in the near-surface environment.

The other and perhaps more familiar genetic connotation of a B horizon is that of a horizon of illuviation. It is the subsoil layer that is the repository of soluble and/or suspendable material eluviated by percolating water from the A and E horizons, but left to reconstitute as water is extracted by plant roots. Depending upon the type of mineral or organic material eluviated from the above horizons, the B horizon is enriched, relative to the parent material in clay, iron oxide (hence red color), organic matter (hence black color), or carbonate (hence white color).

Under the A, E, and B horizons is the material that shows characteristics indicating it has been relatively unaltered by soil-forming processes. By convention, if the material is friable enough to dig with hand tools, it is called a C horizon. If it is hard rock, it is called an R horizon.

B. Common Intrinsic Soil Properties

A complete listing of all the components modern soil scientists are able to observe and measure in a soil is well beyond the scope of the article. Suffice to mention that all of the naturally occurring chemical elements are present in soil. Soils are the recipients of all the organic substance produced by plants and ani-

mals and these substances decompose in the presence of all the inorganic components known to occur in geological minerals. These organic and inorganic derived components are further mixed by every kind of microorganism capable of living in temperature and moisture conditions present in soil. Since the total number of morphological features of a soil is almost infinite, only a few of the more commonly determined features are presented. [See SOIL MICROBIOLOGY.]

1. Particle Size Distribution

Often referred to as texture, this is a measurement of the relative amounts of sand, silt, and clay in a soil sample. This is probably the most useful measure of a soil and its various horizons. Soils with a high proportion of sand have large voids between the particles. All soils have about 50% void space, although this can vary by several points above or below this value. Voids in a soil, commonly called pores, are alternately filled with water or air. Water must pass through these pores when entering the soil or as it is "sucked" to a plant root. Medium-sized pores, sometimes called "capillary pores," hold water against the force of gravity and thereby provide the water plants need during rainless periods. Silt size particles provide this size pore.

Soils with a high portion of their mineral material in clay size have very small pores that hold a great amount of water, but because the pores are so small, water does not easily flow to a plant root. Even though clay soil may contain water, the plants may wilt or die because of their inability to obtain that water fast enough. Very fine organic matter has this same characteristic.

2. Soil Structure

Soil material is not a uniform homogeneous mixture of sand-, silt-, and clay-sized particles. Clay-sized particles adhere to each other and to larger particles. Often particles of any size may be cemented by organic and/or inorganic gels that are quite insoluble. This heterogenous distribution of particle size and cementing agents creates a network that cannot be identified by a simple determination of the amount of sand-, silt-, and clay-sized particles. Also, structure is created and destroyed by pressure as in tillage or simply walking on a wet soil. Roots force their way through soil creating continuous holes which persist after they die and decay. Structure and the most important feature of structure, the continuity of pore space or channels for water and air, are very dependent on a variety of factors including the activity of organisms, roots, and water content. Conditions of structure, while visible in soil samples, are subject to change upon any manipulation of the soil material.

3. Soil Color

This most obvious morphological feature of soil is also a very good indicator of several soil chemical and mineralogical properties. Within local areas soil color serves quite well as a communication tool but on a global basis it is entirely inadequate to represent soil properties. Three basic colors bear relationship to significant soil properties. Black usually identifies a high content of organic matter, although there are black-colored minerals that can belie this interpretation. Also, a high organic matter content can be colored red by iron oxide, in which case any quantitative evaluation of organic matter content by quantification of black color has only local significance.

The red and yellow colors are significant and quite reliable indicators of well-aerated, oxidized conditions in the soil. The red to yellow colors reflect the presence of iron oxides. Red is very indicative of hematite while yellow indicates goethite. These minerals can persist in soil only when they are not solubilized by reduction. Reduction takes place in soil when it is saturated with water for several days when the temperature is high enough for microbial respiration. This saturated and chemically reducing condition removes the iron leaving the silicate minerals uncovered. Mixtures of silicate minerals, whether they be sand, silt, or clay, are gray color. Thus, a gray-colored soil usually indicates that water saturation and reducing chemical conditions are present at least part of the year. Gray to white colors can also be caused by the presence of carbonate so again it is necessary to examine soil color in greater detail to verify what causes that color.

4. Chemical Morphology

Except for the few hints of soil chemistry that can be obtained from soil color, it is necessary to analyze soil to determine its chemical properties. Chemical analysis of soil is extremely complicated by most chemical standards. The difficulty arises from two inherent features of soil. First, every known element is likely to be present in soil; thus, extracting only the element or compound selected for determination is subject to all kinds of interference and contamination. Second, it is seldom informative to determine only the total content of a particular element. Most of the elements of practical interest in soil are present

in several chemical forms and only some of these forms have significance in relating the soil quality to a particular use such as growing plants. [*See* SOIL CHEMISTRY.]

A discussion of soil chemical morphology is well beyond the scope of this article and the reader is referred to the references of methods of soil analysis for further information. [*See* SOIL TESTING FOR PLANT GROWTH AND SOIL FERTILITY.]

III. Soil Classification

Classifying soils has probably been informally done by people working with the soil well before any written communication was available. Black soil, red soil, dry soil, wet soil are but a few common expressions that serve within local communities to express the experience individuals have had with various parts of the land they occupy.

Because soil is geographically fixed, it has only become possible to attempt truly global classifications of soil, based on measured soil properties, since the advent of rapid global transportation. Earlier attempts to express soil properties were based upon concepts related to theories of soil genesis. Names used in these early attempts, such as Lateritic, Alluvial, Podzolic, and Latosol, are so morphologically qualitative that conversion to modern systems is inaccurate at best and most often misleading. They must be considered obsolete.

A. Natural Classification Systems

At present there are two natural classification systems that attempt to reflect soil properties on a global basis. The UNESCO/FAO world soil map project, started in the 1960s, produced a 1:5,000,000 scale map of the world and defined 106 quantitatively defined names for their map units. Although a remarkable advancement in the understanding of soil on a global basis, this work has, unfortunately, not been vigorously expanded. The small number of broadly defined kinds of soil, while serving as a reference among soil scientists around the world, is inadequate to express soil differences at a detail needed to work in individual fields.

Beginning in the 1950s there was an effort by the Soil Survey Staff of the U. S. Department of Agriculture and faculty from the Land Grant Universities in the United States to develop a soil classification system that could include all soils in the world as their properties became known through research. This effort, most formally presented as Soil Taxonomy in 1975, continues. It is a comprehensive system that is constantly being refined to accommodate new findings and especially new methods of quantitatively analyzing soil. At present about 16,000 kinds of soil are defined within the United States and a worldwide estimate is not available. Although Soil Taxonomy and, to a lesser extent, the World Soil Map legend of UNESCO/FAO have worldwide acceptance and are used as standards in the scientific literature, many countries find it desirable to develop unique systems for classifying only the soil within their country. Although these efforts hinder global dissemination of information, they often provide a more satisfying mode of communication among small nationalistic groups of earth scientists concerned with soil-related sciences within that country.

B. Soil Taxonomy

The recognition by the originators of this system that any soil classification system must grow to accommodate new information, but not destroy itself in the process, stands as perhaps the most innovative feature of the system. It is a hierarchical system of six categories with each of the highest four categories defined by a syllable (formative element) in the composed name.

At present there are 11 orders, the highest category in the system. A complete presentation of the system is not possible in this article but the following example may convey the essential features of the system.

It is essential that use of the system follows the key, which contains the quantitative limits of properties permitted in each category. Attempts to classify a soil at any given level in the system, without following the key, often lead to errors.

1. Outline of the Keys to Soil Taxonomy

The reader is cautioned that the following outline is drastically abbreviated and presented only to demonstrate the form of the system. No classification is possible using only what is presented.

The categories that form the hierarchical system are Order, Suborder, Great Group, Subgroup, Family, and Series.

Abbreviated criteria in key to orders	Order name
Organic soils	Histosols
Other soils of volcanic ash	Andisols
Other soils with humus/amorphous subsoils	Spodosols
Other soils with oxide rich subsoils	Oxisols
Other soils with extreme shrink swell properties	Vertisols
Other soils with less than 90 days of moisture	Aridisols
Other soils with acid subsoils	Ultisols
Other soils with thick, dark colored surface	Mollisols
Other soils with slightly acid subsoils	Alfisols
Other soils with weak subsoil development	Inceptisols
Other soils	Entisols

There are two points the readers should note in the abbreviated key. First, the key must be followed sequentially. If the soil being classified meets the requirements of the third order, the subsequent orders are not considered and the user goes immediately to the keys within the Spodosol order. Second, in formulating the name for lower categories, a syllable beginning with a vowel in the order name (underlined) becomes the last syllable as the total name is formulated. For Spodosol, this is od.

2. Abbreviated Example of a Suborder Key

Within each of the 11 orders, there is a key to the suborders of that order. Staying with the Spodosols, the following crudely approximates the key to its suborders:

Abbreviated suborder key (Spodosols)	Suborder name
Spodosols that are saturated with water	Aquods
Other Spodosols with six times more iron than carbon	Ferrods
Other Spodosols with iron/carbon ratio <0.2	Humods
Other Spodosols	Orthods

Note that the formative element has connotations of the criteria. Aquods are wet, Aqua from Latin, i.e., water; iron-rich Spodosols use Ferr, from Latin ferrum, i.e., iron; humus-rich Humods from Latin humus, i.e., earth; and Orth connotes the true or common, from the Greek, Orthos.

3. Abbreviated Example of a Great Group Key

To continue within the Spodosol order, the Aquod suborder is used as an example of the keys to great group:

Abbreviated great group key (Aquods)	Great group name
Aquods with a brittle subsoil	Fragiaquods
Other Aquods too cold to grow crops	Cryaquods
Other Aquods with a hard Si-rich subsoil	Duraquods
Other Aquods with a hard iron-rich subsoil	Placaquods
Other Aquods in the tropics	Tropaquods
Other Aquods with very little iron	Haplaquods
Other Aquods	Sideraquods

The formative elements used are: Fragi, from Latin fragilis, i.e., brittle; Cry, from Greek Kryos, i.e., icy cold; Dur, from Latin durus, i.e., hard; Plac from Greek plax, i.e., flat stone; Trop for tropical; Hapl for Greek haplous, i.e., simple; Sider from Greek sideros, i.e., iron.

4. Abbreviated Example of a Subgroup Key

Using the Sideraquods great group as an example, the following divisions are made for the subgroup category:

Abbreviated subgroup criteria (Sideraquods)	Subgroup name
Sideraquods with organic surface layers	Histic Sideraquods
Other Sideraquods with high pH in subsoil	Alfic Sideraquods
Other Sideraquods with clayey subsoils	Ultic Sideraquods
Other Sideraquods with coarse subsoils	Entic Sideraquods
Other Sideraquods	Typic Sideraquods

Note that the correct name of the subgroup includes the great group name and that the subgroup name is an adjective form. The above examples indicate that the subgroup has certain defined properties that cause it to be somewhat like soils in the Histosol order (Histic); the Alfisol order (Alfic); the Ultisol order (Ultic); the Entisol order (Entic); or Typical of the great group Sideraquods (Typic).

5. Family Category

To complete the formal name through the family category, each soil is named for selected criteria not used in any of the higher categories. These criteria differ depending on the criteria already used.

For most, but not all soils, criteria of particle-size distribution in the subsoil, the mineral composition of the subsoil, and the soil temperature are used. For example, a family name for one kind of Spodosol can be:

Histic Sideraquod; sandy, siliceous, frigid

6. Series Category

Within the United States and in some other countries, further subdivisions are made within each of the families. Criteria used depend upon differences not previously used in the higher categories. It is important to observe that a series must have properties that are within the ranges defined by all of the higher categories, but are defined as different from other series within the same family by some additional criteria. Approximately 16,000 soil series are recog-

nized in the United States at this time. No worldwide estimate can be made.

Series names traditionally are selected to reflect a city or other place near where that soil was first defined. For example, the Miami series, classified as Typic Hapludalfs, fine-loamy, mixed, mesic, was named in 1910 for Miami, Ohio. The series name is the most frequently used designation of soils on detailed soil maps. Higher category names are frequently used for small-scale maps.

C. Technical Classification

While Soil Taxonomy and other systems previously mentioned attempt to classify soils using all properties that can be consistently measured, there exists a multitude of technical classification systems. These systems classify soils according to specific criteria critical to a specific soil use or a particular legal designation. Common examples at this time are various health department criteria defining soils suitable for septic systems and soils not suitable for septic systems. Such technical classifications are subject to change as the regulatory rules change and will be different from one area of the country to another. While they may in many cases mimic the criteria used in Soil Taxonomy, they are not part of the more universal or natural taxonomic systems such as Soil Taxonomy or the UNESCO/FAO system.

Bibliography

Birkeland, P. W. (1984). "Soils and Geomorphology." Oxford Univ. Press, New York.

Buol, S. W., Hole, F. D., and McCracken, R. J. (1989). "Soil Genesis and Classification," 3rd ed. Iowa State Univ. Press, Ames.

Fanning, D. S., and Fanning, M. C. B. (1989). "Soil Morphology, Genesis, and Classification." Wiley, N.Y.

Klute, A. (1986). "Methods of Soil Analysis. Part 1. Physical and Mineralogical Methods," 2nd ed. Soil Sci. Soc. Am., Madison, WI.

Page, A. L., Miller, R. H., and Keeney, D. R. (1982). "Methods of Soil Analysis. Part 2. Chemical and Microbiological Properties," 2nd ed. Soil Sci. Soil Soc. Am., Madison, WI.

Soil Survey Staff (1990). "Keys to Soil Taxonomy," 4th ed. SMSS Tech. Monograph No. 6. Blacksburg, VA.

Soil Survey Staff (1975). "Soil Taxonomy." U.S.D.A. Handbook 436. U. S. Government Printing Office, Washington, DC.

Wilding, L. P., Smeck, N. E., and Hall, G. F. (Eds.) (1983). "Pedogenesis and Soil Taxonomy," Vols. 1 and 2. Elsevier, Amsterdam.

Soil Management

T. S. COLVIN, D. L. KARLEN, T. B. PARKIN

National Soil Tilth Laboratory, USDA-Agricultural Research Service, Iowa

I. Why Manage Soil?
II. How Can We Manage Soil?

Glossary

Conservation tillage Tillage method or sequence that leaves a protective cover of crop residue on the surface that can reduce soil or water loss compared to leaving the soil bare

Crop residue Portion of plants left in the field after harvest such as stems, leaves, or possibly pods or cobs

Fertilizer Organic or inorganic material that is added to the soil to supply elements essential to plant growth. It may be either naturally occurring or manufactured. Ammonia and urea are sources of nitrogen that occur naturally in animal manure but are also manufactured because the supply from manure is limited

Manure Solid or liquid animal waste often mixed with waste feed or bedding. Can be an important source of plant nutrients

Organic farming Production of plants or animals without the use of manufactured inputs such as fertilizer, pesticides, etc; often relies on the recycling or importing of nutrients in plant residue and animal manure

Seedbed Soil prepared by natural or artificial means to promote the placement and germination of seed and growth of seedlings

Soil fertility The ability of the soil to provide 14 essential nutrients such as nitrogen, phosphorus, copper, etc., in proper balance to plants

Soil organic matter The organic fraction of the soil that includes plant and animal residues at various stages of decomposition but generally smaller than 2 mm in diameter

Soil quality The ability of a soil to function in its immediate environment for a particular use and interact positively with the general environment

Soil tilth A qualitative term describing the physical state of the soil. It indicates the ease of tillage, seedbed preparation, seedling emergence, and root growth. It may also indicate the ability of the soil to resist erosion. The best condition for seeding wheat may not be the best condition for growing cranberries

Tillage The operation of machines through the soil to prepare seedbeds and rootbeds, control weeds and brush, manage crop residue, aerate the soil, and cause faster breakdown of organic matter and minerals to release plant nutrients

Soil management is a broad and inclusive collection of human activities, including tillage practices, cropping sequences, cultural practices, organic waste applications, and other physical, chemical, or biological manipulations that are undertaken to work with or improve soil for an intended use such as food, feed, or fiber production.

I. Why Manage Soil?

A. To Grow Food, Feed, and Fiber

The principles of good soil management are universally applicable. They apply in tropical regions of Asia, Africa, or South America just as they do in temperate parts of Asia, Europe, or North America. Developing good soil management practices is important for irrigated lands as well as for rainfed areas. They are important for forest soils and grassland regions as well as those areas used for crop production. Though different from those used for agriculture, soil management strategies are also important for land uses including road construction, building sites, human and animal waste disposal, or recycling operations, or almost any other activity that occurs on the earth's surface. This article, however, focuses on soil management practices that are applicable to crop production.

Techniques and practices of soil management vary greatly from country to country, region to region within a single country, or even from field to field within a locality. The management practices that are best for the problem(s) to be solved in one area may be inappropriate for another area because of differences in soil, climate, capital, human resources, or other factors. Furthermore, practices that are optimum for solving a particular problem in a particular locality may actually change over time because of changes in crops, agricultural amendments or fertilizers, and machinery. For this reason, soil management cannot be effectively discussed in terms of final solutions. The challenge, therefore, is to develop a broad understanding for the variety of practices that should be considered when attempting to correct or prevent some particular problem such as soil compaction, acidity, low fertility, inadequate drainage, or an inability to accept and retain water received through rainfall or irrigation.

Good soil management may be defined as the handling of soil and crops in a manner that ensures crop yields are optimum for the soil and water resources available and that the soils will remain suitable for crop production for an indefinite period. Soils will be kept in good condition for crop production by adhering to three principles of good soil management: namely maintenance of good physical, chemical, and biological conditions. The maintenance of good physical conditions generally refers to maintaining satisfactory soil structure. This is important because of its effect on plant root growth, water relations, and aeration. Maintenance of good chemical conditions usually involves the addition of essential plant nutrients including nitrogen, phosphorus, potassium, calcium, magnesium, sulfur, boron, copper, iron, manganese, and zinc; adjustment of the soil pH to an optimum range of approximately 5.0 to 8.0 by addition of limestone or occasionally (and primarily for specialty crops) acid-forming materials such as sulfur; and sometimes the removal of toxic materials. Maintenance of a favorable biological environment under field conditions generally only requires that an adequate amount of carbon be provided to sustain the micro- and macrofauna and that toxic substances be used judiciously. With this general overview of soil management with regard to production of crops, several specific practices and reasons for their use are examined.

The interaction of plants and soils is required for production of food, feed, and natural fibers consumed or used by humans and other animals. Soils with little or no management provided food for relatively small populations of humans represented by hunting–gathering societies. Archeological studies indicate that tillage was probably first employed in Iraq. As humans domesticated plants and animals, they also began to manage soil through practices, such as tillage and plant selection, to increase yields. A stone hand sickle, presumably used to harvest grain, and other stone implements found at an excavation site in Iraq are thought to have been buried sometime near 11,000 B.C. As civilization expanded, soil management was a key ingredient that led to the production of more food for larger populations.

The origins of many principles of soil management lie hidden in unrecorded history; however, many of the practices used today were also used several thousand years ago. Techniques such as adding manure, lime, and rotating crops have been used for centuries. The Romans had some very excellent agricultural practices as documented by the poet Virgil (30 B.C.) who wrote about rotating crops. Earlier still, Cato (234 to 149 B.C.) told of the benefits of lucerne (alfalfa) in crop production. However, after the downfall of Rome, the practice of crop rotation declined and was actually lost. This was consistent with the loss of most intellectual pursuits in Europe during the "Dark Ages" and therefore resulted in many people living for nearly 1000 years in a frustration of disease, famine, and war.

B. To Remove Limitations to Plant Growth

Higher soil productivity depends on developing management practices that remove or prevent plant growth limitations. These barriers might be physical, such as a very dense or compacted soil layer(s) that is difficult for roots to penetrate; chemical, characterized by the presence of excessive amounts of aluminum or manganese or insufficient amounts of calcium; or biological, if the soil lacks the appropriate microbes such as rhizobium strains that infect plant roots, but then enable them to fix and thus use atmospheric nitrogen gas (N_2) for their growth.

Physical barriers to plant growth are often removed by using tillage. A very visible example of this can be found along the Atlantic and Gulf Coastal Plain in the southeastern United States where deep tillage is used to disrupt a natural hardpan that forms below normal tillage depth because of the size distribution of soil particles and low organic matter concentrations. Unless shattered mechanically, this dense layer restricts plant root growth and prevents the plants from using the entire soil profile to meet its needs for water and nutrients. Even with conservation tillage practices which preserve crop residues near the surface, in-row subsoiling is needed on an annual basis for efficient and profitable crop production.

The application of lime can frequently be used to increase soil pH and thus reduce concentrations of aluminum and manganese which can be toxic to plant roots. The addition of essential plant nutrients through commercial fertilizers or organic sources such as compost, municipal sludge, or animal manure can be used to eliminate many of the chemical barriers to crop production.

Addition of crop residues, manure, or other carbon-containing materials in conjunction with appropriate inoculation of crops such as alfalfa or soybean with the desired species of microorganisms or control of pathogenic microflora is generally sufficient for removing most biological limitations to plant growth. Depending on your point of view, insects, weeds, and some diseases may be biological limitations to plant growth but they can come from parts of the environment other than the soil.

C. To Protect the Soil Resource

Soil resources must also be managed to protect or repair them from damage caused by inappropriate uses or adverse environmental conditions. Soil erosion, which involves detachment, transportation, and deposition of soil materials by wind or water, is one of the primary factors that can deteriorate soil resources. Erosion occurs naturally at a geologic rate, but man's activities often hasten the loss by several orders of magnitude. Agricultural production is responsible for much of the increase in erosion rates, but land uses including road construction, mining, and urbanization also affect soil losses. Management practices that reduce the impact of raindrops, reduce the quantity and velocity of surface water flow, or increase the resistance of the soil to degradation through dispersion and slaking are important strategies that must be developed and used to sustain and improve soil resources.

A renewable resource is one that is produced naturally and continually. Sunlight, at least within a human time scale, is renewable, while petroleum and coal are generally thought of as nonrenewable resources. Soil is a very slowly renewable resource and

can be damaged to the point that it is essentially nonrenewable. It should be protected to ensure that we are able to sustain food, feed, and fiber production into the future. Management practices that sustain or improve soil resources are thus extremely important.

II. How Can We Manage Soil?

A. Manipulation of the Physical Environment

Most plants have a relatively broad range of soil conditions that they can tolerate and a smaller range in which they thrive. The primary physical conditions which affect plant growth include soil texture, depth, structure, temperature, aeration, and water content. Soil texture provides an indication of the relative amounts of sand, silt, and clay size particles that are found mixed together in a particular soil. For road or pond construction, golf courses, or other urban land uses, it may be possible to change soil texture in limited areas by adding large quantities of sand or clay materials. However, it is generally not practical to change soil texture for agricultural purposes. In humid areas, medium- to fine-textured soils are generally considered to be the most productive. Coarse sands or very fine clays present many problems to plants growing on them. Sandy soil tends to be infertile because of leaching and low water retention, while very fine textured soils tend to be slowly permeable and poorly drained. Soil depth, up to a point, determines the soil volume which will be available for plant roots to explore. Thus, any gravel lens, natural hardpan, tillage pan, or subsurface bedrock that reduces the depth of useable soil material may restrict plant growth. [See SOIL FERTILITY; SOIL GENESIS, MORPHOLOGY, AND CLASSIFICATION.]

Soil structure, which generally refers to the arrangement of soil particles into aggregates, affects plant growth in several ways. It affects plants directly by influencing root penetration. An associated structural problem is surface crusting. Soil structure affects plant growth indirectly by determining the number, size, and continuity of pores or voids between the soil particles and aggregates. This influences the aeration of a soil which determines the balance between oxygen and carbon dioxide within the soil atmosphere. Germinating seeds and growing plants need oxygen, even at their root surfaces. If oxygen uptake by seeds or roots is restricted, seedlings and plants will not develop in a normal manner. If air transfer into and out of a soil is slowed by poor soil structure, plant respiration will be retarded and growth will slow. If root growth is restricted by poor aeration, a smaller soil volume will be occupied by roots. This will subsequently restrict the amount of nutrients and water that can be absorbed by the plants. A third way in which poor soil structure can affect plant growth is by interfering with water infiltration and redistribution or percolation. If water cannot infiltrate, it will generally runoff, frequently increasing soil loss through erosion and creating off-site problems because of sedimentation. If internal redistribution of water is restricted by poor soil structure, aeration will generally become the most limiting factor.

To select the best soil management practices, we must determine the optimum physical conditions for plant growth and identify what conditions are currently in place in the field. A soil Tilth Index has been proposed that describes the physical condition of the soil by combining numerical values for the density of the soil, the resistance of the soil to penetration, the organic matter content of the soil, the slipperiness of the soil when it is wet, and the distribution of sizes of aggregates of soil particles.

Each soil condition factor mentioned above, as well as many others, will affect plant growth, but there are also many interactions that are important. The Tilth Index combines soil physical condition indicators by multiplication after converting them to numbers between 0 and 1. The multiplication of the factors together then puts the most limiting factor as a control. A value for the bulk density factor that was near 0 would not allow the Tilth Index to be higher than itself. Several factors that have only medium values by themselves would also give a low Tilth Index when multiplied together.

Tillage is probably the most widely used method of managing soil physical conditions. Machines are available which loosen soil, invert soil, pack soil, and mix soil. Some machines can be adjusted to leave the surface of the soil flat or in ridges and furrows. Machines whose primary function is not tillage, such as planters or fertilizer applicators, can also perform limited tillage. Some tillage that has been done to change soil physical condition may in reality have been more important for its impact on the crop residue cover of the soil. Current research is showing that it may be more important to manage the residue cover than to change physical condition of the soil. However, in the more northern regions of the U. S. corn belt, maintaining crop residues on the soil surface can reduce soil temperatures and negatively affect growth and development of subsequent crops. The increased potential for harboring and transmitting plant pathogens in surface residues is another concern that is being evaluated through current research programs. [See TILLAGE SYSTEMS.]

In the midwestern corn belt of the United States, fall plowing has often been used to loosen and invert the soil. This practice is often followed by other tillage tools that stir and tend to pack the soil into a seedbed that is usually bare. This tillage system has often been called conventional tillage (because it was so widely used prior to 1980) and has usually resulted in the highest yields on somewhat poorly drained soil. The question has been asked whether the disturbance of the soil or the burying of the crop residue is affecting the yields. As an experimental treatment, removing the residue without disturbing the soil has been shown to have yields at least equal to removing the residue, plowing the soil, and putting the residue back on top. This would tend to indicate that the management of the residue may have been the reason for the success of the conventional system rather than the loosening and manipulation of the soil.

In contrast, some well-drained soils currently produce higher yields in field situations when the soil is not disturbed prior to planting. The important point on these soils is not always the soil disturbance, but the maintenance of residue cover that is possible without tillage. There is speculation that the effect of residue cover on soil water content and temperature is the key to understanding these situations.

An ideal management system would use the Tilth Index, a soil quality index, or some other quantitative measure of the soil condition as a benchmark for deciding whether tillage is necessary. Using this approach, the condition of the soil would be determined at any time prior to planting and tillage would be done only when benefits outweighed direct costs, such as fuel, and indirect costs such as increased soil erosion potential.

The outcome of a crop production cycle is dependant on many elements. These include weather and the condition of the soil. Soil condition can be directly manipulated by the producer but the ideal soil condition for a particular year depends on the weather that occurs between planting and harvest. A condition that promotes conservation of soil moisture might be valuable in a dry year and a problem in a year with too much precipitation. Thus, the manager must prepare for a "normal" year for the location.

As agriculture developed, farmers devised ways to use available power and technology. Originally, tillage was done with bare hands and involved only the movement of soil necessary to plant seeds and control weeds. As hand tools were developed, they were substituted for direct contact of hands with the soil but still were human muscle powered. Later, animal and mechanical power substituted for human muscle power.

Until the development of effective herbicides after 1950, there did not appear to be a choice of managing soil physical condition as a separate issue from weed control. Currently, the large majority of land used in producing agronomic crops such as corn and soybeans in North America receive applications of herbicides. Some farmers have developed ways to grow crops with few or no herbicides. These systems often depend on tillage for weed control. The use of the tillage may limit the locations where these systems may be used because of the erosion hazard posed by the loose soil and bare surface that often results from the tillage. [See HERBICIDES AND HERBICIDE RESISTANCE.]

Systems of crop production that use little or no tillage before planting have been developed and successfully used by commercial farmers. In these systems, it is important to know when the condition of the soil is appropriate for the crop to be produced. When proper conditions exist, plants thrive and weeds can be controlled by a combination of cultivation and herbicides. If the use of herbicides is not an option then systems without much tillage may not be feasible, even though herbicides may only be needed as a backup for weed control.

Tillage that has a short-term beneficial effect on plant growth can have long-term detrimental effects on the soil itself. Tillage often aerates the soil and speeds the breakdown of organic matter which releases nutrients for plant growth which can be good for the current year's production. This breakdown over time, however, can reduce the organic matter content of the soil which may reduce the quality or tilth of the soil.

Little evidence of long-term benefits from deep tillage has been presented in scientific literature. Special circumstances, such as a root restricting layer, may require tillage deep enough to assist with root penetration. Often, tilled soil is more susceptible to damage from compaction than untilled soil. This suggests that any tillage, and particularly deep tillage, should only be done when the benefits and long-term consequences are understood. It also suggests that prevention of damage by heavy equipment, operations performed at unfavorable soil moisture conditions, or other causes of damage is extremely important.

Heavy applications of organic material such as leaves, manure, or newspapers have been tried as ways of modifying soil physical properties such as water-holding capacity or bulk density. These applications have been tried both on the surface and in slots dug vertically in the soil. One application that seems to have worked well is the application of broiler litter (chicken manure mixed with bedding) on soils that have been leveled for flooding for rice production. The reasons for the success are not fully understood at this time, but probably relate to the nitrogen and carbon content of the litter along with any special characteristics that it may have. Attempts have been made to modify soil with chemical additives. Examples are the use of buried strips of asphalt to control water, or the use of wetting agents to try to manage movement of water in the soil. There are few, if any, chemical amendments currently in use that strictly modify the physical environment of the soil even though the use of chemicals applied primarily for plant nutrition can also modify soil physical properties.

Earthworms have been artificially introduced into agricultural fields. There is not much information that will allow an informed decision about whether such practices are of value from a cost benefit standpoint. One benefit claimed for heavy earth worm populations is better water drainage through the soil because of the channels left by the worms. Early evidence suggests that maintaining crop residue cover on the soil may be the most important factor in encouraging high populations. In the southern Piedmont, when doublecrop residues are managed so that they remain on the surface, volunteer earthworm populations increase dramatically.

At least one biological management option, choice of crops, has been shown to have an impact on soil physical condition. Crop rotations including crops such as grass or legume hays have been shown to affect the structure of the soil in a positive manner.

B. Manipulation of the Chemical or Nutrient Supplying Environment

Plants depend on the soil for most of their essential nutrients. The exceptions are carbon which is fixed from the air through photosynthesis, hydrogen which comes from the water, and oxygen. Some plants (legumes) have a close association with microorganisms that allow for the capture of nitrogen from the air usually at the cost of the plants feeding the microorganisms. Two elements, carbon and nitrogen, have extensive cycles that include the soil, plants, and animals. They form the basis for many food chains that connect such widely varied life forms as bacteria, plants, rabbits, birds of prey and humans. [See NITROGEN CYCLING.]

The natural physical, chemical, and biological soil conditions or those created through various soil and crop management practices generally determine how efficient a soil will be in supplying nutrients to plants. Cold soil may slow plant growth and root development and make it difficult for plants to take in water or other nutrients. Soil that is too acid or too alkaline may cause nutrients to be either present in toxic concentrations (such as for aluminum or manganese) or unavailable (such as for phosphorus and zinc) to plants. [See SOIL, ACID.]

The pH of the soil is very important in determining soil productivity. Some plants, such as alfalfa (*Medicago sativa L.*), perform at an optimum level when soil is almost neutral (i.e. has a pH near 7). Other plants such as blueberries (*Vaccinium* spp) grow much better when pH levels are below 5. Soil pH can be adjusted either up or down with the addition of appropriate materials such as lime or sulfur. An example of a problem created by a high pH (above 7) is iron deficiency or chlorosis in soybean. In the midwest on high pH soils, some soybean varieties have difficulty getting sufficient iron for photosynthesis. Similar problems have been reported for grain sorghum in the southern plains area of the United States. The problem can be solved by reducing the pH (although this is expensive in that area), spraying the plants with special iron-containing compounds, or using a variety that is not as susceptible to the problem. Selection of a tolerant variety is the most common and least expensive choice and is an example of soil and crop management based on plant selection or biology. Soils that are too acid may cause soybean to suffer from a lack of nitrogen if the rhizobium bacteria that normally fix nitrogen for the plants cannot function well.

Organic amendments, such as crop residue, manure, sludge, and yard waste, can be applied to the soil as a source of carbon which becomes incorporated into the soil organic matter pool and nutrients which become available for uptake by subsequent generations of plants. The exclusive use of such materials as the sole source of nutrients leads to the term organic farming, and if all materials on the farm are continually recycled the practice can be considered a closed system. However, if grain or other plant products are sold from the farm, supplemental amounts of various nutrients, including carbon, may have to be supplied by off-farm inputs (i.e., fertilizer) to replace nutrients contained in the material that is sold. On the other hand, when the primary products sold are produced by animals such as meat, wool, eggs, or milk, the manure from the animals contains much of the original nutrients of the crops that were used to feed the animals. This means that the majority of the nutrients remain on the farm and can be recycled by applying the manure to the crop land.

When specialized farms raise only livestock, there may be a problem with manure. Creative means must be found to allow the manure to be effectively used for the benefit of the soil without becoming an environmental hazard. If this does not happen, limited land area may lead to a problem of manure disposal rather than productive manure use. Current research has shown that some of the highest late-spring soil nitrate nitrogen concentrations are found in fields that have received manure. Preventing an accumulation of phosphorus in soils receiving manure is another challenge facing those who are developing manure management guidelines. This is most difficult if manure is being applied at rates that are sufficient to ensure adequate nitrogen for growing continuous corn.

Developing environmentally acceptable strategies for manure management on specialized livestock farms is not hopeless, since in Iowa, one chicken egg production operation has developed a way to produce fairly dry manure that can be handled, sold to, and managed by local farmers in the same manner as an inorganic, commercial fertilizer material.

The use of cover crops is of relatively recent origin, when compared to green-manuring practices that were utilized by the Greeks more than 300 years B. C. The function of cover crops is to protect the soil in various ways. They prevent soil erosion while growing by protecting the soil from the impact of raindrops and by slowing runoff. When incorporated, cover crops add organic matter to the soil, increase permeability, and thus increase infiltration, slow runoff, and decrease erosion. Cover crops can reduce leaching of nitrogen, potassium, and possibly other nutrients, especially on sandy-textured soils. On fine-textured soils, cover crops have been shown to improve physical properties of aggregation, porosity, bulk density, and permeability. By providing a readily available carbon (food) source, cover crops can cause an increase in microbial activity which subsequently increases aggregation.

Farmer interest in and research emphasis on incorporating cover crops into production systems decreased dramatically during the 1960s. This probably occurred because manufactured fertilizer nitrogen could be substituted for green manure and cover crop additions that supplied essential plant nutrients. Also, herbicide technology developed rapidly during that period, making it very easy to control perennial and annual weed species.

Interest in cover crops for soil erosion control, especially following soybean, was renewed with findings that soil loss from a Grundy silt loam (Midwestern United States) was 35% greater for corn following soybean than for either soybean after corn or a continuous corn rotation. The increased soil erosion following soybean has been attributed to lower dry matter production, less residue cover, and the soil-loosening action of soybean roots. Growing cover crops on Mexico silt loam soils in Missouri improved water quality by reducing nitrate, ammonium, and phosphorus losses when compared to no-till soybean grown without a cover crop. The negative aspect of cover crops was that they decreased soybean yields from 29 to 79%. This was probably due to the use of soil water by the cover crops that was no longer available for the soybean crop.

Cover crops provide an effective method for improving water quality because they accumulate and retain plant nutrients as well as reduce soil erosion. The effectiveness of cover crops with regard to protection of the soil by canopy depends upon (a) density of stand, (b) soil coverage, (c) total amount of cover, (d) average height, (e) rate and period of growth, (f) spacing of plants, and (g) method of harvest, which now would be more accurately termed "method of management." For nutrient and/or biocycling of plant nutrients, these same aerial characteristics, plus the extent and vigor with which the cover crop root systems explore the soil, are also important. If legumes are used as cover crops, they can provide nitrogen through fixation for subsequent grain crops.

In Kentucky, growing hairy vetch as a winter cover crop for 10 years resulted in an additional 20 kg/ha of nitrogen uptake by a subsequent corn crop and resulted in higher grain yields. For more northern locations, however, it has been reported that a major conservation tillage research need for the Midwest is the development of cropping strategies and management schemes that make cover crops more compatible with common crop rotations.

Cooperative research efforts between USDA-ARS scientists and farmers have resulted in on-farm cover crop evaluations during the 1990s. Initial results of those investigations have shown that one reason cover crops are not used more extensively in ridge-tillage systems is that they can lead to nitrogen deficiencies in subsequent corn crops. This apparently occurred because of lower net mineralization of soil organic matter or greater denitrification losses before planting. Additional studies are being conducted to determine the amount of nitrogen temporarily lost because of microbial immobilization.

One of the most difficult challenges for incorporating cover crops into current crop rotations in the Midwest is stand establishment. During the 1950s and 1960s when interseeding and forage establishment were more prevalent, practices using tools such as a cultipacker seeder were developed to interseed directly into a corn crop. Those systems were developed, however, when plant populations for corn were much lower and when standard row width was at least 1 m instead of current widths of 0.75 m or less. The combined effects of higher plant density and narrower rows have contributed to higher corn grain yields with current practices, but with nearly total light interception, it is futile to plant a cover crop until the crop is nearly mature. For much of the Midwest, this results in minimal growing time for establishing cover crops using current germplasm resources.

On-farm research trials in the northern corn belt have shown that for success in much of this region, cover crops should be overseeded when soybean leaves begin to senesce (turn yellow), but before they drop from the plant. A study in Missouri attempted to establish annual or perennial cover crops and subsequently grow no-till soybean after killing 60-cm strips around each row and suppressing cover crop growth between rows with various herbicide combinations. The preliminary observations from this study indicate that competition for water by the cover crop and other weeds may be difficult to overcome.

Winter rye and Italian ryegrass have both been shown to be very effective cover crops for reducing leaching losses of residual nitrogen. A disadvantage of winter rye is that it can be very aggressive during the following spring and deplete available soil water supplies and thus stress the primary crop. This has been reported for sandy soils in the southeastern United States and observed in on-farm experimentation in Iowa. Currently, the use of spring oats seeded in autumn is being evaluated as a cover crop for Iowa. The oats grow rapidly during autumn and provide cover for the soil, but freeze and die in winter and therefore do not deplete soil water reserves in spring.

Oats also provide an excellent companion crop for hairy vetch when broadcast into scenescing soybean.

Commercial fertilizer is commonly used to supply nitrogen, phosphorus, and potassium to crops. The amount of fertilizer elements required by crops should be determined by taking samples of the soil and having them analyzed by commercial or university laboratories. Fertilizer recommendations are usually based on research that relates the level of nutrient measured in the soil, the amount required for best plant growth, and the amount of nutrient required to change the soil status from measured to desired levels. It is possible for the manager to test the soil for nutrients with a kit but it is not a common practice. [*See* FERTILIZER MANAGEMENT AND TECHNOLOGY; SOIL TESTING.]

There is considerable interest in a concept called precision farming or location specific farming along with some other names. The idea is to apply materials including fertilizer and herbicides differentially to specific locations on the field by need rather than at a single rate to an entire field based on average requirements. Measurements on fields that have been uniformly treated in the midwest have shown crop yields varying as much as fourfold from location to location within the field. This indicates a possible opportunity to be more efficient in the use of fertilizers or other inputs.

Farmers who wish to implement this differential management strategy will need equipment that includes computers and other equipment to calculate the position of the equipment within a field and then apply materials according to a prescription. Some farmers have implemented this type of precision without computers but it appears that they might be able to make more complete use of the technology with computers and automated location finding equipment. Computers will probably be required to handle the large amount of data on material applied and resultant crop yield so that this management of small areas can be successful. The economics of this type of practice remain to be worked out.

There is the perception that location-specific application depends on commercially produced materials. It is true that these materials are formulated to allow precise mechanical application and are well suited to this technology. However, with good management and innovation such as that noted in the Iowa chicken manure example, precision application should apply to manure and other biological residues as well.

If this technology is applied properly, there should be environmental benefits as well as economic returns to the farmers. A material that is not applied cannot leave the soil system to become a pollutant. It is also true that materials that are not produced by industry do not leave other waste products behind at the site of manufacture.

C. Manipulation of the Biological Environment

The soil is a holistic life system that is very dynamic. This life ranges from single-celled organisms to complex life forms such as animals and higher plants. A single gram of soil contains billions of microorganisms that may represent in excess of 5000 distinct species. The community that is the soil depends on the life that is within it for many of the cycles that make plant growth possible. When plants and animals die they are decomposed and their components recycled by bacteria, fungi, actinomycetes, yeasts, etc. Some of the soil microbes can cause disease or other problems for plants or animals. This is a risk to life, but without the general biological community in the soil, life as currently known would not be possible. [*See* SOIL MICROBIOLOGY.]

There is much interaction between higher plants and simple organisms. An example is the cooperation that legumes and bacteria use to mutual benefit. The benefit to the plant is a supply of nitrogen in a form that can be used by the plant. Several groups of fungi also form close associations with plant roots and have been shown to improve nutrient and water uptake. These associations are mutually beneficial, with the fungi receiving carbon substrates from the plant. These fungi infect the root cells and extend out into the soil, effectively increasing the soil volume which is explored by the plant rooting system. Nutrients such as phosphorus, nitrogen, zinc, copper, and sulfur can then be absorbed by the fungi and translocated to the plant. It has been observed that the beneficial effect of this association is most pronounced with plant species that do not develop extensive fine rooting systems, such as grasses.

The biological component of the soil can be manipulated by the addition of life forms such as earthworms. Because the inoculated organisms must compete with the indigenous populations for available nutrients, direct inoculation of soil with bacteria or fungi is often not an effective practice. A more effective strategy has been to use direct seed, or root system inoculation. Rhizobia, the nitrogen fixing bacteria that form symbiotic relationships with soybeans and other legumes, is often directly applied to the seed. This is necessary because the host–Rhizobium relationship is a very specific one, dependant upon the species of both plant and the microorganism. Direct inoculation of the rooting systems of nursery plants with specific fungi is also a common practice.

When a new legume crop is introduced to an area, it has been common practice to identify and provide the appropriate bacteria on the seed so that they can work with the plant roots to provide nitrogen. This is called inoculating the seed and was done as the soybean crop was introduced to the United States from Asia. Without inoculation, the crop might grow but not be as productive as it possibly could be.

Introduction of plants and soil microbes has had unforeseen effects, particularly when the distance between source and introduction site is long. For example, the introduction of some plants from one country to another led to their becoming serious weed problems. Johnson Grass [*Sorghum halopense* (L.) Pers.] is a current weed in the southern United States that was introduced as a potential crop for that area with another example being Kudzu [*Pueraria lobata* (willd.) Ohwi].

Often these manipulations of the biological component are accomplished by changing other management practices. For example, increased use of conservation and reduced tillage, and greater awareness of alternative farming systems have resulted in numerous questions regarding the impact of soil fauna on soil quality. This occurs because tillage interactions alter soil and crop residue conditions. As tillage decreases, crop residue decomposition rates decrease and microenvironments that are favorable for soil fauna are created. Comparisons between no-tillage and conventional tillage have shown that as tillage decreases, populations of ground beetles, spiders, and earthworms increase.

Earthworm activity has been shown to reduce surface crusting, hasten decomposition of crop residue mats, and alter the susceptibility of soils to water erosion. Quality and location of residues influence earthworm growth, amounts of ingested soil, number of burrows, and openings to the surface. One negative aspect of earthworm activity is that continuous burrows (macropores) can affect solute transport and increase the potential for rapid movement of surface-applied agricultural chemicals through the soil profile.

Surveys of earthworm species in different agricultural crop management systems in the Midwest are limited. In Indiana, *Lumbricus rubellus* (Hoffmeister), *Aporrectodia turgida* (Eisen), *Octolasium lacteuni* (Savigny), *Eisenia rosea* (Savigny), and *L. terrestris* (L.) are reported in reduced tillage systems in corn (*Zea mays*

L.) and soybean (*Glycine max* (L.) Merr). In Minnesota soils, *L. rubellus* and *A. tuberculata* were the species most often found in fields planted to corn. Recent investigations in Iowa showed that as the amount of tillage increased, earthworm numbers generally decreased. They found the largest number of earthworms where alternate farming practices have been used for more than 20 years. The predominant species was *A. tuberculata*. They also reported that regardless of management practice, the highest number of worms were found in Canisteo soil on the toeslope landscape position. These evaluations show that earthworm populations can be influenced by farming practices throughout the U. S. corn belt region.

Managing the chemical or physical status of the soil can affect the biological environment. Changing the soil pH, a common practice, can dramatically affect both type and quantity of microbial species present. An example is the control of potato scab by keeping the soil pH below 5.2. From the physical condition standpoint, it has been shown that severe tillage of an area can lead to a reduction in earthworm population and may even increase the population of microorganisms that degrade organic matter.

D. Sources of Information

There are a number of organizations or people that can help with questions on soil management. The local extension office in most counties of the United States can answer questions directly or help with contacts at the state agricultural college. The state agricultural college and state department involved with agriculture or natural resources are possible sources of information. The Soil Conservation Service (SCS) which is a part of the U.S. Department of Agriculture (USDA) maintains local offices in most parts of the United States and can help with questions on soil conservation. The USDA also has the Agricultural Research Service that can be contacted directly or through extension or the SCS. There are also national or local private organizations such as the Conservation Tillage Information Center (CTIC) based in West Lafayette, Indiana, or the Rodale Institute that work nationwide or the more local Practical Farmers of Iowa that can answer questions or provide information to assist land or soil managers.

The American Society of Agricultural Engineers (St. Joseph, MI), American Society of Agronomy (Madison, WI), and the Soil and Water Conservation Society (Ankeny, IA) are examples of professional organizations that have printed information available on soil management and can provide names of professionals working in the area.

Bibliography

Campbell, R. B., Karlen, D. L., and Sojka, R. E. (1984). Conservation tillage for maize production in the U. S. southeastern Coastal Plain. *Soil Tillage Res.* **4,** 511–529.

Colvin, T. S., and Gilley. J. E. (1987). Crop residue: Soil erosion combatant. *Crops Soils* **39**(7), 7–9.

Hatfield, J. L., and Stewart, B. A. (eds.) (1992). "Limitations to Plant Root Growth," Vol. 19, Springer-Verlag, New York.

Karlen, D. L., Erbach, D. C., Kaspar, T. C., Colvin, T. S., Berry, E. C., and Timmons, D. R. (1990). Soil tilth: A review of past perceptions and future needs. *Soil Sci. Soc. Am. J.* **54**(1), 153–161.

Karlen, D. L., and Doran, J. W. (1991). Cover crop management effects on soybean and corn growth and nitrogen dynamics in an on-farm study. *Am. J. Alt. Agric.* **6,** 71–82.

Pieters, A. J., and McKee, R. (1938). The use of cover and green-manure crops. *In* "Soils and Men the Yearbook of Agriculture," pp. 431–444. USDA. U. S. Government Printing Office, Washington, DC.

Plaster, E. J. (1992). "Soil Science and Management," 2nd ed. Delmar, Albany, NY.

Singh, K. K., Colvin, T. S., Erbach, D. C., and Mughal, A. Q. (1992). Tilth index: An approach to quantifying soil tilth. *Trans. Am. Soc. Agric. Eng. St. Joseph, MI* **35**(6), 1777–1785.

Zachmann, J. E., Linden, D. R., and Clapp, C. E. (1987). Macroporous infiltration and redistribution as affected by earthworms, tillage, and residue. *Soil Sci. Soc. Am. J.* **51,** 1580–1586.

Soil Microbiology

A. G. WOLLUM II, *North Carolina State University*

Glossary

Aerobe Organism using O_2 as its terminal electron acceptor in its metabolic pathways

Anaerobe Organism using an organic compound more reduced than CO_2 as its terminal electron acceptor in its metabolic pathways

Autotroph Organism which does not require any organic carbon for its energy source or for its growth

Denitrification Biological reduction of the N oxides to a more reduced N oxide or N_2

Facultative anaerobe Organism using O_2 as its terminal electron acceptor, but in its absence uses some oxidized compound, such as NO_3^- or $SO_4^=$

Heterotroph Organism requiring organic nutrients

Nitrification Biological oxidation of NH_4^+ to the products of NO_2^- or NO_3^-

Substrate Compound used for a source of nutrients or for energy for growth or maintenance of microorganism viability

Soil microbiology is that branch of soil science dealing with the microorganisms found the soil and their relationship to soil management, agricultural production, and environment quality. The soil microbiologist not only studies the numbers and kinds of microorganisms found in soil, but is also interested in the effect of microorganisms on nutrient cycling, biocontrol of pests, bioremediation of polluted sites, and survival of introduced microorganisms in the soil, especially as these functions affect crop production, environmental quality, and the restoration of stressed environments.

I. Soil as a Medium for Microbial Growth

The soil is a unique environment for the growth of microorganisms, unlike that microorganisms encounter in traditional culture tubes found in most microbiology laboratories. For this reason it is important to assess the effect of some of the soil physical and chemical properties on the growth and function of microbes. In the natural state, the soil environment is a heterogeneous medium of solid, liquid, and gaseous phases. In an average soil the proportion of solid:free space is about equally distributed. The free space is occupied by either liquid or gas. However as the liquid phase of the soil increases the gaseous phase decreases. For typical conditions the proportions can be thought of as 50:25:25 for solid, liquid, and gas phases, respectively. [*See* SOIL CHEMISTRY.]

The solid phase of the soil is composed of organic or inorganic components, ranging in size from 2000 μm to <2 μm. The larger inorganic fractions are either sands or silts and the smallest size fraction is the colloids or clays. The proportion of the individual solid components in a soil imparts many important characteristics to the soil, ultimately affecting the numbers or activities of the organisms. Generally soils with a higher proportion of sand and silt tend to retain less water and are described as well-drained. Soil with a more even distribution of separates or greater proportion of clay has the potential to be less well-drained, often experiencing an abundance of water and the associated characteristic of being less well-aerated. [*See* SOIL GENESIS, MORPHOLOGY, AND CLASSIFICATION.]

Encyclopedia of Agricultural Science, Volume 4   Copyright © 1994 by Academic Press, Inc.   All rights of reproduction in any form reserved.

The colloidal fraction of the soil has a large and negatively charged surface where nutrients can be retained within the soil. The negatively charged surfaces provide exchange sites for the cationic nutrients. Depending on the charge density, cations adsorbed on the surface of colloids may be difficult to remove by microorganisms. Compared to a conventional culture tube, where the organism is growing in a three-dimensional matrix, in the soil, the organism is essentially growing in a two-dimensional matrix, with respect to the colloid surface. This is true because at most biologically active moisture contents the thickness of the moisture films on the colloids is similar or even smaller than many microorganisms (Table I). In addition to affecting the availability of nutrients, the charge associated with the solid surfaces influences surface potential and diffusion of nutrients to, or diffusion of metabolic products away from, the microorganism. Likewise this charge may affect surface acidity, which in turn affects the availability of nutrients or alters the activity of various extracellular enzymes, either enhancing or inhibiting critical enzyme reactions needed for growth or survival of microorganisms in the soil.

The adsorption of water to charged surfaces alters the structure of the water and affects its availability to microorganisms. Water relations within the soil environment need to be understood in terms of the total soil water potential, which is composed primarily of matrix, osmotic, and other potentials, including a gravitational factor which is most often negligible. The matrix component of the total soil water potential is related to the attraction of the solid surface for water and to surface tension. As the soil becomes drier the amount of energy required to utilize the water increases. The osmotic potential is related to the concentration of the dissolved solutes. Under most soil conditions the contribution of the osmotic potential to total soil water potential is small, except under very dry soil conditions or in environments where evaporative losses are high, and solutes have been concentrated in the soil solution. As total soil water potential becomes low it is more difficult for the organisms to extract water for growth and to maintain membranes intact. [See SOIL–WATER RELATIONSHIPS.]

The gaseous phase of the soil occupies approximately one-half of the free space. All of the atmospheric gases can be found in this space. Oxygen in the soil is somewhat lower than in the atmosphere whereas CO_2 is somewhat higher. These differences are attributable to utilization of O_2 by soil microorganisms and the normal production of CO_2 during various metabolic functions. While total pore (free) space might be equal for two different soils, the two soils might have two distinctive growth patterns for microorganisms. If all of the pores are small, gas exchange and water movement might be severely restricted with the soil tending to become anaerobic. On the other hand if the pores are all of a large size, aeration status might be satisfactory, but the soil might have poor water relations since infiltration and percolation of water might be excessive. Ideally the soil should possess both large and small pores, for optimum moisture and aeration conditions for the microbes.

The last feature distinguishing the soil as medium for microorganisms compared to other cultural conditions is that competition exists among a variety of different organisms for moisture and nutrients. Much of this competition is among microorganisms, such as fungi, bacteria, actinomycetes, but significant competition exists with other forms such as soil animals and plant roots. Figure 1 brings all of the components of the soil together and demonstrates the complex nature of the soil environment for microorganisms. This scheme shows the clays with the adsorbed cations or microorganisms; the soil solution with suspended cations, anions, and microorganisms; and finally the plant roots in the remaining spaces, competing with the microorganisms for nutrients. Understanding how the microorganism grows must be in the context of soil physical, chemical, and biological properties and how they interact.

TABLE I
Relative Sizes of Soil Components

Components	Size (μm)
Sand	2000–50
Silt	50–2
Root hairs/fine roots	±75
Clay	<2
Bacteria, diameter	0.2–2
Fungi, diameter	0.5–3
Pore diameters filled	
0.03 MPa (FC)[a]	5
1.5 MPa (WP)[b]	0.1
Moisture films	
0.05 MPa	<0.1
0.10 MPa	<0.03

[a] Field capacity.
[b] Wilting point.

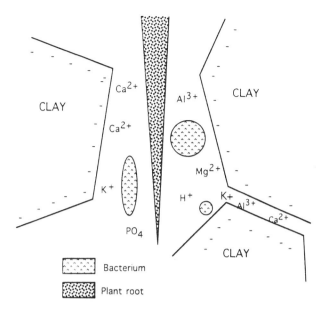

FIGURE 1 Different components of the soil system, including the clays, cations, anions, microbes, and plant roots. Note the negative charge at the surface of the clays. The areas between the clays are the free spaces and are occupied by water or gases. If the moisture film is thick enough the organisms may be free in the soil solution, otherwise the organisms will be intimately associated with the clay surfaces.

II. Microorganisms in Soil

A. Kinds and Distribution

A variety of different size organisms reside in the soil ranging from bacteria to plant roots as well as the suborganismal units referred to as viruses (Table II). The bacteria are most abundant often ranging to an

TABLE II

Kinds and Sizes of Microorganisms or Viruses Found in Soil

Organism or virus	Dimensions (μm)
Tobacco mosaic	0.3×0.02
T_2-Bacteriophage	0.2×0.06
Micrococcus spp.	1.0 (diam)
Pseudomonas aeruginosa	1.5×0.5
Serratia marcesens	1.7×1.0
Bacillus polymyxa	0.6–0.8×2.0–5.0
Bradyrhizobium japonicum	0.5–0.9×1.2–3.0
Nitrosomonas europaea	0.8–0.9×1.0–2.0
Streptomyces spp.	0.5–2.0 (diam)
Mucor hiemalis	8.0 (diam)
Euglena gracilis	50×15
Nostoc spp.	5×13
Neurospora crassa	5.7–11.7 (diam)

excess of 10^8 g^{-1} soil and represent as many as 10^4 different species. The organisms function in a variety of ways, producing various antibiotics, mineralizing organic compounds to inorganic nutrients, oxidizing reduced forms of nutrients, i.e., $S° \rightarrow SO_4^=$, reducing oxidized forms of nutrients, i.e., $NO_3^- \rightarrow N_2$, reducing N_2 to an organism utilizable form(NH_3), and degrading organic matter or various petrochemicals. Other organisms are important plant, animal, or insect pathogens.

Organisms are for the most part more numerous near the soil surface than at deeper depths (Table III). There are many reason why this is true. Normally the soil near the surface has better physical properties, i.e., it is better aerated and moisture relations for the organisms tend to be more favorable. Also the soil is warmer and is more richly supplied with O_2 than the subsoil. The surface soil also has a higher organic matter content, thus providing more carbon for growth of new cells and energy to sustain growth and survival of organisms than at deeper depths in the soil.

It is interesting that anaerobic organisms also exist near the soil surface in an environment normally thought of as being aerobic. This can be explained in the following manner: Soils have structure, in that individual soil particles are united together in more or less stable aggregates. Due to slow diffusion processes the interiors of aggregates can be anaerobic while their surfaces are aerobic. Also as aggregates come together, small pores may result, thus giving rise to a water-saturated environment with a corresponding lack of O_2.

B. Growth and Survival

The growth of soil microorganisms is governed by the interactions imposed by the soil as a whole, e.g., soil physical properties such as porosity, bulk density, texture, water content, and aggregation in concert with certain soil chemical properties such as surface charge, nutrient content, acidity, mineralogy, and organic matter. Each property or interaction among properties will impinge on the final outcome of growth and survival. However, from the standpoint of the microorganism, what essentials are needed to sustain growth or survival? Specifically microorganisms needs carbon, a source of energy (electron donor), and a terminal electron acceptor, provided nutrients, water, etc. are in adequate supply (Fig. 2). For some organisms the soil organic matter can supply

TABLE III

Distribution of Various Kinds of Microorganisms as a Function of Soil Depth

Depth (cm)	Horizon	Aerobic bacteria	Actino's	Bacteria spores	Anaerobic bacteria
3–8	A1		No./g soil		
		1291×10^3	191×10^3	1097×10^3	156×10^3
20–25	A2	1424×10^3	177×10^3	554×10^3	101×10^3
35–40	A2B1	276×10^3	123×10^3	115×10^3	36×10^3
65–75	B2	61×10^3	16×1^3	16×10^3	7×10^3

Adapted from Starc, A. (1942). *Arch. Mikrobiol.* **12**, 329.

both the carbon and the energy needed for growth in the form of carbon compounds more reduced than CO_2. These organisms constitute by far the greatest number and diversity of the organisms in the soil. Known as heterotrophs, these microorganisms contribute to a wide range of activities within the soil. Other soil microorganisms obtain carbon for growth from CO_2 or CO_3^- in the soil solution. These organisms are known as autotrophes and depending on how they obtain their energy are either phototrophes (energy from light sources), represented by many algae and green plants or chemotrophes (energy from the oxidation of inorganic compounds), for example, NH_4^+ to NO_2^- or NO_2^- to NO_3^-.

Regardless of the type of microorganisms found in the soil, all are governed by several "laws." The first law, Liebig's Law of the Minimum, suggests that the growth (increasing numbers, activity, survival, biomass, etc.) of an organism is regulated by the factor which is in lowest supply in relation to what is needed. This law refers to the external or environmental factors regulating microorganisms. On the other hand Shelford's Law of Tolerance suggests that successful growth depends on the needed growth factors remaining within the tolerance range of the organism. Thus this law deals with the biology of the organism itself in relation to growth or activity. Finally Odum's Combined Law suggests that total growth depends on the successful interaction between the limiting factors (Liebig's Law) and the biological tolerances of the organism itself (Shelford's Law).

The energy requirement for the cell is not just for growth. Energy needs may be apportioned to motility, accumulating substrates or nutrients across a membrane, hydrolyses and resynthesis of macromolecules, and maintenance of membrane potentials. These additional needs, apart from growth can be lumped under the general category of maintenance energy. Although energy is frequently limiting for growth, the microorganisms must have enough energy to maintain the integrity of the cell, otherwise it cannot survive and death occurs.

C. Measuring Numbers/Activities

Microorganisms in soils are never static in numbers or activity; therefore, the representation of some number or activity is a property of a particular time, when the soil was sampled. Recognizing that microorganisms are in a dynamic equilibrium and due to the highly complex nature of the soil medium itself, attempts to study microorganisms will be difficult and often laborious. Therefore it is essential that each attempt to characterize some microbial property be firmly supported in advance by a specific set of study objectives.

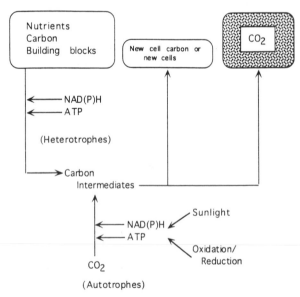

FIGURE 2 Simple model for the growth of microbes.

There are two ways in which to enumerate microorganisms in the soil, one is a direct count and the other an indirect count, using selective media. Both approaches rely on diluting the sample so organisms are in a range which can reliably be counted. In the former technique, an appropriate dilution is selected and the organisms are mounted on a glass slide. Subsequently the preparation is viewed directly using conventional microscopy and the microorganisms are counted or the organisms are stained with an suitable dye prior to counting. When the dye selected is a fluorescent dye, viewing must be done using an epifluorescent microscope.

For indirect procedures, aliquots from suitable dilutions are placed on a selective medium, the medium is incubated, and counts are made of the colonies formed. By varying the medium used, different groups of organisms can be counted. Media can be made selective using different energy sources (e.g., starch or cellulose), adding selective antibiotics (e.g., chloroamphenicol) which inhibit specific groups of microorganisms, moderating the acidity of the solution or combining a specific energy source with an antibiotic, etc. Counts obtained by plating are always less than those obtained when using direct methods (Table IV). There are several reasons why this may be true. Direct counting methods do not normally distinguish between living and dead organisms, where only those cells capable of growing on the medium used would be counted when cultural methods are used. The indirect methods may further underestimate the population because of selective pressures among the community of microorganisms which might prevent a group of organisms from growing on the medium. Further one must deal with the issue of viable, but nonculturable organisms. Not all microorganisms are culturable on currently available media. Thus some microorganisms may be present which are viable, but which cannot be enumerated directly.

Other ways of studying microorganisms in the soil emphasize some important function or property of microorgansims. These methodologies are varied and in the space available cannot be discussed individually. However several techniques are worth mentioning. For the determination of microbial biomass soil samples containing microorganisms are treated so the microbial cells are lysed and the microbial C or N is extracted, measured, and compared to the C or N in paired samples in which the cells were not lysed.

Since CO_2 is respired during growth or cell maintenance, a measure of the activity in a soil sample can be made by determining the amount of CO_2 evolved during a specified period of time. Using ^{14}C-labeled substrates, one could measure $^{14}CO_2$ and determine what portion of the substrate has been degraded. While this doesn't give an estimate of the population size, it does give an indication of the activity of the existing population.

Another way to study activities of organisms is to measure the appearance of product or disappearance of substrate. For instance, if one was interested in the oxidation of reduced nitrogen compounds ($NH_4^+ \rightarrow NO_2^- \rightarrow NO_3^-$), NH_4^+ disappearance could be followed over time or the rate at which NO_2^- or NO_3^- appears could be used to give an indication of the nitrification potential of the soil. Any reaction for which a measurable substrate or product can be assayed can be followed in this fashion. This is also the underlying principle for the determination of many of the extracellular enzyme activities in soil. In some cases, the measurements involve the use of analogous substrates and their subsequent enzymatic products. For instance consider the enzyme alkaline phosphatase. The substrate added to the reaction mixture is p-nitrophenol-PO_4, not normally found in soils.

TABLE IV

Comparison of the Numbers of Microorganisms Found in Soil[a] Based on the Method of Determination

Soil	Direct microscopic count	Selective media (solid)	Selective media (liquid)
		No./g soil	
Spodosol	500×10^6	7.5×10^6	500×10^6
Mollisol	9000×10^6	25.0×10^6	7000×10^6
"Garden soil"	7000×10^6	16.0×10^6	6000×10^6

[a] In the plow layer under perennial grasses [adapted from Krasil'nikov (1958). Soil microorganisms and Higher Plants. Academy of Sciences, USSR].

However, after incubation and in the presence of a phosphatase enzyme, the othro-PO_4 group is cleaved from the parent compound, leaving p-nitrophenol. Under the appropriate conditions p-nitrophenol is colored and the intensity of the color can be used to indirectly quantify the amount of phosphatase enzyme present in the original sample. [See SOIL TESTING FOR PLANT GROWTH AND SOIL FERTILITY.]

III. Soil Organic Matter

A. Unifying Feature in Soil Science

The element carbon (C) is interesting for many reasons. It occurs in a variety of forms from CO_2 to CO_3^-, to reduced compounds such as carbohydrates, and to graphite or diamond. The large variety of C compounds is attributable to the atomic structure of C which permits a variety of bond types. However the soil microbiologist is primarily interested in CO_2 resulting from the metabolic activity of heterotrophic organisms or the more reduced forms which occur as part of organic residues or soil organic matter. The latter is known by a variety of names, many of which are interchangeable. The best known names are probably soil organic matter (SOM) or humus.

The SOM can be considered one of the unifying principles of soil science (Fig. 3). All aspects of soil science interact in some way with the SOM, whether it be biology, chemistry, or physics. From a biological viewpoint, SOM can be considered a source of nutrients for organisms and contributes to the overall negative charge found in soils. Likewise SOM plays an important role in the complexing of Al in acid soil, as well as serving as a source of energy (electron

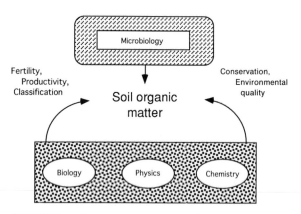

FIGURE 3 Soil organic matter as a unifying principle in soil science, affecting fertility, productivity, classification, conservation, and environmental quality.

donor) for the heterotrophic organisms. From a purely physical standpoint, SOM contributes to the stabilization of soil aggregates, which in turn contributes to a better water-holding capacity and aeration or provides a better means for percolation of water.

B. Composition/Formation

The SOM is composed of a variety of compounds of recognizable chemical structures such as sugars, proteins, lignins, and amino acids to others of less precise structure such as humic acid, fulvic acid, and humins. Although a structure has been proposed for the latter group of compounds, it varies depending on soil parent material, vegetation type, and human activity. These fractions of the SOM have components similar in structure to lignins and polyphenols, as well as a variety of functional groups including OH^-, $COOH^-$, and OCH_3^-. This fraction also contained N in heterocyclic configurations as well as NH^- and amino acids bonded at various points.

Often SOM has been studied and classified using different fractionation procedures (Fig. 4). However considering functional pools, a unified picture emerges, ultimately which may bring together a lot of the theories about SOM. The functional pool approach looks at SOM as microbially active pools. As an additional benefit the functional pools may give an idea of the residence time of different fractions.

Different mechanisms for the formation of SOM have been proposed; however, almost all have certain similarities. Figure 5 brings together common components of many decomposition and formation schemes for SOM. Most models of decomposition depend on size reduction of organic remains via microbes, animals, and physical forces. Subsequently each model requires the breakdown of the organic remains into its constituent components, i. e., chitin, lignin, cellulose, etc. The components are then utilized by microorganisms as a primary energy source with the liberation of CO_2 and the production of microbial tissue. Some of the components may be used for skeletal structures via condensation or polymerization with the formation of a larger molecule (humic substances). The rate at which these reactions occur depends on all of the environmental factors and the nature of the organic remains. Regardless of the mode of formation, more stabilized products are formed.

C. Management Implications

The rate of turnover of organic materials is governed in part by environmental factors and management

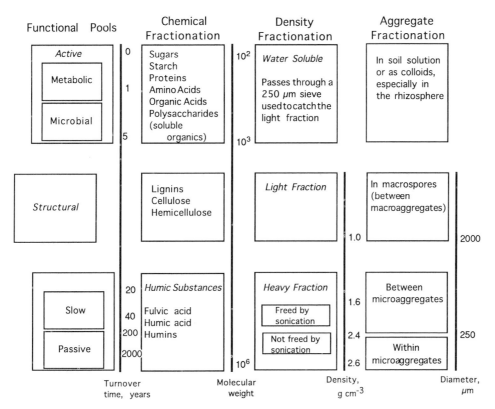

FIGURE 4 Different fractionation schemes used to characterize soil organic matter and their relationship to functional pools as components of soil organic matter.

techniques. Obviously increasing or widely fluctuation temperatures enhance the turnover of SOM. Alternating wetting and drying also contributes to an enhanced rate of turnover. However, it is also known that cultivation may contribute to the degradation of the organic fraction on the soil, but at the same time may provide an important mixing feature. Different cropping systems through rotations, grazing, or no-tillage can influence the SOM. Regardless of the management scheme in place, those practices which enhance the quantity of the SOM fraction, such as rotations, appropriate residue management, and minimum tillage are usually to be favored. Excessive cultivation, monocultures, removal of residues, etc. are among the management practices that should be avoided if SOM management is to be optimized.

IV. Nutrient Cycling

A. Mineralization/Immobilization

Mineralization can be thought of as the biotic reactions resulting in the transformation of the soil organic matter from organic constituents to the formation of inorganic products (C, N, S, P, etc.). The microorganisms are decreasing the biochemical complexity of a component of the ecosystem. For example, during mineralization a protein can go to NH_4^+, CO_2, and $S^=$. The converse of the mineralization reaction occurs during immobilization, where inorganic nutrients are assimilated and converted into organic forms. Following the analogy previously used, the biochemical complexity of the ecosystem is increasing. Since mineralization and immobilization are going on simultaneously, it is the net effect which is observed. If mineralization is greater than immobilization, then the inorganic products will build up. On the other hand if immobilization is greater than mineralization, it will appear that inorganic products are disappearing.

The combined processes of mineralization and immobilization occur as a consequence of growth of the microorganisms, when some utilizable substrate is present in the soil. Assume that an organic substrate in the form of an animal waste product is added to the soil. This product in its simplest form contains a variety of C-based compounds, including proteins. The organisms present in the soil respond to the input

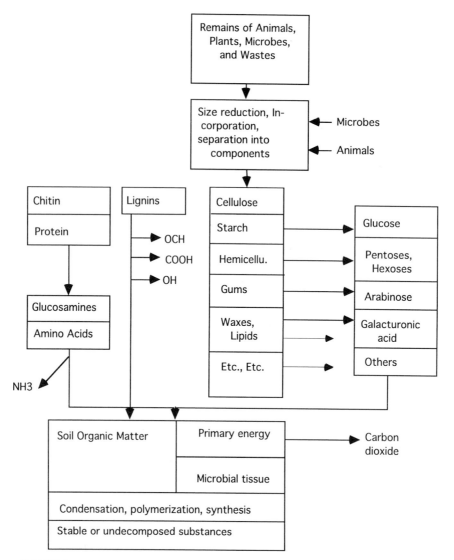

FIGURE 5 Simple model for decomposition of organic residues and formation of the soil organic matter.

of C and energy, by using the material to increase their number. Besides an increase in the total microbial biomass (incorporation of C from the substrate), a corresponding increase in CO_2 is observed and a variety of extracellular enzymes are produced. These enzymes interact with various substrates and NH_4^+, $S^=$, Ca^{2+}, Mg^{2+}, etc. are released from the organic constituents previously added to the soil. Some of these nutrients are immobilized by the microbes themselves because of increased microbial demand during the synthesis of new biomass. However if the demand is less then the amount released, net mineralization occurs. Nutrients arising in this fashion are subsequently available for any other organism, including higher plants or other microorganisms which might be growing in the ecosystem.

B. Oxidation of Inorganic Forms

Once a nutrient is mineralized, many are no longer subject to biological alteration, other than immobilization, e.g., Ca^{2+}, Mg^{2+}, Zn^{2+}, or K^+. However some inorganic forms are subject to further biological reactions. Many of these reactions involve oxidations with the subsequent release of energy for the growth of the organism. The inorganic nutrient forms most likely to be oxidized are forms of N and S. Chemoautotrophic organisms utilize this reaction for producing energy for growth. For N oxidation the process is known as nitrification, while for S it is known merely as S oxidation. Although the organisms participating in these reactions are remarkable similar, they are unique for N and S oxidation. [See NITROGEN CYCLING.]

In nitrification NH_4^+ can be oxidized by species representing five genera. The best known genus is *Nitrosomonas*. The end product of the reaction is NO_2^-; however, in most circumstances NO_2^- does not accumulate, but itself is oxidized to NO_3^- by another group of organisms, the best known of which is *Nitrobacter*. Generally the rate of the overall transformation from NH_4^+ to NO_3^- is controlled by the rate of the oxidation of NH_4^+, thus NO_2^- does not build up. This is fortunate in that much smaller quantities of NO_2^- than of NO_3^- can be toxic to higher plants. One of the side reactions of the nitrification process is progressive acidification. This can be a significant problem in agricultural soils, when ammonical fertilizers are used for a long time without a proper liming program to balance the acidification. While plants can utilize both NH_4^+ and NO_3^-, many of the agronomic crops grow better when supplied with NO_3^-. Nitrification does benefit many crops, but the primary reason for nitrification is the liberation of energy from the oxidation of the reduced N form, enabling the nitrifying organisms to grow.

Sulfur can likewise be oxidized to $SO_4^=$ by chemoautotrophic organisms. The most important genus is *Thiobacillus*. Starting from elemental $S(S°)$, $S^=$, or any S with an oxidation state of $<6^+$, *Thiobacillus* spp. can oxidize the S for the liberation of energy and the subsequent production of the S oxides. Similar to the nitrification reaction, $SO_4^=$ is readily utilizable by plants and is thought of as a preferred S source.

On the one hand, during N and S oxidation, a highly utilizable plant nutrient is produced, but on the other hand, the anionic forms, NO_3^- and $SO_4^=$ are highly leachable. For some situations pollution of groundwater can occur and for some surficial waters nutrient enrichment, called eutrophication, occurs with the leaching of NO_3^- when N fertilizers have been improperly used. Controlling the quantity of and frequency of application can go a long way to minimize the potential for N contamination via leaching. Alternatively using a nitrification inhibitor, such as N-Serve controls the rate of NO_3^- formation. This inhibitor selectively acts on the NH_4^+ oxidizing bacteria, without affecting the NO_2^- bacteria. Although the inhibition is only temporary, the formation of NO_3^- is slowed and when NO_3^- is formed it corresponds more to the plant's need and thus NO_3^- is used by the plant as it is formed without having a large residual amount of NO_3^- found in the soil.

C. Reduction of Inorganic Nutrients

The oxidized forms on some inorganic nutrients can be subject to a series of biological reductions. These nutrients include NO_3^-, $SO_4^=$, Fe^{3+}, and Mn^{3+}. As for the oxidation of certain inorganic nutrients, which are part of the growth processes of the microorganisms, reduction is an important feature of the growth of some organisms. In order for microorganisms to grow they must have a terminal electron acceptor. For the aerobes, O_2 acts as the terminal electron acceptor and in the case of the anaerobes a variety of reduced carbon compounds functions as the terminal electron acceptor. However a group of organisms known as facultative anaerobes utilize O_2, when present, and oxidized compounds, i.e., NO_3^-, in the absence of O_2 as a terminal electron acceptor. These reactions usually occur in the following set of circumstances: an abundant supply of electron donors (reduced C compounds), absence of O_2, and the presence of an appropriate terminal electron acceptor. The best known of these reactions is denitrification.

The ability for denitrification is widespread among bacteria and on the average 10^6 denitrifiers g^{-1} occur in most soils. These organisms have the potential to produce a series of N oxide reductases when the partial pressure of O_2 is low in the system. Initially the denitrifiers utilize O_2 as their terminal electron acceptor; however, if diffusion cannot keep up with demand, the amount of O_2 keeps getting smaller and the organism is induced to produce the reductases essential for denitrification. A typical sequence might be as follows:

$$NO_3^- \rightarrow NO_2^- \rightarrow NO \rightarrow N_2O \rightarrow N_2$$

Each corresponding reduction step has its corresponding reductase, i.e. NO_3^- reductase, NO_2^- reductase, etc., in which the more oxidized form is used as the terminal electron acceptor. Also the three ion species to the right in the equation have the potential to escape from the soil to the atmosphere as a gas.

Denitrification can have both positive and negative aspects. On one hand, a potential leachable form of N can be removed from the ecosystem, thus preventing contamination of ground and surficial waters. However, from a plant production standpoint this series of reactions represents a loss of N which might be used for crop production. The consequence is that more N has to be applied to realize a certain level of production had denitrification not been present. Also the potential liberation of NO and N_2O to the atmosphere could have a significant impact on environmental quality.

Sulfate, Fe^{3+}, and Mn^{3+} also act as terminal electron acceptors for certain facultative anaerobes in the absence of O_2. The consequences of the reduction of these ionic forms are not as obvious as they are for denitrification, as the reduced forms are not lost from the soil ecosystem. However, the reduced forms of Fe and Mn are more toxic to higher plants than the oxidized forms and the SH^- adversely affects some enzymatic reactions.

D. Nitrogen Fixation

The biological reduction of N_2 to a utilizable form of N is a characteristic of only a few bacteria and is known as N fixation. Unlike the chemical reduction of N_2 which occurs at extremely high temperatures and pressures, biological reduction occurs at environmental pressures and temperatures, i.e., 1 atm and 5 to 35°C. Since this is an energy consuming reaction there must be an available energy source present (electron donor). Nitrogen fixation taking place independently of an associated plant or other microorganism is known as nonsymbiotic N fixation or, when in association with an other organism, symbiotic N fixation (discussed later).

Some of the better known nonsymbiotic N fixers are represented by such genera as *Azotobacter*, *Beijerinckia*, *Clostridium*, *Azomonas*, *Nostoc*, and *Anabena*. Nitrogen is reduced to a usable form and is incorporated into the biomass of the N fixing organism. Additions of N to the ecosystem are small until the organism dies and releases its cellular contents into the soil. Except for a few examples the amount of N fixed by these organisms is generally small and is limited by the amount of available energy present. On the average only 5–10 kg N ha^{-1} $year^{-1}$ are fixed by these organisms. An exception to this generalization is the blue green algae, represented by *Anabena* and *Nostoc*, which because of their photosynthetic ability derive their energy from sunlight. These organisms have been reported to fix up to 50 kg N ha^{-1} $year^{-1}$. Like the other nonsymbiotic N fixers any N gain is retained in the fixing cell until it dies and is released to the soil environment.

V. Plant Interactions with Microorganisms

A. Rhizosphere

One cannot understand the full potential of the microbes in the soil without an appreciation of the influence of the plant on the growth and activities of soil microorganisms. The region of soil under the influence of the plant root is known as the rhizosphere. During plant growth, various substances are exuded from the plant root including carbohydrates, amino acids, proteins, organic acids, and vitamins to mention just a few specific compounds as well as complex plant material from root abrasion and broken-off roots. These materials provide an ideal energy and C substrate for the growth and development of microorganisms. Since one of the most prominent limiting factors for microorganisms in the soil is energy and C, the release of these materials to the rooting environment causes a proliferation of microorganisms near the root.

The rhizosphere is not a fixed entity, rather it varies in time and space (Fig. 6). Other zones can be differentiated and are the rhizophane and histoplane. The former comprises the surface of the root, whereas the latter is the intracellular spaces of the plant root. The magnitude of the rhizosphere effect can be quantified by calculating a R/S, where R = number of organisms in the rhizosphere and S = number of organisms in the nonrhizosphere soil. A ratio of >1 indicates a positive rhizosphere effect. Around actively growing

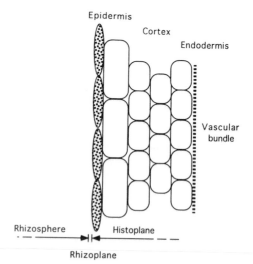

FIGURE 6 Diagram of the rhizosphere in relation to the plant root.

TABLE V

The Numbers of Bacteria in the Rhizosphere and Nonrhizosphere of Different Plants

Organisms/plant	Rhizosphere (R)	Nonrhizosphere (S)	R/S
		No./g soil	
Total bacteria			
Tobacco—RH.211	269.2×10^6	94.7×10^6	2.8
Tobacco—Ch.38	505.4×10^6	94.7×10^6	5.3
Flax—Bison	439.9×10^6	98.3×10^6	4.5
Flax—Novelty	2751.3×10^6	98.3×10^6	28.1
Denitrifiers			
Tobacco—Ch.38	216.3×10^6	44.6×10^6	4.8
Loblolly pine	170.0×10^3	11.2×10^3	15.2
Pond pine	25.0×10^3	2.8×10^3	8.9
Nitrifiers			
Loblolly pine	37.0×10^2	580.0×10^2	0.6
Pond pine	107.0×10^2	17.0×10^2	6.3

Adapted from Lochhead, A. G., and Wollum, A. G. (unpublished data).

plants, soil tends to have a $R/S \gg 1$. Greater activity and often greater diversity of organisms is often associated with the rhizosphere and frequently means a greater abundance of nutrients for plant growth, which in turn stimulates plant growth. Likewise there is a seasonal aspect to the rhizosphere, which tends to be greatest during the warmer and wetter periods of the year. Not only does the environment itself influence the extent of the rhizosphere, but the plant itself, even to a cultivar, may exert a profound effect on microbial development (Table V).

B. Mycorrhizae

The word mycorrhiza is derived from two Greek words: *myco* meaning fungus and *rhiza* meaning root. Literally the word mycorrhiza means fungus root. Hence mycorrhiza refers to a symbiotic association between a specific fungus and the plant root, primarily the smallest order of the secondary roots. Affirming the presence of the association requires in some instances observation of distinct macrocharacteristics of the root, while for others, microscopic examination of root sections is needed for confirmation.

Mycorrhizae are a common feature on most if not all plant roots. The absence of mycorrhizae on a plant is not prima facie evidence the plant is not mycorrhizal in habit. In some instances the association is seasonal and the observer may have looked at the wrong time. Alternatively the plant may be growing off-site and there is no symbiont present or conditions may not

have been appropriate for the formation of the association.

There are two primary classes of mycorrhizal associations. The first class is known as ectomycorrhizae and is recognized by observation of gross root morphologies(Fig. 7) and microscopic structures(Fig. 8). The most distinctive morphological features deal with the branched nature of the fine roots. Normally these fine roots are unbranched and quite long (1000 to 3000 μm); however, when infected with the appropriate fungus, root development is arrested and becomes branched, from dichotomously to multibranched features. In some instances the short root is almost colloroid in nature. Ectomycorrhizae are common on such plant families as Pinaceae, Fagaceae, Betulaceae, Rosaceae, and Myrtaceae, when infected by specific basidiomycetes. It is thought that the

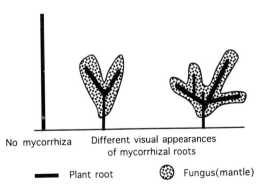

No mycorrhiza   Different visual appearances of mycorrhizal roots

—— Plant root   ⊛ Fungus(mantle)

FIGURE 7 Diagram of the appearance of different roots without and with an ectomycorrhizal association.

branched development of the root arises from cytokinins produced by the plant in response to the infection which affects root development.

The microscopic morphology of the root is distinctive for the ectomycorrhizal association (Fig. 8). To the exterior of the root is a zone called the mantle, composed of fungus, often encircling the fine root. Interior to the mantle the fungus may penetrate the root and develop around the individual cortical cells. The depth of penetration and fungal development depend on the individual plant host and the infecting fungus. Regardless, the fungus does not develop beyond the endodermis of the plant root. Additionally the fungus does not grow into the root cells, remaining entirely intracellular in its infection. The growth of the fungus within the cortical region is often referred to as the Hartig's net.

The other main type of mycorrhizae are the endomycorrhizae. While there can be several endomycorrhizal types, this discussion will be confined to the one commonly known as the vesicular arbuscular mycorrhizae (VAM) and will ignore those associated with orchids (which are somewhat more specialized). Unlike the ectomycorrhizae, for endomycorrhizae, it is virtually impossible to look at a plant root and tell whether it has the associated fungus. Therefore it is necessary to look at the microscopic features of a root section and determine whether it possesses the appropriate features. If the plant is endomycorrhizal, it is likely to have vesicles (V), arbuscules (A), and intercellular hyphae. Vesicles are enlarged structures, often taking on the shape of the cortical cell, and occur

at the ends of hyphae and within the cell (Fig. 9). Arbuscules, likewise, occur at the ends of hyphae within in the plant cell, but have a feathery or branched appearance. Unlike the ectomycorrhizae where the hyphae is confined to the intracellular spaces, for the endomycorrhizae the hyphae can grow both inter- and intracellularly.

The mycorrhizal association benefits the plants in many ways. Mycorrhizal plants have a better nutrient status than nonmycorrhizal plants. This is particularly true for P. It is thought the hyphae extending away from the root literally enlarge the absorbing surface for the plant enhancing nutrient acquisition. Also the mycorrhizal fungi are active producers of phosphatase enzymes and organic acids, which might enhance the solubilities of difficultly available nutrient sources of P. Other benefits also include enhanced disease protection as various mycorrhizal fungi have been shown to produce potent antibiotic substances against a variety of root pathogens. In the instance of the ectomycorrhizae one could argue that the mantle provides a protective covering about the root, thus moderating the rooting environment against extreme stresses. Finally the hyphae from both the ecto- and endomycorrhizal association may contribute to the stabilization of soil aggregates.

C. Nitrogen Fixation

In contrast to the nonsymbiotic forms of N fixation, the symbiotic association between microorganisms, with N fixing capacity and higher plants, has real potential to contribute significant quantities of N to various ecosystems. The best known of the symbiotic

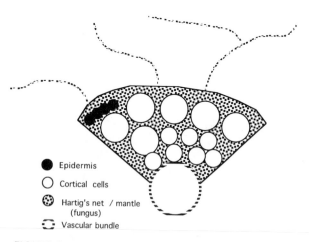

FIGURE 8 Cross-section of an ectomycorrhizal root, showing both fungal and plant features. Note the mantle is to the outer portion of the root, exterior to the epidermis and/or root cortical cells.

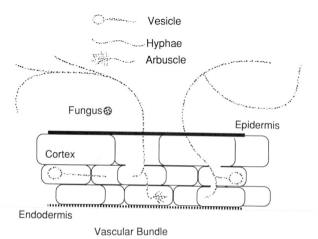

FIGURE 9 Longitudinal section of a plant root, illustrating the different components of an endomycorrhizal association.

N fixers are those found in the family Fabaceae (Leguminosae) associated with either *Rhizobium* or *Bradyrhizobium*. However there are at least 12 other plant families containing genera which will enter into a symbiotic relationship with an actinomycete called *Frankia* which are also capable of fixing N.

For both groups of symbiotic N fixers, infection occurs through root hairs or wounds on the root or both. Once within the plant root the infecting organisms develop toward the cortical regional and illicit a response from the plant which results in the formation of a nodule on the exterior of the plant root. Interior to the nodule the symbiont grows and increases in numbers. Unlike galls consisting of undifferentiated tissue forming on plants roots, nodules are actually modified roots arrested in their development. Thus nodules possess all the necessary transport features of a root and the products of fixation can easily move from the site of fixation to the top of the plant. Conversely photosynthate can be translocated from the top of the plant down to the nodule to support the energy demands of the fixation processes.

Literally 100's of kg N ha^{-1} can be incorporated into the biomass of the plant during a year's time. Initially this N is used to support plant growth, although small amounts may leak from the roots and nodules and be immediately available to other organisms in the ecosystem. However the largest share of N becomes available after the plant dies or the leaves senesce. Subsequently the mineralization of the organic residues results in an increase in the system NH_4^+ which can be used by other organisms, including plants, as a N source or as an energy source by the nitrifying organisms. In the latter instance, the NO_3^- formed can have one of several fates, such as it can be utilized as an N source, leached, or used as a terminal electron acceptor during denitrification processes. In some cropping systems, N fixed via symbiotic means constitutes the only N addition made.

VI. Future Opportunities

At the beginning of the 20th century, microbiologists realized that soil was a living and complex entity and the study of this complex system needed to be done against a background of soil fertility and crop production. This was a turning point for it made the study of soil microbiology practical in terms of an economic output. Since then, there has been great emphasis on the microbiology of N in soil systems, where it went and how much the plant actually used. Also great strides have been made in understanding the basic nature of SOM. Studies of N fixation have concentrated on the effects of inoculation with the proper symbiont and how much N could be expected from the fixation process. While investigators have contributed much to our understanding of the basic biological processes in soil, there is still much to be done.

A. Nutrients

Where it was once fashionable to study biological reactions merely from a crop production standpoint, future studies must also emphasize the environmental impact of excess amounts of nutrients in the ecosystem and how soil biological processes might be utilized to ameliorate adverse environmental conditions. For instance, it might be possible to utilize denitrification as a means for reducing the soil N concentrations when high N content waste materials are added to the soil. At the same time, however, scientists must be aware of and minimize the production of N_2O and loss to the atmosphere which might occur during denitrification.

B. Bioremediation

No longer is it sufficient to study the organic matter of the soil ecosystem just from the standpoint of its physiochemical properties. Although soil has been used for a long time as the final receptor for waste products, there must be a renewed effort to understand those factors limiting decomposition of the wastes, what constitutes a proper loading rate and what happens both to the organic and inorganic constituents of the waste product. Nutrients in organic residues need to be salvaged and reutilized, with the ultimate goal of maintaining clean air and water resources.

The potential of soil organisms to participate in the bioremediation of sites compromised by adverse activities in the environment must be maximized to the fullest. Recent disasters such as petroleum spills or reports of hazardous chemicals in ground or surficial waters underscore the importance of understanding the principles of remediation and how microorganisms might be utilized to overcome such adverse conditions. Not only are studies required on the mechanisms of remediation of different contaminants, but organisms need to be identified which have enhanced activities to degrade noxius chemicals in environmental samples. Likewise optimum conditions for organisms should be identified and implemented on a field scale allowing the establishment of the inoculant organisms in the soil which will maximize the remediation effort.

C. Biocontrol

Increasing concerns about the use of synthetic chemicals as pesticides and the potential environmental and health risks associated with many of these chemicals underscores a great opportunity to use soil microorganisms in biocontrol programs. The success of *Bacillus thuringienesis* to control the balsam woolly aphid suggests that other control opportunities exist. For instance, it may be possible to insert the *B. thuringienesis* genes for balsam wooly aphid control directly into the plant, therefore bypassing the need to use the control organism directly. However before success comes for biocontrol programs, additional organisms and use strategies need to be identified for other disease problems. Basic studies of the ecology of these control organisms may yield important clues as to how to prolong their effectiveness in the soil and plant environment. Advances in these and other areas of soil microbiology will be slow in coming unless there is a resurgence of activity in the study of the bioecology of microorganisms in the soil and rooting environment. [*See* PEST MANAGEMENT, BIOLOGICAL CONTROL.]

D. Biotechnology

In the past, the selection and use of microorganisms with some naturally enhanced property were the norm for many soil microbiologists, whether it was for pesticide degradation, biological N fixation, or some other specific function. These efforts must continue into the future and may provide part of the foundation for utilizing biotechnology in soil microbiology. Thus it may be possible to identify the genes responsible for controlling the enhanced degradation of a PCB or for a supernodulating symbiont for some important grain legume. Inserting these genes into environmentally competent organisms might overcome existing limitations of the natural ecosystem for maximizing a beneficial reaction.

Through ages past, microorganisms have been used to produce a variety of highly esthetic or useful products for both man and animal, i.e., yogurt, light-textured breads, wines, cheeses, antibiotics, etc. For their intended purposes, each microbial product makes life a little easier, safer, or more enjoyable. Today's soil microbiologists have at least two opportunities: unesthetic substrates (i.e., sewage, industrial wastes, animal manures, etc.) and limited resources. The challenge for the soil microbiologist is to use the soil as a support medium to make the undesirable or unesthetic substrates less objectionable and to exploit the residual food and energy potentials of the different substrates while getting more for less in crop production and at the same time maintaining environmental quality.

Bibliography

Dawes, I. W., and Sutherland, I. W. (1992). "Microbial Physiology, 2nd Ed. Blackwell Scientific, Oxford, Great Britain.

Jensen, V., Kjøller, A. and Sørensen, L. H. (1986). Microbial communities in soil. *In* "Proceedings, Federation European Microbiol. Soc. Symposium, Copenhagen, Denmark." Elsevier Appl. Sci., London.

Keister, D. L., and Cregan, P. B. (eds.) (1990). The rhizosphere and plant growth. *In* "Beltsville Symp. Agric. Res." Kluwer Academic, Dordrecht, The Netherlands.

Lynch, J. M., and Hobbie, J. E. (1988). "Microorganisms in Action: Concepts and Applications in Microbial Ecology." Blackwell Scientific, Oxford, Great Britain.

Metting, F. B., Jr. (1992). "Soil Microbial Ecology: Applications in Agricultural and Environmental Management." Dekker, New York.

Soil Pollution

HEINZ HÄNI,

Swiss Federal Research Station for Agricultural Chemistry and Hygiene of Environment, Liebefeld-Berne

Glossary

Buffer capacity Capacity to retain pollutants in the soil so that the biota is protected from adverse effects and subsoil and drinking water are kept pure; buffer capacity is high with high clay and silt content and with high organic matter content

Cation exchange capacity Indicates the total of all cations adsorbed, expressed in milliequivalents per 100 g

Organic matter Fraction of the soil consisting of living organisms of the soil flora and fauna, living and dead plant roots, which may be partly decomposed and modified and newly synthesized organic substances of plant or animal origin; by conventional definition "soil organic matter" does not include coarse plant material or soil vertebrates

pH Indicates the hydrogen ion concentration, or more correctly the H^+ ion activity of the soil solution expressed as the negative logarithm

Pollutants Gaseous emissions from industry, trade, and traffic and from heating installations and waste incineration plants (sulfur dioxide, NO_x, heavy metals, non-readily degradable organic compounds, etc.), which may be emitted as gas, vapor, or dust or enter the soil mixed with precipitation; agrochemicals or other substances which are directly or indirectly applied to the soil for agricultural or non-agricultural purposes; these include fertilizers (commercial fertilizers and manure, sewage sludge, compost), plant treat-

ment products (plant protection agents, pesticides), wood preservations, thawing agents for combatting ice and packed snow, etc.

Redox potential Defined as the electrical potential (in millivolts) which arises from electron transfer from donor to acceptor and specifies the oxidizing or reducing power of the redox system, i.e., the electrical work done

Soil pollution Deals with the contamination of soils by pollutants in the air, from the handling of environmentally hazardous substances and from waste

Soil is the natural basis of life for humans, animals, and plants. It can be impaired both quantitatively and qualitatively. Pollution affects qualitative aspects of soil.

I. Introduction

The most important soil pollutants are heavy metals, acid deposits (see Section IV), and organic substances of low mobility and degradation. Heavy metals occur naturally in soil, normally in rather low concentrations except for special geological situations (e.g., mining sites). Some of the naturally occurring heavy metals are essential for life (e.g., copper and zinc). In soil pollution studies one has to focus on heavy metals of anthropogenic origin (Table I), because these metal forms are usually more soluble than those bound in minerals and ores.

The occurrence of organic pollutants originating mainly from anthropogenic sources is either ubiquitous or specific to waste water.

The ubiquitous organic pollutants are the following:

- Polynuclear aromatic hydrocarbons (PAH), polychlorinated dibenzodioxins (PCDD), and

TABLE I

Anthropogenic Sources of Inorganic Pollutants (Mainly Heavy Metals)

Element	Sources								Agriculture	
	Industry metal[a]	Surface coating[b]	Building materials[c]	Plastics	Chemistry	Waste[d]	Fossil energy	Traffic automobiles[e]	Fertilizers[f]	Plant treatment
Lead	x	x			x	x	x	x		x
Cadmium	x	x		x	x	x	x	x	x	
Chromium	x	x			x	x			x	
Cobalt	x	x			x	x			x	
Fluorine	x		x			x	x			x
Copper	x	x			x	x			x	x
Molybdenum	x	x			x	x	x			
Nickel	x	x			x	x	x	x	x	x
Mercury	x	x			x	x	x		x	x
Selenium	x				x		x		x	
Thallium			x							
Zinc	x	x			x	x	x	x	x	

Source: Meyer, K. (1991). Bodenverschmutzung in der Schweiz, Themenbericht des Nationalen Forschungsprogrammes "Boden."
[a] Production and manufacturing.
[b] Galvanization, enameling, color spraying.
[c] Ceramics, cement, bricks.
[d] Incineration.
[e] Gasoline, abrasion of pneumatics.
[f] Sewage sludge, fertilizers, and manure.

dibenzofurans (PCDF), consequences of emissions from incineration of fossil energy carriers and mixed organic and inorganic substances from vehicles, power stations, industrial plants, and household burning. Some PAH compounds are synthesized naturally by plants and microorganisms. A geogenic basic content of PAH in soils is about 1–10 ppb.
• Phenols, polychlorinated biphenyls (PCB), phtalates, and possibly tin–organic compounds, caused by the inevitable losses, accidents, and inappropriate disposal of technical raw materials.
• Organochlorine pesticides (DDT, DDE, Lindane, etc.), formerly used as plant treatment products.

Pollutants that are specific to waste water are the following:

• Linear alkylbenzene sulfonates (LAS), Nonylphenol (NP), and other surfactants.
• Tin organic compounds from industrial use.

Until a few years ago, soil pollution was not discussed. The soil was considered to be an inexhaustible filter and a favored lasting sink for every type of pollutant. Soil protection only received political importance in the course of discussions on forest decay.

Four areas of prime importance in soil pollution are discussed in this article.

• Proportion of different sources of soil input
• Degree of soil pollution in industrialized countries

• Effects of soil pollution
• Measures against soil pollution

II. Comparison of Pollutant Inputs from Different Sources

In a study on heavy metal contents in the soils of Switzerland, the authors came to the conclusion that different site factors influenced the concentration of the five investigated metals, lead, cadmium, copper, nickel, and zinc:

• Aerosol emissions from traffic, industry, and incineration plants are mostly responsible for increased lead contents in topsoils.
• Some emission sources are locally of importance in elevating cadmium and zinc contents in topsoils. In agriculture, inputs by fertilizers (cadmium), pig slurry (zinc), and plant treatment products (zinc) have to be considered.
• Copper is mainly brought into soils by agricultural practices (pesticides, pig slurry).
• No influence of emission sources and land use can be established for nickel. As increased subsoil contents are found in the catchment area of the glacier of the Rhône in the western part of Switzerland, these contents are probably of geological origin.

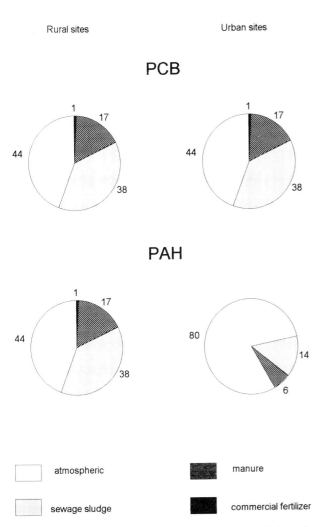

Rural sites   Urban sites

PCB

PAH

□ atmospheric   ▨ manure

▨ sewage sludge   ■ commercial fertilizer

FIGURE 1 Proportions (%) of different sources of pollution of agricultural soils with PCB and PAH [From Diercxsens *et al.*, (1987). *Gas, Wasser, Abwasser*, **66**, 123–132.]

From investigations of sludged soils the approximate contributions of different auxilliary agricultural substances and of atmospheric deposition to the pollution of urban and rural soils with PCB and PAH were deduced (Fig. 1).

The most important carrier of PCB and PAH is atmospheric precipitation; in urban environments, soil pollution with PAH is practically due entirely to atmospheric input.

III. Degree of Pollution

From the already-mentioned Swiss study the conclusion may be drawn that the great majority of agricultural and forest soils contain heavy metal levels which lie below the guide values of the Ordinance Relating to Pollutants in Soil (for this ordinance see Section IV). Excess levels can be explained either by land utilization (e.g., viniculture) or by distinct emission situations. These findings were strengthened by the results of the National Soil Monitoring Network in 1993.

This pattern of great areas of low pollution in which, depending on human activities, so-called hot spots are interspersed may be very similar in other industrialized countries. However, because of the well-known bad air quality in many parts of central and eastern Europe larger areas of polluted soils have to be expected in these countries. In these regions it has been reported that the emission of soil pollutants of anthropogenic origin is about 10-fold higher than natural levels in central Europe. Deposition on forest soils is often twice as high as that on agricultural soils due to the filtering effect of forest canopies. [*See* AIR POLLUTION: PLANT GROWTH AND PRODUCTIVITY.]

Figure 2 shows an example of a polluted area due to a metal smelter. The pollution gradient of soils depends on the type of heavy metal. From Fig. 2, it can be seen that the area polluted by cadmium is larger than the copper-polluted area.

In agricultural practice it is often observed that the heavy metal content in soil goes parallel with the nutrient content. As overfertilization of garden soils is widespread, this phenomenon is very obvious in these soils. It has therefore to be concluded that many of the garden soils belong to the category of polluted soils.

Much less is known about soil pollution by organic chemicals. An interesting investigation exists in the Rothamsted Experimental Station where soils sampled since the middle of the last century were analyzed for polynuclear aromatic hydrocarbons, polychlorinated dibenzodioxins, and dibenzofurans. In the topsoil of the semi-rural site a four- to five-fold increase in the PAH content was observed within the past 100 years. This is also in accordance with findings in the United States. The PCDD and PCDF content in the same soil samples increased by a factor of 2–10.

IV. Effects of Soil Pollution

In order to define the quality of the soil and its protection in a better way, there is a need for further research on soil buffering capacity, compound speciation, soil heterogeneity, and bioavailability of pollutants. Until now, attention has been directed mainly toward

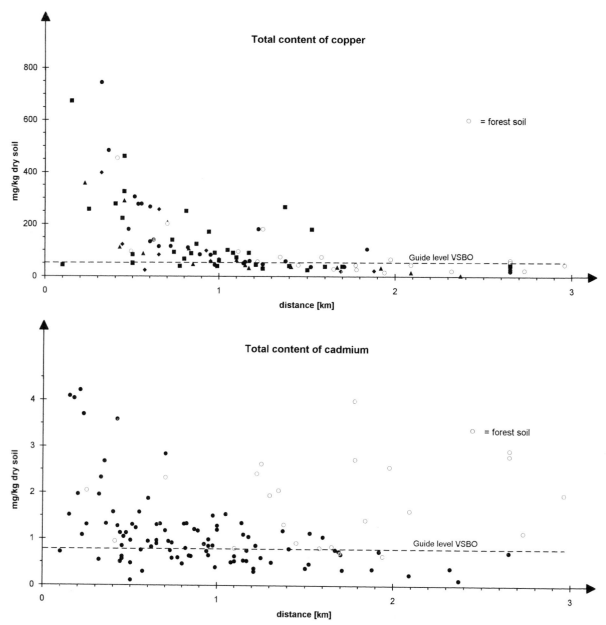

FIGURE 2 Soil pollution by copper and cadmium due to a metal smelter. Dashed line corresponds to the guide level of copper and cadmium in the Swiss Ordinance to Pollutants in Soil. [From Wirz, E. (1990). Kantonales Laboratorium Solothurn, Switzerland.]

chemical and physical properties of soils whereas biological properties have been neglected.

Usually, the soil ecosystem has a capacity to buffer and, thus, to protect the biota from adverse effects of perturbations such as chemical pollution. Only when the buffering capacity of an ecosystem is too small to retain or otherwise counteract inputs of chemical pollution will harmful effects become apparent and the ecosystem will be rendered vulnerable to adverse effects of pollution.

The most prevailing properties of soil which influence adsorption and immobilization of heavy metals are pH, redox potential, salinity, and organic matter content. Salinity directly affects soil structure; organic matter content directly affects the cation exchange capacity.

A. Soil pH

The reaction of a soil, acid, neutral, or alkaline, is expressed by pH which indicates the hydrogen ion (H^+) activity of the soil solution expressed by the negative logarithm. Hydrogen ions either are produced in internal soil processes or originate from external sources:

1. Internal Processes

- CO_2 production in respiration of soil organisms and plant roots.
- H^+ production by plant roots.
- Humification of organic matter producing fulvic and humic acids.
- Oxidation of reduced sulfur and nitrogen compounds to sulfuric acid and nitric acid by weathering or biological oxidation.

2. External Sources

- Pollution by acid deposition (mainly SO_2 and NO_x). The input of natural and anthropogenic substances from the atmosphere to the surface of the earth (soil, vegetation, buildings) is designated as atmospheric deposition. In wet depositions the substances are either dissolved or washed out as particles with the precipitation. The direct sedimentation of dusts or the adsorption of gaseous substances is defined as dry deposition. With regard to the effects on soil the acid-forming substances as SO_2 and NO_x are of prime importance. They are oxidized in the atmosphere and transformed to acids giving rise to the acid precipitation which brings a considerable amount of protons into the ecosystems.
- Ammonia emissions originating from agriculture. In regions of high animal density the emissions of ammonia can at times exceed that of SO_2 and NO_x. Ammonia is converted into ammonium sulfate in the atmosphere leading to neutralization of the acid precipitations. However, the nitrification of ammonium to nitrate in the soil causes temporary acidification.
- Manuring with acid fertilizers like superphosphate and ammonium sulfate. H^+ ions release basic cations from exchangers but pH reduction is only severe when the released cations are removed by leaching or nutrient uptake by plants which take up basic nutrient cations in exchange for H^+ ions excreted by roots. In natural soils pH drop (soil acidification) in the long term is very slight because cations are returned in the litter. The loss can be serious in intensive farming if nutrients are not replaced by manure, fertilizers, and lime.

Soil acidification due to external sources and intensive farming is delayed by a sequence of buffer reactions:

Buffer	PH Range
Carbonate	8.6 > pH > 6.2
Silicate	Whole pH scale (dominating buffer reaction in carbonate free soils pH > 5)
Exchanger	5 > pH > 4.2
Aluminium	4.2 > pH
Aluminium/iron	3.8 > pH
Iron	3.2 > pH

pH has a manifold influence on all the chemical, biological, and physical processes in soils and on soil properties. The most important effects of pH are on nutrient and heavy metal mobility. [*See* Soil, Acid.]

The best conditions for nutrients are found in weakly acid to neutral soils (pH 5.0–7.5). Heavy metals are mobilized under acid soil conditions. It is this mobile fraction which is of the utmost concern for the biota. That is why two levels are set in the Swiss Ordinance Relating to Pollutants in Soil: total heavy metal content to limit the load to a safe level and soluble heavy metal content to assess the bioavailability, determined in a neutral salt extract. Increased metal concentrations in plants, yield reduction, or change of the soil mineralization potential (e.g., its ability to degrade harmful chemicals into harmless inorganic end products) may be cited as important effects of enhanced concentrations of this bioavailable fraction.

As the pH falls below 4.2 (aluminum buffer range) the leaching of aluminum, present as a natural immobile component of soil, is greatly increased. Adverse effects in the ecosystem, such as tree damage and fish kills, begin to be manifested.

B. Redox Potential

Redox potential is high in well-aerated soils with much O_2 dissolved in the soil solution and a high proportion of oxidized compounds (Fe and Mn oxides, hydroxide, nitrate, sulphate), i.e., well-drained soils with a low water table and low content of easily decomposable organic matter.

Redox potential is low in O_2-deficient soils with much reduced compounds (Fe^{II}, Mn^{II}, S^{2-}) and easily decomposable organic matter, i.e., especially in hydromorphic soils. The influence of water in these soils

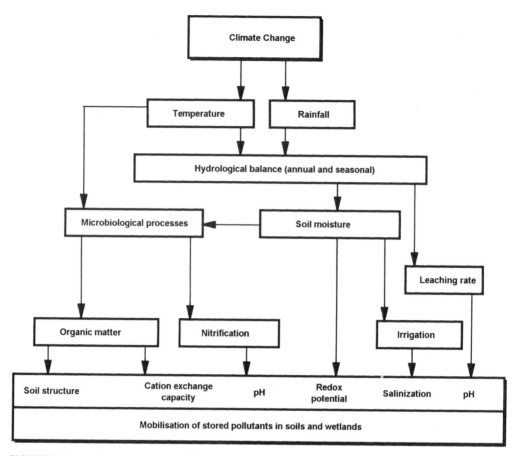

FIGURE 3 How climate change can affect the mobility of heavy metals stored in soils and wetland. [From Stigliani and Salomons, W., submitted for publication.]

is either permanent, due to groundwater, or temporary, due to surface water caused by impeded drainage. [See SOIL–WATER RELATIONSHIPS.]

Soils with high amounts of substances that can be oxidized and reduced are poised, i.e., well-buffered against severe change in redox potential in either direction.

Since H^+ ions are produced by oxidation, pH declines as redox potential increases. The ecological significance of redox potential lies in its effect on nutrient availability. Further, the solubility of heavy metals either adsorbed or occluded in iron and manganese oxides is increased by the reduction of these oxides. [See SOIL, CHEMICALS: MOVEMENT AND RETENTION; SOIL CHEMISTRY.]

C. Changes of Soil Properties

Important factors which can change soil properties are temperature and rainfall. Therefore, the so-called climate change threatens to create soil property alterations, as shown in Fig. 3.

Higher soil temperatures increase microbial decomposition leading to a decrease of the soil organic matter content. In contrast, increasing soil moisture has the effect of increasing organic matter content (and vice versa). [See SOIL MICROBIOLOGY.]

Decreases in the organic matter content of soils cause increases of *heavy metal* mobility due to enhanced erosion and diminished cation exchange capacity, which results in less adsorption. Drying out of wetland soils can mobilize insoluble sulfides which are transformed into soluble sulfates at higher redox potential. Soils with increased salinity have a reduced capacity to store heavy metals. Such soils are formed in regions where the rate of evapotranspiration is greater than the rate of precipitation and saline water is used for irrigation.

From these observations, it is apparent that the capacities of soils to store heavy metals would be significantly reduced under warmer, drier conditions.

The most vulnerable area are those with both high accumulated chemical loads and high storage capacities.

D. Organic Chemicals

PAH, PCB, PCDD, and PCDF have low degradation potentials, while the monocyclic aromatics and the short-chained halogenated aliphatics are readily degraded and moderately leached.

Possible transfers into plants and animals may be assessed by the use of the octanol–water partition coefficient (K_{OW}). K_{OW} is defined as the ratio of a chemical concentration in octanol to that in the aqueous phase of a two-phase octanol/water experimental system at equilibrium:

$$K_{OW} = \frac{\text{concentration in octanol phase}}{\text{concentration in aqueos phase}}$$

Log K_{OW} describes the lipophilicity and hydrophobicity of the chemical in question.

Potential for retention by root surfaces can be envisaged as a sorption process similar to that described for soils. Consequently "high," "medium," and "low"categories are defined as log K_{OW} values of >4.0, >2.5, and <2.5, respectively. The high retention category is intended to identify those compounds which contaminate root crops at the surface.

For potential root uptake and translocation the following categories are used:

Category	Values
High potential for root uptake and translocation:	Log K_{OW} < 3.5 and $T_{1/2}$ > 50 days
Moderate potential:	Log K_{OW} < 4.5 and $T_{1/2}$ > 10 days
Low potential:	Log K_{OW} > 4.5

Potential transfer to animal tissues via soil ingestion will depend on compound persistence in soil and on bioaccumulation potential in terrestrial ecosystems.

V. Measures against Soil Pollution

Because the purification of soils, contrary to air and water, is difficult or even impossible, preventive measures are of prime importance in qualitative soil protection. Once the soil fertility is impaired, its recovery (i.e., sanitation) is very limited. [See SOIL FERTILITY.]

To protect soil, the following measures have to be considered:

- Limits on pollutant emissions from both nonagricultural and agricultural sources.
- Application rules and advisory services for farmers.
- Properly organized waste management systems.
- Surveillance systems for monitoring the level of pollution in the soil.

VI. Conclusion and Summary

Whereas the origin of soil pollutants is known to a great extent, specific gaps in knowledge remain about the fate of pollutants (mainly organic chemicals) in soil. Moreover, the effects of pollutants in biological soil properties are not sufficiently understood. While reducing measures are becoming effective for heavy metals in many countries, the efforts to reduce acid atmospheric depositions have been much less successful. Therefore, research has to be intensified in the risk assessment of soils that have been polluted in former times and in soil acidicification processes. Finally, questions about the influence of climate change on the storage capacity of pollutants in soil may gain growing interest.

Bibliography

Barth, H., and L'Hermite, P. (eds.) (1987). "Scientific Basis for Soil Protection in the European Community." Elsevier Applied Science, London/New York.

Häni, H. (1990). The analysis of inorganic and organic pollutants in soil with special regard to their bioavailability. *Int. J. Environ. Anal. Chem.* **39,**197–208.

Jones, K. C., Stratford, J. A., Waterhouse, K. S., and Vogt, N. B. (1989). Organic contaminants in Welsh soils: Polynuclear aromatic hydrocarbons. *Environ. Sci. Technol.* **23,** 540.

Kjeller, L. O., Rae, C., Jones, K. C., and Johnston, A. E. (1990). Evidence for increase in the environmental burden of polychlorinated dibenzo-*p*-dioxins and furans over the last century. *Chemosphere.*

Meyer, K. (1991). Bodenverschmutzung in der Schweiz, Themenbericht des Nationalen Forschungsprogrammes "Boden," Liebefeld-Bern.

Rosenkranz, D., Einsele, G., and Harres, H.-M. (1988). Bodenschutz, Ergänzendes Handbuch der Massnahmen und Empfehlungen für Schutz, Pflege und Sainerung von Böden, Landschaft und Grundwasser, Erich Schmitt Verlag.

Swiss Federal Office of Environment, Forests and Landscape (1987). "Commentary on the Ordinance Relating to Pollutants in Soil."

Swiss Federal Office of Environment, Forests and Landscape (1993). "National Soil Monitoring Network (NABO) in Switzerland." *Schriftenreihe Umwelt,* Nr. 200.

Ulrich, B. (1986). Natural and anthropogenic components of soil acidification. *Z. Pflanzenernaehr. Bodenkd.* **149,** 702–717.

Vogel, H., Desaules, A., and Häni, H. (1992). Heavy metal contents in the soils of Switzerland. *Int. J. Environ. Anal. Chem.* **46,** 3–11.

Wild, S. R., and Jones, K. C. (1992). Organic chemicals entering agricultural soils in sewage sludges: Screening for their potential to transfer to crop plants and livestock. *Sci. Total Environ.* **119,** 85–119.

Soil Testing for Plant Growth and Soil Fertility

RAYMOND W. MILLER, *Utah State University*

Glossary

Available nutrient That portion of an essential element in the soil that is readily absorbed into plant roots

Cation exchange capacity Quantity of (exchangeable) cations that a soil can adsorb to its negatively charged sites, usually expressed in centimoles$_c$ per kilogram of soil

Chelates Certain organic molecules bonded to one of many metals, particularly iron, zinc, copper, and manganese; a molecule may have several bonds to its metal and natural chelates may be soluble or insoluble; fertilizer chelates are soluble and help to mobilize metals in soil solution

Field correlation Studying the relationship between soil test values from the laboratory with the plant's response to added fertilizer in hundreds of field plots on those same soils

Humus Organic matter remaining in soil after the major portion of added residues (roots, tops, manures) have decomposed

Ions Atoms or groups of atoms that are negatively or positively charged, by gain or loss of electrons

Labile The quantity of a nutrient which is or will become available during a growing season

Peds Units of soil structure formed by natural processes (i.e., blocks, prisms, granules, plates)

Quick tests Term for mostly laboratory tests that can be done quickly to evaluate the soil properties and fertility needs

Soil structure Arrangement and combination of sand, silt, and clay particles into large aggregates or peds (i.e., granular structure, blocky structure, prismatic structure)

Soil texture Terms to describe the proportions of sand, silt, and clay (and coarser fragments) in a soil; a "loam" has about equal physical properties from its sand, its silt, and its clay

Soil testing is a general term for analyses of soil samples to obtain useful information about that soil. Soils are analyzed to permit correction of deficiencies or to correct excesses of harmful constituents. Deficiencies are usually those of nutrient elements; harmful constituents may be strong acidity, toxic elements, or elements taken up by plants that are harmful to animals that consume the plant materials. With the advent of large world populations, wastes have multiplied. Many soil tests are now involved in the determination of the extent of pollution and to reclaim polluted or damaged soils. This section contains soil tests for correcting soil fertility, and the soil tests used in the monitoring and correction of polluted soils.

I. Important Properties of Soils

Soil is the natural media supporting land plants and supplying water and 13 of the 16 essential elements to plants. A few plants benefit from an additional few elements, which are also derived from the soil. In the process of providing and supplying these plant needs, the physical and chemical soil properties can exert dominant influences. The *physical properties* include soil texture (proportions of sand, silt, and clay), soil structure (the shape and porosity of masses of soil particles cemented together), soil aeration (the ease of air exchange into the soil), mineralogy (the kinds of minerals comprising the soil), soil temperature, and the water relationships in the soil. *Chemical properties* include the soil pH (acidity or alkalinity), the concentrations of available nutrients, the presence of toxic concentrations of certain elements, the amount of humus (residue of plant materials after extensive decomposition), and chemically active mineral surfaces that adsorb organic substances and soluble ions. [*See* Soil Chemistry.]

In addition to the physical and chemical properties, the kinds and amounts of *microbes* (thousands of species of bacteria, actinomycetes, fungi, algae, and others) and the large *animals* (earthworms, nematodes, amoeba, insects, slugs) all affect growing plants. Microorganisms decompose soil humus, and minerals weather (decay) releasing nutrients. Certain bacteria make critical chemical conversions in soils (carbon monoxide to carbon dioxide, changing nonusable gaseous dinitrogen of the air to usable amino acids, oxidizing undesirable sulfide to usable sulfate, and many other changes). [*See* Soil Microbiology.]

Thus, soil tests, which are used to predict the availability of one or more deficient nutrients, may indicate which nutrients are adequate or deficient. Nevertheless, the growth of the plant will depend on the suitability of the soil for plant growth. The soil must have adequate oxygen to roots, warm temperatures, adequate but not too much water, a suitable soil pH, adequate nutrients, and many additional factors. [*See* Soil Fertility.]

II. Physical Soil Properties

Soil texture is often a controlling plant growth factor. Soil texture is a measure of how clayey or sandy a soil is. A clayey soil may be very hard when dry, sticky when wet, poorly aerated, and poorly permeable to water. Plant roots may not grow very deep in clays because of poor aeration; their hard crusts when drying may inhibit seedling emergence. Clayey soils have more pore space than do sands, but the pores are smaller and slower in transmitting air and water. Clayey soils hold more water and, in temperate climates, will warm up more slowly than do sandy soils. Clayey soils are more difficult to till, often requiring that it be done within a relatively narrow range of water content.

A soil's texture can be estimated by feeling the soil with ones' fingers when it is dry and as water is added gradually. The exact amounts of clay, silt, and sand in a soil are seldom important. The general texture is,

however, important and can be measured by various methods. Laboratories can measure different sand sizes and coarser fragments (gravel and stones) by sieves. Contents of sands (2 to 0.05 mm diameter), silt (0.05–0.002 mm), and clay (less than 0.002 mm) are readily measured by the amounts that settle out of a water suspension after various times. Approximate rates of fall in water for some of the fractions are

0.5-mm-diameter (medium) sand	21.8 cm sec^{-1}
0.2-mm-diameter (fine) silt	3.5 cm sec^{-1}
0.01-mm-diameter (medium) silt	0.52 cm min^{-1}
0.002-mm-diameter (coarse) clay	0.021 cm min^{-1}
0.0002-mm-diameter (fine) clay	0.30 cm day^{-1}

The amount of soil that falls, after various selected periods of time, can be measured by the pipette method which removes a known volume of the suspended soil at the calculated depth of settling. A simpler method, the hydrometer or Bouyoucus method, measures the lessening solution density with a hydrometer as soil particles fall out of a uniform suspension.

The 12 textural classes most used are shown on the textural triangle in Fig. 1. To determine a texture from the percentages of sand, silt, and clay, adjust the triangle so that the 100% of the fraction being used (say, clay) is at the top and read the percentages of the fraction (clay, in this instance) along lines parallel to the base of the triangle. Do this for two of the fractions. Where they intersect is the soil's texture. All three fractions will intersect at the same point because the textural class assumes that sand + silt + clay = 100%.

Further textural detail is provided by indicating sand sizes, i.e., *fine* sandy loam. If particles larger than sand (coarse fragments) are present, these are named *gravel* (0.2–7.6 cm diameter), *cobble* (7.6–25 cm), *stone* (25–60 cm), and *boulder* (over 60 cm diameter). A sandy loam with coarse fragments (by volume) would be named as follows.

Less than 15% coarse fragments	Sandy loam
15 to 35% gravel-size fragments	*Gravelly* sandy loam
35 to 60% gravel-size fragments	*Very gravelly* sandy loam
Over 60% gravel-size fragments	*Extremely gravelly* sandy loam

The sand sizes and coarse fragment contents cause differences in water movement, water retention, and tillability of the soil. Knowing the kinds and amounts of clay help the analyst to predict stickiness and support strength of the soil when it is wet, hardness when

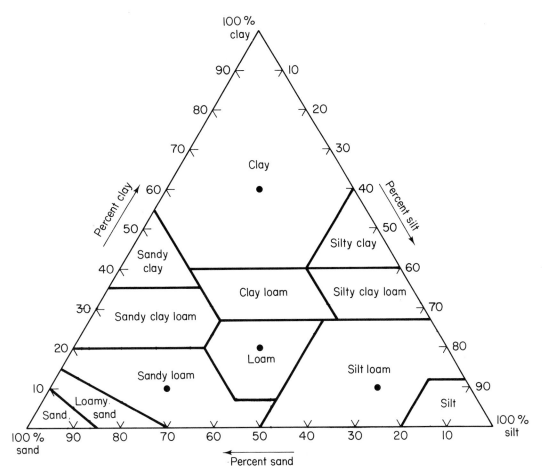

FIGURE 1 Textural triangle for soils.

it is dry, cracking when it is dry, and permeability to water and air.

Soil structure (the term *ped* is used to indicate a unit of soil structure) develops over decades and centuries of time as soils are wetted and dried, swell and shrink, and develop the organic "cements" (plus clay, iron oxides, and silica as cements) that hold (cement) particles together. Structural units are destroyed by decomposition of the humus cements or newly formed by additional humus products and mineral solution and resolidification (precipitation). Soil mixing at the surface (animals, tillage) causes surface soil structural units to have a somewhat spherical shape (granular peds), from a few 10ths millimeter to several millimeters in diameter. Vertical cracks and some horizontal cracking of a soil mass eventually produces vertically elongated prisms (prismatic or columnar) and cube-like (angular blocky or subangular blocky) shapes that range from about 5 to over 100 millimeters across. Compaction or other causes may form horizontal plates (platy) of about 1 to over 10 mm thick. Platy

structure is common below plowing depth (plow pan) and near the surface of noncultivated land as a result of compaction by animals or equipment and of frost action.

Good structure, except possibly platy structure, increases pore sizes between ped units, allowing better aeration, and water and air flow, as well as providing large spaces into which roots can grow. In clayey soils most air and water flow is down through the large pores (cracks) between peds. Tillage can reduce soil structure by mechanical breakage and speeding up humus decomposition (structure cement decomposed). Structure development in clays is slower but eventually is stronger than that in sandier soils. Sands seldom develop much structure, but the pores in sands are already large, and they easily transmit air and water.

Soil aeration indicates the ease with which air can exchange with the soil atmosphere to supply needed oxygen and to remove the carbon dioxide produced as roots respire and humus is decomposed. Sands are well aerated. Air exchange is reduced by poor structure and high clay contents and by excess water that fills the smaller pores and "bottleneck" portions of pores. Oxygen does not move readily through even thin films of water. The reduced aeration in water-blocked pores hinders the oxygen supply to roots and slows growth or causes death of most plants. Only relatively few plants (rice, for example) can bring oxygen down to their roots through their stems.

Soil mineralogy is the combination of minerals making up the bulk soil. Literally hundreds of minerals are present, each one a source of one or more of the approximately 20 important elements in soils. The quantities and kinds of minerals determine the supply of available nutrients and the toxicities that a soil supplies. The kinds of rocks and minerals also affect soil texture (sandstones and quartzite produce sandy soils, limestones and shales produce clayey soils). Some minerals (micas and feldspars) readily produce clays as they weather. Unfortunately, although the soil's fertility is related to the soil's mineralogy, the quantitative relationship of identified minerals and available nutrients is not well documented. Identification of the mineral "suite" in a soil involves microscopic and X-ray diffraction studies and is costly and time consuming. Few mineralogical analyses are done in fertility testing.

Water infiltration, percolation, and drainage are essential to allow rain and irrigation water to penetrate into soil. To avoid excess water (waterlogging), soils must allow water to drain away (percolate). Percolating water does dissolve and remove many soluble nutrients, particularly nitrates and sulfates. Leached soils may lose much of their fertility by this percolation action (leaching away soluble nutrients). Soils with large pores (sands and well-structured soils) are more easily leached than are clayey soils. [*See* SOIL DRAINAGE; SOIL–WATER RELATIONSHIPS.]

Water storage in the soil is crucial to plants in less humid climates; roots absorb water stored in soil pores. Where rainfall is infrequent, soil water must be replaced by irrigation. The quantity of water needed ranges from about 0.3 to 1.0 cm daily in warm growing periods. Sandy soils may store only about 1 to 3 cm of usable water per 30 cm (1 foot) of depth; clayey soils and clay loams may store from 3 to 6 cm of usable water per foot. As this water is absorbed, many nutrient elements dissolved in the water are carried to the plant root. Most or all of the nitrogen, sulfur, calcium, magnesium, boron, and a few other nutrients are supplied to the root surfaces in this absorbed water.

As the water in the upper foot or so of soil is used, the plant may still be able to absorb adequate water from deeper soil layers and continue to grow. However, since the surface soil layer has most of the soil humus (which supplies nitrogen plus other nutrients) and is where fertilizer is applied, water movement in the surface soil supplies many more nutrients than does water in deeper soil layers. As a soil layer dries out, the nutrients contained in that layer become less and less available. If a surface soil dries to 30 or 40 cm deep (the top 30 to 40 cm is where most of that plant's roots are growing), the plant must absorb enough water to grow from deeper soil layers; the nutrient supply will be reduced during the time water is mostly supplied from deeper soil. [*See* SOIL GENESIS, MORPHOLOGY, AND CLASSIFICATION.]

III. Chemical Soil Properties

Soil acidity alters nutrient availability and element toxicity. In soils, soil acidity or alkalinity is referred to as "soil pH" or "soil reaction." Soils that have large amounts of sodium and calcium tend to be alkaline or basic. When soils have been leached through centuries of time in high rainfall areas (over about 500 mm or 20 inches annual rainfall), soils lose much of the sodium and calcium and accumulate hydrogen ion (H^+) from the weak acid of carbon dioxide in water. The common minerals in soils also contain aluminum. The soluble aluminum in the soil forms an acidic aluminum species that adsorbs to the cation exchange capacity sites. When the soil acidity reaches a "strongly acidic" pH of about 4.5, enough soluble aluminum exists to be toxic to many plants. The most common growth problem in strongly acidic soils is aluminum toxicity; too much soluble aluminum is toxic to plant roots and slows microbial processes as well. [*See* SOIL, ACID.]

Acidic soils can be improved by neutralizing some of the acidity with an added "lime." The most common and cheapest lime is powdered limestone, but many alkaline substances (calcium oxide, wood ashes, marl, and powdered egg and sea shells) can be used. The lime is mixed into the soil at rates of about 1 to 10 metric tons per hectare every second, third, or fourth year. The amount and frequency of lime addition depends on (1) the initial acidity of the soil, (2) the total cation exchange capacity or acidic sites occupied, and (3) the sensitivity of the crop to be grown to acidity. Soil pH is usually adjusted to pH above 5.5, commonly near to pH 6.0. There are some "acid-loving" plants that do best when the pH is kept low (azaleas, blueberries, cranberries, pineapples, tea).

Soluble salts are an increasing concern. Soluble salts are the soluble remains of weathered rocks. They are mostly the ions of calcium, sodium, magnesium, chloride, sulfate, and bicarbonate. Too much soluble salts hinder water absorption by plants and cause the plant to die. One reclaims salty soils by leaching the salt from the soil. As environmental concerns increase, however, there is an increasing support to limit leaching of the salts from soils because the salts must end up in ground or surface waters. Accumulations of soluble salts are a problem; what or how to reclaim the land and dispose of the washed-out soluble salts is no less a problem.

Measurement and evaluation of the soil salt content is fairly simple. The electrical conductivity of the extract from a wetted soil is measured. The conductivity, in decisiemens per meter ($dS\ m^{-1}$) indicates the salt content. The approximate scale below is a general guide for conductivity of the extract of a saturated soil paste:

Less than 2 $dS\ m^{-1}$	No plants affected
2–4 $dS\ m^{-1}$	A few plants have reduced growth
4–8 $dS\ m^{-1}$	Many plants have reduced growth
8–16 $dS\ m^{-1}$	Most plants have reduced growth
16–30 $dS\ m^{-1}$	Most plants die or have less than 50% of normal yields.

The tolerance of plants varies enormously; a few common ones are listed below, with tolerance increasing down each list.

Least tolerant 2–6 $dS\ m^{-1}$	Moderate tolerance 6–10 $dS\ m^{-1}$	Most tolerant 10–20 $dS\ m^{-1}$
Strawberry	Blackberry	Tomato
Raspberry	Peach	Broccoli
Avocado	Onion	Spinach
Beans	Many fruits	Fig
Carrot	Pepper	Cantaloupe
Peanut	Soybean	Beets
Clovers	Lettuce	Sugarbeet
	Corn	Cotton
		Barley
		Date palm

The removal of soluble salts is done by leaching. Unfortunately, some clayey soils of high sodium content have poor permeability. In such soils, the major problem is one of soil porosity—the soil does not transmit water well enough to allow easy leaching. Soils of this type must have internal permeability increased, a costly and slow process. Mixing the profile (tillage), mixing in gypsum, or laying shallow drainage lines are all used on various soils.

Cation exchange capacity (CEC) involves a chemical surface reaction. Clays and humus have structural features that cause them to have "net negative charges." These negatively charged sites attract and hold positively charged ions. The ions most often held in the largest amounts are calcium (Ca^{2+}), magnesium (Mg^{2+}), sodium (Na^+), aluminum ($Al[OH]_2^+$ or Al^{3+}), potassium (K^+), and hydrogen (H_3O^+). Small amounts of several other cations also are held. The quantity of the CEC in soils varies from low values in sands to higher values in clays; the highest values are found in organic soils. If all the sites held calcium, the soil's exchange sites per 30 cm of depth could hold from somewhat over 1000 kg per hectare in low-CEC soils to over 10,000 kg of calcium per hectare in soils with a relatively high CEC. These exchangeable ions are not easily removed by leaching but can be replaced by other cations that are soluble in the soil solution, such as potassium or ammonium fertilizers or lime. [See SOIL, CHEMICALS: MOVEMENT AND RETENTION.]

IV. Measuring Available Nutrients

The objectives of soil fertility testing include (1) characterizing the soil to identify any problems of acidity, drainage, texture, or toxicity, (2) assessing the status of the soil's plant nutrients to know what is deficient, and (3) predicting the amount to add of each nutrient element which tests show to be deficient. The tests suitable for use are numerous. The major difficulty in any test lies in interpreting the meaning of the values obtained. A soil sample could be extracted with a variety of strong acids, weak acids, diluted acids, salt solutions, oxidizing or reducing solutions, and alkaline solutions. Each extractant would extract different amounts from subsamples of the same soil. Which value would be correct? Only a good correlation study can provide an answer.

Correlations of laboratory tests to field plot yield data are the most essential parts of the testing program. If the laboratory test values for nutrient "A" are large, the field plot plants should have enough of nutrient "A" in the soil and should not respond to nutrient "A" added as fertilizer. If the laboratory test values for "A" are small, the soil should be low in nutrient "A" and field plot plants should respond to considerable amounts of fertilizer containing nutrient "A". [See FERTILIZER MANAGEMENT AND TECHNOLOGY; SOIL MANAGEMENT.]

The only suitable lab texts are those whose values for a soil are inversely proportional to the fertilizer needed for good growth in field trials on that soil. Thus, many different laboratory tests might individually be well correlated with plant response in field tests and could be used. The perpetual search is for a well-correlated test for each plant nutrient which is quick, cheap, and easy to do but which is not susceptible to easy errors.

Nutrients which are not deficient in most soils are more difficult to correlate with laboratory tests. There are relatively few soils with obvious micronutrient, sulfur, and magnesium deficiencies on which to do the field testing. Thus, soil tests for deficiencies of many micronutrients have been correlated to only a relatively few soils; these tests are only moderately well or poorly established.

Nitrogen (N) is the most often deficient nutrient. Thus, a good predictive laboratory soil test for the amount of N needed in a soil is eagerly sought. Unfortunately, a good, widely used quick soil test for needed N is not presently available. It is the major element that needs to be added to increase growth of lawns and most other crops. N-fixing legumes (bacteria in plant roots utilize atmospheric N_2, which most plants cannot do) obtain some or all of their N by using atmospheric dinitrogen (N_2). The atmosphere has about 79% N_2. In localized areas where intensive field plot tests have been carefully made, measuring soluble nitrate to a depth of 61–92 cm (2–3 feet) has been quite satisfactory. Unfortunately, people do not like the work required to sample to those depths; most soil tests are on the 0–30 cm (1 foot depth).

The reasons why a good soil test for N has been elusive are that the N cycle is very complex—many things can happen to N, sometimes very quickly. First, temporary water logging in a soil for a few days can cause nitrate to be volatilized into the air as dinitrogen gas (denitrification). Second, microorganisms decompose soil organic materials. Most natural soil N is that N released from organic materials (humus, manures, plant wastes) as they undergo decomposition. Decomposition is accomplished by microbes whose activity is regulated by adequate water, temperature, and aeration. The nitrogen contained can be released for plant use if soil N is already high or the N released can be absorbed by organisms to become unavailable microbial tissues if soil N is low. Third, soil nitrate is very mobile in soils and is readily washed into groundwaters by percolating rains or excess irrigation. Fourth, ammonium N fertilizers (ammonium nitrate, ammonium sulfate, urea) applied on the soil surface of arid region (alkaline) soils can be lost by volatilization of the N as ammonia gas (NH_3). These many possible transformations or losses of added N fertilizers make it difficult to predict what the efficiency of added fertilizer N will be. These changes of N in the N cycle are difficult to evaluate accurately when on the site; they are even more difficult to evaluate by the soil tester in a laboratory far away. The analyst has no control over water applied, rainfall, temperature, the physical condition (aeration), or the management of the soil. [See NITROGEN CYCLING.]

Phosphorus (P) and *potassium* (K) soil tests are widely used and accepted. These two elements are the second and third most often deficient plant nutrients. Phosphorus has low solubility in soils and can be deficient in any climatic area, in sandy soils, in intensively weathered soils (stable tropical lands), and in soils with crops having high P demands (vegetables, legumes, potatoes). Only about 10 to 30% of added soluble P fertilizers is used by the crop to which it is added; the rest forms low-solubility mineral precipitates, but stays in the soil. Thus, three to five times more P is added than is used. Yet, the carryover P (that added but not used that season) has little of it available to the next crop. The soil P content will gradually increase in regularly fertilized soils.

Maximum conversion of soluble P to low-solubility P compounds occurs in soils with high contents of soluble calcium or lime (calcium carbonates) and particularly in soils high in free iron oxides (sesquioxides). Weathered soil materials especially in highly weathered tropical soils are high in iron oxides. The weathered tropical soils can have as high as 70 to 80% sesquioxides, to which P readily and strongly adsorbs. Only small portions of added P remain soluble to be used during the growing season. In such soils, placing the P in small "bands" 5 to 10 cm deep and 5 to 10 cm to the side of the planted seed is often the most effective application. The major chemical extractants used for phosphorus soil tests are the following:

- For acidic soils
    Bray No. 1: dilute HCl and dilute NH_4F
    Mehlich No. 1: dilute HCl and dilute H_2SO_4

- For alkaline and calcareous soils
  Olsen test: dilute $NaHCO_3$ at pH 8.5
  Ammonium bicarbonate at pH 7.5

Each of these extractants is correlated with field trials to establish a table of test values as criteria of the fertilizer P needed for various crop groups.

Potassium (K) forms mostly soluble minerals in soils even though its common mineral sources (micas and feldspars) have K in a very low-solubility form. Because K is so slowly soluble from its source minerals, the major K source for a crop is the soil's soluble and exchangeable K. The negative charges on clays and soil humus hold positively charged ions (called cations, cat-i-ons). Most of the K used by plants is from soil's exchangeable K plus any soluble K in the soil solution. Almost any test which measures mostly the exchangeable K has given fairly good correlation to the needs for added K fertilizer. The most common extractant for exchangeable K is ammonium acetate, but various salt solutions, dilute strong acids, and the ammonium bicarbonate extract used for the P test have all been used.

Soils needing added K are usually sandy soils and those acidic soils in humid climates. In arid (irrigated) regions, little or none of the K solubilized by weathering is removed by leaching (percolating rainwaters). However, in high-rainfall, permeable soils, rains can wash out K during the decades and centuries of weathering and leaching. High-K-demand crops (potatoes, bananas, and other sugar- and starch-producing crops) may benefit from additions of fertilizer K even though the soils are normally adequate in K for most crops.

Sulfur (S) is much less likely to be deficient than are N, P, and K. In the past several decades, considerable sulfur was added to soils (1) as a constituent of the fertilizers ammonium sulfate, potassium sulfate, and regular superphosphate; (2) as fallout of "acid rain," which contains sulfuric acid; and (3) as components of some pesticides. These sources of S are still added but less often and in lesser amounts. The higher crop yields and fewer incidental S additions have caused S deficiency to be more common.

Predicting S needs by soil tests has many of the same problems as those mentioned for N. The S cycle has several kinds of losses. Sulfur is volatilized as sulfide gas in anaerobic waterlogged soils, the soluble "end product"—sulfate—is readily leached, and sulfur released during decomposition of organic matter can be made into bodies of new microbes. Because S is needed in much smaller amounts than is N and

because S does come from both humus and various minerals (gypsum, pyrites, others), S is less often deficient than N, P, or K. Consequently, less work on soil tests has been done for S than has been done for N, P, and K.

In some areas where S deficiency is widespread and economically quite important, adequate soil tests have been developed. They are somewhat similar to those for N, which measure the soluble end product of microbial action. For sulfur, this end product is sulfate. The amount of soluble sulfate in the top 61 cm (2 feet) or 92 cm (3 feet) has given the best correlation to plant response in field plots. Unfortunately, soil tests to evaluate S needs are not usually reliable. Often information on the humus content and soil texture is useful; S deficiency is most likely in more sandy, low-humus, acidic soils.

The *micronutrients* boron (B), iron (Fe), zinc (Zn), copper (Cu), manganese (Mn), chloride (Cl), and molybdenum (Mo) are much less often deficient than are N, P, K, S, Ca, and Mg. In various high-rainfall, leached soils boron may be largely washed away and be deficient. Its mineral source tourmaline is of very low solubility; its mineral fertilizer source is borax, a water-soluble deposit. Overall, B is the most commonly deficient micronutrient. Its most common soil test—soluble B in boiling water—is a good test but not convenient to do. Other tests are being studied.

A spectacular and colorful plant deficiency is caused by inadequate iron (Fe); the young leaves of the plant become chlorotic (yellowed) between veins while veins remain green. In extreme cases, leaves may be almost white. Iron deficiency is poorly understood and its correction is the most difficult of all nutrients to accomplish. It is fortunate that relatively few soils and crops have severe Fe deficiency. Most soils have several percentage Fe contents but iron compounds are extremely low in solubility. Plants with Fe deficiency may sometimes contain more Fe than do other plants which are not deficient. Why the plant is deficient is usually unexplained. Because Fe forms such low-solubility compounds when added to soil, correcting deficiencies is usually done by applying a soluble Fe to the foliage. Organic materials (chelates) that bind the Fe keeping the Fe mobile are the most common carriers of iron.

Diagnosing or predicting iron deficiency by soil testing is difficult. Most soil iron moving to roots is believed to do so as naturally produced chelates. So, soil tests employ an extracting solution containing a small concentration of the chelate DTPA (diethylenetriaminepentaacetic acid). Typical extraction values in DTPA for Fe, Zn, Mn, and Cu are shown below:

	Fe	Zn	Cu	Mn
	(mg kg^{-1}			
Low (deficient)	0–2.5	0–0.5	0–0.2	0–1.0
Marginal (barely adequate)	2.6–4.5	0.6–1.0	?	?
High (sufficient)	4.5+	1.0+	1.0+	2.0+

The tests are fair to good where well correlated to field plots. However, there have been limited numbers of studies done and there are relatively few soils exhibiting iron deficiencies. The quality of the soil tests are localized to areas where good correlation work has been done. Alkaline (arid-region) soils are more likely to have iron deficiency than are acidic (humid area) soils. Deficiency is common on peaches, raspberries, some soybeans, roses, and several other ornamental flowers and evergreens.

Soils tests for Zn, Cu, and Mn also are somewhat approximate; they are valuable where good correlation field studies have been done. Values for these are given in a previous tabulation under iron. An extraction with the DTPA chelate, as was done with iron, is a common method to test for available Zn, Cu, and Mn. The most likely soils to have Zn deficiency are arid lands. Deficiency of Zn is common in beans, corn, grapes, sorghum, citrus, and various deciduous fruits.

Copper is infrequently deficient. Since Cu bonds tightly to certain organic groups, Cu is commonly deficient in certain organic soils (peats or mucks). Crops sensitive to low copper levels include alfalfa, rice, barley, citrus, and rice. *Manganese* is probably as often toxic (in strongly acidic soils) as it is deficient. As with Fe, Zn, and Cu, it is less soluble in high pH (alkaline) soils; Mn deficiency is most common in arid region soils. However, where it has been solubilized and leached out of acidic soils in high rainfall areas, Mn is deficient.

Soil tests for Cu and Mn deficiencies are the DTPA extraction but are in limited use and are somewhat approximate except where good extensive correlation has been done. Crops sensitive to low Mn include alfalfa, citrus, fruits, and potatoes. Specific Mn toxicity has been observed in strongly acidic soils growing cotton (crinkle leaf), tobacco, soybeans, and various fruit trees.

V. Plant Growth, Soil Fertility, and Environmental Pollution

Increases in populations, manufacturing, and luxuriant living coupled with the throw-it-away mentality all help to put stress on our earth, water, and air. Many soil tests are increasingly used (1) to predict those problem pollutants that can affect plant growth and (2) to more accurately predict fertilizer needs as one mechanism to minimize pollution. A well-known saying says, "If it ain't broke, don't fix it." The priority need in environmental pollution is to identify that, indeed, pollution exists. When that is determined, it is then possible to ascertain the identity, concentration, hazard, and source of the pollutant. [*See* SOIL POLLUTION.]

Pollution is defined as the addition of any substance to air, water, or soil which makes that resource less desirable for people's use. Thus, pollution can be substances of undesirable odor or taste, heat, increasing "hardness" (calcium and magnesium) in water, toxins, and many other materials. Pollutants can be many things and are frequently not poisons. Agriculture has been blamed for many pollutants, many of which do also come from urban and city runoff waters and volatile chemicals used by all people. This section will briefly review soil tests and problems associated with (1) the nutrients nitrogen (nitrates) and phosphorus (phosphates), (2) heavy metals, (3) toxic organics other than pesticides, and (4) residual pesticides.

Excess *nitrates* in water can cause the health hazard methemoglobinemia (*blue baby disease* or oxygen deficiency) and the less serious *eutrophication* (growth of algae in nutrient-rich water eventually leading to oxygen-depleted waters). Not only is methemoglobinemia frequently a serious problem to young mammals, but it can also, in high concentrations, cause various levels of brain damage and have other effects to adults. Excess nitrate is reduced to nitrite by microorganisms in the mammal digestive tract. Young mammals lack the stomach acidity to hinder this transformation. The nitrite moves into the blood and oxidizes the oxygen carrier so it cannot carry oxygen to the body. Enough nitrate (about 70% of the oxygen carrier changed) can cause the young mammal to suffocate (= blue baby disease = cyanosis). With less nitrate, various damage, but not death, is possible. Drinking water, and thus drinking water sources (groundwater and surface waters) must not exceed 45 parts per million as nitrate. Eating foods high in nitrate (highly N-fertilized forage or "green" vegetables) may add to the nitrate in the body.

Soil testing for nitrates leaving fields or moving deep into groundwaters is increasing. The tests are simple chemically. The difficulty is in collecting deep samples (several feet below crop roots or from groundwaters) and in being able to identify the surface area from which any measured nitrates originated. A third problem is how to increase N fertilization efficiency to avoid overuse. How does one predict from soil tests the amount of fertilizer nitrogen to add, when it should be added, and how it should be added to minimize excess nitrate loss to waters? This needs to be accomplished without allowing a deficiency for the plant's use nor adding excessively to the costs of application. Research on these problems to determine the best practices for efficient yet adequate fertilizer applications is eagerly in progress.

Other forms of nitrogen are also of concern. Nitrogen oxides (burning of organic wastes and fossil fuels) increase the acidity of rain, aid in depletion of the ozone layer (that protects us from excessive ultraviolet or "tanning" rays), and accentuate some respiratory illnesses. Nitrosamines in many foods are increased by nitrite production and are related to formation of some cancers.

Phosphorus is not a health hazard to people. However, as the most often limiting nutrient in water (it has low solubility), added phosphate is the major cause of *eutrophication*. As the algae grow, die, and are decomposed, the waters' oxygen is lowered. In severe conditions fish and other water life die because of insufficient oxygen. Some have referred to such low-oxygen waters as "dead waters." Many older detergents had a soluble hexametaphosphate as a major portion of its "active" cleaning ingredient. An increase in water's phosphorus can also originate from P adsorbed onto soil particles which are eroded into surface waters.

Soil and water tests are used to ascertain the extent of pollution by nitrates and phosphates. Once the areas and extent of pollution are known, more efficient fertilizer and erosion-control practices can be emphasized as needed. Because phosphorus has low solubility and no volatile forms, the mechanisms to reduce pollution by phosphate can be quite different and are usually less complicated than is reduction of pollution by nitrogen.

Heavy metals are considered a serious health-hazard pollutant. Heavy metals are elements, so they never break down further. Usually they have low solubility and mobility in soils; once they contaminate a soil or lake bed, they move in small amounts and only short distances. There are many metals involved which include cadmium (Cd), mercury (Hg), lead (Pb), chromium (Cr), nickel (Ni), zinc (Zn), copper (Cu), beryllium (Be), selenium (Se), arsenic (As), and many others. Their sources are many: burning fossil fuels, sewage sludges, chemical manufacturing wastes,

smelter smoke, electroplating liquid wastes, glazes, putty, paints, and tanning plant liquid wastes.

Soil, water, and plant testing are used to quantify pollutants in soil, water, and foods. Several of these metals (for example Zn and Cu) are plant and animal nutrients and are needed in small amounts, but they are toxic in larger amounts. The plant will take up its nutrients readily but will tend to partially exclude nonnutrients from uptake. Cadmium is one notable exception. Cadmium is readily absorbed and can become a major problem in foods eaten by animals (including people). Monitoring hazardous levels of Cd and other heavy metals is required by law in many states and involves lands on which sewage sludge and some other additives high in hazardous metals are applied.

Various *toxic organics* are common hazards. Excluding pesticides, discussed later in this article, toxic organics include spilled fuels, solvents, spray oils, various materials in sewage sludges, and food processing wastes. The characteristics and variety of these hazards are almost unlimited. Gas, oil, fuel oil, dormant oils, grease solvents, washing detergents, wood preservatives, paint and its wastes, and many other materials can, in particular instances, become hazardous contaminants. The testing for these materials can be complex and require many kinds of instruments and well-trained chemists. [*See* Pest Management, Chemical Control.]

Residual pesticides receive the most scrutiny from those concerned with pollution in agricultural processes. These materials are intended as "pest killers." Many pesticides are harmful also to people. Numerous pesticides are sufficiently hazardous enough that zero measurable levels are allowed in harvested foods. Soil samples and plant tissues are tested for pesticide residues extensively to protect the public against nonpermitted pesticide accumulations. Most analyses are for minute amounts (parts per million parts and parts per billion parts). These residue tests require careful analysis and sensitive gas chromatographs and other expensive equipment for confident and quantitative measurements.

Bibliography

Brady, N. C. (1990). "The Nature and Properties of Soils," 10th Ed. Macmillan, New York.

Miller, R. W., and Donahue, R. L. (1990). "Soils—An Introduction to Soils and Plant Growth," 6th Ed. Prentice–Hall, Englewood Cliffs, NJ.

Tisdale, S. L., Nelson, W. L., Beaton, J. D., and Havlin, J. L. (1993). "Soil Fertility and Fertilizers," 5th Ed. Macmillan, New York.

Soil–Water Relationships

M. B. KIRKHAM, *Kansas State University*

Glossary

Available water Water in soil between field capacity and permanent wilting point; variable units (e.g., percentage or millimeters of equivalent surface water)

Capillary conductivity Hydraulic conductivity under unsaturated conditions; the term is now considered to be obsolete; same units as for hydraulic conductivity (see Diffusivity)

Darcy's law A law relating the quantity of water flowing through the soil per unit time to the hydraulic gradient; the proportionality constant in the law is the hydraulic conductivity; the Darcy law is needed to solve flow problems in saturated and unsaturated soils

Diffusivity Unsaturated hydraulic conductivity times the rate of change of soil matric potential with water content; units: mm^2/sec

Hydraulic conductivity Proportionality constant in Darcy's law; it is considered to be a constant under saturated conditions, but changes with the moisture content under unsaturated conditions; variable units, but often given as m/sec or m/day

Hydraulic gradient In Darcy's law, the difference in the hydraulic head at two points under consideration in the soil divided by the distance between the points; a reference level must be specified; it is a slope (gradient); units: a length divided by a length

Hydraulic head Elevation (height) with respect to a specified reference level, usually the soil surface, at which water stands in a piezometer in water-saturated soil; the definition of hydraulic head can be extended to soil above the water table, if the piezometer is replaced by a tensiometer; the hydraulic head in either case is the sum of gravitational and pressure potentials; units: a length

Infiltration Entry of water into soil; infiltration rate gives the volume of water entering a specified cross-sectional area of soil per unit time; units of infiltration rate: usually expressed as m/sec or m/day

Nonlimiting water range Range of water that can be absorbed by plant roots, and may be smaller than the available water range; the NLWR acknowledges that both aeration and mechanical resistance affect available water; on one end of the scale, oxygen limits root growth and on the other end of the scale, mechanical resistance restricts root growth; the NLWR becomes narrower as bulk density and aeration limit root growth; same units as for available water

Preferential flow Flow of water in continuous non-capillary-sized voids (e.g., cracks, root channels, worm holes) or in zones of locally high conductivity in capillary-sized pores; in preferential flow, water bypasses the matrix pore space

Sorptivity Measure of the ability of soil to attract water by capillary action; units: $mm/sec^{1/2}$

Tension infiltrometer Instrument that can control preferential flow of water through the macropores and soil cracks; the tension infiltrometer evolved into the disc permeameter, which is used when three-dimensional infiltration is being considered; with these instruments, macropore flow is controlled by applying water to soil at water potentials less than zero

Soil–water relationships can be defined as the interactions between water and the solid and porous parts of the soil. For a typical soil, air and water take up

Encyclopedia of Agricultural Science, Volume 4 Copyright © 1994 by Academic Press, Inc. All rights of reproduction in any form reserved.

50% of the space. Organic matter and mineral matter take up the other 50% (Fig. 1). At true saturation, all of the pores are filled with liquid water. At optimum moisture contents for plant growth, the air and water space are about equal, each about 25% of the soil volume. This article will address how the water, solid particles, and pores in the soil are interrelated.

I. Terminology

A. Water Content

Two important expressions used to describe the state of water in the soil are *water content* and *water potential*. The first term gives the amount of water in the soil either by weight or volume and is defined as the water lost from the soil upon drying to constant mass at 105°C. It is expressed either in units of mass of water per unit mass of dry soil (kg/kg) or in units of volume of water per unit bulk volume of soil (m^3/m^3).

B. Water Potential

The second expression utilizies the potential energy status of a small parcel of water in the soil. All water in the soil is subjected to force fields originating from four main factors: the presence of the solid phase (the matrix); the gravitational field; any dissolved salts; and the action of external gas or water pressure. If the force fields in the soil are compared to a reference point, then they can be expressed on a potential energy basis, and each of the four factors can be assigned a separate potential energy value. The sum of these four potential energy values is called the *water potential* of the soil or the *total water potential* to emphasize that it comprises several factors. The reference point for

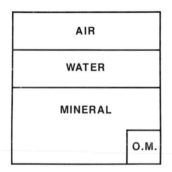

FIGURE 1 Space in a soil. (From Kirkham, D., and Powers, W. L. Copyright © (1972). "Advanced Soil Physics," p. 1. Reprinted by permission of John Wiley and Sons, Inc. Wiley, New York.)

these potential energies is taken as pure free water at some specified height or elevation. Because water is held in the soil by forces of adsorption, absorption, cohesion, and solution, soil water is usually not capable of doing as much work as pure free water. Hence, the water potential is normally negative.

1. Matric (Capillary) Potential

The *matric potential energy* or the *matric potential* is the portion of the water potential that can be attributed to the attraction of the soil matrix for water. The matric potential used to be called the *capillary potential*, because, over a large part of its range, the matric potential is due to capillary action akin to the rise of water in small, cylindrical capillary tubes. However, as the water content decreases in a porous material, water that is held in pores due to capillarity becomes negligibly small, when compared to the water held directly on particle surfaces. The term *matric potential*, therefore, covers phenomena beyond those for which a capillary analogy is appropriate.

The matric potential may be determined with a tensiometer, which measures matric potential of water *in situ*. (The word *tensiometer* refers to the fact that it measures the *soil moisture tension*, a term no longer used in defining the components of the water potential. Soil moisture tension has been represented often with a positive sign, in which case it can be considered to be numerically equivalent, but opposite in sign to the matric potential.) The instrument consists of a porous, permeable ceramic cup connected through a water-filled tube to a manometer, vacuum gauge, or other pressure-measuring device. Water pressure in the manometer comes into equilibrium with the adjacent soil through flow across the ceramic cup. The height of the liquid column at this time is an index of matric potential.

The units used to measure matric potential, and other potentials, become evident, when we consider measurement of matric potential with a tensiometer. The force per unit area, or negative pressure of the water in the porous cup, is the weight per unit cross-section of the hanging column. This is the volume of the column divided by the area multiplied by the density of the liquid water and the acceleration of gravity:

$$P = F/A = mg/A = (V)(\rho_w)(g/A) = (hA\rho_w\, g)/A = h\rho_w g, \tag{1}$$

where P = pressure; F = force; m = mass; g = acceleration due to gravity; A = area; V = volume; ρ_w = density of water; h = height, and the potential (negative pressure) is in units of potential energy or work per unit volume. In the centimeter–gram–second (cgs) system of units, 1020 cm of water would exert a negative pressure of

$$(1020 \text{ cm})(1 \text{ g/cm}^3)(980 \text{ cm/sec}^2) = 999{,}600 \text{ dyne/cm}^2 \qquad (2)$$

or 1×10^6 dyne/cm^2 = 1 bar, because, in cgs pressure units, 1 bar = 1×10^6 dyne/cm^2. The SI (Système International) unit for pressure is the Pascal, which is 1 Newton per square meter and thus 10 bars = 1 MPa or 1 MegaPascal. The unit (dyne/cm^2) is the same as potential energy/volume, because if we multiply the top and bottom of the fraction, F/A, in Eq. (1) by 1 cm (= cm/cm = unity), we get work/volume = potential energy/volume:

$$[(\text{dyne})(\text{cm})]/[(\text{cm}^2)(\text{cm})] = \text{potential energy/volume} = \text{erg/cm}^3,$$

because 1 dyne-cm = 1 erg.

Units of potential energy per unit volume can be converted to units of potential energy per unit mass by dividing by the density of water, which we shall take to be 1 g/cm^3:

$$(1 \times 10^6 \text{ dyne/cm}^2)/1 \text{ g/cm}^3 = 1 \times 10^6 \text{ dyne-cm/}$$
$$\text{g} = 1 \times 10^6 \text{ erg/g} = 100 \text{ J/kg},$$

because 1 joule = 1×10^7 ergs. Or, 1 bar can be considered to be the equivalent of 100 J/kg. Note that the units of matric potential are not equal to potential energy units (ergs; joules), but can be given in units of potential energy/vol or potential energy/mass.

2. Gravitational Potential

The *gravitational potential energy* or the *gravitational potential* is the potential energy associated with vertical position. The reference height or datum assigned can vary according to need and is often based on utility. It is generally convenient to keep the reference level sufficiently low so that one does not get negative values. Solutions to problems are prone to error when negative numbers are used. Land surveyors take their datum at a level below the lowest level that they expect to encounter on their survey. Then all of their levels will be positive. Soil scientists often take either the soil surface or the groundwater level as the reference level. The reference level usually depends upon the direction of water movement: rising or infiltration. If the reference level is below the point in question, work must be done on the water and the gravity potential is positive; if the level is above, work is done by the water and the gravity potential is negative.

3. Solute Potential

The *solute potential energy* or *solute potential* is the portion of the water potential that can be attributed to the attraction of solutes for water. If one has pure water and solution separated by a membrane, pressure will build up on the solution side of the membrane that is equivalent to the energy difference in water on the two sides of the membrane. This pressure, which is usually called the *osmotic pressure*, is numerically equivalent, but opposite in sign, to the solute potential. The solute potential is often called the *osmotic potential*. The osmotic potential is usually ignored in determining water movement in the soil, unless the soil is saline.

4. Pressure Potential

The *pressure potential energy* or *pressure potential* is the potential energy due to the weight of water at a point under consideration, or to gas pressure which is different from what exists at a reference position. Sometimes this pressure potential energy is divided into two separate components: the *air pressure potential*, which occurs under unsaturated conditions when the soil has an air phase, and the *hydrostatic pressure potential*, which occurs when the soil is saturated and there is a hydrostatic pressure from an overlying water phase. In saturated soil, the pressure potential is sometimes called the *piezometric potential*, because it can be measured with a *piezometer*. A piezometer is a tube placed in soil with its top end open to the atmosphere. It also may have openings in the wall at the point where the pressure measurement is to be taken. The level of water in the tube, measured from a suitable reference, is the piezometer reading. Pressure potentials due to gas may be measured with manometers.

5. Other Potentials Defined

Occasionally, a *tensiometer pressure potential*, which is the potential measured with a tensiometer, is defined. The matric potential differs from the potential measured with a tensiometer, because the soil air pressure is maintained at the reference pressure. The reference pressure can be atmospheric pressure. However, the difference between atmospheric pressure and air pressure in the soil is usually ignored, and the potential measured with a tensiometer is considered to be the matric potential. But if one were comparing measurements of matric potential made with a tensiometer on top of a mountain and at sea level, then one would have to consider air pressure differences.

Other potentials may be defined according to need, such as an *overburden potential*, which occurs when the soil is free to move and some part of its weight becomes involved as a force acting upon water at the point in question. But, when a potential that is not zero is neglected, it must be assumed that it is implicitly included in one of those which is explicit in the definition. For example, when overburden potential is neglected, it becomes implicit in the pressure potential or matric potential.

Water moves in response to differences in water potential. The difference is called the *water potential difference*. The *water potential gradient* is the potential difference per unit distance of flow. Water moves from high potential energy to low potential energy. Under nonsaline, unsaturated conditions, the two most important potentials in the soil are the matric potential and the gravitational potential, and both must be considered in determining the direction of flow of water. Under nonsaline, saturated conditions, the two most important potentials in the soil are the (hydrostatic) pressure potential and the gravitational potential, and the difference in the sum of these two potentials, called the *hydraulic head difference*, governs the soil water flow.

6. Hydraulic Head

The *hydraulic head* is the elevation (height) with respect to a specified reference level, usually the soil surface, at which water stands in a piezometer in water-saturated soil. The definition of hydraulic head can be extended to soil above the water table, if the piezometer is replaced by a tensiometer. The hydraulic head in either case is the sum of gravitational and pressure potentials. For unsaturated soil, the pressure potential is the matric potential with a change in sign as noted earlier. Engineers use the term hydraulic head, because it is easier to use units of length than units of potential energy.

Potential energies as expressed as hydraulic heads are the foundation of engineering practice and are used in studies of tile drainage, irrigation, and transport of water and plant nutrients or pollutants in soil. Potentials are at the basis of all saturated and unsaturated flow problems in which the Darcy law, to be defined, is used.

We can see why units of matric potential energy can be expressed in units of length, or head units, if we look at Eq. (1). In Eq. (1), we note that the values (ρ_w and g) in the last term of Eq. (1) can be considered constant on earth, but not the height, h. Acceleration due to gravity does vary with latitude and elevation, according to Helmert's equation (given in handbooks), but the variation is minor. For example, at

Manhattan, Kansas (325 m above sea level; 39° 12′ latitude), we find from Helmert's equation that $g = 979.99$ cm/sec^2, which rounds off to 980 cm/sec^2, the value normally used in solving equations with g. Because g and ρ_w are constant, we can measure matric potential by measuring the height of water in a tensiometer with a ruler. The gravity potential can be measured with a ruler, too, because it is based on the distance above or below a reference point. Therefore, we can get the total head of water under unsaturated conditions (matric potential + gravitational potential) with just a ruler. If the water is under saturated conditions, we can get the total head of water by measuring the height of water in a piezometer with respect to its bottom end and adding this height to the height due to gravity, which is the distance of the bottom end of the piezometer down to the reference level.

II. Static Water

Water is attracted into soil pores predominantly because of the attraction of water to other surfaces (adhesion) and because of capillarity. Surface tension controls the rise or fall of a liquid in a capillary tube. Therefore, we shall now consider surface tension and rise and fall of water in soil pores.

A. Surface Tension

An object is under tension if a pull is being exerted on it. *Tension* is a pull or stretching force per unit area (F/A). The term *surface tension* should not be confused with tension. Surface tension, or more specifically, the *surface tension coefficient*, is an energy per unit area or, equivalently, a force per unit length. But tension is a force per unit area.

Pierre Simon Laplace, the great French mathematician (1749–1827), was the first person to explain mathematically surface tension (1806). A molecule in the body of a fluid is attracted equally from all sides. But a molecule at the surface undergoes a resultant inward pull, because there are no molecules above the liquid causing attraction. Hence, molecules in the surface have a stronger tendency to move to the interior of the liquid than molecules in the interior have to move to the surface. What results is a tendency for any body of liquid to minimize its surface area. This tendency is often opposed by external forces acting on the body of liquid, such as gravity acting on a water drop resting on a flat surface or adhesive forces between water and other materials. Thus, the actual surface may not be an absolute minimum, but rather a minimum depending on the conditions in which the body of liquid is found. Because of surface tension, a thin razor blade or a water beetle can float on the surface of water without breaking through.

B. Water in Capillaries

Surface tension is used to determine the height of rise in capillary tubes. The equation for the height of rise, h_c, of liquid in a capillary tube is:

$$h_c = (2\sigma \cos \alpha)/(r\rho g), \tag{3}$$

where σ = surface tension (surface tension coefficient) of the liquid (units of g/s^2 or dyne/cm), α = contact angle between the liquid and tube, r = radius of tube (cm), ρ = density of liquid (g/cm^3), and g = acceleration due to gravity (cm/s^2). The equation for the height of rise is derived in standard physics textbooks.

C. Soil Moisture Characteristic Curve

If one keeps track of the moisture withdrawn from an initially saturated soil core, as greater tension is successively applied, and then plots on the x axis (abscissa) water content (moisture percent by volume in the soil) (not the water sucked out) and on the y axis (ordinate), tension head (positive units) or matric potential (negative units), the curve so obtained will be the so-called *moisture characteristic* (ABCD in Fig. 2). The moisture percentage on such a curve may be based on oven-dry weight, but in drainage work, as in the figure, the soil moisture characteristic is most useful when the moisture is expressed on a volume basis, because then the surface centimeters (depth) of irrigation water needed to replenish moisture in the sample is obtained from the characteristic. For example, a moisture percentage of 30% by volume at saturation means that, for a 10-cm dry soil layer, one needs to apply 3 cm of water to the surface to bring the 10 cm to saturation.

D. Falling and Rising Water Table: Hysteresis

In Fig. 2, one may think of the tension as being produced by a falling water table. One may verify the following on the figure: Initially (point A), the bulk volume of the soil has all of its pore space, that is, 50% of its bulk volume, filled with water. For 20 cm depth of water table, the moisture percentage at the

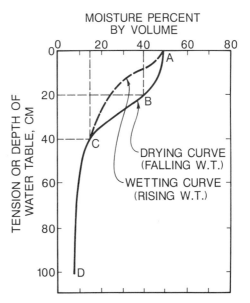

FIGURE 2 A soil moisture characteristic for a loam soil. (From Kirkham, D. (1961). "Lectures on Agricultural Drainage," p. 24. Institute of Land Reclamation, College of Agriculture, Alexandria University, Alexandria, Egypt.

soil surface is 40%; for 40 cm depth of water table, 15%; and for 100 cm depth, 8%. In Fig. 2, if the water table had fallen to 40 cm depth and then risen slowly to the soil surface, the moisture percentages would be those corresponding to the dashed line. The failure of the curve to retrace itself in the reverse direction is called *hysteresis*. In Fig. 2, the soil moisture characteristic ABCD is that of a loam. For finer-textured soils, the curves would be higher. If, for Fig. 2, the water table for the dashed curve had not risen slowly, the moisture percentage for zero depth of water table would be, because of trapped air, less than 50%. Even if the water table rises slowly, there is usually a small amount of trapped air, and, when hysteresis loops are determined experimentally, they are not seen to return to the original point.

If the soil is saturated to the surface and covered by a thin layer of water, there will be no tension in the soil pores (voids). If the water table falls through the soil surface, tension will develop in the soil pores. If the pores are of the same diameter, they will start to drain and the water level in them will fall the same distance the water table falls. The maximum tension that the falling water table can exert on a soil pore at the soil surface will be $\rho_w g h$ dynes/cm², where h is the depth of the water table below the soil surface. If the diameter of the pore is too large to support this tension, the pore will not be subject to the maximum tension.

However, pores in the soil are not the same diameter. Figure 3 illustrates what happens in a soil pore of variable diameter, when the water table falls for six different cases of water table fall. The depth of soil and the length of the pore channel for each case is taken as 15 cm, so that, for the heights of capillary rise shown, the diameter of tube nearest the surface is calculated to be 0.075. Thus, the scale in the horizontal direction is, as seen in the figure (2/0.075 =), 27-fold that of the vertical direction. In part A of the figure, the soil is shown saturated to the surface. In parts B, C, D, E, and F, the water table is shown at successively greater depths. In part B, 4 cm height of water column is held; in part C, also 4 cm. In part D only sufficient water curvature has developed in the narrow neck to support about 5 cm height of water. In part E additional curvature has developed in the narrow neck, such that about 8 cm height of water is supported. In part E the water table is at 13 cm depth and in part F it is at 15 cm depth, a drop of 2 cm. In dropping these 2 cm, the ability of the narrow neck to support the needed 2 cm is exceeded and the pore then empties suddenly and discontinuously to about the level of the water table. This example shows that the emptying of individual pores occurs discontinuously. When the water is removed from a large number of pores, as for any soil sample,

a graph of moisture percentage versus tension (or matric potential) does not show the discontinuous nature of the pore-emptying process. The example also shows that soil pores can be filled with water (saturated), yet the water is under tension in the pores.

In Fig. 4, at the left, three shapes of pores are shown when the water table has fallen from a level A to the level B. The same three pores are shown at the right when the water table has risen from a level C (say) to the level B. At the left, the pores are filled up to the height h_c, the capillary height of rise. At the right, only one pore is filled up to the height h_c; one pore is empty; and one is partially filled. The soil at the left, for the water table falling, has a much higher moisture percentage than the soil at the right for the water table rising.

Figure 4 also gives a physical picture for hysteresis shown in Fig. 2. A soil that is being wet up from a rising water table holds less water than a soil that is being dried down. For the falling water table, water is held in tubes of supercapillary size, if there is a restriction of capillary size at or below the height of capillary lift. Water can be drawn up above a water table, however, only by a continuous capillary opening without supercapillary enlargements. Hence, more water is held in the *capillary fringe*, which is the thickness of saturated water held by capillarity above the water table, above a sinking water table than above a rising water table. These concepts were explained in 1937 by Cyrus Fisher Tolman of Stanford University in his classic book, *Ground Water*.

One concludes from Fig. 4 that applications of subirrigation water to raise the water table will not result in the same amount of moisture in the capillary fringe as will applications of surface water. Subirrigation would provide more soil aeration than surface addition of water. This may be desirable in some cases.

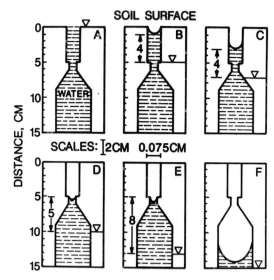

FIGURE 3 The falling water table in a soil pore (channel) of variable diameter. Note the difference in the vertical and horizontal scales. The water table is indicated by an inverted Greek "delta." (From Kirkham, D. (1961). "Lectures on Agricultural Drainage," p. 27. Institute of Land Reclamation, College of Agriculture, Alexandria University, Alexandria, Egypt.

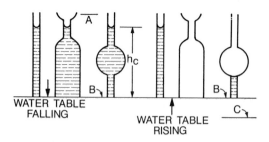

FIGURE 4 Soil pore conditions for a falling and for a rising water table. (From Kirkham, D. (1961). "Lectures on Agricultural Drainage," p. 28. Institute of Land Reclamation, College of Agriculture, Alexandria University, Alexandria, Egypt.

III. Dynamic Water

A. Saturated Soil

1. Darcy's Law

Understanding movement of water in saturated soil is important in drainage and groundwater studies. The French hydraulic engineer, Henry Philibert Gaspard Darcy (1803–1858) determined experimentally the law that governs the flow of water through saturated soil (1856). It is called *Darcy's law* and to illustrate it, let us consider Fig. 5, which shows water flowing through a soil column of length L and cross-sectional area, A.

The law can be stated as follows:

$$Q = -KA(h_2 - h_1)/(z_2 - z_1), \qquad (4)$$

where Q is the quantity of water per second such as in cubic centimeters per second, often called the *flux*; K, centimeters per second, is the *hydraulic conductivity* (the law defines K); heads h_1 and h_2 and distances z_1 and z_2 are as shown in Fig. 5. The reference level here is the x, y plane. The head h_1 is the hydraulic head for all points at the bottom of the soil column, that is, at $z = z_1$, and similarly the head h_2 applies to all points at the top of the soil column, $z = z_2$. The length of the column is $z_2 - z_1 = L$. The negative sign in the Darcy equation is used so that a positive value of Q will indicate flow in the positive z direction. The positive z direction is measured from z_1 to z_2. In the Darcy law equation, the quantity $(h_2 - h_1)/(z_2 - z_1)$ is called the *hydraulic gradient i*; the ratio Q/A is called the flux per unit cross-section or *flux density* $(cm^3/sec)/cm^2$. The ratio Q/A is also called the *Darcy velocity v* or, very often, just the *velocity v*. Therefore,

Darcy's law may be written as $v = -Ki$. The *actual velocity* of the water in the soil is much greater than the Darcy velocity. The actual velocity is on the average v/f, where f is the *porosity* or the *wetted porosity* to emphasize that there is no air in the pores. The porosity is the volume of pores in a soil sample divided by the bulk volume of the sample. The pores can be filled with air and/or water. The percentage porosity in the soil can be determined from the following equation:

$$\% \text{ porosity} = 100\% - (\text{bulk density}/\text{particle density}) \times 100. \qquad (5)$$

The Darcy velocity v means more than flux per unit area Q/A. In Fig. 5, suppose that the supply of water shown dripping into the soil column is abruptly cut off during a short time interval Δt during which h_2 decreases by Δh. We let Δq be the volume of water flowing downward through the soil in Δt. Because Q is the flow per second, we may write Δq as $\Delta q = Q\Delta t$, and we also have by continuity of flow $\Delta q = A\Delta h$. Therefore, $Q\Delta t = A\Delta h$, and $Q/A = \Delta h/\Delta t$. Physically, $\Delta h/\Delta t$ is a velocity; therefore, so is $v = Q/A$. Thus, the Darcy velocity v represents the rate $\Delta h/\Delta t$ approaches dh/dt of fall of surface water in Fig. 5. If the hydraulic gradient is unity (pressure potential same at top and bottom of soil column), then $v = -K$. Thus, it is determined that K is numerically equal to the rate of fall of a thin layer of ponded water into the soil, under only the force of the earth's gravitational pull. We also see that K is the velocity under a unit hydraulic gradient.

Flow in a vertical soil column has been used to derive and illustrate Darcy's law. However, the law and principles developed above apply for flow of water in any direction in the soil.

2. Hydraulic Conductivity

The hydraulic conductivity should not be confused with the *intrinsic permeability*, sometimes just called the *permeability*, of the flow medium. The intrinsic permeability can be used to denote the permeability of the medium without reference to the fluid that is moving. The intrinsic permeability, symbolized by $\bar{k}$ by M. Muskat, a petroleum engineer in the United States well known for his studies in the 1930s and 1940s of fluid flow through porous media, is equal to $K\eta/\rho g$, where K is the Darcy hydraulic conductivity, η is the fluid viscosity, ρ is the fluid density, and g is the acceleration due to gravity. Dimensionally, $\bar{k}$ is an area (L^2). The units of K are m/day, which is the

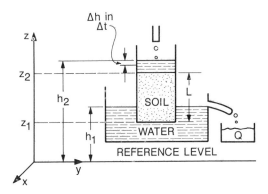

FIGURE 5 Illustration of Darcy's law. (From Kirkham, D., and Powers, W. L. Copyright © (1972). "Advanced Soil Physics," p. 47. Wiley, New York. Reprinted by permission of John Wiley and Sons, Inc.

same as (m^3/m^2)/day. That is, K may be interpreted as the m^3 of water seeping through a m^2 of soil per day under a unit hydraulic gradient.

Hydraulic conductivity in natural field soil is governed by factors such as cracks, root holes, worm holes, and stability of soil crumbs. Texture, that is, the percentage of the primary particles of sand, silt, and clay, usually has a minor effect on hydraulic conductivity, except for disturbed soil materials. The hydraulic conductivity of natural soils in place varies from about 30 m/day for a silty clay loam to 0.05 m/day for a clay. The hydraulic conductivity for disturbed soil materials varies from about 600 m/day for gravel to 0.02 m/day for silt and clay. The value of K can be made higher or lower by soil management. Roots of crops after decay increase K; compaction of soil by animals or machinery decreases K, at least in the surface soil.

Ordinarily one considers K in $v = -Ki$ to be a constant under saturated flow. It is a constant if (a) the physical condition of the soil and of the water does not change in space or time as the water moves through the soil (e.g., the soil is *isotropic*, that is hydraulic conductivity is the same regardless of the direction of measurement) and if (b) the type of flow is laminar, that is, not turbulent. In laminar flow, two particles of water seeping through the soil will describe paths (streamlines) that never cross each other. In turbulent flow, eddies and whirls develop. The possibility of turbulent flow is considered in soil only if the soil is a coarse sand or gravel, and then only if the hydraulic gradients are large (larger than found in most problems of interest to agricultural soil scientists).

3. Laplace's Equation

To solve groundwater seepage and drainage problems, it is desirable to have a general differential equation. It is found that Laplace's equation applies, which is a familiar equation occurring in nearly all branches of applied mathematics. Laplace's equation is derived from Darcy's law and the *equation of continuity*. The equation of continuity states mathematically that mass can be neither created nor destroyed. We can state the equation of continuity in words, as follows: For a volume element x times y times z, the change in velocity of water in the x direction plus change in velocity of water in the y direction plus change in velocity of water in the z direction is equal to the total change in water content, Θ, per unit time of the volume element under consideration. That is, inflow of water in the element minus outflow of water is

equal to the water accumulated. Let us imagine a rectangular x, y, z system of coordinates that is established in a homogeneous porous medium of constant hydraulic conductivity, and let h be the hydraulic head referred to an arbitrary reference level for a point (x, y, z) and let time be t and v_x, v_y, and v_z be the velocity of water flowing in the x, y, and z directions, respectively; then, with Θ being the volume of water per unit volume of bulk soil, from the equation of continuity,

$$- [(\partial v_x/\partial x) + (\partial v_y/\partial y) + (\partial v_z/\partial z)] = \partial \Theta/\partial t \quad (6)$$

and Darcy's law, one may, for incompressible steady-state ($\partial \theta/\delta t = 0$) flow in a porous medium where K is constant, derive the expression

$$(\partial^2 h/\partial x^2) + (\partial^2 h/\partial y^2) + (\partial^2 h/\partial z^2) = 0, \quad (7)$$

as the expression governing groundwater flow. The steady, saturated-flow equation is abbreviated $\nabla^2 h = 0$.

Charles S. Slichter, a mathematician at the University of Wisconsin, was the first to show in 1899 that Laplace's equation applies to the motion of groundwater. Many mathematical solutions for groundwater flow using Laplace's equation have been done by Don Kirkham of Iowa State University.

B. Unsaturated Soil: Diffusivity

So far, we have been considering water flow in saturated soils. Although flow in saturated soils is important, soils are not generally water saturated (saturated meaning that the matric potential is equal to zero).

We now consider concepts of unsaturated flow. Using the equation of continuity and assuming that Darcy's law holds for unsaturated moisture flow, one may derive the following equation:

$$(\partial/\partial x)k(\partial h/\partial x) + (\partial/\partial y)k(\partial h/\partial y) + (\partial/\partial z)k$$
$$(\partial h/\partial z) = \partial \Theta/\partial t, \quad (8)$$

where k is hydraulic conductivity under unsaturated conditions, h is the hydraulic head, and Θ is the fraction of the soil bulk volume occupied by water. If the soil is saturated, the equation reduces to Laplace's equation because k and Θ become constants. In the past, k has been called the *capillary conductivity*, but the term is now considered to be obsolete by the Soil Science Society of America, because a capillary model may not apply to the movement of water under unsaturated conditions. For solutions of Eq. (8), the result has depended upon three factors:

1. We replace h, the hydraulic head, by

$$h = \Psi + z, \tag{9}$$

where Ψ is the called the matric potential or capillary potential (rather than the pressure potential, because the soil is now not saturated) and z is the gravitational head, as before. In 1931, L. A. Richards a (then) doctoral student at Cornell University in New York published the equation in which h is replaced by Ψ and z:

$$(\partial/\partial x)k(\partial\Psi/\partial x) + (\partial/\partial y)k(\partial\Psi/\partial y) + (\partial/\partial z)k(\partial\Psi/\partial z) + \partial k/\partial z = \partial\Theta/\partial t. \tag{10}$$

Equation (10) is known as Richards's equation, a nonlinear, partial differential equation. Such equations are difficult to solve. In 1955, John R. Philip of Australia gave a solution.

2. We introduce a term called the *diffusivity D,* defined by

$$D = k(\partial\Psi/\partial\Theta). \tag{11}$$

D has units of $[mm^2/sec]$. In 1936, Ernest C. Childs in England noted that, under unsaturated conditions, water moves according to diffusion equations.

3. We now make use of a mathematical transformation, so-called the *Boltzmann transformation,* which involves the time t to the one-half power. In 1952, Arnold Klute a doctoral student at Cornell University in New York introduced this Boltzmann variable:

$$\lambda = 1/2\ xt^{-1/2}. \tag{12}$$

He wrote the flow equation in a diffusion form with water content, Θ, as the dependent variable:

$$\partial\Theta/\partial t = (\partial/\partial z)D(\partial\Theta/\partial z) + (\partial k/\partial z). \tag{13}$$

He then restricted himself to the gravity-free case (horizontal flow into a soil column):

$$\partial\Theta/\partial t = (\partial/\partial x)D(\partial\Theta/\partial x). \tag{14}$$

Klute transformed the partial differential equation into an ordinary differential equation by using this Boltzmann variable.

In 1907, Edgar Buckingham of the USDA Bureau of Soils in Washington, DC already had published a bulletin entitled "Studies on the Movement of Soil Moisture," which established the mathematics of unsaturated soil water flow. He saw that the capillary conductivity (the unsaturated hydraulic conductivity) is a function of water content or matric (capillary) potential. The flow equation is sometimes known

as the *Darcy-Buckingham law,* which honors both its discoverers in the saturated and unsaturated realms.

Thus, description of water flow in soil requires the functions $D(\Theta)$ and $k(\Theta)$. In general, it is difficult to measure $D(\Theta)$, especially *in situ.* It is simpler to measure the total effect of the capillary attractiveness of soil, namely the *sorptivity* S $[mm/sec^{1/2}]$, a term defined by Philip in 1969. The sorptivity is equal to the following:

$$S = {}_{\Theta_n}\!\int^{\Theta_s} \lambda\, d\Theta \tag{15}$$

and can be approximated by the following equation:

$$S_o^2 = [(\Theta_o - \Theta_n)/b]_{\Theta_n}\!\int^{\Theta_o} D\, d\Theta \tag{16}$$

where Θ_n is the initial soil water content, Θ_s is the saturated water content, Θ_o is the water content to which the soil surface is wet, and $\frac{1}{2} < b < \pi/4$, often $b \cong 0.55$. Thus, to interpret S_o, in terms of D, requires measurement of Θ_n and Θ_o, which can be easily determined. In theory, to describe flow in a uniform soil, one only requires instruments to measure the sorptivity and the conductivity function from saturation, Θ_s, where $\Theta_o = \Theta_s$, which is at the free water condition of $\Psi_o = 0$, down to $\Theta = \Theta_n$ and $\Psi = \Psi_n$, where commonly $\Psi_n \to -\infty$.

IV. Infiltration

Infiltration rate may be defined as the meters per unit time of water entering into the soil regardless of the types or values of forces or gradients. The term hydraulic conductivity, which has been defined as the meters per day of water seeping into the soil under the pull of gravity or under a unit hydraulic gradient, should not be confused with infiltration rate. Infiltration rate need not refer to saturated conditions. If two rain drops of total volume 2 mm^3 = 0.000002 m^3 fall per day on a m^2 of soil and are absorbed into the soil, the infiltration rate is 0.000002 m/day.

Water entry into soil is caused by matric and gravitational forces. Therefore, this entry may occur in the lateral and upward directions, as well as the downward one. Infiltration normally refers to the downward movement. The matric force usually predominates over the gravitational force during the early stages of water entry into soil, so that observations made during the early stages of infiltration are valid when considering the absence of gravity.

If water infiltrates into a dry soil, a definite *wetting front,* also called a *wet front,* can be observed. This is the boundary between the wetted upper part of the soil and the dry lower part of the soil. If water is infiltrating into soil contained in a clear plastic column, one can observe the progress of the wet front and mark wet fronts as they change with time (Fig. 6). At present, it is impossible to measure the matric potential exactly at the wet front, because it progresses too rapidly into the soil. However, one can measure amount of water infiltrated and the depth and shape of the wet front, and come to important conclusions about the entry of water into the soil. Infiltration is extremely important, because it determines not only the amount of water that will enter a soil, but also the entrainment of the "passenger" chemicals (nutrients, pollutants) dissolved in it.

Four models for infiltration into the soil have been developed. They all deal with one-dimensional, downward infiltration into the soil.

A. Lewis Equation

From work initiated in 1926, Mortimer Reed Lewis, an irrigation engineer at Oregon State College, used the following equation for infiltration:

$$I = \gamma t^a, \tag{17}$$

where I is the cumulative infiltration between time zero and t, and γ and a are constants. Equation (17)

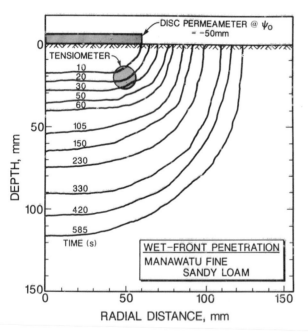

FIGURE 6 Wet fronts for a sandy loam soil. (From Kirkham, M. B., and Clothier, B. E. (1994). Ellipsoidal description of water flow into soil from a surface disc. *Trans. Int. Congr. Soil Sci.* **15**, in press.)

has been erroneously attributed to A. N. Kostiakov, and often appears in the literature as the "Kostiakov" equation. The parameters in Eq. (17) are evaluated by fitting the model to experimental data. By definition, the infiltration rate $i = dI/dt$. Thus, the infiltration rate for the Lewis equation is given by

$$i = a\gamma t^{a-1}. \tag{18}$$

B. Horton Equation

In the 1930s, Robert E. Horton, a pioneer in the study of infiltration in the field, developed the following equation:

$$i = i_f + (i_o - i_f)\exp(-\beta t), \tag{19}$$

where i_o is the initial infiltration rate at $t = 0$, i_f is the final constant infiltration rate that is achieved at large times, and β is a soil parameter that describes the rate of decrease of infiltration.

Horton felt that the reduction in infiltration rate with time was largely controlled by factors operating at the soil surface. These included swelling of soil colloids and the closing of small cracks, which progressively sealed the soil surface. He also recognized that a bare soil surface was compacted by raindrops, but crop cover mitigated their effect. Horton's field data showed that the infiltration rate eventually approached a constant value, which was often somewhat smaller than the saturated permeability of the soil. The latter observation was thought to be due to air entrapment.

C. Green and Ampt Equation

The above models are empirical. W. Heber Green and G. A. Ampt in Australia published in 1911 an infiltration equation that was based upon a simple physical model of the soil. It has the advantage that the parameters in the equation can be related to physical properties of the soil. Physically, Green and Ampt assumed that the soil was saturated behind the wetting front and that one could define some "effective" matric potential at the wetting front. During infiltration, if the soil surface is held at a constant matric potential or head h_o with associated water content Θ_o (e.g., by ponding water over it), water enters the soil behind a sharply defined wet front that moves downward with time (Fig. 7a). Green and Ampt replaced this process with one that has a discontinuous change in water content at the wetting front (Fig. 7b). In addition, they made the following assumptions: (i) The

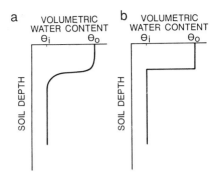

FIGURE 7 Water content profiles during infiltration. (a) A profile that actually occurs during infiltration. (b) A profile corresponding to the Green-Ampt infiltration model. (From Jury, W. A., Gardner, W. R., and Gardner, W. H. Copyright © (1991). "Soil Physics," 5th ed., p. 132. Wiley, New York. Reprinted with permission of John Wiley and Sons, Inc.)

soil in the wetted region has constant properties (K_o, Θ_o, D_o, h_o, where K_o and D_o are the hydraulic conductivity and water diffusivity in the Green-Ampt model, respectively) and (ii) the matric potential (head) at the moving front is constant and equal to h_F.

The Green-Ampt model can be used to calculate the infiltration rate into a horizontal soil column initially at a uniform water content Θ_i such that $\Theta_o > \Theta_i$ and an associated matric potential or head h_o maintained at the entry surface for all times > 0. Using the assumptions of the model and Darcy's law, the following equation can be derived:

$$i = (dI/dt) = \Delta\Theta(D_o/2t)^{1/2}, \qquad (20)$$

where i = infiltration rate, t = time, $\Delta\Theta = \Theta_o - \Theta_i > 0$, $D_o = K_o\Delta h/\Delta\Theta$ is the soil water diffusivity of the wet soil region $0 < x < L$, the depth of the wetting front, and $\Delta h = h_o - h_F > 0$, and K_o is the constant hydraulic conductivity of the wet region, and h_F is the matric potential or head of the moving front. Note in this model that the infiltration rate into the soil is proportional to $t^{-1/2}$. A similar expression is obtained for infiltration into a vertical soil column at short times after infiltration begins.

The model has been used as a conceptual aid in visualizing a complex process. Indirect evaluation of h_F has permitted the model to be used in practical applications.

D. Philip Infiltration Model

J. R. Philip in 1957 suggested an approximate algebraic equation (based on sound physical reasoning) for vertical infiltration under ponded conditions. The

equation, which is simple yet physically well founded, is as follows:

$$I = St^{1/2} + At, \qquad (21)$$

where I is the cumulative infiltration (mm), S is the sorptivity (mm hr$^{-1/2}$), and A is an empirical constant (mm/hr). The first term on the right-hand side of Eq. (21) gives the gravity-free absorption into a ponded soil due to capillarity and adsorption. The second term represents the infiltration due to the downward force of gravity. S and A may be found empirically by fitting Eq. (21) to infiltration data. Alternatively, these parameters may be derived from the hydraulic properties of the soil. This is not possible for other empirical infiltration equations. For horizontal infiltration, cumulative infiltration I is given by

$$I = St^{1/2}. \qquad (22)$$

E. Two- and Three-Dimensional Infiltration

The previous discussion dealt with one-dimensional infiltration in which water is assumed to flow vertically (or more rarely horizontally) into the soil. Multidimensional infiltration theory is an area of soil physics research dominated by the works of J. R. Philip, who published his first paper on the topic in 1966. Sequels to his work have been carried out by Peter A. C. Raats (1971) in the Netherlands and Robin A. Wooding (1968) in New Zealand.

Multidimensional infiltration models have utilized difficult mathematics. However, practical advances in infiltration can be made with simple models. For example, recently, a simple, ellipsoidal description of the pattern of wetting to approximate the depth to the wetting front underneath a disc permeameter, set at Ψ_o and supplying water to soil initially at water content Θ_n, has been described. Wet fronts shown in Fig. 6 were used in developing such an ellipsoidal model.

F. Redistribution

The term redistribution refers to the continued movement of water through a soil profile after irrigation or rainfall has stopped at the soil surface. Redistribution occurs after infiltration and is complex, because the lower part of the profile ahead of the wet front will increase its water content, and the upper part of the profile near the surface will decrease its water content, after infiltration ceases. Thus, hysteresis can have an effect on the overall shape of the water content profile.

V. Preferential Flow

The water flow equations have been derived using the assumption that the soil has a continuous solid matrix, which holds water in pores and films. Field soil, however, has a number of interconnected cracks, root holes, worm channels, and other voids, whose physical properties differ from the surrounding soil matrix. If filled, these continuing flow channels have the capacity to carry large amounts of water at velocities that greatly exceed those in the surrounding matrix. We first define and then consider the characteristics of these voids.

A. Microporosity and Macroporosity

Pores have been classified into different sizes, as follows:

Macropores: diameters ranging from >5000 to 75 μm;
Mesopores: diameters ranging from 30 to 75 μm;
Micropores: diameters ranging from 5 to 30 μm.

It is often more important to characterize soil pores in terms of their function, in particular with regard to their ability to store and conduct water, rather than their diameter. Transport through soil of water with its dissolved chemicals, as well as gaseous exchange, depends critically upon soil pores, and especially upon the continuous and connected macropores.

Functionally, we can distinguish between *macroporosity* and *matrix porosity*. Macroporosity refers to the interconnected pore space of voids, which causes preferential transport of both water and chemicals. When transport occurs through the macropores, there is limited exchange of water between the macropores and the pores of the matrix. Matrix porosity refers to those pores in which the flow through the body of the soil is slow enough so that there is extensive interpore mixing.

If we consider the unit soil pore to be a cylinder of radius r, then the Hagen-Poiseuille law can be used to describe the flow through the pore:

$$q = - (r^2/8\eta) (\Delta P/\Delta x), \qquad (23)$$

where q is the flux density (m/sec), η is the viscosity of water (kg m^{-1} sec^{-1}), and ΔP (Pa) is the pressure difference across the small pipe (pore) of length Δx. Since the flux density increases with the square of the

radius, the macropores can have a great impact on soil-transport processes. This is especially true because the macropores frequently form an interconnected network. However, they are fragile and can easily be disrupted, particularly at the soil surface where they can be rendered ineffective by sealing. Much of the biologically created macroporosity drops off with depth as the populations of soil flora and fauna decline.

B. Macroporosity and Hydraulic Conductivity

Because of macroporosity, the hydraulic conductivity function, $K(\Psi)$ can vary dramatically, mainly as a result of changes in the characteristics of the larger, surface pores that become filled only at high potentials near saturation. Figure 8 shows how the hydraulic conductivity function varies with soil management. At the wet end, the role of macropores is paramount in determining $K(\Psi)$. Here management (e.g., plowing) or natural events (e.g., crusting of the soil after rainfall) can modify rapidly the hydraulic conductivity by altering surface-venting and subsurface connectedness. The upper curve in Fig. 8 shows a soil with macropores, and the lower line shows a soil controlled by matrix flow.

Tillage, especially, affects pore size. Pores are smaller in tilled soils, because tillage pulverizes the soil. When the soil is not tilled, decaying roots and other organic matter create voids. Also earthworms thrive on the organic matter and their populations are greater in soil that has not been tilled. Earthworm holes and root channels are a prime reason for the difference in hydraulic conductivity between cultivated and no-till soil.

C. Tension Infiltrometers

Recognition of the importance of macropores and preferential flow has led to the development of instruments that can be used in the field to control preferential water flow through macropores and soil cracks. The first practical instrument was developed in 1981 by Brent E. Clothier of New Zealand and Ian White of Australia. This simple instrument was known as the *sorptivity tube* or more latterly as the *tension infiltrometer*. Later still it has evolved into the *disc permeameter,* as described by Keith M. Perroux and I. White in 1988. The disc permeameter is used when three-dimensional infiltration is being considered. With these instruments, the amount of macropore flow measured is controlled by applying water to soil at

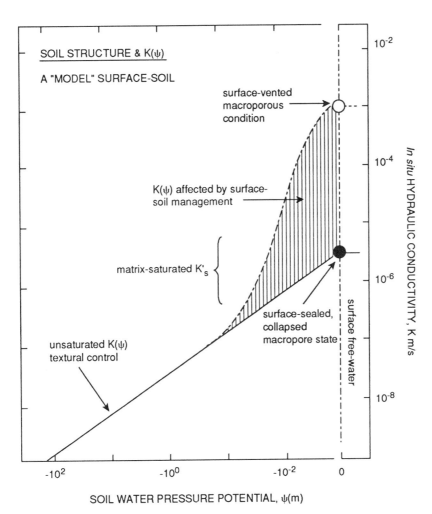

FIGURE 8 A hydraulic conductivity function, $K(\Psi)$. The shaded area identifies the modification that soil management might impart upon the hydraulic conductivity. Also identified by a solid dot is the saturated hydraulic conductivity of the matrix (K_s), i.e., the soil minus those macropores that drain when Ψ_o is less than about -30 mm. (From Clothier, B. E. (1990). Root zone processes and water quality: The impact of management. *In* "Proceedings of the International Symposium on Water Quality Modeling of Agricultural Nonpoint Sources, Logan, Utah, June, 1988." (D. G. DeCoursey, ed.) pp. 659–683. United States Department of Agriculture, Agricultural Research Service, Report No. ARS-81, p. 671.)

water potentials, Ψ_o, less than 0. The maximum diameter of vertical pores, connected to the soil surface, through which water can enter is given by the capillary rise equation (Eq. (3)) and is proportional to the matric potential, $(-\Psi_o)^{-1}$. The more negative Ψ_o, the smaller is the maximum diameter of a pore that can participate in flow from the soil surface. These two instruments are being used to supply water to soil *in situ* at readily selectable, zero or negative pressures. A "ready reckoner" of the relationship between the negative pressure Ψ, where Ψ is in terms of energy per unit weight (in cm of H_2O head), and the capillary diameter d in mm is $-3/d$.

Many water flow processes of interest such as groundwater recharge are concerned only with area-averaged water input. Therefore, preferential flow of water through structural voids does not necessarily invalidate equations that assume homogeneous flow. However, preferential flow is of critical importance in solute transport, because it enhances chemical mobility and can increase pollution hazards.

VI. Soil Water in Relation to Plants

A. Soil Water Budget

The amount of water available for plant uptake has been related to a soil's *water budget*. The three terms associated with the water budget are *wilting point*

(W.P.), *field capacity* (F.C.), and *available water* (A.W.).

1. Field Capacity

To define field capacity we consider the following. In many soils, after a rain or irrigation, the soil will immediately start draining to the deeper depths. After 1 or 2 days the water content in the soil will reach, with time, for many soils, a nearly constant value for a particular depth in question. This somewhat arbitrary value of water content, expressed as a percentage, is called the field capacity. Field capacity is often estimated to be the water content at a soil matric potential of about −0.03 MPa. The field capacity might be measured as 5% of water per unit volume of bulk soil for a sand, which we shall label *A*, and might be measured as 50% per unit volume of bulk soil for a heavy clay, which we shall call *B*.

2. Wilting Point

The wilting point, also called the *permanent wilting point,* may be defined as the amount of water per unit weight or per unit soil bulk volume in the soil, expressed in percent, that is held so tightly by the soil matrix that roots cannot absorb this water and a plant will wilt. The wilting point is usually estimated to be the water content at a soil matric potential of −1.5 MPa. The wilting point might be 2% water per unit volume for the sand *A*, and it might be 20% per unit volume for the heavy clay *B*.

3. Available Water

Plant available water, *A.W.,* may be defined as the difference between field capacity, *F.C.,* and wilting point, *W.P.* The formula is

$$A.W. = F.C. - W.P. \qquad (24)$$

Using the numerical values of *W.P.* and *F.C.* for the sand *A* and heavy clay *B*, we find available water as

(Sand *A*)   *A.W.* = 5% − 2% = 3%
(Heavy clay *B*)   *A.W.* = 50% − 20% = 30%.

The above two *A.W.*'s are in percentages referred to a volume of bulk soil. These *A.W.*'s may be considered to mean that, in 100 cm of the sand *A* profile, there are 3 cm of equivalent surface water in the plant available form; and in 100 cm of heavy clay *B*, there are 30 cm of equivalent surface water in plant available form. The clay soil *B* stores (30 − 3) = 27 cm more of equivalent surface water per meter depth of soil profile than does the sand *A*. From this example, we

see that soil texture can have a large effect on soil water availability.

The terms should be used with caution. They do not apply to certain exceptional soils. The terms should be based on moisture measurements made in the field to a depth of interest, say 100 to 150 cm, not on laboratory measurements. Field capacity is of doubtful value for soils having water tables or layers of widely differing hydraulic conductivity. Some have questioned the use of "field capacity" at all, because the soil water is not static and is always moving, even if the movement is small. In the 1970s, the Soil Science Society of America (SSSA) considered the term obsolete in technical work. However, in recent years, the SSSA has recognized its utility in practical field work, and the term is no longer considered obsolete.

Equation (24) implies to some agronomists that water can be taken up by plant roots with equal ease, from field capacity to the wilting point. This view was promulgated by F. J. Veihmeyer and A. H. Hendrickson at the University of California in Davis, who collaborated for many years starting in the 1920s. For most crops, however, yields are reduced if the water in the soil approaches the wilting point before water is supplied.

4. Nonlimiting Water Range

In 1985, John Letey, a soil physicist at the University of California in Riverside, developed a concept called the *nonlimiting water range* (NLWR), which acknowledges that water may not be equally available to plants between field capacity and the permanent wilting point. The interaction between water and other physical factors that affect plant growth must be considered. Bulk density and pore size distribution affect the relationship between water and both aeration and mechanical resistance. The relationship between water and aeration is opposite to that between water and mechanical resistance. Increasing water content decreases aeration, which is undesirable, but decreases mechanical resistance, which is desirable. The nonlimiting water range may be affected by aeration and/or mechanical resistance (Fig. 9). The NLWR becomes narrower as bulk density and aeration limit plant growth. On one end of the scale, oxygen limits root growth and on the other end of the scale, mechanical resistance restricts root growth. The restriction may occur at a water content higher than the value that would be considered limiting to plants on the basis of plant available water.

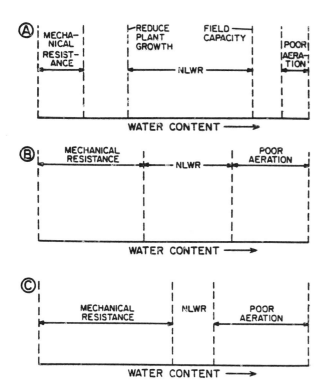

FIGURE 9 Generalized relationships between soil water content and restricting factors for plant growth in soils with increasing bulk density and decreasing structure in going from case A to C. The nonlimiting water range is abbreviated NLWR. (From Letey, J. (1985). Relationship between soil physical properties and crop production. *Adv. Soil Sci.* **1**, 277–294.)

B. Drought and Flooding

Plant water status is primarily described by the same two basic parameters that describe soil water: the water content (Θ) and the energy status of the water, usually expressed as the total water potential or water potential, Ψ. As for soils, under equilibrium conditions, the state of water at a particular point in a plant may be written in terms of the various components of the potential energy, as follows:

$$\Psi = \Psi_s + \Psi_p + \Psi_m + \Psi_g, \qquad (25)$$

where Ψ is the water potential, Ψ_s is the osmotic (solute) – potential component, Ψ_p is the pressure (turgor) – potential component, Ψ_m is the matric component due to capilary or adsorption forces such as those in the cell wall, and Ψ_g is the component due to gravity. For plants, the matric potential and the gravitational potential are usually neglected, and Eq. (25) reduces to

$$\Psi = \Psi_s + \Psi_p. \qquad (26)$$

Wherever plants grow, their development is often limited by either too little or too much water. Drought limits growth more than flooding. About 40% of insurance indemnities for crop losses in the United States are for drought and about 20% are for excess water and flooding. In contrast, insurance indemnities for insect and diseases combined are only about 4%.

Since ancient times, man has been confronted with trying to make dry land productive, as documented by Samuel Noah Kramer of the University of Pennsylvania in Philadelphia, who translated the tablets of the Sumerians, as they were called by the third millennium B.C. The climate of their country, Sumer, is extremely hot and dry, and its soil, left to itself, is arid, wind-swept, and unproductive. The creative and resolute Sumerians turned Sumer into a Garden of Eden through use of irrigation water from the Tigris and Euphrates rivers, and their tablets tell us how they achieved this. [*See* IRRIGATION ENGINEERING: FARM PRACTICES, METHODS, AND SYSTEMS; WATER: CONTROL AND USE.]

Modern dryland research follows upon the basic principles of dryland farming, published in 1911 by John A. Widtsoe of the University of Utah. Widtsoe defined dryland farming as "the profitable production of useful crops, without irrigation, on lands that receive annually a rainfall of 20 inches [51 cm] or less." The methods of soil tillage of Jethro Tull (1674–1741) were at the foundation of Widtsoe's dry farming practices. The basis of the system is to store water in the soil by manipulating either the crops or the soil. Drought-resistant crops, proper tillage (disking, plowing, packing, harrowing), mulching to prevent evaporation, elimination of weeds, and fallowing are all important in dry farming. Several large international research centers focus their research on improving yields under dryland (nonirrigated) conditions. These centers include the International Maize and Wheat Improvement Center (CIMMYT) in Mexico; the International Crops Research Institute for the Semi-Arid Tropics (ICRISAT) in India; and the International Center for Agricultural Research in the Dry Areas (ICARDA) in Syria. [*See* DRYLAND FARMING.]

If the soil is wetter than field capacity, plants may still take up water. But roots need at least 10% by volume air space in the soil to survive, because they obtain oxygen by diffusion from the air. If less than 10% of the soil bulk volume is open to air, then the air-filled pores will not be connected together in a continuous open path to the soil surface and needed oxygen cannot reach the roots to enable them to take up water and minerals. Also, carbon dioxide, evolved from the roots when they take in oxygen, cannot be

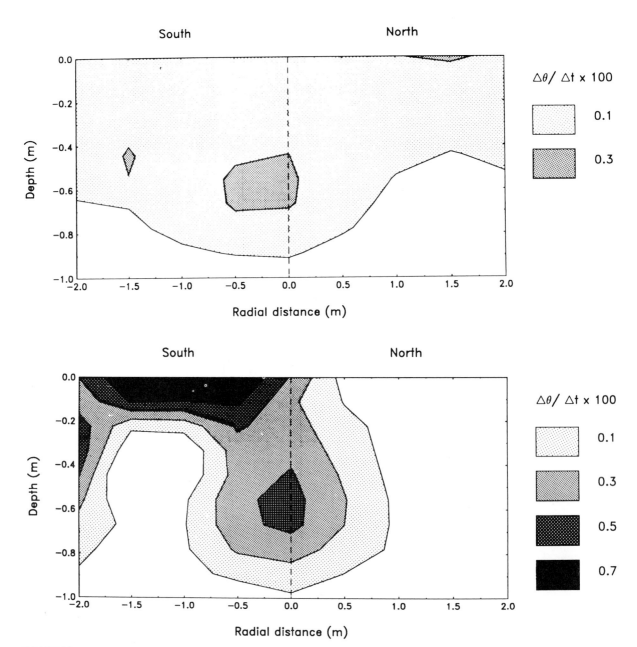

FIGURE 10 Measurement by time domain reflectometry of the changing spatial pattern of soil water content in the rootzone of a kiwifruit vine growing near Palmerston North, New Zealand. The upper figure depicts the average rate of water content change over the 4-week period 11 February–9 March 1992. The lower figure shows that change which occurred over the 2 weeks following irrigation of just the south side on 10 March. Rate of water extraction $\Delta\theta/\Delta t$ is given in units of $m^3\, m^{-3}\, sec^{-1}$. The vine is located at the center. (From Clothier, B. E., and Green, S. R. (1994). Rootzone processes and the efficient use of irrigation water. *Agricultural Water Management* **25**, 1–12.)

removed from the soil when it is too wet. When a soil is flooded, gas exchange between the soil and air is drastically reduced, because gases diffuse much more slowly through water than through air.

C. Root Distribution in Relation to Soil Water

We will consider two examples from recent studies, one done under irrigated conditions and one done under dryland conditions. The two studies show the important relationship between root distribution and soil water.

Greater efficiency in the use of irrigation water will come through a better understanding of the distribution of root systems and the functioning of roots. A recent study done in New Zealand by Brent E. Clothier and Steven R. Green with roots of a kiwifruit vine documents the dominant role of surface roots

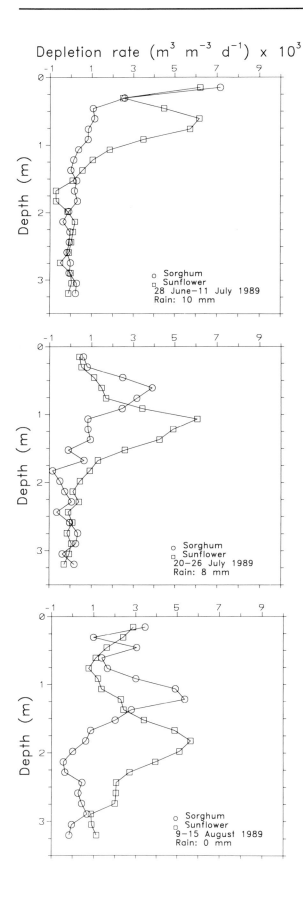

in extracting water under irrigated conditions and demonstrates how irrigation can influence the spatial pattern of root water uptake. In this study, water content was measured by using time domain reflectometry (TDR), which permitted observations of the changing pattern of water content in the soil that occurs as a result of root water uptake (Fig. 10). This new technique for measuring soil water content was developed by G. Clarke Topp and colleagues in Canada in the 1980s and has improved our ability to determine water extraction patterns by roots. In the kiwifruit study, after an initial irrigation, the soil water content was uniform across the rootzone; also, the water uptake rate was quite uniform (Fig. 10, top). Beginning in the 10th week of 1992, just one half of the vine's root zone, the southern half, was wetted by a sprinkler irrigation. Following this differential irrigation of the rootzone, the flow of water in the "wet" southern root increased, but the flux in the "dry" northern root was about halved. Thus, the vine quickly switched its pattern of uptake away from the drier parts of its root zone.

Of greater interest, however, was the depthwise pattern of root uptake observed on the wet side. The preference for near-surface water uptake can be seen (Fig. 10, bottom). The vine continued to extract water in the densely rooted region surrounding its base, but the shift in uptake to the surface roots on the wet southern side was remarkable.

The results show that greater efficiency in irrigation water might be obtained by applying small amounts of water, more frequently. A small amount of irrigation water would be rapidly used by active, near-surface roots. This would then eliminate drainage of irrigation water into the lower regions of the rootzone, where draining water passes by inactive roots and goes to greater depth. The importance of surface roots shows the need for small, high-frequency irrigations.

Under rainfed conditions in semi-arid regions, however, it is important to have crops that exploit water at all depths in the soil, not just the surface, to make maximum use of agricultural water. A crop that depletes water in the upper soil zone could be followed by a crop that depletes water lower in the

FIGURE 11 Soil water depletion rates of sorghum and sunflower during three periods in 1989: (a) 28 June to 11 July, (b) 20 to 26 July, and (c) 9 to 15 August. The depletion rates reported are multiplied by a factor of 10^3; therefore, $1 \text{ m}^3 \text{ m}^{-3} \text{ d}^{-1} \times 10^3 = 0.001 \text{ m}^3 \text{ m}^{-3} \text{ d}^{-1}$. (From Rachidi, F., Kirkham, M. B., Stone, L. R., and Kanemasu, E. T. (1993). Soil water depletion by sunflower and sorghum under rainfed conditions. *Agricultural Water Management* **24**, 49–62.)

soil zone. Thus, the water in the entire soil profile would be available for uptake by crops. Two drought-resistant row crops in semi-arid areas are grain sorghum and sunflower. A recent study done in Kansas showed that the two crops use water at different depths in the soil. Sunflower depleted water to a deeper depth, and had a higher rate of depletion at lower depths, than sorghum (Fig. 11). The results suggest that deep-rooted crops might be planted in rotations with shallow-rooted crops or after irrigated crops to take advantage of water at depth. In a soil with macropores, sunflowers might be grown, because their deep roots would take up water that bypasses the rootzone of shallow-rooted crops.

VII. Conclusion

All terrestrial life depends on soil and water. Civilizations have risen and fallen based on the use or abuse of these two prime resources. This article has tried to explain some of the basic concepts underlying soil–water relationships. A fundamental understanding of water in soil should permit agricultural practices that can be based on sound, scientific principles. With such knowledge, we should be able to sustain the thin layer of wetted soil on the earth's surface, upon which all life is dependent.

Bibliography

Baver, L. D., Gardner, W. H., and Gardner, W. R. (1972). "Soil Physics," 4th ed. Wiley, New York.

Carter, M. R. (ed.) (1993). "Soil Sampling and Methods of Analysis." Lewis, Boca Raton, FL.

Clothier, B. E. (1990). Soil water sorptivity and conductivity. *Remote Sensing Rev.* **5,** 281–291.

Clothier, B. E. (1994). Soil pores. In "Encyclopedia of Soil Science and Technology" (C. W. Finkl, Jr., ed.). Van Nostrand Reinhold, New York, in press.

Gish, T. J., and Shirmohammadi, A. (eds.) (1991). "Preferential Flow." American Society of Agricultural Engineers, St. Joseph, MI.

Hillel, D. J. (1991). "Out of the Earth. Civilization and the Life of the Soil." The Free Press. Macmillan, New York.

Jury, W. A., Gardner, W. R., and Gardner, W. H. (1991). "Soil Physics," 5th ed. Wiley, New York.

Kirkham, D. (1961). "Lectures on Agricultural Drainage." Institute of Land Reclamation, College of Agriculture, Alexandria University, Alexandria, Egypt. (Copy in the Iowa State University Library, Ames, IA.)

Kirkham, D., and Powers, W. L. (1972). "Advanced Soil Physics." Wiley, New York.

Kirkham, M. B. (1990). Plant responses to water deficits. In "Irrigation of Agricultural Crops" (B. A. Stewart and D. R. Nielsen, eds.), pp. 323–342. American Society of Agronomy, Crop Science Society of America, Soil Science Society of America, Madison, WI.

Kirkham, M. B., and Clothier, B. E. (1994). Ellipsoidal description of water flow into soil from a surface disc. Transactions of the International Congress of Soil Science 15 (*in press*).

Soil Science Society of America (1987). "Glossary of Soil Science Terms." Soil Science Society of America, Madison, WI.

van Genuchten, M. Th., Leij, F. J., and Lund, L. J. (eds.) (1992). "Indirect Methods for Estimating the Hydraulic Properties of Unsaturated Soils." Univ. of California, Riverside.

Sorghum

LLOYD W. ROONEY, F. R. MILLER, *Texas A&M University*

Glossary

Bird resistant sorghum Sorghum that contains a pigmented testa with condensed tannins that cause the birds to prefer other food sources; birds eat the bird resistant sorghums when other food is unavailable

Brown sorghum Sorghums containing a pigmented testa and condensed tannins; kernels may appear brown or white because of other characteristics

Decortication Process of removing the pericarp and associated layers from a sorghum kernel by abrasive action; often called dehulling and is done by hand in a mortar and pestle in Africa; the decorticated grain is crushed and used as flour or meal in various products

Phenolics Compounds containing a phenol ring which includes tannins, flavanoids, phenolic acids, and others

Plant color Secondary color of the sorghum tissue (purple, red, and tan are the major colors)

Waxy sorghum Contains only amylopectin in the starch granules; surface of the cut kernel has a wax like appearance

Weathering The deterioration of sorghum in the field by molds, sprouting, and other factors

Sorghum (*Sorghum bicolor*) is a major cereal crop grown in hot, semiarid tropical and dry temperate areas of the world. It is a coarse grass that is heat and drought tolerant. It is the major staple produced in areas of Africa and India, where it is processed into many different traditional foods. Sorghum varies in height and maturity. Hybrid (F_1) sorghums are grown in developed countries and varieties are used in other areas. Sorghum provides large quantities of forage and stover for livestock and building materials and fuel. Sorghum grain is similar to maize in composition and processing properties. It is high in starch and protein content, and its nutritional value is similar to that of maize when it is properly processed. Sorghum is used mostly for livestock feeds in the Western Hemisphere, where it is processed prior to formulating into rations. Sorghum is dry milled into grits, meal, and flour. It is used as an adjunct in brewing lager beer and for malt to produce opaque beer in Africa. Sweet sorghums are used to produce sorghum syrups and molasses. Sorghum hybrids have been improved for yield, disease and insect resistance, and quality by use of germ plasm from the world collection.

I. Introduction

In terms of total world crop production, sorghum [*Sorghum bicolor* (L.) Moench] ranks fifth, with 59 million metric tonnes of total production in 1988. Seventy-eight percent of the sorghum is planted in developing nations. The production of sorghum is concentrated in the United States, Mexico, Nigeria, Sudan, Ethiopia, India, and China. Most African and Asian countries use tall sorghums for food, feed, forage, fuel, and building material. In the Western Hemisphere, sorghum is mainly used for feed and forage. Specialty types are used for syrup, sugar, and alcohol on a limited basis.

Encyclopedia of Agricultural Science, Volume 4   Copyright © 1994 by Academic Press, Inc.   All rights of reproduction in any form reserved.

The sorghum plant originated in the northeast quadrant of Africa. It belongs to the Graminae family, Panicoidea subfamily, and Andropogeneae tribe. Many different taxonomic forms and varieties exist within the species. The commonly used grain types have a large erect stem terminating in a semicompact to compact panicle, whereas the grassy types have smaller stems and narrower leaves, tiller profusely, and have long, lax panicles. The crop is generally handled as an annual, but under some conditions, ratoon cropping of old stubble is a general practice. It is a warm-season, annual crop favored by high day and night temperatures and intolerant of low temperatures. In temperate environments, time from sowing to maturity averages 110 to 140 days. Sorghum plants range in height from 0.6 to 6 m and possess a monoic-hermaphrodite flower that generally self-pollinates. The grain develops on a branched terminal panicle that can be compact or very open. Flowering proceeds from the top of the panicle downward, with each panicle containing from 800 to 3000 kernels.

There is an enormous range of diversity in the sorghum species. The World Sorghum Collection maintained in India has more than 30,000 entries. Sorghum is classed as grain sorghum, forage sorghum, grassy or Sudan-type sorghums, and broomcorn. The latter is grown for its long, fibrous panicle branches that are used to manufacture brooms. The grain of sorghum is classed according to pericarp color (white, yellow, or red), presence or absence of a pigmented testa (with or without tannins), pericarp thickness (thin or thick), endosperm color (white, heteroyellow, or yellow), and endosperm type (normal, heterowaxy, or waxy). These kernel characteristics are genetically controlled. Plant color of sorghum is tan, purple, or red. The tan plant sorghums with a white pericarp are considered to have excellent quality for food processing. A great deal of variation exists in sorghum attributes. For example, a black sorghum found in the western Sudan has very high levels of anthocyanins and condensed tannins.

II. Plant Characteristics

A. Growth and Development

The growth and development of a sorghum plant is similar to that of other cereals. Seed sizes range from approximately 5 to over 80 g per 1000 mature seeds. There is very little association of plant size to seed size. Different types of endosperm affect seedling emergence and vigor, that is, waxy, sugary, floury, and gradations of softer textures. High-quality seed of normal texture germinate rapidly in the soil at temperatures above 16°C. Minimum temperature for germination of sorghum seed is 7 to 10°C, depending on cultivar. Newly emerged seedlings can withstand freezing temperatures (-2 to -3°C) for a short period of time, but more mature plants are killed by freezing temperatures. Optimum temperature for growth appears to be approximately 27 to 30°C, but is modified by drought, wind, and relative humidity. Sorghum is a short-day plant because floral initiation is hastened by short days (less than 12 hr) and delayed by longer days. F. R. Miller and colleagues demonstrated that varieties have different photoperiod requirements and some varieties respond to differences in day length of as little as several minutes.

B. Maturity and Height

Generally, temperate grain sorghum hybrids require 100 to 140 days from planting to maturity. In tropical areas, the crop is usually planted prior to the onset of rains, and harvest is completed after the rains have subsided. Yield and maturity are related phenomena. Yields generally increase as time to maturity increases, up to a point where the requirements for growth become limiting, then yield decreases. Sorghum varieties and hybrids differ in their ability to tolerate different plant populations, fertility, and irrigation levels. Some hybrids respond differently to insecticides and weed control chemicals. They also respond differently to stresses and production technologies. The yield is variable, and the best cultural practices should be applied to obtain the full potential of each hybrid.

Sorghum height is a variable trait that is under simple genetic control. In most areas of the world, taller plants are preferred, but in those areas where mechanical harvesting is practiced, shorter stature is required. Among presently grown materials, there is a positive correlation between height and yield. As height is increased above 1.5 m, problems of lodging also become important. Height is controlled by four recessive, nonlinked, brachytic dwarfing genes. A single recessive gene may reduce height by 50 cm or more. Most grain sorghum hybrids developed in the United States are recessive at three height loci (three dwarfs), generally dw_1, Dw_2, dw_3 and dw_4. The dw_3 gene is unstable, and mutations to dominance result in a higher than normal frequency of tall plants in otherwise short hybrids.

Maturity in sorghum has been used to regulate the time of harvest to escape grain deterioration, seed molds, and insect damage and to maximize yield. There is a wide array of maturity differences from 60 to 300 + days to maturation. When sorghum varieties differ in maturity, it is the result of a response to temperature and photoperiod. Research has demonstrated that maturity differences in most sorghum cultivars are controlled by four genes (Ma_1, Ma_2, Ma_3, and Ma_4) and an allelic series at each locus. Rate of growth is reflected through maturity differences and total leaf production is correlated to maturity. Rate of leaf production varies only between 2.8 and 3.5 days per leaf, furthermore, both height and rate of growth are limited under stress conditions.

The genetics of height and maturity of sorghums grown primarily in the Americas are understood sufficiently to permit easy manipulations of that germ plasm. However, the American material represents a rather limited genetic base from which single-gene mutations have been selected. It is unreasonable to believe that all the variation in height and maturity among diverse sorghums can be explained by these genes. However, height does appear to be more simply controlled than does maturity, at the World Collection level.

C. Morphology

Grain color varies from white translucent to a very deep reddish-brown with gradations of pink, red, yellow, brown, and intermediates. Grain color is determined by pigmentation in the pericarp, testa, and endosperm. Specific genes determine the color of each of these parts. Pericarp color is controlled by R-Y-genes. A red pericarp contains R-Y- genes, white pericarp contains rryy or R-yy genes, and lemon yellow pericarps are rrY-. A pigmented testa occurs when B_1-B_2-ss and B_1-B_2-S- are present. These genotypes (B_1-B_2) contain condensed tannins and are referred to as brown sorghums. The pericarp color of a sorghum with B_1-B_2-S- genes is brown regardless of the pericarp genetics. White grain is preferred for human food and milling; brown has been generally found undesirable because of its bitter taste, intense color, and seed dormancy. However, brown sorghums are grown in certain areas of the world because they are more resistant to molds, weathering, and bird attack. In some areas brown sorghum is grown because other sorghums are destroyed. Argentina grows a high proportion of brown, bird-resistant, high-tannin sorghum.

Red grain is most frequently grown in the United States, where it is used primarily for livestock and poultry feed. However, larger quantities of white sorghums are grown in some areas because of good yields and improved quality of the white and yellow grains for processing. Most U.S. hybrids contain yellow endosperm genes that give the endosperm a pale yellow appearance. There is a strong movement toward production of tan plant hybrids. Disease or insect damage to the grain often causes colored spots in the pericarp and endosperm of sorghums with red and purple plant color. These stains affect grain appearance and processing properties.

The stem and leaf midrib are either sweet or non-sweet and dry or juicy, with gradations of both of these characteristics. Sweet stem is genetically recessive to non-sweet. These traits are important in forage sorghum quality and disease and drought resistance. Leaves of the sorghum plant appear alternately on the stem. In dwarf varieties, leaf sheaths overlap, but generally on taller types, portions of the internodes are exposed. Leaf size is a function of stem size and maturity. A cutinized layer covers the leaf and retards desiccation; during periods of drought, sorghum leaves infold or roll to reduce water loss.

The sorghum infloresence is a panicle, which varies in shape from compact to very open and lax and in size from 10 to 50 cm or more in overall length. Length and width of the panicle are inversely related. The panicle is a continuation of the vegetative axis. Primary branches appear at nodes within the panicle, and these branches are arranged in whorls, one above the other. The final branches bear one or several spikelets in which seeds are borne. Spikelets appear in pairs—the sessile one is fertile and the pedicellate one is staminate or neuter. Each sessile spikelet contains a primary and secondary floret. The ovary in the primary floret develops into the seed following fertilization. Some varieties that allow the development of both florets within the spikelet produce twin-seed. The seed are contained within the glumes and are covered by the glumes to varying degrees (25–100%).

D. Flowering

Anthesis occurs during the night or early morning hours, but is affected by climatic conditions. Flowering begins on the uppermost panicle branch and follows a regular downward progression and a horizontal plane around the panicle. If the pedicellate spikelets are staminate, a second wave of flowering begins at the tip moving downward after the primary wave has moved into the lower half of the panicle. The flowering process of one spikelet may be completed in 20 to 30 min, but the spikelet may remain open 2 or 3 hr. Flowering may span 6 to 15 days, depending on panicle size, temperature, and variety. A time span of 6 to 9 days (average 7 days) is usual; most of the spikelets on a panicle flower between Days 3 and 6. An adapted hybrid planted on uniform land generally completes anthesis in 10 to 15 days, but many stress factors cause nonuniformity. Anthers dehisce as they are exserted from the spikelet, or soon thereafter, and release pollen. A single panicle may produce from 20 to 100 million pollen grains. Stigmas are receptive for 1 to 2 days before anthesis and remain receptive for 8 to 16 days. Although sorghum is a self-pollinated species, natural outcrossing occurs and may range from 0 to 30+%, but averages less than 2%.

III. Sorghum Conversion Program

The cornerstone to sorghum improvement has been the tropical conversion program, a cooperative TAES–USDA project initiated in 1963, which changes tall, late-maturing tropical sorghum cultivars into short, early-maturing, nonphotosensitive types while retaining nearly 98% of the original genetic diversity. Tropical sorghums normally do not produce seed in temperate areas, thus the converted lines are extremely useful to sorghum breeders in temperate areas. Partially converted lines have been returned to Africa and have made significant improvements in sorghums in the tropics. Materials from the conversion program have dramatically changed the U.S. sorghum industry. Important economic traits obtained are disease and insect resistance; the stay-green trait, which improves drought tolerance; white grains on tan-colored plants, which produces improved quality; and many other properties. This long-term program continues to provide elite genes for sorghum improvement around the world. The benefits have been shared by sorghum programs through free exchange of elite germ plasm. Most new cultivars or hybrids released from sorghum programs have material from the conversion program in their pedigrees.

IV. Physiology

Sorghum has a lower osmotic concentration of the leaf juices than does maize, but that of the stem, crown, and root juices is higher in sorghum. Sorghum stems have a low moisture content and low transpiration ratio. Most data suggest that sorghum requires from 255 to 294 kg of water per kilogram of dry matter produced. Sorghum is slow to wilt and recovers well after rain or irrigation, making it more drought resistant than maize. Following drought induced wilting, sorghum leaves will recover within 5 days after watering. Whereas, maize was irreparably damaged.

Sorghum is not immune to drought however, high temperatures and moisture stress can affect growth, cause sterility problems, and substantially reduce yield. High temperatures between germination and floret initiation can result in lower grain yield. Plants exposed to high temperatures before floral initiation and at the late panicle development stage often have floret abortion.

Even though sorghum is drought tolerant, it responds well to supplemental irrigation. The amount of water required to produce maximum yields of sorghum is not a fixed value because temperature, relative humidity, wind, and soil moisture interact to determine the rate of both evaporation and transpiration. In some years the water requirement may drop to 41 to 46 cm and in a hot, dry year may go to 61 to 66 cm to produce maximum yields.

When sorghum plants begin to use water for germination, the rate for the first 2 or 3 weeks of development is slow (0.13–0.25 cm per day). A peak use of up to 0.84 cm per day may occur during the late boot and early heading stage, then water use rate averages about 0.64 cm per day from boot through the dough stage, which is a critical period. At this time sorghum will use about 7.6 cm of water in a 12-day period. Irrigation or water management is essential to maximize crop yields and includes land preparation methods and timing of irrigations, selection of planting seed, seeding rates, and amounts of fertilizer, herbicides, and insecticides.

Natural soil fertility is not generally sufficient to maintain a crop for maximum production. Sorghum requires relatively large amounts of nitrogen, phosphorous, and potassium; lesser amounts of calcium, magnesium, and sulfur; and small amounts of seven trace elements for proper plant growth. The most effective method to determine fertilizer needs is a soil test. The rule of thumb to follow in nutrient requirements for sorghum is that each 1000 kg of grain yield removes 13.6 kg of N, 4.5 kg of P_2O_5, and 13.5 kg of K_2O. Sorghum grows best when soil pH is between

6 and 7.5. If pH should drop below 6, lime can be added to bring it back into the optimum range.

At anthesis or approximately 60 to 70 days past emergence, about one-half of the total plant weight has been produced, and nearly 70% of the nitrogen, 60% of P_2O_5, and 80% of the K_2O have already been taken up. These values indicate the importance of nutrition during the early growth of the sorghum plant.

Within the first 30 to 35 days after plant emergence, nearly all growth is in the leaves. Floral differentiation occurs in photoperiod-insensitive material at approximately this time. Then the culm or stem begins rapid growth and continues until maximum leaf weight is reached (approximately 60 days) and maximum stem weight is obtained at 65 days past planting. The panicle size remains small and increases slowly in weight until about 18 days past differentiation, after which it increases rapidly in weight. Following pollination, the grain dramatically increases in weight, sometimes faster than the rate at which total dry matter accumulates in the plant. This lowers the stem weight because stored materials are moved from the stem to the developing seed. Most sorghums increase in dry weight until 30 to 38 days past anthesis, at which time maximum dry weight is attained. Maximum rates of dry matter accumulation occur 8 to 14 days past anthesis. More vitreous kernels reach harvestable moisture (12–15%) 45 to 60 days after anthesis. Softer kernels lose moisture at a slower rate.

V. Hybrids

In the more developed countries, sorghum is produced using F_1 hybrids provided by a sophisticated seed industry. Sorghum hybrids yield 20 to 50% more grain than varieties. They are more tolerant of drought and other adverse growing conditions. The yield increase comes from more grain per plant. Seed size is not significantly different between parents and the hybrid, although the hybrid has more leaf area and thus has a greater photosynthetic area. It has been suggested that the greater yield may be attributed to a more rapid cell division of the apical meristem.

Fertile sorghum hybrids are produced by growing specific parents (inbred lines) together in seed grower crossing fields (Fig. 1). Cytoplasmic male sterility is the key to hybridization in sorghum. Because the male-sterile plants do not disseminate viable pollen, these plants can be fertilized by pollen from the otherwise normal pollen-producing plants. Cyto-

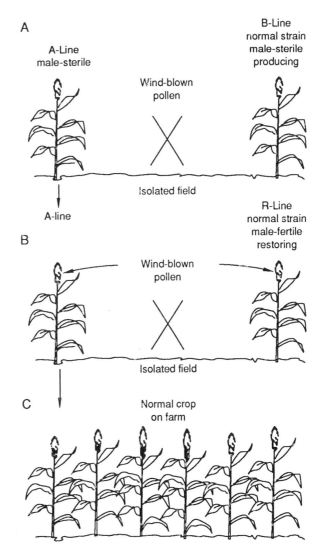

FIGURE 1 Methods for producing parental and hybrid seed of sorghum. (A) Parental crossing field; (B) Seed grower crossing field; (C) Single cross (A × R) sorghum hybrid.

plasmic–genetic male sterility is inherited maternally. This form of male sterility results from incompatibility between the cytoplasm of the female and nuclear factors contributed by the male parent. Cytoplasmic male sterility was found when cytoplasm from a milo sorghum was used with nuclear factors from kafir.

Sorghum hybrids originated in Texas, thus male and female parents were derived from germ plasm selected in a temperate-zone climate. As a result of this, the first hybrids developed in Texas were not suited to tropical areas, where floral differentiation occurs in short days and grain fill is accomplished under increasingly hot nights, which causes reduction in harvestable yield. Tropically adapted temperate-zone sorghums have been developed that have increased grain yields in the tropics.

Yield of grain under dryland cultivation averages 1800 to 4000 lb per acre. Under irrigation, yields of sorghum grain range from 6000 to 12,000 lb per acre. Yield is dependent on specific hybrid potential, fertility, availability of water, cultural management, and related biotic and abiotic stresses. In many important sorghum producing areas, cultivars are grown because a seed industry does not exist to supply hybrids. This limits the productivity of sorghum.

VI. Grain Structure and Physical Properties

The sorghum kernel is considered a naked caryopsis, although some African types retain their glumes after threshing. The kernel weight varies from 3 to 80 mg. The size and shape of the grain vary widely among sorghum races. Commercial sorghum grain has a flattened-spherical shape 4 mm long, 2 mm wide, and 2.5 mm thick with a kernel weight of 25 to 35 mg. Bulk density or test weight and grain density range from 708 to 60 kg/m^3 and 1.26 to 1.38 g/cm^3, respectively.

The sorghum caryopsis is composed of three anatomical parts: pericarp, endosperm, and germ. The relative proportion of these structures varies but in most cases is 6, 84, and 10%, respectively. The pericarp is the fruit coat and is fused to the sorghum seed. It originates from the ovary wall and is subdivided into three distinctive parts: epicarp, mesocarp, and endocarp. The epicarp is the outermost layer and is generally covered with a waxy film impermeable to water. The mesocarp varies in thickness and contains starch granules. The dominant gene Z affects thickness of the mesocarp; homozygous recessive ZZ produces a thick, starchy mesocarp. The endocarp plays a major role during water uptake and germination.

The seed is composed of the seed coat (or testa), endosperm, and germ. The endosperm tissue is triploid, resulting from the fusion of a male gamete with two female polar cells, a double fertilization. The testa is derived from the ovule integuments; in brown sorghums, it is thick and contains condensed tannins. It is sometimes referred to as a subcoat or undercoat and can be purple or brown in color. In nonbrown sorghums the testa is difficult to find without high-magnification microscopy.

The endosperm is composed of the aleurone layer and peripheral, corneous, and floury areas. The aleu-

rone consists of a single layer of rectangular cells adjacent to the tube cells or testa. Aleurone cells contain a thick cell wall, large amounts of proteins (protein bodies) and enzymes, ash (phytic acid bodies), and oil bodies (spherosomes). The peripheral endosperm adjacent to the aleurone layer is composed of dense cells containing large quantities of protein and small starch granules. These layers affect processing and nutrient digestibilities of sorghum. Processing by steam flaking, micronizing, popping, and reconstitution is designed to disrupt endosperm structure to improve digestibility.

The corneous and floury endosperm cells are composed of starch granules, protein matrix, protein bodies, and a thin cell wall rich in β-glucans and hemicellulose. In the corneous endosperm, the protein matrix has a continuous interphase with the starch granules with protein bodies embedded in the matrix. The starch granules are polygonally shaped and often contain dents from protein bodies. The appearance is translucent or vitreous. The opaque-floury endosperm is located around the geometric center of the kernel. It has a discontinuous protein phase, air voids, and loosely packaged round-lenticular starch granules and is opaque to transmitted light. Genetics and environment affect the proportions of floury to corneous endosperm (kernel texture) in sorghum kernels. Texture is related to grain hardness but is not the same.

The germ is diploid owing to the sexual union of one male and one female gamete. It is divided into two major parts: the embryonic axis and scutellum. The embryonic axis develops into the new plant; it is subdivided into a radicle and plumule. The radicle forms primary roots, whereas the plumule forms leaves and stems. The scutellum is the single cotyledon of the sorghum seed. It contains large amounts of oil (spherosomes), protein, enzymes, and minerals and serves as the connection between the endosperm and embryonic axis.

VII. Composition

Sorghum composition (Table I) varies significantly owing to genetics and environment. Starch (75–79%) is the major component, followed by protein (6.0–16.1%) and oil (2.1–5.0%). Protein content (N × 6.25) of sorghum is more variable and usually 1 to 2% higher than in maize. Approximately 80, 16, and 3% of the protein is in the endosperm, germ, and pericarp, respectively. Generally, sorghum contains 1% less oil and significantly more waxes than

TABLE I

Composition of Sorghum Grain[a]

Component	Mean	Range
Protein (N × 6.25) (%)	10.6	5.5–17.0
Ether extract (%)	3.4	2.2–4.0
Crude fiber (%)	2.5	2.0–3.0
Ash (%)	2.0	1.8–2.2
Nitrogen-free extract[b] (%)	80.0	75–86
Starch (%)	74.1	68–78
Soluble sugars (%)	2.1	1.8–2.2
Essential amino acids[c] (g AA/100 g protein)		
Lysine	2.1	1.6–2.4
Leucine	14.2	12.0–16.3
Phenylalanine[d]	5.1	4.0–5.5
Valine	5.4	4.5–6.2
Tryptophan	1.0	0.7–1.2
Methionine[e]	1.2	1.0–1.6
Threonine	3.3	2.8–3.5
Histidine[f]	2.1	1.8–2.3
Isoleucine	4.1	3.7–4.7

[a] All values are expressed on a dry matter basis for sorghum samples analyzed in the past 27 years, excluding endosperm mutants.
[b] Calculated by difference.
[c] FAO/WHO suggested pattern (g AA/100 g protein): lysine, 5.44; leucine, 7.04; phenylalanine + tyrosine, 6.08; valine, 4.96; tryptophan, 0.96; methinine + cysteine, 3.52; threonine, 4.0; isoleucine, 4.0.
[d] Phenylalanine can be partially spared by tyrosine.
[e] Methionine can be partially spared by cysteine.
[f] Histidine is considered an essential amino acid only for children.

does maize. Sorghum starch is composed of 70 to 80% amylopectin and 20 to 30% amylose. Waxy sorghums contain starch with 100% amylopectin and have properties and uses similar to those in waxy maize. Amylopectin and amylose have an average molecular weight of $8–10 \times 10^6$ and $1–3 \times 10^5$, respectively.

The main protein fraction in the kernel is the prolamines (kafrins) followed by glutelins. The alcohol-soluble prolamine fraction comprises 50% of the protein. These proteins are hydrophobic, rich in proline, aspartic, and glutamic acids, and contain little lysine. They are mainly found in protein bodies and are affected by nitrogen fertilization. Glutelins are high-molecular-weight proteins mainly located in the protein matrix. The lysine-rich protein fractions, albumins and globulins, predominate in the germ. High-lysine sorghums such as "P-721" and some Ethiopian types contain lower and higher levels of kafrins and albumins/globulins, respectively. The higher-lysine sorghum cultivars are soft or dented and are not produced commercially.

Most of the fiber is present in the pericarp and cell walls. Aleurone and endosperm cell walls are associated with ferulic and caffeic acid. Around 85% of the dietary fiber is insoluble; it is mainly composed of hemicellulose and cellulose. The soluble fraction is rich in pentosans and β-glucans. Approximately 70 and 30% of the pentosan are alkali and water soluble, respectively.

The germ and aleurone layer are the main contributors to the lipid fraction. The germ provides about 80% of the oil. The fatty acid composition consists mainly of linoleic (49%), oleic (31%), and palmitic (14.3%) acids. Sorghum contains 0.1 to 0.3% of an indigestible carnaubalike wax that is located on the epicarp, and also on the leaves and sheaths. Refined sorghum oil is very similar to maize oil in quality.

Most of the minerals are concentrated in the pericarp, aleurone, and germ. The ash fraction is rich in phosphorus and potassium and low in calcium and sodium. Most of the phosphorus is bound to phytic acid. The germ and aleurone are rich in fat-soluble and B vitamins. Carotenes are found only in yellow and heteroyellow endosperm cultivars. The carotenes are bleached by the sun; levels in mature grain are significantly lower than those of yellow maize.

All sorghums contain phenolic acids and most contain flavonoids, but only brown sorghums contain condensed tannins, which protect the kernel against preharvest germination and attack by insects, birds, and molds (fungi). Brown sorghum always have a pigmented testa (B_1-B_2-ss) and some have tannins in the pericarp (B_1-B_2-S-). Sorghums without a pigmented testa do not contain any condensed tannins. Birds can and do consume brown sorghums when other food is unavailable; in fact, animals consume greater amounts of bird-resistant sorghums (brown) than nonbird-resistant (nonbrown) sorghum in rations. The amount of weight gain is similar, but the feed efficiency is lower with brown sorghum. Sorghum does not contain any tannic acid, although some articles erroneously report condensed tannins as tannic acid. Assays for tannins based on colorimetric procedures for phenols give unreliable data for sorghum.

VIII. Market Classes

The Federal Grain Inspection Service (FGIS) recognizes four classes of sorghum: sorghum, white sorghum, tannin sorghum, and mixed sorghums. The class sorghum contains sorghum kernels with any color pericarp and endosperm as long as they do not contain a pigmented testa. The white sorghum class consists of kernels with white or colorless pericarp without a pigmented testa. The tannin sorghum class has kernels that contain pigmented testa and condensed tannins. Mixed class sorghum has more than 3% of tannin sorghum in other sorghum grains. The tolerance levels for foreign material were reduced in 1992.

In South Africa, sorghum standards have been established for malting and feed sorghums. The brown or tannin sorghums are not desired for malting by commercial maltsters. Brown sorghums can be malted by using special procedures to inactivate the tannins. For traditional malting by local artisans, the brown sorghums are malted because the white sorghums are preferred for food.

It is difficult to distinguish brown or tannin sorghums from red or even white sorghums in market channels. The FGIS uses a chlorox bleach test to determine sorghum kernels with a pigmented testa. The bleach/alkali removes the pericarp and the black or intense brown kernels with a pigmented testa can be easily identified when compared with standards. The percentage of brown kernels can be determined and is generally related to quantity of tannins. Argentina and a few other countries produce high-tannin sorghums for export, although the tannin content significantly reduces the value of sorghum.

IX. Traditional Uses of Grain

A. Milling

Thirty percent of world sorghum production is consumed directly by humans. For production of most traditional foods, sorghum is first dehulled with a wooden mortar and pestle. The grain is usually washed, placed in the mortar, and pounded vigorously with the pestle. The abrasive action frees the pericarp from the kernel above the aleurone layer on a nonbrown sorghum. Thick pericarp cultivars with hard endosperm and round kernels are preferred for dehulling or decortication. The bran or pericarp is separated from the grain by washing with water or by winnowing the sun-dried grain. Most sorghums are decorticated to remove 10 to 30% of the original grain weight depending on kernel hardness. It is impossible to dehull soft kernels because they disintegrate. Mechanical decortication with rice milling

equipment or abrasive disks is becoming more popular in many countries, particularly in urban areas.

The decorticated kernels are reduced to flour by hand pounding in the mortar and pestle. However, in urban areas, the housewife takes the dehulled grain to a small mill, where it is milled into flour or meal. The mill usually uses attrition mills with stones or steel plates that produce a smooth-feeling flour. Flour is sieved to obtain fractions with acceptable particle size for specific products. Attrition milling gives better flours than hammermilling, which produces gritty flour that imparts harsh texture to sorghum products.

The milled products from sorghum have a short shelf life because they contain lipids, thus the women mill sorghum daily. The lack of shelf-stable sorghum products is a major disadvantage. Many consumers have switched from sorghum foods to other cereals that are convenient to prepare.

B. Traditional Food Uses

The major categories of traditional foods are fermented and unfermented flat breads, fermented and unfermented thin and thick porridges, steamed and boiled cooked products, snack foods, and alcoholic and nonalcoholic beverages. Worldwide, the most popular unfermented flat breads are roti in India and tortillas in Central America. For rotis, a portion of the flour is gelatinized, mixed with more flour and warm water, and kneaded into a dough. The dough is shaped or rolled into a circle that is baked on a hot griddle. For tortilla production, whole or decorticated sorghum is lime-cooked, steeped overnight, washed, stone ground into a masa, shaped into thin circles, and baked on a hot griddle. The disc puffs during baking. Fresh roti and tortillas have good flavor and texture but they stale rapidly.

The most popular fermented breads are injera, kisra, and dosai consumed in Ethiopia, Sudan, and India, respectively. About 80% of the Ethiopian sorghum is used for production of injera. To make injera, the sorghum flour is mixed with water and a starter from a previous batch of injera. Part of the fermented batter is cooked to gelatinize the starch, cooled, and added to the fermenting batter. Then after fermentation for 24 to 48 hr, the batter is poured onto a covered greased pan for baking. The fermentation is very active, so many small bubbles form on the surface of the bread. Baked injera is a large, thin, flexible bread with many uniformly distributed air bubbles (fish eyes) on the surface. Kisra is similar but is much thinner. Dosai is produced from a mixture of black gram, sorghum, and rice flour. These products are consumed with spicy fillings and have excellent taste.

Porridges are fermented or cooked with acid or alkali. Tô is an unfermented stiff porridge very popular in West Africa. Decorticated sorghum flour is cooked in plain water or water acidified with tamarind juice or made alkaline with the leachate of wood ashes (potash). Popular fermented porridges are ogi and nasha consumed in West and East Africa, respectively. For these, whole sorghum is soaked in water and allowed to ferment for 2 to 3 days. The wet grain is crushed in a slurry of water and sieved to remove the bran. The throughs are allowed to ferment longer. Excess water is decanted and the resulting slurry cooked in water or milk.

For couscous production, sorghum flour is kneaded with enough water to form agglomerates. The particles are forced to pass through a coarse screen and then steamed. Sometimes the cooked couscous product is sun-dried, screened to a given particle size, and used as a convenience food. It is rehydrated when required. Couscous is eaten with special sauces and is an excellent food, but tedious to prepare. Decorticated sorghums are often cooked like rice. Special types of small-seeded, very hard sorghums are used as a substitute for rice.

Opaque beer is a traditional alcoholic beverage produced from malted sorghum. The sorghum is soaked in water for 12 to 24 hr and allowed to germinate for several days until the sprouts reach a certain stage. The germinated sorghum (malt) is sun-dried, crushed, and mixed with water, which is heated and held long enough to allow the malt enzymes to convert the starch into sugars. Then it is filtered to remove some of the sprouts and pericarp pieces. The filterate is brought to boiling, cooled, and placed in a fermentation pot that contains yeast from a previous batch of beer. Fermentation occurs overnight or longer and the beer is drunk while actively fermenting. The beer has high solids content, a low pH, a sour flavor, and a pink or red color when produced from red or brown sorghums. There are many variations in the type of opaque beers, with some sweet, nonsour products that are very good tasting. The length of fermentation and the extent of souring are related. Most opaque beer is very sour.

X. Industrial Uses

A. Wet Milling

Industrial uses of sorghum are similar to those of maize. Sorghum is wet-milled to produce starch with properties and uses similar to those of maize starch. Sorghum is more difficult to wet-mill than maize, and sorghum by-products are less desirable. Sorghum is wet-milled in the Sudan and possibly in Nigeria, where the grain is significantly less expensive. Wet-milling of sorghum in the United States was discontinued in the 1970s for economic reasons.

B. Sweet Sorghum

Sweet sorghum biomass, the entire above ground portion, is used for ethanol production. Yields of alcohol (182 proof) per tonne of sorghum grain are comparable to those of maize (387 vs. 372 liters). The commercial technology required to ferment sweet sorghum biomass into alcohol has been highly developed in Brazil. One tonne of sweet sorghum biomass has the potential to yield 74 liters of 200 proof alcohol.

C. Sorghum Syrup and Molasses

Sweet sorghum types are available that have been used to produce syrup and molasses, and special varieties are grown. The plants are cut, stripped of leaves, and pressed to force sap from the stalks. The juice is evaporated to form a strong-tasting syrup that is referred to as sorghum molasses. This process is common in the southern United States. Alternatively the juice can be processed and used for sugar production. This procedure is well developed but is not used commercially. Sorghum molasses or syrup has a strong aroma and unique flavor.

D. Dry Milling

Sorghum has been dry-milled into a wide variety of products, including low-fat grits, flour, acid-modified flour, and other products. The sorghum is tempered, decorticated with abrasive mills, and degerminated by impaction. The germ is separated from the endosperm particles by gravity separation. Good yields of low-fat grits are possible, especially with the new white, harder endosperm sorghum grains. The grits are used as a brewing adjunct in production of lager beer depending on the relative price of competing adjuncts. The most desirable grit has light color, bland flavor, and low oil content. The grits have been fortified with soy grits and used in U.S. food aid shipments to Africa, where sorghum is preferred.

E. Malting

Sorghum malt is produced extensively in South Africa. Pneumatic malting and floor malting is used.

The malt is used for alcoholic beverages, weaning foods, and breakfast foods. Sour opaque beers are produced commercially in large factories. Sorghum malt is mixed with cooked maize grits and allowed to sour for several hours. Then the soured mixture is added to additional malt and cooked corn grits to saccharify the starch. Finally, the mixture is incubated with yeast and consumed as a sour, opaque, actively fermenting beer. Sorghum malt is preferred for color and flavor. A significant portion of the sorghum grown in southern Africa is used for industrial malting. Prepared malts and beer powders for home brewing are popular products in South Africa. [See BREWING TECHNOLOGY.]

In Nigeria, sorghum and maize are being used to produce lager beer without barley malt following the government ban on the importation of barley and barley malt. Therefore, Nigerian breweries are producing clear (lager) beer from a combination of malted sorghum, sorghum and/or maize grits, and commercial enzymes that convert the starch to fermentable sugars. Sorghum malt has low diastatic power so commercial enzymes are required. In many processes, sorghum malt is not used because malting causes considerable dry matter losses. Economically, the use of grits and commercial enzymes is practical. The clear beer is of good quality with slightly different taste and keeping properties compared to those of barley malt lager beer. Recently, the ban on barley has been lifted in Nigeria.

F. Baked Products

Sorghum grits, meal, and flour can be used to produce a wide array of baked goods when mixed with wheat flour. Sorghum does not contain gluten, thus the amount of sorghum flour in the blend depends on the quality of the wheat flour, the baking procedure, formulation, and quality of the baked products desired. It is possible to produce nonwheat sorghum–cassava starch breads by gelatinizing the cassava starch. Such breads have intermediate loaf volume and stale rapidly.

G. Snacks and Cereals

Sorghum can be puffed, popped, shredded, and flaked to produce ready-to-eat breakfast cereals. Extrusion of sorghum produces acceptable snacks, cereals, and precooked porridges. Waxy and heterowaxy sorghum hybrids produce tender extrudates with excellent mouth feel. Micronized waxy sorghum flakes give granolas excellent texture.

XI. Nutritional Value

Sorghum has proximate composition, amino acid contents, and nutritional value similar to those of maize. However, because of its lower fat content, sorghum usually has slightly lower gross, digestible, and metabolizable energy than does maize. The protein digestibility of sorghum is 5% lower than that of maize. However, fermentation, malting, and other processing methods significantly improve nutritional value. Brown sorghums have lower nutritional value than sorghums without tannins; tannins lower protein digestibility and feed efficiency. Malting significantly enhances the digestibility and biological value of sorghum. Malted brown sorghums have greatly improved nutritional value, and decortication improves their protein digestibility and reduces their tannins.

Lysine and threonine are the first and second limiting amino acids of sorghum. There are high-lysine cultivars that contain approximately 50% more lysine and promote better weight gains in weaning rats. However, they have soft, floury endosperms and produce low yields of grain. Research to develop sorghum hybrids with harder endosperm and higher lysine continues with slow progress. The high-lysine types found in Ethiopia continue to be grown on a limited basis because they have excellent taste.

XII. Animal Feeds

The feeding value of sorghum for livestock species is generally considered to be 95% or more of the feeding value of yellow, dent maize. Brown sorghums are considered to have 85% of the feeding value of maize. Sorghum must be properly processed to enhance its digestibility. Poultry and swine feeds use ground sorghum extensively depending on relative costs and feeding value. Because sorghum is low in yellow pigments, additional carotenoids are used in rations where yellow-pigmented broilers are desired. [See FEEDS AND FEEDING.]

Sorghum is used extensively for dairy and beef cattle rations. In feedlots in the Great Plains, sorghum comprises 60 to 80% of the diet. Sorghum in these feedlots (up to 200,000 head) is usually steam-flaked and mixed with roughage and supplements and fed to the cattle immediately. The grain is sieved to remove foreign material, conditioned to about 18% moisture, steamed for 15 to 30 min, allowed to equilibrate for 15 min at 100°C, and flaked by large rollers. For good feed efficiency, the flakes of sorghum must be very thin and resistant to breakage during handling. The addition of moisture to the grain is an advantage to the feedlot operator.

Popping, micronizing, exploding, and reconstitution have been used to process sorghum for feedlot cattle. These methods, if properly used, will yield the feeding efficiency of steam-flaked sorghum. They afford an advantage for smaller feedlots because a source of steam is not required. Reconstitution and early harvesting require less energy for processing, but grain storage is a costly problem.

XIII. Sorghum Improvement

In the United States, new sorghum inbreds with white kernels and tan plant color have been released by the Texas Agricultural Experiment Station. They produce new hybrids with significantly impoved food, feed, and processing properties combined with good agronomics and tolerance to production hazards. A number of seed companies are developing or have released white or yellow hybrids, some with tan plant color. The tan grains have reduced levels of anthocyanin pigments and produce processed feeds with a light color. These improvements make sorghum more attractive for use in feeds and foods. For example, the white sorghums produce lighter-color grits at significantly higher yields than do red sorghums. White, tan plant homozygous, and heterowaxy hybrids are available for use in specific applications. The waxy grain has interesting processing properties, including greater expansion during extrusion, tender flakes useful in granola, and significantly improved steam-flaking characteristics. Some data suggest that waxy grains are more efficiently utilized by ruminants and swine.

International sorghum improvement was begun fairly recently, yet significant improvement has been made in sorghum yields and grain quality in many areas. However, in West Africa the new improved sorghums were attacked by head bugs and molds that essentially destroyed the grain. Efforts to breed sorghums with resistance to molds and head bugs have been only partially successful. Only photosensitive varieties consistently escape the head bugs, so efforts to increase yields have been largely thwarted. Improved local photosensitive types with tan plant and good-quality grain for food processing are required. Sorghum is an important food and feed crop that will continue to be improved by commercial seed companies and government research activities.

Bibliography

FAO. (1988). "Production Yearbook 1987. FAO Statistics," Vol. 41. Food and Agriculture Organization, Rome.

Harlan, J. R., and deWitt, J. M. J. (1972). A simplified classification of cultivated sorghum. *Crop Sci.* **12,** 172–176.

Miller, F. R., Barnes, D. K., and Cruzado, H. J. (1968). Effect of tropical photoperiods on the growth of sorghum when grown in 12 monthly plantings. *Crop Sci.* **8,** 499–502.

Murty, B. R., Arunachalam, V., and Saxena, M. B. L. (1967). Classification and catalogue of a world collection of sorghum. *Indian J. Genetics Plant Breeding* **27** (Spec. No.), 1–312.

Rooney, L. W., and Miller, F. (1982). Variation in the structure and kernel characteristics of sorghum. *In* "International Symposium on Sorghum Grain Quality" (L. W. Rooney and D. S. Murty, eds.), pp. 143–162. ICRISTAT, Patancheru, India.

Rooney, L. W., and Serna-Saldivar, S. O. (1990). Sorghum. *In* "Handbook of Cereal Science and Technology" (K. J. Lorenz and K. Kulp, eds.), Chap. 5. Marcel Dekker, New York.

Rooney, L. W., Earp, C. F., and Khan, M. N. (1982). Sorghum and millets. *In* "CRC Handbook of Processing and Utilization in Agriculture" (I. A. Wolf, ed.), Vol. II. CRC Press, Boca Raton, FL.

Rooney, L. W., Kirelis, A. W., and Murty, D. S. (1986). Traditional foods from sorghum: Their production, evaluation and nutritional value. *In* "Advances of Cereal Science and Technology" (Y. Pomeranz, ed.), Vol. VIII. American Association of Cereal Chemists, St. Paul, MN.

Stoskopf, N. C. (1980). "Cereal Grain Crops." Reston Publishing, Reston, VA.

Vanderlip, R. L. (1972). "How a Sorghum Plant Develops." Kansas Agricultural Experiment Station, Manhattan, KS.

Soybean Genetics and Breeding

JAMES R. WILCOX, *USDA-Agricultural Research Service, Indiana*

Glossary

Cultivar Strain of plants, developed by breeding and selection, that is uniform in characteristics and grown under cultivation; soybean cultivars are inbred lines, phenotypically homogeneous, and genetically stable

F_1, F_2, F_3, etc. Designation used for successive generations of inbreeding or filial generation; F_1 is the immediate progeny of a cross, the F_2 the self-pollinated progeny of the F_1, the F_3 the self-pollinated progeny of F_2, etc.

Genotype Genetic make-up or identified genes of an individual; genes may be identified by observable traits of individuals or their progeny

Heritability Extent to which traits are controlled by the genotype of an individual or strain and are transmitted from parent to offspring; heritability is often expressed as the ratio of genotypic to phenotypic variability and may be expressed as a percentage

Inbred line In soybean breeding, a line developed by successive generations of selfing, following hybridization, in which individuals making up the inbred lines are phenotypically homogeneous and genotypically homozygous; inbred lines with superior attributes may be designated as cultivars

Linkage group Association of genes that tend to be inherited together because of their proximity on the same chromosome; genes in different linkage groups are inherited independently

Phenotype Observable traits of individuals that are due to the interaction of the genotypes, or genetic constitutions, of the individuals with the environment

Restriction fragment length polymorphism (RFLP) Fragment of DNA that has been cut by enzymes, and identified by electrophoretic techniques; these RFLPs are used as marker sites on chromosomes that make up the soybean genome

Transgenic plants Genetic modification of a plant's genome by inserting DNA from different genotypes, usually from different species; transgenes are the genes transferred from different donor genomes and expressed in the recipient genome

Soybean, one of the world's major oilseed crops, is grown commercially in nearly 50 countries. Soybean oil is the major edible vegetable oil produced in the world; the residual meal is an important high-protein supplement of livestock feeds. Soybean genetics deals with the inheritance of both simple and complex traits of the plant, many of which are important in the development of improved cultivars. Various breeding methods are used to develop cultivars with high seed yield, resistance to pathogens, and seed compositional traits important in the utilization of the crop.

I. Introduction

The soybean, *Glycine max* (L.) Merr., introduced from China in the late 1700s, was not grown commercially in the United States until the early 1900s. Initial production of soybean was primarily for hay or silage or the crop was plowed into the soil as a green manure. It was not until 1941 that the U. S. acreage of soybean harvested for seed exceeded the acreage harvested for forage and other purposes. Soybean, grown on about 24 million hectares, is now the major oilseed crop produced in the United States and the residual meal is the primary source of high-quality protein in livestock feed rations. [*See* SOYBEAN PRODUCTION.]

Soybean seed of commercially grown cultivars averages 41% protein and 21% oil, on a moisture-free seed basis. About 95% of the oil is used as an edible oil in salad or cooking oils, and in margarines and shortenings. Industrial uses of the oil include components of paints, varnishes, plastics, lubricants, and printing inks. Soy protein has an excellent balance of essential amino acids, with only the sulfur containing amino acids slightly lower than the requirements for an ideal feed. Soybean meal is a key ingredient in pet and livestock feeds and is the primary source of protein in poultry rations. Less than 5% of soy protein is used for edible purposes as soy flour, protein concentrates and isolates, textured proteins, and in specialty foods such as tofu.

Soybean breeding programs were initiated in the United States in the 1930s by scientists in the U. S. Department of Agriculture (USDA). Early released cultivars were direct selections from soybean germplasm introduced from China, Japan, and Korea. The first cultivar developed from hybridization was "Lincoln," released in 1944. Almost all cultivars released in the United States prior to 1970 were developed by USDA-Agricultural Research Service (ARS) and State Agricultural Experiment Station soybean breeders. These cultivars were grown on virtually all the U.S. acreage planted to soybean. The Plant Variety Protection Act, passed in 1970, provided protection to breeders of self-pollinated crops against unauthorized production of cultivars. This encouraged cultivar development by commercial interests and now most of the soybean acreage in the northern United States is planted to cultivars developed by private companies. In the southern United States a greater portion of the acreage is planted to cultivars developed by publicly funded breeding programs. [*See* CULTIVAR DEVELOPMENT.]

The soybean is a self-pollinated plant and the small amount of outcrossing that occurs, less than 1% is due to pollen transmission by insects. Controlled pollinations between selected parents are tedious to make and result in one to three seeds per successful pollination. The mode of pollination and difficulty in making controlled crosses affect breeding methods used to improve the soybean. Released cultivars are genetically stable inbred lines, maintained by harvesting pure seed of each cultivar.

II. Qualitative Genetics

The soybean has a $2n$ chromosome number of 40 and is considered to be a functional diploid of polyploid origin. Genetic studies have identified over 200 loci, some with multiple alleles, that control reaction to pathogens and insects, plant growth and morphology, physiological and biochemical traits, and chemical composition of the seed. About 70 loci have been associated in 19 linkage groups, or segments of chromosomes.

Biochemical techniques have been used to identify small fragments of DNA electrophoretically. Over 500 of these restriction fragment length polymorphisms (RFLP) have been mapped to specific sites on all 20 soybean chromosomes. These RFLPs are used as reference points to map identified genes on individual chromosomes. In addition, the RFLPs are used to locate multiple sites on chromosomes that are associated with the expression of quantitatively inherited traits. Knowing the number and locations of sites controlling the expression of specific traits of soybean increases the efficiency of breeding for these traits. [*See* PLANT GENETIC ENHANCEMENT.]

A Genetic Type Collection for qualitatively inherited traits is a part of the soybean germplasm collection maintained by the USDA-ARS at Urbana, Illinois. The Genetic Type Collection includes strains that contain all published genes of soybean, a collection of near-isogenic lines containing various combinations of genes, a linkage collection containing combinations of linked genes, and a cytological collection containing interchanges, inversions, deficiencies, trisomics, and tetraploids of soybean. [*See* PLANT GENETIC RESOURCES; PLANT GENETIC RESOURCE CONSERVATION AND UTILIZATION.]

Many economically important traits of soybean are controlled by genes with qualitative effects (Table I). The two major growth types of soybean, determinate (*dt1*) and indeterminate (*Dt1*), affect flower development and, indirectly, plant height. Genes affecting time of flowering and maturity, *E1–E4,* have been used in combination with alleles at the *Dt1* locus to develop cultivars uniquely adapted to specific production systems.

Reactions to major pathogens of soybean are controlled by genes with qualitative effects. Genes for resistance have been incorporated into improved soybean cultivars to minimize losses due to these pathogens. Several genes have been identified that affect chemical composition of soybean seed. Cultivars have

TABLE I

Genes Controlling Traits of Economic Importance in Soybean

Gene	Phenotype
	Growth and morphology
DT1	Indeterminate plant type
dt1	Determinate plant type
E1-E4	Time of flowering and plant maturity
	Pathogen resistance
Rpg1	Bacterial blight (*Pseudomonas syringea* pv. *glycinea*)
rxp	Bacterial pustule (*Xanthomonas campestris* pv. *glycines*)
Rcv	Cowpea chlorotic mottle virus
Rpv1, rpv2	Peanut mottle virus
Rsv1, rsv1-t, Rsv2	Soybean mosaic virus
Rmd	Powdery mildew (*Microsphaera diffusa*)
Rpm	Downy mildew (*Peronospora manshuruca*)
Rcs1-Rcs3	Races of frogeye leafspot (*Cercospora sojina*)
Rpp1-Rpp3	Races of soybean rust (*Phakopsora pachyrhizi*)
Rbs1, Rbs2	Races of brown stem rot (*Phialophora gregata*)
Rps1-Rps7	Races of Phytophthora rot (*Phytophthora sojae*)
Rdc1, Rdc2	Races of stem canker (*Diaporthe phaseolorum* var. *caulivora*)
rhg1, rhg2, rhg3, Rhg4	Races of cyst nematode (*Heterodera glycines*)
	Variants for seed protein and oil
1x1-1x3	Absence of lipoxygenase enzymes Lx1, Lx2, Lx3
ti	Absence of Kunitz trypsin inhibitor
fan[1]	Low linolenic acid
fap1[2]	Low palmitic acid
fap2[2]	High palmitic acid
fas, fas^a, fas^b[3]	High stearic acid

Adapted with permission from Palmer, R. G., and Kilen, T. C. (1987). Qualitative genetics and cytogenetics. *In* "Soybeans: Improvement, Production, and Uses" (J. R. Wilcox, ed.) 2nd ed., pp. 125–209. ASA, CSSA, SSSA, Madison, WI.

[1] Wilcox, J. R., and Cavins, J. F. (1987). Gene symbol assigned for linolenic acid mutant in the soybean. *J. Hered.* **78,**410.

[2] Erickson, E. A., Wilcox, J. R., and Cavins, J. F. (1988). Inheritance of altered palmitic acid percentage in two soybean mutants. *J. Hered.* **79,**465–468.

[3] Graef, G. L., Fehr, W. R., and Hammond, E. G. (1985). Inheritance of three stearic acid mutants of soybean. *Crop Sci.* **25,**1076–1079.

been developed that lack the lipoxygenase enzymes L2 and L3, resulting in improved flavor of oil and of soy food products. The cultivar "Kunitz," that lacks the Kunitz trypsin inhibitor, produces seed with improved protein digestibility that can be fed to finishing hogs without first preheating to inactivate this trypsin inhibitor. Cultivars with low linolenic acid have improved oil flavor and stability and those with altered levels of palmitic and stearic acids have potential use in specialty markets for soybean oil.

III. Quantitative Genetics

Most soybean traits of economic importance including seed yield, plant maturity, plant height, lodging resistance, seed size, and protein and oil content of the seed are quantitatively inherited. These traits are controlled by few to many genes and may be strongly influenced by environment.

Quantitatively inherited traits of soybean are controlled by genes with additive genetic effects. That is, the many individual genes that control the expression of these traits each have small effects that combine in an additive fashion to control the level of expression of a trait. Since soybean cultivars are true-breeding inbred lines, these additive effects can be fixed during the development of inbred lines and maintained in selections released as new cultivars.

A. Heritability of Traits

The degree of genetic control of a quantitatively inherited trait is frequently expressed as the heritability of that trait. Estimates of heritability are applicable only to the population from which they are derived. However, when different traits are measured in a single population, or in different populations, the relative heritability of the traits can be determined. Heritabilities for traits of economic importance and of primary interest to soybean breeders are shown in Table II. Seed yield, economically the most important trait of soybean, typically has a low heritability relative to other traits. In contrast, plant maturity, percentage seed protein, and percentage seed oil are traits that are highly heritable. Heritability estimates are used to predict progress that can be made by selecting for a specific trait in a breeding population. In general, greater genetic improvement results from selecting for a trait with a high heritability than when selecting for a trait with a low heritability.

B. Interrelationships Among Traits

Quantitatively inherited traits may be associated with each other to varying degrees depending upon the population in which these traits are segregating. Correlations between traits may be higher in segregating populations where parents differ greatly in measured traits than where small differences exist between parental values. Table III lists typical correlations between seed yield and other quantitatively inherited traits in soybean. In these populations there is no

TABLE II

Heritability Estimates in Percentage for Quantitatively Inherited Traits in Progenies from Different Soybean Crosses

Trait	Cross 1	Cross 2	Cross 3	Cross 4	Cross 5	Cross 6
Seed yield	38	23	10	39	52	58
Seed weight	68	53	44	92	92	88
Plant height	75	82	70	66	82	90
Lodging	54	59	51	60	63	70
Maturity	78	84	79	75	90	92
Seed protein	63	—	57	76	86	81
Seed oil	67	—	51	74	88	82

Adapted with permission from Burton, J. W. (1987). Quantitative genetics: Results relevant to soybean breeding. *In* "Soybeans: Improvement, Production, and Uses" (J. R. Wilcox, ed.), 2nd. ed. pp. 211–247. ASA, CSSA, SSSA, Madison, WI.

association between seed yield and oil content of the seed. In contrast, in most of these populations there is an inverse relationship between seed yield and seed protein content. This inverse relationship has limited progress in developing cultivars with superior seed yield and high seed protein.

Correlations among traits may simplify or complicate breeding efforts to develop inbred lines with specific combinations of traits. Soybean breeders may use selection indices when selecting for multiple, correlated traits. These selection indices are numeric values that put different emphasis on the selected traits and are usually based on heritability and economic value of the traits and on correlations among the traits.

IV. Sources of Genetic Variability

Genetic variability provides the basis for breeding improved cultivars; without variability there are no opportunities for genetic improvement. Genetic variability exists in germplasm collections and is created by making crosses among selected parents, followed by self-pollination to permit segregation for observable traits.

A. U.S. Soybean Germplasm Collection

The USDA-ARS maintains about 14,000 soybean accessions at Urbana, Illinois. These accessions have been collected from primary centers of origin for soybean, China, Japan, and Korea, and from other countries where soybean research has resulted in the development of diverse germplasm. The collection contains accessions of *Glycine sojae,* a wild, annual relative that has the same chromosome number and is cross-compatible with the cultivated soybean. There are accessions of 15 other perennial *Glycine* species that generally are not cross-compatible with the cultivated soybean without the use of special tech-

TABLE III

Estimates of Phenotypic Correlations of Seed Yield with Other Traits in Progenies from Six Soybean Crosses

Trait correlated with seed yield	Cross 1	Cross 2	Cross 3	Cross 4	Cross 5	Cross 6
Seed weight	−0.07	0.20	0.10	−0.01	0.21★★	0.21
Plant height	0.32★★	0.44★★	−0.13	−0.04	0.02	0.26
Lodging	0.36★★	0.27★	−0.21★★	0.03	−0.20★★	−0.26
Maturity	0.37★★	0.37★★	0.13	0.08	0.22★★	0.37
Seed protein	—	−0.42★★	0.22★★	−0.34★★	−0.17★	−0.14
Seed oil	—	0.05	−0.01	0.26	0.08	0.07

Adapted with permission from Burton, J. W. (1987). Quantitative genetics: Results relevant to soybean breeding. *In* "Soybeans: Improvement, Production, and Uses" (J. R. Wilcox, Ed.), 2nd ed., pp. 211–247. ASA, CSSA, SSSA, Madison, WI.
★, ★★ Exceeds the 5 and 1% probability levels, respectively.

niques to culture immature embryos from interspecific crosses.

The germplasm collection is an important reservoir of genes that has been essential to the development of improved cultivars. About 20 of these accessions have provided the germplasm for 95% of released cultivars. In addition, the germplasm collection has contributed genes for pathogen, nematode, and insect resistance that have been essential for successful soybean production in areas where these pests limit seed yields. The collection has also contributed genes for improved chemical composition of the seed that will increase both uses and markets for soybean. This collection is the ultimate source of genetic variability for soybean improvement.

B. Cultivars and Breeding Lines

Two commonly used sources of genetic variability for cultivar development are previously released cultivars and improved germplasm registered with the Crop Science Society of America. Descriptions of both registered cultivars and germplasm are published in the journal *Crop Science*. Registered germplasms may not merit release as cultivars but are genetically improved sources of unique traits.

Superior lines from various soybean improvement programs are an important source of genetic variability for soybean improvement. These lines may not possess all the attributes required for release as improved cultivars but have combinations of characteristics that make them useful as parents. Cooperative performance tests of superior breeding lines, conducted by soybean breeders, provide a method for exchange of this genetic material.

C. Transgenic Plants

The development of transgenic plants provides the opportunity to increase genetic variability for soybean beyond limits imposed by intra- and interspecific cross compatability. Current technology permits foreign DNA from totally unrelated species to be introduced and expressed in the soybean genome. At present, transgenes controlling tolerance to specific herbicides, resistance to insects, and increased methionine in seed proteins have been successfully incorporated into soybean. This technology provides opportunities to extensively increase genetic variability, particularly for qualitatively inherited traits of soybean.

V. Breeding Objectives for Soybean

A. Seed Yield

The primary breeding objective for soybean improvement programs has been high seed yield. Soybean is sold by weight or volume of seed; therefore, increasing seed production per unit area is essential in the development of an improved cultivar. Selection for seed yield in a breeding program is usually delayed until homogeneous, inbred lines are developed; this minimizes genetic variability within lines and maximizes genetic variability among lines. Since seed yield has a low heritability and is strongly influenced by environment, reliable estimates of the genetic potential for seed yield are determined by replicated performance trials at different locations and over several years. Seed yields of inbred lines that are greater than parental yields result from transgressive segregation where new gene combinations affecting seed yield accumulate in inbred lines that were not present in parent cultivars. Soybean breeders have increased the genetic potential for seed yield an average of 0.5 to 1.0% per year over the past 50 years.

B. Plant Maturity

Maturity date is an important attribute for improved soybean cultivars. Soybean cultivars begin their reproductive phase in response to varying lengths of the dark period. The date that cultivars flower strongly influences the date they mature; therefore, cultivars are adapted to specific bands of latitude where seasonal variation in length of the dark period is associated with growing season. Soybean germplasm is classified into 13 maturity groups, from 000 through X. The 000 germplasm lines are adapted as full-season lines in the higher latitudes; X germplasm lines are adapted to low latitudes in close proximity to the equator.

Germplasm used in breeding programs may include parents from diverse maturity groups, so selection for suitable maturity for a production area is essential. Since maturity is a highly heritable trait, selections can effectively be made on a single-plant basis in early segregating generations following a cross. Soybean breeders have developed productive cultivars in each of the maturity groups and have expanded the range of maturity groups to include 000 and X.

C. Plant Height

Selection has resulted in the development of cultivars that vary from about 0.75 to 1.00 m in mature plant height when grown in productive environments. In the higher latitudes of the midwestern United States or southern Argentina, indeterminate cultivars are grown to obtain adequate plant height for high seed yields. In the lower latitudes of the southern United States and South America, determinate cultivars are grown to limit plant height during the long growing season. A few determinate cultivars have been developed for production in the midwestern United States. These cultivars average 0.50 to 0.70 m in mature plant height and are typically seeded at 1.5 times the normal seeding rate to obtain high yields of these short-statured plants.

D. Lodging Resistance

Lodging, the tendency of plants to lean away from vertical growth, may limit plant photosynthesis during the growing season and interfere with harvest when plants are mature. Lodging tends to increase as plant population increases since individual plants are taller and have thinner stems when grown at high populations. Lodging resistance was not an important trait when cultivars were grown for fodder or as a green manure and older cultivars frequently lodged badly. Breeding efforts have been very successful in developing cultivars that are resistant to lodging and produce high seed yields at normal plant populations. Determinate cultivars developed for the Midwest are very resistant to lodging, even at high plant populations, because of their short stature.

E. Seed Size

Seed size, commonly expressed as weight/seed, receives only limited attention in most soybean breeding programs. Seed of currently grown cultivars range in size from about 100 to 200 mg/seed. Within this range there is little relationship between seed yield and seed size. Soybean genotypes with exceptionally large or exceptionally small seeds do not produce as high yields as cultivars with the normal range of seed size. Seed size may be an important attribute of soybean cultivars developed for specialty markets. Very small seed, 80 to 100 mg, is preferred for the production of natto, a fermented food product in which the integrity of the seed is partially maintained. Large-seeded cultivars, 180 to 250 mg, have traditionally been preferred for the production of tofu, a curd developed by precipitating proteins from soy milk.

F. Seed Oil Content

Soybean cultivars typically average 20 to 22% oil in the seed and this value has not changed appreciably in 50 years of soybean breeding. Since there is no close association between seed yield and oil content, soybean breeders have been able to successfully increase seed yield while maintaining high oil content. Cultivars have been developed with 23% oil, which is near the maximum value of accessions in the germplasm collection. Recent breeding efforts have altered the fatty acid composition of soybean oil, providing opportunities for developing cultivars with unique fatty acid composition for specialty markets for soy oil.

G. Seed Protein Content

Protein content of currently grown cultivars ranges from 39 to 41% and, like oil content, has not been increased in 50 years of soybean breeding. Accessions are available in the germplasm collection that contain 52% protein in the seed. The strong inverse relationship between protein and oil has precluded the development of soybean with both high protein and high oil (Fig. 1). Disincentives for breeding to increase seed protein in soybean are: (i) soybean is purchased on a weight or volume basis with no premium for chemical composition of the seed and (ii) the moderately strong inverse relationship between seed yield and seed protein.

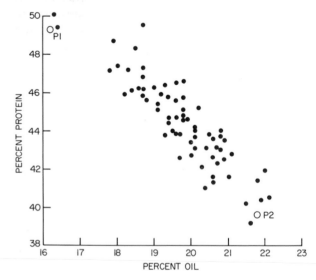

FIGURE 1 The inverse relationship between seed protein and oil content in progenies from a cross between "Pando" (P1) a high-protein parent and "Woodworth" (P2) a high-oil parent.

Increasing seed protein has recently become an important breeding objective to maintain the competitive place of U. S. soybean in world markets. Both recurrent selection and backcrossing breeding methods have been used to increase seed protein of breeding lines. However, in breeding populations the highest protein breeding lines generally are not the highest yielding lines. Backcrossing high seed protein into high yielding cultivars has been very successful in overcoming the inverse relationship between seed yield and protein. There has been virtually no success to date in overcoming the inverse relationship between seed protein and oil.

H. Disease Resistance

There are about 35 different pathogens that cumulatively cause annual losses estimated as high as 12% of the soybean crop in the United States. Some of these pathogens can be successfully controlled by the use of resistant cultivars. Breeding for resistance to specific pathogens that reduce seed yield or quality of seed produced is an integral part of most soybean improvement programs.

Bacterial diseases that reduce seed yield include bacterial blight (*Pseudomonas syringae* pv *glycinea*) and bacterial pustule (*Xanthomonas campestris* pv *glycines*). Selection for high seed yield and favorable agronomic traits has indirectly resulted in high levels of resistance to bacterial blight. Widely grown cultivars rarely show blight symptoms in breeding nurseries or production fields while accessions from the germplasm collection may show severe leaf blight when grown in these same areas. The *rxp* gene for resistance to bacterial pustule has been incorporated into virtually all cultivars grown in the southern United States, eliminating the 8 to 11% yield losses commonly associated with susceptibility to this disease.

Virus diseases for which genes for resistance are available include cowpea chlorotic mottle virus (*Rcv*), peanut mottle virus (*Rpv1* and *Rpv2*), and soybean mosaic virus (*Rsv1* and *Rsv1-t*). These virus diseases may reduce seed yield or cause discoloration of seed coats that reduce the value of the seed. Since economic losses due to virus diseases are not severe, breeding for resistance to viruses receives limited attention in most breeding programs.

Diseases caused by fungi cause the greatest yield losses in soybean and also are responsible for poor quality seed, resulting in lowered prices to the producer. Phytophthora root rot (*Phytophthora sojae*) can cause pre- and postemergence damping off of suscep-

tible seedlings severe enough to require replanting of production fields. Damage may be as insidious as slightly reduced plant growth with subsequent losses in seed yield. This disease has been effectively controlled with the development of resistant cultivars. As new races of the pathogen became prevalent, additional genes for resistance were bred into new cultivars. Sources of field resistance, that are nonrace-specific, have been identified and are being bred into cultivars that will be resistant to a wide spectrum of races of the pathogen.

Brown stem rot (*Phialophora gregata*) causes internal browning of the pith and vascular tissue and foliar necrosis of susceptible cultivars. The disease is widespread in the midwestern United States and can result in yield losses as high as 44%. Several cultivars have been developed with moderately high levels of resistance to the pathogen.

Stem canker (*Diaporthe phaseolorum* var. *caulivora*) is characterized by a lesion encircling the base of soybean stems during early reproductive stages of the plant resulting in plant death. Virulent races of the pathogen have become prevalent in the southern United States causing yield losses as high as 100%. Resistant cultivars have been developed by incorporating into them one of two genes for resistance to the pathogen.

Sudden death syndrome (*Fusarium solani*) causes a foliar necrosis and eventual leaf loss as soybean enters the reproductive stages of development. The disease frequently occurs in production fields that have optimum growing conditions and high yield potential. Limited information is available on the genetics of resistance to the pathogen. Cultivars have been identified that have a high level of resistance and these are being used as parents to develop additional high yielding, resistant cultivars.

Soybean rust, caused by *Phakopsora pachyrhizi,* is a widespread foliar disease in the orient that can cause yield losses as high as 40 to 50%. The disease has not been identified in North America but has been found in Puerto Rico and South America. The disease can be controlled by the development of resistant cultivars, using the *Rpp1* and *Rpp2* genes.

Two pathogens adversely affect seed quality and result in lower prices for seed lots exhibiting disease symptoms. The *Diaporthe–Phomopsis* complex causes cracked, shrivelled, and moldy seed and reduces seed germination. Resistant accessions have been identified in the germplasm collection and have been used as parents to develop cultivars with a moderate level of resistance to the pathogen. Purple seed stain, a discoloration of soybean seed caused by *Cercospora kikuchii,* may be widespread in soybean producing areas under environmental conditions that favor the pathogen. Cultivars differ in susceptibility to this disease and soybean breeders select against extreme susceptibility, thus limiting disease problems under most production conditions. [*See* PLANT PATHOLOGY.]

I. Nematode Resistance

The soybean cyst nematode, SCN (*Heterodera glycines*), is the most destructive and widespread nematode attacking soybean. The minute worms feed on soybean roots causing extensive yield losses in southern, southeastern, and midwestern states of the United States and in China and Korea. Genes for resistance to specific races of the nematode have been incorporated into resistant cultivars using various breeding procedures. Each of these cultivars is resistant to a limited number of races of the nematode. The soybean accession PI 437654 is resistant to all known races of SCN and the resistance in this accession has been incorporated into the cultivar "Hartwig."

Root knot nematodes (*Meloidogyne* spp.), particularly *M. arenaria, M. incognita,* and *M. javonica,* can cause yield losses up to 90% on susceptible soybean grown in light-textured soils in warm climates. Nematode feeding results in galls up to 20 mm in size on plant roots, interfering with water and nutrient transport within the plant. Even though the genetics of resistance to root knot nematodes is not well understood, breeders have been successful in developing cultivars with high levels of resistance to this pest.

J. Insect Resistance

Foliar-feeding and pod-feeding insects reduce soybean yields more severely in the warmer climates of low latitudes than in cooler climates of higher latitudes. Identified resistance to insects has taken two forms, (i) antibiosis, an adverse effect of the plant on insect growth, survival, and reproduction, and (ii) antixenosis, an adverse effect on insect behavior, such as visitation by insects. Antibiosis has been used in the development of cultivars with general resistance to foliar feeding insects. Antixenosis, in the form of dense pubescence covering the soybean plant, has been used to discourage both foliar- and pod-feeding insects.

VI. Breeding Methods Employed

Soybean breeding includes (i) creating genetic variability for specific traits, and (ii) identifying and selecting desireable variants for these traits. Breeding methods commonly employed in soybean improvement include pedigree, single seed descent, early generation testing, backcrossing, and recurrent selection. Each of these methods has been used to develop cultivars that have been released for commercial production.

A. Pedigree Method

The pedigree method has been used to combine favorable traits from two or more parents. Following a cross between selected parents, progenies are inbred from the F_1 through successive generations while maintaining the genetic relationship or pedigree of each selected individual. Several hundred F_2 plants are commonly grown from a cross and from these selections are made based on phenotypic attributes. Selected plants are grown in individual progeny rows in the F_3 generation and selections are made first among phenotypically desirable rows, and then for phenotypically desirable plants within rows. The process is repeated in successive generations, typically growing one generation each year in the field, until plants within rows are phenotypically uniform. Selected rows in advanced generations are harvested and evaluated in succeeding years in replicated performance trials. Advantages of the pedigree method of breeding are that selections can be made in early generations based on highly heritable phenotypic traits such as disease resistance, plant maturity, and morphological traits such as plant height. Breeding lines are evaluated in successive years under different environments, creating opportunities for the expression of traits and for effective selection. Typically one generation is grown per year so several years are required to identify lines for evaluation in replicated performance trials. This breeding method is not used extensively today but it was the primary soybean breeding method used until about 1970.

B. Single-Seed Descent

Single-seed descent, or a modification of this method, is currently the most commonly used breeding method to develop improved soybean cultivars. Following the F_1 generation from crosses between selected parents, the F_2 generation is grown and one seed from each F_2 plant is advanced to the next generation. The process is repeated, without selection, in successive generations until the desired level of inbreeding is attained, usually the F_4 or F_5 generation. Individual plants are then selected based on phenotypic traits and seed from these plants is increased to produce adequate seed for replicated performance trials. Since each F_2 plant is represented by a single F_4 or F_5 plant, genetic variability in the F_4 or F_5 generation is equal to the variability in the F_2 generation.

The single-seed descent method of breeding has several advantages in soybean improvement. Since no selection is practised in early generations and only one seed per plant is needed, several generations can be grown each year using winter nurseries or indoor growth facilities. Plants can be grown in very limited space and either photoperiod is controlled or growth regulators are used to minimize plant size since only one seed is needed from each plant. The primary disadvantage to this breeding method is that the identity of superior plants in each generation is lost. Therefore, superior F_2 and F_3 plants cannot be identified and additional selections made from progenies of these superior plants.

C. Early Generation Testing

Early generation testing is a breeding method designed to identify early in the breeding program soybean lines that have superior yield potential. The method utilizes evaluation of breeding lines in replicated performance trials during the development of inbred lines. Crosses are made between selected parents and the F_1 and F_2 generations grown as spaced plants to insure adequate seed production for performance tests. Initial performance tests are conducted in the F_3 generation evaluating F_3 lines from selected F_2 plants. Based on results of these tests, both crosses and F_2-derived lines with superior yield are identified and evaluated a second year in replicated F_4 performance trials conducted in multiple-row plots. F_4 plants selected from the border rows of these multiple-row plots are retained from those plots with superior performance. The F_4 plants from selected plots are evaluated as F_5 progeny rows, and then in the F_6 generation in replicated performance trials. The primary advantage of this breeding method is the identification in early generations of crosses and breeding lines that have superior yield potential. If superior F_2 lines can be identified early in the program, advanced generation selections can be made from progenies of these superior lines. This method requires extensive performance trials and data collection in all stages of the breeding program.

D. Backcrossing

Backcrossing is a widely used breeding method to transfer a specific trait identified in a donor parent to a recurrent parent that has superior attributes. A cross is made between the recurrent parent and the donor parent and as soon as progeny are identified that carry the desired trait from the donor parent, these progeny are crossed back to the recurrent parent. The process is repeated, using selected progeny from each backcross generation to again cross back to the recurrent parent until the phenotype of the recurrent parent is recovered, in addition to the trait transferred from the donor parent. Usually five to seven backcrosses are required to completely recover the phenotype of the recurrent parent. In each backcross generation progeny with the desired trait may be identified as early as the F_1 generation if the trait is dominant or in the F_2 generation if the trait is recessive.

Backcrossing has been used extensively in soybean breeding to incorporate specific genes for disease resistance into superior cultivars . For example, resistance to specific races of *Phytophthora sojae* have been incorporated into many soybean cultivars. When the resistant, backcross-derived form of the cultivar is released, the year of release of the resistant cultivar is appended to the name of the original cultivar, e.g., "Williams 82," "Century 84," and "Hobbit 87" are resistant forms of the cultivars Williams, Century, and Hobbit that were released in 1982, 1984, and 1987, respectively.

The advantage of the backcross breeding method is that success in cultivar improvement is assured. With an adequate number of backcrosses the phenotype and performance of the recurrent parent are recovered plus the desirable trait from the donor parent. The limitation of this breeding method is that no improvement is made for traits other than the one transferred from the donor parent.

E. Recurrent Selection

Recurrent selection, a breeding procedure more widely used with cross-pollinated crops, has been used successfully to improve soybean. This breeding procedure is used to improve quantitatively controlled traits by gradually accumulating in breeding lines genes that affect the expression of these traits. Selected parents are intermated in all combinations, and their F_1 progeny may be intermated to assure random assortment of genes controlling the desired trait. Progeny from the intermatings may be inbred one or two generations, and then evaluated in performance trials and a percentage of the best lines for the desired trait is selected. These selected lines are again intermated, either in all combinations or at random, to redistribute the genes controlling the trait. After performance trials, superior lines for the trait are again selected for the next cycle of intermating. The process is repeated for successive cycles. Recurrent selection has been used to accumulate genes affecting maturity, seed yield, and chemical composition of seed including oil, protein, and fatty acid composition of the oil.

The advantage of recurrent selection is that genes controlling quantitative traits can be effectively accumulated in breeding lines. Most traits of economic importance in soybean are controlled primarily by additive effects of genes and recurrent selection is effective in accumulating genes with additive effects. Selections can be made at any stage of a recurrent selection program, further evaluated in performance trials, and, if warranted, released as improved cultivars.

Recurrent selection requires extensive crossing among selected parents in each generation. Hand pollinations, which are difficult and time consuming to make, may limit the number of selections that can be intermated in each generation. Genes that cause male sterility in soybean have been incorporated into recurrent selection populations to facilitate intermating; selection to eliminate the genes for male-sterility is done during inbreeding to develop homozygous lines for release as cultivars.

VII. Performance Testing of Improved Germplasm

Soybean breeding lines, inbred to phenotypic uniformity, are evaluated in replicated performance trials to determine their merit for economically important, quantitatively inherited traits. These trials are conducted in multiple-row plots, 4 to 6 m in length, and replicated two to six times at a location. Multiple-row plots usually vary from 4 to 10 rows with spacing between rows from 0.75 m for 4-row plots to 0.20 m for 10-row plots. Only the center 2 to 6 rows are harvested to minimize effects of adjacent plots on yield determinations. Performance data, including maturity date, plant height, plant lodging, and seed yield are commonly recorded on these plots. In successive years of performance trials data may also be recorded on seed size and on protein and oil content of a sample of seed of each inbred line. Usually 10 to 15% of the superior lines identified in each years' performance trials are retained for evaluation in successive years of testing.

Initial performance trials are usually conducted at one location with two or three replications. Second-and third-year performance trials are conducted at more locations, usually two to four, and with three to four replications at each location. Economically important traits of soybean, particularly seed yield, are strongly influenced by environmental factors including temperature and rainfall that vary among years and locations. In soybean performance trials conducted at different locations and in different years, differences among years and among locations may be greater than differences among breeding lines. Therefore, soybean breeders conduct performance trials at multiple locations and years to identify breeding lines that can be expected to exhibit superior performance as improved cultivars.

In public breeding programs, superior breeding lines identified in state trials are entered into cooperative performance trials for each maturity group, 00 through VIII. These tests are conducted by soybean breeders and pathologists who grow the trials at multiple locations across the entire area of adaptation for each maturity group. Data are recorded on morphological traits, pest reactions, agronomic characteristics, and chemical composition of seed for each superior breeding line. These data are the basis for decisions as to which breeding lines merit release as improved cultivars. Individuals participating in these tests may use superior lines entered by any soybean breeder as parents in their breeding program. This policy promotes widespread use of superior breeding lines as parents for the development of improved cultivars. Commercial breeding programs conduct similar extensive performance trials of breeding lines at multiple locations across the area of adaptation of selected lines.

VIII. Increase and Distribution of New Cultivars

Soybean cultivars are maintained and distributed through seed certification programs with four classes of seed to maintain cultivar purity and identity. Breeder seed, produced and controlled by the breeder, consists of seed from individual plants of a cultivar that have been grown in progeny rows and selected for uniformity of phenotypic traits. In the United States, breeder seed may be produced from single plants only once, then maintained as a bulk seed lot. In many European countries, single plants are selected from a cultivar each year, their progeny evaluated for uniformity, and seed from uniform rows bulked to produce annual lots of breeder seed.

Foundation seed is initially produced from breeder seed and, in the USA, is maintained in successive generations by designated foundation seed organizations in each state. In Europe, foundation seed is usually produced each year from new lots of breeder seed.

Registered seed, produced from either breeder or foundation seed, and certified seed, produced from registered seed, may be produced by any grower interested in producing these classes of seed. Foundation, registered, and certified seed must be produced according to specific standards including field inspections of the cultivar during the growing season and inspections of harvested seed for genetic purity. Genetic purity standards for the three classes of certified seed are 99.9% for foundation seed, 99.75% for registered seed, and 99.0% for certified seed. In addition, seed of all classes must not contain more than 0.05% weed seed. Both registered and certified seed are sold to soybean growers for farm production of commercial soybean.

Comprehensive soybean breeding programs involve cooperative efforts of plant breeders with plant pathologists, nematologists, entomologists, and increasingly with molecular geneticists. Scientists in each of these disciplines contribute their expertise to the development of improved soybean cultivars. The development of an improved cultivar normally takes 7 to 10 years from the time a cross is made between selected parents until seed is available for farm production. In the first 2 years, inbred lines are developed that represent the variability available among progenies of a cross. The following 3 to 5 years are spent identifying inbred lines with superior attributes using replicated performance trials. Finally, about 3 years are required to increase seed of a new cultivar to amounts required for general farm production.

Bibliography

Fehr, W. R. (1987). Soybean. In "Principles of Cultivar Development" (W. R. Fehr, ed.), Vol. 2. Macmillan, New York.

Jensen, N. F. (1988) "Plant Breeding Methodology." Wiley, New York.

Stalker, H. T., and Murphy, J. P. (eds.) (1991). "Plant Breeding in the 1990s." CAB, UK.

Wilcox, J. R. (ed.) (1987). "Soybeans: Improvement, Production, and Uses," 2nd ed. American Society of Agronomy, Crop Science Society of America, Soil Science Society of America, Inc., Madison, WI.

Soybean Production

GARY E. PEPPER, *University of Illinois*

Glossary

Bradyrhizobium Genus name of bacteria which are capable of establishing a symbiotic relationship with roots of legume plants; metabolic activity of the bacteria converts atmospheric nitrogen to a form useful to meet plant nutritional needs

Cation exchange capacity Capacity of soil to bond (with ionic forces) positively charged ions, which exist in equilibrium with the soil solution, which provides nutrients to the plant

Determinate growth Plant growth pattern which terminates vegetative development with the onset of flowering and seed production

Green manure crop Crop grown to improve soil, particularly in regards to nutrient supplying ability

Hectare Land area equal to 10,000 square meters, which is equal to 2.47 acres

Herbicide Chemical pesticide for control of weeds

Lodging Bending over or falling over by plant stems

pH Numerical value, ranging from 0 to 14, indicating the degree of acidity or alkalinity; a value of 7.0 is neutral, values <7 are acid and values >7 are alkaline

Photoperiodic response Response which occurs as a result of duration of the daylength

Shatter Splitting open of fruits (pods) on the plant, which results in dropping of seed or grain produced onto the ground

Variety (cultivar) Group of plants, within a species, which differ from the rest of the species because of their unique genetic composition

Vegetable oil Oil derived from plant tissues, chiefly from the seed or fruit portions of the plant

The soybean plant (*Glycine max* L.), a member of the Legume plant family, produces grain rich in both protein and edible oil. Because of its yield potential across a fairly wide geographic range, it provides large amounts of protein and oil required by the world's populations. With an annual life cycle, cultivated soybean is generally spring planted and matures before the onset of cold weather in the fall. As a member of the legume family, it converts atmospheric nitrogen to a plant useable form when proper strains of *Bradyrhizobium* bacteria are present in the root zone.

I. Introduction

The soybean evolved in southeastern Asia, where literature indicates its cultivation has been going on at least 3500 years in that area of the world. The soybean seed, or food products made directly from it, still constitutes a portion of the diet for many Asian populations. In western cultures, soybeans tend to be utilized indirectly through livestock, which consume the protein-rich meal made from the crop.

The soybean was brought to the western world on trading ships, arriving in North America in 1765. It was first grown in the area which is now Georgia. In 1851 soybeans were first introduced to Illinois, and within 3 years were disseminated to many midwestern farmers. Major increases in soybean production began during World War II, and acres grown in the United States reached a peak in the 1970s.

Early soybean use in the United States generally did not involve the harvest of grain, for it was grown for soil improvement (green manure) or for forage (hay or pasture) purposes. Because soybean production results in nitrogen fixation from the atmosphere, it provides nitrogen fertility which benefits the next crop produced. Since the introduction of soybean preceded the availability of commercial nitrogen fertilizer, its production was a means for farmers to enhance yields in crops responsive to nitrogen. The low cost of nitrogen fertilizer today generally does not make it economically viable for the soybean to be produced solely for its nitrogen contribution to the succeeding crop.

For seed harvest, early soybean production required a great deal of hand labor—making harvest as a cash grain impractical. Availability of the first grain combines, during the 1920s, made it feasible for farmers to produce the soybean as a grain crop. During this time a greater appreciation for the soybean protein and oil content also developed. Both of these stimulated interest in growing soybean for grain harvest.

Current soybean use in the United States and throughout the world is based primarily on grain protein and oil content. Livestock feeding consumes the majority of the protein meal produced from the grain, but many prepared foods often contain soybean flour, protein, or other grain components. Substitute or simulated meat products are produced from soybean protein as well.

Edible soybean oil is primarily consumed as cooking and salad oil, salad dressing, frying oil, and margarine. Because it has a very mild flavor, the oil is desirable for cooking purposes. Additionally, because of its relatively low level of fatty acid saturation, it is one of the most desirable oils for health conscious populations. Soybean is the major source of vegetable oil used in the United States today.

Alternative uses for soybean exist, but thus far have consumed only a small portion of the crop harvested. Nonfood uses of soybean include the manufacture of paints, adhesives, plastics, and inks. Soybean oil can also be used as an alternative, and renewable, fuel to power diesel engines.

A large portion of the soybeans produced in the United States are exported. World demand for protein and edible oil will only expand as the world's population grows, helping insure continued demand for the soybean. A summary of U.S. soybean production and export is shown in Table I.

TABLE I

U.S. Soybean Production and Exports, 1930–1991

	Thousand metric tons	
Year	Production	Exports
1930	381	0
1940	2123	0
1950	8138	762
1960	15,106	3674
1970	30,675	11,813
1980	48,938	19,706
1990	52,422	15,161

Major world soybean producers are the United States, China, Argentina, and Brazil. Argentina and Brazil are relatively new producers and exporters, having greatly expanded the scope of their production since the early 1980s. China, with its large population, consumes most of its production, leaving Argentina and Brazil as major competitors to U.S. farmers on the world market. South American competitors have the advantage of low priced land for expanded production, but are hindered by grain transportation to an export facility. Table II summarizes soybean production by the world's major producers.

II. Production Practices

A. Variety Selection

Selecting the best adapted varieties is basic to successful and profitable soybean production. Farmers need to use the most productive varieties with a maturity adapted to their area. In addition, other agronomic traits and disease resistance are criteria considered in choosing varieties. [See SOYBEAN GENETICS AND BREEDING.]

Soybean maturity is described by Maturity Groups, with Roman numerals used to designate the relative maturity. Earlier maturing soybeans, which require fewer days to reach maturity, are used at greater latitudes where the growing season is shorter. Later maturing varieties are used at latitudes closer to the equator. Thirteen Maturity Groups, from OOO (earliest) to X (latest) are used to describe soybean maturity. It is basically the photoperiodic (daylength) response effect on flower initiation in different varieties which makes them adapted to differing latitudes. For that reason, varieties cannot be moved very far north or south of their region of adaptation before they become too late, or early, in maturity. Figure 1 indicates the general areas of North America where different maturity groups are best adapted.

TABLE II

Soybean Production by Major World Growers

Country	1972	1982	1992
	(1000 metric tons produced)		
United States	34,921	60,697	53,892
Argentina	82	4137	10,479
Brazil	3674	12,793	18,508
China	6287	9009	9608

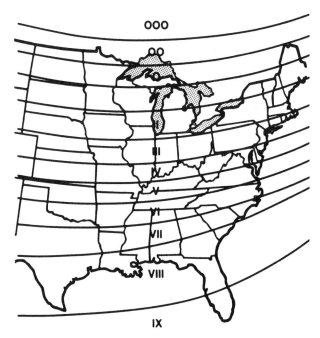

FIGURE 1 Distribution of Soybean Maturity Groups Adapted to North America. [Reprinted with permission from Scott, W. O., and Aldrich, S. R. (1983). "Modern Soybean Production," 2nd ed. S. & A. Publications, Inc., Champaign, IL.]

After farmers identify the Maturity Group(s) best adapted to their area, varieties with greatest yield potential and other desirable traits need to be identified. Many private seed companies have research programs which provide farmers with improved soybean varieties. In addition, land grant universities in soybean growing regions have variety development programs as well. Together, these two sources have released hundreds of new soybean varieties. Universities in soybean growing regions have variety testing programs which provide data useful to farmers as they select their soybeans.

Other varietal characteristics needing consideration include the ability of different varieties to resist lodging, as well as disease problems likely to appear in the farmer's fields. The ability of soybeans to stand well until harvested has been dramatically enhanced by plant breeding efforts. Resistance to several commonly occurring diseases, such as Phytophthora root rot (caused by *Phytophthora megasperma* (Drechs.) f. sp. *glycinea* Kuan and Erwin), brown stem rot (caused by *Phialophora gregata* (Allington and Chamberlain) W. Gams), and cyst nematodes (caused by *Heterodera glycines* Ichinohe), has been genetically incorporated into many varieties.

It is important for farmers not only to purchase the best varieties, but also to purchase quality seed of the most desirable varieties. Quality seed can be identified based on the germination score, vigor, and freedom from disease and mechanical damage to the seed. High germination levels and vigor will enhance the probability of a good stand emerging after planting. Freedom from seed-borne disease helps reduce infection of seedlings early in the season. Seed which are mechanically sound (not cracked or split) will have a greater percentage of undamaged seedling embryos within the seed. All these factors combine to enhance the probability of a good healthy stand of soybeans. Planting good quality seed does not guarantee a perfect stand, but without quality seed it is unlikely a good stand can be achieved.

An alternative to purchasing seed is to plant soybean seed which were harvested by the farmer the previous year. This is most likely to occur when the farmer is particularly pleased with a variety's yield and apparent seed quality. Because soybean is a self-pollinated species, varieties do not change genetically from generation to generation. Thus, it is possible for seed harvested one year to serve as planting seed for the next crop. The risk farmers face when using their own seed may be low quality, for exceptionally good management is needed to maintain quality. The advantage to farmers using their own seed is some economic savings.

B. Crop Rotations

Soybean yield tends to benefit from planting the crop in a rotational sequence, i.e., not planting soybean after soybean. Most soybeans are planted in fields which produced corn or some other grass crop during the previous year. Rotating crops in a field helps reduce pest problems, enhancing yield potential. Diseases that survive only on living soybean plants will be diminished in years when soybean is not produced. Planting crops such as corn, which differ considerably from soybean, allows the use of different herbicides for weed control as well. Weed management tends to be more effective when herbicide use varies with cropping seasons.

An additional benefit to soybean grown in rotation is a reduction in allelopathic effects from the previous soybean crop. Allelopathic effects, recognized only in recent years, can be described as a syndrome induced by chemicals released from decomposing crop residue, which has a yield limiting effect on that same crop when it is continuously grown. The greater the decomposition of crop residue, before a crop is planted again, the less damaging are allelopathic effects on that crop's growth and production. Crop rotation away from soybean allows greater decomposition of soybean crop residue, which reduces allelopathic effects which will be suffered by the next soybeans planted.

C. Seedbed Preparation for Planting

Tillage used for seedbed preparation varies greatly from farm to farm. All farmers do not have the same equipment for tillage and planting the crop, and soybean are grown on a wide range of soil types. These two factors combine to dictate the use of different tillage methods. Fields also have different topographic features, which relate to the potential for soil erosion. Concerns regarding soil erosion can greatly influence the type and amount of tillage most appropriate for preparing a field for soybean planting. The crop preceding soybean will also influence the amount of crop residue present in a field, which also determines tillage required to prepare a suitable seedbed for planting. [See TILLAGE SYSTEMS.]

Tools used to prepare fields for planting in various tillage systems include plows, disks, and field cultivators. Many farmers now use a chisel plow, in place of the traditional moldboard plow. Both the fuel required to accomplish needed tillage and greater crop residue remaining on the soil surface to control erosion favor use of the chisel plow.

The number of times the soil is worked with a disk, field cultivator, or other tillage tool after plowing is dependent on the extent to which the farmer desires to prepare a clean seedbed. Soil type, the extent of soil freezing and thawing during winter, and the level of crop residue help determine tillage needs for seedbed preparation.

Farmers are tending to reduce the amount of tillage done in their fields. As a result, more residue from the previously grown crop remains on the soil surface at planting time. This is an effective means to help protect and hold soil in place—reducing erosion potential from both wind and water. Planting equipment has been developed to allow soybean planting with considerable crop residue levels on the soil surface.

Many farmers view reduced tillage as a means to reduce the cost of producing soybean—for less time and equipment is needed for field work. As tillage is reduced, there is generally a greater need for herbicides to chemically control weed problems in the crop. A farming system which involves no tillage prior to planting is dependent on herbicides and some cultivation during the growing season to control weeds.

A final reason farmers are reducing tillage is that government support programs are not available to farmers who create excessive erosion problems with their farm operations. Farmers must be responsible for the potential erosion problems they generate, or they will not be entitled to government programs helping assure financial stability in farming.

Application of some herbicides can be combined with the use of a tillage tool such as a disk or field cultivator. Herbicide, sprayed immediately in front of the tillage tool, is incorporated at a shallow depth in the soil. Further incorporation of the herbicide, to insure uniform mixing, may be done with another tillage trip through the field prior to planting.

D. Soil Fertility—Mineral Nutrition

Soybean, as with all crops, depends on the soil to provide adequate mineral nutrition for normal growth and development. Nutrients most commonly supplied to soybean are phosphorus (P) and potassium (K). Each bushel of soybeans removes P contained in 386 g P_2O_5 and K contained in 590 g K_2O. For these, and other soil-derived nutrients to be available to roots, the soil pH level needs to be in the range of 6.0 to 6.5. Maintaining soil pH in this range benefits the activity level of the nitrogen fixing bacteria *Bradyrhizobium* as well.

Soil phosphorous and potassium levels must be maintained at recommended test levels to avoid nutritional stresses. Individual states have guidelines for maintaining soil test levels of P and K required to meet crop needs. Guidelines are based on soil fertility research, done in the differing soil types found across soybean producing areas. On soils with good cation exchange capacity, P and K can be applied before the year in which soybeans are grown. On soils with low or little capacity to retain applied P and K, more frequent applications are needed.

Liming, to raise the soil pH, should be done as needed with lime rates based on soil testing results. Between a pH of 6.0 and 7.0, soybean tends to optimize grain yields. Generally, maintaining a soil pH between 6.0 and 6.5 is most cost effective for farmers. Below a pH of 6.0, or above 7.0, mineral availability may become a yield limiting factor.

Because soybean fix nitrogen (N) with the assistance of *Bradyrhizobium* bacteria, nitrogen fertilizer is generally not applied. During early seedling growth, as the first two or three leaves develop, nitrogen fixation is initiated as *Bradyrhizobium* infect the soybean root. Small applications of N at planting time will often result in darker green seedlings, as nitrogen nutrition in plant tissues will be enhanced during early growth stages. Most positive effects of nitrogen applied at planting would be expected to be seen in sandy soils where irrigation is used.

Most areas producing soybeans have an established *Bradyrhizobium* population in the soil, because the bacteria can survive several years in the soil even if soybeans are not produced. Fields where soybeans have never been produced may lack needed populations of *Bradyrhizobium*, however. To insure the presence of the nitrogen-fixing bacteria, seed can be inoculated prior to planting. The bacteria, most frequently mixed into a ground peat carrier, is made to adhere to seed with a sugar-water solution, insuring the bacteria will be nearby the seedling as it becomes established. Alternative methods for introducing the needed *Bradyrhizobium* include granule and slurry products which are placed in the furrow with the seed at planting.

Several mineral nutrients are needed in very small amounts by soybean, but are just as essential as P and K to normal growth and production. Because of the small amounts taken up by the crop, those nutrients are typically called "micronutrients." Occasionally, a field may be found deficient. If not available in sufficient quantity from the soil, micronutrient deficiencies may be corrected with a nutrient spray application when deficiency symptoms become apparent. A small amount of the micronutrients can also be applied along with other fertilizer material if a deficiency is suspected based on previous crop growth or soil testing results.

E. Date of Seeding

In the northern hemisphere, the majority of soybeans are planted during the month of May. Delaying planting often results in reduced grain yield, and extreme planting delays will also put the crop at risk of fall frost damage. The impact which planting delays have on soybeans planted across the Corn Belt is presented in Table III. Penalties to yield are associated with delayed planting in southern latitudes of the United States as well.

Soybeans in some areas are planted following the harvest of winter wheat or other small grain cereal crops which mature in early summer. This practice is referred to as double-cropping soybeans. A fairly small portion of soybeans grown in the Corn Belt

TABLE III

Seeding Delay Effects on Soybean Yield in Central Corn Belt States

Seeding date	Percent yield potential
Early May	100 %
Mid May	100
Late May	95
Early June	90
Mid June	70
Late June	60

are planted as double-crop, but in the southern and southeastern states, double-crop planting accounts for a considerable portion of total soybean acres planted. Table IV documents double-crop plantings in southern and southeastern states.

Planting dates used for soybeans in southern latitudes of the United States must consider photoperiodic (daylength) effects on the crop. Because soybean flowering is induced by exposure to a sufficiently short day, planting too early will induce premature flowering, which results in excessively short plants with reduced yield potential. Southern varieties are determinate in growth, and thus stop growing vegetatively when flowering begins. To avoid complications due to photoperiod effects, growers in southern latitudes of the United States generally plant the majority of their soybean during May, with some planted in late April and early June.

F. Planting Row Space

Most soybeans are planted in rows spaced 30 to 36 in. apart. A yield advantage is sometimes associated with row spacings more narrow, such as 7–10 in. Enhancement of yield in narrow rows can be ex-

TABLE IV

Double-Crop Planting of Soybeans in Selected States, Average of 1990–1992

State	Percent of acres seeded as double-crop
Illinois	4 %
Indiana	4
Kansas	2
Arkansas	31
Georgia	46
Kentucky	38
N. Carolina	30
S. Carolina	41

plained basically by greater sunlight energy interception by the crop canopy through the season.

Arranging a crop of soybean in narrow rows allows the canopy to fully intercept sunlight available by an earlier date in the season. Full interception of light earlier in the season allows a greater total amount of light to be intercepted by the canopy through the cropping season. Greater total light interception by a crop during the growing season can result in enhanced yield. Yield advantages associated with narrowed row spacing in soybeans tend to be larger in more northern latitudes than in southern regions.

While narrowed rows offer farmers greater yield opportunity, they may create both opportunities and challenges in regards to weed control. The plant canopy cover generated by narrow row plantings can help suppress weed growth by the shade imposed on weeds. At the same time, rows more narrow than 30 in. cannot generally be cultivated for weed control; thus, herbicides must be relied upon for weed control.

Narrow row soybeans, because they cover the soil with vegetation in fewer days, can also protect the soil from erosion. The plant canopy covers the area between rows, protecting the soil from the force of beating raindrops, which reduces the water erosion potential.

G. Plant Densities

Soybeans can maximize their yield potential across a rather wide range in plant densities. To a great extent, soybean can adjust or compensate for the population at which it is planted. Field studies evaluating plant density effects on soybean have indicated that stands of 300,000 to 370,000 plants per hectare are needed for optimum soybean yields. Across this range in plant densities, if plants are reasonably uniform in their distribution, soybeans tend to maximize their yield potential with timely planting.

Growing soybeans at insufficient plant densities encourages development of large branches low on the main stem. While branches produce grain, the position of these branches is not conducive to efficient mechanical harvest. Large branches attached low on the main stem may be laying on the soil at crop maturity. At harvest the combine may fail to collect grain if it is produced on branches positioned too close to the soil. At appropriate population ranges branches on the soybean tend to be fairly short, and emerge from the main stem well above the soil surface.

At excessively high plant densities, the soybean stem tends to be abnormally tall and structurally weak, which may allow the crop to lodge, causing harvest losses. In addition, soybeans which lodge during the grain filling period of development have a reduced ability to fill seed, due to reduced light distribution and photosynthesis in leaves.

Varieties with consistently short stems tend to stand better than average, and thus may be seeded at higher densities. Weak stemmed, or tall varieties, may need to be planted at slightly lower than average seeding rates, so that lodging can be avoided.

H. Pest Management

1. Weeds

In every soybean crop, weed management must be considered. Several approaches can be used to manage weeds—all intended to help reduce competition to the crop. In virtually every soybean field herbicide is used to manage weeds. In addition, mechanical control (tillage before planting and/or between row cultivation) is used in the majority of fields. Methods used for weed management depend on the type and density of weed problems, tillage systems used by the farmer, equipment available, and budgetary considerations. [See WEED SCIENCE.]

Herbicide options for soybeans are numerous, and change each year with new products and formulations available. Depending on chemical characteristics of the herbicide(s) used, application may be made during seedbed preparation, immediately after planting is completed, or after emergence of the crop and weeds. Farmers that use reduced or no-till production programs, and consequently do not have the opportunity to incorporate chemicals during seedbed preparation, must depend on herbicides which can be applied after planting or after the crop and weeds emerge. Those using narrow rows, which cannot be cultivated for weed control, are greatly dependent on herbicides suitable for application after planting or emergence of the crop. [See HERBICIDES AND HERBICIDE RESISTANCE.]

Herbicide selection for weed control needs to be based on weed problems anticipated in the field. Some herbicides provide effective control of grasses, but not broadleaf weeds, while others control broadleaf weeds but not grasses. A few help control both broadleaf and grass weeds.

In addition to considering weed species present, herbicide selection is influenced by cost of the product, time when application is needed, potential for soybean damage, carryover to future crops grown in the field, and environmental considerations. Newer herbicides tend to be most costly, but often provide weed control at a lower rate of chemical per acre. Reduced rates per acre are beneficial, since environmental concerns exist. Equipment available for application may influence the herbicide used, because different types of equipment are needed to apply herbicides at different times in the cropping year. Some herbicides are slow to breakdown or decompose in the environment, so they may potentially injure subsequent crops planted in the same field, or may create a greater risk to the environment. Applying herbicides properly, and at the proper time and rate, will minimize any potential danger or threat to both the crop and environment.

Mechanical weed control in soybean may be accomplished during seedbed preparation, as weed seed may be buried deep enough to prevent their germination. Also, early germinating weeds are destroyed by tillage. A rotary hoe, which is used soon after crop emergence, also is a form of mechanical weed control as it breaks up the upper soil layer and dislodges small weed seedlings.

Cultivation between rows for weed control is typically done once or twice in fields where preplant tillage was done and spacings between rows permit equipment operation. Cultivation can be done until the crop is large enough that row middles become filled with vegetation. In no-till planted fields, cultivation between rows is not done, which preserves the soil cover of crop residue.

2. Insects

At lower latitudes, with a longer growing season and milder winter, insects in soybean tend to be more of a problem. Various insects feed on different soybean plant parts—leaves, stems, roots, or developing grain. Sufficient insect damage can reduce the soybean's ability to yield. Minor feeding damage, however, may not result in detectable yield loss. Both the extent of damage and developmental stage of the soybean plant determine if control of insects present is warranted. Research on integrated pest management, which has been conducted in a farmer's area, is the best guide to understanding when insect control measures are economically justified.

Insect problems vary from year to year in regards to the specific insects present and the size of their populations. Weather plays a role in winter survival, reproduction rates, and distribution or movement of insects from field to field. Because insect problems are not always associated with soybean production, it is best to manage problems as they become apparent

and threaten crop productivity. In addition to cost saving, it is more environmentally friendly to apply insecticides only when they can be justified.

3. Diseases

Disease problems can greatly limit soybean production potential. Disease incidence and severity are determined in large measure by local weather patterns. Some diseases may thrive under very humid or wet conditions, while others may tend to do best in hotter and dryer conditions. While the farmer cannot control weather, through variety selection management of several diseases may be accomplished.

Many varieties available to farmers now have genetic resistance to some diseases which are frequently encountered. Unfortunately, genetic resistance is not available for all diseases which can infect soybean. From those varieties adapted to their area, farmers must look for those which have disease resistance in addition to the yield and agronomic characters desired.

Cultural practices such as the use of disease-free seed, providing adequate soil fertility, and the use of crop rotations, will all help reduce disease incidence in soybeans. Use of disease-free seed may prevent a disease from being introduced to a field. Providing adequate fertility keeps plants more vigorous, and better able to tolerate the stresses of disease. Crop rotations, when adequate in duration, reduce pathogen numbers in a field if they need living soybean plants to survive and multiply.

Chemical control, in the form of a seed treatment, can be used to manage some disease problems which are seed-borne. Seed treatment may also be useful to manage diseases which are soil-borne and which often impact early seedling growth. Late season fungal-induced diseases which damage leaves can be managed with foliar sprays. The use of fungicides to control late season leaf diseases will only be profitable if the environment favors disease development, and if the crop is of relatively high value. Soybeans produced for planting seed purposes might be considered to have a relatively high value, compared to those grown for delivery to the grain market. [See FUNGICIDES.]

The soybean cyst nematode problem is often included in discussion of pathological problems of soybean. The cyst nematode, a microscopic round worm, causes root damage which stresses soybeans through reduced water and nutrient uptake, which in turn reduces yield. The cyst nematode problem has migrated across virtually the entire soybean growing region of the United States. [See PLANT PATHOLOGY.]

Management of the cyst nematode problem needs to include crop rotation and planting resistant varieties. The longer the time interval between susceptible soybean crops, the greater the number of cyst nematodes which die due to the lack of a suitable food supply. Planting a nonhost crop such as corn, followed by soybean variety resistant to cyst nematode, followed by another nonhost crop, tends to dramatically reduce cyst nematode populations in a field. Such a crop rotation will not eliminate the problem, but will reduce its severity to a level that a susceptible variety generally can be grown in the fourth year of the rotation. During the fourth year, the few remaining cyst nematodes increase in number, necessitating the start of another 4-year rotation cycle. Farmers using the 4-year rotation to manage their cyst nematode problems need to have cyst counts done on soil samples collected after the third year of the rotation—to insure populations have been adequately suppressed to allow production of a susceptible variety.

Varieties which are resistant to cyst nematode contain genes imparting resistance to specific races of the pest. Planting varieties resistant to a specific race(s) each time soybean is produced will encourage the increase in populations of nematode races to which varieties are not resistant, which then reduces soybean yield potential in the field. The 4-year rotation uses a susceptible variety in the fourth year. The purpose of planting the susceptible variety is to encourage a resurgence of nematodes for which genetic resistance is available.

4. Scouting and Pest Management

Scouting soybean fields, which is simply monitoring pest levels throughout the season on a regular basis, is the first step to control potential pests. Once a pest is identified, and the intensity or severity of the problem determined, the most appropriate and profitable course of action can be determined. The most profitable response to minor pest problems may be to do nothing, for treatment costs might exceed the value of potential crop damage. In contrast, higher levels of infestation may require immediate action to preserve crop profitability. To most effectively manage pest problems, soybean producers need to be aware of pests in their fields and their potential for damage.

I. Harvest

Once mature and sufficiently dry, soybeans are well suited to mechanical harvest with a combine. A primary consideration in harvesting soybeans is grain moisture level. Harvesting when grain moisture is in the range of 12 or 13% adds to harvest efficiency and helps maintain quality in the harvested crop. Soybeans are "toughest" at about 13% moisture; thus, they resist cracking and splitting at that moisture level, and pods thresh easily when grain is at 12 or 13%. Pods are not likely to shatter as plants are cut by the sickle of the combine at these moisture levels compared to lower levels. Moisture levels of 13% or less are also needed for safe storage of soybeans. If soybeans are above 13% moisture, drying of grain is needed for safe storage. Soybeans are sold on the basis of 13% moisture in grain, with higher moisture in the grain resulting in drying charges levied again the seller.

Soybean harvest equipment available influences the efficiency of this critical phase of soybean production. Some combine sickle bars may not follow the contour of the soil. If so, a portion of the soybean yield may escape the sickle bar and collection by the combine head. The better the sickle bar follows the soil contour, the greater the percentage of the crop that will be harvested.

Equipment adjustment and operation are critical to efficient harvest. Reel speed on the combine platform and forward travel speed both influence movement of the crop material into the head of the combine. Excessive reel speed causes shattering of pods; essentially threshing seed before they can be delivered inside the harvest equipment, resulting in harvest losses.

Internal adjustments of the combine need to be made based on the seed size and moisture content. Adjustments in the threshing cylinder may be needed based on soybean seed size. Cylinder speed needs to be adjusted to consider the "toughness" of pods, which is related to grain moisture at harvest. Cylinder speed needs to be fast enough to efficiently thresh seed from pods, yet not so fast that unnecessary cracking and splitting of grain occurs. Airflow within the combine needs to be adjusted so that chaff, dirt, and other crop debris is separated from the grain.

Estimates are that 2–3% soybean yield loss is typical during harvest, despite the farmer's best efforts. Losses are the total amount of crop which shatters from pods prior to combining, those lost in front of the grain head, cracks, splits, and unthreshed beans which remain in pods discarded out the rear of the combine.

III. U.S. Production and Utilization

A. Production Regions and Costs

Major soybean producing states in the United States are in the midwest. Illinois and Iowa have been major soybean producing states since it has been grown for grain harvest. In the past 10 years, Illinois and Iowa together have produced a third of the total U.S. crop (Table V). Production in other midwest states make major contributions to total U.S. production as well. Total production by the six states listed in Table V have averaged two-thirds of the total U.S. crop from 1984 to 1993. Highest yields per hectare have been achieved in Illinois, Iowa, and Indiana during that period.

States in the south and southeastern United States also produce soybeans, but both farm land devoted to the crop and yield per hectare are considerably lower than in the midwest. Yield per hectare tends to be relatively low in many southern areas for a number of reasons. The soybean is often planted after the harvest of small grains (double-cropped), which restricts yield potential. Due to chemical and physical characteristics, soils across much of the south and southeast tend to have lower productivity. In addition, insect and disease problems more frequently reduce yield of soybean in that region.

Total production costs per hectare for soybean vary across regions in the United States. All soybean production budgets include items such as seed, lime, and fertilizer charges, as well as machinery expenses and labor. Charges for land, pest management, and possibly irrigation, have a strong influence on the cost of production per unit of soybean produced in various areas of the United States.

Land, pest management, and irrigation costs vary greatly across areas producing soybean. Regardless of location, a major charge in a soybean production budget is for land. Land charges in the midwest tend to be highest, but highest yields per hectare are obtained in that region. Regardless of location, producers have to manage weeds, but may have other pests to manage as well. For weed control, virtually all soybean fields are treated at least once with herbicide. At lower latitudes, with warmer and longer growing seasons, management of insects is often needed and increases costs of production. Thus, total pest management costs are likely to be higher in southern regions. To reduce dry weather stress, some areas in the south or southeast are irrigated, which also adds to production costs.

Soybean yield per hectare, which varies greatly in the United States, does not always reflect the margin of profit made by the farmer. The total cost per unit of production determines whether soybean production is profitable. Total cost per unit soybean harvested tends to be higher in southern latitudes, because of actual expenses and yields harvested. The lack of profitability associated with soybean production in this region has resulted in many farmers reducing the farm area devoted to production in recent years. In contrast, farmers in the midwest enjoy higher yield potentials, and also have lower pest management costs, which tend to make production more profitable.

B. Protein and Oil Separation

Chemical components of cultivated soybean make it necessary that the grain be cooked before consumption by most animals. Raw soybeans contain trypsin inhibitors, which reduce digestion of protein in monogastric animals. Cooking the soybean destroys these inhibitors. Cooking of soybean is accomplished during processing, which is typically referred to as "crushing." The crushing sequence not only cooks soybean, but separates the oil and protein rich fractions in the grain. A bushel of soybeans yields a little over 11 lbs of oil and 47 lbs of protein-rich meal.

Soybean crushing begins with cracking the grain to loosen the hull (seedcoat) from the seed. Hulls are separated, while the balance of the grain proceeds to rollers which create thin flakes from the pieces of soybean. Hexane then flows through the soybean flakes, extracting the oil. Hexane is recovered from the hexane–oil mix, and is used again. Soybean meal,

TABLE V

Major Soybean Producing States, Average Total Production, and Yield per Hectare for the Period 1984–1993.

State	Total production metric tons	Average yield (kg/ha)
Illinois	9,310,908	2567
Iowa	8,498,472	2560
Indiana	4,622,244	2580
Minnesota	4,474,140	2231
Missouri	3,781,183	2056
Ohio	3,767,361	2466
U.S.	52,302,055	2197

from which oil has been extracted, is then cooked to drive off the hexane remaining. Hexane is recovered from the cooking meal, and used again in the processing. Hulls removed at the start of processing are often recombined with the meal. If hulls are not remixed with the meal, protein level in the meal is higher.

Oil extracted from soybeans is refined to produce the vegetable oil needed for salad oil, shortening, margarine, and other edible oil items. Soybean meal, produced when oil is extracted from soybean, serves as a protein feed supplement for many livestock species. Protein levels in the meal vary with the soybean variety processed, and the degree to which hull material is recombined with the meal after oil extraction. Soybean meal typically has a protein content of 44%.

C. Consumption

The majority of the soybean crop produced in the United States is consumed by our food and feed industry, with the remainder available for export markets. Poultry and swine consume about 75% of the meal derived from the crop, with beef, dairy, and other livestock using smaller portions. Salad, cooking, baking, and frying oil account for roughly 80% of the soybean oil consumption in the United States. Manufacture of margarine consumes about 15% of the soybean oil in the United States. Table VI summarizes

TABLE VI

Sources of Edible Fats and Oils for the United States and World, 1991

Source	Percent of total consumed by	
	U.S.	World
Soybean	74%	27%
Corn	8	[a]
Cottonseed	5	7
Coconut	1	5
Palm	1	20
Rapeseed	—	16
Sunflower	—	13
Others	11	12

[a] Included in other sources.

edible oil and fat consumption in the United States and indicates the relatively large role played by soybeans.

Industrial uses of soybean oil consumes a relatively small portion of that produced. In recent years, a soybean-based ink has become available, and is used to print many government documents, newspapers, and magazines. Using ink based on soybean oil, rather than petroleum, is viewed as an environmental advantage, as well as creating new markets and demand for the crop. The use of soybean oil as a liquid fuel, replacing or being mixed with diesel, is currently being developed. Because of air pollution concerns in major metropolitan areas, an expanding market for soybean oil used for fuel purposes is anticipated. Both the reduced particle emissions from soybean fuel and the renewable nature of the fuel make it a promising market for the soybean crop.

A material made from soybean meal and recycled newspapers has recently been developed, and in many instances may have the potential to replace wood. The material can be used in furniture, flooring, and paneling applications. Additional industrial applications to consume both soybean meal and oil will no doubt result as a consequence of research on soybean utilization.

Bibliography

Ashlock, L. O., et al. (1988). "Soybean Diagnostic Guide." American Soybean Assoc., St. Louis, MO.

Golbitz, P. (1992). "'92 Soya Bluebook" (P. Golbitz, ed.). Soyatech, Inc., Bar Harbor, ME.

Illinois Agricultural Experiment Station (1987). "Illinois Research—The Soybean" (M. Overmier and M. Theis, eds.), Vol. 29, Nos. 2–3. Urbana, IL.

Iowa Cooperative Extension Service (1982). "How A Soybean Plant Develops—Special Report 53" (J. C. Herman, ed.) rev. ed. Iowa State Univ. Cooperative Extension Service, Ames, IA.

Scott, W. O., and Aldrich, S. R. (1983). "Modern Soybean Production," 2nd ed. S & A Publications, Inc., Champaign, IL.

Wilcox, J. R. (ed.) (1987). "Soybeans: Improvement, Production, and Uses," 2nd ed. American Society of Agronomy, Madison, WI.

Structures

LOUIS D. ALBRIGHT, *Cornell University*

Glossary

Confined animal housing systems (CAHS) Building systems to confine animals used for agricultural production and the associated electrical and mechanical systems associated with the production

Controlled environment agriculture (CEA) Industry that produces horticultural crops (primarily flowers and vegetables) within controlled environment structures (greenhouses, growth rooms, etc.)

Environment Word having two connotations: related to buildings it is generally taken to mean the environment inside buildings but is also used for exterior environment, as in natural settings surrounding a farmstead

Environmental stress Any situation in an organism's microenvironment that induces an adaptive response; a stress may be acute or chronic and adaptation to the stress may or may not occur; depending on type and level of environmental stress, the effect on the organism may or may not be negative

Environmental stressor Factor present in the microenvironment that induces environmental stress on an organism

Homeothermic Animals that maintain an approximately constant internal body temperature through a carefully regulated balance between the rate at which metabolic heat is produced and the rate at which it is dissipated

Indoor air quality Relatively subjective index used to describe how closely aerial conditions (combinations of humidity, dust, odors, vaporous contaminants, etc.) match the needs of the occupants

Lower critical temperature Effective environmental temperature at the lower end of an animal's zone of thermoneutrality

Mechanical ventilation Ventilation of a building using mechanical means, generally fans; in agricultural buildings which house animals or grow plants, fans are typically of the propeller type and ducts to distribute fresh air are not generally used; in product storage buildings fans may be of propeller or centrifugal type and ducts to distribute fresh air are commonly used

Microenvironment Combination of environmental factors in the immediate vicinity of an organism, including air temperature, relative humidity and other aerial constituents, light intensity and quality, air velocity and turbulence intensity, sound intensity and frequency, and all other environmental factors important to the organism

Natural ventilation Ventilation of a building using only passive means: thermal buoyancy and/or wind-induced pressures

Thermoneutrality The temperature at which a homeothermic organism is most comfortable and exhibits no behavioral response characteristic of heat or cold; neither vasodilation nor vasoconstriction dominates in blood vessels near the skin; piloerection for heat loss suppression and moisture evaporation for cooling from the skin or respiratory systems are minimized.

Upper critical temperature Effective environmental temperature at the upper end of an animal's zone of thermoneutrality

Agriculture comprises a complex industrial process and buildings used for agricultural production should be integrated into a total system that provides at least the following: (1) desirable conditions to the housed animals or plants and the workers involved with them, (2) high production capabilities, (3) labor and energy efficiency, (4) economic effectiveness, and (5) limited environmental impacts outside the building. Agricultural structures are designed to modify microenvironments. Environmental modification is important to reduce weather- and microenvironment-induced stresses on the animals or plants and, in the case of stored crops, provide conditions that promote long-term quality retention and a minimum of spoilage and loss. The modification may be as simple as providing a sun shade for cattle in a warm climate, or as complex as a totally controlled facility for raising and storing food crops in a (now being planned) lunar colony.

To a significant extent, the design of agricultural structures has evolved in response to social, esthetic, economic, and political forces as much as in response to scientific input. Although design of today's agricultural structures is based more firmly on engineering principles, all the nonscientific factors listed are likely to continue defining, in part, the future development of agricultural structures.

I. The Need for Agricultural Structures

Most agronomically important crops are grown outdoors. Agriculturally important animals are raised with little or no shelter throughout much of the world. However, continuous exposure to the vagaries of weather and climate can impose stresses that limit production, increase morbidity, enhance exposure to injury and predation, and may ultimately prove fatal. This is true for both plants and animals.

Modern agriculture is sufficiently competitive economically that avoidable production losses cannot be accepted. This has led to various systems to house animals and plants and ameliorate the microenvironments they experience. The evolutionary process has been a long one. Records show, for example, mica sheets were used to create crude greenhouses to produce out-of-season cucumbers for Roman emperors. From earliest times, caves (where available) were used to shelter animals during the worst weather. Confined animal housing systems and controlled environment agriculture have matured greatly since then. Today's fully automated poultry house for 30,000 (or more) laying hens, dairy barn for hundreds of milking cows, or multihectare, highly automated, tomato production greenhouse controlled by a computer are simply

steps along the natural progression from yesterday's primitive environmentally modified facilities toward tomorrow's totally enclosed and automated food production facilities on earth and in lunar (and beyond) colonies.

Agricultural buildings are, in effect, industrial production facilities. The agricultural activity within a building can be represented as an interacting collection of biological and physical processes and material transformations. A factor that sets an agricultural building apart from typical industrial buildings is the relative importance of the biotic system housed by the agricultural building. True, a factory must be staffed by people (at least today, before robot-run factories are the rule) but the people have a relatively small effect on the building itself. In an agricultural building the biotic system strongly affects the environment within the building and the environment provided by the building is critical to the welfare and production of the biotic system housed within.

The specific needs to be met by animal housing, product storage buildings, and greenhouses have led engineers to develop unique structural design and construction techniques. Generally, construction must be simple to limit costs because relatively large floor areas must be covered, areas that encompass an economic activity having relatively low return per unit area (contrast the yearly income from a dairy barn to the yearly income from an electronics equipment manufacturer, for example, having the same floor area).

Agricultural buildings often are not subject to the same constraints of building and other codes imposed on structures for human occupancy. This has permitted greater freedom for design innovation. However, aerial conditions within agricultural structures (high humidity in greenhouses, organic acids, dust, and other air contaminants produced by animal wastes, as examples) impose severe restraints on the choice of materials that may be used. Wood has been the material of choice for most animal housing facilities. Wood is relatively inexpensive and not subject to the corrosion characteristic of iron and steel. Steel buildings have been used to house animals, but often specially coated structural members are needed to limit corrosion. As an extreme, exhaust ventilating fans in swine housing are likely to have fiberglass bodies to avoid the corrosion that can destroy a steel body within 6 months of operation. In greenhouses, the need for sunlight has restricted construction to use of a structural covering of plastic or glass over a lightweight frame of steel, aluminum, or wood.

II. Planning Agricultural Structures

Every building must ensure its occupants (animal and human) will not be exposed to risks due to the building's construction. Every state in the United States has a building code devised to assure such safety. Local governments may impose additional restrictions. Such codes usually require construction in compliance with specific standards, or in accord with accepted engineering practice. In addition, energy performance standards have been adopted by many state and local governments. These codes may or may not apply to agricultural buildings, depending on local interpretation. Many codes specifically exempt agricultural buildings from certain provisions, but exemptions are not uniform and neither are they uniformly interpreted. Thus, in any construction it is necessary to consult with local building officials and obtain the necessary permits.

Site planning is an important component of agricultural building design. Important considerations include: water drainage (surface and subsurface), vehicle access, equipment parking, internal traffic patterns, exposure to winds and the prevailing wind direction and speed, adequate separation from human living areas, access to fields, solar exposure, storage, appearance, pollution hazards (internal and external to the site), labor efficiency in the context of the entire operation, waste management, feed distribution, electric and other utilities, soil characteristics, topography, production volume, and expectations for future expansion (for example, some experts recommend to plan the site assuming the operation will eventually double in size).

Topography is important for drainage, solar exposure, and snow control. Surface drainage requires a slope of 2 to 6%. Terraces and diversion ditches are used to intercept surface water. Such intercepts are usually grassed to limit erosion, and mowed to facilitate movement of water. Subsurface drainage can be achieved by drain tiles and pipes and is necessary for all building foundations and below-grade structures. A south facing slope will enhance drying, which is a benefit after rains. Tree windbreaks or windbreak fences provide protection from both winter storms and drifting snow. Windbreaks slow the wind for 10 to 20 height equivalents downstream of the break and 5 to 10 upstream. Several rows of evergreen trees provide an excellent windbreak, but a constructed windbreak may be desired until trees grow to sufficient height. The constructed windbreak should not be solid—an 80% solid windbreak provides better wind and snow protection than does a solid one.

Space requirements depend on the animals or plants being raised. Overcrowding causes animals to be stressed and perform poorly, and is likely to increase disease and injuries. As examples, recommended floor areas for some agriculturally important animals are listed in Table I.

TABLE I

Recommended Floor Areas per Animal Used for Design of Confined Animal Housing Systems

Animal	Floor area, m²/head
Swine	
Nursery pig	0.3
Growing pig	0.6
Finishing pig	0.8
Beef animal, confinement barn	
Cow/calf unit	4
To 250 kg	2
Over 250 kg	3
Dairy animal, total confinement	
Tie stalls	1.4 (W) × 1.8 m
Free stalls	1.2 (W) × 2.3 m
Sheep, ewes, w/solid floor broilers	
To 4 weeks of age	0.05
4 to 10 weeks of age	0.1
10 weeks to adult	0.2

III. Materials for Agricultural Structures

Agricultural buildings must be constructed to withstand four types of loads: dead, live, wind, and snow. Dead loads are vertical loads due to the weight of the construction materials and permanently installed equipment. Live loads are movable, such as equipment, animals, products, and stored materials. Design live loads are typically less in modern agricultural buildings than in public and commercial buildings. Wind loads may be horizontal or vertical (e.g., uplift) but do not include tornado winds. Snow loads are vertical loads applied to the horizontal projection of the roof.

Wood is frequently the construction material of choice. It is workable on the site, amenable to do-it-yourself construction, reasonably inexpensive, and retains its strength for a relatively long time in a fire. It also is subject to decay by fungi and damage by insects. Wood used for agricultural construction may be natural, or treated to resist decay. However, care is required in selecting the type of wood preservative, for volatile chemicals used in the preservative treatment may continue to evaporate and cause damage to plants if used in greenhouses, for example. Many new techniques are available to improve the strength to weight ratio of wood construction and use lumber that otherwise would be discarded. Use of laminated solid beams, box beams, and wooden I beams are three such techniques.

Concrete and masonry are commonly used for foundations, floor slabs, and walls. Air-entrained concrete is often recommended to resist weathering and the destructive actions of animal wastes. Slotted floors in animal housing are usually made of reinforced concrete slats.

Plastics have found several applications in agricultural building construction. The most obvious is foamed plastics used for insulation. Closed cell foam insulation is recommended in damp conditions. In addition, various plastic surface treatments have been used to improve the longevity and cleanability of walls and ceilings. Such surface treatments are typically integral with prefabricated panels. Rigid, clear plastic panels are available for greenhouse covering. The panels may be single layer, but numerous panels are now available having two plastic walls connected by internal webs that provide both strength and an air space for thermal insulation. One or two layers of plastic film (e.g., polyethylene) are also used extensively for low-cost greenhouse covering. Glass is, of course, widely used as a greenhouse covering.

Steel and aluminum have been widely used in agricultural buildings, for both framing and cover. Many storage buildings and farm shops, and some animal housing buildings, are mostly or all metal. Virtually all greenhouse framing is metal, in contrast to the extensive use of wood (e.g., cypress) in the past.

IV. Animal Housing

A. General

Confined animal agriculture has been characterized by several trends. One has been continued growth in the sizes of operations and the numbers of animals housed at single locations. Another is the trend away from combining animal housing and human housing at the same location—the "farmstead"—and a concomitant move toward more careful site planning. In fact, increased specialization has led to animal agriculture operations having no cropland base and where all feed must be purchased. A third trend is the growing involvement of third-party professionals in planning the production unit and selecting systems and components. A fourth is an increasing regulation for environmental reasons of animal and other wastes generated within the production unit.

The dominant development in animal housing during the past half century has been a long series of design modifications to increase animal housing density and deal with the resulting need for more precisely modulated environmental control. The poultry industry (especially the egg producing industry) has been the most evident example of increased housing density. Some swine facilities have also recently been designed and constructed to mimic the principles of laying hen confinement—confinement of the animals in cages that are stacked (spaced) vertically to increase space efficiency. Buildings having high animal densities are typically ventilated using mechanical ventilation. Simultaneously, primarily in the dairy industry, average herd sizes have increased to the point where stanchions/tie stalls are no longer labor efficient and free stall housing has emerged as the dominant housing method. Free stall housing is generally based on a large, open, naturally ventilated building where the air temperature remains close to that outdoors. Thus, we see change in two directions—one based on carefully controlled environment and active environmental modification, and one based on limited or no environmental control and passive environmental modification. [See DAIRY CATTLE PRODUCTION; POULTRY PRODUCTION; SWINE PRODUCTION.]

B. Mechanically Ventilated Animal Housing

Animal housing typically comprises a single air space, in contrast to industrial, commercial, and residential buildings for humans. This simultaneously simplifies and complicates the science and art of environmental control.

Mechanically ventilated housing generally corresponds to what is termed "warm housing" in which air temperature is maintained above freezing and often within a fairly narrow zone, when possible. Domestic animals are homeothermic with typical body temperatures of

Cattle: 38.5°C	Goats: 40°C
Horses: 38°C	Swine: 39°C
Sheep: 39°C	Chickens: 41.7°C

For comparison, human deep body temperature is 37°C.

A well-known relationship can be used to predict the rate at which warm-blooded animals generate body heat,

$$\text{Heat, watts per killogram body mass} = k \, (\text{body mass, kg})^{0.75},$$

where k is a constant that depends on body form. This relationship has been based primarily on adult animals in their natural habitats. Animals that are in the unnatural state of high production (growth, milk, eggs, etc.) can be expected to have a higher metabolic rate than predicted by standard values of k. The degree to which the standard values are exceeded depends on the degree of rapid growth and production. More accurate data may be found in engineering handbooks and the research literature.

The temperature range best for animals within a building is that which produces conditions of thermoneutrality, shown schematically in Fig. 1. The low temperature end of the thermoneutral zone is termed the lower critical temperature (LCT) and can be used as the lower limit of desired temperature for cold weather environmental control. The high temperature end is termed the upper critical temperature (UCT) and environmental control should endeavor not to exceed the UCT for more than short times during a day. Some evidence shows animals are able to compensate for short periods (several hours) above

the UCT by, for example, taking advantage of night time coolness. In addition, animal management may be simplified by proper environmental modification that takes advantage of the lack of comfort below the LCT. For example, control of air flow and resulting temperature in a swine facility can create zones within pens below the LCT and zones above it. Pigs, being naturally clean animals, will then use the colder parts of the pens only as dunging areas and rest only in the warmer parts of the pen.

Temperature control of animal housing buildings to attain thermoneutral conditions is typically more effective during cold weather than during hot periods. Considerations of cost (installed and operating) limit the number of methods available in a practical sense for temperature control—refrigerated air conditioning, for example, is not used. The thermoneutral zone for mature animals is typically well below their deep body temperatures and is a factor that depends on their rate of production or growth, the feed characteristics (energy content) of their diet, the presence and amount of bedding, the thermal radiation balance of the animal, relative humidity, and air movement and turbulence intensity. In mechanically ventilated housing for mature animals, metabolically produced heat is often the only source of heat for the air space. Mature animals (with their greater body mass) produce more heat per unit area of housing space and usually exhibit a lower thermoneutral zone. When immature animals are housed, supplemental heat is often required.

Today's trend to greater animal housing density and genetic manipulation (breeding) to develop high-producing animals results in a great deal of heat production within the ventilated space. The amount of heat is typically sufficient to balance heat loss through the structural cover and ventilation and yet maintain air space temperature at or above the lower critical temperature unless the outdoor air temperature is extremely cold (e.g., below $-20°C$). On the other hand, the high heat production rate does not usually permit temperature control to within the thermoneutral region when outdoor air temperature is near or above the upper critical temperature. A maximum installed ventilation capacity of one complete air exchange per minute is typical in most mechanically ventilated animal housing, which limits the temperature rise of the ventilating air to perhaps 2°C, but in many regions of the world there are many hours of weather at or above the thermoneutral region. Evaporative cooling (either by cooling the air prior to its being introduced into the air space or by introducing a fine water mist

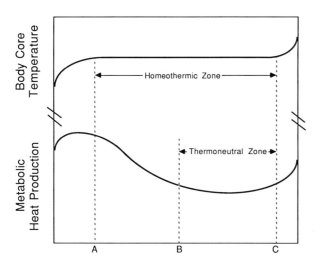

FIGURE 1 Body core temperature and metabolic heat production as functions of the effective environment temperature. To the left of A is the region of hypothermia and to the right of C is the region of hyperthermia. Between B and C, temperature regulation is by physical means and to the left of B increased heat loss to the environment can be compensated only by increased feed consumption and metabolism.

within the air space) is the most typical means of environmental cooling. Evaporative cooling is most effective in dryer climates, but even in moderately humid climates there is some potential for its use during the hottest time of day when the relative humidity is usually at its lowest. The defining factor is the difference between the outdoor dry bulb and wet bulb temperatures (the so-called wet bulb depression). A well-maintained evaporative cooling system should be able to bring the cooled air to within 2°C of the wet bulb temperature, which is a rule that can be used to assess the possible benefits of evaporative cooling. Mechanical refrigeration is usually thought to be too expensive for environmental modification in animal housing, except perhaps in localized zones such as providing cooled air directed at the animal's head for inhalation.

Mechanical ventilation of animal housing can be one of three types, depending on the locations of the fans:

1. Negative pressure, where one or more fans exhaust air from the air space. Air pressure within the space is slightly below that of outdoors (ideally between 10 and 20 Pa difference). Fresh air is drawn into the building through planned inlets and some enters through the many small openings (air leaks) in the building shell—the so-called infiltration. This is the most typical arrangement for mechanical ventilation of animal housing.

2. Positive pressure, where one or more fans push fresh air into the air space (usually through some form of widely distributed inlet area). Air pressure within the space is slightly above that of outdoors. Air from the space is exhausted through planned outlets and exfiltration occurs through air leaks in the building shell.

3. Neutral pressure, where fans are at both the inlets and outlets and the net pressure within the air space is approximately the same as that outdoors, and air infiltration/exfiltration is minimized.

Most mechanically ventilated, negative pressure, animal buildings (usually rectangular in shape, perhaps 15 m wide and up to 100 m or more long) are designed to draw air across the shortest dimension of the air space. Fans are typically located on the more sheltered (leeward) side of the building and inlets (often essentially continuous) may be located on the opposite side or on both sides. An alternate location for the inlets is along the center line of the ceiling, with air drawn through an insulated plenum constructed within the attic space. This concept of ventilation (a short distance from inlet to exhaust) was developed to limit the temperature rise of the air as it passes

through the air space. Recent innovations ("tunnel" ventilation) are based on the opposite. Air is drawn through the building in the long direction, which significantly increases air speed within the space. Higher air speeds and the resulting greater turbulence intensity are thought to increase animal and worker comfort during hot weather.

Two principles are important in design and control of mechanical ventilation systems. One is that the ventilation rate (volumetric rate of air flow) is determined almost exclusively by the fans. The second is that air distribution and its subsequent mixing within the air space are determined almost exclusively by the inlets. Inlets typically include movable baffles that automatically adjust to modulate the effective area of air flow and thereby the inlet air velocity and indoor to outdoor pressure difference. Ample air mixing results from adequate inlet air speed which results, in turn, from a sufficient pressure difference from inside the building to outside. Pressure differences in the range of 10 to 20 Pa are usually adequate, leading to inlet air speeds from 4 to 6 m per second. The standard Bernoulli equation of classical fluid mechanics can be used to relate air speed and pressure difference. Control of the total system is best accomplished by modulating the fans based on indoor air temperature (trying to keep within the thermoneutral region) and adjusting the inlets based on the indoor-to-outdoor air pressure difference.

Ventilation systems such as described above work best with air spaces that encompass few or no obstructions such as partial or complete walls, pens having high and solid sides, and massive feeding structures, as examples. Such obstructions lead to dead air zones and subsequent unhealthy conditions. The systems also work best when the building is constructed to have as little air leakage—infiltration—as possible. Air leaks act as unplanned and uncontrollable inlets and provide paths of ventilation that short circuit the planned ventilation system.

Fans may be speed controlled and modulated to vary the ventilation rate, or may be single speed and activated and deactivated in groups (staged) as the ventilation need changes. Energy efficiency is an important criterion in fan selection and efficiency data are often available from the manufacturer and from independent testing laboratories. However, efficient fans do not remain efficient if permitted to become dirty or misadjusted. Cleaning and adjusting at least twice yearly is often recommended because of the dusty and humid operating conditions in most animal housing.

C. Naturally Ventilated Animal Housing

Naturally ventilated animal housing exists as two types—so-called "cold" buildings and "modified-environment" buildings. Neither type attempts to maintain indoor conditions above the housed animals' lower critical temperature during cold weather. However, building construction and animal care expenses are generally less, compensating for the resulting increased feed intake. Conditions during warm weather are often superior to those in mechanically ventilated animal housing.

Cold buildings are lightly insulated, large, open structures having an open front or large ventilation openings on their two long walls, smaller ventilation openings along their roof ridge, and no attic spaces. The side wall ventilation openings may be partly closed during winter to limit chilling winds and blowing snow, but indoor air temperature generally remains no more than a few degrees above the outdoors. Because the air can be very cold the buildings are generally used only for large and mature animals—dairy or beef cattle, for example. Such animals do not suffer when conditions are well below their lower critical temperatures and simply eat more to compensate for the increased heat loss to their environment. There is seldom any true control of either air flow or temperature in naturally ventilated buildings. The roof may be insulated to suppress condensation on the underside of the roof during cold and clear nights and reduce radiant heat loads on the housed animals during midday in the summer.

Modified environment buildings are insulated to a greater extent but still rely on wind effects and thermal buoyancy for ventilation. Movable vent panels are opened and closed in response to indoor air temperature in an attempt to keep the buildings from freezing. This type of housing may be used for dairy and beef animals but also for (for example) dairy calves and heifers and finishing swine and gestating sows, which are not highly susceptible to cold temperatures.

A critical time for proper operation of naturally ventilated buildings is during cold and still weather. Ventilation must be in response to thermal buoyancy when there is no wind. If thermal buoyancy is to work, at least two elevations of openings must exist—one at the high point of the air space and one low. A vent along the ridge of the building is usually the high opening, and remains open year around. A cap over the ridge vent to prevent rain entry is usually detrimental in regions where winter snows are frequent, for the ridge cap acts as a snow fence to cause snow to be driven through the vent, possibly creating a snow drift inside the building. Roof slope is important to facilitate warm air movement toward the vent; a slope of 1:4 is the recommended minimum and 1:3 is often used. Because air moving toward the roof vent is the warmest and most humid in the building, roof insulation is typically used, not to conserve heat, but to limit condensation on the under side of the roof.

Natural ventilation is typically combined with free stall housing for dairy cattle. The animals are penned in groups and are free to wander between a feeding and a resting area. This system is best suited to herds of at least 80 animals, where the herd can be divided into four reasonably sized groups having similar milk production and thus similar nutrition needs. The animals are taken in groups two or three times a day to be milked in a separate milking parlor. Manure is typically handled by automatic scrapers and bedding is used only in the resting stalls, if at all. Permanent mats may be used instead to replace bedding, some forms of which have occasionally been implicated in the spread of mastitis.

Dairy calves are often housed in a very simple type of naturally ventilated structure—the calf hutch. Calves are very susceptible to disease and when housed closely together in a ventilated room can pass a variety of diseases among themselves. This led, approximately two decades ago, to using small (1.2 × 2.4 m × 1.2 m high) hutches (boxes) open on one end and with no floor, with the open end facing away from prevailing cold winds (and usually south for solar gain). The insides of the hutches are bedded, as with straw. Either there are small fenced spaces outside the open ends or calves are tethered to the hutches. The hutches are separated sufficiently that there is no calf-to-calf physical contact and hutches are moved between occupants to limit soilborne transmission of diseases and parasites. Calves are placed into hutches within hours of birth, while they still retain the ability to produce brown adipose tissue (BAT, a form of body fat that is high in energy content and quickly available to the animal). Even in the coldest weather calves adapt well to this system, grow well, and show almost no morbidity. However, since the calves must be cared for daily, this has not proven the most popular system for farm workers (e.g., a natural reluctance to work outdoors to feed a group of calves during a blizzard) and thus a modification, based on housing calves in open-front sheds (usually facing south), has become popular.

The concept of the so-called "FLEX" house was first applied successfully in the poultry industry, and more recently to dairy housing. In concept, the FLEX house is a combination of a closed, mechanically ventilated building for winter operation and an open, naturally ventilated building for summer operation. Movable, but sealable, side wall vents are constructed, opened wide during warm weather, and closed except for a small, continuous inlet opening during cold weather. Fans are used only when the vents are closed. This form of housing takes the modified open front building concept one step further, permitting temperature control to within the animals' thermoneutral zone during cold weather, yet providing the advantages of natural ventilation during warm weather.

V. Greenhouses

Commercial greenhouses must serve several purposes. The paramount purpose is to provide stress-free environments to plants to encourage growth and development at rates that are optimally profitable. Concomitantly, efficiency of production, labor, and energy must be enabled. Plant growth may be in hydroponics, artificial media in containers, or soil (or raised soil beds), depending on the crop and grower preference. The trend is toward less growing in soil and more toward hydroponics (especially for greenhouse-grown vegetables). Growing plants hydroponically requires careful management of the nutrient solution to assure sufficient dissolved oxygen, and pH and nutrient control. An alternative gaining acceptance is aeroponics, which is a system in which the roots are sprayed with a fine mist of nutrient solution. Aeroponics assures adequate oxygen supply to plant roots. [See HORTICULTURAL GREENHOUSE ENGINEERING.]

Numerous regulatory pressures are forcing rapid changes in greenhouse site planning. Primary among these are regulations prohibiting discharges of water containing detectable amounts of the chemicals (fertilizers, growth regulators, pesticides, herbicides) used in the greenhouse industry, and other water pollutants. These discharges may arise from draining excess water used for watering plants (plants are often overwatered to prevent salts build up in the rooting medium), draining the condensate that forms during cold weather on the inside of the greenhouse cover, and even roof runoff, which carries with it contaminants from local and regional air pollution. Where regulatory pressures are greatest, "zero discharge" green-

houses may soon be required. In part these demands can be addressed by using ebb and flow systems or by capturing and recycling water used within the greenhouse, but site planning should also include an area for containing and treating large volumes of water, as from roof runoff. In addition, concerns for light pollution near residential areas may limit site selection options if night time plant lighting is planned.

Pollution problems are not confined to effects arising from the presence of the greenhouse operation. Water and air contaminants can have very negative effects on crop growth. Normal water contaminants such as calcium and magnesium that cause water "hardness" are not detrimental to plant growth. Less common contaminants such as boron are detrimental to certain plants. The background salts level in groundwater, if sufficiently concentrated (as may be the case in arid climates and near oceans, for example), may cause the total salts level to be too high after soluble fertilizer is added to the water, and be detrimental to plant growth. Air pollution can also negatively affect plants. For example, the presence of a nearby, heavily travelled highway may generate sufficient air pollution (NO_x, for example) to significantly reduce plant growth and perhaps even plant quality to the point where they cannot be sold.

Structural design loads that must be considered are generally the same type as with other buildings. However, the design snow load is typically less than for other building types because heat conducted from within a heated greenhouse is sufficient to melt snow nearly as quickly as it falls. In greenhouses constructed of many sections, joined at the eaves (gutter-connected), special heating pipes are placed under the joined eaves to melt snow and prevent its accumulation to a dangerous depth. Another difference in greenhouse design load assumptions is the type of live load that may be anticipated. Heating and ventilating equipment, hanging baskets of growing plants, carts for moving plants and materials that are suspended from tracks attached to the frame, and movable screens and curtains used for energy and light control may all be hung from a greenhouse frame. This has led to a recommendation that greenhouses be designed for a live load of 75 kg/m^2, the same as the recommended minimum design load for snow. Greenhouses are very light weight, making it doubly important that anchorage to the ground be able to resist the uplift forces generated by winds; a design wind speed of 35 m/sec (130 km/hr) is recommended.

Most greenhouses used for commercial production can be classified into six basic frame types, shown in Fig. 2. The hoop house is especially useful in the nursery industry for over-wintering plants and has also been widely used as an inexpensive structure for growing situations that last for only part of the year, such as growing bedding plants. The gutter-connected styles can cover many hectares under a single roof and usually form sections approximately as wide as they are long.

The greenhouse environment encompasses numerous environmental parameters. Greenhouse crop production must emphasize quantity, quality, and timing of product availability. Placing any of these three ahead of the others is difficult. The importance of timing is not as obvious as the other two, but flowers for holidays are worthless if late and vegetables that do not reach market at the contracted time may constitute a breach of contract. Plant growth in greenhouses is subject to the inconsistency of weather, especially solar insolation, and thus crop management is a highly refined skill.

Photosynthesis is driven by the light energy in the wavelength band from 390 to 700 nm. This wavelength band is the "photosynthetically active radia-tion," or PAR. Growth is little affected by where, within this band, the energy is received, although certain morphological developments depend on receiving some energy in specific parts of the spectrum (e.g., red or blue). Some plants adapt well to 24-hr lighting while other species require a dark period each day for proper development. Photoperiodism is exhibited relative to flower initiation in some species. Certain species are short day obligates (e.g., chrysanthemums), some are long day obligates (e.g., fuchsia), some are daylength-intermediate obligates, while others are day neutral.

Supplemental greenhouse lighting for growth is generally accomplished using metal halide or high-pressure sodium luminaires. Uniformity of lighting is perhaps more critical for uniformity of plant growth than it is for lighting for human vision. The human eye responds logarithmically to light intensity and is thus insensitive to relatively large changes of the intensity. Plants respond essentially linearly to light; thus, a 10% variation of illumination can lead to a 10% variation of growth but be undetectable to the human eye. Supplemental greenhouse lighting for photoperiod control is often accomplished using incandescent lamps and relatively low light intensities, and light uniformity is not critical.

Temperature is another critical environmental parameter although its effects on plant growth are complex and not understood in fine detail. General practice is to heat to a specific night temperature (a blueprint condition determined by best plant response) and increase the day temperature 5 to 8°C above the night temperature. Space heating is often by hot water or steam, although forced hot air is also common. The crop may be heated using localized systems such as root zone (often provided by a warmed floor) or infrared heating systems, which require special controllers. Ventilation is by mechanical ventilation in most instances, although natural ventilation alone may be adequate in cool climate regions. Supplemental lighting and heating interact, for the lights emit infrared radiation which can heat the plant canopy several degrees above ambient air temperature.

Carbon dioxide is a nutrient required for photosynthesis. Whether supplementing carbon dioxide will provide additional plant growth depends, however, on whether it is the factor limiting growth at the time. If light levels are low, adding carbon dioxide will have little effect. If light levels are intense, inadequate access to carbon dioxide during the mid-day is likely to limit photosyntheses and thus supplementing can

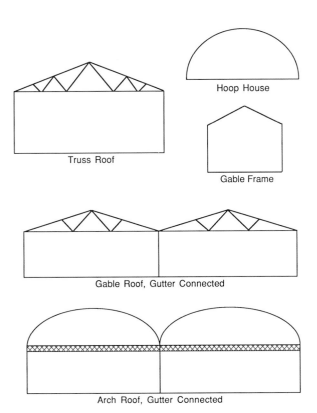

FIGURE 2 Six generic greenhouse frame types.

double plant growth rate. Unfortunately, frequently during the times when carbon dioxide supplementation would be most beneficial greenhouses are vented (mid-day, when solar intensity and the resulting heat load are greatest).

The carbon dioxide may be supplied from compressed gas or be in liquid form, or may be derived from exhaust gases from a natural gas or oil combustion unit (e.g., a central boiler) if care is taken to prevent incomplete combustion and the resulting ethylene (and other air pollutants) production. Special, high-efficiency burners are often recommended to limit introduction of harmful combustion products into greenhouses.

Ventilation system design in greenhouses must include consideration of air speed near the plants. If the air is stagnant, carbon dioxide can become locally depleted even while being added elsewhere in the greenhouse. Conversely, air speeds that are too high encourage excessive evapotranspiration, causing the leaf stomata to close and limit carbon dioxide uptake and thereby photosynthesis. As a general recommendation, air speeds of 0.1 to 0.2 m/sec are considered a good compromise. If areas of air stagnation are a problem, horizontal air flow and mixing can be added to a greenhouse. Horizontal air flow is induced by small (e.g., 0.4 m diameter) propellor fans spaced at even intervals around the greenhouse and directing air to flow in a racetrack pattern around the structure.

Because light environment is so critical to growth and quality of plant growth, especially during winter, the structural cover of a greenhouse should be highly transmissive to short-wave solar radiation. Greenhouse orientation also affects the light environment somewhat. A common recommendation is to have ridges of stand-alone greenhouses oriented east/west in northern zones (above approximately 35 N latitude, where the winter sun is low in the sky) to expose the largest possible greenhouse cover area for light interception during mid-day (when most of the sun's energy is received). Greenhouse ranges composed of gutter-connected units are recommended to have ridge lines oriented north/south so the shade lines of structural elements do not create zones of shade that move little during the middle of the day, retarding plant growth and development in those zones. In southern regions, stand-alone greenhouses are recommended to be oriented north/south to limit overheating during the day. Shade cloth is also used to reduce solar gain during the summer.

Greenhouses require a great deal of heating energy in cold climates. Because the light environment is so critical, normal insulation techniques do not apply. Double glazing the structural cover can reduce heat loss significantly, but the most effective insulation methods involve movable curtains deployed at night over the crop, creating an attic space under the greenhouse roof. Most greenhouse heating is required during the night (estimated to be approximately 70% of total heat needed in cold climates); thus, deployable insulation (thermal screens) can be reasonably effective even though they are stowed during the daylight hours. Advanced designs of thermal screens incorporate translucent materials and can double as shade cloth systems for crop protection during the heat of day during summer.

Greenhouse cooling is first accomplished by ventilation and then by evaporative cooling. Evaporative cooling may be produced by drawing ventilation air through wetted pads or by generating a very fine fog (mist) into the greenhouse. Evaporative cooling systems can provide cooling unless the outdoor relative humidity is very high. Mechanical refrigeration is prohibitively expensive for application in commercial CEA facilities.

VI. Product Storage

Drying and storing agricultural products requires specialized structures. In many cases these structures are purchased as whole units and are brought to the farm complete or in fabricated modules. Grains, especially, are harvested, dried, and then stored on the farm until use or sale. Drying is critical for preservation of grain and to prevent mold and fungi growth and grain spoilage. Certain fungi, if permitted to proliferate, produce compounds (mycotoxins) highly toxic to animals and humans. Drying typically reduces grain moisture content to 12 to 13%, on a wet basis. Some crops (e.g., oil seeds) must be dried to an even lower moisture content. Once dried, these crops can often be stored for several years with little deterioration. [See Grain, Feed, and Crop Storage; Postharvest Physiology.]

A very specialized form of storage has been developed, primarily for apples, although cabbage and celery also may be stored using the technology. The technology is controlled atmosphere (CA) storage. Storage in CA conditions reduces the respiration rate of the stored product by approximately half, extending storage life for apples, for example, by several months and making them available year around. The structure for CA storage is a tightly sealed and refrigerated building (or room) in which the atmospheric composition is carefully controlled. The oxygen content is lowered to a few percent (the exact value depending on the crop) and the carbon dioxide concentration is raised from ambient to several percent. This combination of actions greatly suppresses, but does not kill, the living organism which is the fruit or vegetable. The organism's metabolic rate is slowed sufficiently that respiration does not as rapidly consume the stored sugars, etc., in the product. When such food sources are depleted, the product dies and decay commences.

Extremely careful construction and control are required to construct and operate a CA storage and it is a technology not economically amenable to small-scale application. It is not unusual for several growers to cooperate to build, operate, and use in common a CA storage facility. Because of the modified atmosphere inside a CA storage, great care must be taken to avoid accidental suffocation by entering a CA room before it has been sufficiently purged with fresh air prior to removing the stored product and special life support equipment is required to enter such a room should some repair or other action be required before the storage would normally be opened.

Bibliography

Albright, L. D. 1991. "Environment Control for Animals and Plants." American Society of Agricultural Engineers, St. Joseph, MI.

ASHRAE (1989). "Handbook of Fundamentals," Chapts. 9, 10. American Society of Heating, Refrigerating and Air Conditioning Engineers, Atlanta, GA.

ASHRAE (1991). "HVAC Applications" Chapts. 21, 22. American Society of Heating, Refrigerating and Air Conditioning Engineers, Atlanta, GA.

Aldrich, R. A., and Bartok, J. W. (1989). "Greenhouse Engineering." Northeast Regional Agricultural Engineering Service. Ithaca, NY.

Barre, H. J., Sammet, L. L., and Nelson, G. L. (1988). "Environmental and Functional Engineering of Agricultural Buildings." Van Nostrand Reinhold, New York.

Clark, J. A. (1981). "Environmental Aspects of Housing for Animal Production." Butterworths, London.

Esmay, M. L., and Dixon, J. E. (1986). "Environmental Control for Agricultural Buildings." Van Nostrand Reinhold, New York.

Hellickson, M., and Walker, J., (eds.) (1983). "Ventilation of Agricultural Structures." American Society of Agricultural Engineers, St. Joseph, MI.

Langhans, R. W. (1990). "Greenhouse Management." Halcyon, Ithaca, NY.

Sugarbeet

STEPHEN KAFFKA, F. JACKSON HILLS,†

University of California, Davis

Glossary

Biomass Dry matter produced by plants
Bolting Formation of seed stalks by the sugarbeet
C3 Photosynthetic system of most plants of temperate regions
EC European community
ET Evapotranspiration—the loss of water from a given area by evaporation from the soil surface and by transpiration from plants
Mg/ha (Megagrams per hectare) Similar to metric tons/ha; When multiplied by 0.446 equals short tons (2000 pounds) per acre
Petiole Stalk of a leaf
Photosynthesis Process by which green plants utilize the sun's energy to produce carbohydrate from carbon dioxide and water
Stand Number and distribution of plants after emergence from seed
Sucrose $C_{12}H_{22}O_{11}$, the sugar of world commerce
Ton Two thousand pounds, when multiplied by 1.102 equals one metric ton (Mg)

Sugarbeet and sugarcane produce nearly all of the world's supply of sucrose, the "sugar" of commerce. A crop of the temperate regions, sugarbeet is intensively farmed and is one of the most efficient plants

†Deceased.

used in the production of food for humankind and animals.

I. Classification, Origin, Adaptation, and Production

Sucrose is synthesized in most plants as a temporary storage product for photosynthetically reduced carbon, and is the most common form of carbon translocated in plants. Most plants convert photosynthate to starch for long-term storage. However, sucrose accumulates to an exceptional degree in two species, sugarbeet (*Beta vulgaris* L.) and sugarcane (*Saccharum officianarum* L.), which together form the basis for greater than 90% of the world's sugar trade. The sucrose derived from these two species represents approximately 11% of the world's food supply, and 0.2% of all the carbon fixed via photosynthesis by the world's crops each year. The most recent estimate for world sugar (sucrose) production is 114.3 million tons, of which one-third is derived from sugarbeet, and two-thirds from sugarcane. [*See* SUGARCANE.]

A genus of the family Chenopodiacee, sugarbeet is one of a diverse and useful group of cultivars from the same species that includes swiss chard, fodderbeet, and red beet. The first modern sugarbeets originated as selections made in the middle of the 18th century from fodderbeets grown in then German Silesia, but food and medicinal uses of the genus are much older. A precursor is known to have been used as food as early as dynastic times in ancient Egypt. In 1747 a German chemist, Andreas Marggraf, demonstrated that the crystals formed after a crude extraction from pulverized beet roots were identical in all properties with sugarcane crystals, and attempts to derive sugar from beets originate from his work. His student, Karl Achard, developed processing methods for sugar extraction from the beet, and made the first selections of higher sugar type beets. The blockade of shipments of cane sugar to Europe by the British during the Napoleonic wars stimulated a more intensive search for sweeter beets, a plant breeding program, and the construction of many crude factories in France and elsewhere to produce sugar from the sugarbeet. After Waterloo and the lifting of the British blockade, the incipient sugarbeet industry in France declined but the modern sugarbeet had been created and the efficacy of sugar extraction from beet had been demonstrated. The first successful commercial factory in the United States was constructed by E. H. Dyer at Alvarado, California, in 1879. Soon after, sugarbeet culture and factories expanded in many states. In 1917 there were 91 factories opening in 18 states. However, by 1989 there were only 36 operating factories in 13 states processing sugarbeet grown on about 550,000 ha. The major sugarbeet producing states in the United States are California, Colorado, Idaho, Nebraska, North Dakota, Minnesota, Michigan, Texas, and Wyoming.

Sugarbeet is grown predominantly in regions with temperate, Mediterranean, or arid climates. For the most part, beet-producing regions lie north and south of the 30th parallels. Sugarcane production is confined to tropical and subtropical zones. Table I contains data for sugarbeet production in the major beet-producing regions of the world. All of these regions except the EC, China, and Turkey also must import sugar from sugarcane-producing countries to meet a portion of their sugar demand. Sugar consumption has been growing at roughly the same rate as world population or 2% per year. There are substantial differences in per capita sugar consumption among nations. In part these differences are cultural, but per capita consumption also is correlated with wealth and is highest in Europe and lowest in China and Africa.

II. Industry Organization

Beet sugar production worldwide often is vertically integrated. Companies that process sugar from the beet root have considerable influence over all aspects of production from the area planted through the sale of the final product. The crop is of little value without a processor to extract the sugar, and once a sugar factory is constructed, a company must have a reliable supply of beets. Usually, there is a closer and more cooperative relationship among growers and companies than is found with other agronomic commodities. In the United States, the crop is grown most often under contract between the individual grower and a processing company. The contract specifies the area that can be grown, various details concerning the delivery of beet roots, and the method on which payment to the grower will be based. Typically, contracts guarantee the grower a share of the return the processor realizes from the sale of sugar. They often contain quality incentives. Sugarbeet growers, through the formation of local associations, influence the terms of the contract and inspect company operations, such as the method of sampling delivered sugarbeet methods of sucrose analysis and tare determinations. In the United States, sugarbeet processors and grower associations band together to influence national policy and legislation concerning the growing of sugarbeet.

In both Europe and the United States, sugarbeet variety improvement and seed production are carried

TABLE I

Sugarbeet Land Area, Root Yield, and Percentage Sugar Recovered for the World's Important Production Regions[a]

Region	Area planted (1000 ha)	Beet yield (Mg/ha)	% Sugar recovered	Sugar yield (Mg/ha)	Ratio of domestic production to consumption[b]
European Community[c]	1966	49.4	16.2	7.98	123
Eastern European Nations[d]	1055	32.5	12.5	4.05	(Not available)
Former Soviet Union	3150	22.8	10.4	2.38	60
United States	564	45.8	13.6	6.24	82
China	740	22.1	10.5	2.3	106
Japan	72	55.6	18.0	10.0	35
Turkey	391	37.7	12.8	4.8	103

[a] Three-year average (1990–1992). USDA-Foreign Agricultural Service. Sugarbeets are also grown in countries other than those listed, but the area planted is generally small.
[b] All sugar sources. China and the United States also produce sugarcane.
[c] Belgium-Luxembourg, Denmark, France, Germany, Italy, The Netherlands, Spain, and the United Kingdom.
[d] The former Czechoslovakia, Hungary, Poland, Romania, the former Yugoslavia, and the Baltic States: Estonia, Latvia, and Lithuania.

TABLE II

Approximate Water Use Efficiency (WUE) and Nitrogen Use Efficiency (NUE) of Various Crops Grown at Davis, California, Compared on Biomass, Harvested Yield, and Human-Digestible Energy Basis

Crop or product	Season Et (mm)	Biomass (kg ha^{-1})	WUE$_b$ (kg ha^{-1} mm^{-1})	HI	WUE$_h$ (kg ha^{-1} mm^{-1})	WUE$_f$ (MJ ha^{-1} mm^{-1})	NUE$_f$ (MJ ha^{-1} kg^{-1} N)
Corn	710	22,000	32.6	0.5	16.3	203	765
corn → milk	—	—	—	—	—	96	—
Barley	390	10,000	25.6	0.4	11.5	136	—
barley → beef	—	—	—	—	—	22	—
Dry bean	570	6,000	10.5	0.4	4.2	50	—
Sugarbeet	780	20,000	25.6	0.4	11.5	180	1810

Note. WUE$_b$, water use efficiency per unit biomass; WUE$_h$, water use efficiency per unit harvested biomass; WUE$_f$, water use efficiency per unit digestible energy; NUE$_f$, nitrogen use effiiciency per unit digestible energy. Typical ET and biomass values based in part on Loomis and Wallinga (1991). Alfalfa: efficient or inefficient user of water? [*In* "Proceedings, 21st California Alfalfa Symposium, Davis, CA" (S. Mueller, ed.). NUE calculations based on Hills *et al.* (1983). Fertilizer nitrogen utilization by corn, tomato, and sugarbeet. *Agron. J.* **75**, 423–426.]

out primarily by private companies. However, the USDA developed most of the varieties grown in the first half of the 20th century in the United States and current variety development often uses genetic lines derived from USDA research. Most countries have variety testing programs to assure the use of cultivars that are productive and well adapted.

III. Growth and Development of the Sugarbeet Crop

The sugarbeet is a remarkable plant. A rapidly growing crop is capable of high rates of sucrose accumulation. California has regions which are ideally suited to commercial sugarbeet production. The world's commercial record has come from a field in the Salinas Valley and equalled 19.0 Mg ha^{-1} of sucrose from a crop grown over a 240-day period (115 Mg ha^{-1} of roots at 16.5% sucrose). Averaged over the total period of growth, the crop accumulated 185 kg total dry matter ha^{-1} day^{-1} (44.7 Mg total DM/240 days) and 80 kg sucrose ha^{-1} day^{-1}. Sucrose accumulation is not uniform throughout the growing season. Initially it is relatively slow. Peak sucrose accumulation rates are considerably higher than the average reported for a cropping season and likely exceed rates of 100 kg sucrose ha^{-1} day^{-1}. More typical crops reach half the biomass and sugar yields of record crops. An average hectare of sugarbeet in California produces 56 Mg of roots containing 15% sucrose. Upon processing, the beets yield 7.4 Mg of recoverable sugar, 3.4 Mg of dry root pulp, and 98 kg of monosodium glutamate, an amino acid salt used to enhance the flavor of foods. The sugarbeet pulp left after sucrose extraction is used widely in

the dairy and beef cattle industries as a feed supplement due to its highly digestible fiber and energy content. Another 6.7 Mg dry matter of beet tops may be left in the field to fertilize subsequent crops or used as feed for cattle or sheep. When the beets are harvested, approximately 150 kg N, 20 kg P, and 150 kg K ha^{-1} are removed with them. These amounts of nutrients are roughly similar to those removed by a 10 Mg ha^{-1} crop of corn grain. Because beets are efficient at accumulating photosynthate in a useful form, they are also efficient convertors of agricultural inputs such as water and nitrogen (Table II). One of the reasons sugarbeet requires relatively low use of fertilizer nitrogen is its efficiency in recovering residual soil nitrogen from previous crops or decomposed organic matter. [*See* NITROGEN CYCLING.]

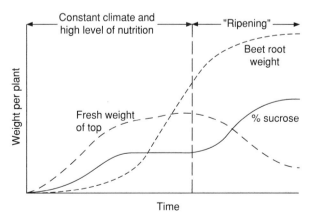

FIGURE 1 Schematic representation of growth of the sugarbeet. In a constant, favorable climate, vegetative growth continues indefinitely (Fig. 2). An increase in the sucrose concentration of the beet root is dependent on external factors, principally cool night temperatures and nitrogen deficiency (Courtesy of Albert Ulrich).

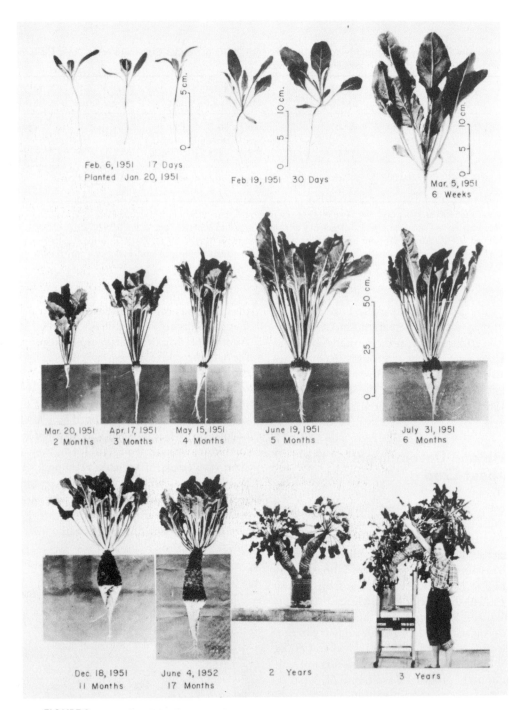

Feb. 6, 1951   17 Days
Planted Jan. 20, 1951

Feb. 19, 1951   30 Days

Mar. 5, 1951
6 Weeks

Mar. 20, 1951
2 Months

Apr. 17, 1951
3 Months

May 15, 1951
4 Months

June 19, 1951
5 Months

July 31, 1951
6 Months

Dec. 18, 1951
11 Months

June 4, 1952
17 Months

2 Years

3 Years

FIGURE 2   Growth and development of sugarbeets grown for 3 years with a plentiful nutrient supply in a climate favorable to vegetative growth. Bolting (seed stalk production) will not occur until induced by cold temperature (Courtesy of Albert Ulrich).

Figure 1 illustrates the growth and development of a sugarbeet plant. Under such appropriate conditions, the plant develops quickly from seed with the seedling emerging from the soil as soon as 5 days after planting. The taproot grows rapidly and may reach 30 cm or more by the time the first true leaf is developed. During the first 30 days, growth is confined primarily to leaves and fibrous roots. After about 30 days both top and storage-root growth proceed rapidly with tops reaching near maximum fresh weight in 60 to 90 days. Subsequently, with favorable climate, top growth remains fairly constant but storage roots con-

FIGURE 3 (A) The sugarbeet grows from 6 to 10 months before it is harvested for the sugar (sucrose) in its root. (B) Bolting sugarbeets. Seed stalks are induced by a period of cold temperature.

tinue to grow rapidly for another 20 to 24 weeks. Beyond that period, crown (stem) growth constitutes an increasingly larger percentage of the commercial storage root. As the storage root increases in size, there is a constant translocation of sucrose from the leaves to the root where it stored primarily in concentric rings of vascular tissue derived from secondary cambium initiated early in the root's development and in root parenchyma cells that enlarge during growth. On a fresh weight basis, the sucrose content of the root remains relatively constant until suitable external factors cause the concentration to increase. A rapid increase in root sucrose content is correlated with cool night temperatures in the fall of the year coupled with a nitrogen deficiency. Both of these conditions slow vegetative growth, particularly top growth, and the photosynthetically produced sucrose accumulates in roots as storage rather than as new vegetative growth. Figure 2 shows sugarbeet plants

at various stages of growth over a 3-year period in a constant, favorable climate. Sugarbeet is a biennial and when the growing plant (Fig. 3A) undergoes prolonged exposure to cold tempeatures (approximately 90 days at 5 to 7°C) followed by warmer temperatures and longer day lengths, seed stalk production ("bolting") takes place (Fig. 3B). In the United States, sugarbeet seed is produced most efficiently in the Willamette Valley of Oregon, where winter temperatures are low but the roots do not freeze, allowing seed producers to manipulate the plant's biennial habit.

Most sugarbeet varieties currently grown are monogerm hybrids that out-yield older, open-pollinated types by from 10 to 20%. The use of monogerm seed, discovered by V. F. Savitsky in the late 1940s, eliminates seed balls with multiple embryos and crowding of seedlings when plants emerge. In turn, this improves the operation of mechanical thinners or eases thinning by long-handled hoes, and makes it easier to plant directly to a stand. Before planting, seed is processed and graded to permit precision planting, and is treated to protect germinating seedlings from soil fungi and insects.

IV. Management Practices and Production Problems

In most sugarbeet growing regions, the earlier the planting and longer the growing season, the higher the yield, provided that temperatures at planting are conducive to rapid growth and plants are not retarded by diseases or other problems.

Seeds are planted in rows from 50 to 76 cm apart. Within a row plants should be spaced at least 13 cm apart. Closer spacings tend to encourage vegetative growth at the expense of sugar yield. When plants are too far apart or spacings uneven, sugar yield is lost as well. Where conditions are conducive to good field emergence (50% or better) seeds can be planted 10 to 15 cm apart with the expectation that the resulting stand will not need to be thinned. Many fields, however, are planted at closer seed spacings and, with good emergence, require the use of mechanical or hand thinning to space the plants from 13 to 30 cm within the row. Good stands of sugarbeet planted in rows 50 cm apart contain from about 154,000 to 67,000 plants per hectare.

Generally, nitrogen fertilization is required for profitable sugarbeet production. However, sugar yield is sensitive to the timing of nitrogen availability, requiring ample amounts early for maximum vegetative growth but also a period of nitrogen deficiency prior to harvest for proper sugar accumulation in the storage roots. Figure 4 shows a typical response of a sugarbeet crop to fertilizer nitrogen. Highest sugar yields, a function of root yield and sucrose concentration, usually are achieved with a fertilizer rate that nearly maximizes root yield. However, this rate can be considerably less than the rate required for maximum total biomass production (roots plus tops) and usually is not the rate giving the highest root sucrose concentration. Data in Figure 4 indicate that application of 112 kg fertilizer N/ha resulted in maximum sugar yield and maximized profit to the grower. In this instance, plant analyses indicated that the crop was deficient in nitrogen for about 8 weeks prior to harvest. [See FERTILIZER MANAGEMENT AND TECHNOLOGY.]

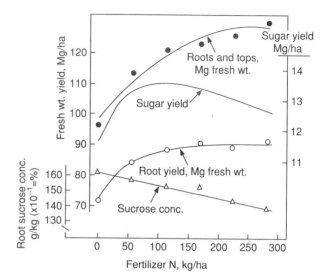

FIGURE 4 Response of sugarbeet to fertilizer nitrogen. Maximum sugar yield is produced at the N rate that nearly maximizes root yield (112 kg N ha^{-1} in this case), but far less than the N rate that maximizes total crop yield (roots + tops).

Sugarbeet can serve as a nitrogen scavenging crop to prevent possible nitrate pollution of groundwater. The crop has been shown to require from 25 to 50% less fertilizer nitrogen than corn (*Zea mays* L.) and when fertilized to produce maximum sugar per hectare recovers from fertile soil 2.5 to 3.5 times the amount of nitrogen applied as fertilizer. Sugarbeet tops, when returned to the soil, can reduce by 50% the amount of fertilizer nitrogen required for a following wheat crop under California conditions. The analysis of sugarbeet petiole (leaf stalk) samples collected in a systematic program can prevent the under- and overuse of fertilizer nitrogen.

Sugarbeet is a C3 plant with broad, dark green, succulent leaves. In arid areas of the temperate zone it must be irrigated. Careful and timely irrigations are essential to a good sugarbeet yield. Either furrow or sprinkler irrigation is possible. Sprinkler irrigation, though more costly, has the advantages of improving seedling emergence and using less water in the early stages of plant growth. Irrigation water requirements range from as little as 600 mm of water per hectare per season in a cool climate where the soil is filled with plentiful winter rain to as much as 1200 mm per hectare in a hot, dry climate with limited precipitation. [See IRRIGATION ENGINEERING, FARM PRACTICES, METHODS, AND SYSTEMS.]

Controlling pests and diseases is important for profitable crop production. Sugarbeet should not be planted in fields heavily infested with weeds. Moderate weed infestation is controlled by crop rotation and a combination of chemical and mechanical methods. Sugarbeet is susceptible to preemergence and post-emergence seedling rots known collectively as the damping-off diseases. Other important diseases which must be controlled in areas where they occur are: curly top, a virus disease transmitted by the sugarbeet leafhopper; sugarbeet yellows, a virus complex transmitted primarily though not exclusively by the green peach aphid; powdery mildew (*Erisphe polygoni* DC) and Cercospora leafspot (*Cercospora beticola* Sacc.), diseases caused by leaf fungi; rhizomania, caused by a virus (beet necrotic yellow vein) transmitted by a soil-borne fungus (*Polymyxya betae* Keskin); and the sugarbeet cyst nematode (*Heterodera schachtii* Schmidt) and root-knot nematodes (*Meloidogyne* sp.). Strategies for the control of these diseases involve development of resistant varieties, attention to time of planting, isolation of new plantings from old sugarbeet fields that can serve as sources of virus inoculum, the selective use of fungicides, soil fumigation, and careful attention to crop rotation.

V. Future Prospects

The land area planted to sugarbeet, and the sugar yields achieved in most of the principal beet-producing countries have remained stable or increased only slightly over the last decade or more. However, planting has expanded rapidly in China during the last several years as that country seeks to increase its domestic sugar production. Beet and sugar yields have increased in the northern European countries in the last several years (Table III). In the United States, yields have not changed significantly for over a decade. Stable sugarbeet yields over the last decade in the industrialized nations with intensive agriculture suggest that a yield plateau has been reached with the crop. Long-term trends for yield and sucrose percentage for California are depicted in Fig. 5. They reflect the successes and problems of modern, intensive cropping throughout the 20th century. Curly top virus was the first major challenge that struck the industry in the 1920s. Starting with the decade of the 1930s, yields began to increase and reached a peak in the early 1950s. Yields then stagnated or declined due to problems associated with the yellows virus complex. When these were diagnosed and a management program based on isolation was introduced in the late 1960s, yields rose once again as overall management improved, input use intensified, and superior varieties were developed and planted. However, yields have remained relatively stable during the last two decades.

There is potential for yields to improve significantly in some regions of the world. Those achieved in the Soviet Union are lower than in Poland and other eastern European countries with comparable climates, while those of eastern Europe are lower than yields achieved in comparable regions of western Europe.

TABLE III

Yield Trends in Selected Countries with an Industrialized Agriculture (Mg/ha)

Year	France Beet yield	France Sugar yield	Germany Beet yield	Germany Sugar yield	Netherlands Beet yield	Netherlands Sugar yield	Great Britain Beet yield	Great Britain Sugar yield	United States Beet yield	United States Sugar yield	Japan Beet yield	Japan Sugar yield
1992/93	53.0	9.40	48.5	7.72	56.9	9.35	46.5	7.85	44.4	6.4	54.0	9.51
1991/92	53.6	9.76	49.0	7.54	58.5	9.24	46.2	7.82	45.0	6.05	57.2	10.83
1990/91	53.8	9.99	44.2	6.72	69.7	10.73	41.7	7.08	44.8	6.28	55.5	9.72
1989/90	56.0	9.85	44.2	6.71	56.3	9.70	41.2	6.81	43.5	6.00	50.9	9.26
1988/89	59.0	10.17	39.8	6.13	54.3	8.73	41.2	7.16	42.8	5.86	53.5	9.79
1987/88	53.6	8.81	44.3	6.20	53.2	8.39	39.8	6.64	50.2	6.84	53.9	9.58
1986/87	50.8	8.81	42.1	6.96	55.8	9.59	40.2	7.09	47.4	6.88	53.6	9.51
1985/86	51.2	9.26	43.4	6.53	48.4	7.44	38.0	6.51	45.8	6.08	54.5	8.79
1984/85	53.0	8.50	45.2	5.89	53.9	7.87	43.4	7.30	45.2	5.95	53.9	8.67
1983/84	48.6	5.07	44.7	5.20	44.3	6.57	40.8	5.89	44.6	6.03	46.3	6.99
1982/83	55.1	8.01	43.6	6.15	59.3	9.16	49.5	7.63	45.6	5.87	58.7	9.57
1981/80	54.1	6.69	34.3	6.06	56.9	8.72	35.4	5.68	50.3	6.06	45.3	7.26
Mean	53.5	8.69	43.6	6.48	55.6	8.79	42.0	6.96	45.8	6.19	53.1	9.12
SE	0.76	0.43	1.1	0.21	1.76	0.32	1.13	0.2	0.69	0.1	1.13	0.31
CV%	4.9	4.7	8.7	5.0	11.0	5.2	9.3	5.4	5.2	5.0	7.4	6.9

Source. USDA-Foreign Agriculture Service (1992).

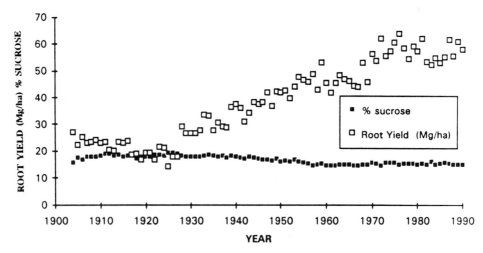

FIGURE 5 Trends for long-term sugarbeet yield and sucrose percentage in California (1904–1990).

Likewise, yields in China are much lower than those of Japan. These differences suggest that there is undeveloped yield potential in these large beet-producing regions, as well as room for improvement in extraction technology.

Just as sugarbeet owes something of its modern development to international conflict, so its future production may depend in part on the nature of international trade agreements. At times, the world has experienced a sugar surplus. In 1992, production is expected to exceed demand by approximately 0.7%. Some countries are more dependent on sugar production for their trade than others, Cuba (a sugarcane producer) being the most striking example. While sugar production is less important in nations that produce sugarbeet, the crop has an important biological role in crop rotations and an important economic role in providing income to farmers. This is especially true in the European Community. Also, established industries representing significant capital investment have been developed to process the beets into sugar. Sugar is a basic commodity and some nations would prefer not to become dependent on imports for their entire domestic supply. The cost of growing and processing sugarbeet in the industrialized world is higher on average than equivalent costs for sugarcane. This is due in part to differences in labor and other costs, and the value of assets devoted to crop production in the industrialized and developing nations. It is unclear how trade issues affecting sugarbeet production will be resolved in the future.

Bibliography

Abshahi, A., Hills, F. J., and Broadbent, F. E. (1984). Nitrogen utilization by wheat from residual sugarbeet fertilizer and soil incorporated sugarbeet tops. *Agron. J.* **76**, 954–958.

Bray, W. E., and Thompson, K. J. (eds.) (1985). "Sugarbeet—A Growers Guide". Broom's Barn Exp. Sta., Higham, Bury St. Edmunds, England.

Fick, G. W., Loomis, R. S., and Williams, W. A. (1975). Sugarbeet. "Crop Physiology" (L. T. Evans, ed.), pp. 259–296. Cambridge Univ. Press. Cambridge.

Hawker, J. S. (1985). Sucrose. "Biochemistry of Storage Carbohydrates in Green Plants" (P. M. Dey and R. A. Dixon, eds.), pp. 1–51. Academic Press, NY.

Hills, F., Jackson, Sailsbery, R., and Ulrich, A. (1982). "Sugarbeet Fertilization," Bulletin 1891. Univ. of Calif., Division of Agriculture and Natural Resources, Oakland, CA.

Hills, F. J., Broadbent, F. E., and Lorenz, O. A. (1983). Fertilizer nitrogent utilization by corn, tomato, and sugarbeet. *Agron. J.* **75**, 423–426.

Hills, F. J., Winter, S. R., and Henderson, D. W. (1990). Sugarbeet. *In* "Irrigation of Agricultural Crops" (B. A. Stewart and D. R. Nielsen, eds.). American Soc. of Agronomy, Madison, WI.

Johnson, R. T., Alexander, J. T., Rush, G. E., and Hawkes, G. R. (eds.) (1971). "Advances in Sugarbeet Production: Principles and Practices." Iowa State Univ. Press, Ames, IA.

Lewellen, R. T. (1992). Use of plant introductions to improve populations and hybrids of sugarbeet. *In* "Use of Plant Introductions in Cultivar Development, Part 2" (A. L. Shands and L. E. Weisner, eds.). Crop Science Society of America, Madison, WI.

McGinnis, R. A. (ed.) (1982). "Sugar Beet Technology," 3rd ed. Sugarbeet Development Foundation, Denver, CO.

Sailsbery, R. L., Hills, F. J., Bendixen, W. E., Brendler, R. A., and Henderson, D. W. (1985). "Stand Establishment," Bulletin 1877. Agric. Exp. Sta., Univ. of Calif., Oakland, CA.

Ulrich, A., and Hills, F. J. (1990). Plant analysis as an aid in fertilizing sugarbeet. *In* "Soil Testing and Plant Analysis" (R. L. Westerman, ed.), 3rd ed. Soil Science Society of America, Madison, WI.

Ulrich, A., and Hills, F. J. (1969). "Sugarbeet Nutrient Deficiency Symptoms, A Color Atlas and Chemical Guide." Agric. Exp. Sta., Univ. of Calif., Oakland, CA.

Whitney, E. D., and Duffus, J. E. (eds.) (1986). "Compendium of Beet Diseases and Insects." The American Phytopathological Society, St. Paul, MN.

Sugarcane

DON J. HEINZ, ROBERT V. OSGOOD, *Experiment Station, Hawaiian Sugar Planters' Association*

PAUL H. MOORE, *USDA-Agricultural Research Service, Hawaii*

I. Taxonomy and Botany
II. Distribution and Improvement
III. Yields and Crop Cycles
IV. Cultural Practices
V. Processing and Utilization
VI. Contemporary Issues

Glossary

Bagasse Fibrous plant residue remaining after the sugar-containing juice is extracted by crushing sugarcane through milling units

Brix Percentage by weight of soluble solids in a water solution

Juice Sap expressed from the sugarcane stalk that contains dissolved sucrose formed by the plant

Massecuite Suspension of sugar crystals in their mother liquor produced during the first stages of vacuum pan crystallization

Molasses By-product remaining after crystallized sugar has been removed, by centrifugation, from the mother liquor of condensed sugarcane juice

Ratoon Sugarcane plant regrowth from germination of underground buds following harvest of the crop

Raw sugar Product of cane sugar factories, intermediate crystalline product of about 96% sucrose resulting from the removal of impurities and the evaporation of water from sugarcane stalk juice

Refined sugar Product of a sugar refinery where raw sugar is processed to remove remaining nonsugar impurities to produce a range of sugar products for human consumption

Ripening Developmental phase of the sugarcane plant at the end of the crop cycle when, owing to climate, cultural practices, flowering, or growth regulators, the crop reaches maturity, slows accumulation of fresh weight, and increases the accumulation of sucrose

Sugar Normally the disaccharide sucrose but occasionally the invert monosaccharides glucose and fructose.

Sugarcane, or sugar cane, is the common name given originally to the sucrose-storing species and now to the interspecific hybrids of the genus *Saccharum*, grown as the improved cultivars of contemporary sugarcane production. Cultivated sugarcane is a robust, vegetatively propagated perennial grass that is generally limited to latitudes within 30° of the equator or to ocean-warmed coastal areas (20°C mean air temperature isotherm) lying outside this belt (Fig. 1). The prolonged growing seasons of the tropics, coupled with the high production efficiency of sugarcane, result in extraordinarily high crop yields. Although sugar for food remains the most important product of sugarcane, by-products are a significant part of its economic production. The technologies used worldwide in sugarcane cultivation and processing range from those of low-input farming, essentially unchanged over the last millennium, to the high-input, extensively mechanized, and sophisticated technologies of modern corporate farming and factory processing. [*See* SUGARBEET.]

I. Taxonomy and Botany

A. Taxonomy

Sugarcane is a member of the genus *Saccharum*, which belongs to the family Gramineae of the order Poaceae and class Monocotyledoneae. The extensive prehistoric distribution of sweet canes by mankind, and the wide hybridization among the various forms, obfuscate taxonomic relationships among this group. At the lower hierarchic levels, the taxonomy of *Saccharum* and its relationship to intercrossing genera re-

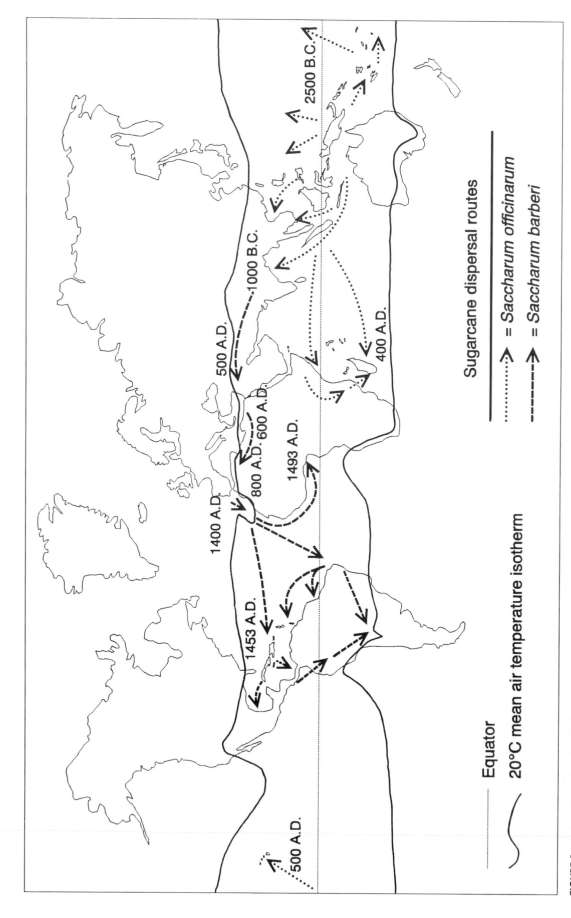

FIGURE 1 Origin, dispersal, and world distribution of sugarcane. [Modified after Daniels, J., and Roach, B. T. (1987). *In* "Sugarcane Improvement through Breeding" (D. J Heinz, ed.), p. 66. Copyright 1987 by Elsevier Science Publishers B. V., Amsterdam; and Blume, H. (1985). "Geography of Sugar Cane: Environmental, Structural and Economic Aspects of Cane Sugar Production." Verlag Dr. Albert Bartens, Berlin.]

main controversial. Characteristics of the different species of the genus are presented in Table I.

Saccharum officinarum L., type species for the genus, is the one species with continuous acceptance since Linnaeus' 1753 description. Classification of other species varies by authority. It is generally considered that sugarcane has two wild species and three or four domesticated ones. The wild species *Saccharum spontaneum* L. has a wide distribution throughout the tropics of Africa, Asia, and Oceania, whereas *Saccharum robustum* Brandes and Jeswiet ex Grassl are restricted to Melanesia and parts of Indonesia. *Saccharum sinense* Roxb., the sugarcane of China, and *Saccharum barberi* Jesw., the sugarcane of India, are considered as one species by some authorities but two by most. The domesticated *Saccharum edule* Hassk., grown as a garden vegetable for its abortive inflorescence, is restricted primarily to Melanesia and is considered to be a product of introgression of *S. officinarum* or *S. robustum* with other genera.

B. Botany

1. Plant Morphology

Sugarcane is a tall, robust, clump-forming grass (Fig. 2). Culms, usually called stalks or stems, shed their lower leaves. Aerial stalks are unbranched, stout to slender, differentiated into nodes and internodes with prominent, annular leaf scars; adventitious root primordia in a several-tiered band at each node; an intercalary meristem or growth ring above each root band; and an ovoid or deltoid axillary bud prominent in the root band. The lateral buds are inserted alternately along the stalk in the axil of leaves. Leaves are differentiated into long (1 to 2 m) blades and shorter (0.5 m), culm-clasping sheaths.

Each node is capable of giving rise to a new plant and is used for crop propagation. The shoot roots arise from underground nodes, and the axillary buds located at these nodes give rise to tillers. Depending on the clone and growing conditions, more than 100 stalks can be produced from one bud, but only 5 to 10 survive the competition in densely planted field conditions.

Sugarcane can be propagated through sexual seed. The sugarcane inflorescence is a large, open panicle with several orders of branching upon which are pairs of spikelets composed of short segments easily separated by brittle joints. Each spikelet of a pair is oblong and contains a single complete flower with long tufts of hair at its base, imparting a general silky appearance to the entire panicle (Fig. 2).

Following fertilization and development of the mature seed, the panicle disarticulates to scatter the hair-

TABLE I

Principal Characteristics of the Different Species of the Genus *Saccharum* and Number of Clones in the World Collections of Sugarcane

Species (chromosome no.)	Common name	Sucrose content (%)	Fiber content (%)	Stem diameter (cm)	Adaptability	Germplasm collection (no.)	
						United States[a]	India[b]
S. officinarum (2n = 80)	Noble	High 18–25	Low 5–15	Thick	Tropical and subtropical	568	762
S. sinense (2n = 110–120)	Chinese	Medium 12–15	High 10–15	Medium 1.4–2.2	Tropical and subtropical	38	29
S. barberi (2n = 82–124)	Indian	Medium 13–16	High 10–15	Medium 1.7–2.1	Tropical and subtropical	57	43
S. spontaneum (2n = 40–128)	Wild	Very low 1–4	Very high 25–40	Slender 0.5–0.9	Tropical and subtropical	450	724
S. robustum (2n = 60 and 80)	Wild	Low 3–7	Very high 20–35	Medium 1.1–1.7	Tropical wetlands	135	144
S. edule (2n = 60–80)	Edible	Low 3–8		Medium 1.1–1.8	Tropical		
Erianthus	Related genus	Very low	Very high		Tropical and subtropical	196	201

Note. Range values are the mean ± 1 SD of data reported on germplasm collections. Reports summarized are: 1. Sugarcane Genetic Resources. I. *Saccharum spontaneum* L. (1983). Sugarcane Breeding Institute, Coimbatore, India. 2. Sugarcane Genetic Resources. II. *Saacharum barberi,* Jeswiet; *Saccharum sinense,* Roxb. Amend Jeswiet; *Saccharum robustum,* Brandes et Jeswiet ex Grassl; *Saccharum edule,* Hassk (1985). Sugarcane Breeding Institute, Coimbatore, India.
[a] Maintained by the USDA, ARS, Miami, FL.
[b] Maintained by the Sugarcane Breeding Institute, Coimbatore, India.

leaf — blade

leaf — sheath

node — axillary bud
node — root band
node — leaf scar

internode

FIGURE 2 Sugarcane growth habit and details of stalk segment used as a propagule.

covered caryopses called "fuzz." Fuzz is planted in the breeding program to develop improved cultivars.

2. Physiology

Factors that maximize the amount of light absorbed by the crop are optimum leaf area per stalk and number of stalks per unit land area. These factors vary considerably with age, environment, and cultivar. The single-sided leaf blade area for commercial hybrids is approximately 0.05 m^2 per leaf; around 65 to 80 thousand stalks ha^{-1} survive to harvest and consist of one internode produced every 7 to 10 days. The laminar leaf blade of sugarcane has stomata for gas exchange on each side, and the photosynthetic meso-phyll cells are arranged in the typical C-4 Kranz anatomy. Vigorous plants will carry 10 to 14 fully formed leaves for a two-sided leaf area of 1.0 m^2 per stalk, providing a leaf area index of 3 to 7.

Leaf area expansion is coupled with rate of leaf formation and stalk growth; all are closely related to air temperature. Although sugarcane shows increasing rates of photosynthesis with increasing solar radiation up to full sunlight, solar radiation is not as limiting to development as is temperature. [*See* PHOTOSYNTHESIS.]

Sugarcane was the plant which led to the discovery of C-4 photosynthesis, and it is acclaimed as a leading performer in rates of photosynthesis. Sugarcane is reported to have carbon fixation rates as high as 2.8 mg CO_2 m^{-2} sec^{-1} (63 μmol cm^{-2} sec^{-1}). Under exceptional circumstances, total dry matter produced by sugarcane may average 40 g m^{-2} day^{-1} and exceed 150 t ha^{-1} $year^{-1}$, more than half of which is partitioned into the harvested stalk which contains 30% dry matter composed of approximately equal amounts of sucrose and fiber.

II. Distribution and Improvement

A. Origin and Development as a World Crop

The origins of sugarcane are lost in folklore and mythology. Sugarcane appears in Indian mythology at about 1000 B.C., and sugar production is recorded from the Orient from 500 B.C. These facts support the hypothesis that sugarcane originated in northern India (*S. barberi*) or southern China (*S. sinense*). However, archeological records indicate that sugarcane (*S. officinarum*) originated in New Guinea as early as 2500 B.C., and myth extends this date to 6000 B. C. Cytogenetic evidence supports the hypothesis that *S. officinarum,* which is found only in cultivated settings, was domesticated from *S. robustum*. Since numerous forms of both these species are concentrated in New Guinea and adjacent islands of Melanesia, we assume that domestication of sugarcane occurred in this area. *S. officinarun* subsequently spread to Indochina and Bengal by 1000 B.C. (Fig. 1) to hybridize with *S. spontaneum* in India and China to produce the domesticated *S. barberi* and *S. sinense*.

Dispersal of *S. officinarum* into Indonesia, Malay, China, India, Micronesia, and Polynesia apparently took place during prehistoric times (Fig. 1). The spread of *S. officinarum* from Polynesia to Hawaii took place with native migrations around 500 A.D. and from Indonesia to Africa about 400 A.D. Concurrently, *S. barberi* hybrids were spread from India to the Middle East, then eastward to the Mediterranean from 600 A.D. to 1400 A.D., and finally to the New World beginning with the second voyage of Columbus in 1493. Sugarcane rapidly spread throughout Central and South America during the 1500s so that by 1600, Latin American cane sugar production was the most important in the world. Sugarcane first reached the continental United States (Louisiana) in 1750.

S. officinarum, called "noble canes," which were first observed by Europeans on their explorations in the Pacific Ocean, were higher in sucrose and lower in fiber than the Indian canes and were quickly spread throughout sugarcane growing areas. However, they were more susceptible to diseases and insects and required a program of continuous replacement of susceptible clones.

B. Breeding and Selection

The importance of cultivar development is related to the facts that sugarcane is grown as a monoculture, without crop rotation, and without fallow for tens or hundreds of years. This allows time for pests and pathogens to adapt and accumulate to crop-damaging levels. Steadily increasing yield potential makes it advantageous to replace cultivars about every 10 years.

Sugarcane underwent accelerated genetic improvement following the observation in 1858 that it produced viable seed. Until this time, it was not known that sugarcane could reproduce sexually. Following a particularly disastrous disease complex called Sereh in Java during the late 1800s, the Dutch in 1888 established an innovative breeding and selection program. The early stimulus for sugarcane breeding was to incorporate the disease resistance, hardiness, and tillering capacity of *S. spontaneum* into the sugar-producing germplasm of the noble canes. A key event in this breeding effort was the production in 1921 in Java of cvs. POJ 2725 and POJ 2878, the first of the so-called nobilized canes, which are present in the pedigrees of nearly all modern sugarcane cultivars.

Cytological studies of *S. officinarum* × *S. spontaneum* hybrids revealed a curious phenomenon which remains an enigma to the present day. The production of nobilized cultivars resulted from selection of progeny with higher chromosome numbers containing the somatic complement (NN) of the noble female parent (80 chromosomes) plus the gametic number (S) of the *S. spontaneum* male.

$$F_1$$
$$NN (80) \times SS (96) \rightarrow NNS (80 + 48 = 128)$$

This behavior of restitution of the female chromosomes persisted through another backcross generation to the noble but not the third. Similar chromosome behavior is seen when *S. barberi/ S. sinense* is crossed to the nobles, as was done in India to produce the "Co" clone series, which were equally important progenitors of today's cultivars.

Today, parents are selected on the basis of their yield potential, disease and pest resistance, and progeny performance. Breeding programs have been under way long enough in most producing areas so that unique, adapted germplasm lines have been developed for the various ecological niches in each area. Crossing is conducted using paired, known combinations, or multiple combinations in a polycross. Generally, flowering stalks are excised in the field and placed in an acid solution, which allows the stalk to live long enough for cross-pollination and maturation of seed.

Selections from seedling populations take place after 8 to 10 months of growth, are asexually propagated, and go through one or more additional visual stages of selection before being placed in field yield trials. It takes 10 to 15 years from crossing to release of a new cultivar. Yield potential has increased at about 1% per year over the last 50 years.

C. Germplasm Evaluation and Preservation

Modern commercial sugarcane cultivars have germplasm from *S. officinarum, S. spontaneum, S. robustum,* and *S. barberi/S. sinense* but are very limited in genetic diversity. Over 60% of the world's commercial cultivars are derived from only three clones of *S. officinarum,* possibly four clones of *S. spontaneum* and *S. barberi/S. sinense,* and two clones of *S. robustum.* This limited sampling of clones has sparked an interest in widening the germplasm base to increase yield potential and pest resistance. Hybrids of *S. spontaneum* accessions from southeast Asia have shown promise for increasing yield potential under certain conditions in Louisiana, Hawaii, Argentina, Australia, and South Africa.

Since 1875, over 25 expeditions have collected *Saccharum* species and related genera in Indonesia (Irian Jaya, Kalimantan, Sulawesi, and Moluccas), Papua New Guinea (including New Britain), India, China, Thailand, The Philippines, and Taiwan. Sampling techniques on these expeditions emphasized broad sampling of clonal types to ensure the collecting of diverse genetic material.

The genera and species of *Saccharum,* related genera, and numbers of clones in the world collections of sugarcane are listed in Table I. To the degree possible, the two locations are duplicate clonal repositories. Seed from 160 clones of *S. officinarum,* stored in liquid nitrogen for long-term preservation, are in the U.S. National Seed Repository at Fort Collins, Colorado.

Geographical areas with endangered germplasm needing further collection are in Pakistan, Burma, and Irian Jaya. Classification and characterization of the collections are now under way to develop core collections of each of the groups, to determine genetic diversity and the best methods for preserving and maintaining the germplasm.

III. Yields and Crop Cycles

A. Regional Productivity and Yields

The 1990 cane sugar production of 98.2 million metric tons (Mmt) of sugar included 69.8 Mmt centrifugal raw sugar, 12.8 Mmt noncentrifugal raw sugar, and the equivalent of 15.6 Mmt sugar that was fermented into ethanol (Table II). Countries with the largest area under cane cultivation are Brazil, India, China, and Cuba; collectively these four countries account for 59% of the area under cultivation and 67% of the cane sugar production worldwide.

The world average of 61 t cane ha^{-1} and 5.82 t sugar ha^{-1} represent fresh weight yields and product yields well above those for other crops. The highest fresh weight crop yields are generally ascribed to tuber crops, e.g., potatoes average 15.1 t ha^{-1}; but this is only 25% of world average cane production. The highest product yields are generally ascribed to the cereal grains, e.g., 3.70 t ha^{-1} maize grain, which is 64% of the processed sugar yield of cane. Therefore, although the total productivity of sugarcane ranks only about eighth among crops, this is primarily due to the processed character of its product, sucrose, and its smaller area under cultivation; on a dry weight basis, sugarcane yields are the highest among crops.

Factors that contribute to high yields of sugarcane are its perennial growth habit and continuous accumulation of sucrose in the vegetative plant structure. Crop cycles vary from less than 10 months in temperate areas such as Pakistan and Louisiana, where killing frosts set rigid seasons, to 24 months in Peru and South Africa, and sometimes longer in Hawaii (Table II). Most of the sugarcane in other parts of the world is grown in 14- to 18-month plant crops and 12-month ratoons. Crop cycles average just over 15 months for the highest-producing countries. Sugar yields are also affected by the length of the harvest and milling season. In most countries, milling is limited to the 5 or 6 months in the coolest part of the year that produces the ripest cane. At the other extreme are Hawaii with a 10- to 12-month harvest season and Louisiana with a 3-month harvest season.

B. Production Efficiency of Sugar Yield

The yields of cane sugar per hectare can be used for comparing the efficiency of production among differ-

TABLE II

Sugarcane Production and Yield Statistics for Countries Producing More Than 500,000 Tons Centrifugal Raw Sugar in 1990

Region Country	Area harvested (1000 ha)	Cane production (1000 t)	Cane yield (t ha^{-1})	Sugar, CR[a] production (1000 t)	Sugar, N[b] production (1000 t)	Sugar E[c] production (1000 t)	Sugar yield[d] (t ha^{-1})	Growth period (months)	Harvest and milling season	No. of ratoons
Africa	1202	72,982	60.7	7,572[c]	89		6.37			
Egypt	118	11,143	94.7	975			8.26	12–18	Jun–Dec	8–9
Mauritius	76	5,548	72.8	624			8.21	12–24	May–Jan	3–7
S. Africa	272	18,700	68.8	2,230			8.20	12–18	May–Dec	7–8
Swaziland	40	3,800	95.0	500			12.50			
Asia	7229	426,006	58.9	29,578[c]	11,130		5.63			
China, PR	1068	63,970	59.9	4,937[c]	430		5.02	10–16	Nov–Apr	1
India	3430	220,000	64.1	11,946	8,200		5.87	9–18	Sep–Mar	1–2
Indonesia	369	25,503	69.1	2,180	45		6.03	12–16	May–Oct	0–1
Pakistan	854	35,493	41.6	1,993[c]	1,150		3.68	12	Oct–Jul	1
Philippines	315	24,800	78.7	1,740	21		5.59		Sep–Apr	1
Thailand	686	33,561	48.9	3,641	615		6.20	10–14	Nov–Jun	2–3
N & C America	2701	173,278	64.1	17,016[c]	246		6.39			
Cuba	1350	77,000	57.0	8,050			5.96	12–20	Oct–Jun	4
Dominican Republic	170	7,000	41.2	620	38		3.87	11–18	Nov–Jun	4–6
Guatemala	109	7,400	67.8	726	58		7.19		Nov–Jun	
Mexico	350	34,893	99.7	3,406			9.73		Nov–May	2–3
USA (FL, LA, TX)[f]	265	17,246	65.1	1,981			7.47		Oct–May	1–4
United States (Hawaii)[g]	29	5,938	203.8	744			25.54	20–36	Jan–Dec	0–2
S. America	5327	332,016	62.3	12,972[c]	1,303	15,630	5.61			
Argentina	330	16,000	48.5	1,367	240		4.14	10–16	Jun–Nov	6–7
Brazil[h]	4269	263,604	61.7	7,900	240	15,630	5.57	12–16	Jun–Oct	5
Colombia	304	24,466	80.6	1,695	978		8.79	16–18	Jan–Dec	5
Peru	62	6,965	112.3	603	21		10.06	16–24	Jan–Dec	4–8
Venezuela	100	7,000	70.0	557	10		5.67		Sep–Aug	
Oceania	414	30,559	73.8	4,094			9.89			
Australia	340	26,226	77.1	3,570			10.50	12–16	Jun–Dec	2–5
World total[i]	16,878	1,035,096	61.3	69,752[c]	12,768	15,630	5.82			

Source. "FAO Yearbook Production," Vol. 44 (1990). Food and Agriculture Organization of the United Nations.

[a] CR, centrifugal raw sugar.

[b] N, noncentrifugal raw sugar.

[c] E, equivalent amount of raw sugar fermented to ethanol.

[d] Tons sugar per hectare based on total production of centrifugal plus noncentrifugal raw sugar plus fermented equivalent raw sugar.

[e] Regions and countries producing both cane and beet sugar; the FAO statistics were reduced by fraction of cane sugar to total sugar from data in "FO Lichts World Sugar Statistics 1990/91."

[f] FL, Florida; LA, Louisiana; TX, Texas. Data from "Agriculture Statistics 1991," United States Department of Agriculture. U.S. Government Printing Office, Washington, DC.

[g] Data from "Hawaiian Sugar Manual 1991," Hawaiian Sugar Planters' Association, Aiea, HI.

[h] FAO data on Brazil fail to credit 68% of the sugar production that is diverted to ethanol fermentation. Ethanol data for Brazil from personal communication with G.R. Machado, Centro de Technologia Copersucar, Piracicaba, SP, Brazil.

[i] The total for the world is greater than that for the continents listed, and totals for continents are greater than the sum of the countries listed.

ent countries and regions and for evaluating factors contributing to these efficiencies. The top-ranking countries or regions in total efficiency of production are Hawaii, Swaziland, Australia, Peru, and Mexico (Table II). Total efficiency of cane sugar production depends upon the biomass produced, which is expressed in terms of the yield of sugarcane per hectare and the sugar recovery, i.e., the amount of sugar produced as a percentage of the crushed cane. Sugar recovery depends on the sugar mill recovery efficiency and the quality (i.e., sugar vs nonsucrose impurity content) of the cane.

Biomass is the factor that contributes most to production efficiency. The importance of biomass is revealed in this data set by comparing the coefficient of determination between biomass and sugar yield ($r^2 = 0.87$) vs sugar recovery, defined as tons sugar per ton of cane, and sugar yield ($r^2 = 0.33$). Consequently, greatest productivity gains have been made through efforts to increase biomass. [See BIOMASS.]

IV. Cultural Practices

Sugarcane is grown over a wide range of climatic, economic, and social environments. This results in diverse cultural practices, ranging from unmechanized, low material inputs and low yields of undeveloped regions to highly mechanized crop cultivation with high inputs of fertilizers, insecticides, as well as irrigation and growth regulators to achieve high yields. This latter cropping system is covered in the following discussion.

A. Planting and Ratooning

Preparation varies according to soil conditions and the mechanized capabilities of the farm. Soils include the major tropical and subtropical orders with extreme differences in organic matter and physical characteristics.

The sugarcane crop is planted by machine or by hand with vegetative stem cuttings called "seed," seedpieces, or setts sometimes treated with heat and a fungicide. The propagation material is cut from seed fields or, more typically, from designated areas of commercial fields. In areas subject to freezing or drought during germination and early growth, long seed consisting of whole stalks with 10 to 15 buds may be used. Under less severe conditions, seedcane is cut into smaller sections of 0.3 to 0.6 m, which includes 3 or 4 buds.

Sugarcane is planted at row widths varying from 0.9 m in areas having short cropping seasons to 1.8 m, depending on mechanization and length of crop cycle. An exception to this occurs when sugarcane is planted in alternating wide (1.8 m) and narrow (0.9 m) interrows to accommodate a single drip irrigation tube between the narrow interrows.

Depth of planting is a compromise between shallowness needed for a high percentage of emergence from the soil and depth needed for avoiding freeze killing and dehydration and for ensuring adequate buds for good tillering.

Sugarcane can be germinated in a nursery and then transplanted to the field, but this technique is generally too costly to be widely used for normal field operations. It may be used for rapid spreading of new cultivars or as a way of certifying that the clone is free of diseases.

Multiple ratoon crops of sugarcane may be harvested from a single planting by regrowth from stubble. Ratoons originate from germination of axillary buds on the short underground internodes remaining after the above-ground stalk is harvested. The number of ratoons possible from a single planting is the result of an interaction of the multiple factors of cultivar, soil type, depth of planting, disease incidence, weed infestation, and how badly the stool was damaged by harvest. It is common to grow 2 or 3 ratoons; under ideal conditions the number can exceed 10.

Most sugarcane crops are "fired" or "burned" either as a standing crop prior to harvest or occasionally after harvest to remove the accumulated dead leaf trash. However, the crop may be harvested unburned, in which case the residual leaf trash may reduce soil water loss, soil erosion, and weed growth and improve establishment of the ratoon crop.

B. Fertilization

Nutrients are supplied from the residue of the previous crop, in irrigation water, and from applied fertilizer. Sugarcane is an efficient user of nitrogen (N) based on dry matter yield. Management of the timing and placement of N is critical for the production of high yields of sugar; high levels of N are required for the rapid early growth of the crop, but plant N levels must be low near time of harvest to promote maximum sucrose storage. Leaf blade N is used as an index of nitrogen status of the crop to optimize fertilizer applications, especially in long-cycle crops. [See FERTILIZER MANAGEMENT AND TECHNOLOGY.]

The requirements of potassium (K) and phosphorus (P) are highly variable; soil analysis is used to determine required applications. The requirement for P is high on upland soils owing to the adsorption or fixation of P under acidic conditions. As a result, fertilizer P is usually applied in amounts greatly in excess of the actual crop requirement. [See SOIL FERTILITY; SOIL TESTING.]

Sugarcane grown on acidic upland soils may benefit from liming (application of calcium carbonate) to improve the availability of P and to reduce the availability of toxic concentrations of aluminum and manganese. Calcium silicate is used as an amendment in muck soils of Florida and in amorphous sesquioxide soils of Hawaii and South Africa.

Critical tissue levels and deficiency symptoms for most elements are well documented; nevertheless, nutrients other than N, P, K, and Ca are rarely used on a wide scale. Spot applications of minor elements are occasionally made to correct local mineral nutrient deficiencies.

C. Water Requirement and Application

The high quantity of biomass produced requires a large amount of water. In Hawaii, areas with less than 200 cm of rain annually receive irrigation. About 60% of Hawaii's cane land is irrigated, and 90% of this is through drip systems. Other methods of irrigation include adjustment of the water table and water application by flooding, furrow irrigation, or sprinklers. The method used depends on availability of water, labor, operational energy, land slope, technical skill of the farmer, yield return, and material availability and costs. [See IRRIGATION ENGINEERING, FARM PRACTICES, METHODS, AND SYSTEMS.]

The most technically difficult, but labor- and water-conserving system, is drip irrigation, which utilizes plastic tubes to uniformly distribute water along the crop row. Because of the low pressure and small distribution orifices, water entering the drip irrigation system must be free of suspended solids, which are removed by screening and filtration. Chlorination reduces biological growth in the tubing; otherwise the growth would plug orifices and disrupt water distribution. Drip irrigation in Hawaii has improved water distribution efficiency, increased yields, and reduced labor costs compared to the earlier furrow and sprinkler systems.

Under controlled conditions, sugarcane exhibits a linear relationship between total dry matter production and water consumption (7 to 9 g liter^{-1}). A large proportion of the world production of sugarcane is not irrigated and is subjected to alternating wet/tropical and dry/subtropical seasons. If there are no prolonged periods of drought during the wet growing season, the crop yield potential is roughly 1 t cane stalks cm^{-1} evapotranspiration. Therefore, it is possible to use evaporation data and water budget analysis to estimate yields and to characterize factors limiting this potential.

D. Pests

1. Diseases

Sugarcane is susceptible to at least 8 bacterial, 152 fungal, and 7 viral diseases; the major diseases worldwide are smut, rust, red rot, leaf scald, ratoon stunt disease, and viral diseases (Table III). Most growing areas impose quarantine to prevent the distribution of disease pathogens, but diseases are fairly widely distributed around the world, requiring the planting of resistant cultivars to control them. [See PLANT PATHOLOGY.]

TABLE III

Major Sugarcane Diseases of the World: Causal Organism, Common Name, and Type of Infection

Causal organism	Common name	Symptom[a]
Bacterial diseases		
Clavibacter xyli subsp. *xyli*	Ratoon stunt	S
Pseudomonas rubrilineans	Red Stripe	L,S
Xanthomonas albilineans	Leaf scald	L,S
Xanthomonas campestris pv. *vasculorum*	Gumming	L,S
Fungal diseases		
Bipolaris sacchari	Eye spot	L
Ceratocystis paradoxa	Pineapple	sett
Cochliobolus stenospilus	Brown stripe	L
Fusarium moniliforme	Pokkah boeng	T
Glomerella tucumanensis	Red rot	L,S
Mycovellosiella koepkei	Yellow spot	L
Peronosclerospora sacchari	Downy mildew	L
Puccinia melanocephala	Rust	L
Stagonospora sacchari	Leaf scorch	L
Ustilago scitaminea	Smut	S
Viral, viruslike, or mycoplasma diseases		
	Chlorotic streak	L
	Fiji disease	L,S
	Grassy shoot/ white leaf	L,S
		L
	Streak	L
	Sugar cane mosaic	

[a] L, leaf; T, top leaf spindle and apex; S, systemic and stalk; sett, seed piece.

Phytosanitary measures such as heat therapy can temporarily control some of the diseases. The seed-piece rotting diseases can be controlled with appropriate fungicides, otherwise no fungicides are used for control of sugarcane diseases. [*See* FUNGICIDES.]

2. Weeds

Although sugarcane is a robust grass, it competes poorly with weeds owing to its relatively slow early growth rate and wide interrow spacing. After the canopy closes, the crop can compete with most weeds. Perennial grasses and vines are the most serious weed problems. Nevertheless, many annual broadleaf and grass species also infest the crop and reduce yields. Particular weed species tend to be regionally important problems. [*See* WEED SCIENCE.]

Weed control techniques include mechanical cultivation and application of pre- and postemergence herbicides. Integrated methods of control are used with reliance on cultivation and the use of herbicides just after planting until canopy closure. Nonchemical methods of control such as trash blanket culture resulting from harvest of unburned cane are being used in some regions. [*See* HERBICIDES AND HERBICIDE RESISTANCE.]

3. Insects

Insects of the orders Homoptera, Lepidoptera, Coleoptera, and Hymenoptera can be serious pests of the sugarcane plant; termites of the family Isoptera sometimes destroy setts, preventing germination; army worms, cutworms, and stalk borers may be damaging to young crops. Among the most destructive insect pests to older plants are the larvae of the stalk-boring moths and beetles, the root grubs of beetles, and other locally important insects. Other insects such leafhoppers cause little direct damage and serve as vectors for the spread of diseases, especially viral diseases such as Fiji disease.

Control of insects is based on integration of cultural practices and use of host genetic resistance, biological agents, and a small amount of chemicals. Most success has been experienced with host resistance and the introduction of biological control insects. In some areas of the world insecticides are used on particular sugarcane insect pests, but none are currently used in Hawaii. [*See* INTEGRATED PEST MANAGEMENT; PEST MANAGEMENT: BIOLOGICAL CONTROL; PEST MANAGEMENT: CHEMICAL CONTROL; PEST MANAGEMENT: CULTURAL CONTROL.]

4. Nematodes

Nematodes are potentially a serious threat to sugarcane, especially to crops grown on sandy soils. There is considerable genetic resistance to nematodes so that control can be achieved through an active breeding and selection program for these pests. However, nematicides are used in some areas. [*See* NEMATACIDES.]

5. Rodents

Rats gnaw cane and may be very damaging primarily by attracting boring insects and facilitating the entry of pathogenic microbes. In general, rodents prefer soft, low-fiber cultivars of high sugar content. Gnawed stalks soon ferment and deplete sugar owing to infection by various organisms, the major cause of losses. Control is by genetic resistance and poison baits. Susceptible cultivars without control may experience up to 80% of the stalks damaged by rats, and damaged stalks may cause a 50% reduction in yield.

E. Flower Prevention

Flowering, called tasseling or arrowing, can be quite detrimental to yields, especially when the crop cycle extends months beyond time of flowering. Since flowers are monopodal, stalks cease production of new leaves and internodes after flowering, apical dominance is broken, allowing the germination of axillary buds, the stalks may become pithy, reducing sugar content and thus resulting in lower yields.

Sugarcane flowering is initiated when the day lengths in autumn shorten to about 12.5 h; panicle emergence occurs 3 months later. Since induction of flowering occurs only once annually during a 3-week period, treatments can be applied shortly before this period to prevent it. Flowering can be prevented by moisture stress, by light interruption of the night, and most practically and successfully by chemical inhibition with herbicides or growth regulators, especially with application of the growth regulator ethephon 15 to 30 days prior to the induction period. In Hawaii, such treatments are used on heavily flowering cultivars grown in heavily flowering environments, resulting in yield increases of around 0.5 t sugar ha^{-1}.

F. Ripening

Cultivars differ during crop development in the fraction of dry weight growth partitioned into fiber to support increase in size and into stored sucrose. Generally, throughout the crop cycle, the tissue moisture percentage drops steadily from about 85% in very young cane to 70% in mature cane. Meanwhile sucrose rises steadily from less than 10% to more than 45% of the dry weight. This trend of development results in juice with a Brix of 20 or more, of which more than 90% is sucrose. This natural trend of maturation is referred to by sugarcane growers as ripening. Ripening can be stimulated by decreased water availability, cool temperature, low levels of nitrogen, and growth-regulating chemicals. In many sugarcane growing areas, significant levels of natural ripening occur during the cool, dry winter season. However, in areas like Hawaii, the dry season coincides with rapid growth during summer and the wet season is the time of cool, growth-limiting temperatures. Therefore, in Hawaii, seasonal ripening is not sufficient for optimal production. In addition, optimal economies of employing labor and operating mills and other specialized equipment necessitate harvesting throughout most of the year. Consequently, alternatives to natural ripening are employed. In Hawaii, a combination of limiting nitrogen application to the early part of the crop cycle, withholding water at the end of the crop cycle, and application of growth-regulating chemicals are used to ripen the sugarcane crop. Compounds with potential to enhance ripening are glyphosate, ethephon, and fluazifop. Glyphosate is the only ripener used commercially in Hawaii.

G. Harvesting

Most of the world's sugarcane crop is harvested by hand. Where labor is unavailable or too costly, machines are used. Because of the high biomass yields and varied terrains under cultivation, sugarcane harvesting equipment is always heavy-duty. Custom manufactured sugarcane harvesters are suitable for annual crops having relatively low yields. These specialized harvesting machines are usually equipped with ground level knives and a topping mechanism to harvest the crop while removing the immature top with its attached leaves. Such equipment is generally not suitable for high-yielding biennial crops such as that grown in Hawaii.

Mechanization of harvesting operations has increased the losses from wet weather harvesting by increasing the quantity of extraneous material which must be handled both in transport and in the mill. These losses usually balance the lower overhead costs when equipment and operation costs are spread over a long harvesting season.

V. Processing and Utilization

A. Milling and Raw Sugar Production

The production of centrifugal cane sugar and products from juice fermentation is capital-intensive as it in-

volves complex factory processing (Fig. 3). The cane crop delivered from the field is normally weighed as it enters the factory where it is cleaned and then prepared by shredding and crushing. The prepared cane passes through a milling tandem where water is added to facilitate extraction of juice, leaving the fibrous residue, or bagasse, as the first by-product. The extracted juice typically contains about 12% solids, of which about 87% is sucrose. An alternative to milling is the diffusion process in which the cane is finely shredded and placed in a tank where the sugars are washed out from the ruptured juice storage cells. Bagasse after dewatering is carried by conveyors to the boiler furnaces or to storage.

The juice from the extraction unit is clarified by lime or other agents (e.g., magnesium oxide) and heat to precipitate soil and organic matter. The clear juice is evaporated to thick syrup from which the sugar is crystallized. Finally, the massecuite (mixture of sugar and impurities) is separated in the centrifugals into raw sugar and the by-product molasses.

In the developing countries of Africa, Asia, and South America, a noncrystalline sugar called jaggery, gur, panella, or khandsari is produced without the extensive and expensive separation of crystalline sucrose for centrifugal sugar production. These noncentrifugal sugars are for local market consumption instead of world trade. In processing noncentrifugal sugars, the expressed juice may or may not be clarified prior to being concentrated. After concentration the syrup is put into earthenware pots or molds in which the syrup solidifies. Countries with high production of noncentrifugal sugar include India, Pakistan, Colombia, and Thailand (Table II).

One ton (1000 kg) of processed sugarcane in Hawaii provides approximately 125 kg sugar, 160 kg bone dry bagasse, and 34 kg molasses. Because of its calorific value, bagasse has been traditionally used as fuel in the boiler furnaces of the sugar mills. One ton of bone dry bagasse fiber has the energy equivalent of 2 bbl fuel oil.

B. Refining

Raw sugar, which is 96 to 99% sucrose, also contains high- and low-molecular-weight colorants that are removed during the refining process. Refining involves dissolving raw sugar and treatment with adsorbents such as bone char or granular carbon to remove the colorants. This is followed by recrystallization and centrifugation to form refined white sugar and refiners molasses. For the production of liquid refined sugar used in beverages and canning,

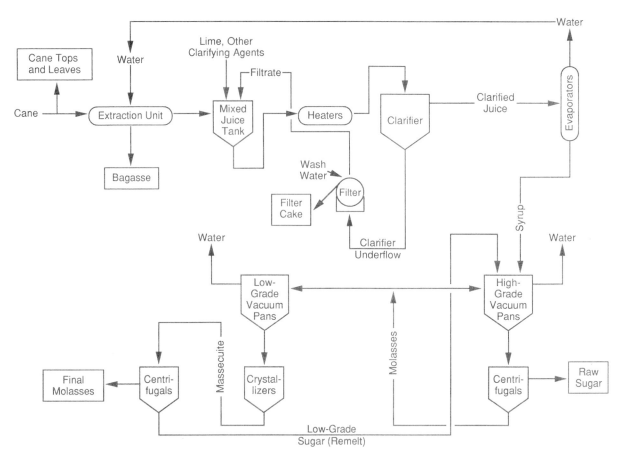

FIGURE 3 Simplified flow diagram of centrifugal cane sugar factory processes and prime products.

the recrystallization step is omitted. Brown sugar is produced by crystallization in massecuites containing molasses and by addition of such molasses to the refined sugar.

C. By-products

The by-product uses to which sucrose bagasse and molasses have been applied are varied and numerous (Table IV). Bagasse is composed of cellulose, hemicellulose (pentosans), and lignin. Fiber products, primarily paper, can be obtained from the cellulose while furfural and its derivatives are obtained from the pentosans, and plastics are potentially derived from the lignin. Molasses solids consist of 60% combined sucrose and invert sugars and about 13% inorganic salts, with the remainder being organic nonsugars. Because molasses is rich in sugars it is used primarily as a feed supplement, chemical raw material, and a nutrient for microorganisms producing a number of organic compounds such as ethanol, butanol, acetic acid, citric acid, and glutamic acid. The principal product of sug-

arcane, sucrose, is primarily a food, but research has shown that this also can be used as a raw material for production of higher value products (Table IV).

VI. Contemporary Issues

A. Sugarcane Burning

Prior to harvest, the sugarcane crop is burned in most high production areas to reduce the amount of biomass trash transported to the mill. Burning generally improves sugar recovery. However, if burned cane is left in the field for extended periods, substantial degradation may occur. Loss of sucrose is especially rapid when the air temperature is high. Environmental objections to field burning are related to the release of particulate plant material, CO_2, and other gases. Although cane is routinely harvested unburned in some regions, notably Queensland, Australia, harvesting is still more efficient following burning. Sugarcane trash resulting from green harvest may be

TABLE IV
Actual and Potential By-products of the Cane Sugar Industry

Bagasse, cane tops, and leaves	Sucrose	Molasses
Power generation	Foods and beverages	Animal feed
Charcoal		Potassium
	Invert syrup	fertilizer
Gasification products	Fructose	Ethanol
Pulp and paper	Fatty acid esters	Amino acids
Fiberboard	Poly(hydroxybutyric)	
	acid	Vitamins
Particleboard	Polyether polyols	Antibiotics
Animal litter	Chlorosucrose	
	sweetener	CO_2
Mulch	Sucrose octaacetate	Citric acid
Furfural	Sucrose octabenzoate	Yeast
Cellulose/glucose	Sucrose acetate/	
	isobutyrate	Acetone/butanol
Xylan/xylose/		
xylitol	Ethanol	
Lignin	Dextran gum	
Ethanol	Xanthan gum	
Single-cell protein	Gluconic acid	
	Itaconic acid	

burned after harvest to aid in cultivation for planting the next crop.

Methods to separate leafy biomass from millable cane at the factory might allow improved recovery of sucrose and thus negate the advantage of burning. A higher value for cogenerated electricity would encourage growers to recover leafy trash rather than burn it in the field.

B. Soil Conservation and Groundwater Protection

Sugarcane is an excellent soil conservation crop, especially where multiple ratoons are grown and where the cropping cycle is long.

Recent legislation in the United States requires growers of annual crops and certain commodity crops, including sugarcane, to reduce soil erosion on land classified as highly erodible. Approved cropping practices vary according to the soil erosion risk.

Groundwater stewardship is another environmental issue of concern. Crop protection chemicals, primarily herbicides, are being detected in groundwater at the parts per billion level. Steps under way to reduce the level of contamination include rotation of herbicides, use of lower rates with more effective timing, and replacing broadcast application with band application.

Surface run-off water containing nutrients and pesticides will require development of yield response curves, more efficient application methods, and soil conservation methods to minimize the potential for environment contamination.

C. Biomass and Cogeneration

Excess bagasse can be used to generate electricity for sale to public utilities. In Hawaii, 1.0 t processed cane results in the sale of 70 kWhr of electricity in excess of that required for the mill and plantation use. The proportion of electricity supplied by the plantations for public use can be significant, especially in the less populated areas. Cogenerated electricity from sugarcane currently supplies about 20% of the total energy on three of the four sugar-producing islands of the state of Hawaii. One cogeneration factory is in place in Florida; others are obtaining permits. Cogeneration from sugarcane in Mauritius reportedly supplies 20 to 30% of that island nation's electrical power. In addition, some countries, e.g., The Philippines, are showing increased interest in recovering crop leaves and tops for use as cogeneration fuel.

D. Fermentation Products

The fact that sugarcane juice could develop intoxicating qualities was known in ancient times; however, the preparation of sugarcane rum as a by-product from molasses began during the 17th century with the development of the sugar industry in the Caribbean. In addition to potable alcoholic products, various grades of ethyl alcohol from molasses are produced in several countries.

The greatest experience with sugarcane fermentation has been in Brazil where about two-thirds of the sugarcane crop is directly used for ethanol production. Brazil began ethanol production in 1975 as a direct consequence of the 1973 world oil crisis. The ethanol industry was developed to lessen Brazil's dependence on imported oil since it had a high capacity for sugarcane production (Table II). Since the beginning there has been a dramatic increase in production, reaching 1.3×10^6 m^3 anhydrous alcohol and 10.5×10^6 m^3 hydrated alcohol during the 1990 milling season. The total 11.9×10^6 m^3 ethanol is roughly equivalent to 200,000 bbl per day of petroleum. Part of this ethanol has been used as a solvent and for the production of important derivatives for chemical industries (Table IV). However, the primary use is for automotive fuel; in 1988, approximately 3.6 to 4.0 million vehicles were running purely on hydrated ethanol (30 to 33% of the total Brazilian fleet). Low prices of petroleum and an excess of gasoline has forced the Brazilian government to withhold subsidies for the ethanol industries, reducing the number of ethanol-driven cars. Future production capacity will be determined by the relationship between gasoline and sugar prices. The Brazilian experience has shown how to implement a large bioenergy program and the critical role played by government support programs.

E. Increased Value Products

The general conversion of sucrose by chemical processes into products of greater worth is generally termed sucrochemistry. These products are derived through fermentation, synthesis, or degradation (Table IV).

F. Biotechnology

Sugarcane improvement through traditional breeding methods has had a phenomenal success, but current rates of yield increases are slow. The tools of biotechnology, including cell and tissue culture, genetic engineering, molecular biology, and genome analysis, have the potential for accelerating genetic gains.

Considerable success has been met in learning how to manipulate foreign genes for the improvement of sugarcane through genetic transformation. Most phases of tissue culture have been developed for sugarcane. This has allowed transient transformation of sugarcane protoplasts through electroporation and stable transformation of embryogenic tissue cultures into plants transformed with selectable marker genes.

Native sugarcane genes are being cloned and used to transform sugarcane to confirm the suspected function of these genes.

Identifying and characterizing the genes for manipulation are being done with molecular markers (RFLPs, restriction fragment length polymorphisms; and RAPDs, random amplified polymorphic DNA). Molecular markers have produced the first genomic maps of sugarcane. Genome maps will be used to direct breeding efforts in a more efficient manner, assess genetic diversity, and detect major genes, as well as to develop phylogenetic and evolutionary relationships among the *Saccharum* species. Ultimately, a saturated genome map will allow the use of markers, based on their map position, to clone agronomically important genes for subsequent use in transformation.

Bibliography

Blackburn, F. (1984). "Sugar-cane." Longman, Singapore.

Blume, H. (1985). "Geography of Sugar Cane: Environmental, Structural and Economic Aspects of Cane Sugar Production." Verlag Dr. Albert Bartens, Berlin.

Heinz, D. J. (ed.) (1987). "Sugarcane Improvement through Breeding." Elsevier, Amsterdam.

Laluce, C. (1991). Current aspects of fuel ethanol production in Brazil. *Crit. Rev. Biotechnol.* **11**(2); 149–161.

Meade, G. P., and Chen, J. C. P. (1977). "Cane Sugar Handbook: A Manual for Cane Sugar Manufacturers and Their Chemists." Wiley, New York.

Paturau, J. M. (1989). "By-products of the Cane Sugar Industry: An Introduction to Their Industrial Utilization." Elsevier, Amsterdam.

Payne, J. H. (ed.) (1990). "Cogeneration in the Cane Sugar Industry." Elsevier, Amsterdam.

Samuels, G. (1969). "Foliar Diagnosis for Sugarcane." Adams, Chicago.

Sustainable Agriculture

MIGUEL A. ALTIERI, *University of California, Berkeley*

Glossary

Agroecology Agroecological approach to the study and management of agricultural systems

Agroecosystem Agricultural system which encompasses interacting biological, technical, and socioeconomic factors, some of which are under human control, for the purpose of producing food and fiber

Agroforestry Food production system which includes multipurpose trees as part of the ecosystem

Biodiversity Collection of animal, plant, and microbial species which provide key ecological services to local agroecosystems

Ecosystem System made up of a community of plants, animals, and other organisms and their interrelated physical and chemical environment

Intercropping Planting of two or more crops together in various configurations of time and space

Monoculture Highly simplified cropping system which involves the planting of only one crop in a season

Shelterbelts Barrier zone of trees, plants, or shrubs planted to protect crops, soil, etc. from strong winds or to provide habitat for beneficial insects and wildlife

Sustainable agriculture refers to a mode of farming that attempts to provide long-term sustained yields through the use of ecologically sound management technologies such as crop diversification, organic soil management, and biological pest control. The principles of agricultural sustainability are provided by agroecology, a scientific methodology which regards agricultural systems as ecosystems (hence, the term agroecosystem) and, as such, farming and research are not concerned with high yields of a particular commodity, but rather with the optimization of the system as a whole. It also requires us to look beyond production economics to consider broader issues of ecological stability, sustainability, social equity, and cultural acceptability. For this reason, a wider definition of agriculture as sustainable means that it is

- ecologically sound: the quality of natural resources is maintained and/or enhanced;
- economically viable: farmers can produce enough for self-sufficiency and obtain adequate income by emphasizing efficient use of locally available resources;
- socially just: resources and power are distributed in such a way that the basic needs of all members of society are met, and their rights to land use, adequate capital, market opportunities, and technical assistance are assured;
- humane: all forms of life (plant, animal, human) are respected.
- adaptable: rural communities are capable of adjusting to the constantly changing farming conditions.

I. Introduction

In agricultural development, raising production is often given primary attention, but there is an upper limit to the productivity of agroecosystems. When this is exceeded, agroecosystems may degrade and collapse. For this reason in sustainable agriculture the performance criteria to evaluate agroecosystems must, in addition to productivity, be broadened to include properties of sustainability, equity, and stability.

Encyclopedia of Agricultural Science, Volume 4   Copyright © 1994 by Academic Press, Inc.   All rights of reproduction in any form reserved.

1. Sustainability relates to the ability of an agroecosystem to main production through time, in the face of long-term ecological constraints and socioeconomic pressures. It also relates to the resiliency of an agroecosystem, i.e., its ability to recover after being subjected to stress. Productivity in agricultural systems cannot be increased indefinitely. A ceiling is placed on potential productivity by the physiological limits of crops, the "carrying capacity" of the habitat, and the external costs incurred during efforts to increase production. This point is the "management equilibrium" where the agroecosystem, considered to be in equilibrium with environmental and management factors, produces a sustained yield. The characteristics of this balanced management will vary with different crops, geographical areas, and energy inputs and, therefore, will be highly "site specific."

2. Equity is a measure of how evenly the products of the agroecosystem (income, produce, etc.) are distributed among the local producers and consumers. However, equity is much more than simply a matter of an adequate income, good nutrition, or a satisfactory amount of leisure. Many aspects of equity are not easily definable or measurable in scientific terms. To some, equity is reached when the distribution of opportunities or incomes within producing communities really improves. Clearly, although "improvements" may be a step toward equity, they do not guarantee the establishment of a more "equitable" society. Generally, this is dependent on the political structure of each country.

3. Stability is the constancy of production under a given set of environmental, economic, and management conditions. Some ecological pressures are rigid constraints in the sense that the farmer is virtually unable to modify them. In other cases, the farmer can improve the biological stability of the system by choosing more suitable crops or developing methods of cultivation that improve yields. The land can be irrigated, mulched, manured or rotated, or crops can be grown in mixtures to improve the resilience of the system. The farmer can supplement family labor through the use of either animals or machines, or by employing other people's labor through various means. Thus, the exact nature of the response does not depend solely on the environment, but on other social factors as well. For this reason the concept of stability must be expanded to embrace socioeconomic and management considerations. Three other sources of stability can be defined:

a. *Management stability*. Derived from choosing the set of technologies best adapted to farmers' needs and resource base. Initially, the application of industrial technology usually results in substantial increases in yield, as less and less land is left fallow and soil, water, and biotic limitations are bypassed. At the same time there is always an element of instability associated with the new technologies. The farmers are keenly aware of this, and their resistance to change often has an ecological basis.

b. *Economic stability*. Associated with the ability of the farmer to predict market prices of inputs and of the product and to sustain farm income. Depending on the sophistication of this knowledge, the farmer will make trade-offs between production and stability. To study the dynamics of economic stability in traditional agriculture, data must be obtained on total production, yields of important commodities, cash flow, off-farm income, net income, and the faction of total production that the farmer sells or trades.

c. *Cultural stability*. Dependent on the maintenance of the sociocultural organization and context that has nurtured traditional agroecosystems through generations. Rural development cannot be achieved when isolated from the social context, and it must be anchored to the traditions of local people. In order to fully understand the concept of stability, an integrated analysis must be adopted, since total stability results from the interplay of so many different causal factors.

4. Productivity is a quantitative measure of the rate of and the amount of production per unit of land or input. In ecological terms, production refers to the amount of yields or end product, and productivity is the process for achieving that end product. In ecological terms, production refers to the amount of yields or end product, and productivity is the process for achieving that end product. Yield per unit area can be one indicator of the rate and constancy of production, but it can also be expressed in other ways, such as per unit of labor input or per unit of cash investment or as energy efficiency ratios. When patterns of production are analyzed using energy ratios, it becomes clear that traditional systems are exceedingly more efficient than modern agroecosystems in the use of energy. A commercial agricultural system typically exhibits output/input ratios between 1 and 3, whereas traditional farming systems exhibit ratios from 10 to 15. Farms are both energy-consuming and energy-producing systems, but they also provide food, income, jobs, and a way of life for many agrarian societies. These are indexes that should be included in the overall evaluation.

In analyzing production/stability features of agro-ecosystems, it must be recognized that farmers have a fixed quantity of land, family labor, and capital with which to meet their subsistence goals, promote diversity of diet and income sources, minimize risks, maximize harvest security, and optimize returns under low levels of external inputs.

When the above indicators of performance are used to evaluate the viability of modern agroecosystems, it becomes apparent that although, historically, the introduction of new technology has greatly increased short-term productivity, it has also in the long term lowered the stability, sustainability, and equity of the total agricultural system. Today there is growing awareness of the social and environmental costs that are associated with large-scale, specialized production systems. Concerns include:

a. increased cost of, and dependence on, external inputs of chemicals and energy
b. decline in soil productivity from soil erosion and nutrient loss
c. contamination of surface and groundwater from fertilizers and pesticides
d. hazards to human and animal health and to food quality from agrochemicals
e. demise of family farms and local markets

When compared with traditional farming systems in developing countries, industrialized agricultural systems appear in the long-term more ecologically fragile and unsound (Fig. 1). In developing countries, small farmers place a higher value on reducing risk than on maximizing production. Through diversifi-

cation and recycling, small farmers are usually interested in optimizing the productivity of scarce farm resources, not necessarily in increasing land or labor productivity. Also, small farmers choose a particular production technology based on decisions made for the entire farming system and not only for a particular crop. [*See* FARMING SYSTEMS.]

II. Requirements of a Sustainable Agricultural System

Modern agriculture today faces the challenge of producing an economically viable crop while preserving the integrity of the local, regional, and global environment. The opportunities lie in the application of ecological theory to farm management. Agronomists must consider the interactions of all important biological and physical components of the cropping systems and must integrate this knowledge at the community level if they are to meet the twin challenges of economic growth and environmental sustainability. Agroecology is central to this integration of agronomy and ecology. Agroecology proposes that the basic tenets of a sustainable agroecosystem are the conservation of renewable resources, adaptation of the crop to the environment, and maintenance of a moderate but sustainable level of productivity. The production system must: (1) reduce energy and resource use and regulate the overall energy input so that the output : input ratio is high; (2) reduce nutrient losses by effectively containing leaching, run-off, and erosion and improve nutrient recycling through the promotion of legumes, organic manures and compost, and other effective recycling mechanisms; (3) encourage local production of food items adapted to the natural and socioeconomic setting; (4) sustain a desired net output by preserving the natural resources (by minimizing soil degradation); and (5) reduce costs and increase the efficiency and economic viability of small and medium-sized farms, thereby promoting a diverse, potentially resilient agricultural system. Table I describes the attributes of sustainable farming systems which rely on internal resources when compared to conventional systems that rely mostly on resources external to the farm.

As shown in Fig. 2 from a management viewpoint, the basic components of a sustainable agroecosystem include: (1) vegetative cover as an effective soil- and water-conserving measure, met through the use of no-till practices, mulch farming, use of cover crops,

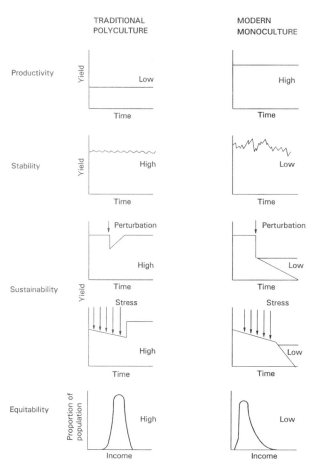

FIGURE 1 Long-term trends of ecological indicators in traditional versus modern agroecosystems.

TABLE I

Comparison of Ecological Characteristics between Conventional (External Input-Dependent) and Alternative (Internal Input-Dependent) Agroecosystems

	Alternative	Conventional
Sun	Main source of energy	Energy used as "catalyst" for conversion of fossil energy
Water	Mainly rain and small irrigation schemes	Increased use of large dams and centralized water distribution systems
Nitrogen	Collected from air by legumes and recycled	Primarily from synthetic fertilizer
Minerals	Released from soil reserves and recycled	Mined, processed, and imported
Weed and pest control	Biological and mechanical	With pesticides
Energy	Some generated and collected on farm	Dependence on fossil fuel
Seed	Some produced on-farm, local varieties	All purchased hybrids
Management decisions	By farmer and community	Some provided by agribusiness
Animals	Produced synergistically on farm	Feed lot production at separate locations
Cropping system	Rotations and diversity enhance value of all of above components	Monocropping
Labor	Most work done by the family living on the farm	Most work done by hired labor
Capital	Initial source is family and community; any accumulation of wealth is reinvested locally	Initial source is external indebtedness or equity, and any accumulation flows mainly to outside investments

etc.; (2) a regular supply of organic matter through the regular addition of organic matter (manure, compost) and promotion of soil biotic activity; (3) nutrient recycling mechanisms through the use of corp rotations, crop/livestock mixed systems, agroforestry and intercropping systems based on legumes, etc.; (4) pest regulation assured through enhanced activity of biological control agents, achieved by introducing and/or conserving natural enemies.

III. Restoring Biodiversity in Agroecosystems

Modern agriculture implies the simplification of biodiversity and reaches an extreme form in crop monocultures. The end result is the production of an artificial ecosystem requiring constant intervention. In most cases this intervention is in the form of agrochemical inputs which, in addition to boosting yields, result in a number of undesirable environmental and social costs.

As a consequence, modern agroecosystems are unstable and breakdowns manifest themselves as recurrent pest problems such as soil degradation and pollution of water systems. Worsening pest problems have been linked to the expansion of crop monocultures at the expense of vegetation diversity which, more often than not, provides key ecological services to ensure crop production and protection. Therefore a major concern in sustainable agriculture is the mainte-

nance and/or enhancement of biodiversity and the role it can play in restoring the ecological balance of agroecosystems so that sustainable production may be achieved. Biodiversity performs a variety of renewal processes and ecological services in agroecosystems (Fig. 3), when they are lost, the costs can be significant.

A major strategy in sustainable agriculture is to restore agricultural diversity in time and space through crop rotations, cover crops, intercropping, crop/livestock mixtures, etc.

Some of the ecological features of these alternative cropping systems are:

a. *Crop rotations.* Temporal diversity incorporated into cropping systems, providing crop nutrients and breaking the life cycles of several insect pests, diseases, and weeds.

b. *Polycultures.* Complex cropping systems in which two or more crop species are planted within sufficient spatial proximity to result in competition or complementation, thus inhibiting or enhancing yields.

c. *Agroforestry systems.* An agricultural system where trees are grown together with annual crops and/or animals, resulting in enhanced complementary relations between farm components and increased multiple use of the landscape.

d. *Cover crops.* The use of pure or mixed stands of legumes or other annual plant species under fruit trees for the purpose of improving soil fertility, enhancing biological control of pests, and modifying the orchard microclimate.

e. *Crop/livestock mixtures.* Animal integration in agroecosystems aids in achieving high biomass output

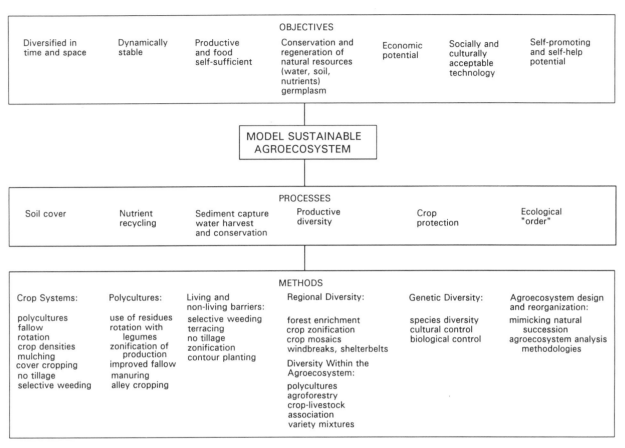

FIGURE 2 Objectives and processes in the design of a model sustainable agroecosystem.

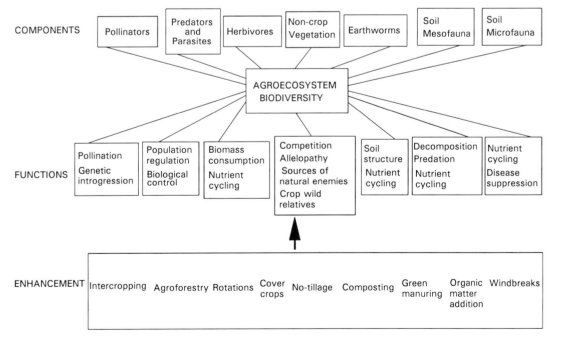

FIGURE 3 The integration of resources, components, and functions for multiple use farming systems.

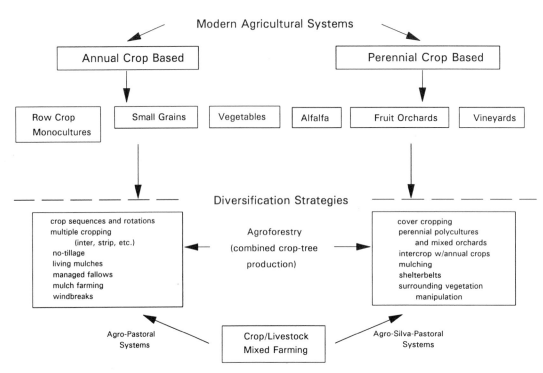

FIGURE 4 Diversification options for annual or perennial crop-based cropping systems.

within a given ecological and socioeconomic setting, complementing nutrient cycling, and optimizing management of pasture–crop rotations. As seen in Fig. 4, different options to diversify cropping systems are available depending on whether the current monoculture systems to be modified are based on annual or perennial crops. Diversification can also take place outside of the farm, in crop–field boundaries with windbreaks, shelterbelts, and living fences, for example, which can improve the habitat for wildlife and beneficial insects, provide sources of wood and organic matter, resources for pollinating bees, and, in addition, modify wind speed and the microclimate.

When biodiversity is restored to agroecosystems a number of complex interactions between soils, plants, and animals are established; the idea is to exploit complementary interactions and synergism that may result in beneficial results such as enhanced pest control, nutrient cycling, and soil conservation. When diversified cropping systems are assembled the possibilities of complementing interactions or "synergisms" between agroecosystem components are enhanced (Fig. 3), resulting in one or more of the following effects: (a) continuous vegetation cover for soil protection, (b) constant production of food, ensuring a varied diet and several marketing items, (c) closing of nutrient cycles and effective use of local resources, (d) soil and water conservation through mulching and wind protection, (e) enhanced biological pest control through diver-

sification, (f) increased multiple use capacity of the landscape, (g) sustained crop production without the use of environmentally degrading chemical inputs.

IV. Biodiversity and Pest Management

Several studies have explored the relationships between vegetational diversity and pest reduction in diversified cropping systems (Fig. 5). The literature is full of examples of experiments documenting that diversification of cropping systems often leads to reduced pest populations. The studies suggest that the more diverse the agroecosystem and the longer this diversity remains undisturbed, the more internal links develop to promote greater insect stability. It is clear, however, that the stability of the insect community depends not only on its trophic diversity, but on the actual density-dependence nature of the trophic levels. In other words, stability will depend on the precision of the response of natural enemies (predators and parasites) to an increase in the population of herbivorous pests.

Although most experiments have documented insect population trends in single versus complex crop habitats, a few have concentrated on elucidating the nature and dynamics of the trophic relationships between herbivores and natural enemies in diversified agroecosystems. Several lines of study have been developed:

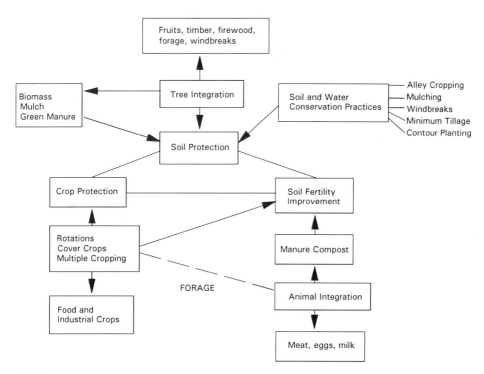

FIGURE 5 Complementary interactions in diversified cropping systems resulting in enhanced soil protection, soil fertility, and biological crop protection.

a. *Crop–weed–insect interaction studies.* Evidence indicates that weeds influence the diversity and abundance of insect herbivores and associated natural enemies in crop systems. Certain weeds (mostly Umbelliferae, Leguminosae, and Compositae) play an important ecological role by harboring and supporting a complex of beneficial arthropods that aid in suppressing pest populations.

b. *Insect dynamics in annual polycultures.* Overwhelming evidence suggests that polycultures support a lower herbivore load than monocultures. One factor explaining this trend is that relatively more stable natural enemy populations can persist in polycultures due to the more continuous availability of food sources and microhabitats. The other possibility is that specialized herbivores are more likely to find and remain on pure crop stands, which provide concentrated resources and monotonous physical conditions.

c. *Herbivores in complex perennial crop systems.* Most of these studies have explored the effects of the manipulation of ground cover vegetation on insect pests and associated enemies. The data indicate that orchards with rich floral undergrowth exhibit a lower incidence of insect pests than clean cultivated orchards, mainly because of an increased abundance and efficiency of predators and parasitoids. In some cases, ground cover directly affects herbivore species which discriminate among trees with and without cover beneath.

d. *The effects of adjacent vegetation.* These studies have documented the dynamics of colonizing insect pests that invade crop fields from edge vegetation, especially when the vegetation is botanically related to the crop. A number of studies document the importance of adjoining wild vegetation in providing alternate food and habitat to natural enemies which move into nearby crops.

The available literature suggests that the design of vegetation management strategies must include knowledge and consideration of (1) crop arrangement in time and space, (2) the composition and abundance of noncrop vegetation within and around fields, (3) the soil type, (4) the surrounding environment, and (5) the type and intensity of management. The response of insect populations to environmental manipulations depends upon their degree of association with one or more of the vegetational components of the system. Extension of the cropping period or planning temporal or spatial cropping sequences may allow naturally occurring biological control agents to sustain higher population levels on alternate host or prey and to persist in the agricultural environment throughout the year.

A classical example of the effects of diversity on pest populations is the role of the native blackberry bush (*Rubus* sp.) in vineyards of the Central Valley of California in the control of an important insect pest, the grape leafhopper *Erythroneura elegantula*. Long considered the key pest in many grape agroecosystems, this foliage-feeding leafhopper inflicts severe damage on vines and great losses in fruit yield when present in large numbers. Insecticides have often failed to give effective control of the leafhopper or their use has aggreveted other pest problems, such as spider mites. Entomologists had known that the parasitic wasp, *Anagrus epos,* ovipositing in the eggs of the grape leafhopper kept the pest under control in some vineyards, but not in others.

The riddle was solved when it was realized that the wasp spent its winters parasitizing a different insect on *Rubus.* Since the leaves fall off grapevines in the winter and the grape leafhopper retreats to the edge of the vineyard and becomes inactive, the nonhibernating parasitic wasp has no shelter, food, or means of survival in this environment. Nearby blackberry bushes, however, keep their leaves during winter and host their own economically unimportant leafhopper species, *Dikrella cruentata,* all year round. When entomologists checked the eggs of this blackberry leafhopper, they found considerable parasitism by *Anagrus.* Thus, the weedy blackberry patches were providing a winter home for this important natural enemy of the key grape pest. Accordingly, it was growers with blackberry bushes in the vicinity of their vineyards who had the least grape leafhopper problems. *Anagrus* adults migrating back to the vineyards in the spring kept grape leafhopper numbers at low levels from the beginning of the season. Since this discovery, many growers have solved their major leafhopper problems with the planting of blackberry bush refuges in shady areas near their vineyards.

Recent studies in California have shown that prune trees planted next to vineyards allow early-season buildup of *A. epos.* After surviving the winter on an alternate host, the prune leafhopper, *Anagrus,* moves into the vineyard in the spring, providing grape leafhopper control up to a month earlier than in vineyards not near prune trees. Researchers now recommend that prune trees should always be planted upwind from the vineyard (but managed as a typical commercial prune orchard) and to plant as many trees as is economically feasible, since the more trees there are, the more productive the refuge is likely to be.

The beneficial effects of diversification are also evident in annual cropping systems. Strip cropping, a form of intercropping characterized by two or more alternate rows of crops, is common in the United States for corn/soybean. In California, cotton–alfalfa strip cropping has been tested for *Lygus* bug control with encouraging results. The effect of this system is that the alfalfa strips act as a trap crop when the invading *Lygus* colonize the cotton fields. Also, the strips serve as an insectary for natural enemies of other cotton pests. The natural enemies leave the alfalfa strip and enter the adjacent cotton to attack eggs and small larvae of the bollworm, cabbage looper, and beet armyworm.

In the coastal areas of Northern California, populations of cabbage aphids (*Brevicoryne brassicae*) and flea beetles (*Phyllotreta cruciferae*) can be significantly reduced in broccoli when this crop is grown intercropped with fava beans, wild mustard, vetch, barley, or with living mulches of various clover species. There are a number of other studies evaluating crop mixtures that exhibit reduced insect pest incidence. This reduction may be the result of an increased predator/parasitoid population, higher availability of alternate food for natural enemies, decreased colonization and reproduction of pests, chemical repellency, masking and/or feeding inhibition from nonhost plants, prevention of pest movement, and/or emigration and optimum synchrony between pests and natural enemies.

V. The Goal of Sustainable Agricultural Development

Sustainable agriculture refers to those forms of agriculture that:

1. Seek to optimize the use of locally available resources by combining the different components of the farm system, i.e., plants, animals, soil, water, climate, and people, so that they complement each other and have the greatest possible synergetic effects;

2. Seek ways of using external inputs only to the extent that they are needed to provide elements that are deficient in the ecosystem and to enhance available biological, physical, and human resources. In using external inputs, attention is given mainly to maximum recycling and minimum detrimental impact on the environment.

The central goal in sustainable agriculture is not to achieve maximum yield, but long-term stabilization. Sustaining agricultural productivity will require more than a simple modification of conventional management techniques. The development of self-sufficient, diversified, economically viable, small-scale agroecosystems comes from novel designs of cropping and/or livestock systems managed with technologies adapted to the local environment that are within a farmer's resources. At the farm, regional, and national level, sustainable agriculture implies the need for closely monitoring and carefully managing flows of nutrients, water, and energy in order to achieve a balance at a high level of production. Management principles include harvesting water and nutrients from the watershed, recycling nutrients within the farm, managing nutrient flow from farm to consumers and back again, using aquifer water judiciously, enhancing biodiversity, and using renewable sources of energy. As these flows are not confined by farm boundaries, sustainable agriculture requires management not only at farm level but also at district, regional, national, and even international levels.

Energy and resource conservation, environmental quality, public health, and equitable socioeconomic development should be considered in making decisions on crop species, rotations, row spacing, fertilizing, pest control, and harvesting. Many farmers will not shift to alternative systems unless there is a good prospect for monetary gain, brought about by either increased output or decreased production costs. Different attitudes will depend primarily on farmers' perceptions of the short-term and near-term economic benefits of sustainable agriculture.

It is crucial that scientists involved in the search for sustainable agricultural technologies be concerned about who will ultimately benefit from them. This requires recognizing that political determinants enter at the point when basic scientific questions are asked and not only at the time when technologies are delivered to society. Thus, what is produced, how it is produced, and for whom it is produced are key questions that need to be addressed if a socially equitable agriculture is to emerge. When such questions are examined, issues of land tenure, labor, appropriate technology, public health, research policy, etc. unavoidably arise. Increasingly scientists interested in promoting sustainable agriculture will have to become involved in meeting the adequate policy scenarios that promote sustainability.

Bibliography

Altieri, M. A. (1987). "Agroecology: The Scientific Basis of Alternative Agriculture." Westview Press, Boulder, CO.

Altieri, M. A., and Letourneau, D. (1982). Vegetation management and biological control in agroecosystems. *Crop Protect.* **1,** 405–430.

Conway, G. R., and Barbier, E. B. (1990). "After the Green Revolution: Sustainable Agriculture for Development." Earthscan, London.

Edwards, C. A., Lal, R., Madden, P., Miller, R. H., and House, G. (1990) "Sustainable Agricultural Systems." Soil and Water Conservation Society, IA.

Francis, C. A., Butler Flora, C., and King, L. D. (1990). "Sustainable Agriculture in Temperate Zones." Wiley, New York.

Reijntjes, C., Haverkort, B., and Waters-Bayer, A. (1992). "Farming for the Future: An Introduction to Low-External-Input and Sustainable Agriculture." MacMillan, London.

Swine Production

WILSON G. POND, *USDA-Agricultural Research Service, Children's Nutrition Research Center, Baylor College of Medicine*

Glossary

Barrow Male castrated before sexual maturity
Boar Male swine of any age
Finishing pig Young swine generally weighing more than 50 kg but not yet heavy enough for slaughter
Gilt Female swine of any age to second pregnancy
Growing pig Young swine after weaning, generally weighing less than 70 kg
Hog Swine of either sex, generally referring to immature gilts, barrows, or boars
Market hogs Finished hogs sold for slaughter
Pig In the United States, refers to young swine of either sex; in Europe, refers to all ages and either sex
Shoat Young weaned swine of either sex, generally weighing less than 50 kg
Slaughter pig Young swine ready for slaughter, usually weighing 90–130 kg
Sow Female swine having produced one or more litters
Stag Male castrated after reaching sexual maturity
Suckling pig Young swine before weaning
Swine Hoofed mammals of the family Suidae, genus *Sus*, species *scrofa* (*domesticus*)
Weanling pig Young swine after weaning

Swine production refers to that portion of animal agriculture devoted to the conversion of feed resources to pork. The enterprise varies from small "backyard" efforts in which household kitchen wastes and locally grown feedstuffs are fed to pigs to provide pork for home use to large highly specialized pork production systems geared for large commercial production. Pork production, regardless of the size of the enterprise, represents a major human food resource and requires inputs related to capital, labor, feed resources, physical facilities, disease control, waste management, marketing, and product quality assurance. The integration of all inputs and outputs into pork production systems at the farm, regional, national, and international level is an ongoing interdisciplinary effort.

I. Trends in Swine Production

Pork continues to occupy an important position as a food source in affluent societies as well as in developing countries with slower economic growth. The world swine population is growing at a faster rate than that of the human population; this is a reflection of the sustained demand for pork in all parts of the world. Total world meat consumption has continued to increase during the past decade to about 170 million tons in 1990 (32 kg/capita). Pork accounts for about 40% of total (70 million tons in 1990) and remains the first among all meat sources in total consumption, followed in descending order by beef, poultry, sheep, and goats.

A. Regional Distribution in the United States

Swine production in the United States continues to be concentrated in the Midwest where maize and grain sorghum production are concentrated, even though human population centers are remote from these areas. Of the approximately 80 million swine slaughtered annually in the United States, about 20 million are produced in the state of Iowa; the six states of Iowa, Illinois, Minnesota, Indiana, Nebraska, and North Carolina produce nearly two-thirds of the total pork in the United States. Other states ranking in the top 10 in swine production are Missouri, Ohio, South Dakota, and Kansas.

About three-fourths of the swine marketed in the United States are produced on farms raising more than 1000 head annually. This trend accompanies a steady reduction in the number of farms reporting swine.

B. World Distribution

The world swine population has increased steadily for many decades and in 1991 was approximately 860 million. China is the world's leading pork consumer and produces 35% of the world's pork. Differences among regions in animal reproductive rates and animal weights at slaughter result in discrepancies among countries between census figures and annual pork production. Asia has about one-half of the world's total swine, but produces about 40% of the world's pork; Europe (including the former USSR) has about 30% of the world's swine and produces 42% of the world's pork; corresponding figures for other continents are North and Central America, 12% and 14%; South America, 6% and 3%; Africa, 1.3% and 0.7%; and Oceania, 0.6% and 0.7%, respectively.

II. Pork as Human Food

A. Nutrient Composition

Pork, along with other meats, provides protein of higher nutritive value and mineral elements more efficiently used by the body than those present in most plants. Pork is an excellent source of some of the mineral elements and a poor source of others. For example, it is high in phosphorus, but almost devoid of calcium; it is high in potassium, but low in sodium; it is an excellent source of iron, and a good source of zinc, manganese, and magnesium. Also, pork is an excellent source of vitamins and, like other animal products, it contains vitamin B_{12} which is absent from plants. The nutrient content of pork and the percentages of the recommended daily vitamin allowance supplied by a 100 g (3 ounce) serving of cooked pork loin are summarized in Table I. [*See* MINERALS, ROLE IN HUMAN NUTRITION.]

TABLE I

Nutrients Contained in Pork

Nutrient	Amount
Protein	20.7%
Fat	6.9%
Water	71.5%
Minerals	0.9%
Calories	151 kCal of gross energy
Thiamin	1.13 mg/100 g (70% of daily adult requirement)
Riboflavin	0.33 mg/100 g (14% of daily adult requirement)
Niacin	6.8 mg/100 g (29% of daily adult requirement)
Vitamin B_6	0.50 mg/100 g (25% of daily adult requirement)[a]
Vitamin B_{12}	0.9 μg/100 g (20% of daily adult requirement)

[a] Based on raw fresh cut (about 85% of cooked value).

The long-term acceptance of pork as a major food source has been a result of its high nutritive value and the variety of processing and cooking methods available for its inclusion in many cultures. In many third world cultures, pigs kept to supplement family income are fed largely household waste and food gleaned locally and, in turn, provide a valuable source of protein, vitamins, and other nutrients to children and adults in an otherwise impoverished environment.

B. Properties Affecting the Acceptability of Pork to Humans

1. Pork Quality Factors

The amount of pork consumed in relation to alternative meat sources is dependent on cultural, religious, economic, and esthetic factors. Economic and esthetic forces, which are generally independent of cultural and religious constraints, are addressed briefly here. The share of the total market for animal products captured by pork is closely related to costs and supply of alternative sources, i.e., beef, lamb, and poultry, the production of which in turn, is driven by many of the same forces that control cost of production and marketing of pork. As world trade of food animal products has expanded, the economic factors determining the ultimate consumption of pork globally and in specific regions have become more complex. Esthetic aspects of pork as a food have a major impact on its acceptance. Pork is less variable than beef or lamb in recognized palatability factors (tenderness, juiciness, color, aroma, flavor) so that differences in age, breed, and environment have a relatively small effect on its quality. Color, firmness, and water-holding capacity are included together as a general appraisal of pork quality, ranging from pale, soft, exudative (PSE) to dark, firm, dry pork. Between these extremes is the most desirable. The pale color and excessive exudation of PSE pork creates merchandizing problems in the retail store. Recognition of the fact that PSE pork has a genetic basis has permitted the industry to reduce its incidence drastically by selection of animals free of this trait.

Much remains unknown about all of the factors involved in pork quality, the relative importance of each factor, and the degree to which pork acceptability can be controlled through husbandry practices, marketing and slaughtering procedures, and meat processing and technology. A major marketing constraint on the sale of pork from intact males is the objectionable odor and flavor perceived by some individuals. Fat-soluble male hormone derivatives such as 5-α-androst-16 ene-3-one, responsible for the "boar odor," are detected in most males by 6 months of age. Since boars grow faster, require less feed per unit of weight gain, and produce leaner pork than castrated males, there is economic incentive for their production. In some regions of the world, intact males are sold without price reduction to take advantage of their more efficient production, but in other regions, such as the United States, meat from intact males is discounted at the marketplace and sold as a component of sausage.

2. Health Factors

a. Fat Content and Composition Advances in swine breeding, feeding and management have transformed the composition of pork in the past 30 years to a relatively low-fat product. The average percentage of fat in pork in the United States is now about 7% of retail carcass weight compared with about 25% in the 1960s. This translates to a 50% reduction in calorie content of pork carcasses (300 kCal/100 g in the 1960s compared with a value of 150 now). Pork is relatively high in unsaturated fatty acids and its fatty acid composition resembles that of the diet fed to the animal. Thus, the stereotypic image of pork as a high-calorie food high in saturated fatty acids is erroneous. The cholesterol content of pork is about 70 mg/100 g, a value similar to that of beef and lamb and less than that of butter, cheddar cheese, eggs, and many seafoods. The digestibility of pork is high and contrary to myth, there is no evidence that pork fat (lard) differs from that of other animals and plants in digestibility by humans. [See FATS AND CHOLESTEROL, ROLE IN HUMAN NUTRITION.]

b. Disease organisms The parasite, *Trichinella spiralis,* may infect swine and cause trichinosis in hu-

mans consuming improperly cooked pork from infected animals. While still a serious potential health risk in many regions of the world, reliable methods of identification of infected animals have reduced the incidence of infection in swine to nearly zero in regions where swine production utilizes modern technology. Safe methods of killing the organism in infected pork (heating to 170°F, freezing for 20 days at 5°F, or subjecting the pork to high-energy radiation) have reduced the danger of infection drastically. Reported human cases of trichinosis in the United States number less than 100 annually, and effective drugs are now available for treatment.

Other infectious agents such as Salmonella and Campylobacter bacteria may contaminate pork and other food products, but public awareness of precautionary measures and careful practices of inspection and surveillance by federal and state agencies and by the industry itself of animal and carcass handling and processing en route to the consumer provide a dependable supply of safe and wholesome pork.

C. Wholesale and Retail Cuts of Pork

The proportion of the live animal that is available as edible lean meat is often referred to as "percent lean cuts." These lean cuts are the shoulder (Boston butt plus picnic), loin, and ham. The lean cuts constitute 40% or more of the weight of typical market weight swine, but more than 75% of the value under U.S. pricing conditions. The lard yield from a U.S. No. 1 market pig is about 10% of the retail carcass weight in pigs in the United States now, compared with 35% forty years ago and 16% twenty years ago. About 50% of the weight of a 78-kg carcass is made up of the wholesale cuts [ham, loin, shoulder and side (spare ribs and cured bacon)]; the remainder is skin, fat, jowl, tail, feet, and trimmings. [See ANIMAL BY-PRODUCTS FROM SLAUGHTER; MEAT PROCESSING.]

Carcasses also yield important organs such as brain, liver, and kidney. The wholesale cuts, showing the location of each component on the carcass, are illustrated in Fig. 1. Methods of carcass breakdown and nomenclature vary in different countries and regions, but the same general approaches are used in separating and merchandizing the various cuts in all markets. Regions also vary in the choice of cuts that are processed into cured products, e.g., bacon in the United States is from the belly, while bacon in Canada and Europe is often from the shoulder. In many places within the developing countries, constraints on post-slaughter handling are imposed by lack of modern abattoirs and refrigeration and inadequate dis-

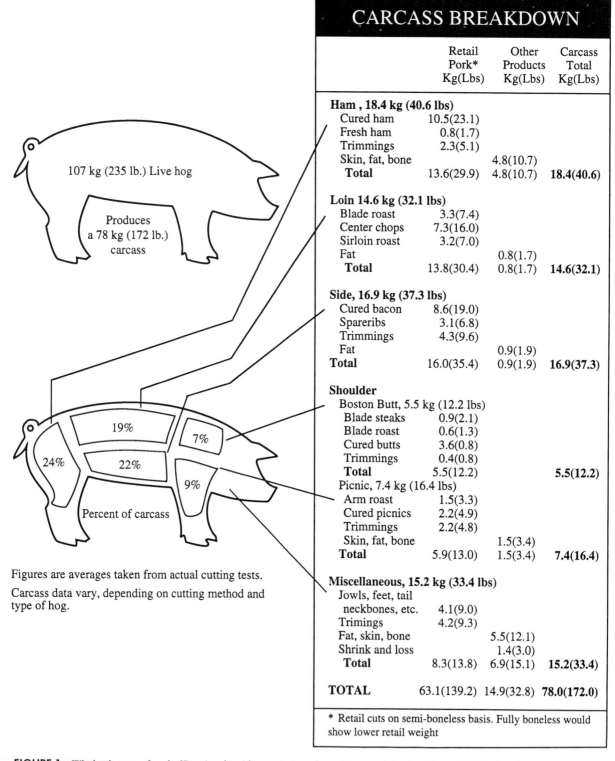

CARCASS BREAKDOWN

	Retail Pork* Kg(Lbs)	Other Products Kg(Lbs)	Carcass Total Kg(Lbs)
Ham , 18.4 kg (40.6 lbs)			
Cured ham	10.5(23.1)		
Fresh ham	0.8(1.7)		
Trimmings	2.3(5.1)		
Skin, fat, bone		4.8(10.7)	
Total	13.6(29.9)	4.8(10.7)	**18.4(40.6)**
Loin 14.6 kg (32.1 lbs)			
Blade roast	3.3(7.4)		
Center chops	7.3(16.0)		
Sirloin roast	3.2(7.0)		
Fat		0.8(1.7)	
Total	13.8(30.4)	0.8(1.7)	**14.6(32.1)**
Side, 16.9 kg (37.3 lbs)			
Cured bacon	8.6(19.0)		
Spareribs	3.1(6.8)		
Trimmings	4.3(9.6)		
Fat		0.9(1.9)	
Total	16.0(35.4)	0.9(1.9)	**16.9(37.3)**
Shoulder			
Boston Butt, 5.5 kg (12.2 lbs)			
Blade steaks	0.9(2.1)		
Blade roast	0.6(1.3)		
Cured butts	3.6(0.8)		
Trimmings	0.4(0.8)		
Total	5.5(12.2)		**5.5(12.2)**
Picnic, 7.4 kg (16.4 lbs)			
Arm roast	1.5(3.3)		
Cured picnics	2.2(4.9)		
Trimmings	2.2(4.8)		
Skin, fat, bone		1.5(3.4)	
Total	5.9(13.0)	1.5(3.4)	**7.4(16.4)**
Miscellaneous, 15.2 kg (33.4 lbs)			
Jowls, feet, tail neckbones, etc.	4.1(9.0)		
Trimings	4.2(9.3)		
Fat, skin, bone		5.5(12.1)	
Shrink and loss		1.4(3.0)	
Total	8.3(13.8)	6.9(15.1)	**15.2(33.4)**
TOTAL	63.1(139.2)	14.9(32.8)	**78.0(172.0)**

* Retail cuts on semi-boneless basis. Fully boneless would show lower retail weight

107 kg (235 lb.) Live hog

Produces a 78 kg (172 lb.) carcass

24%   19%   7%

22%   9%

Percent of carcass

Figures are averages taken from actual cutting tests.

Carcass data vary, depending on cutting method and type of hog.

FIGURE 1 Wholesale cuts of pork. [Reprinted, with permission, from "Meat and Poultry Facts, 1993." American Meat Institute.]

tribution systems. In these areas, meat from freshly killed swine is sold immediately, with little effort directed toward identifying and separating conventional wholesale cuts.

III. Life Cycle and Physiological States

The generation interval in swine is about 1 year. The early sexual maturity, prolificacy, and short gestation period of swine compared with other food animals, and the associated high heritability of the traits involved, make possible relatively rapid changes in growth efficiency and body composition. Females and males reach puberty at about 6 months of age and can be mated by 8 months of age to produce a litter at about 1 year of age (gestation is 114 days). Average number of pigs born per litter is 9–12 and an average of 8–10 pigs are weaned at 3 to 5 weeks of age. After weaning, pigs are usually full fed a nutritionally complete diet throughout the growing–finishing period of about 4 months at which time they are marketed for pork or retained as breeding animals (5 to 6 months of age). Lactating sows do not normally ovulate during the suckling period, but within 1 week after their pigs are weaned, they will ovulate and become receptive to the male. Mating at this first postweaning estrus usually results in a pregnancy, and a second litter is born 3.9 months later. Therefore, it is common for one sow to produce 2–2.5 litters of 8–10 market weight pigs yearly, weighing an average of 230 pounds per pig (total of 3680 pounds of live weight) at 5 to 6 months of age.

A. Body Size and Growth

Eleven-day-old embryos begin to show signs of attachment to the endometrium. However, true implantation to form the placenta does not occur until about Day 18 (embryo length of 5–10 mm). By Day 20 the crown–rump length is about 10 mm and the fetus can be used for gross laboratory study. From this stage onward, the rate of fetal growth is tremendous. From a crown–rump length of 2.5 cm and weight of 1.5 g at 30 days, the fetus grows to a crown–rump length of 30 cm (12 times the 30-day length) and a weight of about 1200 g (800 times 30-day weight) at birth. The number of developing fetuses is inversely related to the weight of individual fetuses at term. Viable young have been known to weigh as little as 400 g and more than 2000 g at birth after a normal

gestation. The newborn pig contains about 82% water, 12% protein, 5% minerals, and 1% fat.

The body weight during the 4- to 5-week suckling period doubles during the first week and is six to ten times the birth weight by 4 weeks. Postweaning growth is plotted in Fig. 2 and body protein accretion during the same period (64 to 154 days of age) for females, males, and male castrates is shown in Fig. 3. Changes in body composition of genetically obese, lean, and contemporary swine from 10 weeks to 24 weeks of age are depicted in Fig. 4. The steady increase in fat accretion is evident in animals of all three genotypes. The greater protein deposition of intact males than of females and of females than of castrates emphasizes the effect of sex hormones on patterns of growth and ultimate carcass value of swine. Unresolved problems with boar odor (see previous section) in intact males has precluded the widespread capture of their increased lean meat production.

Animals are marketed at 5 to 6 months of age weighing 220 to 240 pounds. Those retained for breeding are normally placed on limited feed intake to avoid excessive fatness. By breeding age of 8 months, females weigh 260 to 300 pounds and males weigh 280 to 320 pounds. Body weight and skeletal size continues to increase until 3 years of age or beyond, despite restricted feed intake after market weight is attained. Mature females often weigh in excess of 500 pounds and mature boars may reach 800 pounds or more, depending on how liberally they are fed after maturity.

B. Reproduction and Lactation

A high reproductive rate is essential in a successful swine enterprise. Knowledge of the anatomy and physiology of male and female reproductive tracts is important for maximization of reproductive efficiency. The reproductive tract and endocrine control of reproduction of female and male swine share the same general features as those of other mammals. The female reproductive tract includes two ovaries, fallopian tubes, uterus (consisting of the body and two uterine horns), cervix, vagina, and vulva. The uterine horns are long and tortuous to accommodate numerous developing fetuses. In the mature sow, they may be 1 m or more long when extended. The ovaries are lobular, owing to follicles in varying stages of development. There may be 10 to 25 individual mature follicles. Puberty (onset of estrous cycle, i.e., first ovulation) occurs at about 6 months of age in most breeds, although in some Chinese breeds it occurs at less than 4 months. Puberty, which coincides

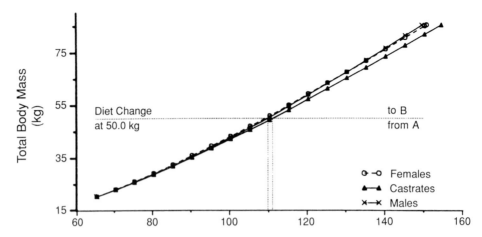

FIGURE 2 Empty body weight curves (live body weight minus gastrointestinal tract contents) of contemporary crossbred female, male, and castrated male pigs from age 64 to 154 days as generated by computer simulation. [Reprinted from Pomar *et al.,* (1991). *J. Animal Science* **69**, 1468–1488.]

with first estrus and sexual receptivity, is influenced by season of the year, social environment, and degree of spacial confinement. Relocation or exposure to a boar consistently advances puberty. The number of ova released per estrus increases gradually over the first several estrous cycles. There is a large range even among normal animals kept under adequate husbandry, partly due to breed differences. Although age at puberty is several months, the number of ova available for release in the course of a lifetime, determined in prenatal life as oogenesis, is complete by Day 100 after conception. The estrous cycle length (onset of one estrus to the onset of the next) is important from the standpoint of planning breeding dates. Length of the cycle averages 21 days (range is about 18–24 days). During proestrus (1–3 days),

females are alert to the approach of the boar, will mount other females, and accept mounting by diestrus females, but will not tolerate mounting by a boar. During estrus, the swollen vulva and vaginal discharge first observed during late proestrus are accompanied by restlessness (fence-walking, agitation), mounting of other animals, and acceptance of the boar. The female in estrus will mate for a period of 2–3 days, and because ovulation lasts over several hours, mating on two successive days of estrus often results in birth of larger litters owing to improved synchrony of contact between newly released ova and spermatozoa. Since the estrous cycle is under endocrine control, it can be altered by exogenous hormones. Technology, including the use of prostaglandins in combination with reproductive hormones and

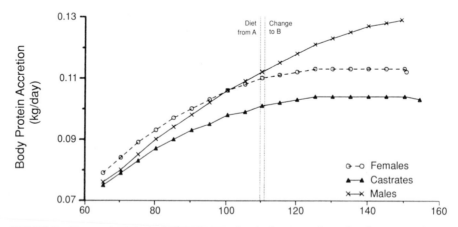

FIGURE 3 Changes in daily body protein accretion in female, male, and male castrate pigs as generated from computer simulation show the greater lean tissue growth rate of intact males than of castrates and the intermediate position of females. [Reprinted from Pomar *et al.* (1991). *J. Animal Science* **69**, 1468–1488.]

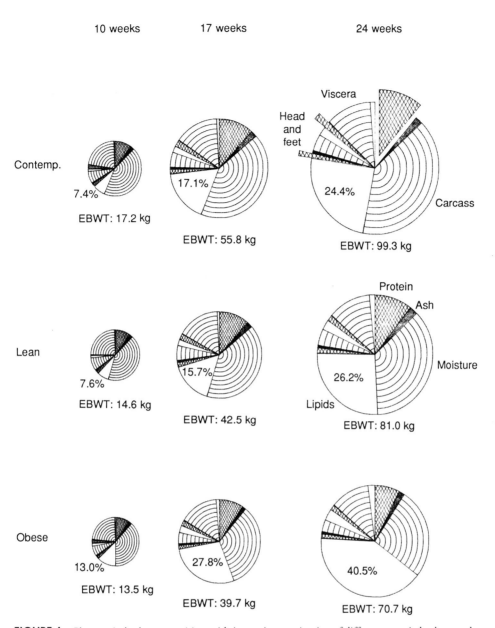

FIGURE 4 Changes in body composition with increasing age in pigs of different genetic background. Percentages shown are for carcass lipids as a fraction of empty body weight (EBWT). [Reprinted, with permission, from *Pork Production Systems,* (1991). Van Nostrand Reinhold, NY]

their derivatives, is available to apply these therapies in commercial swine production, particularly as a means of using artificial insemination for genetic improvement and for tighter control of reproduction schedules in individual enterprises. Artificial insemination in concert with estrous cycle synchronization has not been widely applied to date in the swine industry owing more to economic considerations than to technical limitations. [*See* ANIMAL REPRODUCTION, AN OVERVIEW OF THE REPRODUCTIVE SYSTEM; ANIMAL REPRODUCTION, MALE; ANIMAL REPRODUCTION, NONPREGNANT FEMALE; ANIMAL REPRODUCTION, PREGNANCY.]

Males produce viable sperm by about 4 months of age, but generally are not used for breeding until they have attained larger size and mature sexual behavior at 6–8 months of age. The male reproductive tract of swine includes all of the typical accessory organs of the mammal. The testes migrate out of the body cavity to the scrotum at about 100 days of prenatal life. The tail of the epididymis forms a cap over the dorsal end of the testis. In normal castration, the epididymis and the attached tunica vaginalis are removed with the testes. Stored sperm leave the epididymis via the vas deferens. The seminal vesicle, Cowper's (bulbourethral) gland, and prostate gland all contribute to semen volume, which may exceed 500 cc per ejaculate. Ten or more sows can be inseminated from a single ejaculate. Techniques for freezing semen for use in artificial insemination are available. Modern genetic evaluation procedures are expected to stimulate the commercial use of this technology. As superior boars are identified, the opportunity to extend their use to more sows and more herds will be enhanced by artificial insemination.

Prenatal deaths occur in 30–40% of developing young between Days 1 and 114 of gestation. More than half of these losses occur during the first 25 days and most of the remainder occur before midgestation. Mummified fetuses represent deaths that occur after 40 days and are differentiated from stillborn pigs by partial resorption. The causes of these large prenatal losses are not fully understood, but limited uterine capacity and high ovulation rate have been identified as two distinct but interrelated major components of the problem. The transfer of swine embryos from the uterus of one female to that of another is a useful tool as a means of increasing the number of progeny obtained from genetically superior animals. Another option with potential application is the manipulation of embryonic cells in culture which can then be cloned and inserted into the embryo. International transfer of swine germplasm by these approaches offers advantages over traditional transportation systems.

Lactation provides the means by which essential nutrients and immunological protection reach the neonate. The immune protection of colostrum (mammary secretion during the first days of lactation) is more critical in swine than in many other animals. Placental transfer of immune antibodies is almost nil, leaving colostrum as the principal source of neonatal protection against pathogenic agents. The normal duration of lactation in swine is 6–8 weeks, but nutritional needs of the rapidly growing pig exceed those provided in milk after about 3 to 4 weeks, because the peak of lactation is reached at about 4 weeks. Therefore, pigs are usually weaned at 3 to 5 weeks and the sow enters postweaning estrus within a few days and can be mated to produce another litter. Milk production efficiency in swine is very high and nutrient yield per unit body weight in highly productive sows is greater than that in dairy cattle (sow milk contains nearly 20% dry matter compared with 12% in cattle). [See LACTATION.]

Newborn piglets begin suckling immediately and do so at hourly intervals over the 24-hr day and thereafter throughout lactation. Daily milk yields of 6 kg have been recorded over an 8-week lactation (288 kg total). Milk yields of 5 to 10 kg daily with an energy concentration of 1.2 kcal per kg are expected in lactating sows and are partly dependent on the number of nursing pigs. This high level of production allows rapid growth of piglets during the first few weeks of postnatal life. Systems of early weaning are available in which the pig is weaned at 1 or 2 days of age to a liquid formula containing milk products. Growth approaching or exceeding that obtained with sow-reared littermates can be achieved, but only if frequency of feeding and amount consumed at each meal approximate sow-rearing conditions. Such early-weaning programs allow the possibility of rebreeding the sow earlier than normal to maximize the total pigs produced per calendar year. The economics of such a program will be affected by the relative prices of sow feed versus milk-replacer formula and differences in the efficiency with which nutrients are partitioned for milk production, maternal nutrient stores, and piglet growth.

IV. Genetics and Breeding Systems

The genetic aspects of the swine production system set both the limits and potential for performance of the system. Breeding stock selection systems have evolved as a means of accelerating genetic improvement from the traditional visual appraisal approach to modern computer-based performance testing and genetic evaluation procedures. The wide genetic diversity of swine is evidenced by the large number of breeds and groupings in different regions of the world of swine having unique characteristics and appearance. There are currently probably more than 100 recognized breeds and more than twice as many genetic groups of swine with traits unlike those of other groups. This vast number of gene combinations provides the basis for animal breeders to capitalize on the plasticity of swine to improve biologic efficiency and animal vigor and to create populations of swine to meet human needs most effectively. Representative breeds and types of pigs are illustrated in Fig. 5. Early breeders of purebred swine contributed to changes in animal performance and appearance through livestock shows and fairs and advertising. In this form of breeding, producers kept replacement females from young animals to replace older breeding animals being culled. Replacement boars were purchased from other breeders as a means of introducing new genes. As the merits of crossbreeding became evident as a means of improving productivity (the term heterosis or "hybrid vigor" was introduced to describe the greater than expected improvement in a given performance trait in the offspring of crossbred swine than in those of offspring of swine of the same breed), the swine industry of the United States adapted the approach by the producers of rotating two or more breeds to provide replacement breeding stock. Various crossbreeding systems have evolved from the original systems, e.g., rotational crossing, terminal crossing, rota-terminal crossing, all aimed toward improved breeding stock. Genetic improvement by selection for specific heritable traits has been affected by the development of performance testing programs (both central and on-farm). The rate of genetic improvement in any particular trait is determined by four factors: intensity of selection, accuracy of selection, genetic variability for the trait, and generation interval. Progress can be relatively rapid for most heritable traits in swine because of the short generation interval (1 year) and the wide genetic variability in most of the economically important traits, i.e., growth rate, body leanness, and efficiency of feed utilization. Significant development of statistical procedures has gone into modern genetic evaluation of swine breeding stock. Procedures such as the swine testing and genetic evaluation system (STAGES) are used to assist purebred breeders in evaluating their swine and in decisions related to their individual breeding plans. As such systems are accepted and used by the industry, the theory of quantitative genetics finds valuable practical application. [See ANIMAL BREEDING AND GENETICS.]

Rapid advances in molecular biology have created new opportunities for genetic improvement in swine. The functional basis for genetic variation in economically important traits, such as growth and lactation, relates to hormones, enzymes, and various intracellular processes. Progress is underway in elucidating the genetic code for directing synthesis of specific proteins. It is possible to trace segregation of genetic factors previously not observable as they are transmitted between generations. However, the complexity of the processes complicates progress, because many DNA combinations code for many different proteins involved in the many body processes. The location and identification of simple genetic codes for major proteins ultimately will allow greater manipulation of these major genes. Recombinantly derived hormones and other metabolites are already used to enhance lean growth and production. As an example, porcine somatotropin produced from *Escherichea coli* bacteria is effective in increasing leanness and is safe for use in swine production. Transgenic animals produced by these transfer techniques have also been produced, e.g., transgenic swine with high somatotropin production; however, associated changes in other metabolic processes in these transgenic animals have discouraged commercial application of the technology to date.

V. Nutrition and Feed Formulation

Feed represents 55–85% of the total cost of commercial swine production, depending mainly on the relative costs of feed, labor, and housing in a particular case. Therefore, the formulation of nutritionally balanced diets must be based on selection of economical as well as nutritious feed ingredients. Swine have a digestive system with limited ability to utilize cellulosic and other fibrous feeds; therefore, they are in direct competition with humans for available food supplies. The degree of competition is related to cultural differences in food preferences. For example, wheat and potatoes are not usually fed to swine in the United States, as the demand for human consumption holds the price too high, but in other parts of the world these crops are commonly fed to swine. Similar relationships exist for other crops in other parts of the world. [See FEEDS AND FEEDING.]

A. Nutrient and Energy Requirements

Nutrient (defined as any chemical entity required by the animal to meet metabolic needs) and energy requirements for swine correspond closely with those required by humans. The known requirements of swine follow:

Water.
Fatty acids. Linoleic and arachidonic acid are required and some fat (0.06% of diet) is needed for absorption of fat-soluble vitamins.
Protein. Proteins are probably not required as such, except in neonates who receive immune proteins intact from milk; the ability to absorb these proteins from the intestinal tract lumen is lost during the first 2 days after birth. Of approximately 25 amino acids in nature, the following are considered indispensable for swine because they are not synthesized from other metabolites in body tissues and therefore must be included in the diet: arginine (for growth only), histidine, isoleucine, leucine, lysine, methionine (50% replaceable by cystine), phenylalanine (30% replaceable

Poland China boar

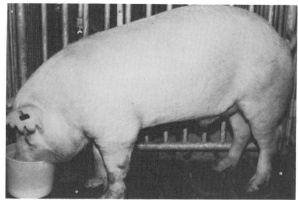

Chester White barrow

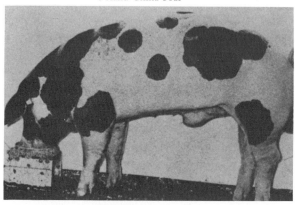

Spotted boar

Miniature sow

Yorkshire boar

Landrace gilt

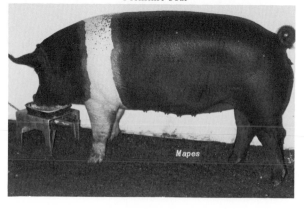

Hampshire gilt

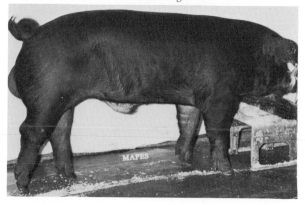

Duroc boar

FIGURE 5 Breeds and types of swine

Berkshire boar

Pietrain gilt

Ming sow (China)

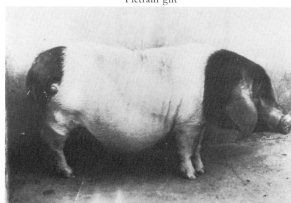

Jinhua gilt (China)

Meishan boar (China)

Ningfiang boar (China)

FIGURE 5 *Continued*

by tyrosine), threonine, tryptophan, and valine. The remaining amino acids are considered dispensable (nonessential) because they are synthesized in the body from nonspecific sources of nitrogen and other metabolites. Thus the total protein requirement can be met by including adequate amounts of all of the indispensable amino acids plus sufficient nonspecific sources of nitrogen in the diet to synthesize the non-essential amino acids.

Energy (Calories). Calories can be supplied by fat (9 Cal/g) or carbohydrate (4 Cal/g) or by the breakdown of protein (5 Cal/g).
Fat. Although the caloric density of fat is about 2.25 times that of carbohydrates, most swine feeds are high in carbohydrates and low in fats.
Carbohydrate. There is no proof that carbohydrates are required as a source of energy, but since all natural feedstuffs contain some carbohydrate, it becomes an

academic question. If a dietary requirement exists, it is as glucose.

Vitamins. The fat-soluble vitamins are A, D, E, and K. The water-soluble vitamins are biotin, choline (replaceable by methionine), folic acid, niacin (nicotinic acid), pantothenic acid, riboflavin, thiamin, vitamin B_6, vitamin B_{12}, vitamin C (ascorbic acid), inositol, and paraaminobenzoic acid (PABA). Biotin and vitamin K requirements are normally met by microbial synthesis in the large intestine, but when coprophagy is prevented, as in swine raised in confinement in slatted floor pens, deficiencies have been reported. Vitamin C synthesis in the body normally meets the metabolic requirement for the vitamin, except in young pigs exposed to the stress of early weaning.

Inorganic Elements. Elements required in large amounts (major elements) include calcium, magnesium, phosphorus, potassium, sodium; elements required in small amounts (minor elements) include: chlorine, cobalt (as a constituent of vitamin B_{12}), copper, iodine, iron, manganese, selenium, sulfur (as a constituent of sulfate, and of thiamin, methionine, cystine, and several other organic compounds), and zinc. [*See* ANIMAL NUTRITION, NONRUMINANT; ANIMAL NUTRITION, PRINCIPLES.]

B. Life-Cycle Feeding

The quantitative nutrient requirements differ for each productive function, i.e., growth, pregnancy, lactation, and maintenance. The daily amount of swine feed is adjusted to accommodate the special requirements of each physiological stage, and the composition of the diet is changed to match the physiological needs at each stage. The protein (amino acid) requirement, expressed as a percent of the diet, is highest in the neonate and declines gradually with age. Growing swine are normally fed *ad libitum,* so the protein concentration in the diet is reduced as body weight increases and concentrations of other nutrients are also adjusted downward during the growing period. Expression of nutrient requirements as a percent of diet allows the formulation of diets designed to meet all nutrient requirements for growth when the diet is offered *ad libitum.* In mature animals, body weight must be controlled to avoid obesity by limiting daily feed allowance, except in lactation. Lactating sows require large energy intake to accommodate adequate milk production and are normally fed *ad libitum.*

Commercially prepared diets are formulated to meet specifically defined periods of the life cycle: gestation, lactation, preweaning, growing period (early postweaning), finishing period (late postweaning), and nonpregnant, nonlactating females, and males.

C. Feedstuffs

A broad array of feed resources is available worldwide from which to formulate balanced diets for all stages of the life cycle. Feedstuffs can be classified broadly according to their major contribution of nutrients to the total diet.

Energy sources. Carbohydrates are the most abundant form of energy in plants and, as such, are the most widely available sources of energy for swine feeding. Grains and their by-products are the most important sources of carbohydrates. Each of these sources of energy also supplies important amounts of protein, vitamins, and inorganic elements. The major grains used in swine feeding are corn (maize), sorghum (milo), barley, oats, rye, wheat, triticale, rice, and their distillery and milling by-products. The amounts of these by-products available in a particular region are governed by the way in which the respective crops are utilized for human consumption. For example, rice, the most important crop in Asia, is a staple food for billions of people, but a variety of by-products of the milling process supplies large quantities of rice bran and screenings for swine feeding. Likewise, wheat bran and other seed coat fractions are available as by-products from the milling process for swine feeding in the United States. Roots and tubers, including cassava and potatoes, as well as bananas, plantains, sugar beets, and their products are major sources of energy for swine feeding in many regions and cane molasses, citrus and citrus pulp, and many other high-carbohydrate plant materials are used in swine production throughout the world. Household kitchen wastes and food discarded from hotels, restaurants, and institutions contribute additional amounts of energy and other nutrients to swine production. Animal fats, including tallow, lard, and fish oils as well as vegetable fats from such plants as coconut, soybean, cottonseed, maize, safflower, sesame, and others, are by-products of other food and industrial uses and are used in swine feeding.

Protein sources. Next to energy, protein is the nutrient class needed by swine in the largest amount. A wide variety of protein sources is available from both plants and animals.

Animal proteins. By-products of abattoirs include meat meal, meat and bone meal, blood meal, fish meal, shrimp meal, krill meal, hatchery waste, feather meal, and animal and poultry wastes, while dried whey comes from cheese plants. All are utilized in swine feeding.

Plant proteins. Oilseed meals are the most important plant proteins in swine feeding. These meals are by-products of plant oils extracted for human consumption. Soybean meal is by far the greatest source of plant protein used in the United States and in many parts of the world. Other important plant protein supplements resulting from fat extraction are coconut meal, cottonseed meal, linseed meal, peanut meal, canola meal, rubberseed meal, safflower meal, sesame meal, and sunflower meal. Several grain legumes provide significant amounts of protein used in swine production. These include whole soybeans, dry beans, kidney beans, mung bean, lima bean, chick pea, cow pea, pigeon pea, and field pea; their use for swine is normally confined to sources not meeting standards for human consumption. Legumes whose vegetative parts are used for swine feeding include alfalfa and sweet lupin.

Single cell protein (SCP). Single-cell protein sources, i.e., algae, bacteria, fungi, and yeast, are undergoing thorough investigation for nutritional value and safety for human and animal consumption. Some of these SCPs are grown on such hydrocarbons asn-alkenes and methanol. Others, e.g., yeast and fungi, are grown on sulfite-waste liquor, a waste product of the wood pulping industry. Blue–green algae, *Arthrospira platensis,* can be grown successfully on swine effluent. All of these SCP sources are high in well-balanced protein and can be produced in large quantities on waste materials or by-products of other processes.

Synthetic amino acids. For many years the feed industry had pure lysine and methionine available from microbiological production at prices competitive for use in swine feeds in limited amounts. Now, gene-splicing techniques are available to mass-produce these and other amino acids microbiologically. These breakthroughs in biotechnology should provide the basis for greater use of synthetic amino acids and a reduction in conventional plant and animal protein use in future swine production.

Inorganic element and vitamin sources. Most energy and protein sources provide some vitamins and inorganic elements but usually it is necessary to balance the diet with specific sources of these essential minor ingredients. Common salt is added to almost all swine diets as a source of sodium and chloride. Calcium and phosphorus sources include bone meal and products such as dicalcium phosphate and rock phosphate; oyster shell, limestone, and gypsum are common sources of calcium, but devoid of phosphorus. Most plant energy and protein sources are marginal or deficient in calcium and the phosphorus is present largely as phytic acid phosphorus which is poorly utilized by swine. Therefore most swine diets must be supplemented with both elements. Other inorganic elements usually deficient in common ingredients are iodine, iron, selenium, and zinc. Commercially formulated swine feeds usually contain inorganic salts of these trace elements plus manganese and copper to ensure against deficiency. Synthetic sources of vitamins provide the opportunity to supplement swine diets with pure vitamins to supplement those provided in energy and protein sources used in the diet. Inclusion in the diet of a variety of feedstuffs of plant and animal origin made it possible in earlier times to avoid serious vitamin and inorganic element deficiencies, before the identities and metabolic functions of these nutrients were recognized. In general, animal products and green forages are good sources of vitamins and minor elements. As swine production has moved to confinement rearing, the opportunity for ingestion of these essential nutrients from forages and soils has decreased, adding to the importance of dietary supplementation with pure sources of these nutrients.

VI. Swine Diseases

Many infectious, metabolic, and nutritional diseases affect swine. Some of the infectious diseases, e.g., brucellosis, leptospirosis, erysipelas, and tuberculosis, are of particular significance because the organisms are pathogenic to humans. All of these zoonoses are treatable in humans; their importance in swine production makes their control of high priority. Metabolic and nutritional diseases of swine, although of less importance from a public health standpoint, require continued surveillance in herd health programs. [*See* ANIMAL DISEASES.]

A. Infectious Diseases

The practice of veterinary medicine has gradually evolved from a major focus on treatment of diseases in individual animals to emphasis on preventive herd health maintenance in which the veterinarian and swine producer work together in applying modern principles of disease prevention and control. The common infectious diseases of swine are generally divided into bacterial, viral, and mycoplasmal diseases. Important bacterial diseases include Haemophilus infections, causing pleuropneumonia, polyserositis, and arthritis; Pasteurella pneumonia; Bordetella infections, causing respiratory diseases, including atrophic rhinitis (whose etiology may also involve Pasteurella and possibly other agents); tuberculosis; swine dysentery; salmonellosis; colibacillosis; mastitis; erysipelas; leptospirosis; brucellosis; streptococcal diseases; anthrax; and clostridial infections. Important viral diseases include swine influenza, transmissible gastroenteritis, pseudorabies (Aujeszky's disease), hog cholera, African swine fever, swine pox, porcine adenovirus, porcine enterovirus, porcine cytomegalovirus, foot-and-mouth disease (aftosa), swine vesicular disease, vesicular stomatitis, vesicular exanthema, porcine rotavirus; rabies, reovirus, congenital tremors, encephalomyocarditis, porcine endemic diarrhea, Japanese encephalitis, porcine parvo virus infection, and swine infertility and respiratory syndrome (SRIS). Important mycoplasmal diseases include Mycoplasma pneumonia, Mycoplasma arthritis and Mycoplasma polyserositis.

Internal and external parasites impede productivity in the absence of appropriate control programs. Small intestinal parasites, *Ascaris suum* (roundworm), *Strongyloides ransomi* (threadworm), and *Trichinella spiralis* (trichina); large intestinal parasites, *Trichuris suum* (whipworm), *Oesophagostomum* spp. (nodular worm); and lung (*Metastrongylus* species) and liver (*Fasciola hepatica*) parasites all adversely affect swine health. They can be controlled by judicious use of anthelmintics and by good sanitation. Common external parasites are *Sarcoptes scabiei* (sarcoptic mange mite) and *Haematopinus suis* (louse). These parasites are controlled by external application of insecticides or by systemic application of ivermectin which also controls internal parasites.

Improvement of animal performance through disease control is increasingly recognized as an important component of efficient swine production. Control and treatment by medication is costly. Acquired immunity is achieved for protection from many infectious diseases by vaccination and other forms of immunization. New approaches to vaccine production, such as vaccines produced by recombinant DNA (gene splicing) technology, are available, e.g., foot-and-mouth disease vaccine and pseudorabies vaccine, and others should be forthcoming.

Swine producers, particularly those involved in purebred or seedstock production, routinely introduce new breeding animals into their herds. These introduced animals are potential sources of infectious disease. For each specific pathogen, choices must be made for the best control program to preserve herd health. Many herds are derived and maintained as SPF (specific pathogen-free) enterprises by removing pigs from the mother by surgery and raising them in laboratory conditions before their introduction into the herd as future breeding stock in order to break the infection cycle for many pathogens. Breeding stock is not the source of all pathogens; many pathogens are transmitted by rodents, birds, people, and even by feed, dust particles, and aerosol suspensions. Traffic control even to the point of requiring employees and visitors to shower and change clothes before entry into the facility is becoming commonplace in large swine production facilities.

B. Metabolic and Nutritional Diseases

Swine are affected by a large array of metabolic disorders of importance in commercial pork production.

Some of these, including gastric ulcers, osteoporosis, osteochondrosis, photosensitization, and porcine stress syndrome (PSS), have their counterpart in humans and other animals, and result in significant economic losses. Genetic and environmental variables share in contributing to these disorders, and husbandry and feeding may modify their incidence and severity. Marginal levels of one or more nutrients are contained in most homegrown feedstuffs not fortified with commercial sources of vitamins, mineral elements, and protein. These marginal deficiencies are manifested as reduced growth or efficiency of feed utilization, often so slight as to go unrecognized.

Frank deficiencies of several specific nutrients are associated with specific typical clinical signs, e.g., zinc (parakeratosis), iron (baby pig anemia), selenium, and vitamin E (hepatosis dietetica, mulberry heart disease), calcium, phosphorus, or vitamin D (osteoporosis, rickets), calcium–phosphorus imbalance (fibrous osteodystrophy), and niacin (necrotic enteritis). Toxic effects of specific nutrients are of some practical concern, e.g., skeletal abnormalities in newborn piglets from sows fed excess vitamin A during early gestation; calcification of soft tissues in pigs fed excess vitamin D or diets containing plants that contain active metabolites of vitamin D; liver damage and death in pigs fed excess copper commonly fed to promote growth.

Mycotoxins (toxic metabolites of several fungi that commonly infect grains and oilseeds) are a serious threat to swine reproductive function and growth of young pigs. Contaminated feed can be fed safely only if diluted with uncontaminated feed or by the inclusion in the diet of agents such as zeolites and other aluminosilicate minerals that may decrease the absorption of the toxins from the digestive tract.

VII. Production Systems

Swine production has evolved to be a primary enterprise on many farms as a means of converting processed feedstuffs and breeding stock resources into marketable pork products. The concept of a "systems approach" analogous to the production of goods in other industries has become important in commercial pork production. Modern production often occurs in environmentally controlled facilities with automated feed delivery and manure disposal (Fig. 6). This technology requires highly skilled personnel and careful record keeping and cost accounting. The major controllable inputs are the breeding system, the breeding stock, the feedstuffs, and the formulated diets. The output from the production system determines the

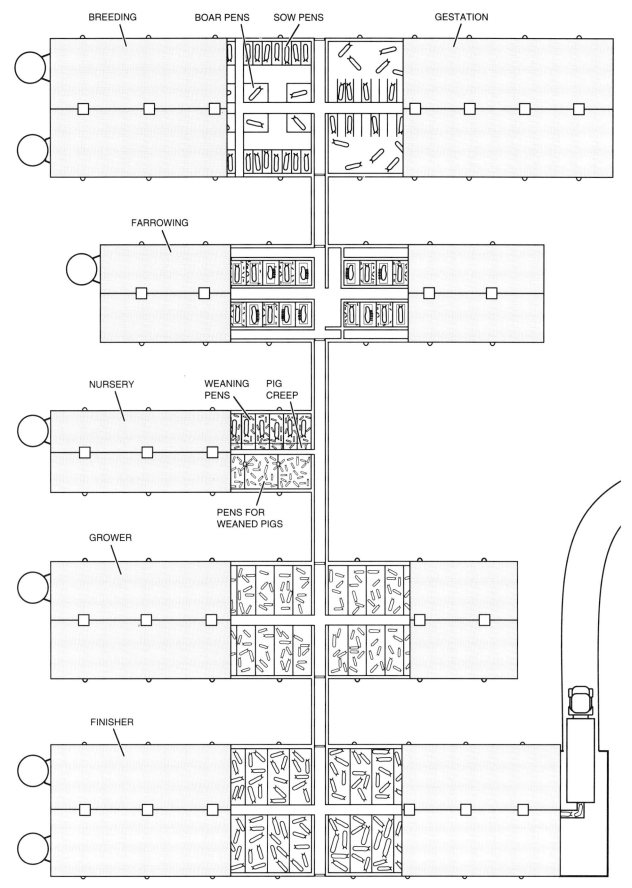

FIGURE 6 Environmentally controlled total confinement unit keeps pigs indoors throughout the life cycle. [Reprinted, with permission, from Scientific American, May, 1983.]

income to offset costs and possibly a margin of profit for the enterprise. Income is determined by number of animals marketed, weight of each animal, and value (price received) per unit weight. Thus, briefly stated, the profitability of the enterprise is determined by the efficiency of the production system in integrating the inputs and outputs to maximize efficiency and overcoming the effects of extraneous factors such as climate and disease. Environmentally controlled facilities and effective disease control programs have evolved in response to the need to minimize the impact of these variables on animal productivity.

Life-cycle feeding systems that address the changing nutritional requirements of swine during specific stages of growth, reproduction, and lactation, coupled with least-cost diet formulation by computer, have been developed. Also, the application of genetic principles to select for economically important heritable traits, e.g., lean tissue growth, feed utilization, reduced fat accretion, and reproductive efficiency, has been integrated into the plan and design of pork production systems.

Management of the pork production system requires appropriate approaches to the execution of the plan (construction and adaptation of physical facilities, financial arrangements, labor supply, feed formulation and delivery, manure disposal, genetically defined breeding stock, swine husbandry, market outlet); adjustment to unforeseen occurrences (changes in feed supplies or costs, changes in market prices or options, disease outbreaks, availability of new technology); problem identification; and problem resolution.

The accumulated knowledge acquired over many years of research on the reproductive and growth biology of the pig has provided a data base to allow the collection of the knowledge in the form of a set of computer programs to simulate the numerous alternative courses of action in pork production and predict the likely outcome. These computer simulation models, together with management information systems, provide potential support to the manager's decision making. Such computerized systems, termed integrated decision support systems (IDSS), currently are in use in several countries in research aimed toward guiding pork production.

VIII. The Future of Swine Production

A. Consumer Demand for Pork

The demand for pork among consumers in the United States has increased in proportion to population

growth during the past 50 years; in 1992, 7.8 million metric tons of pork were produced to meet the per capita demand for approximately 31 kg. Although the United States ranks third, behind Mainland China and the European Community (which includes Belgium, Luxembourg, Denmark, France, West Germany, Greece, Ireland, Italy, Netherlands, Portugal, Spain, and United Kingdom) in annual pork production (Table II), imports of pork in 1992 exceeded exports (29,300 and 185,000 metric tons, respectively). This importation put the United States third behind only West Germany and the former Soviet Union in total pork imported among countries of the world.

Pork consumption in other parts of the world continues to increase, particularly in developing countries where per capita incomes are improving and stimulating greater consumption of animal products. Per capita consumption of pork in 1992 was highest in Denmark (65.8 kg), followed by Sweden, Poland, Germany, Spain, and Hungary, all with consumption greater than 40 kg per capita; by Taiwan, Hong Kong, Singapore, France, Canada, and the United States, with values between 30 and 39 kg; and by the United Kingdom, China, Japan, Korea, Australia, and the former Soviet Union, with values ranging from 15.6 to 18.5 kg. Mexico and Brazil consumed 9.5 and 6.9 kg per capita, respectively, and all other countries consumed less. Projections by the United Nations of human population growth indicate that total population will, except for the most conservative scenario, equal or exceed 10 billion by 2030.

Swine production is closely tied to grain consumption, which is by far the largest single component of global agriculture. Global consumption of all grains

TABLE II

Top 10 Pork-Producing Countries in Thousand Metric Tons, 1992[a]

1. China, Mainland	26,330
2. European Community—12[b]	13,735
3. United States	7,816
4. Former Soviet Union	4,875
5. Poland	1,998
6. Japan	1,430
7. Canada	1,200
8. Brazil	1,150
9. Taiwan	1,120
10. Mexico	830

[a] Carcass weight equivalent.
[b] European Community—12 includes Belgium–Luxembourg, Denmark, France, Germany, Greece, Ireland, Italy, Netherlands, Spain, United Kingdom, and Portugal.

has grown at an annual rate of 1.6% since 1979. It is assumed that this rate will continue to 2030, resulting in a doubling of total consumption of grains (human food and animal feed) to 3.3 metric tons in 2030. More than 90% of the total growth in grain consumption is projected to be in the developing countries, mostly in Asia. The coarse grains, e.g., maize, sorghum, and millet, are projected to increase more rapidly (3.2%) than the principal food grains, i.e., wheat (2.3%) and rice (1.3%). The reason is the high income elasticity of demand for meat and other animal products, for which the coarse grains are feedstuffs. Increased land area devoted to coarse and food grain production and increased yields per hectare will be required to meet these projected needs. Ultimately, the long-term future of swine production likely will be determined not only by the degree to which pork is preferred in the diet relative to alternative foods, but by constraints imposed by agronomic, ecological, economic, and demographic forces external to biological characteristics of the pig.

B. Animal Performance

For the foreseeable future, animal performance will improve for most of the relevant traits of economic importance in pork production. This seems predictable, based on rapidly developing technology in all aspects of biology and engineering, e.g., recombinant DNA technology for production of nutrients, vaccines, and metabolic modulators; genetic manipulation including advanced methods in population genetics and in transgenics; application of nutrient repartitioning agents such as porcine somatotropin and β adrenergic agonists to improved growth, lactation, and reproduction; new vaccines and other disease control procedures; refinements in design and management of pork production systems that maximize production; and marketing efficiency. As the knowledge base of nutritional requirements for each phase of the life cycle enlarges, further refinements will be made in tailoring nutrient intake to age, gender, genetic makeup, and body composition.

The use of recombinant DNA technology will hasten the cost-effective substitution of individual amino acids into the diet at appropriate levels and combinations to enhance efficiency of growth and will save significant amounts of traditional high-protein supplements. Recombinant DNA techniques also will find increased application in the production of hormones, digestive enzymes, growth factors, and other metabolites to be administered in the feed or other delivery systems, e.g., subcutaneous implants to im-

prove lean tissue growth. As the use of nutrient repartitioning agents such as porcine somatotropin and β adrenergic agonists increases, the resulting improvement in lean tissue accretion will stimulate reevaluation of the nutrient requirements of these animals and may signal a further increment of improvement in overall pork production efficiency. Females and males may be housed separately during the finishing period and diets specially tailored to their differing nutrient needs will be fed. As technology for suppressing secondary sex characteristics (objectionable odor in the meat) of intact boars is refined, the use of boars rather than castrates for pork production will be common in the United States as it already is in many other countries to capture the innate superiority of the intact boar to the male castrate in growth rate and lean tissue production.

The development and use of nonconventional and newly identified sources of energy and protein from plants and animals for use in feeding swine will continue, and such crops as grain amaranth, several seed legumes, and forages may find greater use. Blue–green algae, yeasts, and bacterial cells grown in culture may be genetically engineered to produce feed resources with specific desired nutritional composition. As the knowledge of intestinal microbial populations and large intestine physiology in the pig expands, greater utilization of feedstuffs high in lignocellulose and other fermentable substrates may be forthcoming. The identification of new microbes with high cellulose-splitting ability that thrive and compete well in the milieu of the large intestinal environment may create the opportunity for new feeding strategies in areas where conventional high-concentrate feedstuffs are scarce or expensive due to their high demand for human consumption.

C. Animal Well-being

Societal concerns about the well-being of animals have escalated in recent years and these concerns have engendered heightened attention by food animal producers to the impact of production practices on their animals. Practices that have received the most attention in animal agriculture are those related to space and restricted movement. In swine production, the restraint of sows in gestation stalls and farrowing crates has been brought into question in this regard. Farrowing crates first came into use as an effective means of protecting piglets from injury and death caused by crushing or overlaying by the mother. This and most other husbandry practices were developed to reduce costs of production and improve the comfort and productivity of the animal. It has become increasingly accepted by pork producers and others associated with the industry that pigs (and other farm animals) are sentient creatures with the capacity to suffer; it follows that those working with pigs have a moral responsibility for their welfare, a concept accepted by most pork producers for many years. The Farm Animal Welfare Council of the United Kingdom in 1993 described the five freedoms of farm animals (including pigs) as freedom from hunger, thirst, and malnutrition; freedom from discomfort; freedom from pain, injury and disease; freedom to express normal behavior; and freedom from fear and distress. Implicit in this description is the acceptance of the moral responsibility to provide pigs with a reasonable quality of life and a humane death. This implies obligations for ensuring well-being during all of life, including transit to slaughter and death itself.

It is clear that the sustainability of pork production, aside from resource-related constraints, will in the long term be determined by consumer acceptance of pork. The degree of acceptance will be determined by consumer perceptions not only of the product itself, but of the conditions under which it was produced, including an assurance of acceptable animal well-being.

Limited knowledge concerning the impact of the environment and husbandry practices on animal well-being has curtailed an effective response by swine producers to the concerns raised by those who have challenged the acceptability of current production practices. Research funding to answer biological questions of animal well-being is now emerging and several important questions need to be addressed: What are the scientific measures of swine well-being? How do the behaviors of swine vary in different environments? How are their responses affected by genetic and environmental factors? How do animals utilize different amounts and kinds of space in relationship to group size and composition? What are the appropriate indicators of stress, pain, and suffering, and how are they measured? All of these and many more researchable questions must be addressed to provide adequate information for fair and informed legislative decisions and sound public education. Issues of animal well-being will continue to receive greater attention by researchers, consumers, and producers as intensive pork production systems become more prevalent around the world.

D. Environmental Stability and Ecological Balance

Swine production, like all of animal agriculture, must be approached in such a way as to promote environ-

mental stability and ecological balance. Intensive swine production potentially may have negative effects on the environment. Odors produced by swine formerly went relatively unnoticed, but encroachment of agricultural areas by human activities, e.g., residential expansion, has created concerns about air pollution; pollution of water by swine waste run-off must be controlled by appropriate design and placement of intensive swine production facilities. A major agricultural impact on water quality originates from crop production which requires fertilization of soils with inorganic and organic (manure) materials and the use of herbicides and pesticides. Broad awareness of these problems has awakened efforts to devise systems of swine production that eliminate the negative impact of these practices on the environment, e.g., efforts to reduce the use of chemical pesticides and herbicides by genetic manipulation of plants to improve resistance to insect pests and diseases, advanced methods of manure management, and nutrient preservation to reduce nitrates in the water supply. [See ANIMAL WASTE MANAGEMENT.]

Tillage and irrigation practices have contributed to soil erosion and water pollution, and a conflict between agriculture (including pork production) and the human population for use of available water. Soil and water conservation programs and cropping practices, e.g., irrigation, cropping methods, and pasture and range management, must be tied closely with swine production methods, e.g., waste management, feed resource allocation, and facilities design. The needs and goals of swine production must be adapted to fit on a local and global basis within the broad context of agriculture, forestry, rangeland, and animal ecological systems and must adapt to demographic changes in the human population. The interrelationships among swine production, production of other animals and crops, and the human population in competing for available resources must be tuned in the future, more than ever before, to the preservation of environmental quality and ecological balance. The maintenance of this delicate balance is attainable if the research needed to improve swine production systems and provide sound information at all levels for informed decisions can be done and the information can be effectively transmitted.

Bibliography

Crosson, P., and Anderson, J. R. (1992). "Resources and Global Food Prospects: Supply and Demand for Cereals to 2030." The World Bank, Washington, DC.

Durning, A. B., and Brough, H. B. (1991). "Taking Stock: Animal Farming and the Environment." Worldwatch paper No. 103, Worldwatch Institute, Washington, DC.

Food and Agriculture Organization, United Nations (1992). "FAO Production Yearbook." FAO, Rome, Italy.

Food Animal Integrated Research for 1995. (1995). "Linking Science and Technology to Societal Benefits: Research Priorities for Competitive and Sustainable Food Production from Animals," pp.1–17. Food Animal Sciences and Forum for Animal Agriculture, FASFAS, Champaign, IL.

Leman, A. D., Straw, B., Glock, R. D., Mengeling, W. L., Penny, R. H. C., and Scholl, E. (1986). "Diseases of Swine." 6th Ed. pp. 1–930. Iowa State Univ. Press, Ames, IA.

National Pork Producers Council (1993). "Pork Facts 1993–1994," pp. 1–25. NPPC, Des Moines, IA.

National Research Council (1988). "Nutrient Requirements of Swine." 9th Revised Ed., pp. 1–90. National Academy Press, Washington, DC.

Pond, W. G. (1983). Modern pork production. *Sci. Am.* **248,** 78–87.

Pond, W. G., Maner, J. H., and Harris, D. L. (1991). "Pork Production Systems: Efficient Use of Swine and Feed Resources," pp. 1–439. Van Nostrand Reinhold, New York.

Webster, A. J. F. (1993). The challenge of animal welfare. *In* "Proceedings, VII World Conference on Animal Production. Edmonton, Alberta, Canada," Vol. 1, pp. 513–524.

Tariffs and Trade

ANDREW SCHMITZ, TROY G. SCHMITZ,
University of California, Berkeley

Glossary

Countervailing duty Tariff imposed by the importing country in response to export dumping by exporters (i.e., the exporter either sells below cost of production or sells abroad at a price below that charged in the home market)

Large-country tariff One which can make the importer better off. Because there is a "terms of trade effect," the producer gain plus the government revenue effect is larger than the consumer cost in the case of an optimal tariff

Optimal-revenue tariff Set by the government to maximize government tariff revenue from imports; this tariff has the effect of restricting trade even more than for the optimal large-country tariff

Small-country tariff One which makes the importing country worse off since the producer gain plus the government revenue collected from the tariff is smaller than the consumer cost of the tariff due to higher prices

Tariff Policy instrument which drives a price wedge between what the exporters receive and what the importer pays

Tariffs and Trade can be defined as a branch of economics dealing with the theory and measurement of international protection. The theory applies to manufacturing as well as to agriculture; however, the empirical content of this article applies only to agriculture. From theory, one can easily deduce why certain producers and other special interest groups lobby for tariffs.

Almost every nation protects its industries from foreign competition. One such protectionist instrument is the tariff. This is an instrument used by importers of a specific commodity; it drives a wedge between export and import prices. For example, if a country imposes a dollar per pound tariff on beef imports then, excluding all other factors such as transportation costs, the price in the exporting nation is one dollar below the price producers receive in the importing country. Often the term "duty" is used interchangeably with the concept of tariff, and these terms will be used interchangeably in this discussion. First, we explore the theory of tariffs and then examine some empirical data relating to their importance. Tariffs are widespread. Especially in agriculture, tariffs—along with certain nontariff barriers such as quotas—have, for many years, stalled global trade negotiations under the General Agreement on Tariffs and Trade (GATT).

I. Tariff Theory

There are many types of tariffs. Those of major importance are discussed below and are: small-country tariffs, large-country tariffs, optimal-revenue tariffs, general equilibrium tariffs, countervailing duty, effective tariff rates, and scientific tariffs.

A. Small-Country Tariffs

The following demonstration assumes that a small-country importer can impose a tariff without affecting the price charged by the exporter. Norway, for example, can establish tariffs and quotas on apple imports without affecting the prices charged for apples by exporting countries. The following demonstration is based on this assumption. In Fig. 1 the supply for apples is S while the demand is D. At a world free-trade price of P_w, the nation imports Q_1Q_2 of apples; domestic production is Q_1 while consumption is Q_2.

Suppose the country imposes a tariff of size T. What are the effects? (1) Price rises in the importing country from P_w to P_1. (2) Internal production increases from Q_1 to Q_1'. (3) Demand decreases from Q_2 to Q_2'. (4) Imports are reduced to $Q_1'Q_2'$. As a result of the tariff, producers in the importing country gain (measured by area P_1abP_w), consumers lose (measured by area $P_{1a'b'}P_w$), and the government gains tariff revenue (measured by area R or $aa'dc$). As measured in conventional economic terms, there is a net cost from the tariff of the two cross-hatched areas ($abc + a'b'd$).

As with many of the demonstrations to follow, tariffs benefit producers in importing countries along with the agra-business complex that both sells inputs to agriculture and markets the final product. This is why producers and the entire agra-business complex lobby (and are usually quite successful) for tariff protection. [See MACROECONOMICS OF WORLD AGRICULTURE.]

B. Large-Country Tariffs

Large countries may affect export prices when they impose tariffs. For example, as a major importer of fresh grapes, the United States might well force down the export price of grapes from Chile by increasing the tariff as demand in the United States falls. This can result in net economic gains in the importing country. Consider Fig. 2. Suppose a tariff of t^0 is introduced. Unlike the small country case, the export price is affected by the tariff. The price facing the

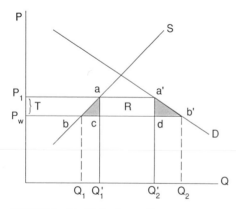

FIGURE 1 Tariffs in the small-country case.

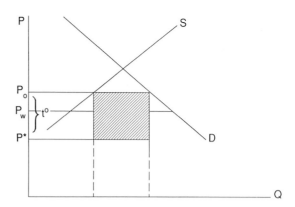

FIGURE 2 Tariffs in the large-country case.

importing consumer increases, causing demand to drop; however, if the price facing the exporter remained the same and the export supply was unchanged, an export surplus would be created. Because the exporter's excess supply schedule (which shows the amount available for export at various border prices) is upward sloping, the price must drop to $P\star$ to equate supply and demand in the exporting country. [See PRICES.]

There are cases where a tariff can result in net economic gains. Note that the government collects the entire cross-hatched area as tariff revenue. It, plus the producer gain, more than offsets the loss to consumers as a result of the tariff. Thus, tariffs result in a net economic or social welfare gain in the importing country.

An "optimal" tariff is one that maximizes social welfare (producer gain plus tariff revenue minus consumer loss). This is achieved when the duty-paid price is the same as the price at the intersection point of the demand curve D with the sum of S and the marginal outlay curve of the foreign excess supply curve. This type of tariff can lead to a welfare gain because the importer is exerting "monopsony" power against the exporter.

Often tariffs are variable in nature. For example, instead of the fixed tariff t^0 in Fig. 2, suppose the government in the importing country wanted to maintain the internal producer price at P_0 but supplies in the exporting country fluctuated because of weather. In response, the importer would adjust the tariff level (i.e., it would use a variable levy).

The above assumes that the exporter does not retaliate even though the exporter is harmed by the tariff (note earlier that export prices fell as a result of the tariff). The important situation which emerges with tariffs is that the amount which the importing country gains is less than what the exporting country loses. This is why from a global perspective, where both importers and exporters are taken into account, free trade is optimal.

C. Optimal-Revenue Tariffs

Governments do use tariffs to advertently collect revenue from imports. The tariff which maximizes government revenue is generally not one of those shown earlier. Conceptually this tariff is set so the government can exploit both exporters and domestic consumers. In Fig. 3 the excess supply curve is ES, while ED is the excess demand curve for the importer. Under free trade, the world price is P_w and Q_w is imported. The optimal tariff referred to earlier is t^0 (where the marginal outlay curve, MO, crosses the excess demand curve), which results in imports being reduced to Q^0. However, this is not the optimal revenue tariff. It is $P_1 - P_2$ per unit of import (determined by the intersection of MO and MR where the latter is the marginal revenue schedule to ED). The tariff revenue collected is P_1abP_2. Note that imports are $Q^\star$, which are below those under the optimal tariff.

D. General Equilibrium Tariffs

The effects of tariffs can also be shown for more than one country (Fig. 4). The aggregate production possibility for agriculture and manufacturing is represented by X_1X_2. At relative prices (terms of trade) represented by P_1, the output of manufacturing is M, while A of agriculture is produced. This is under no trade. At free trade, the relative price is P_2. Output of agriculture increases to $\overline{A}$ but production of manu-

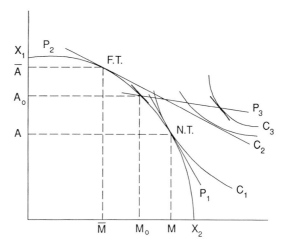

FIGURE 4 Tariffs in general equilibrium.

facturing decreases to $\overline{M}$. Welfare is improved under free trade (C_2 which indicates consumer welfare lies above C_1).

A tariff causes production to fall between the free-trade and no-trade points. For example, for a tariff which changes the terms of trade to P_3, agricultural output is A_0 and M_0 represents manufacturing output. This tariff is welfare improving (C_3 lies above C_2).

In all the cases where tariffs are welfare improving, the important assumption is that the trading partner does not retaliate. Under extreme retaliation, tariffs can be welfare reducing since, at the extreme, tariffs would become trade prohibitive.

E. Countervailing Duties

Border disputes often arise over accusations of unfair trade. One form is dumping where an exporter sells to an importer at a price below the cost of production or sells abroad at a lower price than it charges its domestic customers. For example, in Fig. 5, total supply in the exporting country is S_Q. The demand in the exporting country is D_d, while the demand in the importing country is D_f. Now, if the exporter sells quantity $Q^\star$ at a price $P^\star$ in the home market and $Q^{\star\star}$ at $P^{\star\star}$ abroad, export dumping occurs. The importer (whose demand is D_f) can retaliate with a countervailing duty (e.g., D^0). This will cause the exporter not to price discriminate, at which time the importer will remove the duty. The result will be free trade resulting in price P^0. Less is shipped abroad than before (Q^0 instead of $Q^{\star\star}$) and more is consumed domestically.

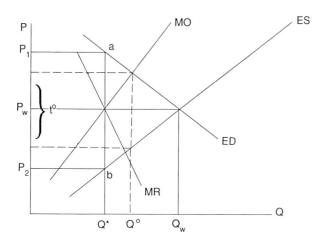

FIGURE 3 The optimal revenue tariff.

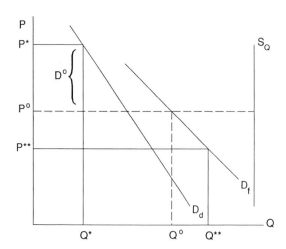

FIGURE 5 Export dumping and retaliation.

F. Effective Tariff Rates

A distinction is usually made between "nominal tariff" rates and "effective tariff" rates. The above discussion has focused on nominal tariffs since only tariffs on the final product are considered. Where inputs into production are traded and tariffs are also levied on the importation of these inputs, the tariff structure for the entire industry has to be considered. The rate of protection to the industry is called the "effective protective rate."

The nominal tariff rate can be misleading in cases where tariffs are imposed on related raw materials or intermediate products. As a result, the traditional nominal tariff rates may not give an accurate picture of the extent of protection afforded any given industry or the height of the average tariff of a country.

G. The Scientific Tariff

A scientific tariff structure includes noneconomic arguments for protection; however, it is difficult to reconcile the conflicting objectives of protection in a single scientific tariff structure. Tariffs are used to promote noneconomic objectives of various kinds through their influence on domestic production and consumption of certain products. Examples of the many tariffs classified as scientific include the following:

1. A tariff to promote national self-sufficiency and independence.
2. A tariff to promote diversification and industrialization or agriculturalization.
3. A tariff to promote a way of life.
4. A tariff to increase military preparedness.

5. A bargaining tariff.
6. A tariff to promote food security.

Each of these tariffs have associated costs and benefits. Consider, for example, a tariff to promote a way of life. This, along with other arguments, has been used to support high prices for farmers in the European Community (EC) and in Mexico. As Barkema noted,

> The Mexican government has a long tradition of safeguarding the interests of the nation's large number of small farmers. About a third of the Mexican population live in rural areas, and about a fourth are employed in production agriculture. The primary objective of Mexican farm policy is to boost incomes to small farmers, thereby minimizing rural unrest and slowing the pace of migration to Mexico City and other crowded urban areas. An important component of Mexican farm policy is restricting imports of low cost farm products from the United States and elsewhere. By blocking farm imports at the border, Mexican farm policy pushes up farm prices and incomes.

While farmers benefit from tariffs, there are some associated costs. One such cost is an increase in food prices paid by the urban people. These costs, in part, motivated Mexico's entry into the GATT and North American Free Trade Agreement (NAFTA) negotiations.

Some of the tariffs listed under the scientific tariff above actually fall into the earlier tariff categories. For example, a bargaining tariff could fit into the category of countervailing duties, since in essence an importing nation when it imposes a countervailing duty is retaliating or bargaining with an exporter to remove unfair trade practices.

Of the tariffs listed, the most popular one appears to be the tariff that promotes food security and food self-sufficiency. Strong arguments for food security have been made in view of world famine and food shortages during war time. As we will show in the empirical section, the problem with such an argument is that a policy put in place to achieve food security generally ends up resulting in excess production. For example, food security was an argument for introducing a high level of farm price supports in the European Economic Community. Over time, because of these high supports, the EC became a major exporter of food and found itself in a food overproduction situation, having to export at highly subsidized rates. In this example the EC achieved much more than any reasonable degree of food security or self-sufficiency. In other words, a food security, self-sufficiency policy ended up with some undesirable economic consequences. [*See* WORLD HUNGER AND FOOD SECURITY.]

II. How Important Are Tariffs?

A. United States and Mexico

For certain products and countries, tariffs represent a significant barrier to international trade. Recent U.S. agricultural export statistics are shown in Fig. 6. Japan is the largest importer, followed by the EC, Canada, and Mexico. For the 1990–1992 period, U.S. exports to Japan were roughly $8 billion. The United States has been in almost continual negotiation with each of these major trading partners in attempts to improve market access. In this section we consider the North American trade situation and, in the following section, the EC situation.

There have been attempts at trade liberalization through the Canadian and United States Trade Agreement (CUSTA) and with the proposed NAFTA. The latter seeks to remove the numerous barriers that restrict agricultural trade in North America. The primary players in the NAFTA accord have been the United States and Mexico since, under CUSTA, many farm trade issues between Canada and the United States were already addressed. A breakdown of U.S. farm trade with Canada and Mexico is shown in Table I. Fruits, juice, and vegetables comprise the largest component of U.S. exports to Canada, while livestock and products are the largest component of exports from Canada to the United States. U.S. exports to Canada are slightly greater than U.S. imports from that country. Grains, oilseeds, and products comprise the largest component

TABLE I

U.S. Farm Trade with Canada and Mexico in 1990

	To Canada		To Mexico	
U.S. exports	$1000	%	$1000	%
Livestock and products	802,216	19	662,068	26
Grains, oilseeds, and products	848,609	20	1,287,490	50
Fruits, juice, and vegetables	1,709,397	41	237,020	9
Other	837,193	20	367,038	14
Total	4,197,415	100	2,553,616	100

	From Canada		From Mexico	
U.S. imports	$1000	%	$1000	%
Livestock and products	1,491,822	47	466,199	18
Grains, oilseeds, and products	775,334	25	71,298	3
Fruits, juice, and vegetables	208,211	9	1,346,360	52
Other	605,018	19	726,851	28
Total	3,152,385	100	2,610,708	100

Reprinted with permission from A. Barkema (1992). North American Free Trade Agreement, what is at stake for U.S. agriculture? *Econ. Rev. Fed. Reserve Bank Kansas City,* 3rd Quarter, 7.

of U.S. exports to Mexico, whereas fruits, juice, and vegetables are the largest component of U.S. imports from Mexico. The value of U.S. imports from Mexico roughly equals the value of U.S. exports to that country.

Mexico used an array of tariff and nontariff barriers to protect its many small farmers from foreign competition, while the United States restricted imports to protect the domestic horticultural industry and to ensure the safety of food imports from Mexico (Table II). Mexico restricted the imports of U.S. farm products with import license requirements and tariffs ranging up to 15% for grain and oilseed products and up to 20% for various meat, dairy, and horticultural products. The average tariff on U.S. farm exports to Mexico was in the neighborhood of 5% in 1992. Note that license requirements were also in place and acted to enforce import quotas. Even though tariffs have been reduced, license requirements remain and are a major restriction on many of the most important U.S. farm exports to Mexico. For example, import licenses for corn and wheat are not granted until the entire domestic crop is used. Also, import licenses for horticultural crops close the Mexican border to U.S. imports during the Mexican harvest season. A combination of license requirements with tariffs restricts imports of U.S. poultry and dairy products.

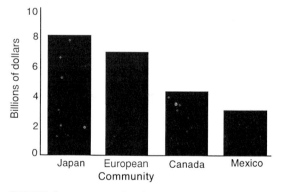

FIGURE 6 U.S. agricultural exports, 1990–1992 average. [A. Barkema (1992). "North american free trade agreement, what is the state for U.S. agriculture?" *Econ. Rev. Fed. Reserve Bank Kansas City,* 3rd Quarter, 6]

TABLE II

Major Restrictions on Farm Trade between Mexico and the United States, 1992

| Products | Import restrictions imposed by | |
	Mexico	United States
Livestock products	20% tariff on most pork products	Dairy and meat quotas
	10% tariff and license requirement on poultry products	Tariffs on many dairy, meat, and poultry products
	10–20% tariff and license requirement on most dairy products	1.2% tariff on live cattle
	Sanitary requirements	Sanitary requirements
Grains and oilseeds	0–20% tariff on most grains	Some small tariffs
	Seasonal 10% tariff on soybeans	
	Seasonal 15% tariff on sorghum	
	License requirements	
Horticultural products	10–20% tariff	Seasonal tariffs up to 25% on many fresh vegetables
	License requirements	35% tariff on dried onions, garlic, cantaloupe, melons
		Phytosanitary regulations

Reprinted with permission from A. Barkema (1992). North American Free Trade Agreement, what is at stake for U.S. agriculture? *Econ. Rev. Fed. Reserve Bank Kansas City,* 3rd Quarter, 8.

In terms of U.S. trade barriers, tariffs are intertwined with stringent technical regulations on food imports which guard the quality and safety of the U.S. food supply. The average tariff facing Mexican farm exports to the United States is about 6%, which is slightly greater than the average tariff facing U.S. farm exports to Mexico. However, there is one important difference. Generally Mexican farm exports to the United States are subject to relatively few quantitative restrictions (i.e., quotas or import licensing schemes). The U.S. horticultural industry receives the highest protection, with an average 8% tariff on U.S. imports of horticultural products from Mexico. Seasonal tariffs reach as high as 35% and are assessed during the U.S. harvest season.

To highlight that tariffs are not the only major barrier to trade, quality, health, and sanitary standards also play a prominent role in regulating U.S. imports of horticultural and livestock products from Mexico. The United States, for example, regulates the use of

farm chemicals on imported horticultural crops. It also maintains strict health and sanitary standards on livestock product imports, and imports of fresh citrus products are generally restricted to those grown in a few areas of Mexico that have been certified "fly free."

It is possible to put together numbers on tariff and nontariff barriers between Canada and the United States and to show how these have changed due to CUSTA. Likewise, it is possible to tabulate the tariff and nontariff barriers present in agricultural trade between the EC and the United States. As is the case between Mexico and the United States, for certain products there are significant tariff barriers to trade as well as significant nontariff barriers such as quotas and licensing schemes.

B. The United States and the EC

Barriers to agricultural trade between the United States and the EC have been at the heart of the problem to achieve any resolution under the GATT. Even though there have been several years of trade negotiations under the auspices of GATT, there had been no resolution as of January 1, 1993. The United States and the EC are major competitors in international agricultural markets; they are also major trading partners. The EC accounts for roughly one fourth of U.S. agriculture exports. A summary of program supports for agriculture in both the United States and the EC by major commodities is presented in Table III. Note that tariffs play a role as an instrument for supporting agriculture. For example in the United States, tariffs play a role in supporting the income of dairy farmers and of livestock producers. In the EC, tariffs are important for dairy, grains, livestock, and sugar. The term "variable import levies" appears in Table III. This is simply a variable tariff which moves up and down depending on market supply and demand conditions.

The EC uses variable levies on imports on U.S. beef, veal, and live animals. The actual levy has ranged from 0 to 114% of the basic levy, depending on the relation of the EC internal prices to what is called "guide prices."

Concerning dairy products in the EC, butter and skim milk are purchased at fixed intervention prices. A threshold (minimum import) price for milk and dairy products is enforced by variable levies that are equal to the difference between the threshold and world prices. Table IV is presented to show the complexity of agricultural programs, including border protection measures such as tariffs for one sector—the

TABLE III

Summary of Program Supports for Agriculture, United States and EC

Commodity	United States	EC
Dairy	Price supports maintained by tariffs, quotas, and government purchases.	Price supports maintained by intervention purchases.
Grains	Deficiency payments.	Variable import levies. Export refunds. Production quotas. Consumption subsidies.
	PIK entitlements.	Price supports maintained by intervention purchases.
	CCC inventory operations and commodity loans.	Variable levy. Export refunds.
Livestock	Beef: tariff, quota (countercyclical), and purchases (4/86–9/87).	Beef price supports maintained by intervention purchases.
	Other: general (research and development, inspection).	Variable import levies and export refunds on all products.
Oilseeds	CCC inventory operations and commodity loans.	Deficiency payments.
Sugar	Price supports.	Price supports maintained by intervention purchases.
	Import quotas.	Variable import levies. Export refunds. Production quotas.

Reprinted with permission from Newman, M., Fulton, T., and Glaser, L. (1987). "A Comparison of Agriculture in the United States and the European Community." Economic Research Service, U.S. Department of Agriculture. Foreign Agricultural Economic Report No. 233, p. 38, Washington, DC.

grain sector for the United States and the EC. Note that the United States does not have any border protection measures for grains with reference to the EC; however, the EC uses a threshold (minimum import prices) which is enforced by variable levies which are adjusted daily to equal the difference between threshold and world prices. This is also applied to the grain content of processed products. Table IV also shows the price support and the production control measures, and the stock and surplus disposal measures used in both countries. The EC has high price supports and its policy does not constrain agricultural production, although reforms introduced in 1992 sought to change this. On the other hand, in order for a U.S. producer to participate in the farm program, acreage set asides are required.

Concerning our earlier discussion, note that to dispose of surplus stocks the EC uses export subsidies which are set weekly as the difference between EC and world price changes. For commodities such as wheat, the EC has moved from a major importer to a major exporter, largely through the maintenance of high price supports using variable import levies. This has allowed EC farmers to increase production significantly, thus the EC has become one of the largest wheat exporters in the world. [*See* CROP SUBSIDIES.]

III. Case Studies

There is some evidence available which suggests that certain tariffs discussed theoretically have been used.

A. EC Variable Levies

A major study by Carter and Schmitz tested whether the EC was pursuing an optimal tariff strategy (modeled previously in Fig. 2), with its introduction of the variable levy system. It found that this was an optimal tariff strategy, and there were significant economic gains from such a policy. The results are shown in Table V. However, these results apply not only to the EC, but to China and the C.I.S., which are major wheat importers as well. As theory suggests, there is a loss in consumer welfare from the tariff because of higher prices; however, this is more than offset by the gain in producer revenue and by the gain in import tariff revenue. Note (from Table V) that the gain in tariff revenue is larger than the gain in producer revenue. The net gain from pursuing this strategy was roughly $3.8 billion.

As pointed out earlier, tariffs maintained for a long period of time encourage overproduction. This is essentially what happened in the European Common Market (ECM) with respect to wheat production. When the Common Agricultural Policy (CAP) was introduced (the early 1960s), the EC was a major importer; by the early 1990s the EC was a major exporter along with the United States and Canada. The EC leads both Argentina and Australia as a major wheat exporter. As a result of these dynamics, the optimal tariff strategy by the EC is no longer valid since the EC is now a net exporter.

TABLE IV

Grain Program Supports, United States and EC

	Price support measures	Production control measures	Stock and surplus disposal measures	Border protection measures
United States	Price supports maintained through nonrecourse loans to producers at established loan rates using the crop as collateral. If the market price falls below the loan rate, then producers may keep the loan and forfeit the crop.	Production is limited through voluntary producer participation in acreage reduction programs (participation is required for loan and deficiency payment eligibility). Voluntary paid land diversion programs have periodically been offered to increase acreage set-asides.	Commodity certificates for public stocks have been issued as partial payment for deficiency payments, the conservation reserve, the export enhancement program, PL 480, and wheat donations under Section 416.	None.
	Income supports maintained through deficiency (direct) payments to producers. The payment rate is the difference between a target price and the higher of either the loan rate or the market price. Commodity certificates redeemable for government stocks have been used as part of the deficiency payments.	Participating producers may reduce permitted planted acres up to 50% and still receive 92% of their deficiency payments.	Farmer-owned reserve (FOR) maintained for longer term (3 – 5 years) storage of wheat and feed grains.	
EC	The EC is obligated to purchase all grain offered that meets minimum standards at intervention prices that are fixed annually. A co-responsibility levy (production tax) reduces effective producer receipts by 3% on marketed grain. For durum wheat, direct payments are made to producers in low-yield areas. Wheat and rye meeting higher standards receive up to 7% higher prices than for the minimum qualities.	Up to 45 million acres of cropland will (by 1990) be placed in a conservation reserve for 10 years. A production threshold is set and, if a 3-year average of actual production exceeds the threshold (adjusted for imports of nongrain feeds), price support increases are supposed to be adjusted downward. Annual price setting remains at the discretion of the EC Council of Agricultural Ministers, however.	National intervention agencies hold stocks purchased at the intervention level. Surpluses are disposed of with export subsidies that are set weekly as the difference between EC and world price changes.	Threshold (minimum import) prices enforced by variable levies that are adjusted daily to equal the difference between threshold and world prices. This is also applied to the grain content of processed products.

Reprinted with permission from Newman, M., Fulton, T., and Glaser, L. (1987). "A Comparison of Agriculture in the United States and the European Community." Economic Research Service, U.S. Department of Agriculture. Foreign Agricultural Economic Report No. 233, p. 41, Washington, DC.

TABLE V

Welfare Gains to Wheat-Importing Nations with the Imposition of the Optimal Import Tariff

Welfare effect	Net gain $U.S. millions
1. Loss in consumers' surplus	−9439
2. Gain in producers' surplus	5971
3. Import tariff revenue	7202
4. Net gain (3 + 2 − 1)	3734

Source. Calculated. C. Carter and A. Schmitz (1979). Import tariffs and price formation in the world wheat market." *Am. J. Agricult. Econ.* **61,** 520.

B. Japanese Beef Imports

Considerable controversy has surrounded the Japanese beef policy, which has been highly restrictive in allowing imports into the country from the United States and elsewhere. For many years, the Japanese restricted beef imports through the use of an import quota. Prior to April 1, 1990, the primary mechanism used to protect the domestic beef industry was "on the quantity of beef" which could be imported; but, on April 1, 1990, the quota was replaced by a 70% tariff. What was this tariff to achieve?

First, the tariff supports beef producers' incomes in Japan. Second, Japanese beef prices are much higher than those in many trading nations. Third, the tariff allows the Japanese government to collect substantial income on imports via tariff revenues. Wahl, Hayes, and Schmitz test the extent to which the beef tariff is optimal from a society standpoint, or whether it is used to maximize the revenue collected by the Japanese government from the tariff. Interestingly, a tariff in the neighborhood of 70% was found to maximize government revenue (Fig. 4), while one of 50% was closer to maximizing social welfare (Fig. 3). Thus, the Japanese proposal to lower tariffs to 50% implies that they are moving toward an optimal social welfare position. Note that the optimal revenue tariff is higher than the optimal welfare tariff, as suggested by theory.

In terms of the Japanese, the government's behavior is consistent with the hypothesis that the Japanese government acts as a self-interested middleman. As the theory shows, an optimal revenue tariff is akin to a government middleman, which essentially exerts monopsony power on sellers and monopoly power on buyers. In terms of the Japanese beef tariffs, Fig. 7 shows the tariff revenue as a function of tariff levels. As the graph indicates, the tariff revenue is roughly

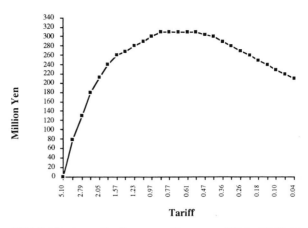

FIGURE 7 Japan: Beef import tariff revenues (1993). [Wahl, T., Hayes, D., and Schmitz, A. (1992). "The Japanese beef policy: Political preference function" in Agriculture and Trade in the Pacific Rim: Toward the Twenty-First Century" (Coyle, W. T., Hayes, D., and Yamauchi, H., eds.), p. 303. Westview Press, Boulder/San Francisco.]

at a maximum for tariffs that range between 70% and 100%.

C. Canada–United States Potash Dispute

The theory of a countervailing duty and its impact, as discussed previously, has been applied to several agricultural cases, including the potash dispute between Canada and the United States. Potash is a major fertilizer component used in U.S. agriculture, and Canada is a major supplier. On 10 February 1987, two American firms (Lundberg Industries of Dallas, TX, and New Mexico Potash Corp. of Memphis, TN) filed a lawsuit against several Canadian producers for dumping potash in the United States at prices which were alleged to be 43% below the cost of production. In 1987 these two firms accounted for less than 15% of the potash consumed in the United States. The suit was filed through the U.S. Department of Commerce and the U.S. International Trade Commission. The International Trade Commission agreed on 3 April 1987 that there was unfair price discrimination and on 21 August 1987 the United States announced preliminary duties on Canadian potash. Canada did respond by raising prices by over 30% and adjusted production accordingly. In response, the United States removed duties on potash entering the U.S. market. What were the effects?

The users of potash in the United States stood to lose because potash prices were raised as a result of the court action brought by American potash producers. On the other hand, potash producers stood to gain from their legal pursuit. Ironically, the U.S. farmers in this case lost much more from the legal transaction than what the U.S. potash producers gained. This was because the U.S. producers essentially were receiving a subsidy from the Canadian government on potash being produced in Canada and shipped into the U.S. market. U.S. potash producers gained roughly $13 million, Canadian potash producers gained roughly $108 million, and U.S. farmers lost roughly $70 million (Table VI). The net effect from the countervailing duty was positive–both for Canada and the entire North American market (approximately $51 million).

D. Tariffs and Quotas

As the earlier tables suggest, quotas are used extensively to restrict imports. In the United States, for example, these are common for sugar and peanuts. In Canada, they are commonplace for supply-managed products such as eggs and poultry. Quotas differ from tariffs in at least one important respect. Under a tariff, financial benefits flow to the government in the form of tariff revenues but, under import quotas, the financial benefits more often flow to exporters in the form of higher prices. There are exceptions, however. In the Japanese beef case, when quotas were in place prior to their replacement with tariffs, the Japanese collected the quota rents. However, in the U.S. sugar case, the quota rent actually is retained by exporters of sugar to the United States. In Canada, the importer quota rents are received by private importers such as retailers and food processors.

There has been a general move to replace quotas with tariffs, as has been the case for Japanese beef. Table VII shows Canadian implicit tariffs (i.e., the equivalent tariff that would raise the border price to the internal quota price) on chicken imports. These cases are roughly equivalent to the protection afforded by existing sugar quotas. At times the implicit tariff

TABLE VI

Effects of U.S. Potash Countervailing Duties

U.S. potash producers	+$ 12.9 million
Canadian potash producers	+$108.4 million
U.S. farmers	−$ 70.4 million
Net effect	+$ 50.9 million

Source. Picketts, V. J., Schmitz, A., and Schmitz, T. G. (1991). Rent seeking: The potash dispute between Canada and the United States. *Am. J. Agricult. Econ.* **73**, (2), 255–265.

TABLE VII

Canada: Chicken Prices and Implicit Tariffs in the 1980s

Year	Canadian price[a]	U.S. price[b] C$/kg	Transport cost[c]	Implicit tariff (%)
1980	1.662	1.207	0.094	29.9
1981	2.007	1.225	0.096	56.0
1982	1.955	1.193	0.098	55.6
1983	2.092	1.340	0.098	48.8
1984	2.286	1.594	0.104	36.9
1985	2.032	1.534	0.110	25.3
1986	2.182	1.744	0.111	18.8
1987	2.082	1.390	0.106	42.1
1988	2.115	1.527	0.098	32.1
1989	2.478	1.535	0.094	55.3

Source. Moschine, G., and Meilke, K. D. (1991). Tariffication with supply management: The case of the U.S.–Canada chicken trade. *Can. J. Agricult. Econ.* **39**, 61.
[a] Wholesale price in Ontario. *Source.* Agriculture Canada.
[b] U.S. 12-city wholesale price. *Source.* USDA (expressed in Canadian currency).
[c] *Source.* see text.

exceeds 50%. If GATT is resolved in line with current proposals, not only will "tariffication" of quotas proceed, but also tariffs will be lowered over time.

IV. Conclusions

In conclusion, we present some empirical evidence on the effects of trade liberalization in agriculture. These results are for removal of not only tariff barriers but also nontariff barriers, including quotas. Thus, the results overstate the economic impacts of removing tariff barriers. Numerous large-scale models have been developed to estimate the impact of free trade, and these models were developed largely in response to the GATT negotiations.

A. The Organization for Economic and Cooperation Development (OECD)

According to the OECD, the world market effects of trade liberalization by commodity are as follows.

Wheat The price rises 18% and production increases 0.5%. World trade declines 1.5%.
Rice The price rises 21% and production increases 1%. World trade increases 37%.
Feed grains The price rises 11% and production increases 2%. World trade declines 5%.
Bovine and ovine meat The price rises 17% and production increases 3%. World trade jumps 35%.

Dairy The price rises 31% and production increases 2%. World trade goes up to 13%.

Other animal products The prices are unchanged and production rises 1%. World trade increases 17%.

Protein feeds The price rises 13% and production increases 2%. World trade rises 5%.

B. The Tyers and Anderson Model (TA)

According to TA, the world price and trade effects of industrial market economy liberalization only on agricultural markets are:

Wheat The world price rises 2% and trade declines 1%.

Coarse grains The world price increases 1% while the trade rises 19%.

Rice The price rises 5% and trade increases 32%.

Beef The price increases 16% while the traded amount rises 195%.

Pork and poultry The price rises 2% and trade increases 18%.

Dairy The price jumps 27% and trade increases 95%.

Sugar The price increases 5% and trade increases 2%.

C. Food and Agricultural Policy Research Institute (FAPRI)

Generally the FAPRI results are much higher with respect to trade liberalization than the results from the other studies. Significant changes are expected to occur within the EC itself when it implements a 15% set-aside requirement and lowers intervention prices. Under this CAP reform alone, FAPRI estimates that wheat prices will increase somewhere in the neighborhood of 18%, corn 11%, barley 8%, soybeans 12%, and soybean oil 23%. However, only minor changes will occur in soybean meal, beef, pork, poultry, and dairy.

The impact of trade liberalization is significant, especially with respect to world prices for agricultural commodities. Some commodities are affected more than others; this is clearly the result of the level of protection that currently is afforded various commodities. Estimates of the effects of liberalizing trade differ. This is not surprising, given the complexity of international markets and the shifting dynamics of their interaction. But almost all of the estimates conclude that eliminating all tariffs and other trade barriers would improve the world's economic condition. However, whether producers would gain from freer trade depends on the type of product produced and the level of government support through such measures as deficiency programs. In the United States, some farm groups would lose from free trade (if all farm support measures were removed) because the positive price increase effect from liberalized trade would be less than the negative effect caused by the reduction in various forms of nontariff government support.

Acknowledgment

The author thanks Dr. Kirby Moulton and Dr. Jerry Seibert for their comments on earlier drafts.

Bibliography

Barkema, A. (1992). North American free trade agreement, what is the state for U.S. agriculture? *Econ. Rev. Fed. Reserve Bank Kansas City*, 3rd Quarter, 5–20.

CARD Report (1993). "The Periodical of Policy Research from the Center for Agricultural and Rural Development," Vol 6 (1). Iowa State Univ., Ames, IA.

Carter, C., and Schmitz, A. (1979). Import tariffs and price formation in the world wheat market. *Am. J. Agricult. Econ.* **61** (3), 517–522.

Moschine, G., and Meilke, K. D. (1991). Tariffication with supply management: The case of the U.S.–Canada chicken trade. *Can. J. Agricult. Econ.* **39,** 55–68.

Newman, M., Fulton, T., and Glaser, L. (1987). "A Comparison of Agriculture in the United States and the European Community." Economic Research Service, U.S. Department of Agriculture. Foreign Agricultural Economic Report No. 233. Washington, DC, 38–41.

Sarko, R. N. (1986). "Agricultural Trade Model Comparison: A Look at Agricultural Markets in the Year 2000 With and Without Trade Liberalization." National Center for Food and Agricultural Policy Discussion Paper Series No. RR87-01. Renewable Resources Division, Resources for the Future, Washington, DC.

Wahl, T., Hayes, D., and Schmitz, A. (1992). The Japanese beef policy: Political preference function. *In* "Agriculture and Trade in the Pacific Rim: Toward the Twenty-First Century" (W. T. Coyle, D. Hayes, and H. Yamauchi, eds.), pp. 295–304. Westview Press, Boulder/San Francisco.

Tea

CHEN ZONGMAO, YU YONGMING

Tea Research Institute, Chinese Academy of Agricultural Sciences

Glossary

Harvesting index Ratio of economic yield and total biological yield. The harvesting index of tea plants varies according to the location, it generally ranges between 7.5 and 14.7%, compared with 30% or more for other crops

Pluckable shoot Terminal bud of the tea shoot that develops to attain the pluckable maturity; plucking standard of the shoot is determined according to the different kinds and grades of tea; shoots with one bud and two to three leaves are generally plucked and ready for manufacture

Tea polyphenol One of the important components constituting the tea quality; it is a mixture of polyhydroxy phenolic compounds existing in tea plants; main components include catechins (flavanols), flavones, flavonols, anthocyanins, and phenolic acids

Tea plant (*Camellia sinensis*) originated in the southwest part of China, and has been cultivated for more than 3000 years. Now, tea plants are cultivated in 54 countries around the world. Nearly one-half of the population in the world consumes tea. Tea, coffee, and cocoa are the three most popular beverages in the world.

I. Development of the Tea Industry

The discovery and utilization of tea originated during the "Shen-Nong" era of ancient China, around 5000 to 6000 years ago. Originally, tea was used as a medicine for various ills; it can be traced back to the "Xi-Han" era (200 B.C.). Tea production has been developed rapidly since the Tang dynasty (618–907 A.D.), and has been accepted as a beverage; however, tea has achieved popularity in other parts of the world only since the middle of the 17th century. Commercial cultivation of tea gradually expanded to Indonesia, India, and Sri Lanka until the middle of the 19th century. The tea cultivation history in Africa is relatively short. The first record of cultivation in Africa is in 1850; however, the tea industry was developed until the middle of the 20th century. Now, tea plants are distributed worldwide ranging from 42° N to 33° S. It is now grown commercially in tropical and subtropical regions of Asia, Africa, and South America, and also in limited areas in North America and Australia. In 1990, the tea-growing area in the world amounted 2.45 million ha, total output amounted 2.51 million tons, and green tea comprised about 21% of the total. The average yield per unit area in the world is around 1004 kg/ha. Eight major tea-producing countries (India, China, Sri Lanka, Kenya, Turkey, Indonesia, formerly Soviet Union, and Japan) accounted for 86% of the world production. Virtually all tea produced in Japan and about 60% of that produced in China is green tea. India is the largest tea producer; nearly all of which is black tea. The world total exports amounted 1.125 million ton in 1990, and is about 40% of total tea production. The exported tea from Sri Lanka has surpassed that of India since 1990, and is the greatest in the world (Table I).

II. Agrobotanical Characteristics

Although the tea plant is an ancient plant with a long history, the confusion and modification in nomencla-

TABLE I

Tea Production in the Major Tea-Producing Countries

Country	Tea production ($\times 10,000$ t)					
	1940	1950	1960	1970	1980	1990
India	21.16	27.85	32.11	41.85	56.96	71.47
China[a]	—	6.22	13.58	13.60	30.87	51.50
Sri Lanka	10.77	13.90	19.72	21.22	19.14	23.41
Kenya	0.49	0.68	1.38	4.11	8.99	19.70
Indonesia	8.34	3.54	6.78	4.40	9.97	15.04
Turkey	—	0.02	0.59	3.34	9.59	13.12
USSR	1.13	—	3.77	6.68	12.98	11.00
Japan	5.82	4.18	7.76	9.12	10.23	8.99

[a] Taiwan is not included.

ture have continued for almost two centuries. As early as 1753, Linnaeus described the tea plant as *Thea sinensis*, and it was modified to *Camellia sinensis* in August of same year. Since then, the genus name of *Thea* and *Camellia* has had a checkered history. In the second edition of *Species Plantarum*, Linnaeus abandoned the former name and described the two species separately: *Thea bohea* and *T. viridis*. Watt in India named *Camellia thea* in 1907; Cohen-Stuart in Indonesia used a new name of *Camellia theifera*. In 1950, a famous Chinese botanist, Qian Chongshu, nomenclatured *Camellia sinensis*. Sealy in the U.K. (1958) also gave the same name and included two varieties: var. *sinensis* (small-leaf variety) and var. *assamica* (large-leaf variety). Since that, despite some papers contributing to the botanical name of tea plant, uniformity has been achieved.

Botanically, tea belongs to the order Theales, family Theaceae, genus *Camellia*. All varieties and cultivars of tea belong to a single species, *Camellia sinensis*. Tea plant is a perennial evergreen; the aerial portion of tea plant is grown as tree, semi-tree, and shrub depending on the influence of the external environment. The China variety (var. *sinensis*) tea plant usually grows into a shrub about 1–2 m high, characterized by more or less virgate stems. Leaves are small, hard, dark-green in color with a dull surface. The *Assam* variety (var. *assamica*) is described as a erect tree with many branches, 8–12 m high. Leaves are 15–20 cm long, light-green in color, with glossy surface.

The fresh shoots are the economic harvest of tea plant. The phyllotaxy of leaves on the shoot is alternate. The leaf pose on the stem includes erect, semierect, horizontal, and drooping according to the variety. Leaves are leathery in texture, with silvery or light-yellow colored hairs on the undersurface of tender leaves. There are 7–15 pairs of veins on the

leaf. The lateral veins curve upward and connect with the upper veins, forming a close transporting network, which is characteristic of the leaves of tea plants. Leaves are serrated at the margin. The first several new leaves at the flushing period of the tea shoot usually have a characteristic small size, being thick and brittle with a blunt apex; the petiole is wider and flat, and called fish-leaf or in Indian terminology the *Janam*. Its position on the shoot is of the very greatest importance when considering standards of plucking. The tea manufactured with the fish-leaf are of low quality. Sometimes the leaf primodium differentiates from the vegetative bud of tea plant ceasing growth prematurely instead of developing into the normal leaf. It is termed the dormant bud or in Indian terminology the *Banjhi*. Normal tea shoots show the distinct periodicity of growth, i.e., after the development of several normal leaves, the *Banjhi* bud forms, thus completing a full periodic shoot growth rhythm.

Tea flowers are bisexual with a slight fragrance and are white in color. Their diameter is 20–55 mm. The morphology of the flower is one of the important indexes in the classification of the tea plant. The fruit of the tea plant is green in color, three-celled, thick-walled, and shinny at first but then duller and slightly rough later. Tea seed is brown in color, thin-shelled, about 1 cm in diameter, and semiglobose in shape.

III. Nutrition and Cultivation

Tea plants can be grown over a considerable range of conditions from temperate climates to hot, humid subtropics and tropics. However, the optimum mean daily ambient temperature for tea growth is ranges between 20 and 30°C. When the mean ambient temperature is higher than 30°C, the growth of the tea plant is retarded. The tolerance of tea plant to the minimum temperature varies with the varieties, it generally ranges between -3 and $-15°C$. Tea plants require not only certain amounts of rainfall, 1000–1700 mm annually, but also rainfall that is well-distributed during the whole year, especially the growing season.

Tea plants are not overcritical to soil. The range of soil types on which tea is grown in the major tea-producing countries in the world is remarkably wide. Tea plants are very sensitive to the acidity of soil. They cannot survive in alkaline soils. The optimum pH of soil for tea growing ranges between 4.5 and 6.5. Table II shows the physiochemical parameters of a high-yielding tea garden in China. [*See* SOIL, ACID.]

The tea output per unit area is proportional to the coverage in tea garden. For the purpose of obtaining the maximum productivity within short period, a density of more than 12,000–20,000 bushes per hectare in large-leaf varieties and 45,000–60,000 bushes (20,000 bushes × 3 rows) in small- to medium-leaf varieties is recommended. The economic age of the tea plant is generally around 40 years. It is recommended to pull out and replant the new clones when the tea plants reach this age. However, such techniques as collar-pruning and heavy-pruning of old bushes are adopted in China, Sri Lanka, and other countries in order to obtain the benefits during the early period.

The principle of fertilization is to compensate the nutrients removed by the crop and eluted by the rainfall in a timely manner. Ordinarily, the schedule of fertilization is determined according to the nutritional status in the tea soil, the yield level in the previous pruning cycle, and the yield predicted by agrometeor-ological conditions. On this basis, the level of nitrogen application is controlled around 240–300 kg per hectare and half amounts of potassium are added; the level of phosphorus is fixed at amounts of 60–90 kg P_2O_5 per hectare and applied every 2 years. [*See* FERTILIZER MANAGEMENT SYSTEMS.]

The requirements for microelements by tea plant are few. It is not important in most of the tea-producing areas; however, deficiencies were found in some particular instances. For example, in areas of Malawi and Japan are copper deficiencies, part of the soil in Sri Lanka and east African countries are zinc deficient, part of the areas in Indonesia, east Africa, and Zaire are magnesium deficient. So, the application of microelement fertilizer produced significant effects in some instances.

The direct effect of shading is to modify the situation of light, airflow, temperature, and humidity as well as to decrease the physical damage of solar radiation; the indirect effect is to minimize the excessive evaporation of water from leaves. Besides, the fallen leaves of the shading tree increase the source of organic matter; however, shading increases the incidence of tea blister blight (*Exobasidium vexans*) due to the shade tree minimizing the solar radiation. So, the benefit and risk analysis of shading are a disputed issue, possibly because of the wide geographical distribution and various climate conditions. It is regarded that shading is necessary in tea areas with a maximum temperature higher than 35°C and relative humidity lower than 40%.

Although the total rainfall in a year may be adequate for the production of green leaves in most tea areas in the world, the distribution of this rainfall month

TABLE II

Main Physiochemical Parameters of High-Yielding Tea Garden in China

Physical characteristics		Chemical characteristics	
Effective soil horizon > 80 cm		Acidity	Water extracts pH 4.0–5.5
			Salt extracts pH 3.5–5.0
Ploughing horizon > 20 cm		Exchangeable Al	Al^{3+} 1–4 mg/100 g
Soil texture	Sandy-loam to heavy loam	Exchangeable Ca	Ca^{2+} < 4.0 mg/100 g (CaO < 0.1%)
Bulk density (loam)	Surface 1.0–1.2 g/cm^3	Degree of base saturation (loam)	Ca^{2+} < 50%
	Subsoil 1.2–1.45 g/cm^3		Mg^{2+} around 10%
			K^+ > 5%
Porosity	Surface 50–60%	Tillage horizon	Organic Matter > 1.5%
	Subsoil 45–50%		Total N > 0.1%
Ratio of three phases	Surface Solid: 50		Available N > 1.00 mg/kg
	Liquid: 20		Quick acting P > 10 mg/kg
	Gas: 30		(dilute HCl Extracts)
	Subsoil Solid: 55		Quick-acting K > 80 mg/kg
	Liquid: 30		(NH$_4$Ac extracts)
	Gas: 15		
Water-permeable coefficient > 10^{-3} cm/sec			

by month is often inadequate. This can be regulated by irrigation. Irrigation not only supplements the water supply to tea bush, but also modifies both the atmospheric and the soil environment. It was also proved that the shoots from irrigated gardens had higher polyphenol content. The optimum time for irrigation can only be decided according to the local situation. However, it is believed that irrigation is most beneficial when it carried out early in the dry season before the water deficiency is severe.

Pruning is a "necessary evil" to the tea plant. The objects of pruning are to maintain the plant permanently in the younger phase, to stimulate the growth of shoots, and to build an rational height of frame. In mature tea gardens, light-pruning and heavy-pruning should be done alternately. The best time for pruning is during a dormant period, because this is the time that the carbohydrates reserves within the tea plant are at a higher level. Pruning during drought season is not suitable. The rational for the plucking system is based on the fact that certain amounts of regrowth leaves remain on the plucking table, thus guaranteeing to supply enough carbohydrates to the tea shoots. Generally, the terminal bud is removed together with one to three leaves for manufacture. The interval of the plucking cycle on the tea plant mainly depends on the growth rate of the plant, generally 5–14 days. In most areas of the former USSR and Japan, plucking has been fully mechanized; however, most of the world's tea is plucked by hand.

Tea plant is a C3 plant with high photorespiration; the utilization ratio of the tea plant of solar radiation energy is far lower than that of other crops. According to a study in India, only 7% of the photosynthetic products are used in the growth of the tea shoot, 9% in the formation of frame branches, and 84% is exhausted during respiration and other metabolic actions. How to improve the harvesting index via the breeding route or through cultivation is a problem to be solved in the future.

IV. Kinds of Tea and Manufacture

The fresh leaves plucked from the tea plant are manufactured into various kinds of tea including black tea, green tea, Oolong tea, scented tea, etc., by means of different manufacturing methods. Fresh leaves treated with high temperature (de-enzyming or steaming) at the beginning of manufacture, to deactivate the polyphenol oxidase localized within the cells of leaves and to stop the fermentation, and to maintain the

original green color, are termed unfermented tea (green tea). On the other hand, when the process begins with dehydration and leaves are not treated with high temperature, the tea polyphenols are oxidized completely by the enzyme, and produce fermented tea (black tea). When the enzymes in the tea leaves are not completely deactivated and the tea polyphenols are not oxidized fully, these products are the intermediate of black tea and green tea, termed semi-fermented tea (Oolong tea).

Black tea is the major kind of tea consumed in the world. The key process in the manufacture of black tea is fermentation. Congou black tea is manufactured by the most traditional processes including withering, rolling, fermentation, and drying. For the convenience of brewing, the tea cutter was developed first in India, and the rolling process was changed to a rolling and wringing processes; thus, the broken black tea product was produced. This kind of manufacture makes more water-extracts with same quantity of tea, thus improving the efficiency of the raw material. Subsequently some alternative manufacturing machines and methods were developed successively in India, East African countries, and China, include the Rotovane process, CTC process (crushing, tearing, curling), LTP process (Laurie tea processor). The production of CTC black tea was increased rapidly in the past 10 years.

The production of green tea is mainly concentrated in China and Japan, with a small-scale production in the former USSR, India, Indonesia, and Turkey. The basic manufacturing processes of green tea include de-enzyming, rolling, and drying. The de-enzyming process comprises pan-de-enzyming and steam-de-enzyming. The steamed green tea is the major tea product consumed in Japan. Due to the different terminal drying process, it can be classified into roasted and baked green tea. The roasted green tea is the major tea consumed in China and the African countries. The baked green tea is the raw material of scented tea. The propensity of the tea adsorbing flavors is used in the manufacture of scented tea. The baked green tea is mixed with dried fresh flowers to impact fragrance and aroma. The most popular flowers used in the scented tea are Jasmine, Michelia, Zhulan, Dae-dae (Citrus aurantaium var. amara), osmanthus, and rose. Oolong tea is a kind of semi-fermented tea. Its basic manufacturing process includes Shai-Qing (sunlight withering), Zuo-Qing (light rolling), de-enzyming, rolling, and drying. Not only the special tea variety and strict plucking standard are necessary, but also the elaborating manufacturing technique is required.

The plucking requirement for Oolong tea is different from that of other kinds of tea. It is recommended that shoots with three to four leaves be plucked as the raw material when the *banjhi* is formed on the terminal of shoot. Due to the distinct characteristic of various tea varieties and degree of fermentation process, different styles of Oolong tea are produced, such as "puochong" (light fermentation), Tie-Quan-Yin, and Shui-Xian (heavy fermentation).

Black–black tea is mainly produced in China and also on a limited scale in the former USSR. The manufacturing processes include de-enzyming, primary rolling, Ou-Dui (treatment of high temperature and humidity), secondary rolling, and drying. The fresh leaves used in the manufacture of black–black tea are rather coarse. Ou-Dui process is the special process in the manufacture of black–black tea and the key process in determining the quality of black–black tea. The products include Hei-Mao-Cha and Pu-Er. It is consumed in the minority nationality region of China, southeast Asian countries, Hong Kong, and Mongolia, and the former USSR.

Besides the above mentioned kinds of tea, there are many kinds of remanufactured tea made using the above made tea as the raw material, such as instant tea, brick-tea, fruit-flavored tea, and health-protecting tea (mixture of tea and Chinese traditional medicine).

V. Consumption and Customs

There are 125 countries and regions in the world that import tea. The imported amount by the former USSR in 1990 was 231,000 tons; this was the first time it surpassed the imports of U.K. and occupies the first place in the world. The United Kingdom was the largest tea importing country for a historical period. The imports amounted 141,900 tons in 1990, and occupied the second place. Imports of tea are listed successively in the following order: Pakistan, United States, Egypt, Iran, Iraq, and Poland. Ireland has the highest average annual consumption of tea per capita, according to statistics from 1986–1988, (3.07 kg/year), followed by Iraq (2.95 kg), Qatar (2.91 kg), the U.K. (2.84 kg), and Turkey (2.73 kg). The following characteristics can be summarized about world tea consumption during recent years: (1) the consumption of the largest tea importing country (U.K.) historically showed a decreasing tendency. (2) The internal consumption in the major tea-producing countries (India and China) increased rapidly. (3) The proportion of imports from the former

USSR and eastern European countries were increased from 8.7% in 1980 to 24.4% in 1990; those of Asian and African countries were increased from 35.5% in 1980 increased to 43.7% in 1990. On the other hand, the imports of western European countries were decreased from 25.0% in 1980 to 21.7% in 1990. (4) The proportion of CTC black tea in the total world black tea trade increased significantly from 39% in 1980 to 47% in 1990. The proportion of tea bags and instant tea in the total tea trade increased.

The custom of tea drinking in China and Japan mainly adopts the brewing form, and in India, Sri Lanka, and European countries mainly adopts the cooking style. People from Asian and northern African countries prefer the green tea, and the black tea is the type most consumed by most parts of the world. Perfumed tea is popular in south American countries and mint green tea is popular in northwest African countries as well as buttered tea, salted tea, and Rei-tea in the border area of China. Instant tea, iced tea, liquid tea, and various tea bags which are simple and fast were developed with the changing life styles. Additionally, tea drinking with tea as the raw material was developed popularity in the markets of China, India, and Indonesia.

VI. Tea Biochemistry

The quality of various kinds of tea is based on the contents and constitutions of various chemical components. Twenty-eight elements were discovered in tea plants. Tea contains more potash, manganese, fluorine, aluminum, and selenium than other plants. Tea is also rich in vitamins, especially vitamin C. It was reported that the content of vitamin C in 100 g green tea is as high as 100 mg. However, 90% of the vitamin C contained in tea fresh leaves is destroyed during the fermentation stages of black tea manufacture. The content of vitamin B group in green tea and black tea is around 10 mg per 100 g made tea. They are water soluble and hence 90–100% is extracted into the infusion during brewing. Vitamin E is exists mainly in the lipid fraction of made tea, and the content is around 14–80 mg per 100 g made tea.

Twenty-five amino acids are reportedly contained in made tea. The total content in tea shoots is as high as 2–4%. Among those, theanine is the highest and represents more than 50% of the total amino acids. It plays a special role not only in the nitrogen metabolism of the tea plant, but also in determining the taste and quality of tea infusion.

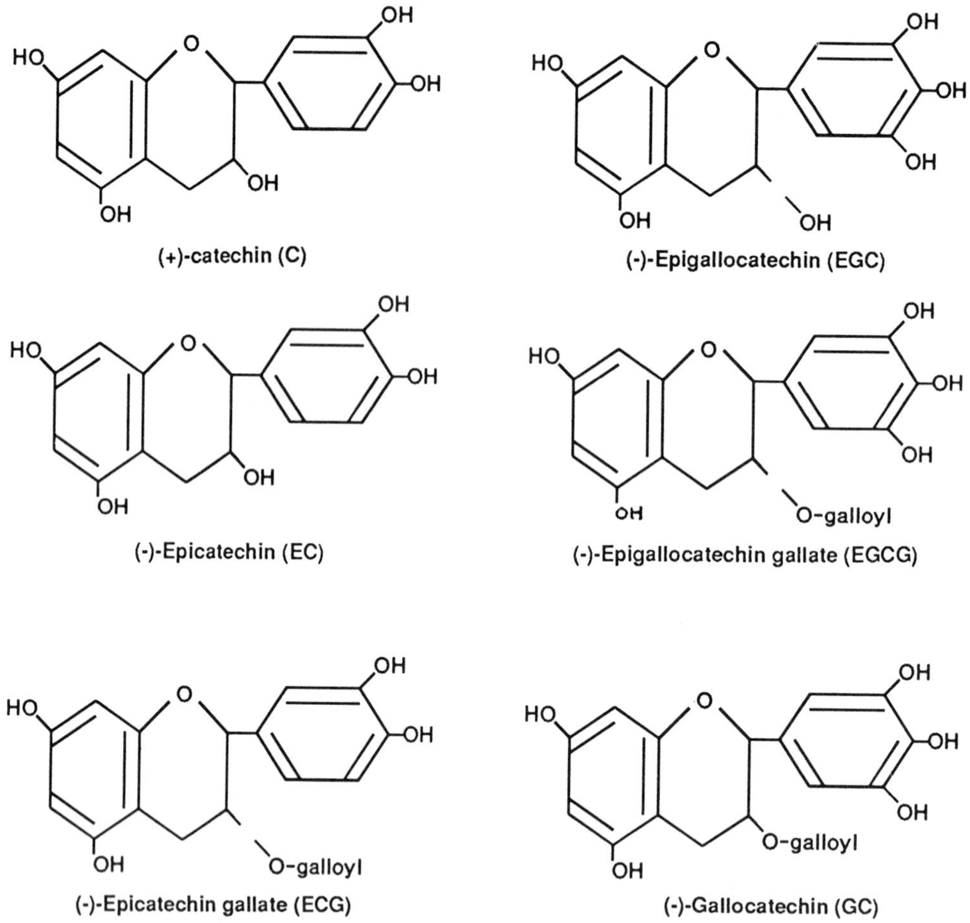

FIGURE 1 Major catechins in tea.

Caffeine has been reported to be present in dry weight basis at 3–4%. It is soluble in water. Its mild stimulation and astringent effects are considered to be one of the reasons for the popularity of tea.

The most important and characteristic components in tea are the polyphenols. The total content of tea polyphenols expressed as percentage of dry weight leaf is around 20–30%. They are the key compounds that determine the taste and color of infusion and have proved to have beneficial effects on human health. The most important compounds in tea polyphenols are the catechins. The content of catechins in tea is around 12–24% and represents more than 50% of the total amounts of tea polyphenols. Six kinds of catechin compounds were isolated from tea. They are the various derivatives of catechins and gallic acid, including (i) catechin (C), (ii) epi-catechin (EC), (iii) gallocatechin (GC), (iv) epicatechingallate (ECG), (v) epigallocatechin (EGC), and (vi) epigallocatechingallate (EGCG). Generally, the content of the latter three catechins are relatively high. Their structure is listed

in Fig. 1. These catechin compounds condense to theaflavin and thearubigin during the manufacturing process of black tea. The formation of these compounds makes the infusion orange-red in color.

A. Chemical Basis of Tea Tasting

The taste of tea is based on the taste threshold value of chemical components in tea and the reaction of sensory organs to these components. The compounds which play the major role in taste are tea polyphenols, amino acids, and polysaccharides. The most important standard for the green tea is "freshness and fullness." The "freshness" is a reflection of amino acids, and the "fullness" is a reflection of the suitable ratio of amino acids and tea polyphenols. The standard of black tea is "strong, fullness, and briskness." The catechins and theaflavin are the most important compounds determining the tasting of black tea. "Strong" depends on the content of water extracts.

Briskness and fullness of taste mainly depend on the suitable ratio of caffeine, theaflavin, and amino acids. The conjugation of these compounds and caffeine creates the astringency feeling and strong taste.

B. Chemical Basis of Tea Color

Different kinds of tea have distinct color. This includes the color of made tea and color of infusion. The color is based on certain chemical compounds. For example, the color of green tea is mainly determined by the chlorophyll and some flavone compounds, such as vitexin and isovitexin. Chlorophyll a is deep green in color and chlorophyll b is yellow-green in color. So, the different proportions of these two chlorophylls constitute the different grade of green color. The color of black tea is black in made tea and orange-red in infusion. These colors are formed by the theaflavin and thearubigin which are polymerized by catechins. Theaflavin is yellow in color and thearubigin is red in color. Different ratios of these two compounds constitute the different degrees of color. If the catechins are overoxidized, the theafluvin (fluvin = brown) is formed which causes the infusion to be an unpleasant dark-brown color. Semifermented Oolong tea is generally dark green–brown color in made tea and yellowish red color in infusion. It is due to the fewer oxidized products of polyphenols.

C. Chemical Basis of Tea Aroma

Tea aroma constitutes a group of flavor compounds. According to the combination of various flavor compounds, the aroma characteristic of various kinds of tea is formed. Up to now, more than 500 flavor compounds were identified in tea, although they existed only a small amount (0.03–0.05% in fresh leaves on dry basis, 0.005–0.01% in green tea, and 0.01–0.03% in black tea). These compounds play an important role in determining the quality of tea. Some of these flavor compounds exist in the intact fresh leaves; however, most of them are formed during the processing process. Alcohols are the greatest flavor components in fresh leaves. There are more than 230 identified flavor components in green tea with the alcohols and pyrazines in the greatest proportion. Alcohols are contained in the intact fresh leaves, but pyrazines are formed during the drying process. Four hundred four flavor compounds were identified in black tea, which include the alcohols, aldehydes, ketones, and ethers. With regard to semifermented tea (such as Puo-chong tea), the alcohols and ketones are the most abundant, especially geraniol, jasmone lactone, nerolidol, indole, etc. Those compounds make the characteristic floral flavor. There were 48 flavor compounds identified in Oolong tea. In the Oolong because of heavy fermentation, linalool and its oxidative products and the benzyl alcohol are the most abundant.

VII. Tea and Human Health

In addition to the best-known effects of relieving fatigue and sobering the mind, it has been proved by modern medical research that tea also possesses the following effects:

Prevention from tooth-caries: It was proved that the fluorine contained in tea are an effective anticary. A study carried out in Japan in which subjects drank 100 ml tea infusion containing 1 g made tea (corresponding to 0.35 ppm F) per day. Results showed that the percentage of caries decreased 19.5–21.3%. Besides the fluorine, tea polyphenols (especially the theaflavin) inhibit activity of glucosyltransferases excreted by teeth-decaying bacteria (*Streptococcus mutans*). Therefore, the transforming process from sucrose to mutan was inhibited, thus minimizing the opportunity of adhension of bacteria on the surface of the tooth-bed.

Antimicrobial action: Use of tea as an anti-inflammatory therapy can be traced back to ancient China. Green tea and black tea showed broad bacteriostatic spectrum *in vitro* including the *Salmonella paratyphi, S. typhi, Vibrio cholera, Shigella dysenteriae*, etc. Besides, it can also inhibit or neutralize the toxin formed by bacteria, such as *Cholera* toxin. *Cholera hemolysia, Staphylococcus aureus* A toxin. Green tea showed the most potent bacteriostatic action among the various kinds of tea. The active components of this action are catechins, especially EGCG.

Hypertension and blood-glucose depressing action: It was proved that ECG, EGCG, and theaflavin have a notable blood tension depressing effect. A new type of tea (Gabaron tea) was developed in Japan by anaerobic treatment of fresh leaves and it was found that the tea contained a large amount of γ-aminobutyric acid. According to the clinical experiment, it showed a significant hypertension depressing effect.

High blood-glucose is a biochemical expression of diabetic patients. A complex of tea EGCG and aluminum hydroxide showed a notable blood-glucose depressing effect, which is comparable to that of Tolbutamide, a well-known blood-glucose depressing medicine. A mixture of polysaccharide compounds and diphenylamine isolated from tea was proved effective in the curing of diabetes.

Effect on cardiovascular disorder: High level of blood cholesterol induces deposit of lipids on vessel walls and causes obstructed coronary arteries, atherosclerosis, and the formation of thrombus. So, decreasing the level of blood lipid is the basis for controlling atherosclerosis and other cardiovascular disorders. Investigation showed that EGCG and ECG decrease the level of total cholesterol, free cholesterol, total lipid, and triglyceride in plasma and liver significantly. Catechin, theaflavin, and thearubigin possess the actions of anticoagulation of blood platelet, anti-hemagglutination, and the promotion of fibriolysis. The clinical experiment using the extract of Tu-cha, Oolong, and green tea showed effectiveness in the prevention of atherosclerosis.

Anticarcinogenic and antimutagenic activity: Scientists in various countries have carried out much research on the anticarcinogenic and antimutagenic effects of tea since the end of the 1970s. Subjects were administered different tea materials (including fresh leaves extract, green tea extracts, EGCG, ECG, tea polyphenols, etc.) orally and treated with various potent carcinogens simultaneously. All tea materials showed anticarcinogenic activity to various degrees. Even when a low concentration of 0.05% tea polyphenols was orally administered, significant anticarcinogenic activity was also exhibited. These positive results have been reported on many kinds of cancer including skin cancer, liver cancer, lung cancer, stomach cancer, intestine cancer, etc.

With regard to the mechanism on the anticarcinogenic and antimutagenic activity of tea, it was proved that tea not only had a dismutagenic and bioantimutagenic activity, but also had inhibitory effects on both stages of initiation and promotion of carcinogenesis.

Bibliography

Bokuchava, M. A., and Skobeleva, N. I. (1986). Tea aroma. *In* "Development in Food Science" (I. D. Morton and A. J. MacLerd eds.), Vol. 3B, pp. 49–84. Elsevier, Amsterdam.

Zongmao, C. (1991). Contribution of tea to human health. *In* "World Tea." Record of the Opening Session of International Symposium on Tea Science, p. 12–20. Shizuoka, Japan.

Zongmao, C. (ed.) (1992). "China Tea Classics" (Chinese), pp. 786. Shanghai Civil, China.

Flament, I. (1989). Coffee, cocoa and tea. *Food Rev. Internatl.* **5**(3), 317–414.

Temperate Hardwoods

MARC D. ABRAMS, DAViD A. ORWIG, *Pennsylvania State University*

Glossary

Clear-cutting Removal of the entire forest by logging for the purpose of timber procurement and regenerating light demanding species in the next stand
Climax Final stage or end point of succession resulting in a self-perpetuating forest community comprised of generally shade-tolerant species
Crown classes Vertical position of a tree in the forest canopy, generally classified as dominant, codominant, intermediate, or overtopped
Deciduous Trees that drop their leaves at the end of each growing season
Forest ecology Study of the interrelationships of forest organisms to one another and the environment
Forest type Unit of forest vegetation that is essentially uniform in general appearance and vegetation structure and composition
Gap-phase species Plant species whose successful regeneration or, in the case of trees, overstory recruitment depends on periodic small-scale disturbances that create holes in the forest canopy and increase light to the forest floor
Succession Gradual change which occurs in vegetation in an area over time in which one seral stage replaces another, leading to the end point of succession or climax

Soil The weathered superficial layer of the earth's crust with which is intermingled living organisms and the products of decay

In the broadest sense hardwoods include all tree species in the class of seed plants called Angiosperms, which have seeds enclosed in a developed ovary or fruit. The other major class of seed plants is the Gymnosperms which means "naked seeds," because they are borne on the surface of an appendage and not enclosed in a fruit. Gymnosperms also include many tree species such as pines, spruces, firs, redwoods, and cypress. Angiosperms are divided into two subdivisions—the dicotyledons (two seed leaves) and the monocotyledons (one seed leaf). Monocotyledon families include grasses, orchids, and palms and are generally devoid of tree species, with the exception of certain palm species. Thus, dicotyledonous Angiosperms are the subdivision with almost all of the hardwood tree species. While most research on this subject has been conducted with hardwoods in the temperate regions of the northern hemisphere, they actually occur in most regions of the world, including the equatorial regions, southern hemisphere, and, to a lesser extent, arid, desert environments. They are a very diverse class of trees and can grow under a wide range of temperature, light, moisture, and soil conditions. Within the United States well over 100 hardwood species have important economic or social value. Such highly valued species as walnut, cherry, oak, maple, and hickory are all hardwoods. Historically hardwood forests have represented the primary commercial natural resource in developing countries.

I. Introduction

This article focuses on hardwood forests within the temperate region of the northern hemisphere. In par-

Encyclopedia of Agricultural Science, Volume 4 Copyright © 1994 by Academic Press, Inc. All rights of reproduction in any form reserved.

289

ticular, we emphasize the phytogeography and ecology of forests within eastern North America, including climatic, edaphic, and physiographic factors associated with the major forest types, but also discuss hardwood forests within the western United States, Europe, and Asia. For eastern North America, pre-European settlement composition will be described where available, and the effects of disturbance on forest composition and successional relationships are discussed for the major vegetation types.

Temperate hardwood forests of the eastern United States dominate the region from east of the 95th meridian and between 28°N and 48°N latitudes. Geographically, they stretch from the northern tip of Minnesota eastward to central Maine, southward to northcentral Florida, and westward into eastern Texas. Forests of the region are primarily deciduous, although conifer-dominated forests occur in the northeastern, northcentral, and southeastern portions of the biome. Eastern woodlands have a wealth of species due to differences in topography, climate, soils, geological history, disturbance regimes, and land utilization that vary from region to region. Forests typically experience moderate average annual temperatures throughout four distinct seasons. These areas experience a variety of growing season lengths ranging from less than 90 days in northern Wisconsin to 300 days in the southeastern Coastal Plain. Due to the impacts of man, hardwood forests within the last 300 years have been altered to the point where virtually none of the original forest remains undisturbed. Different portions of the landscape have been harvested, burned, and stripped of topsoil and nutrient reserves. Due to their resiliency, however, new hardwood forests have developed following the catastrophic disturbances, although species composition may be significantly different than that in the original forests.

Much of the initial information concerning presettlement forest conditions and present-day forest composition in eastern North America is derived from the extensive work of Dr. E. Lucy Braun. Eastern hardwood forests were originally divided by Braun into nine major associations. For the purpose of this article we have divided the forest into six distinct associations based on the dominant species in each location: northern hardwood–conifer, maple–beech–basswood, mixed-mesophytic, oak–hickory, oak–pine, and southern evergreen (Fig. 1).

The different forest types present on a particular site result from many factors, although climate, physiography, and soil type are typically the most im-portant. Eastern forests contain a variety of soil types associated with different physiographic regions (Fig. 2, Table I). Forests in the northeast and the Lake States are typically composed of young acidic spodosols and inceptisols formed from glacial deposits under cool, moist conditions. Mid-Atlantic and midwestern forests are composed of deep alfisols and ultisols which have subsurface clay accumulations. Weakly differentiated inceptisols are also common in these forests. Deep, highly weathered ultisols dominate the entire southeastern region westward into Texas, although localized areas of alfisols and inceptisols are present along the Mississippi River. These soil differences, as well as annual climatic differences, influence species occurrence and distributional limits. Typically, climate becomes warmer from north to south and markedly drier from east to west within the eastern forest region (Figs. 3 and 4).

II. Forest Associations of the Eastern United States

A. Northern Hardwood–Conifer

This northern vegetation type is characterized by diverse physiography, cold, snowy winters, and glacial soils. It forms one of the larger forest associations, encompassing most of the New England, Adirondack, and Superior Upland physiographic provinces in addition to the northern portions of the Central Lowland and Appalachian Plateau provinces (Fig. 1). Several coniferous species including eastern hemlock (*Tsuga canadensis*), eastern white pine (*Pinus strobus*), red pine (*P. resinosa*), and jack pine (*P. banksiana*) occupy this transition zone between the conifer-dominated boreal forests to the north and deciduous forests to the south. Deciduous species such as sugar maple (*Acer saccharum*), red maple (*A. rubrum*), northern red oak (*Quercus rubra*), American beech (*Fagus grandifolia*), basswood (*Tilia americana*), and yellow birch (*Betula alleghaniensis*) form pure hardwood stands or mixed stands with conifers. A mix of paper birch (*B. papyrifera*), bigtooth aspen (*Populus grandidentata*), and quaking aspen (*P. tremuloides*) is also important throughout much of the Lake States.

Hardwoods in this association generally inhabit mesic sites consisting of moderately well-drained to well-drained soils of medium to heavy texture. In addition to spodosols and inceptisols, hardwood species also inhabit sites composed of alfisols in the aspen-birch dominated portions of the Lake States. Alfisols

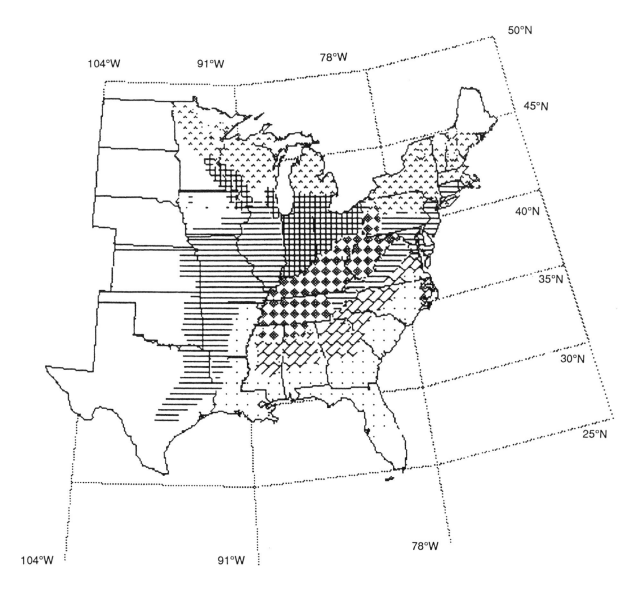

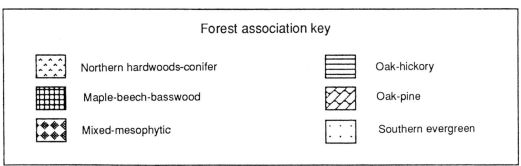

FIGURE 1 Major vegetation associations within the eastern United States.

FIGURE 2 Major physiographic provinces in the eastern United States [Adapted from Barnes, B. V. (1991). Deciduous forests of North America. *In* "Ecosystems of the World." 7. "Temperate Deciduous Forests" (E. Rohrig and B. Ulrich, eds.), pp. 219–344. Elsevier Science, New York].

have subsurface horizons high in bases and clay accumulation and therefore are more fertile than spodosols and inceptisols. Hard, impermeable subsurface layers, or fragipans, are also common in alfisols throughout the northeast, resulting in poorer drainage and more mesic site conditions. Excluding hemlock, conifers tend to inhabit dry, fire-prone environments such as eskers, dry outwash sands, and rock outcrops. However, white pine can also be found occupying swamps and mesic ravines as well as former old-field sites throughout New England. Young spodosols or inceptisols formed from Wisconsin-age glacial deposits are typical soils in this type. Similar to spodosols, inceptisols are acidic in nature, but have weakly differ-

TABLE I

Forest Associations, Physiographic Provinces, and Major Soil Orders within Eastern Hardwood Forests[a]

Forest association	Physiographic province(s)	Dominant soil order
Northern hardwoods–conifer	New England; Adirondack Central Lowland; Appalachian Plateau; Superior Upland	Spodosols; Inceptisols; Alfisols
Maple–beech–basswood	Central Lowland	Alfisols
Mixed-mesophytic	Appalachian Plateau; Interior Low Plateau	Alfisols; Ultisols; Inceptisols
Oak–hickory	Ozark Plateau; Central Lowland; Appalachian Plateau; Ridge and Valley; Blue Ridge	Ultisols; Inceptisols
Oak–pine	Piedmont Plateau; Coastal Plain	Ultisols
Southern evergreen	Coastal Plain	Ultisols; Inceptisols

[a] Adapted from Orwig and Abrams (1993). Temperate forests of the eastern United States. *In* "Conservation and Resource Management" (S. K. Majumdar, E. W. Miller, D. E. Baker, E. K. Brown, J. R. Pratt, and R. F. Schmalz, eds.), pp. 97–116. Pennsylvania Academy of Science.

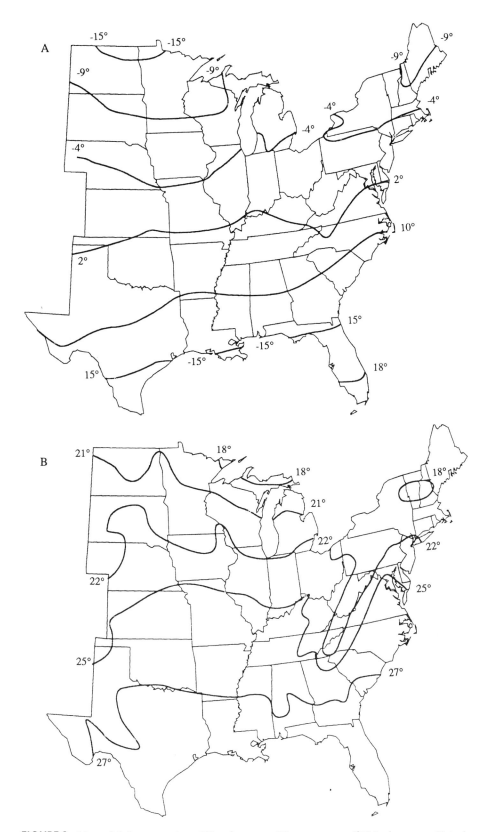

FIGURE 3 Normal daily mean winter (A) and summer (B) temperatures (°C) in the eastern United States [Adapted from Conway, M., and Liston, L. (1990). "The Weather Handbook." Conway Data, Inc., Norcross, GA].

FIGURE 4 Mean annual precipitation (cm) by state [National Climate Data Center (1990). "Comparative Climatic Data for the United States through 1989." Asheville, NC].

entiated horizons with little accumulation of clay or iron.

B. Maple–Beech–Basswood

This association includes both the beech-sugar maple and sugar maple-basswood regions described by Braun (1950, "Deciduous Forests of Eastern North America." Hafner Press, New York). Located within the Central Lowland physiographic province and the northern fringes of the Appalachian Plateau, mesophytic forests of this association are strictly limited to areas of Wisconsin glaciation (Fig. 1). The climate is humid continental with summers being generally warmer than those of the nearby northern hardwood forests. Shade-tolerant sugar maple is the prominent species throughout the region, as it shares overwhelming overstory dominance with American beech on the gently rolling till plains of Ohio and Indiana, and with American basswood (*T. americana*) within the Driftless section located in southwestern Wiscon-

sin, northwestern Illinois, northeastern Iowa, and southeastern Minnesota. Common associates of this association include northern red oak, slippery elm (*Ulmus rubra*), American elm (*U. americana*), red maple, tulip poplar (*Liriodendron tulipifera*), and occasionally white ash (*Fraxinus americana*), black cherry (*Prunus serotina*), and eastern hemlock. Understory vegetation generally consists of seedlings and saplings of the dominant overstory trees and associated species. Because of their shade tolerance, sprouts of beech and basswood, along with sugar maple seedlings can establish themselves in the forest understory. Prior to spring leaf expansion, ephemeral herb species are locally abundant, capturing the early season sunlight. Swamp and bottomland forests throughout many northern forests are dominated by American elm, silver maple (*Acer saccharinum*), yellow birch, larch (*Larix laricina*), and northern white cedar (*Thuja occidentalis*).

Maple–beech mixtures inhabit sites which are composed primarily of mesic alfisols. These soils are well-drained to moderately well-drained, fertile silt or clay loams. Sites within this association remain moist throughout the growing season as a result of soil texture and relatively flat topography. This favorable climate aids in tree growth and reduces the risk of natural and anthropogenic fires. Maple–basswood sites are slightly drier and vary from areas of fine-textured glacial drift in central Minnesota to nutrient-rich loess (wind-deposited loamy soils) sites in southern Wisconsin.

C. Mixed-Mesophytic

This region was originally classified separately as mixed and western mesophytic forests and is characterized by high structural complexity and species diversity. The vegetation contained within the Appalachian Plateau and the Interior Low Plateau regions is one of the most floristically rich collections of overstory species in North America . The broad classification of this group is required due to the highly varied dominance of many different overstory species, commonly 25 tree species or more per hectare. The association stretches southward from the Appalachians of western Pennsylvania and eastern Ohio through West Virginia and into the Cumberland mountains of Kentucky and Tennessee (Fig. 1). Yellow buckeye (*Aesculus octandra),* white basswood (*Tilia heterophylla),* and cucumbertree (*Magnolia acuminata*) are characteristic indicator species whose limits help define the southern and western boundaries of this vegetation type. Additional overstory associates include American beech, tulip poplar, sugar maple, black cherry, American basswood, northern red oak, white oak (*Quercus alba),* white ash, and eastern hemlock. Similar to the overstory, a large assemblage of species comprises the understory layers including redbud (*Cercis canadensis),* sourwood (*Oxydendron arboreum),* dogwood (*Cornus florida),* witch hazel (*Hamamelis virginiana),* hornbeam (*Ostrya virginiana*) and ironwood (*Carpinus caroliniana).*

A variety of habitats ranging from exposed ridges and convex slopes, to protected valleys and mountain coves facilitate the wide array of species found in this association. Perhaps more important are the long, warm growing seasons and the deep, melanized soils which comprise many of these forests. Deciduous mull litter composed of a mixture of organic matter and mineral soil is abundant throughout the association. The humus-darkened soils are a collection of inceptisols, alfisols, and ultisols and are considered to be some of the most productive soils on the continent.

The deep alfisols in southwestern Pennsylvania and northwestern West Virginia contain a high base status because they have been formed from shale, limestone, and calcareous shale bedrock. Local ultisols are also deep, moist soils, although they contain a much lower base status because they have been derived from acid sandstones, shale, and phyllite. These unglaciated soils also have thin subsurface accumulations of clay and weatherable minerals.

D. Oak–Hickory

Immediately east and west of the mixed mesophytic association lies the oak–hickory association. The original oak–hickory and the oak–chestnut regions of Braun are included in this association, making it the largest eastern forest association (Fig. 1). Former oak–chestnut forests are now oak–hickory mixtures due to the eradication of overstory chestnut (*Castanea dentata*) by chestnut blight disease during the early part of this century. By the early 1930s, the fungal parasite, *Endothia parasitica,* had killed virtually all mature chestnut trees throughout most of its range. A large, western portion of this vegetation type extends from the Texas Coastal Plain north through the Ouachita and Ozark Plateau provinces into the Central Lowland Province (Fig. 1). Oak-hickory forests may also be found in portions of southern Minnesota, Wisconsin, and Michigan. Vegetation growing in close proximity to the tallgrass prairie region may form a forest–prairie transition type consisting of scattered, open-grown oaks with a grassy understory in Missouri, Iowa, and eastern Nebraska and Kansas. Eastern portions of these forests presently stretch from the previously glaciated sections of southern New England southward along the Ridge and Valley and Blue Ridge physiographic provinces into western North Carolina and eastern Tennessee (Fig. 1).

White oak maintains high, widespread importance throughout the oak-hickory association. A variety of additional oak species comprise overstory positions in different geographic locations within this type. Well-developed oak-hickory forests dominate the more xeric landscape located west of the mixed-mesophytic association. In addition to the ubiquitous white and black (*Q. velutina*) oaks, prominent southern species in the Ozark and Ouachita provinces include post oak (*Q. stellata),* blackjack oak (*Q. marilandica),* and Shumard oak (*Q. shumardii).* In the Central Lowland section, bur oak (*Q. macrocarpa),* northern pin oak (*Q. ellipsoidalis),* and chinkapin oak (*Q. muehlenbergii)* assume greater importance. Dogwood is a common understory species along with persimmon (*Diospyros virginiana*), redbud (*C. canadensis*), serviceberry (*Amelanchier* spp.), pawpaw (*Asimina triloba*), and red mulberry (*Morus rubra*). Oak savannah woodlands are common in the western Central Lowlands province, where xeric conditions preclude the formation of closed forests. The most successful upland species on these savannas include drought-tolerant post oak, blackjack oak, bur oak, black oak, white oak, and black hickory (*C. texana*).

Important overstory species east of the mixed-mesophytic forest type include red oak, black oak, chestnut oak (*Q. prinus*), and scarlet oak (*Q. coccinea*). Tulip poplar, red maple, and various hickories including pignut (*Carya glabra*), mockernut (*C. tomentosa*), bitternut (*C. cordiformis*), and shagbark (*C. ovata*) commonly share canopy dominance with oaks. Common understory trees include dogwood, sassafras (*Sassafras albidum*), red maple, witch hazel (*H. virginiana*), and tupelo (*Nyssa sylvatica*). In addition, short-lived chestnut sprouts are still locally abundant in many eastern forests. Ericaceous shrubs such as *Vaccinium, Kalmia,* and *Rhododendron* spp. are also prevalent in oak–hickory understories on acidic sites. Since elevation is highly variable within this association, vegetation common in mixed-mesophytic, maple–beech–basswood, and northern hardwood forests may be found in various amounts on steep slopes, ridges, and mountain coves. Characteristic bottomland associates of this vegetation type include sycamore (*Platanus occidentalis*), river birch (*Betula nigra*), boxelder (*Acer negundo*), red maple, and various willows (*Salix* spp.).

Climatic, topographic, and edaphic differences impact the variety of species observed in different locations within this vegetation type. Oak–hickory mixtures of the western Ouachita and Ozark provinces are comprised primarily of ultisols, although limestone and dolomite are also common soil constituents of the plateau regions. Similar to northern hardwood sites, oak forests of the northern Central Lowlands contain sandy glacial tills and outwash plains. Eastern oak–hickory forests experience more precipitation than western portions of the association and, therefore, contain more mesic species on upland sites. The majority of eastern oak forests are found on characteristically mountainous terrain ranging from gently sloping to steep sites comprised of inceptisols, ultisols, or a mixture of both. Moist valley floor sites typically contain limestone-derived soils, while many of the dry ridges and upper slopes contain soils originating from highly weathered, acidic sandstone or shale.

E. Oak–Pine

This region could be considered an eastern extension of the oak–hickory association, although the codominance of pine species characterizes this association. The majority of this vegetation type resides within the gently rolling Piedmont Plateau province which encompasses Virginia, the Carolinas, and portions of Georgia, as well as the Coastal Plain forests of Alabama and Mississippi (Fig. 1). Common oak and hickory species found in eastern oak–hickory forests are the dominant canopy associates along with a mixture of transitional, even-aged pine forests containing loblolly pine (*Pinus taeda*), shortleaf pine (*P. echinata*), and Virginia pine (*P. virginiana*). Species such as willow oak (*Q. phellos*), sweetgum (*Liquidambar styraciflua*), and tulip poplar obtain local importance throughout the region, whereas longleaf pine (*P. palustris*) is locally important in Alabama. In addition to the abundant dogwood, common understory species include sourwood, tupelo, red maple, and American holly. Similar oak–pine mixtures are also found within Coastal Plain forests of New Jersey, Delaware, and Maryland. Interesting variants of this vegetation type are found in the fire-prone pine barrens of New Jersey, Cape Cod, and Long Island which are dominated by pitch pine (*P. rigida*), and occasionally shortleaf pine, in association with dense, short-statured scrub oaks (*Q. ilicifolia* and *Q. prinoides*).

Climatically, this association is very similar to that of the southern evergreen association, experiencing relatively mild winters, hot summers, and long growing seasons of up to 240 days. Temperatures, however, are typically cooler in the oak–pine type (Fig. 3). Gentle slopes comprised almost exclusively of weathered ultisols prevail throughout this vegetation type. These soils are predominantly acidic, sandy loams derived from crystalline and metamorphic rock parent materials.

F. Southern Evergreen

This vegetation association is confined to the relatively young Coastal Plain, encompassing the entire southeast from Virginia to the Gulf Coastal areas of Texas (Fig. 1). Longleaf pine is the characteristic species along with the evergreen angiosperms, live oak (*Q. virginiana*) and evergreen magnolia (*Magnolia grandiflora*). Spanish moss (*Tillandsia usneoides*) commonly blankets these forests, accentuating their evergreen character. Additional overstory constituents on more xeric sites include slash pine (*P. elliotii*), loblolly pine, turkey oak (*Q. laevis*), bluejack oak (*Q. incana*), blackjack oak, and sand post oak (*Q. stellata* var. *margaretta*). On more mesic sites, hardwoods such as laurel oak (*Q. laurifolia*), sweetgum, southern red oak, white ash, beech, and tulip poplar become more prominent. Common understory species include American holly, dogwood, ironwood, hornbeam, inkberry (*Ilex glabra*), and saw-palmetto (*Serenoa repens*). Extensive swamp and bottomland forests are also common in southern forests along river floodplains, where sweetgum attains its peak abundance and biomass. Baldcypress (*Taxodium distichum*), swamp tupelo (*N. sylvatica* var. *biflora*), water tupelo (*N. aquatica*), black willow (*Salix nigra*), water hickory (*C. aquatica*) and overcup oak (*Q. lyrata*) flourish in these frequently flooded areas. Additional variations of the southeastern evergreen forest include sand pine scrub, dominated by sand pine (*P. clausa*) and understory scrub oaks (*Q. geminata*, *Q. myrtifolia*, and *Q. chapmanii*), and sandhill vegetation dominated by longleaf pine, slash pine, and turkey oak with a wiregrass (*Aristida stricta*) understory.

Southern evergreen forests experience a mild climate with abundant precipitation distributed evenly throughout the year. Humidities in excess of 70% are common and growing season lengths may exceed 300 days. Gentle topography prevails on the ultisol-derived, sandy uplands. Many sites are seasonally flooded and, therefore, soils typically experience mottling. Clay hardpans are also common in southern ultisols, causing further saturation by impeding soil drainage. Xeric sites are located on sand hills stemming from ancient shorelines in portions of the Carolinas, Georgia, western Florida, and southern Alabama and Mississippi. Broad bottomland forests, including the alluvial plain of the Mississippi River, are composed of younger inceptisols. These seasonally wet soils also experience mottling and have an organic surface horizon.

III. Presettlement Versus Present-Day Conditions

Forest species composition is rarely stable for extended lengths of time because of disturbance factors, climatic changes, and successional dynamics. Present-day composition may significantly differ from forests which existed prior to the settlement of European man in the 17th and 18th centuries. However, since few trees presently remain from that time period, past forest history is often reconstructed from written historical accounts of land surveyors and from palynology, the study of pollen sediments. Original land survey records have been used in northeastern and midwestern states to reconstruct forest composition of the last several hundred years. Surveyors described vegetation encountered along township boundary lines and listed the species of each corner "witness" or bearing tree. Past vegetational composition has also been interpreted from similar metes and bounds land surveys, which were common in southern land-grant states. Despite potential bias due to surveyor preferences for certain tree species, historical records are still an accurate tool for determining presettlement forest composition. Preserved pollen extracted from lake and bog sediments has been used to determine the broad-scale climatic changes and associated vegetational changes of the last several centuries, including shifts from pine and spruce to oak-dominated forests throughout most of the eastern United States. Table II describes presettlement forest conditions which were constructed from land survey records and pollen data from different portions of eastern hardwood forests.

More recent changes in forests have occurred primarily due to anthropogenic disturbances. Therefore, pre- and postsettlement forest composition may differ markedly from region to region. Although some white pine–hemlock–northern hardwood forests have remained relatively unaltered since European settlement, many have undergone dramatic changes as a result of anthropogenic disturbances. Following clear-cutting and burning, former hemlock–birch–maple forests in Wisconsin developed overstories dominated primarily by red oak, a species of typically low importance in presettlement forests. Similarly, red oak importance in Massachusetts increased from 7% in presettlement white pine forests to nearly 20% in present-day forests as a result of clearing and logging. An additional striking example of vegetational change due to logging was recorded in hemlock–hardwood forests of the Allegheny Plateau in Pennsylvania, where black cherry and red maple percentages of 1–5% in presettlement forests increased to 23 and 27%, respectively, in present-day forests.

Mixed-mesophytic and oak–hickory forests are currently devoid of the once-dominant chestnut, as only root sprouts of this blight-infected species remain today. As mentioned previously, former chest-

TABLE II

Presettlement Forest Composition in Various Eastern Hardwood Forests[a]

Forest region	State	Presettlement vegetation
Northeast	ME, VT	Spruce spp., yellow birch, balsam fir, beech, birch spp.
	NY, NH, PA	Beech, hemlock, sugar maple, white pine
North-Central	WI, MI, MN	Hemlock, sugar maple, beech, white pine, yellow birch
	MN	Sugar maple, basswood, American elm
	MI	White oak–bur oak savanna
Midwest	IN	Beech, sugar maple
	IL	White oak, red oak, sugar maple, black oak
	OH	White oak, black oak, beech, chestnut
	KY	Beech, sugar maple, white oak
	IN	Bur oak–black oak savanna
Central Plains	MO	White oak, bur oak, blackjack oak savanna, post oak
	KS	Tallgrass prairie
	OK	White oak, shingle oak
Mid-Atlantic	PA	White oak, black oak, white pine, hickory
	NJ	Oak–chestnut
	VA, NC	White oak, red oak, black oak
Southeastern	Entire Coastal Plain	Longleaf pine
	GA, LA	Longleaf pine, white oak
	FL	Magnolia, beech

[a] Adapted from Orwig and Abrams (1993). Temperate forests of the eastern United States. In "Conservation and Resource Management" (S. K. Majumdar, E. W. Miller, D. E. Baker, E. K. Brown, J. R. Pratt, and R. F. Schmalz, eds.), pp. 97–116. Pennsylvania Academy of Science.

nut forests were replaced with a group of species including red oak, chestnut oak, black oak, red maple, sweet birch (*Betula lenta*) and pignut hickory. In addition, eastern oak–hickory forests have undergone repeated logging and clearing since settlement, resulting in maintenance of oak in some forests and increases in oak in others, including former oak–pine forests. Midwestern oak–hickory forests also experienced shifts in species composition during postsettlement years as a result of agriculture and fire exclusion. Only 2600 hectares of oak savanna currently remain of the 11–13 million hectares present at the time of settlement. In Wisconsin, bur oak savannas became closed white oak–black oak forests, while rolling prairies in Kansas expanded to closed chinkapin oak–bur oak gallery forests. Naturally occurring southern

oak–pine and southern evergreen forests presently contain less pine and more oak and hickory species than during presettlement times. Because pine species are relatively short-lived and fire frequency has been reduced, the succession without disturbance naturally favors the more shade tolerant hardwoods which become established in the understory.

IV. Disturbance Factors

Historical disturbances such as fire, logging, wind, insects, disease, and animals have played a major role in shaping the structure of many forest communities. Fire has been a naturally recurring force in the majority of temperate forests for thousands of years. In North America, presettlement fires caused by lightning or Indian burning occurred frequently in the Central Plains, mid-Atlantic, and southeastern states. Fires were less frequent but more catastrophical in the upper Lake States and infrequent in northeastern states. Indians used fire for a myriad of tasks including cooking, heating, lighting, hunting game, driving off mosquitos, clearing underbrush, and maintaining grasslands. Although some have debated the extent of Indian burning, it certainly affected local forest composition. Frequent fires during presettlement times presumably affected many forests by eliminating later successional species such as beech and maple, and favoring more resistant oak species. Thus, fire suppression since the beginning of the 20th century has permitted shade-tolerant trees to survive and inhabit understory positions in many forests. [*See* Forest Ecology; Silviculture.]

Windthrow is another natural disturbance which has influenced forest structure for centuries. Wind disturbances typically cause scattered blowdowns of mature trees, creating canopy gaps and a subsequent release of already established individuals or establishment of new species. This "gap-phase" species replacement is common in old-growth hemlock forests, where slightly less tolerant sugar maple, beech, and yellow birch inhabit overstory hemlock gaps. Although windthrow typically occurs as small-scale localized events, less frequent catastrophic windthrow has occurred historically in forests as a result of tornadoes, hurricanes, or heavy localized thunderstorms. Glaze, or ice storms, and early snow prior to leaf fall have similarly affected forests by killing or damaging many overstory trees and stimulating compositional changes, including accelerating succession by releasing shade-tolerant understory trees.

Logging and land clearing for agriculture have also affected a large proportion of hardwood forests. Remaining tracts of land which have escaped logging or clearing are scattered remnants typically located on rough terrain. In addition to the aforementioned compositional changes that occurred following logging, agricultural abandonment following land clearing of hardwood forests also led to drastic compositional changes in various forest types. Old fields in New England were typically invaded by white pine, while abandoned fields of the southeast were commonly invaded by Virginia, shortleaf, or loblolly pines. Dramatic increases in early successional conifer forests resulted from the large-scale agricultural abandonment in the 1800s and early 1900s, initiating the natural conversion to oak–pine and eventually mixed oak forests seen today.

Considerable changes in forest structure may arise due to pathogens or insects, which can cause localized damage and mortality of tree species or can totally eliminate a species such as chestnut. An additional tree species which was recently eliminated from the overstory of many eastern lowland and mesic forests is American elm. Dutch elm disease, caused by the fungus *Ceratocystis ulmi*, along with phloem necrosis disease, resulted in the demise of this dominant species in the 40 years following its introduction into Ohio from Europe in 1930. Common species replacing elm include hackberry (*Celtis occidentalis*), box elder (*Acer negundo*), black cherry, black ash (*Fraxinus nigra*), red maple, and yellow birch. American elm has not been eliminated from understory positions and should persist for generations by short-lived individuals, as seen to a lesser extent in chestnut. Oak wilt (*Ceratocystis fagacearum*), a vascular disease transmitted by sapfeeding beetles, has historically caused mortality of red and black oaks and a subsequent increase in black cherry in midwestern and north-central forests. In addition, beech bark disease (*Nectria coccinea* var. *faginata*) has resulted in extensive mortality of American beech in northern forests over the past few decades. [*See* PLANT PATHOLOGY.]

Hardwood species are also affected by a variety of insects including the destructive gypsy moth (*Lymantria dispar*), which defoliated over 7 million acres of northeastern deciduous forests in 1990 alone. Widespread defoliation can result in considerable oak mortality and may possibly alter species composition. Additional insect pests which incur heavy localized tree damage include the hemlock woolly adelgid (*Adelges tsugae*), in northern hardwood–conifer forests, and

the southern pine beetle (*Dendroctonus frontalis*) in pine forests of the southeast and Gulf Coastal Plain.

In many northern forests, deer have been a common disturbance factor limiting stand development by removing understory vegetation. Following heavy cutting cycles in the late 1800s and early 1900s, white-tailed deer (*Odocoileus virginianus*) populations exploded and severely diminished hemlock and other northern hardwood regeneration. Consequently, a shift in species dominance occurred in Michigan forests from hemlock to sugar maple, whereas in many Pennsylvania hardwood stands that suffered total elimination of understory vegetation, arrested succession from fern and grass species was the result. It has been estimated that deer have been directly responsible for more than 85% of regeneration failures within several forests of the Allegheny Plateau.

V. Western *Populus* Forests

Few of the eastern hardwood species persist west of 97° longitude, which is a north–south boundary from western Minnesota through eastern Texas. Eastern tree species that grow beyond that point are generally found in riparian (river and stream) ecosystems. In these communities, eastern cottonwood (*Populus deltoides* var. *deltoides*) and plains cottonwood (*P. deltoides* var. *occidentalis*) are particularly important. These cottonwood species often grow in association with black (*Salix nigra*) and peachleaf (*S. amygdaloides*) willows, as well as hackberry, green ash, box elder, river birch and slippery elm. In addition, trembling aspen (*P. tremuloides*) grows across the entire North American continent, from Nova Scotia to Alaska and occurs as a mosaic of clonal (sprout origin) forests throughout the western United States. These highly valued forests grow primarily along streams and in wet meadows, but can be found in dry plateaus and mountains. Trembling aspen is intolerant of shade or understory conditions and is perpetuated primarily by root sprouting (called suckering) following periodic burning or cutting. In the absence of such disturbances this short-lived species will be replaced by more shade-tolerant trees such as spruce and fir.

VI. Western Oak Forests

As we discussed earlier oak species are one of the most important genera in eastern hardwood forests. Many different oak species also occur in the western

United States, but often under significantly drier conditions than those in the east. Because of the drier conditions many western oak species exist as shrubs, rather than full-sized trees. In the southwestern intermountain region, gamble oak (*Quercus gambelii*) is the most common oak species. It grows as a shrub or small tree in dense thickets on dry foothills, canyons, and lower slopes. It is slow growing, but its acorns and leaves provide valuable forage for a variety of wildlife in the region. Other oak species in the southwestern United States are Mexican blue oak (*Q. oblongifolia*), Arizona white oak (*Q. arizonica*), and emory oak (*Q. emoryi*).

In contrast to the small stature of these southwestern oaks, the oak woodlands in the West Coast States contain a variety of species that obtain full tree size. Oak woodlands typically occur in the Central Valley and foothills of California and the interior valleys of Oregon. These woodlands are savanna-like in nature, with widely-spaced trees and a grassy understory. The dominant deciduous oak species in these communities are Oregon white oak (*Q. garryana*), blue oak (*Q. douglasii),* California white oak (*Q. lobata*), and Engelmann oak (*Q. engelmannii*). Two evergreen oaks, coast live oak (*Q. agrifolia*) and interior live oak (*Q. wislizenii*), may also be important. Typical of oak savannas in the Central Plains States, these western oak woodlands may be dependent on fire for their survival and perpetuation. Oak species throughout the United States are generally light demanding and do not reproduce well in the shade of their own canopy. Periodic understory burning maintains the open nature of these forests and the grassy understory as well as prevents the successional replacement of oak species by the typical climax of fir and Douglas-fir.

VII. Forests of Europe

Temperate hardwood forests of Europe are classified as mixed conifer–hardwood and are much less species diverse than analogous forests in North America or Asia. The primary hardwood ecosystems are dominated by beech and/or oak. European beech (*Fagus sylvatica*) dominates in the plains, low plateaus, and lesser mountain ranges of central and western Europe. These forests are best developed on slightly acid brown soils, where this species grows in association with sycamore maple (*Acer pseudoplatanus*) and linden tree (*Tilia cordata*). Beech trees tend to be tall and small in diameter and grow in dense forests. This may reflect the fact that trees are of coppice (sprout)

origin from frequent cutting for charcoal or fuelwood production and that beech is a highly shade-tolerant species. Nonetheless, like many species that grow in late successional forests, beech often regenerates most prolifically in single tree gaps that temporarily increases light to the forest floor. Episodic increases in light around existing beech trees generally triggers the production of root sprouts, which represents an important mode of regeneration for this species. Beech forest can also occur on leached or podzolic soils and grow with oak (*Quercus petraea* and *Q. robur*). When sites are not suitable for beech due to rocks, slopes, exposure, and drainage, it may be replaced by forests of *Q. robur*, *Carpinus betulus*, *Castanea sativa*, or *Pinus sylvestris*. In the Alps, Pyrenes, and Carpathian mountain ranges, beech forests grow to an elevation of 600 to 1300 m, after which they are replaced by higher elevation fir, spruce, larch, and pine forests.

European oak forests exist when site conditions facilitate periodic burning due to being drier and having dense understories and proper fuel conditions, thus eliminating other temperate hardwoods and perpetuating the fire-adapted oak species. Not surprisingly, mediterranean ecosystems in southern Europe that burn with great regularity are dominated by *Quercus ilex*. Temperate oak forests are dominated by *Q. robur* to the north and east and extend from southern Finland to northern Scotland. *Quercus petraea* has a range similar to that of European beech, while *Q. pubescens* grows from the Mediterranean to Nancy, France, to the Bohemia region of central Europe. *Quercus cerris* occurs from the Atlantic ocean to central and western Europe.

Forests of England are dominated by *Q. robur* on heavy lowland soils, *Q. petraea* on sandy soils, and *Fagus sylvatica* on calcareous soils. Associated species with *Q. robur* include *F. sylvatica*, *Carpinus betulus*, *Tilia cordata*, and *T. platyphyllos*. *Quercus petraea* forests are mixed with *Q. ilex* (which was introduced from southern Europe), *Betula pubescens*, and *B. pendula*. Calcareous woods dominated by beech also contain *Tilia*, *Acer campestris*, *Ulmus glabra*, and *Fraxinus excelsor*. Other tree genera or species important to the forests of England include *Platanus*, *Salix*, *Juglans*, *Acer platanoides*, and *Populus*.

VIII. Forests of Asia

Both Japan and China contain a significant amount of land dominated by cool-temperate and warm-temperate, broad-leaved, deciduous hardwood forests. The dominant genera in these countries are remarkably similar to that of eastern North America, including *Fagus, Quercus, Acer, Fraxinus, Populus, Betula,* and *Pinus.* Cool temperate forests of Japan are dominated by beech (*Fagus crenata* and *F. japonica*) and the oak, *Quercus crispula.* There are a large number of species mixed in these forests, including many maples (e.g., *Acer mono, A. micranthum,* and *A. japonicum*), *Acanthopanax, Fraxinus lanuginosa, Tilia japonica,* and *Magnolia obovata.* Forests on particularly wet sites may contain *Aesculus, Cercidiphyllum, Betula, Alnus,* and *Cornus.* Warm-temperate hardwood forests in Japan are dominated by mixed oak species and *Castanopsis.* The principal oak species are *Q. gilva, Q. salicina, Q. acuta, Q. glauca, Q. myrsinaefolia,* and *Q. sessilifolia.* In some localities evergreen conifers may be present, including species of *Abies, Tsuga, Podocarpus, Torreya, Picea, Crytomeria,* and *Chamaecyparis.* These species occur on stoney, steep, mountainous habitats and comprise small groups of trees within the hardwood forests. On dry habitats *Quercus phillyraeoides,* with small leathery leaves, may be particularly important. This oak species is the Japanese analogue to *Q. ilex* of southern Europe.

Deciduous hardwood forests of China can be divided into four different forest types: mixed-mesophytic, mixed northern hardwood, birch-dominated, and temperate deciduous broad-leaved. Mixed-mesophytic forests occur in southern China and are dominated by over 50 species of *Acer* and multiple species of *Tilia, Betula, Carpinus, Celtis, Fraxinus, Quercus, Ulmus,* and *Phellodendron.* Over 60 genera are known to exist as canopy tree species in these diverse forests, with no one species acting as a superdominant. Mixed northern hardwood forests located in northern China are represented by more than 20 tree genera, the most important being *Acer, Betula, Pinus koraiensis, Quercus, Fraxinus, Juglans, Maackia, Phellodendron,* and *Ulmus.* Birch forests dominated by *Betula ermani, B. costata, B. dahuria,* and *B. platyphylla* forms the upper altitudinal reaches of temperate deciduous oak forests and mixed northern hardwood forests near Siberia. At higher elevations, below the montane coniferous zone, birch species form nearly pure stands except for occasional *Populus, Salix,* and *Sorbus* species. Temperate deciduous broad-leaved forests exist in the subhumid regions of central China in between the mixed-mesophytic forests of the south and the mixed hardwood forests to the north. In general, these forests are dominated by the deciduous oaks *Quercus mongolica, Q. dentata, Q. liaotungensis, Q. acutissima, Q. variabilis,* and *Q.*

serrata and the evergreen oaks *Q. baronii, Q. glauca,* and *Q. spinosa.* Lower elevation oak forests may be mixed with *Celtis, Fraxinus, Juglans, Populus, Ulmus, Carpinus,* and *Acer.* Most oak forests have their canopy dominated by a single oak species. In drier habitats *Q. mongolica* and *Q. dentata* form open, savanna like stands.

IX. Global Change and Future Forests

As we have discussed above, vegetational change is a dynamic process attributable to many factors including disturbance regimes, site conditions, and prevailing climatic conditions. Climate will probably be the most important factor controlling future vegetational change. Although climatic changes over the past several hundred years have been small, it is predicted that unprecedented climatic change may occur over the next few centuries. Atmospheric carbon dioxide (CO_2) concentrations have risen steadily and are projected to nearly double from the already inflated present levels by the mid-21st century. Increases in CO_2 and other atmospheric trace gases may cause global temperatures to increase several degrees (°C), which could significantly alter forest structure and productivity. Recent predictions based on projected global temperature increases propose declines of spruce and northern pine species. As global temperatures increase, a synergistic effect between vegetation, drought, and fire may occur as the potential for severe fires are predicted to increase, which in turn may lead to increases in vegetation which can tolerate high fire frequency. Therefore, oak and hickory populations are predicted to experience an overall expansion in most temperate forests.

Atmospheric pollutants such as ozone, sulfur dioxide, and nitrogen oxide may also influence future forest composition. These pollutants have been hypothesized to contribute to forest decline in many temperate forests by inhibiting photosynthesis, leaching soil cations, and increasing soil aluminum toxicities. Due to the complexities of our atmosphere and the many interactions present within and among ecosystems, predictions about climatic trends and associated vegetative changes are tenuous at best. Predictive models which take into account species' responses to past environmental changes, potential species' migration rates, and possible climatic feedbacks have been utilized to simulate future scenarios in hardwood forests. More information concerning long-term atmospheric and climatic trends as well as species, population, and ecosystem responses to fluctuating conditions are necessary to accurately predict the future composition of temperate forests of the northern hemisphere. [*See* AIR POLLUTION: PLANT GROWTH AND PRODUCTIVITY.]

Bibliography

Abrams, M. D. (1992). Fire and the development of oak forests. *Bioscience* **42,** 346–353.

Barnes, B. V. (1991). Deciduous forests of North America. *In* "Ecosystems of the World" 7. "Temperate Deciduous Forests" (E. Rohrig, and B. Ulrich, eds.), pp. 219–344. Elsevier Science, New York.

Braun, E. L. (1950). "Deciduous Forests of Eastern North America." Hafner Press, New York.

Conway, M., and Liston, L. (1990). "The Weather Handbook." Conway Data, Inc., Norcross, GA.

Eyre, E. H. (ed.), (1980). "Forest Cover Types of the United States and Canada." Society of American Forestry, Washington, DC.

Jahn, G. (1991). Temperate deciduous forests of Europe. *In* Rohrig, E. and B. Ulrich, eds. "Ecosystems of the World." 7. "Temperate Deciduous Forests" (E. Rohrig and B. Ulrich eds.), pp. 377–502. Elsevier Science Publisher, New York.

National Climatic Data Center (1990). "Comparative Climatic Data for the United States through 1989." Asheville, NC.

Numata, M. (ed.) (1974). "The Flora and Vegetation of Japan." Kodansha Scientific Books, Tokyo.

Orwig, D. A. and Abrams, M. D. (1993). Temperate forests of the eastern United States. *In* "Conservation and Resource Management" (S. K. Majumdar, E. W. Miller, D. E. Baker, E. K. Brown, J. R. Pratt, and R. F. Schmalz, eds.), Pennsylvania Academy of Science.

Wang, C.-W. (1961). "The Forests of China." Maria Moors Cabot Foundation Publ. No. 5. Harvard University Press, Cambridge, MA.

Thermal Processing: Canning and Pasteurization

ARTHUR A. TEIXEIRA, *University of Florida*

I. Technology Overview of Thermal Processing
II. Scientific Principles of Thermal Processing
III. New Developments

Glossary

Aseptic processing Filling and hermetically sealing a previously heat-treated commercially sterile food into a separately sterilized package or container under a sterile environment

Commercial sterilization Relatively severe heat treatment at temperatures above 100°C to inactivate heat-resistant bacterial spores for long-term preservation of foods to be stored at normal nonrefrigerated conditions; heat treatment times and temperatures calculated on the basis of achieving sufficient bacterial inactivation in each food container to comply with public health standards and to insure that the probability of spoilage will be less than some minimum; foods are rendered safe but not "sterile" in the medical sense in that they are not completely free of all possible microorganisms (all references to "sterilization" in this article imply commercial sterilization)

Canning Method of food preservation which results in hermetically sealed containers of food that have been sterilized by heat so they may remain shelf stable over long periods of storage at normal nonrefrigerated storage conditions; the severity of heat treatments needed for this purpose depends upon whether microbial activity is further hindered by low pH and/or water activity of the specific food product

Lethality Reduction in population of target microorganisms as a result of exposure to a lethal temperature history, and expressed as the number of logarithm cycles in population reduction

Slowest heating point Location within a container of food that is last to respond to heat that is penetrating inward from all surfaces, usually the geometric center of the container for solid-packed foods or food containers that are continuously agitated during processing; for containers with liquid products that are held motionless during processing, the slowest heating point may lie somewhat below the geometric center because of naturally occurring convective currents that arise during heating of the liquid contents

Retort Large industrial-sized pressure vessel or cooker in which filled sealed food containers are exposed to pressurized steam for sterilization at temperatures above 100°C

Pasteurization Relatively mild heat treatment at temperatures below 100°C to inactivate heat-sensitive bacterial cells for temporary preservation of foods to be stored under refrigeration

Sterilizing value Time in minutes at a constant reference process temperature that will produce the same lethality as that delivered by the actual temperature history experienced at the slowest heating point in food container during a retort process, and is symbolized by F_0

Thermal process Specifically, the heating of foods in retorts after they have been filled and hermetically sealed in airtight containers for sufficient time and temperature to render the product commercially sterile; generally, any method of heating to accomplish the purpose of heat sterilization or pasteurization

Thermal processing covers the broad area of food preservation technology in which heat treatments are used to inactivate microorganisms to accomplish either commerical sterilization or pasteurization. Sterilization processes are used with canning to preserve the safety and wholesomeness of ready-to-eat foods over long terms of extended storage at normal nonrefrigerated temperature without additives or preservatives, while pasteurization processes are used to extend the refrigerated storage life of fresh foods.

Encyclopedia of Agricultural Science, Volume 4 Copyright © 1994 by Academic Press, Inc. All rights of reproduction in any form reserved.

I. Technology Overview of Thermal Processing

A. Sterilization versus Pasteurization

Both sterilization and pasteurization are thermal processes which make use of heat treatments for the purpose of inactivating microorganisms in foods. However, they differ widely with respect to the classification or type or microorganisms targeted, and thus the range of temperatures that must be achieved, and the type of equipment systems capable of achieving such temperatures. Pasteurization is used to inactivate vegetative bacterial cells, food-borne pathogens which have a relatively low heat resistance. These organisms can be effectively inactivated when exposed to temperatures in the range of 75–95°C, which is below the boiling point of water at standard conditions. These are also the organisms of concern when attempting to prolong the safety and wholesomeness of fresh foods intended for limited periods of refrigerated storage. The more highly heat-resistant bacterial spores remain unaffected by pasteurization, and will eventually spoil the food. Thus, pasteurization is a relatively mild heat treatment used in conjunction with refrigerated storage. [See FOOD MICROBIOLOGY.]

In order to achieve long-term microbial stability in foods, it is necessary to inactivate the more highly heat-resistant bacterial spores which require temperatures in the range of 110–150°C. These temperatures are well above the boiling point of water at standard conditions, and can only be achieved with the use of water (or steam) under pressure in specialized equipment. Because of the severity of these heat treatments, they also accomplish the objectives of pasteurization, and are capable of rendering the food commercially sterile. Thus, this type of heat treatment is known as sterilization, and much of the article will address thermal processing applied to sterilization of canned foods (canning).

B. Retort Processing

There are two fundamentally different process methods by which canning is accomplished in the food industry. These two methods are known as retort processing and aseptic processing. In retort processing, foods to be sterilized are first filled and hermetically sealed in cans, jars, or other retortable containers; they are then heated in their containers using hot steam or water under pressure so that heat penetrates the product from the container wall inward;

both product and container become sterilized together. In aseptic processing, a liquid food is first sterilized outside the container by pumping it through heat exchangers which deliver very rapid heating and cooling rates. Then, the cool sterile product is filled and sealed in a separately sterilized package under a sterile environment at room temperature. Thus, retort processing can be thought of as "in-container" sterilization, and aseptic processing can be thought of as "out-of-container" sterilization. Each of these canning methods will be described more fully.

In retort processing (in-container sterilization), the food to be sterilized is first filled and hermetically sealed in rigid, flexible, or semirigid containers such as metal cans or trays, glass jars, retort pouches or plastic bowls or trays which are then placed within large steam retorts (pressure vessels that work like giant pressure cookers). Once the retorts are full of containers to be sterilized, the retort doors are closed tightly and the air is replaced by hot steam under pressure to achieve temperatures above the atmospheric boiling point of water. A common retort temperature for sterilizing canned foods is 121°C (250°F), at approximately one atmosphere of added internal pressure. After the containers have been exposed to the sterilizing temperature for sufficient time to achieve the desired level of sterilization, the steam is shut off and cooling water is introduced to cool the containers and reduce the pressure, thus ending the process. Once the retort pressure has returned to atmosphere, the doors can be opened, and the processed containers removed for labeling, case-packing, and warehousing to await distribution to the market place.

As would be expected, considerable time, effort, and labor are required to repeatedly unload and reload the retorts after each retort load or batch of containers has completed the sterilization cycle. This is known as a batch retort operation which can become very labor-intensive for large-scale production. Modern food canning plants that produce large volumes of canned foods operate with great efficiency by using continuous retort systems. In continuous rotary retort systems, filled and sealed containers travel in single file along automated conveying tracks into a series of continuous retorts. They enter through a rotating pressure-seal valve that works like a revolving door to maintain the steam pressure inside the retort while introducing container after container from the outside atmosphere at speeds approaching 500 units per minute. Once inside the continuous retort, the containers travel slowly along a rotating helical path (much like being pushed along by riding within the groove

FIGURE 1 Continuous rotary sterilizer system. [Courtesy of FMC Corporation. Reprinted with permission from Teixeira, A. (1992). Thermal process calculations. *In* "Food Engineering Handbook". (Heldman and Lund, eds.), Chapt. 11 Fig. 28, p. 599. Copyright © 1992 by Marcel Dekker, Inc., New York.]

of a rotating screw) until they exit the opposite end of the retort through a similar rotating pressure-seal valve (see Figs. 1 and 2). In a continuous system of this type, the containers move directly from the high pressure steam retort into a cooling retort which is filled with cooling water instead of hot steam to accomplish the cool-down portion of the process. The cool sterilized containers are then conveyed automatically to the labeling, case packing, and warehousing operations as described earlier.

An alternative to the continuous rotary retort system described above is the continuous hydrostatic retort system, which makes use of two U-shaped columns of water over 20 m high separated by a pressurized steam chamber in which the containers are sterilized. Both columns of water are open to the atmosphere at the top and are open to the steam chamber at the bottom. One column serves as the entrance water leg while the other serves as the exit leg. Meanwhile a chainlink-driven conveyor travels continuously through the system carrying cradles of

incoming containers up along the outside wall to the top of the inlet water leg and then down the inlet water leg into the steam chamber. The conveyor speed and length of its path within the steam chamber are designed so as to deliver a sufficiently long residence time of exposure to the hot steam so the containers are fully sterilized before they are carried up the exit leg and down the other side where they automatically transfer to the conveying tracks that take them away for labeling, case packing, and warehousing (see Figs. 3 and 4).

C. Aseptic Processing

The retort temperatures and times required to make food microbiologically safe may also cause unavoidable quality degradation. For these heat-sensitive products sterilization temperatures and times are chosen which will produce a commercially sterile product, but with minimum quality degradation. Because in a retort the container is heated from the outside,

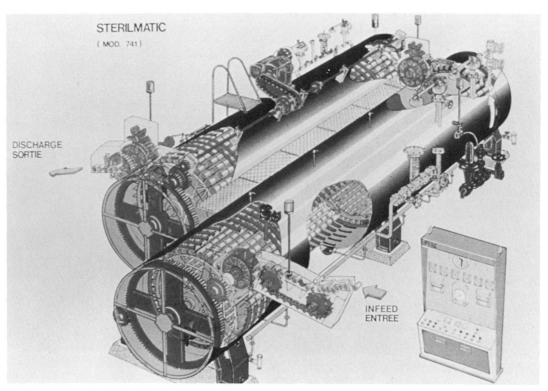

FIGURE 2 Cutaway view of continuous horizontal rotary sterilizer. [Courtesy FMC Corporation. Reprinted with permission from Teixeira, A. (1992). Thermal process calculations. *In* "Food Engineering Handbook" (Heldman and Lund, eds.), Chapt. 11, Fig. 27, p. 598. Copyright © 1992 by Marcel Dekker, Inc., New York.]

it is apparent that the food next to the container wall reaches the process temperature much sooner than the material in the center of the container particularly with solid foods that heat by conduction. As a result, the major portion of the product must be held at an elevated temperature much longer than is necessary to render it sterile while time is being used to assure that sufficient sterilization is reached at the slowest heating point of the container. Obviously the container size, the product consistency, and its ability to conduct heat exerts a very measurable effect on the required time–temperature relationship. Large containers require much longer processing times. Thus, the quality of solid food is generally poorer in larger containers as compared to the same food processed in small containers.

Following the above logic further, it can be reasoned that if the food can be taken out of the container altogether, the distance for heat penetration can be reduced by a minimum if the food can move as a liquid through very narrow tubes or channels in heat exchangers, or exposed directly to hot steam in a fine spray or thin liquid film. This is the concept behind out-of-container sterilization or aseptic processing mentioned earlier. Aseptic processing is essentially limited to liquid foods that can be pumped or sprayed through heat exchangers which are capable of heating the product almost instantaneously to the sterilizing temperature, and cool it down just as quickly. The exposure time that is needed at the sterilizing temperature is achieved by letting the heated product flow through an insulated holding tube of sufficient length before entering the cooling section of the heat exchanger. The main drawback to this processing concept historically has been the difficulty in avoiding recontamination of the cool sterile product from subsequent exposure to the atmosphere or package when attempting to package it for long-term storage. These drawbacks have since been overcome by the development of sophisticated aseptic packaging and filling systems which are capable of forming, filling, and sealing sterile packages with sterile liquid products under controlled sterile environments.

D. Pasteurization Processes

Just as with retort and aseptic methods of canned food sterilization, pasteurization can be carried out by either in-container or out-of-container processes. The main difference from sterilization is that the lower

FIGURE 3 Exterior view of continuous hydrostatic sterilizer. [Courtesy FMC Corporation. Reprinted with permission from Teixeira, A. (1992). Thermal process calculations. *In* "Food Engineering Handbook" (Heldman and Lund eds.), Chapt. 11, Fig. 29, p. 600. Copyright © 1992 by Marcel Dekker, Inc., New York.]

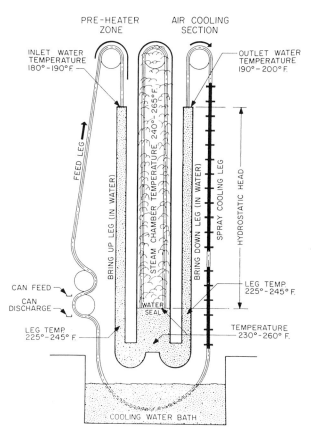

FIGURE 4 Operating schematic of a continuous hydrostatic sterilizer for canned foods. [Reprinted with permission from Teixeira, A. (1992). Thermal process calculations, in "Food Engineering Handbook." (Heldman and Lund eds.), Chapt. 11, Fig. 30, p. 601. Copyright © 1992 by Marcel Dekker, Inc., New York.]

temperatures used for pasteurization do not require the need for operating under pressure. Thus, the equipment systems needed for pasteurization are much simpler in design and easier to operate and maintain.

Normally, liquid foods with delicate heat-sensitive quality attributes like milk and fruit juices are pasteurized out-of-container using high temperature-short time (HTST) heat exchangers to pasteurize with minimum quality degradation prior to filling in clean packages. These HTST pasteurization systems are similar to the aseptic process systems used in sterilization except that they operate at lower temperatures and at atmospheric pressure, and they do not require rigid aseptic filling conditions. Some liquid dairy products, such as dairy cream and coffee whitener, are given a sterilization heat treatment by operating the heat exchanger under pressure to achieve sterilizing temperatures, but are filled into conventional sanitary cartons without aseptic filling systems. Such products are marketed as "ultra-pasteurized" with markedly longer storage life under refrigeration. [*See* DAIRY PROCESSING AND PRODUCTS.]

Less heat-sensitive foods as well as most nonliquid foods are pasteurized in-container much like the retort process for sterilization, except that an open tank of

hot or near-boiling water is sufficient, and there is no requirement to use pressure vessels like retorts or autoclaves. A third method of pasteurization, known as "hot fill," makes use of the high pasteurizing temperature reached by the product in a batch tank or mixing kettle as part of the product preparation. The clean empty containers are filled with the hot product and sealed. They are held upright for a few minutes to transfer sufficient heat to the container walls and bottom; they then are inverted for an additional few minutes to complete pasteurization of the container lid and seal area using heat transferred from the still hot product. Most canned fruits, fruit preserves, and acidified (pickled) products are pasteurized in this way.

Note that the food examples given above for the "hot fill" method of pasteurization are nonrefrigerated foods which enjoy long-term storage at room temperature without the use of sterilization heat treatments. That is because they are high-acid foods (pH<4.5) which cannot support the growth of heat-resistant spore forming pathogens. High-acid foods are subject to spoilage principally by yeasts and molds, which have low heat resistance and can be inactivated by pasteurization heat treatments, alone. These are technically canned foods, but are essentially processed by the use of pasteurization technology. That is why it is important to distinguish between high-acid and low-acid canned foods in the context of thermal processing.

II. Scientific Principles of Thermal Processing

A. Important Interrelationships

An understanding of two distinct bodies of knowledge is required to appreciate the basic principles involved in thermal process calculation. The first of these is an understanding of the thermal inactivation kinetics (heat resistance) of food-spoilage-causing organisms. The second body of knowledge is an understanding of the heat transfer considerations that govern the temperature profiles achieved within the food container during the process, commonly referred to in the canning industry as heat penetration.

Figure 5 conceptually illustrates the interdependence between the thermal inactivation kinetics of

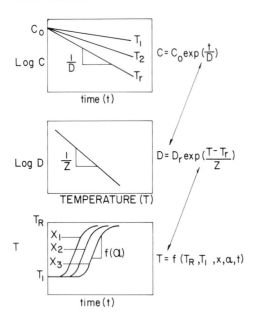

FIGURE 5 Time and temperature dependence of the thermal inactivation kinetics of bacterial spores in the thermal processing of canned foods. [Reprinted with permission from Teixeira, A. (1992). Thermal process calculations, *In* "Food Engineering Handbook" (Heldman and Lund, eds.), Chapt. 11, Copyright © 1992 by Marcel Dekker, Inc., New York.]

bacterial spores and the heat transfer considerations in the food product. Thermal inactivation of bacteria generally follows first-order kinetics and can be described by a logarithmic reduction in the concentration of bacterial spores with time for any given lethal temperature, as shown in the upper family of curves in Fig. 5. These are known as survivor curves. The decimal reduction time, D, is expressed as the time in minutes to achieve one log cycle of reduction in concentration, C. As suggested by the family of curves shown, D is temperature dependent and varies logarithmically with temperature, as shown in the second curve. This is known as a thermal-death-time (TDT), curve and is essentially a straight line over the range of temperatures employed in food sterilization. The slope of the curve that describes this relationship is expressed as the temperature difference, Z, required for the curve to traverse one log cycle (achieving a tenfold change in D). The temperature in the food product, in turn, is a function of the retort temperature (T_R), initial product temperature (T_I), location within the container (x), thermal diffusivity of the product (α), and the time (t), as shown by the heat penetration curves at the bottom of Fig. 5.

Thus, the concentration of viable bacterial spores during thermal processing decreases as a function of the inactivation kinetics, which are a function of temperature. The temperature, in turn, is a function of the heat transfer considerations, involving time, space, thermal properties of the product, and initial and boundary conditions of the process. This interrelationship is illustrated by the functional expressions given in Fig. 5.

B. Microbiological Considerations

When subjected to a lethal temperature, a population of viable bacterial spores will decrease logarithmically at a rate which can be defined by the decimal reduction time (D) described earlier in reference to Fig. 5. As shown on the second curve of Fig. 5, D is temperature dependent and will take on different values at different temperatures in an exponential relationship, which will appear as a straight line on a semilog plot of D versus temperature. This is known as a thermal death time (TDT) curve, shown in more detail in Fig. 6. The slope of this curve reflects the temperature dependency of D and is used to derive the temperature dependency factor Z, which is expressed as the temperature difference (usually in degrees Fahrenheit) required for the curve to traverse one log cycle, or the

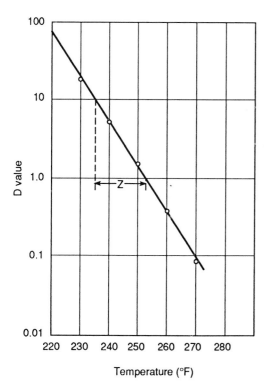

FIGURE 6 Thermal death time (TDT) curve showing temperature dependency of D value (decimal reduction time of microorganisms) given by temperature change (Z) required for 10-fold change in D value. [Reprinted with permission from Teixeira, A. (1992). Thermal process calculations. *In* "Food Engineering Handbook". Chapt. 11, Fig. 6, p. 570. Copyright © 1992 by Marcel Dekker, Inc., New York.]

temperature difference required for a 10-fold change in the D value.

Once the TDT curve has been established for a given microorganism, it can be used to calculate the time–temperature requirements for any idealized thermal process. For example, assume a process is required that will achieve a six-log-cycle reduction in the population of bacterial spores whose kinetics are described by the TDT curve in Fig. 6, and that a temperature of 235°F has been chosen for the process. The TDT curve shows that the D value at 235°F is 10 min. This means that 10 min will be required for each log cycle reduction in population at that temperature. If a six-log-cycle reduction is required, a total of 60 min is required for the process. If a temperature of 270°F had been chosen for the process, the D value at that temperature is approximately 0.1 min, and only 0.6 min (or 36 sec) would be required at that temperature to accomplish the same six-log-cycle reduction.

C. Sterilization *F* Value

The example process calculations carried out using the TDT curve in Fig. 6 showed clearly how two widely different processes (60 min at 235°F and 0.6 min at 270°F) were equivalent with respect to their ability to achieve a six-log-cycle reduction for that organism. Therefore, for a given Z value, the specification of any one point on the line is sufficient to specify the sterilizing value of any process combination of time and temperature on that line. The reference point that has been adopted for this purpose is the time in minutes at the reference temperature of 250°F, or the sterilizing F value for the process. Since the F value is expressed in minutes at 250°F, the unit of lethality is 1 min at 250°F. Thus, if a process is assigned an F value of 6, it means that the integrated lethality achieved by whatever time–temperature history is employed by the process must be equivalent to the lethality achieved by 6 min of exposure to 250°F.

To illustrate, the example process calculation using the TDT curve in Fig. 6 will be repeated by specifying the F value for the required process. Recall from that example that the process was required to accomplish a six-log-cycle reduction in spore population. All that is required to specify the F value is to determine how many minutes at 250°F will be required to achieve that level of log-cycle reduction. The D_{250} value is used for this purpose, since it represents the number of minutes at 250°F to accomplish one log-cycle reduction. Thus, the F value is equal to D_{250} multiplied by the number of log cycles required in population reduction, or

$$F = D_{250} (\log a - \log b), \qquad (1)$$

where a is the initial number of viable spores and b is the final number of viable spores (or survivors).

In this example, $D_{250} = 1.16$ min as taken from the TDT curve in Fig. 6, and $(\log a - \log b) = 6$. Thus, $F = 1.16(6) = 7$ min, and the sterilizing value for this process has been specified as $F = 7$ min. This is normally the way in which a thermal process is specified for subsequent calculation of a process time at some other temperature. In this way information regarding specific microorganisms or numbers of log cycles reduction can be replaced by the F value as a process specification.

Note also that this F value serves as the reference point to specify the equivalent process curve discussed earlier. By plotting a point at 7 min on the vertical line passing through 250°F in Fig. 6, and drawing a curve parallel to the TDT curve through this point, the line will pass through the two equivalent process points that were calculated earlier (60 min at 235°F, and 0.6 min at 270°F). Alternatively, the equation of this straight line can be used to calculate the process time (t) at some other constant temperature (T) when F is specified.

$$F = 10^{[T - 250/Z]}t. \tag{2}$$

Equation (3) becomes important in the general case when the product temperature varies with time during a process, and the F value delivered by the process must be integrated mathematically, such as at the center of a container of solid food.

$$F = \int_0^t 10^{[T - 250/Z]}dt. \tag{3}$$

D. Heat Transfer Considerations

In traditional thermal processing of canned foods, the situation is quite different from the idealized processes described above. Containers are placed in steam retorts which apply heat to the outside wall. The product temperature cannot respond instantaneously, but will gradually rise in an effort to approach the temperature at the wall followed by a gradual fall in response to cooling at the wall. In this situation, the sterilizing value delivered by the process will be the integrated result of the time–temperature history experienced at the slowest heating point of the container, which is determined by heat penetration tests. The primary objective of heat penetration tests is to obtain an accurate recording of the product temperature at the slowest heating point of the container over time while the container is being heated under a controlled set of retort processing conditions. This is normally accomplished through the use of thermocouples inserted through the container wall so as to have the junction located at the slowest heating point. Thermocouple lead wires pass through a packing gland in the wall of the retort for connection to an appropriate data acquisition system in the case of a still cook retort. For agitating retorts, the thermocouple lead wires are connected to a rotating shaft for electrical signal pick up from the rotating armature outside the retort.

The precise temperature–time profile experienced by the product at the slowest heating point will depend on the physical and thermal properties of the product, size and shape of the container, and retort operating conditions. Therefore, it is imperative that test containers of product used in heat penetration tests be truly representative of the commercial product with respect to ingredient formulation, fill weight, headspace, can size, and so on, and that the laboratory or pilot plant retort being used is capable of accurately simulating the operating conditions that will be experienced during commercial processing on the production-scale retort systems intended for the product. If this is not possible, heat penetration tests should be carried out using the actual production retort during scheduled breaks in production operations. [*See* FOOD PROCESS ENGINEERING: HEAT AND MASS TRANSFER.]

E. Process Calculations

Numerical integration of Eq. (3) is the most versatile method of process calculation because it is universally applicable to essentially any type of thermal processing situation. It makes direct use of the product temperature history at the slowest heating point of the container obtained from a heat penetration test or predicted by a computer model for calculating the process sterilizing value delivered by a given temperature–time history.

In fact, this method is particularly useful in taking maximum advantage of computer-based data logging systems used in connection with heat penetration tests. Such systems are capable of reading temperature signals received directly from thermocouples monitoring both retort and product center temperature, and processing these signals through the computer. Both retort temperature and product center temperature are plotted against time without any data transformation. This allows the operator to see what has actually happened throughout the duration of the process test. As the data are being read by the computer, additional programming instructions call for calculation of the incremental process sterilizing value at each time interval between temperature readings and summing these over time as the process is under way (numerical integration of Eq. (3)). As a result, the accumulated sterilizing F value is known at any time during the process and can be plotted on the graph along with the temperature histories to show the final value reached at the end of the process. An example of the computer printout from such a heat penetration test is shown in Fig. 7.

III. New Developments

Thermal processing has been in use as a predominant method of food preservation since the middle of the

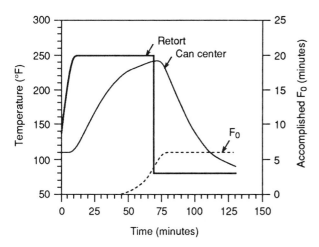

FIGURE 7 Computer-generated plot of measured retort temperature and calculated center temperature and accomplished F_0 for a given thermal process. [Reprinted with permission from Teixeira, A. (1992). Thermal process calculations. *In* "Food Engineering Handbook" (Heldman and Lund, eds.), Chapt. 11, Fig. 16, p. 585. Copyright © 1992 by Marcel Dekker, Inc., New York.]

19th century. Thus, people throughout the world have become quite familiar with canned foods packed in traditional metal cans and glass jars. Perhaps less apparent is the important role that this technology has had and continues to have in promoting and sustaining the health and well-being of populations throughout the world. Although the major portion of canned foods produced throughout history has been used to help feed the consuming public, this technology has also played a very strategic role in major world events. The famous "C"-rations which supported military troops through the first and second world wars were canned food rations. These rations remained safe and wholesome for consumption after long periods of storage and handling under highly stressful and abusive conditions.

Developments in new packaging materials and retort systems have brought about a host of innovative new canned food products that are often not recognized as being canned foods. By the end of the 20th century for example, most canned food rations for the military consisted of flexible retort pouches for use by infantry in combat because of their convenience,

comfort (soft), and light weight when being carried on maneuvers. For feeding large numbers of military troops in field kitchens, canned foods came as fully prepared meals in large institutional-size rectangular steam-table trays ready to heat and serve by the kitchen staff.

Back on the home front, the increasing popularity of the microwave oven demanded canned foods in microwavable containers that were ready to "pop and zap." This has led to the increasing success of complete prepared meals in convenient microwavable lunch bowls or dinner trays that can be placed directly in the microwave oven and then taken directly to the dinner table as an attractive serving dish. Such products are hardly recognizable as traditional canned foods, but they are.

Perhaps least recognizable, however, is the important use that thermal processing technology has played in the pharmaceutical and health care industry. Large quantities and varieties of sterile solutions are required daily in various surgical and patient care procedures. Sterile saline solutions, irrigation solutions, intravenous solutions with dextrose or glucose, and dialysate solutions, along with a host of other large-volume parenteral solutions in glass, plastic, flexible, and semi-rigid containers are sterilized in retort systems using the technology of canning for food preservation. Such products, of course, are not thought of nor considered to be canned foods, but in fact represent a very important use of thermal processing technology throughout the world.

Bibliography

Lopez, A. (1987). "A Complete Course in Canning and Related Processes." CTI, Baltimore.

Lund, D. B. (1975). *In* "Principles of Food Science" (Karel, Frenema, and Lund, eds.). Marcel Dekker, New York.

Teixeira, A. A. (1992). Thermal process calculations. *In* "Food Engineering Handbook" (Heldman and Lund, eds.), Chapt. 11. Marcel Dekker, New York.

Teixeira, A. A., and C. F. Shoemaker (1988). "Computerized Food Processing Operations." Van Nostrand Reinhold, New York.

Toledo, R. (1991). "Fundamentals of Food Process Engineering." Van Nostrand Reinhold, New York.

Tillage Systems

PAUL W. UNGER, *USDA-Agricultural Research Service, Texas*

Glossary

Aggregate (soil) Unit of soil structure composed of many individual soil particles, usually formed by natural processes rather than by artificial processes, and usually less than 10 mm in diameter

Arable land Land so located that production of cultivated crops is economical and practical

Clean tillage Process of plowing and cultivation that incorporates all crop residues with soil and prevents the growth of all plants, except those of the crop being grown

Conservation tillage Any tillage system for which the object is to conserve soil and water. In practice, it is any tillage or tillage and planting system that results in at least 30% of the surface being covered with crop residues to control erosion by water after a crop is planted. To control erosion by wind, crop residues equivalent to at least 1.1 Mg/ha of small grain residues must be retained on the soil surface

Conventional tillage Tillage operations normally performed in preparing a seedbed for a given crop in a given geographical area

Erosion Detachment and movement of soil or rock by water, wind, ice, or gravity. For soil erosion on land used for crop production, water and wind are the prime erosive agents

No-tillage Procedure whereby a crop is planted directly into a soil with no preparatory tillage since harvest of the previous crop; usually, a special planter is used to prepare a narrow, shallow seedbed immediately surrounding the seed being planted

Seedbed Soil zone into which seed is planted

Tillage is defined as the manipulation, generally mechanical, of soil for any purpose, but, in agriculture, it is usually restricted to modifying the condition of the upper soil layers for crop production. Hence, a *tillage system* is the combination of tillage operations that is employed to modify the soil conditions for crop production in a given situation.

Since ancient times, farmers have sought ways to improve soil conditions for the crops that provided food and fiber for themselves and feed for their livestock. Early farmers used sticks to scratch the soil so that seeds could be covered, thus providing better conditions for seed germination and seedling establishment than that which occurred when the seeds were strewn on the soil surface. Even today, farmers in parts of the world still use sticks to punch holes in soil to plant their seeds. In other cases, the hoe is the common tillage implement of the farmer.

In developed countries, soil manipulation for crop production has become a highly mechanized and sophisticated process. A large array of tillage equipment has been developed to manipulate soils in an attempt to provide improved conditions for crops. For many years and in many cases, intensification of tillage to achieve the "ideal" soil condition was attempted. Within the last few decades, however, equipment, labor, energy, and other crop production costs have greatly increased. In addition, alternate pest (weed, insect, and disease) control practices have been developed. As a result, critical assessments have been made regarding the amount of tillage required to achieve satisfactory crop yields under a wide range of conditions. This has led to the use of less intensive tillage systems in many situations. Increased concern regarding the environment has accentuated the need to carefully assess the intensities and types of tillage systems used for producing crops because intensive tillage often results in increased soil erosion by wind and water.

I. Types of Tillage Systems and Equipment

A. Clean (Conventional) Tillage

Conventional tillage systems are those sequences of operations normally performed for the production of a given crop grown in a given geographical area. Certainly, what may be "conventional" in one area may not be so in another. Also, system designation as "conventional" changes with development and adoption of new practices. However, under current usage, conventional tillage is clean tillage in most situations, and that designation will be adhered to in this report.

By definition, clean tillage (or clean culture, clean cultivation) is the process of plowing and cultivation that incorporates all crop residues and prevents growth of all plants, except the particular crop being grown. The residues usually are covered by inversion-type tillage early in the interval between crops. In some systems, however, the first operation (as with disking) may only partially mix the residues with soil, then further mix them with subsequent tillage so that little or no residues remain on the surface when the next crop is planted. Unwanted vegetation between crops is controlled by various tillage operations (plow, disk, sweep, chisel, rod-weeder, etc.). Weeds during the crops' growing season are controlled by cultivation, hoeing, or herbicides. Although the value of plowing has been questioned for many years, clean cultivation is still widely practiced under many conditions. Only with the introduction of conservation tillage systems within the last 30 to 40 years has a trend toward less plowing developed.

B. Conservation Tillage

A widely accepted definition of conservation tillage is any tillage sequence that results in at least 30% of the soil surface being covered with crop residues after the next crop is planted to control water erosion. To control wind erosion, crop residues equivalent to at least 1.1 Mg/ha of small grain residues must be present during the major wind erosion period. However, more residues may be needed to effectively control erosion under some conditions and less under others.

Stubble mulch tillage, reduced tillage, and no-tillage are types of conservation tillage.

1. Stubble Mulch Tillage

Stubble mulch tillage was developed primarily to help control wind erosion that was rampant in the U.S. Great Plains during the major drought of the 1930s. The value of this practice for also controlling water erosion and for conserving water was soon recognized. Hence, the stubble mulch tillage system is now widely used as a year-round system of managing crop residues for effective erosion control while, at the same time, controlling weeds and conserving water.

Stubble mulch tillage is accomplished with sweeps or blades that undercut the soil surface to sever weed roots and prepare a seedbed while yet retaining adequate residues on the soil surface to control erosion. Water conservation benefits are derived from controlling weeds that could use soil water, from surface residues that enhance water infiltration and suppress water evaporation, and, in some cases, from disrupting soil surface crusts, which could reduce water infiltration.

In general, stubble mulch tillage is better adapted to semi-arid or arid regions than to subhumid or humid regions, based on yields reported for crops in different regions. Possible reasons for good responses to stubble mulch tillage in the drier regions include lower nitrification in soil, which prevents overstimulation of plant growth and, in combination with greater water infiltration, improves the water-nutrient balance for crops. Better weed control possibly is another factor because weeds may not die if rain occurs soon after stubble mulch tillage. Because rain probability is lower in dry regions, weed control should be better.

2. Reduced Tillage

Controlling weeds is a major reason for tillage. Therefore, if weeds can be controlled by other means, the need for tillage is reduced, and one such means is the use of herbicides. In recent years, a wide array of herbicides has been developed for controlling weeds in many crops, which has resulted in the development of various reduced or minimum tillage systems. In these systems, herbicides usually are relied upon to control weeds during at least a part of the crop production cycle. However, in contrast to no-tillage, the entire soil surface is disturbed one or more times by tillage for seedbed preparation or crop planting. The reduction in tillage may be in intensity or in frequency of the operation. Some examples of reduced tillage systems that may still meet the surface residue amounts required for conservation tillage are:

1. *Fall (autumn) chisel, field cultivate.* Chiseling loosens a soil, but retains most residues on the surface. Field cultivating undercuts the surface, thus also retaining residues on the surface.

2. *Disk and plant.* Disking incorporates about 50% of surface residues at each operation. Hence, disking can retain adequate residues on the surface, if used sparingly and if adequate amounts are present initially.

3. *Till-plant.* Tillage with sweeps or blades that undercut the surface at the time of planting can retain sufficient residues on the surface to control erosion. By delaying tillage until planting, the surface can remain fully covered with residues during most of the year.

4. *Strip tillage.* Only a narrow band of soil is tilled in a strip tillage system, often with a rotary tiller. By attaching a suitable planter, tillage and planting can be achieved in one operation. Residues remaining on the surface between the tilled strips provide continuing protection against erosion.

5. *Herbicide-tillage combinations.* For these systems, herbicides are relied upon to control weeds, at least during a part of the crop production cycle. In general, tillage is performed as needed to control troublesome weeds, to loosen the soil, and to produce a seedbed. In some situations, tillage is performed to reduce surface residue amounts or to shift surface residues to improve conditions in the row zone for crop planting. The latter may also be used to hasten soil warming in the zone where the crop is planted. [*See* HERBICIDES AND HERBICIDE RESISTANCE; WEED SCIENCE.]

3. No-Tillage

With the no-tillage system, crops are planted directly into the soil with no preparatory tillage since harvest of the previous crop. The planting usually is accomplished by special planters that open a narrow slot or punch a hole in the soil for seed placement at the desired depth. The crops usually are not cultivated and weeds are controlled with herbicides. No-tillage is synonymous with no-till, zero-tillage, slot planting, ecofallow, sod planting, chemical fallow, and direct drilling, which are terms frequently found in the literature.

All crop residues are retained on the soil surface with a no-tillage system. Hence, no-tillage is widely recognized and is being promoted for its erosion-control benefits. When adequate amounts of residues are present, they help control water erosion in three ways. First, they protect soil surfaces from the bombarding action of falling raindrops, which can dislodge soil particles from the soil mass and render

them subject to subsequent removal from the land by flowing water. Second, residues help maintain favorable water infiltration rates, which results in less water flow across the surface to transport dislodged soil particles from the land. Third, surface residues retard the rate of water flow across the surface, thus providing more time for some of the water to infiltrate into the soil and more time for soil particles to settle from the water before they can be transported from the land. For wind erosion control, surface residues, when adequate amounts are present, reduce the wind at the soil surface to nonerosive velocities.

Besides the erosion-control benefits, other advantages ascribed to no-tillage systems as compared with clean tillage or even other conservation tillage systems include improved water conservation (greater water infiltration and reduced evaporation), increased use of land, equal or greater crop yields, reduced energy requirements, reduced labor requirements, reduced equipment inventories, reduced wear and tear on farm equipment (tractors, plows, etc.), and greater net returns to the farming enterprise. The no-tillage system generally is well-suited for use on well-drained and moderately well-drained soils.

Results with no-tillage often are poor on poorly drained soils and where weeds are difficult to control with herbicides. Other disadvantages of the no-tillage system, at least under some conditions, include delayed planting due to lower soil temperatures in cool climates, increased use of chemicals, shift in weed populations, carry-over effect of herbicides, adverse effects of herbicides on adjacent crops, high cost of herbicides, greater pest problems (insect, disease, rodent), lack of adequate residues, greater soil compaction, and a need for a greater level of management by the farm operator.

Major improvements in planting equipment for no-tillage crop production have been made in recent years. Thus, most crops can now be planted by the no-tillage method. Improved sprayers have been developed also, which, along with improved herbicides, permit effective weed control in most cases. There is, however, concern about the greater use of chemicals in no-tillage systems with respect to the environment, especially with respect to water quality. Some chemicals (herbicides) readily move with water, thus contamination of both surface and groundwater is possible. Other chemicals are adsorbed on soil particles and are lost from fields when erosion occurs. Surface water contamination should be lower with no-tillage because it usually reduces runoff (increases infiltration). The increased infiltration, however, may cause water containing soluble chemicals to move deeper into the soil, thus possibly contaminating underground water supplies. To minimize surface and underground water contamination, all chemicals (herbicides, insecticides, fertilizers) must be applied at recommended rates and times, and according to established practices.

C. Ridge Tillage

Ridge tillage is a method of land preparation for crop production that involves deliberately raising the seedbed level above that of the surrounding soil. Reasons for using ridge tillage include improving drainage in the seed zone, allowing improved management of crop residues in a tillage system, and providing for improved soil conditions through cycling of crop residues in the plant root zone. To initiate a ridge-tillage system, ridges are built at the last cultivation of the previous crop or as soon as possible after harvest of that crop. The ridges are built from soil derived from the areas between the crop rows. Before planting the next crop, standing residues may be shredded, thus moving some residues into the furrows. At planting, a one-pass operation scrapes the ridge tops to move remaining residues into the furrows and to expose moist soil into which seed is planted. The ridges are built again at the last cultivation, which begins the next cycle.

Ridge tillage generally is better than no-tillage on poorly drained soils because it provides for improved aeration of the plant root zone. Other advantages of ridge tillage include early soil warm-up, thus allowing more timely crop establishment; good erosion control due to residues remaining on the surface for a major portion of the year; more timely planting than where more intensive tillage systems are used (under wet soil conditions, planting can be accomplished instead of first plowing to prepare a seedbed); lower costs than where more intensive tillage methods are used; and the potential for reduced soil compaction because wheel-track traffic can be confined to certain furrows.

II. Goals of Tillage

A. Overall Goals

The overall goals of tillage are (1) to create soil conditions that will result in crop growth and yields at a satisfactory level, (2) to help protect the environment, and (3) to protect soil resources so that an adequate amount of arable land will be available to future generations on which to grow their food, fiber, and feed crops. The first of these goals usually is of primary concern for producers, and may be of major concern also for policy makers and society as a whole. The producers' goals regarding tillage center around crop production at a satisfactory level to provide the required products for sale and possibly for the families' food and fiber needs as well as feed for livestock. The tillage system employed must result in production at a level that will provide favorable returns to producers' investments so that long-term economic viability can be achieved. Certainly, many producers are concerned also about the environment as well as maintaining the productivity of the land for future generations.

Concern about the environment has increased greatly in recent years, and will increase in the future. Tillage systems employed may affect the water, air, and esthetic quality of the environment. Hence, to meet the environmental standards that regulatory agencies and society as a whole have set or expect, tillage systems are being closely scrutinized regarding their affect on the environment.

The world's area of arable land is finite. All arable land at present is not available for crop production and additional amounts are being constantly removed from cultivation for such purposes as transportation (highways and airports), commercial ventures (factories, businesses, and warehouses), parks, and residential areas. Will there be enough arable land on which future generations can grow their food, fiber, and feed crops? For the near future, adequate amounts are available. However, the productivity of the land must be preserved because the world's human population continues to increase rapidly, which is causing increased demands for food and fiber. Even at present, arable land is severely limited in some regions of the world, which is contributing to famine in some countries. Tillage systems employed may enhance, maintain, or decrease soil productivity. They also may result in soil degradation, which may render them unsuitable for crop production in the future. Therefore, careful selection and evaluation of tillage systems are essential for maintaining the long-term productivity of soils suitable for crop production.

B. Specific Goals

Specific goals for tillage are varied and numerous, and many of them complement one another. The goals include seedbed preparation, weed control, water conservation, erosion control, plant residue incorporation (when excessive amounts are present), fertilizer and pesticide incorporation, soil aeration improvement, irrigation land preparation, insect habitat destruction, and plant rooting depth improvement.

1. Seedbed Preparation

Successful crop production is greatly dependent upon successful seed germination and seedling establishment, which rely on beginning the crop growth cycle with a well-prepared seedbed. In a well-prepared seedbed, viable (live) seeds readily absorb water when placed and firmed in contact with moist soil. A well-prepared seedbed also provides for adequate aeration and soil temperatures for timely seed germination and seedling emergence and establishment. Tillage is widely used for seedbed preparation, but no-tillage crop production systems are gaining acceptance for some crops.

The crop to be grown has a major influence on the type of seedbed required. Crops having small-size and high-cost seed, for example, some vegetables, grasses, alfalfa, and clovers, require a seedbed of relatively small soil aggregates to assure uniform planting depth and adequate seed–soil contact. In contrast, larger-seeded crops, for example, corn, soybean, small grains, sorghum, dry bean, and cotton, do not require a seedbed primarily composed of small aggregates. The implement used and the depth and speed of its operation strongly influence the size distribution of aggregates resulting from a tillage operation on a given soil. Soil water content at the time of tillage also influences aggregate size distribution. Implements that invert the plow layer (moldboard and disk plows) often result in a rough soil condition that requires additional tillage with a disk or harrow to achieve a satisfactory seedbed. Even so, the resultant seedbed may not be as fine as that achieved by use of implements (disk harrows and rotary tillers) that mix the upper soil layers. Rotary tillage is especially suited for obtaining a good seedbed for small-seeded crops.

2. Weed Control

Weed control is essential for successful crop production because weeds compete with crop plants for water, light, nutrients, and space. Until the development of herbicides, a primary reason for tillage was to control weeds. Although tillage operations often achieved both weed control and seedbed preparation, fewer tillage operations would have been necessary if weeds were not a problem or if they were controlled by other means. Such control became possible when herbicides were developed to control weeds in many crops. At present, tillage is still used in many cases, but proper use of appropriate herbicides often makes tillage unnecessary for weed control.

3. Water Conservation

All crop plants require water, but competition for water is increasing among agricultural, residential, industrial, and recreational users. Hence, water conservation is of prime interest where water supplies for agriculture are limited because water deficiencies can greatly reduce crop yields. While deficiencies seemingly are more common, excess water also is detrimental to crop production under some conditions. Tillage systems can be used to conserve water on or remove excess water from cropland, depending on such factors as crop row orientation relative to soil slope, surface roughness resulting from tillage, amount of crop residues remaining on the surface after tillage, presence of soil surface crusts, and degree of disruption by tillage of soil layers that impede water movement. In general, water conservation is improved by row orientation across the slope (contour tillage), increased surface roughness, increased surface residues, and reduced surface crusting, either through greater water infiltration or by reduced soil water evaporation. Water removal from land is enhanced by row orientation with the slope (up and down the slope), smooth soil surfaces, low surface residue amounts, and crusted surfaces. Disruption of impeding layers can enhance water conservation by allowing more water to infiltrate a soil, but it can also enhance water removal by allowing drainage to depths beyond the reach of plants, thus avoiding possible harmful affects of excess water. [*See* SOIL AND WATER MANAGEMENT AND CONSERVATION.]

4. Erosion Control

The tillage system used strongly influences the potential for soil erosion, both by water and by wind. Whereas clean tillage often results in highly erodible soil conditions, conservation tillage systems are widely recognized for their erosion control benefits because they are designed to retain crop residues on the soil surface.

Water erosion control under conditions where surface residues are not used can be achieved by tillage that helps retain water on the land. The same practices that help conserve water (see Section III.B.3) also help control erosion by water because, if water is retained on the land, it cannot transport soil particles from the land.

For wind erosion control, surface residues, when adequate amounts are present, reduce the wind at the soil surface to nonerosive velocities. Where residues are not available or present in adequate amounts, wind erosion control can be enhanced by using tillage practices that result in a rough, cloddy surface; bring nonerodible soil aggregates to the surface and bury erodible soil materials; or provide ridges perpendicular to the direction of prevailing winds.

5. Plant Residue Incorporation

With irrigation and in high-precipitation regions, crops may produce more residues than needed for controlling erosion and amounts that interfere with tillage, pest control, planting, and other crop production operations. They also may adversely affect seedling growth and, consequently, crop yields. Large amounts of residue are of concern mainly where annual cropping and double cropping (more than one crop grown annually) are practiced because of the relatively short time between harvest of one crop and planting of the next crop. Although equipment is available for planting crops under high-residue conditions, it may be desirable to incorporate some of the residues, and various types of tillage equipment are available for this purpose. Any tillage operation results in some residue incorporation. Moldboard and disk plows result in the greatest, disks in intermediate, and sweep or blade plows in the least amounts of residue incorporation. Careful selection of tillage system is essential for assuring that adequate residues will be retained on the land for erosion control where residues are relied upon to help control erosion.

6. Fertilizer and Pesticide Incorporation

Fertilizers that move readily with water such as some nitrogenous materials can be surface-applied and still effectively provide nutrients to crops, but anhydrous ammonia, a gaseous form of nitrogen fertilizer, must be placed in soil to avoid significant losses. Anhydrous ammonia is injected into soils under pressure, usually through chisel point openers. Such openers help loosen a soil, but do not invert the surface or have a major effect on surface residues. In contrast, other fertilizers such as phosphorus materials usually must be incorporated with soil either in narrow bands or over the entire field to be effective. Where lime is needed to alleviate acid-soil conditions (low soil pH), it usually also must be incorporated to be effective. Phosphate fertilizers and lime can be incorporated with a variety of tillage implements. Depending on the method used and the resultant degree of residue incorporation, remaining amounts of residues may be inadequate to achieve effective erosion control. [See FERTILIZER MANAGEMENT AND TECHNOLOGY.]

As for fertilizers, some pesticides are surface-applied, others must be incorporated. Incorporated pesticides for weed and insect control must be mixed uniformly across the entire field for maximum effectiveness. Greater effectiveness of pesticides is achieved with tillage implements such as disk harrows and rotary tillers that mix the soil than with implements that invert the soil (moldboard or disk plows) or only loosen the soil (chisels and sweep plows).

7. Soil Aeration Improvement

Proper air supplies in the plant root zone are essential for good plant growth. While a crop such as rice can grow in water, others must have good access to air (oxygen) that is supplied to plant roots through pores in the soil. Coarse-textured soils (sandy soils) usually have no aeration problems, but fine-textured soils (clay soils and some silty soils) have fine pores that restrict air movement and, hence, may cause poor aeration. Poor aeration can be overcome by tillage that loosens dense or compacted soil zones. However, if the soil initially is in good physical condition, good aeration can be maintained by use of conservation tillage, especially no-tillage, because it does not disturb the channels resulting from decayed plant roots, burrowing insects, and earthworms.

Poor aeration can also be overcome by performing tillage in a manner that results in drainage of excess water from the land. The drainage may occur as water flows across the surface in furrows or especially designed channels (terraces, waterways), or through an underground drainage system (pipes, tiles, etc., or a mole-drain system). The latter is installed by pulling a bullet-shaped cylinder through the soil, thus forming an unlined channel for water flow to a suitable outlet.

8. Irrigation Land Preparation

Land surface preparation is critical where flood or graded-furrow irrigation systems are used because the goal is to achieve uniform water application over the entire area. For flood irrigation, the entire surface is leveled, usually in basins that retain the applied water until it infiltrates into the soil. Special land-leveling equipment, often in conjunction with some type of clean tillage to loosen the soil, is used to level the land. [*See* IRRIGATION ENGINEERING: FARM PRACTICES, METHODS, AND SYSTEMS.]

Graded-furrow irrigation is practiced on land having slight, relatively uniform slopes. To improve uniformity in fields, some land planing (moving soil from high to low points in the field) may be required. Once the desired slopes have been established, ridge- and furrow-forming tillage (lister or disk-bedder) is performed. Then the water is applied to the land at the upslope end and allowed to flow downslope to irrigate the field. Land preparation for graded-furrow irrigation generally involves clean tillage.

In many cases, no special land preparation is used for sprinkler irrigation because center-pivot or lateral-move systems are capable of traversing land with uneven slopes. However, for systems that apply water at low pressure and at a relatively high rate, special small depressions are often needed on the land surface to minimize or prevent water losses by runoff. Construction of these depressions is accomplished by using tillage to form ridges and furrows along the direction of travel of the sprinkler system, then diking the furrows at short distances (about 3 m) with special furrow-diking equipment. With properly designed systems, greater than 95% efficiencies of irrigation water applications have been achieved.

9. Insect Habitat Destruction

Certain insects survive from one crop to the next in crop residues. Thus, plowing under of crop residues has long been promoted as an effective means of controlling such insects. Insects controlled or at least kept in check by plowing under crop residues include the Hessian fly for wheat, wheat jointworm, European corn borer, grasshoppers, and cotton boll weevil and pink bollworm. In general, clean tillage is more effective than conservation tillage for destroying insect habitats. Where surface residue retention is essential for other purposes (for example, erosion control and water conservation), effective insect control in some cases can be achieved by crop rotations or by timely applications of insecticides.

10. Plant Rooting Depth Improvement

Plants depend on the water and nutrients stored in soil to sustain them between precipitation or irrigation events or nutrient applications. When plant root growth is restricted by dense, impervious layers in the soil, the water and nutrients available to plants may not be adequate to provide for the desired level of plant growth. Hence, deeper loosening of such

soil could result in more water and nutrients being available to the plants.

Tillage can be used to alleviate such naturally occurring or traffic-induced (farming equipment or animal) zones, provided they are sufficiently near the surface to be reached by the tillage implement. A variety of implements (plows, disks, chisels, sweeps, subsoilers, etc.) are available for soil loosening. The implement selected should be capable of reaching and effectively loosening the restrictive zone. Common implements (plows, sweeps, chisels, etc.) usually are limited to the upper 0.20 to 0.30 m of a soil. Deeper loosening is possible with special subsoilers. Under some conditions, soils have been loosened to depths of 1.50 m with special equipment.

III. Effectiveness of Different Systems for Attaining the Goals

A. Clean Tillage

The overall and specific goals of tillage discussed above can be attained through proper use of clean tillage under most crop production conditions. Exceptions are on highly erodible soils where clean tillage usually results in major soil losses by water or wind, even under normal rainstorm or wind conditions. During major rainstorms or windstorms, devastating soil losses may occur under some conditions where clean tillage is used. Clean tillage may also result in less-than-desirable water conservation where water infiltration is low, as on sloping soils and unstable soils for which a surface seal develops during water (rainfall or irrigation) application, and where water losses by evaporation are high. Evaporation is greater from bare (clean tilled) than from residue-covered soils under most conditions.

B. Conservation Tillage

The overall and specific goals for tillage can be attained by using some type of conservation tillage under most crop production conditions. Stubble mulch and reduced tillage generally are as effective as clean tillage for most goals, but usually result in more effective soil and water conservation than clean tillage. Plant residue incorporation is not a goal with stubble mulch or reduced tillage. Rather surface residue retention usually is the goal and an advantage of using these systems. Insect habitat destruction may be less than desirable with stubble mulch or reduced tillage than with clean tillage under some conditions. To prepare land for irrigation, as by surface leveling, a residue-free surface usually is needed to achieve uniform and trouble-free operation of the equipment. Therefore, stubble mulch and reduced tillage would not be satisfactory in most cases.

Good crop production is achieved by using no-tillage in many cases, which suggests that this system is effective for attaining the goals for tillage. Certainly, the no-tillage system is highly effective for controlling erosion and conserving water under many conditions because of the greater amounts of crop residues retained on the soil surface. However, just as certainly, residues, fertilizers, and pesticides cannot be incorporated; land cannot be prepared for irrigation; insect habitats cannot be destroyed; and plant rooting depth cannot be mechanically increased where a no-tillage system is used. Where these goals are essential, they must be performed before converting to a no-tillage system.

No-tillage is not adaptable to soils in a degraded condition, and such condition must be corrected before using no-tillage. However, no-tillage is capable of improving a soil by (1) reducing erosion, (2) improving water conservation for improved crop production and, hence, more residue production for further improvements in soil and water conservation, (3) increasing plant rooting depth by not disturbing channels in soil that result from plant root decay, earthworms, and insects, and (4) promoting microbiological activity in soils, which can result in improved soil physical condition and, hence, an improved seedbed for crop establishment. Overall, no-tillage is the cropping system most capable of sustaining the long-term productivity of soils under most conditions.

C. Ridge Tillage

As for clean and conservation tillage, the overall and specific goals can be attained by using ridge tillage under most conditions. An exception is land preparation for irrigation, especially where land surface shaping (for example, leveling) is needed. Where such operation is needed, it must be performed before adopting a ridge tillage system.

In general, erosion control and water conservation should be better with ridge tillage than with clean tillage, but possibly not as good as with conservation tillage, especially with no-tillage. No-tillage provides for continuous surface protection by residues, even after crop planting. In contrast, some bare soil is exposed at planting where ridge tillage is used, and this

could result in erosion by water or wind as well as less water infiltration and greater evaporation under some conditions. Clean tillage results in bare surfaces for prolonged periods, which renders soils subject to erosion and water losses until a crop becomes well established, unless the tillage system used results in surface conditions that minimize or prevent soil and water losses.

IV. Summary

Farmers have sought ways to improve soil conditions for crop production since ancient times. While primitive implements are still used in some countries, soil manipulation for crop production has become a highly mechanized and sophisticated process in developed countries. Many tillage implements have been developed to manipulate soils in an attempt to improve conditions for crops.

Tillage intensification to achieve the "ideal" soil condition was common in many cases for many years. In recent decades, however, alternate practices for controlling pests (weeds, insects, diseases), long a major reason for tillage, have been developed. Such practices along with increased concern for the environment and increasing production costs have resulted in critical assessments regarding the amount of tillage needed to achieve satisfactory crop production under many conditions. As a result, clean tillage, usually an intensive form of tillage that results in crop residue incorporation with soil, is being replaced in many cases by less intensive forms of tillage, for example, conservation and ridge tillage, that result in crop residue management on the soil surface.

The overall goals of tillage are to achieve satisfactory crop production, help protect the environment, and preserve the soil resources for use by future generations. Specific goals for tillage include seedbed preparation, weed control, water conservation, erosion control, residue incorporation, fertilizer and pesticide incorporation, soil aeration improvement, irrigation land preparation, insect habitat destruction, and plant rooting depth improvement. These overall and specific goals can be attained by proper use of any of the various tillage systems in most cases. However, the degree of attainment varies with the system used; other goals are not attainable with some systems.

In general, erosion control and water conservation are greater with conservation tillage, especially no-tillage, than with clean tillage; ridge tillage gives intermediate results. Because conservation and ridge tillage involve crop residue management on the soil surface, major operations such as land leveling to prepare land for irrigation must be done before these tillage systems are adopted. Also, fertilizer and pesticide incorporation and deeply loosening a soil mechanically are not possible with no-tillage in most cases, but they can be accomplished with a reduced tillage system.

Tillage systems will continue to be used to obtain desirable conditions for satisfactory crop production. A variety of systems are available, and the system selected should be used properly so that the overall and specific goals for tillage can be attained.

Bibliography

Gerik, T. J., and Harris, B. L. (eds.) (1987). "Conservation Tillage: Today and Tomorrow." Proc. Southern Region No-Tillage Conf., College Station, TX, July 1987. Texas Agric. Exp. Stn., College Station, Misc. Publ. MP-1636.

Lal, R. (Guest ed.) (1987). Special issue: Ridge tillage. *Soil Tillage Res.* **16** (2–3).

Logan, T. J., Davidson, J. M., Baker, J. L., and Overcash, M. R. (eds.) (1989). "Effects of Conservation Tillage on Groundwater Quality—Nitrates and Pesticides." Lewis Publishers, Inc., Chelsea, MI.

Singh, R. P., Parr, J. F., and Stewart, B. A. (eds.) (1990). "Dryland Agriculture: Strategies for Sustainability." *Adv. Soil Sci.* **13**.

Sprague, M. A., and Triplett, G. B. (eds.) (1986). "No-Tillage and Surface-Tillage Agriculture: The Tillage Revolution." Wiley, New York.

Unger, P. W. (1984). "Tillage Systems for Soil and Water Conservation." *FAO Soils Bull.* **54**.

Unger, P. W. (ed.) (1994). "Managing Agricultural Residues." Lewis Publishers, Inc., Chelsea, MI. (in press).

Unger, P. W., Sneed, T. V., Jordan, W. R., and Jensen, R. (eds.) (1988). "Challenges in Dryland Agriculture—A Global Perspective." Proc. Int. Symp. on Dryland Farming, Amarillo/Bushland, TX, August 1988. Texas Agric. Exp. Stn., College Station.

Unger, P. W., and Van Doren, D. M., Jr. (eds.) (1982). "Predicting Tillage Effects on Soil Physical Properties and Processes." *Am. Soc. Agron., Soil Sci. Soc. Am.,* Spec. Publ. **44**.

Wiese, A. F. (ed.) (1985). "Weed Control in Limited-Tillage Systems." Monograph No. 2, Weed Sci. Soc. Am., Champaign, IL.

Tobacco

CHARLES S. JOHNSON, T. DAVID REED, *Virginia Polytechnic Institute and State University*

Glossary

Burley tobacco Stalk-cut, air-cured tobacco type; cured leaves are reddish-brown in color, with lighter body, greater absorbency and filling power, lower sugar content, and higher alkaloid content than other types

Fire-cured tobacco Stalk-cut tobacco that is cured in widely ventilated barns with open fires under the tobacco; the fires produce smoke that is allowed to contact the tobacco and is the only source of artificial heat; cured leaves of fire-cured tobacco are light to dark brown in color with moderate to heavy body and strong flavor

Flue-cured tobacco Tobacco that is sequentially harvested as leaves ripen; flue-cured tobacco leaves are cured according to a precise schedule of heat and moisture control; leaves are lemon to orange-yellow in color, with a sweet aroma and a slightly acidic taste, and with a relatively high sugar content and relatively low alkaloid content

Layby Final cultivation of a tobacco crop in which soil from the middle of the row is thrown up against the tobacco to form a large bed, which is needed for good root system development for nutrient uptake and to help keep mature tobacco plants upright

Nicotine Most abundant alkaloid in tobacco and one of the primary leaf constituents desired in tobacco products; nicotine content is generally balanced with carbohydrate and sugar levels within cured tobacco leaves

Order Condition of cured tobacco leaves in which their moisture content is high enough so that leaves are soft and malleable, but not so high as to be predisposed to molds and rots; also referred to as "condition" or "case"

Oriental tobacco Class of tobacco traditionally grown in Greece and Turkey; oriental tobacco is commonly primed and air-cured to produce lemon-colored leaf that possesses a characteristic flavor; cured oriental leaf has a relatively high sugar content and a relatively low alkaloid content, with many nonvolatile acids and volatile flavor oils

Priming Removal of tobacco leaves from the stalk, traditionally performed by hand; leaves are generally harvested from the stalk as they ripen, so that bottom leaves (often called "primings") are removed first and top leaves last; in flue-cured tobacco (the predominant tobacco type harvested by priming) approximately three to five leaves are removed at each harvest, "priming," or "pulling"

Stalk-cut tobacco Tobacco types that are harvested by cutting the entire plant or stalk, and are usually air- or fire-cured; burley tobacco is the predominant stalk-cut tobacco type

Tobacco *Nicotiana tabacum,* a solanaceous plant species cultivated for its leaves, which are smoked or chewed for their content of nicotine

Topping Removal of the apical inflorescence, usually along with several small tip leaves; most tobacco types are "topped" at or near the onset of flowering to increase the size, thickness, body, and nicotine content of leaves

Tobacco is a solanaceous plant whose leaves are harvested, cured, and smoked. Although Christopher Columbus was the first European to record the use of tobacco, native Americans and, possibly, the Chinese had been cultivating and smoking tobacco for centuries before. Since Columbus' time, tobacco culture has spread throughout the world. Tobacco seedlings are generally grown in outdoor plant beds before being transplanted in fields. Tobacco fields are fertilized with nitrogen, phosphorus, and potassium at or before transplanting. The crop grows slowly during the first month of the growing season when fields are cultivated. Once cultivation has been completed, the crop grows very quickly and must be protected from a number of pests and diseases during the growing season. Growth of undesired lateral shoots must also be controlled after removal of apical inflorescences. Some types of tobacco, such as burley, are harvested by cutting the entire plant from the roots. Other types, particularly flue-cured tobacco, are harvested by sequentially removing leaves from the stalk. The tobacco curing process manages the moisture content and temperature of tobacco leaves to obtain the desired levels of nicotine and reducing sugars within the leaf. Different tobacco products require varying levels of these constituents. New uses for tobacco are currently being explored. New technologies manipulate tobacco physiology to produce industrial chemicals, food supplements, antibiotics, and enzymes.

I. Classification, Origin, and History of Tobacco

The word "tobacco" generally refers to *Nicotiana tabacum,* although *Nicotiana rustica* is used for similar purposes in some parts of the world. The word tobacco is of Spanish origin. It may have arisen from the name of Y-shaped tubes or pipes used by native Americans for smoking, from the Tabasco province of Mexico, or from the West Indian island of Tobago. The genus name *Nicotiana* and the term nicotine were derived from the name of the French ambassador to Portugal, Jean Nicot, who introduced tobacco to France in 1560. The genus *Nicotiana* is in the family *Solanaceae* and contains 3 subgenera, 14 sections, and 64 species. *Nicotiana* is primarily a New World genus, but 15 species are native to Australia. *Nicotiana tabacum* is a perennial allotetraploid with 24 chromosomes. Although *N. tabacum* probably originated from a natural hybridization of *N. sylvestris* and *N. tomentosiformis* in Brazil or Central America, it has never been found in the wild state.

Native Americans cultivated *N. tabacum* throughout the Western Hemisphere in pre-Columbian times. The Chinese may also have grown and used tobacco long before Columbus landed in the Bahamas in 1492. Although *Nicotiana* species are not native to the east-

ern part of North America, native Americans cultivated and used *N. rustica.* European explorers observed native Americans chewing and sniffing tobacco, as well as smoking it in pipes, rolling it into cigars, and pouring it into "cigarettes" made from palm leaves.

Tobacco use spread rapidly through the world following Columbus' voyages, mostly smoked in cigarlike forms or in pipes. Tobacco culture spread to Europe, Asia, and Africa during the last half of the sixteenth century. The first confirmed reference to a cigarette was made in 1518 in Mexico, but modern cigarettes may have developed in Spain, where "papeletes" were used as early as 1635. Use of papeletes spread to France, where significant improvements were made, and where the product was first called a "cigarette." Cigarettes remained a minor form of tobacco use until late in the 1800s. Development of high-speed cigarette-making machines and the introduction of the "American blended cigarette" revolutionized the tobacco industry and dramatically increased demand for tobacco leaf.

Because manufacturers of tobacco products require specific leaf characteristics, they tend to be very concerned that specific producing areas continue to produce consistent quantities of the type of tobacco leaf that they need. Therefore, tobacco producers tend to enjoy a more stable demand, resulting in higher prices, for their product than that experienced for most other agricultural commodities. Most classes of tobacco are highly suited to coarse-textured soils of low inherent fertility, which are often also poorly suited for production of alternative crops. Tobacco production has tended to dominate areas where it has become established.

The United States Department of Agriculture classifies cultivated tobacco into 8 classes and 26 types, reflecting differences in plant genetics, curing methods, fertilization and management, and soil and weather characteristics of the geographic regions where each is produced (Table I). Cultivated tobacco is grown in most countries of the world. *Flue-cured tobacco* is the most widely grown tobacco type. The term "flue-cured" reflects the heating systems used in early curing barns, when hot air was transported into the barns via flues. Until around 1875, flue-cured tobacco was harvested by cutting the entire stalk, and thereafter the "priming" method of sequential harvest began. In the United States, it is produced from southern Virginia to north Florida. Major flue-cured tobacco-producing countries include Brazil, China, India, the United States, and Zimbabwe. Flue-cured

TABLE I
Characteristics of Different Tobacco Types

Class/type of tobacco	Soils	Nitrogen fertilization (kg/ha)	Leaves per plant	Harvest initiation (weeks after topping)	Harvest method	Curing method	Cured leaf color
Flue-cured	Sandy loams	56–112	18–24	2–10	Primed	Heat	Lemon to orange
Fire-cured	Silt loams	140–168	12–16	4–6	Stalk-cut	Heat + smoke	Light to dark brown
Light air-cured							
Burley	Silt loams	140–280	18–22	3–4	Stalk-cut	Air	Straw to brown
Maryland	Sandy loams	67	16–20	3–4	Stalk-cut	Air	Shades of brown
Dark air-cured	Silt loams	140–168	15–18	4–6	Stalk-cut	Air	Shades of brown
Cigar filler	Silt loams	56–112	12–16	2–3	Stalk-cut	Air	Dark brown
Cigar binder	Sandy/silt/clay loams	224	15–18	2–3	Stalk-cut	Air	Dark brown
Cigar wrapper	Sandy loams	168–235	15–30	N/A	Primed	Air	Light tan to gray brown
Perique	Sandy loams	140–168	12–14	3–4	Stalk-cut	Air, then fermented	Black
Oriental	Wide variety	0–224	24–30	N/A	Primed	Open air	Lemon to dark brown

tobacco is described as possessing full body and being rich in aroma and flavor. Fire-cured and air-cured tobaccos are *stalk-cut tobacco types.* In contrast to flue-cured tobacco, fire-cured and air-cured tobaccos are harvested by cutting the aboveground portion of the plant near ground level. Harvested plants are typically speared onto a wooden stick. Once the leaves have wilted, plants are placed in wooden curing barns. Leaves remain on the stalk during the curing process. The curing process does not involve any heating, but is controlled by adjustments in ventilation. Cured leaves are "stripped" from the stalk, separated into grades, and tied or baled for auction. Most *fire-cured tobacco* is grown in Virginia, Kentucky, and Tennessee. It has a distinctive aroma obtained by "smoking" leaves over open fires that burn hardwood, such as oak or hickory.

Burley tobacco, most cigar tobacco types, dark, air-cured, Maryland, and Virginia sun-cured tobacco types are all examples of *air-cured tobacco. Burley tobacco* originated from a genetic mutation discovered by Mr. George Webb of Higginsport in Brown County, Ohio, in 1864. Most of the burley tobacco grown in the United States is produced in Kentucky, Tennessee, Virginia, North Carolina, and Ohio. Much burley tobacco is also produced in Brazil, China, Italy, and Malawi. *Maryland tobacco* is grown on the light, sandy loam soils of southern Maryland, whereas the *dark air-cured tobacco* types are grown on heavy silt loams in Kentucky and Tennessee or on sandy loam soils with a heavy clay subsoil in Virginia. *Cigar tobaccos* are divided into three classes: cigar filler tobacco, cigar binder tobacco, and cigar wrapper tobacco.

Shade-grown cigar wrapper tobacco is produced in fields enclosed by cloth tents. The artificial shade and protection from wind movement provided by the tents produce the thinner, longer, smoother, small-veined leaves that are needed to wrap cigars. Shade tents are constructed by erecting a wire frame supported by stout posts. Tents are usually 33 feet wide and 125 feet long.

Oriental tobacco is produced in Bulgaria, Greece, Turkey, and Yugoslavia. Leaves are much smaller than those produced by other tobacco types. Harvested leaves are gathered into bundles, sewn onto cotton twine, allowed to wilt in the shade for 24 hr, and then placed in racks or frames in direct sunlight. Curing structures must be covered each night to prevent formation of dew on the strung leaves. After curing, leaves are temporarily hung in garlands, but are sold in bales.

II. Commercial Production of Tobacco

A. Seedling Production

The commercial production of tobacco begins with the growing of seedlings to be transplanted to the field. Management of transplant production systems is particularly important because the grower is dependent on the availability of healthy transplants. Tobacco seed has traditionally been started in plant beds or seedbeds owing to the difficulty of direct-seeding in the field. The seed is relatively delicate and is very small (ca. 11,000 to 12,000 seeds per gram). The use of plant bed techniques provides the grower with the ability to control environmental conditions and thereby ensure favorable conditions for seed germination and seedling growth. The following practices for producing tobacco transplants are general procedures that hold for most types of tobacco produced in most areas of the world.

1. Site Selection

Plant beds should be located on deep, fertile, well-drained soils with good moisture-holding capacity. Plant bed sites with a southern or southeastern exposure and a windbreak on the northern or western sides will have the most favorable local weather conditions. Surface water drainage is very important; plant bed sites should have a gentle slope and may include drainage ditches, if necessary, to eliminate standing water in the beds. Permanent plant bed sites are often established, although rotation of individual plant beds within a permanent site is advisable. Plant beds should be located near a clean water source for irrigation and near the grower's home to make day-to-day management more convenient.

2. Soil and Fertility Management

A cover crop should be grown on plant beds between tobacco growing seasons to maintain the physical condition of the soil and to minimize weed growth. Tobacco plant beds can be constructed to any size, but are usually 2.7 to 4.6 m wide and of variable length. The size of a plant bed, particularly width, is generally determined by convenience in seeding and maintaining the area. All plant material or residue must be removed before seeding. This is often accomplished by disking plant bed areas in the fall and allowing several months for plant residue to decompose. Just prior to seeding, plant bed areas are moldboard-plowed or disked toward the center of the bed. This pattern of working the soil should leave the center of the bed slightly higher than the surrounding area. This "crowning" of the plant bed improves surface drainage, a common plant bed problem. After the plant beds have been plowed, the soil should be harrowed or raked until it is well-pulverized and smooth, and free of clods (important for adequate seed-to-soil contact and thus good germination). To reduce soil compaction, the use of tractors and other heavy equipment directly in the beds should be avoided following final tillage operations. Plant beds are fumigated, with methyl bromide or a similar fumigant to control soil-borne pathogens and weeds.

Plant beds are fertilized with "complete" or mixed fertilizers containing nitrogen, phosphorus, and potassium. Preplant fertilizers are worked into the soil to a depth of 5 cm. Although organic fertilizers have been used on tobacco plant beds, mineral fertilizers are now generally recommended. Nitrogen is normally the predominant ingredient in tobacco plant bed fertilizers, and though nitrogen fertilizers can have several forms, at least 35 to 50% of the nitrogen in a preplant plant bed fertilizer should be in the nitrate form, rather than as ammonium. Additional fertilizer applications are usually recommended only when nutrient deficiencies are encountered. The most common nutrient deficiencies involve nitrogen and sulfur. Nitrogen deficiencies can be corrected by applying a nitrate-nitrogen fertilizer. Sulfur deficiencies are usually corrected with sulfate of potash-magnesia or magnesium sulfate.

3. Seeding

Plant beds are usually seeded 60 to 65 days before a grower plans to transplant his or her crop. Plant beds have traditionally been seeded by hand. The seed is evenly broadcast over the bed by mixing a small quantity of seed with a much larger amount of an inert material (sand, lime, ashes, etc.) or fertilizer (nitrate of soda). Whatever the method, tobacco seed should be evenly scattered over the soil surface, rolled (with a water-filled drum), and lightly irrigated or rained upon to ensure good seed-to-soil contact. Beds are lightly covered with a layer mulch of straw, pine needles, or similar material to keep the seed moist and slightly raise the cover off of the small seedlings. Seeding rate, the number of seed per unit area, is a very important parameter because seedling density largely determines a number of very important characteristics of tobacco transplants. Beds are generally seeded at a rate of 1 ounce of seed to 600 to 800 square yards of plant bed. Beds that are too dense will result in tall, spindly transplants, whereas too few plants will result in short plants with large leaves. A desirable transplant has some stem elongation (12 to 15 cm), that is, a strong stem that is not woody and is the approximate diameter of a wooden pencil.

4. Moisture Management

Tobacco plant beds need to be watered whenever the soil begins to dry. Irrigation may be needed only intermittently in temperate regions such as the tobacco-growing areas of the United States. In drier areas of the world, however, more extensive irrigation is necessary. Soil type and the type of plant bed cover also influence how much and how often plant beds must be watered. Irrigation is needed more frequently with sandy soils and when more porous cover materials are used. Plant beds should be watered often, but lightly during the first 3 weeks after seeding. Plant beds should be irrigated with a greater quantity of water less frequently once seed have germinated. Plant beds should be irrigated slowly, so that water can be absorbed as it is applied.

5. Cover Management

Once the plant beds are seeded, they must be protected by covering with one of several types of material, generally manufactured of cotton, nylon, polyethylene plastic, or spun polyester. In some areas outside of the United States, plant beds may be covered with thatching grass, banana leaves, or a chopped grass mulch. Plant bed covers protect developing plants against cold and wind and help maintain soil moisture. Caution must be exercised when using plastic covers as they may produce excessively high temperatures if not managed properly. Growers using plastic covers perforate the cover, usually with a hand-drawn rolling punch, in order to provide additional cooling under the plastic covers. Covers should be removed when temperatures outside the plant bed reach 30°C for two consecutive days and replaced if nightly low temperatures fall to below 7°C.

6. Mechanization

Many U.S. tobacco producers are adopting a number of new production practices for tobacco plant beds, primarily to reduce the labor involved in raising tobacco transplants. Narrower, raised plant beds (1.2–1.8 m wide vs. 2.7 m wide) are being used to facilitate use of tractor-mounted field equipment to maintain the bed and to reduce surface water drainage problems. Mechanical or precision seeding using pelleted or coated seed is being used to more closely approach optimal plant populations within plant beds and to improve the seedling uniformity. "Clipping" or the removal of leaf tips extending above the terminal buds of seedlings has become a standard production practice for most growers in the United States. Regular clipping will increase transplant size and uniformity and may be used to delay transplanting if field conditions warrant. Lawn mowers and tractor-mounted rotary mowers are often used for clipping plant beds. The increased seedling uniformity made possible by these new practices allows growers to remove a larger percentage of the seedlings within a plant bed at any given time, thus increasing the effi-

ciency of the transplanting operation. Further labor reductions can be obtained by "undercutting" plant beds, that is, by pulling a tractor-mounted metal blade through the soil just below seedling root systems.

7. Greenhouse Transplant Production

The use of greenhouse technology is a recent alternative to outdoor tobacco plant beds. Although Canadian growers have utilized greenhouse culture for many years, the practice has become common in the United States only since approximately 1989. Greenhouse technology provides the grower with more control of growing conditions, produces more uniform transplants, and eliminates hand labor associated with pulling transplants from a plant bed. The principal disadvantage is the capital investment in the structure, which is not generally used for the production of other crops or commodities. [See HORTICULTURAL GREENHOUSE ENGINEERING.]

Greenhouse systems used for tobacco transplant production differ primarily according to how the plants receive water. In an overhead-watered greenhouse, plastic trays are filled with soilless media and placed closely together on the greenhouse floor. Water is applied with an overhead irrigation system. Trays must be watered frequently during the day to ensure that the media is not allowed to dry. Nutrients are provided with water-soluble fertilizers applied in the irrigation water. Growth of the seedlings may be regulated by the amount and frequency of water and fertilizer application. Overhead-watered greenhouses are direct-seeded using specially coated seed that may be placed individually into each cell of the trays. Generally 1175 plants per square meter are grown in overhead-watered greenhouses.

A second production system is the greenhouse float system, which utilizes Styrofoam trays or "floats" that are filled with soilless media and floated in shallow, water-filled bays. Floats may hold 200 to 392 plants, producing 884 to 1744 plants per square meter, respectively. Fertilizer is dissolved in the water and thus constantly available to the tobacco seedlings. Growth is regulated primarily through clipping of the seedlings with a rotary mower that is hung from a rail that passes over the plants. Clipping is necessary to increase transplant uniformity in direct-seeded float or overhead-water greenhouses. Although float greenhouses are direct-seeded, small-scale float systems may be used for hand transfer of purchased miniplugs (commercially grown seedlings) or small seedlings that growers may start themselves. Float beds used for miniplugs or seedling transfer are generally very small, producing limited acres of transplants, but do not require the heating systems necessary for germination of direct-seeded floats. The disadvantage of transfer beds is the labor required for hand transfer of the young seedlings. Direct-seeded greenhouses may be used to produce as much as 150 to 200 acres of transplants.

Proper management is very important for successful transplant production in either a greenhouse or outdoor float bed. Sanitation is essential to prevent pest problems, and contamination with field soil must be avoided to prevent the introduction of soil-borne pathogens in the greenhouse. Trays used for seedling growth and all equipment that may come in contact with plants should be kept clean and sanitized to prevent the introduction and spread of pathogens. Proper greenhouse ventilation and air movement are necessary to prevent high temperatures that may injure or kill young seedlings. The typical greenhouse used for tobacco transplant production has side curtains that are raised and lowered to allow for proper ventilation. Air movement in the greenhouse may be further enhanced with the use of "horizontal airflow" fans that are suspended from the top of the greenhouse to provide a circular pattern of air movement throughout the greenhouse. Unlike outdoor plant beds, water quality is an important consideration of greenhouse transplant production. Water analysis can be used to determine the most appropriate fertilizer and whether water treatment is necessary.

B. Leaf Production

1. Fundamental Soil Considerations

Soils best suited for tobacco production tend to have a well-drained, open-textured topsoil with good water-holding capacity over a heavier-textured, more clayey subsoil. Tobacco producers can maintain and improve soil tilth and quality by rotating tobacco with other crops, by appropriate tillage, and by using recommended practices to minimize soil pests. Tobacco is a heavy user of soil nutrients and thus commercial production requires the addition of relatively high levels of fertilizer. The practice of regular soil sampling and analysis is important to determine the most appropriate and economical fertilization program, and whether the addition of lime is necessary. Soils used for flue-cured tobacco are generally infertile and the grower relies on proper fertilizer selection and precise application to provide sufficient amounts of necessary nutrients in the most appropriate forms. Other tobacco types may be grown on more fertile

soils, although the addition of fertilizer is necessary to provide sufficient nutrient levels at the appropriate time for crop development. [See FERTILIZER MANAGEMENT AND TECHNOLOGY.]

2. Fertilization

Nitrogen is the most important nutrient in tobacco production. How well the crop matures and ripens depends on the amount and availability of nitrogen. Nitrogen rates vary from 56 to 112 kg/ha for flue-cured tobacco to 140 to 280 kg/ha for burley and dark tobaccos (see Table I). Although green manures may be used with most tobaccos, their use must be avoided with flue-cured tobacco as nitrogen availability is critical for proper maturation and ripening. Tobacco is also a heavy user of potassium or potash (K_2O) with normal use rates of 112 to 168 kg/ha. Soils commonly used for tobacco are inherently low in phosphorus. However, years of tobacco production and the use of high-phosphorus fertilizers have resulted in a buildup of soil phosphorus levels in most fields used for tobacco. The phosphorus recommendation for most tobacco soils is 45 to 90 kg/ha.

A typical fertilization program includes two applications of fertilizer. Usually a complete fertilizer, containing nitrogen, phosphorus, and potassium, is applied either before, at the time of, or shortly after tobacco is transplanted in the field. Depending on phosphorus soil test levels, the analysis ratio (N : P : K) of the complete fertilizer will be 1 : 1 : 3, 1 : 2 : 3, or 1 : 3 : 3. A second application of nitrogen or nitrogen and potassium (depending on soil analysis) is made during an early cultivation of the crop. The sidedress fertilizer analysis ratio will depend on potassium soil test levels and may be either 1 : 0 : 0, 1 : 0 : 1, or 1 : 0 : 3. Care must be taken during fertilizer applications that too much fertilizer is not applied at one time or placed too closely to the roots of young plants. Otherwise, root injury and stand losses may occur due to high fertilizer salts levels.

A typical tobacco crop may remove approximately 62 and 25 kg/ha of calcium and magnesium, respectively. Fertilization specifically for these two essential nutrients is generally not necessary as both are supplied in complete analysis fertilizers used for tobacco, and from lime applied to maintain proper soil pH. The pH of tobacco soils should be maintained between 5.6 and 6.2 to ensure proper micronutrient availability and to remain compatible with other crops grown in tobacco rotations. Although a number of micronutrient deficiencies have been observed in tobacco, their occurrence is not common; therefore, specific micronutrient fertilization is not generally required.

3. Land Preparation and Cultivation

Fields in which tobacco is to be grown are prepared by plowing with a moldboard or chisel plow and disked to prepare 25 cm of loose soil and good tilth within the top 12 cm. The soil should be free of clods and fine enough to allow firming of the soil around the transplant. Tobacco is generally planted into raised beds or ridges to provide better drainage and aeration of the soil around the plant. However, not all tobacco is planted into beds owing to the time and expense of the bedding operation and the potential for beds to dry excessively. [See TILLAGE SYSTEMS.]

Tobacco is usually cultivated two to four times to control weeds, to prevent soil crusting (thus increasing water penetration and improving soil aeration) and to place soil around the base of the plant. Each cultivation is directed to successively build up a row ridge to improve surface drainage and reduce the chance of plants drowning in waterlogged soils. The last cultivation occurs near the point when the plants become too tall to pass under the equipment used for cultivation and is called the "layby" cultivation. Application of certain herbicides and fungicides to the soil may occur with the layby cultivation.

No-till or reduced tillage has been researched and evaluated for several years as a way of reducing potential soil loss in tobacco production. The yield and quality of such tobacco are usually slightly lower than with conventionally grown tobacco. However, the development of better broadleaf herbicides for tobacco promises to alleviate some of the limitations of reduced tillage production.

4. Topping and Sucker Control

The production of tobacco with acceptable quality and high yields requires the topping and control of sucker growth. Topping is the removal of the apical bud at the time of inflorescence bud emergence and development. Allowing the flower to fully develop diverts resources from leaf production, thus reducing the yield and quality of the cured tobacco. The height or number of leaves per plant will vary according to tobacco type (see Table I). To produce maximum yield, plants should be topped as soon as they reach the desired stage.

Topping is generally done by hand, although some flue-cured tobacco growers have adopted mechanical topping machines to reduce hand labor requirements. Removal of the "top" or inflorescence breaks apical dominance within the plant and allows axillary buds or "suckers" present in each leaf axial to develop and grow. Allowing suckers to grow will reduce yield and is detrimental to the quality of the cured tobacco. In early tobacco culture, suckers were regularly removed by hand in a procedure called "suckering." Chemical growth regulators are now used to minimize the growth of suckers and greatly reduce the hand labor required. The use of these materials was first developed in the 1940s. Today, chemical sucker control usually involves the sequential application of one or more materials. Contact chemicals (fatty alcohols) act upon young, actively growing suckers through desiccation. Systemic chemicals act by preventing cell division either locally (flumetralin) or throughout the entire plant (maleic hydrazide).

5. Pest Control

Diseases, insects, nematodes, and weeds can severely damage tobacco crops. Although diseases and nematodes are often considered bigger problems for tobacco than insects and weeds, virtually all tobacco producers must include insects and weed control practices in their tobacco production plans.

Table II lists many of the most important tobacco diseases. Many of these syndromes (e.g., black shank) kill plants by destroying plant roots. Plant-parasitic nematodes are microscopic roundworms that live in soil and feed on roots, particularly of flue-cured tobacco. Root-knot nematodes are the most important nematode pests of tobacco. Because leaves are the part of the tobacco plant that is harvested and sold, foliar diseases can severely reduce tobacco yield and quality. Fungi and bacteria cause a number of leaf spot diseases that are important tobacco problems, especially blue mold. A number of viruses can also stunt tobacco plants and severely distort tobacco leaves. Various fungi cause molds or rots that damage cured tobacco leaves in storage. Parasitic plants can also infect tobacco plants: broomrape (species of *Orobranche*), witchweed (*Striga gesneroides*), and dodder (*Cuscuta campestris*) can infect the stems or roots of tobacco plants and remove nutrients that would otherwise be used to increase tobacco yield and quality.

Crop rotation, early destruction of tobacco debris after harvest, and resistant varieties are the foundation of tobacco disease control. Growers are highly encouraged to use all of these practices together, rather than relying on only one method to control a disease problem. However, pesticides are frequently needed to control diseases and nematodes in tobacco fields either because pathogen populations are so large that

TABLE II

Important Diseases of Tobacco

Root and stem diseases		Foliar diseases	
Common name(s)	Causal agent(s)	Common name(s)	Causal agent(s)
Fungi			
Black root rot	*Thielaviopsis basicola* (Berk. & Br.) Ferr.	Anthracnose	*Colletotrichum gloeosporoides* (Penz.) Penz. & Sacc.
Black shank	*Phytophthora parasitica* Dast. var. *nicotianae* (B. de Haan) Tucker	Blue mold	*Peronospora tabacina* Adam
Charcoal rot	*Macrophomina phaseolina* (Tassi) Goidanich	Brown spot	*Alternaria alternata* (Fr. ex Fr.) Kiessel.
Collar rot	*Sclerotinia sclerotiorum* (Lib.) de Bary	Frogeye	*Cercospora nicotianae* (Ellis & Everh.)
Damping-off	*Pythium* spp. *Rhizoctonia solani* Kühn	Gray mold or dead blossom leaf spot	*Botrytis cinerea* Pers.:Fr.
Fusarium wilt	*Fusarium oxysporum* ex Fr. f. sp. *nicotianae* (J. Johnson) W.C. Snyder & H. N. Hans.	Ragged leaf spot	*Ascochyta nicotianae* Pass.
Sore shin	*Rhizoctonia solani* Kühn		
Southern stem rot or blight	*Sclerotium rolfsii* Sacc.		
Tobacco stunt	*Glomus macrocarpus* (Tul. & Tul.) and *Glomus microcarpus* (Tul. & Tul.) Gerd. & Trappe.		
Verticillium wilt	*Verticillium dahiae* Kleb.		
Bacteria			
Granville or bacterial wilt	*Pseudomonas solanacearum* (Smith) Smith	Angular leaf spot and and wildfire	*Pseudomonas syringae* pv. *tabaci* (Wolf & Foster) Stevens
Hollow stalk and black leg	*Erwinia carotovora* subsp. *carotovora* (Jones) Bergey *et al.*		
Nematodes		**Viruses**	
Brown root rot or lesion	*Pratylenchus* spp.	Alfalfa mosaic virus beet curley top virus cucumber mosaic virus	
Root-knot	*Meloidogyne incognita* (Kofoid & White) Chitwood, *M. arenaria* (Neal) Chitwood, *M. javanica* (Treub) Chitwood, *M. hapla* Chitwood	peanut stunt virus potato virus Y tobacco etch virus tobacco leaf curl virus tobacco mosaic virus tobacco necrosis virus tobacco rattle virus tobacco ringspot virus tobacco streak virus tobacco stunt virus tobacco vein mottle virus tomato spotted wilt virus	
Stem break	*Ditylenchus dipsaci* (Kuhn) Filipjev		
Tobacco cyst	*Globodera tabacum* subsp. *solanacearum* (Miller & Gary) Behrens, *G.t. tabacum* (Lownsbery & Lownsbery) Behrens, or *G.t. virginiae* (Miller & Gray) Behrens		

they overwhelm the effects of these cultural practices or because some other factor prevents effective use of one or more of these cultural control methods. Although fungicides are commonly applied to tobacco plant beds, most tobacco disease control chemicals are applied to fields just before transplanting. Pesticides for control of diseases or nematodes are rarely applied directly to tobacco leaves in the field. [See NEMATICIDES; PEST MANAGEMENT: CULTURAL CONTROL.]

Although a principal constituent of tobacco leaves (nicotine) is used to control insects on other crops, insect pests remain an important problem in tobacco production. Some insects that damage tobacco avoid nicotine by feeding on plant tissues with minimal levels of nicotine, whereas others have developed metabolic pathways to excrete or detoxify nicotine before the chemical can exert negative effects upon them. Most of the important insect pests of tobacco are listed in Table III.

Early destruction of tobacco roots and stalks after harvest and early topping and effective sucker control practices are encouraged to reduce overwintering populations of insect pests. Early topping and improved sucker control practices are also promoted to improve control of aphids and hornworms. Transplanting earlier and avoiding excessive use of fertilizers are also recommended to improve control of to-

TABLE III
Important Insect Pests of Tobacco

Common name(s)	Scientific name
Insects that damage roots and stems	
Cutworms	*Agrotis, Feltia, Peridroma,* and *Spodoptera* spp.
Flea beetles	*Epitrix hirtipennis* (Melsheimer)
Mole crickets	*Scapteriscus* spp.
White fringe beetles	*Graphognathus* spp.
Wireworms	*Conderus vespirtinus* and *C. falli*
Insects that damage leaves in the field	
Aphids	*Myzus nicotianae* Blackman
Budworms	*Heliothis virescens* (Fabricius)
Cabbage loopers	*Trichoplusia ni* (Hübner)
Flea beetles	*Epitrix hirtipennis* (Melsheimer)
Grasshoppers	*Melanoplus* spp.
Hornworms	*Manduca* spp.
Japanese beetles	*Popillia japonica* (Newman)
Potato tuberworms	*Phthorimaea uperculella* (Zeller)
Stink bugs	*Acrosternum, nezara,* and *Euschistus* spp.
Thrips	*Thrips tabaci* and *Frankliniella* spp.
Whiteflies	*Bemisia tabaci* (Gennadius)
Insects that damage stored tobacco leaves	
Cigarette beetles	*Lasioderma serricorne* (Fabricius)
Tobacco moths	*Ephestia elutella* (Hübner)

bacco insects. However, insect control in tobacco remains even more dependent on pesticide use than control of diseases and nematodes. No insect-resistant varieties are available, and cultural methods to reduce pest incidence are usually insufficient to provide acceptable control by themselves. Insecticides are usually applied to tobacco fields just before transplanting to control soil insects. Some soil insecticides also control some foliar insect pests, but insecticides are commonly sprayed on tobacco fields during the growing season on an as-needed basis. Many tobacco growers in the United States now use biocontrol (in the form of a *Bacillus thuringiensis* bait) to control budworms.

Weed control is an important part of producing a quality tobacco crop because weeds compete with tobacco for fertilizer, sunlight, and water. Weeds also increase trash in harvested tobacco and provide alternate hosts for tobacco pests and diseases. Crop rotation and properly timed and executed tillage and cultivation practices often provide significant weed control for tobacco. Hand-hoeing of tobacco plant beds and fields remains an important part of tobacco weed control, especially for small farmers. However, herbicides are commonly used where persistent weed problems exist and where labor costs for hand-hoeing are prohibitive, particularly for flue-cured tobacco in the United States. Most tobacco weed control programs focus on minimizing weed populations in plant beds and fields until the crop is large enough to shade out weed seedlings. Although most grasses can usually be controlled in tobacco fields, broadleaf weeds can sometimes choke whole tobacco fields, even when all available weed control methods have been used. All currently available tobacco herbicides act by inhibiting the germination of weed seed. Consequently, tobacco plant beds are fumigated with methyl bromide before seeding and tobacco fields are treated with herbicides just before transplanting. Herbicides are also sometimes applied to tobacco fields just after the final cultivation to provide full-season weed control. Minimal weed growth during the harvest season is particularly important when mechanical harvesters are used. [See WEED SCIENCE.]

6. Tobacco Harvesting Systems

The timing of tobacco harvest is a critical factor in tobacco production. Growers try to harvest only "ripe" tobacco; "mature" tobacco leaves have reached their full size and operate at maximum effectiveness. Ripe tobacco leaves are mature, but are no longer operating at peak efficiency. Farmers detect the onset of this senescence by a chlorosis or yellowing of tobacco leaves that results from the breakdown of chlorophyll. The intensity of these changes varies for each tobacco type and may also be influenced by environmental conditions. This yellowing indicates that carbohydrate and nitrogenous compounds within the leaves are being converted into more soluble, mobile forms. Tobacco ripeness is a physiological state occurring after this conversion has begun but before the process has advanced to the point that these compounds have actually left the leaves.

Flue-cured, cigar-wrapper, and oriental tobaccos are sequentially harvested or "primed" because they need to have a relatively high sugar content. Sequential harvesting of individual leaves allows these tobacco types to continue conversion of carbohydrates to reducing sugars for a longer period of time. Delayed harvesting also generally results in lower levels of nitrogenous compounds such as nicotine. Leaves toward the bottom of the stalk usually ripen before those toward the top of the plant. Several (three to five) flue-cured tobacco leaves are primed at each harvest. Priming aids or "taxi-type" harvesters were introduced in the 1950s that transported harvest labor through flue-cured tobacco fields. Mechanical leaf-tying machines were developed in Canada and spread throughout the United States. A machine for harvesting flue-cured tobacco was introduced in 1971. Mechanical harvesting of flue-cured tobacco is becoming more common as labor costs continue to rise. Other tobacco types, such as air-cured tobaccos and burley, are harvested by cutting stalks just above the soil. Harvested plants are left in the field until their leaves begin to wilt. After wilting, plants are placed in curing barns, where leaves are cured while remaining attached to plant stalks.

7. Curing Tobacco

Curing tobacco involves the use of ventilation and temperature to reduce the water content of harvested leaves in order to manage the continued conversion of carbohydrates within tobacco leaves to simple sugars such as glucose, fructose, and sucrose. The length of time that tobacco is cured directly influences the sugar content of the final product. Farmers learned to smoke tobacco in the curing process to minimize rots and to prepare the leaf for storage and transport to market. Early in the nineteenth century, planters in North Carolina and Virginia began to use heat in the curing process to cure leaves to an even lighter color, a golden yellow. The use of flues to supply fireboxes from fuel outside of the barn was patented by Dr. David G. Tuck of Halifax, Virginia, in 1830. However, flue-

curing did not become widespread until after the Civil War. Flue-curing of primed leaves was not completely adopted in the United States until almost 1920. Flues were gradually replaced by thermostatically controlled burners that used oil or gas. "Bulk-curing" was first used on a farm in Robeson County, North Carolina, in 1960. This new curing method reduced harvesting labor by 50% compared to use of conventional barns that contained leaf tied onto wooden sticks. Almost all flue-cured tobacco grown in the United States is now bulk-cured.

Flue-cured tobacco is cured for only 3–6 days, resulting in relatively high levels of reducing sugars. Wet and dry bulb thermometer readings are used to manage airflow, relative humidity, and temperature within curing barns. R. L. Ragland of Virginia proposed the curing regime for flue-cured tobacco that is still being used today. His process included four distinct stages: (1) yellowing of the leaf, (2) fixing the color of the leaf, (3) drying the leaf, and (4) drying the leaf stems. In the "yellowing stage," fans recirculate air through the harvested leaves to minimize molds and rots while air temperatures within the curing barns are raised very gradually. Almost all the starch in the leaves is converted to sugars during this stage. The degree of carbohydrate-to-sugar conversion is judged based on the intensity of the change in leaf color from green to yellow. Once the yellowing phase has been completed, chemical changes within the leaves (indicated by leaf color) are "fixed" by increasing temperatures and the proportion of ambient to recirculated air to dry the leaf lamina. The final "killing-out" stage of curing flue-cured tobacco involves increasing air temperatures further to remove remaining moisture from within leaf stems to prevent seepage of water back into leaf lamina and to minimize problems with storage rots and molds.

Sun-cured tobaccos are cured for 2–4 weeks, without any precise controls. Some air-cured types, such as oriental, are not cured within a structure but dry out on racks in shady areas with minimal protection from the weather. Most air-cured types, however, are cured within barns for 3–6 weeks. This slow and gradual process minimizes the sugar content of these types of tobacco. The amount of environmental control used during curing varies, but the walls and roofs of curing barns usually allow growers to adjust airflow through the barns to some degree. Artificial heat or fans are used only in rare cases of excessively moist conditions.

Fully cured tobacco leaves are dry and too brittle to be handled easily. This condition limits storage problems, but must be corrected to market the product. Therefore, one of the first stages of market preparation is often to "condition" or bring the tobacco "in order". Under humid conditions, cured leaves can absorb enough atmospheric moisture to become soft and malleable. However, in some tobacco production areas, and in some years, cured leaves must be steamed or misted prior to being sold.

8. Marketing Tobacco

Cured leaf was originally packed into hogsheads and shipped overseas. Later, tobacco was sold through inspection warehouses, followed by sales "at the barn door" to domestic dealers and manufacturers. Loose leaf sales of flue-cured tobacco were first recorded at Neel's Warehouse in Danville, Virginia, in 1858, where tobacco was sold in stacks of hand-tied bundles, called "hands." Flue-cured tobacco was sold in piles of untied tobacco beginning in the 1970s. Burley marketing switched to bales of untied leaves in the late 1970s and early 1980s. Inspection and use of standardized federal grades of U.S. tobacco on warehouse floors was initiated in 1929. Growers were required to predesignate warehouses for marketing their crop beginning in 1974.

Cured tobacco leaf is generally sold at auction. Flue-cured tobacco producers in the United States bundle loose leaf in large burlap sheets. These bundles are lined up on the floor of an independently owned warehouse. Sheets are untied to allow government graders to classify the tobacco according to a system that attempts to describe leaf size, color, and physical condition. Tobacco is sold as auctioneers and buyers move along the rows of sheets taking bids on each pile of tobacco. Burley tobacco is sold similarly, with the exception that farmers sort burley tobacco leaves as they strip them from plant stalks, and then press the cured leaves into bales. Other tobacco types are still prepared for market by tying into "hands" composed of several leaves that are twisted or tied together. These hands are placed in neat piles for presentation at the warehouse or sales area. Dark air-cured tobacco in Kentucky is purchased while still in the curing barn. In Brazil, individual tobacco farmers contract with a buyer before planting. In some African countries, producer cooperatives process the tobacco and market the crop by auction or private contract.

Tobacco producers are not directly identified in auction systems for marketing tobacco as codes are used to keep track of a producer's crop. This pseudo-anonymity helps preserve the rights of both buyers and sellers to nullify a sale for appropriate reasons.

In the United States, tobacco producers who do not receive an auction price equal to or higher than a "support price" can place their tobacco under loan to a government-administered, producer-owned cooperative for a designated "support price." The cooperative processes and stores the leaf and attempts to sell it via a bidding system. This system was instituted to stabilize supply and demand for tobacco. The system also guarantees a minimum price for U.S. producers.

III. Tobacco Propagation for Research

All *Nicotiana* species produce very small seeds (10,500/g for *N. tabacum*) and delicate seedlings. Seed should be sown in a sterile medium such as vermiculite, a sterilized sand : loamy soil : peat moss mixture, or fumigated soil. A 10-cm pot should be sown with 40–50 seed. Seed should be covered with a fine layer of medium after sowing, which needs to remain moist until emergence, but should not be watered from above. Seedlings should emerge within 5–7 days at ambient air temperatures between 21 and 27°C. Species other than *N. tabacum* may take as long as 30 days to germinate. Seedlings in vermiculite should be fed with 150 ml of Hoagland's solution 1 and 2 weeks after germination. Freshly harvested seed may be dormant, which can usually be overcome by placing seed in a 2% sodium hypochlorite solution (2:3 solution of bleach and water) for 15–30 min. Treated seed should be rinsed with water and placed briefly in acetone. Seedlings should be transplanted into 5-cm-diameter containers when they are about 4 cm tall. Plants should be fed weekly with Hoagland's solution, but care should be exercised to avoid overwatering. *Nicotiana* species that produce large mature plants should be transplanted a second time about 3–5 weeks after the first transplanting.

Most *Nicotiana* species can be asexually propagated, although with varying difficulty, using stem cuttings, axillary shoots (suckers), or leaves. *Nicotiana* species can also be grafted. Haploid plants are very useful for research because they can be cultured in large numbers, screened for any number of inherited traits, and then transformed back into a diploid state. Viable plants of *Nicotiana* species can be obtained by culturing either anthers or pollen. The ploidy status of haploid plants is usually confirmed (often by root tip cytology) before treatment to convert them back to a diploid state. Diploid plants may be obtained by culturing midvein sections from mature leaves of diploid plants or by culturing plants from axillary buds treated with colchicine. Vegetative organs of *Nicotiana* species may also be cultured separately. Root cultures are initiated by germinating disinfected seed and then incubating the seed on a sterile rooting medium. Shoot tip culture involves removing and surface sterilizing the apical 1 cm of a plant stem, cutting the meristematic tissue from the bud, and transferring the tissue to a sterile rooting medium. Leaves can be cultured by transferring meristematic tissue onto a suitable nutrient medium that does not stimulate root formation. Plant reproductive organs can also be cultured for research purposes.

Nicotiana species were among the first used in developing plant tissue culture methods and are a commonly used model system in basic plant research. Cells are usually obtained by aseptically transferring pith tissue from within plant stems onto a solid agar or liquid growth medium. Cultures are incubated in the dark under moist conditions for 3–5 weeks. Once established, callus tissues need to be transferred frequently to maintain an uninterrupted supply of healthy, continuously growing plant cells. However, these techniques also have a number of limitations. Wherever possible, therefore, tissue cultures need to be compared with intact plants. Cultures need to be checked periodically against the specific plant from which the original culture was taken to verify that the culture retains sufficient resemblance to the original explant.

IV. Tobacco Products

Tobacco is currently produced by farmers for the commercial manufacture of products that are smoked (cigars, cigarettes, and pipe tobacco) or chewed (chewing tobacco, snuff). Once sold, tobacco is grouped by purchasers into homogeneous mixtures of leaves with a similar "style." These mixtures possess a specific set of desired characteristics that is described by a classification system that may be unique to each manufacturer. The midribs of leaves are then separated from leaf lamina in a process called "stemming." Lamina and stems are then "redried" separately and packed for storage. Cured leaf is stored under conditions to minimize insect damage, molds, or loss of color. Leaf is often stored for up to 18 months before use.

The most commonly used type of cigarette is known as the "American blended" cigarette. It is so known because of the extreme degree to which bur-

ley, flue-cured, Maryland, oriental, and reconstituted tobaccos are mixed or blended with various additives to result in a given taste and aroma. Blended cigarettes, versus those made from a single or limited number of tobacco types, originated in the United States. This style of cigarette is increasingly replacing other types because blended cigarettes are characteristically milder.

Cigarette manufacture initially involves processing leaf to obtain a thorough mixture of tobacco cut into small pieces, followed by inserting this mixture into a paper tube to form a cigarette. The manufacturing process requires precise control of the moisture content of the tobacco. For this and a number of other reasons, each of the different tobacco types used in blended cigarettes is initially processed separately.

When tobacco is removed from storage for cigarette manufacture, it is first "conditioned," "ordered," or "brought into case" by adding moisture. Flavorings and other additives are also often added to leaf lamina of burley tobacco at this stage of processing. "Casing" is the process of adding flavorings and modifiers to tobacco by soaking, spraying, or dipping leaf lamina before it is cut into narrow strips called "rag." Cased tobacco is "toasted" at high temperatures to reduce harshness, and then reordered. Sugars, herbs, botanical oils, resins, and gums are added to tobacco to improve taste and aroma and to improve the moisture-holding capacity of the tobacco. These additives may be applied before (casing) or after cutting. Additives are also sometimes applied to cigarette packaging.

Leaf stems are preconditioned with water and then crushed. In many countries, crushed stems are cut, dried, and cooled before use or storage. In the United States, water-soluble materials are removed from crushed stems, mixed with additives, and then added back to a fibrous matrix to form "reconstituted sheet."

The processing lines for each type of tobacco merge just before the tobacco is cut into rag. This cutting operation cuts the tobacco into narrow strips, the width of which influences smoking characteristics, as well as the firmness of the cigarette. The cut rag is then deposited onto paper fed from large bobbins. Most cigarette paper is made from flax and must possess a uniform and precise permeability to allow cigarettes to burn properly. Cigarette paper also tends to hold cigarette ash together to minimize flaking of hot ash outward during smoking. The paper is rolled and gummed around cut tobacco rag to form a long cylinder that is cut into appropriate lengths. Filters, if desired, are placed on the cut cigarettes by a separate machine that is integrated with the cigarette maker. Paper or cellulose acetate fibers (called "tow") within cigarette filters remove particulate matter from tobacco smoke. Carbon is also sometimes used in cigarette filters to remove certain gases from inhaled tobacco smoke.

Cigars may be hand-rolled or manufactured by machine. They are composed of 85% "filler," 10% "binder," and 5% "wrapper" type tobaccos. Binder and wrapper tobacco are often made from reconstituted tobacco sheet. Filler tobacco is rolled into a cigar shape and wrapped in binder tobacco to produce a "bunch." A wrapper leaf is spiraled around the outside of each bunch, from the fire to the head end, to prevent the cigar from unwrapping as it is being smoked.

Pipe tobaccos are blended and conditioned similarly to cigarette manufacture, though the tobacco is maintained at a higher moisture content. Heavier styles of burley and flue-cured tobacco may be blended with heavy sun-cured, air-cured, or fire-cured leaf. Pipe tobacco is sometimes heavily cased. Small quantities of Perique or Latakia tobacco may also be included in blends of pipe tobacco. Tobacco rag may be cut in varying widths for pipe tobacco and may be baked or pressed.

There are four types of chewing tobacco: loose or scrap leaf, plug, fine-cut, and twist. Most chewing tobacco today is loose leaf, which is mostly dark air-cured tobacco from Pennsylvania and Wisconsin. Leaves are stemmed and cut and may or may not be heavily cased with sweeteners. Plug chewing tobacco is the original type of chewing tobacco. Leaves were soaked in honey and "plugged" into green hickory or maple logs in Kentucky and Missouri, and rum and licorice were frequently added as well. Plugs are now manufactured by pressing leaves in a mold and wrapping the plug with fine-textured, elastic leaves, usually flue-cured tobacco. Fine-cut chewing tobacco is manufactured from air-cured and fire-cured tobacco produced in Kentucky, Tennessee, and Virginia. It is held between the cheek and gum, rather than being chewed. Twist-type chewing tobacco is composed of burley, air-cured, and flue-cured tobacco leaves that are twisted together.

Snuff is manufactured from fire-cured and dark air-cured tobacco. Leaves are packed and aged as for other uses, but are heavily reconditioned and repacked to ferment for about 2 months. Fermented tobacco is dried and ground into a fine powder that may be blended with flavorings or scents or left plain. Dry snuff is held between the lower lip and the gum of the user. Wet snuff, like fine-cut chewing tobacco, is held between the cheek and gum. Europeans, however, inhale snuff through each nostril. Some North Africans consume a wet snuff made from leaves of *N. rustica*.

V. Future Uses of Tobacco

Tobacco is one of the plant species most widely used in basic agricultural and botanical research. Many call it the "white mouse" or the "*Escherichia coli*" of the plant kingdom. Much research has also been conducted to identify uses for tobacco other than for human consumption. Some of these uses have existed for many, many years, and others involve technological innovations on the forefront of science. Most alternative uses involve using various parts of the tobacco plant or require extraction of certain specific components from tobacco leaves. Nicotine has been used for centuries as a natural insecticide, and tobacco can also be used as a fiber source to produce paper. Research has also evaluated tobacco for use as poultry feed, animal bedding, and as a fertilizer and soil conditioner. The use of tobacco stems and stalks to retain ammonia gas in poultry manure has also been investigated.

Most of the exciting new uses for tobacco involve manipulation of tobacco physiology to obtain products other than nicotine. Tobacco leaves are a chemical factory that could be manipulated to produce industrial chemicals and food supplements. Half of the soluble protein in tobacco is a type of protein referred to as Fraction I protein, which is a tasteless, odorless substance that can be extracted from tobacco in an extremely pure form. It also has an amino acid composition very similar to that of milk, giving it a specific nutritive value for humans that is much higher than that from soybeans, and even comparable to that of human milk. Tobacco also produces relatively large quantities of Fraction II protein, which has a specific nutritive value only slightly lower than that of Fraction I types. In addition, tobacco plants have already been developed, through the use of biotechnology, that produce valuable antibiotics and enzymes. Research is continuing to develop practical and commercially viable tobacco production systems focused on industrial proteins and enzymes, pharmaceuticals, and antibiotics.

Bibliography

Akehurst, B. C. (1981). "Tobacco." Humanities Press, New York.

Chaplin, J. F., Baumhover, A. H., Bortner, C. E., Cart, J. M., Graham, T. W., Hauser, E. W., Heggestad, H. E., McMurtrey, J. E., Jr., Miles, J. D., Nichols, B. C., Ogden, W. B., and Skoog, H. A. (1976). "Tobacco Production," Agric. Info. Bull. 245. U.S. Department of Agriculture, Agricultural Research Service, Washington, D.C.

deBardeleben, M. Z. (1987). "Dictionary of Tobacco Terminology." Philip Morris, New York.

Durbin, R. D. (ed). (1979). "*Nicotiana*: Procedures for Experimental Use," Tech. Bull. 1586. U.S. Department of Agriculture, Washington D.C.

Grise, V. N. (1993). "Tobacco Situation and Outlook," TS-222. Commodity Economics Division, Economic Research Service, U.S. Department of Agriculture, Washington, D.C.

Guerstel, D. U. (1961). Essay on the origin of tobacco. *Tobacco Sci.* **5,** 15–17.

Hawks, S. N., and Collins, W. K. (1983). "Principles of Flue-Cured Tobacco Production," Hawks and Collins, Raleigh, NC.

Moffat, A. S. (1991). "Plant Pharmers Transform Tobacco to Produce Proteins." Genetic Engineering News, New York.

Shew, H. D., and Lucas, G. B. (eds). (1991). "Compendium of Tobacco Diseases." APS Press. St. Paul, MN.

Tso, T. C. (1990). "Production, Physiology, and Biochemistry of Tobacco Plant." IDEALS, Inc., Beltsville, MD.

Wernsman, E. A., and Matzinger, D. F. (1980). "Tobacco. Hybridization of Crop Plants," pp. 657–668. American Society of Agronomy/Crop Science Society of America, Madison, WI.

Tomato Production in Protected Cultivation

HARRY W. JANES, *Rutgers University*

Glossary

Photomorphogenesis Influence of light on the development and organizational structure of a plant

Plant factory Ultimate in controlled environment agriculture where all aspects of the production cycle are under the control of the grower; this system is based on the belief that we know exactly what the plant needs and when it needs it; the development of such a system would allow a grower to control and predict production much like in a factory, where the system can be made as efficient as possible

Plant growth model Blueprint from which a grower can work; such a model is based on a basic understanding of the crop and how it will respond to environmental changes at any time during its developmental cycle

Soilless culture Production of plants in a medium other than natural soil; this includes the use of a totally liquid growing medium (hydroponics) or the use of an aggregate such as peat, vermiculite, perlite, gravel, or sand either alone or in combination; the medium must be sterile and be able to provide the plant with nutrients and air without releasing any toxic material into the nutrient solution

Tomatoes are consumed worldwide. They are produced primarily in the field and can be shipped to areas where environmental conditions prevent field production in all or part of the year. Generally, the production of tomatoes miles and/or days from the point and/or time of sale will result in a product with reduced quality. It is possible to grow tomatoes year round at a point close to consumption on a commercial basis under controlled environmental conditions (i.e., greenhouses). Through a description of the methodologies used to grow greenhouse tomatoes, we will explore the production of a quality product by accurate environmental control and manipulation. Remember there can be two ways in which yield and quality can be enhanced. One is by breeding a new cultivar with certain desirable characteristics. The second, and the one explored here, is through an understanding of how temperature, light, humidity, CO_2 and nutrition interact to effect the plant during different stages of development.

I. Introduction

Tomato fruit are produced and consumed worldwide (over 135,000,000 tons/year). They can provide between 20 and 40% of an adult's requirement for vitamins A and C based on an average of 100–125 g of tomato consumed per average salad. Table I lists the nutritional content of a 100-g tomato. The popularity of the tomato rests not only on its wide production range but also on its unique flavor. The perception of flavor is influenced by many chemical constituents. Primary among these are sugars and acids that interact to provide sweetness, sourness, and flavor intensity. Usually high sugars and high acids are needed for the best flavor. In tomato, fructose and citric acid are of primary importance in flavor development. The fleshy part of the fruit contains sugar but not much acid, whereas the gel contains high acid. Usually fruit with high gel content and both high sugar and acids are perceived to have better flavor. Table II lists some of the main chemical constituents in a ripe tomato fruit.

The quality of the fruit relies not just on the flavor but also on the firmness, shelf life, and appearance of

TABLE I

Nutritional Information for a 100-g Tomato

Calories	23
Water	94%
Protein	0.8 g
Carbohydrates	4 g
Fat	0.6 g
Cholesterol	0
Crude fiber	0.6 g
Minerals and vitamins	
Sodium	8 mg
Potassium	21 mg
Vitamin A	1100 IU (22% RDA)
Vitamin C	18 mg (30% RDA)
Thiamin	0.05 mg (3% RDA)
Riboflavin	0.05 mg (3% RDA)
Niacin	0.6 mg (3% RDA)
Iron	0.5 mg (3% RDA)
Folic acid	0.01 mg (2.5% RDA)

Source: Nutritive value of foods. *Home and Garden Bull.* **72**, 56–61. Human Nutrition Information Service, U.S. Department of Agriculture.

the fruit. Generally speaking these latter features are more important than flavor to marketers and distributors. Appearance refers to size, shape, color, and defects. Tomatoes are often picked at a "green" stage (see Table III for ripeness classification) and shipped great distances to market. These fruit ripen in transit and can be treated with ethylene gas to promote ripening. With this procedure, tomatoes with good appearance can be marketed many miles and several days from the field. However, the flavor may suffer when fruit are harvested prior to the "breaker" stage with the development of off-flavors or lack of flavor. Fruit harvested at the "breaker" stage and held at 20°C will develop the best overall flavor and appearance. "Mature green" fruit can be stored for up to 7 weeks

TABLE II

Organic Chemical Content of Tomato Fruit as Percentage of Dry Weight

Protein	8
Glucose	22
Fructose	25
Sucrose	1
Citric acid	9
Malic acid	4
Minerals	8
Cellulose	6
Pectin	7

Source: J. G. Atherton and J. Rudich (eds.). (1986). "The Tomato Crop." Chapman & Hall, New York.

TABLE III

Ripening Stages

Stage	Description
Green	Mature size, entirely light to dark green
Breaker	First appearance of pink, no more than 10% of surface
Turning	More than 10% but less than 30% of the surface is pink
Pink	More than 30% but less than 60% of surface is pink
Light-red	More than 60% but less than 90% of the surface is red
Red	Over 90% of the surface is red, ripe

Source: Retail Guide. (1994) California Tomato Board, Fresno, CA.

at 4% O_2, 2% CO_2, and 5% CO. These fruit can still attain a marketable quality for an additional 1–2 weeks at 20°C, however, flavor will suffer.

Tomato quality depends on developing the proper appearance and flavor during both the preharvest growing period and the postharvest handling period. The focus of this section will be the preharvest "growing" conditions. In an even more narrow sense we will concentrate on the environmental conditions necessary to produce quality fruit. This will be done within the framework of the production of tomatoes in protected cultivation.

In places where the natural environmental conditions prevent the production of tomatoes in the field, fruit can be produced in controlled environmental facilities, usually greenhouses. These facilities are used to produce high-quality fruit at an increased cost to the consumer. The increased retail price is paid because of the availability of quality product when normally only poorer-quality fruit transported great distances are available. The ability of the greenhouse grower to manipulate the environment has led to research elucidating climatic influences on tomato growth and development. In addition, unique production systems have been developed that incorporate this knowledge in a cost-conscious manner. Indeed, the modern commercial greenhouse operation is making a slow but steady transition from a general farming operation to a highly sophisticated plant factory, a place where a computer is a valuable tool in day-to-day operations as well as in long-term decision making. The ability to control the growing environment, coupled with a more thorough understanding of tomato growth, has provided the impetus for this transition. [*See* HORTICULTURAL GREENHOUSE ENGINEERING.]

This article will describe what can be done environmentally in the greenhouse and give some examples of plant responses to these manipulations. Given that one goal of the commercial grower is to minimize operational costs by reducing energy inputs while optimizing profits from the best possible plant growth, an understanding of plant–environment interactions that lead to the development of plant growth models is necessary to accomplish this goal.

The concept of growing quality crops on a predictable and controllable basis, that is, in a plant factory, is becoming a reality. However, much work needs to be done, particularly in the area of plant response to various temperature, light, CO_2, humidity, and nutrient levels at different stages of plant development. Additionally, we will address some of the economic considerations necessary to a viable business, as well as some of the various production methods in use today and some possibilities for tomorrow.

II. Environmental Control of Tomato Growth

A. Temperature

A greenhouse is totally dependent on its heating and cooling systems. Energy is used to operate vents, fans, boilers, and pumps in an attempt to maintain temperatures acceptable for plant growth. Greenhouses are intensive consumers of energy and energy costs are a significant part of the operational expenses. On the other hand, productivity in greenhouses can be over four times greater than that in the same area of field. Therefore, much effort has been expended to develop heating and cooling systems that are energy efficient. In colder climates, energy conservation strategies, as well as alternative heating systems, have been developed.

Several management practices have proven very beneficial for greenhouse tomato seedling (young tomato plants that have not yet produced visible flowers) growers. Two of the most effective appear to be soil heating in conjunction with energy-saving thermal blankets. A properly managed greenhouse so equipped has resulted in nearly 60% reduction in fuel oil used per year.

Soil heating of a tomato seedling crop, for instance, speeds germination and seedling development and allows one to start the crop later than normal. This eliminates 2–3 weeks of operation during the coldest time of the year. Soil heating of low-growing crops also allows the night air temperature to be lowered about 3°C or more, further reducing energy require-

ments. In greenhouses with a floor heat storage system, because the floor mass is so large, there is a gradual decay in greenhouse air temperature throughout the night rather than the abrupt change that occurs in most greenhouses at sundown. In combination with a thermal blanket, the decline of the night air temperature is further slowed.

Extremely exciting possibilities exist in combining a floor heating system with low-temperature water typically rejected as waste heat from industrial sources. This system can be designed so that 34°C water can be used effectively to heat greenhouses. Cogeneration systems, that is, burning one fuel (e.g., natural gas or methane from landfills) to produce both heat and electricity, also offer benefits to the greenhouse operator.

From the standpoint of the engineer, systems can and have been designed to control temperature. But most of our information deals with heating, because most commercial greenhouse operations are active in areas that are too cold rather than too hot for field production. However, cooling and ventilating systems are a necessary and important part of the greenhouse design. Nonetheless, cooling in areas of high relative humidity and warm outside temperatures is accomplished only with prohibitive energy and capital costs. Most practical systems use shade, outside air movement through the greenhouse, and evaporation as the principal means of reducing excessive heat in the greenhouse. Solar radiation may cause the air that is moving through a greenhouse to raise 10°C or more as it travels from inlet to outlet. Even with the use of a traditional evaporative cooling system that consists of a porous pad down which water runs and through which the outside air is drawn, there are significant temperature gradients through a greenhouse. A more recent development has been evaporative cooling using a high-pressure fog system that sprays fine water droplets (0.02 cm diameter) evenly throughout the greenhouse. These droplets easily evaporate. Typically, one nozzle is placed every 5 m² with temperature reductions of 2–7°C depending on relative humidity.

The existence of these heating and cooling systems with the subsequent environmental control they provide has prompted commonsense questions such as: What temperature is best for plant growth? Should there be a differential day/night regime? Do all stages in the growth of a plant respond optimally to the same temperature? What about the environment of the root zone? To balance the desire for optimal plant growth with the efficient use of energy, these somewhat simple questions need to be accurately answered.

It appears that specific answers to heating and cooling needs are complex and depend on the genetic makeup of the plant, its physiological age, and previous environmental history. Some examples of the usefulness of root zone heating and the interaction of root zone and air temperatures on growth will illustrate the complex nature of temperature control and how it can be manipulated to provide an optimal product.

In-depth studies with tomatoes reveal a maximum growth plateau that slopes upward from about 16–30°C (Fig. 1). Above and below these points, significant growth retardation occurs. This graph illustrates a fairly general phenomenon that has led growers to develop rules of thumb for their greenhouse environmental control. Although the plateau for root zone temperature is fairly broad, it is quite obvious that certain temperatures are better than others for growth and that the cost of operation must be balanced against this growth response. However, the fact that precise information is needed before such decisions can be made is evident. Furthermore, an interaction between air and root zone temperature is shown in Figs. 2 and 3. These data suggest that increases in plant growth associated with root temperature increases may be due to some effect on the very early growth. The data show that the phase before rapid growth begins may be shortened by some increases in root temperature. Data collected during the rapid growth phase indicate that root temperature variation had little or no influence during that phase, which suggests that root temperature has a significant

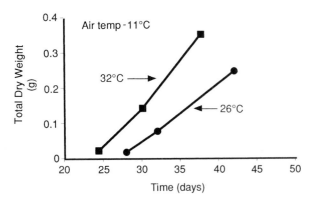

FIGURE 2 Plant dry weight as affected by growth at 11°C air temperature and root temperatures of 26 and 32°C. [From M. Mellata and H. W. Janes. (1987). Interrelation of root and shoot temperatures on dry matter accumulation and root growth in tomato seedling. *J. Hort. Sci.* **62**, 49–54.]

growth effect early in crop development. Once the root system is established, air temperature becomes more important for growth.

Maximum growth of tomato plants may be achieved only by maintaining air temperature at an optimal level. Low air temperature limits growth and growth rate even when root temperature is not low. Increases in root temperature do not increase growth response to an extent that can compensate for reductions in growth rate at low air temperatures. Root zone heating may be useful in optimizing growth at a given air temperature, especially if applied during

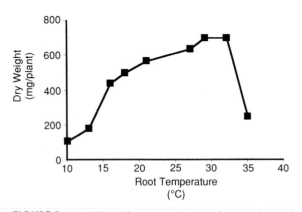

FIGURE 1 The effect of root zone heating for 2 weeks on the growth of tomato seedlings. [From J. Hurewitz and H. W. Janes. (1983). Effect of altering the root-zone temperature on growth, translocation, carbon exchange rate, and leaf starch accumulation in the tomato. *Plant Physiol.* **73**, 46–50.]

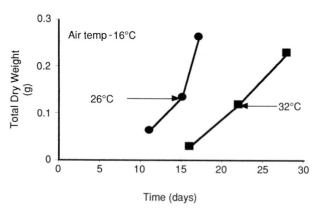

FIGURE 3 Plant dry weight as affected by growth at 16°C air temperature and root temperatures of 26 and 32°C. [From M. Mellata and H. W. Janes. (1987). Interrelation of root and shoot temperatures on dry matter accumulation and root growth in tomato seedling. *J. Hort. Sci.* **62**, 49–54.]

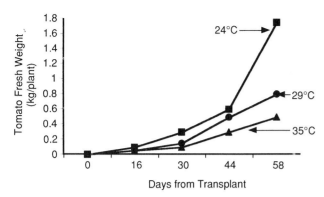

FIGURE 4 The effect of root zone heating on the accumulation of fresh weight by tomato plants following flowering. [From G. Giacomelli and H. W. Janes. (1986). The growth of greenhouse tomatoes in nutrient film at various nutrient solution temperatures. *Soilless Culture* **2**, 11–20.]

very early growth. High root temperature, however, may reduce growth rate, adversely affecting growth. The interrelationship of root and shoot activity ultimately determines the outcome of plant growth, so the temperature environment of each component is important. At extremes of hot or cold, either may have a critical effect on growth. However, when neither temperature is limiting, shoot temperature rather than root temperature appears to have the dominant effect on plant growth.

Within certain limits of air temperature (17–25°C), the optimal root zone temperature for tomato seedling growth is between 27 and 32°C. However, Figs. 4 and 5 show that prolonged growth at a root zone temperature of 29°C results in considerable decreases in both growth and crop productivity. There is a considerable difference in response to temperature depending on the age of the plant, its stage of physiologi-

cal development, and the duration of a particular temperature treatment. It is clearly seen by looking at root metabolism (Fig. 6 and Table IV) that temperature has specific short- and long-term effects. Though promoting respiration and ATPase activity in the short term (30 min), a similar temperature inhibits these processes over the long term (7 days).

The air temperature is of primary importance in the development of flowers following initiation. In particular, higher day temperature seems to be more effective in promoting growth than higher night temperature. Anthesis (flowering) can be delayed up to 18 days by giving temperatures of 10 versus 15°C for 14 days after floral initiation. In the winter under conditions of low irradiance, some floral abortion may occur under warm air temperatures (e.g., 21°C). Once the flower has developed, successful fertilization must occur to produce good-quality fruit. The germination of the pollen grain in tomato can also be affected by temperature. Generally it takes longer to germinate at lower temperature than at higher (5 hr at 10°C vs. 1 hr at 25°C). Germination must take place between 10 and 35°C. In the summer, short periods of time at 40°C without adequate ventilation will result in the failure of the egg to develop properly. Temperatures above 25°C at night and above 40°C during the day or below 10°C at night cause the most damage to greenhouse-grown tomatoes. It is recommended that night temperatures be in the range of 15–20°C (Table V).

The information presented here suggests that temperature regulation is a much more complex issue than it appears to be on initial reflection. The efficient operation of heating and cooling systems requires a thorough knowledge of the plant material and the desired end product.

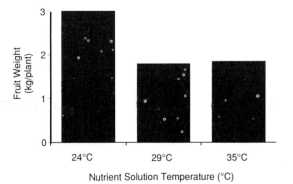

FIGURE 5 The effect of root zone heating on average marketable yields (fruit > 90 g) of tomato. [From G. Giacomelli and H. Janes. (1986). The growth of greenhouse tomatoes in nutrient film at various nutrient solution temperatures. *Soilless Culture* **2**, 11–20.]

TABLE IV

Length, ATPase Activity, and Respiration Rate of Isolated Tomato Roots Grown at Two Temperatures[a]

Temperature (°C)	Length (mm)	ATPase (μmoles P_1/mg protein/hr)	Respiration (μmoles O_2/min/ m/g dry wt)
28	97	45.0	39
33	72	6.0	24

Source: H. W. Janes, C. Chin, and J. Bachmansky. (1988). Growth and metabolism of tomato roots grown in tissue cultures held at various temperatures. *Hort Science* **23**, 773.

[a] Roots were grown for 7 days at the temperatures indicated but ATPase and respiration measurements were made at 28°C. In each column, means are significantly different by LSD = 1%.

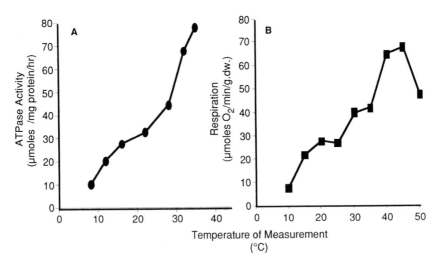

FIGURE 6 Respiration rate and K^+-stimulated ATPase activity as a function of assay temperature. Roots were grown for 7 days at 28°C and the measurements were made at various temperatures following 30 min of incubation of the roots at these temperatures. [From H. W. Janes, C. Chin, and J. Bachmansky. (1988). Growth and metabolism of tomato roots grown in tissue culture held at various temperatures. *HortScience* **23,** 773.]

TABLE V

Optimal Temperatures during Different Stages of Tomato Development

Stage	Temperature (°C)
Germination	16–29
Seedling growth	21–24
Fruit set	
Night	14–17
Day	19–24
Red color development	20–24

Source: J. G. Atherton and J. Rudich (eds.). (1986). "The Tomato Crop." Chapman & Hall, New York.

B. Light

Low winter light levels represent the single most limiting factor preventing continuous year-round production of greenhouse crops. Low light quantity is a major limiting environmental factor to plant growth for 6 months of the year in the Northern Hemisphere. This low light effect is exacerbated by a high incidence of cloud cover along coastal regions. Increasing fertility and better control of temperature, water, or CO_2 result in only marginal improvements in plant growth when light is limiting.

Because winter light is inadequate for production, tomato growers are unable to deviate from a spring–fall cropping strategy. Under winter light, only limited vegetative growth is possible. The production of vegetative crops such as lettuce in the Northern Hemisphere is greatly reduced in December and January, with the production time increasing from 6 to 10 weeks and total yields decreasing by 50%. Production of a reproductive crop, such as the tomato, is virtually arrested (Fig. 7). However, supplemental lighting in the greenhouse can be used to induce both photoperiodic and photosynthetic effects. Photosynthetic lighting can ease undesirable seasonal effects such as reduced flower production in tomato. Increases in flower number in response to both high intensities and long daylengths have been demonstrated. There is a linear relationship between total irradiance (400–700 nm) and the rate of seedling

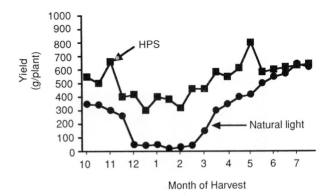

FIGURE 7 Comparison of the production of tomato plants grown with and without supplemental light. HPS lighting is used to supplement the natural radiation. [From R. McAvoy, H. W. Janes, B. Godfriaux, M. Secks, D. Duchai, and W. Wittman. (1989). The effect of total available photosynthetic photon flux on single truss tomato growth and production. *J. Hort. Sci.* **64,** 331–338.]

growth in both tomato and lettuce regardless of light source in the winter.

It was found in the 1940s that the growth rate and yield of certain tomato varieties increased as the number of hours of lighting increased. However, varietal differences are broad. Longer light periods may allow the grower to lower the greenhouse night temperature and save fuel dollars. By increasing the photoperiod to 16 hr there is a significant increase in growth and yield of tomatoes during November and December, and 16-hr photoperiods may allow a lowering of the night temperature. The intensity of the supplementary light is extremely critical. If the normal daylight is extended with high-intensity light, the growth and yield of the plants are enhanced. However, if low-intensity supplemental light is used, the flowering can be delayed.

The same total light intensity given over 8 or 16 hr can dramatically alter tomato growth. A 16-hr day results in an increased net assimilation rate as well as higher chlorophyll levels. However, flowers appeared one or two nodes lower on plants given only 8-hr days. The faster growth rates under 16-hr days would more than balance out the faster flowering with 8-hr days and result in higher yields. In England in midwinter, day lengths of less than 6 hr result in absolutely no growth and that growth is proportional, at this time of year, to light intensity or duration.

Lighting during November and December will cause flowering to occur 10–14 days earlier than normal, which translates into an increase of 4.7 tons of fruit per acre over the life of the crop. Furthermore, with increased lighting in the winter, the number of misshapen fruit declines. Also, color development and fruit quality, as measured by taste panels, are enhanced by supplementary lighting.

Research in this area can become extremely complicated owing to the interaction between lighting and various other environmental and physiological conditions. An experiment run for 1 week may give you one answer and that for 2 weeks another answer. Table VI illustrates the problem. If the same amount of supplemental light is given for a 33-day period during tomato seedling growth, with high light being provided in one of the three 11-day periods, the end result is quite different depending on which period received the high light. Vegetative plant growth responded differentially to the total light integral, depending on when it was applied during the growth cycle. However, for the production of a tomato crop it is best to provide light earlier in development rather than later.

TABLE VI

The Influence of an 11-day High-Light Treatment Applied Differentially during Seedling Development on Vegetative Growth[a]

Growth variable	Light treatment	Sampling date			
		Day 6	Day 11	Day 22	Day 33
Total dry weight (g)	HLL	0.05b[b]	0.32b	3.53b	14.27a
	LHL	0.02a	0.12a	4.47b	13.92a
	LLH	0.02a	0.11a	2.31a	19.44b
Leaf area index (cm²)	HLL	0.06b	0.32b	2.41b	3.04a
	LHL	0.03a	0.16a	2.32ab	2.95a
	LLH	0.03a	0.16a	1.82a	3.38a
Leaf area ratio (cm²/g)	HHL	276a	249a	254b	195b
	LHL	408b	356b	188a	192b
	LLH	446b	360b	298b	158a
Plant height (cm)	HLL	0	6.1b	32.7b	75.3b
	LHL	0	4.2a	26.8a	63.9a
	LLH	0	4.1a	29.3ab	66.8a

Source: R. McAvoy and H. Janes. (1990). Cumulative light effects on growth and flowering of tomato seedlings. *J. Am. Soc. Hort. Sci.* **115,** 119–122.
[a] Each number is the mean of 15 plants.
[b] Data followed by different letters indicate significant differences between light treatments on a certain sampling date at the 5% level as determined by Duncan's multiple range test.

Additionally, the interaction between supplementary lighting and seasonal changes in night temperatures deserves some mention. Both leaf formation and growth increase with both light intensity and temperature. However, an increase in temperature also meant an increased number of nodes prior to floral initiation. Whether increased growth rates under warmer temperature regimes with supplementary lighting will offset the delay in flowering remains to be seen. This will play an important role in the timing of a crop.

The effects that light has on plant growth are not limited to its involvement in the photosynthetic process. There are numerous examples of the action of light (duration and quality) on growth, flowering, and plant hormone activity. It would be a mistake to assume that by changing the photoperiod one was only altering the rate of sugar formation. For tomato, the length of the light period has little effect on flowering, that is, tomatoes are day-neutral plants. However, there is some evidence to suggest that some tomato cultivars are quantitative short-day plants. By increasing the length of the day with low levels of incandescent light, the number of leaves below the first inflorescence can be increased, but the plant will still flower. Additionally, daylight–dark cycles that deviated too greatly from a 24-hr cycle of 12 hr light and 12 hr darkness were inhibitory to plant growth. In a 48-hr period if all the plants received the same

TABLE VII

Growth of Tomato in Different Durations of Light with Equal Total Light[a]

Light regime	Leaf area	Dry weight leaves	Fresh weight stems	Dry weight stems
18 hr 200 μE/m^2/sec 6 hr dark (control)	100.0	100.0	100.0	100.0
24 hr 150 μE/m^2/sec	59.8	40.1	66.0	65.8

Source: F. Bradley and H. W. Janes. (1985). Carbon partitioning in tomato leaves exposed to continuous light. *Acta Horticulturae* **174**, 293–302.

[a] In each column, values are not significantly different at $P \leq 0.05$. Values represent the average of five plants per treatment, expressed as percentage of control.

quality and quantity of light in alternating light–dark cycles of 6, 12, o4 24 hr, the tomatoes grown under 6- and 24-hr light regimes exhibited growth inhibition. It is clear that with tomato seedlings, equal light intensity given over 18 or 24 hr results in different plant growth rates (Table VII). [*See* PHOTOSYNTHESIS; PLANT PHYSIOLOGY.]

Photosynthetic period has also been found to affect carbon export in tomato. Translocation and partitioning of carbohydrate was altered by the duration of the photosynthetic period or possibly by the duration of the dark period rather than the absolute light intensity. More sugar is translocated out of the leaves under a 16-hr photoperiod than under an 8-hr photoperiod, even when the total amount of carbon fixed in photosynthesis is the same (Table VIII).

The interactions of photomorphogenic factors controlling sugar export and its partitioning within the plant need to be seriously addressed, as they are directly related to crop yield. Photomorphogenic effects

TABLE VIII

The Light Period Effect on Carbohydrate Movement Out of the Leaf (Translocation)[a]

Length of light period (hr)	Photosynthetic rate (g CH$_2$O/ m^{-2}/hr)	Total carbohydrate fixed daily (g/m^{-2})	Total carbohydrate translocated daily (g/m^{-2})
8	0.74b	5.95a	3.46a
16	0.37a	5.87a	4.88b

Source: S. Logendra and H. W. Janes (1992). Light duration effects on carbon partitioning and translocation in tomato. *Scientia Horticulturae* **52**, 19–25.

[a] Values in columns followed by the same letter are not significantly different at $P < 0.05$.

are known to modify the distribution of photosynthesis products. This may have significance for artificial lighting, as the spectral pattern of certain popular light sources is deficient in blue light and heavy in the near infrared region relative to sunlight, and so photomorphogenic changes are probable.

Selection of a light source is not easy given the various types available. One of the most common light sources is the fluorescent lamp; however, it is not practical for commercial application. The practical use of the fluorescent source is limited by its unwieldy size, its low-intensity discharge, and safety regulations requiring moisture barriers to protect the bulb in the wet greenhouse. The high-pressure sodium (HPS) light source is an attractive source for commercial use. The fixture is fairly compact and the bulb has a life of up to 20,000 hr. The HPS lamp is the most efficient, after the low-pressure sodium lamp, in terms of the percentage of the total input energy, which is converted to visible light. With the HPS lamp 25% of the total input energy is emitted as visible light. Metal halides range from 12 to 20%; fluorescent lamps are 20% efficient in this conversion. The low-pressure sodium (LPS) lamp has a 27% efficiency. The LPS lamp, a monochromatic light source, has a short bulb life, and the fixture is also much larger than that of the HPS lamp. Considering all factors—ballast and fixture size, safety, energy conversion efficiency, spectral distribution, and bulb life—the HPS lamp is the most commercially applicable of the available light sources for supplemental lighting in the greenhouse.

Spectral distribution of any artificial light source is always a concern because the sunlight spectrum is never completely reproduced by any single light source. The discrepancy between an artificial light source spectrum and the solar spectrum is significant as light quality has been shown to influence plant growth and development. Table IX shows that add-

TABLE IX

Light Quality Effect on Tomato Response to Continuous Light[a]

Continuous light treatment	Chlorophyll (mg/gfw)	Starch (% DW)	Leaf death (#/plant)
Fluorescent	0.22	4.46	2.83
Fluorescent + far-red	0.49	7.17	1.17

Source: S. Globig, I. Rosen, and H. W. Janes. (1994). Continuous light effects on photosynthesis and carbon metabolism. *Acta Horticulturae*.

[a] In each column, values are not significantly different at $P < 0.05$.

ing far-red light (730 nm) to fluorescent light provided to tomatoes on a continuous basis can delay leaf death and alter starch levels.

We also need to know the optimum ratio of the various wavelength intervals, particularly in the blue, red, and far-red regions. This can be illustrated by considering the response of flowering in tomato under cool white fluorescent lights or fluorescent lights and incandescent lamps. In the latter case, the plant receives more far-red light and the time to first flower opening is reduced by 2 days.

A caution needs to be issued here regarding supplemental lighting for tomatoes. Continuous light can result in severe damage with significant decreases in growth and possibly death of the plant (Table VII). It is recommended that at least a 6-hr dark period be provided. Seedlings will be more quickly affected by continuous light than older plants. Also, reducing the "night" temperature in comparison to the "day" will delay the injury appearance. Older leaves of injured plants will lose chlorophyll and turn yellow, and young leaves will not develop chlorophyll and will appear white. Obviously, photosynthesis is decreased and a reduction of growth results. If the continuous light is not stopped, the plant can die.

C. Carbon Dioxide

The use of CO_2 enrichment in the greenhouse has taken on added significance in recent years. With the advent of energy-conserving techniques to prevent heat loss from greenhouses, they are now sealed better and much tighter to outside airflow. Although energy is saved, the CO_2 levels can dramatically decrease when plants are photosynthesizing in a closed greenhouse. This problem is particularly acute during clear, cold days when photosynthetic levels may be high and air exchange between the interior of the greenhouse and outside air is small. Also, the use of supplementary lighting at night makes CO_2 enrichment even more necessary as depletion of the CO_2 concentration will result in dramatic decreases in photosynthesis and plant growth while wasting the energy spent on lighting. Increased levels of CO_2, possibly as a consequence of promoting overall plant growth, will also speed up the date for first flowering in tomato. It is likely that increases in fruit production to CO_2 enrichment in the winter are largely the result of more flowers reaching maturity.

In tomato, levels of CO_2 between 1000 and 1500 μl/liter of air provide adequate substrate to maintain high photosynthetic rates as well as increased

translocation of carbohydrate out of the leaves, resulting in increased whole-plant growth. However, CO_2 concentrations above 5000 μl/liter can be dangerous to both humans and plants. Though CO_2 injection should be practiced, too much of a good thing can cause trouble. CO_2 can be added to the greenhouse from a supply of liquid CO_2 that is distributed throughout the greenhouse via a fan-tube system. This is the cleanest way of adding CO_2. The most prevalent way of producing CO_2 is by suspending an open-flame burner in the greenhouse; generally, propane or natural gas is burned. These burners can be controlled by commercially available computerized systems that can monitor and regulate CO_2 levels. The burners have an advantage of adding some heat to the greenhouse. When using CO_2 generated by burning propane or other fuels in the greenhouse, however, it is possible that production of volatile pollutants such as ethylene, propylene, and oxides of nitrogen and sulfur may occur. At first glance, CO_2 enrichment appears to be a positive process that should be practiced by greenhouse operators, because it is clearly associated with increased rates of photosynthesis and plant dry matter accumulation. However, there appear to be long-term and short-term effects of high CO_2 concentration on tomatoes, with increased photosynthetic rates not persisting over long time periods (Fig. 8).

To complicate matters further, the nitrogen fertilizer status of the plant can influence the amount of carbohydrate translocated out of the leaf following exposure to high CO_2 levels. This points out the fact that, as with light and temperature, the response to above ambient CO_2 levels for long or short periods of time needs to be studied prior to deciding (1) how to most efficiently apply this material and (2) whether

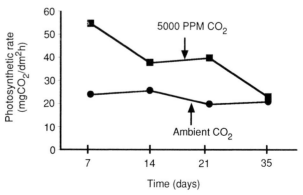

FIGURE 8 The effect of high carbon dioxide on photosynthesis of whole tomato seedlings.

or not long exposure to CO_2 above ambient levels is warranted.

Before concluding our discussion of CO_2, it should be mentioned that companies in Europe are marketing equipment that will add CO_2 to the irrigation water. They contend that CO_2 benefits root growth as well as photosynthesis. In tomato seedlings it would appear that short-term exposure of the roots (less than 12 hr) to high concentrations of CO_2 will result in increased whole-plant growth (Fig. 9), however, high CO_2 levels and/or long durations can limit growth. These CO_2 effects are due not to increased photosynthesis, but possibly to a more specific effect of CO_2 on nutrient uptake by the plant roots.

D. Humidity

The amount of water in the air plays a significant role in plant health. Too much water can lead to the proliferation of disease-causing organisms and result in the inability of pollen to be released and move to the stigma. High humidity is a concern in some greenhouses because measures taken to conserve heat also serve to raise the relative humidity. Under high light levels, raising the relative humidity to about 90% was shown to actually increase growth. The growth of young tomato seedlings may be accelerated by enhanced CO_2 assimilation resulting from the increased number of open stomates at higher humidity. However, humidity seems to have much less of an effect on tomato growth and development than do light, temperature, CO_2, or nutrients. Additionally, the uptake and distribution of certain nutrients like

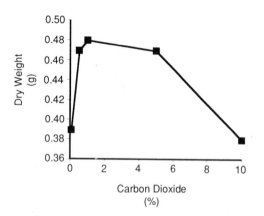

FIGURE 9 The effect of carbon dioxide concentrations (0.03, 0.5, 1, 5, and 10%) on the dry weight growth of tomato leaves. The root systems of 5-week-old tomato plants were treated for 12 hr with CO_2. [From Yurgalevitch and H. Janes. (1988). Carbon dioxide enrichment of the root zone of tomato seedlings. *J. Hort. Sci.* **63**, 265–270.]

calcium can be seriously affected by the relative humidity of the greenhouse. Young leaves will have low calcium levels if the humidity is high (95%), whereas fruit will have low calcium levels if the night humidity is below 50%. This is due to the method of calcium transport into these different organs. Leaves receive calcium as a result of transpiration (evaporation of water from stomates), whereas the fruit relies on root pressure to supply calcium. The lack of calcium in the ovary and young fruit can result in a serious condition called blossom end rot. Fruit with this physiological disorder are unsalable.

E. Nutrition

In controlled environment culture, the commercial production of tomatoes is done using some type of soilless growing method. Usually either a form of hydroponic culture called the nutrient film technique (NFT) or a nonsoil growing media is used. Current popular nonsoil media are rockwool and a mixture of peat moss, vermiculite, and perlite (referred to as a peat-lite mix). Rockwool is manufactured from crushed rock heated to over 600°C. The molten material is lengthened into strands that are pressed and cut into a variety of shapes and sizes. These systems have replaced natural soil for several reasons, most significant being the expenditures of energy, particularly the labor cost needed to transport and sterilize soil. Additionally, the replacement of soil with soil of equal quality is difficult. NFT, rockwool, and to some extent peat-lite mixes provide a grower with constant quality year-in and year-out without the need to initially sterilize to remove weed seeds, fungi, insects, and bacteria. Furthermore, soilless culture allows easier manipulation of the environment and the ability to provide the proper nutrients for healthy tomato growth.

An in-depth discussion of tomato nutrition will not be given here. However, Tables X and XI show the nutrient levels recommended for tomato and provide some generalized descriptions of deficiency symptoms. The reader is cautioned that providing fertilizer above optimum levels will result in growth inhibition. It should also be a goal to provide the plant with no more than necessary, which saves dollars on fertilizer but also protects the environment. Frequent overwatering or disposal of nutrient solution in an NFT system will result in higher fertilizer levels leaching into the ground-water, which can lead to the overproduction of algae and other microorganisms. Every effort should be made to collect and recycle

TABLE X

Optimal Nutrient Levels in the Fertilizer Solution for a Tomato Crop

Element	Concentration (ppm)[a]
Nitrate-nitrogen (NO_3-N)	150–200
Phosphorous (P)	50
Potassium (K)	200–400 [P_2O_5 = 1140]
Calcium (Ca)	150–300 [K_2O = 240–480]
Magnesium (Mg)	50
Iron (Fe)	5
Manganese (Mn)	1
Copper (Cu)	0.1
Zinc (Zn)	0.1
Boron (B)	0.2
Molybdenum (Mo)	0.05

Source: H. M. Resh. (1989). "Hydroponic Food Production." Woodbridge Press, Santa Barbara, CA.
[a] 1 ppm = 1 oz. per 7500 gallons.

the nutrient solution. The solution will need to be frequently tested to make sure the proper nutrient levels are maintained. Additionally, the pH should be maintained between 5.5 and 6.0. Probably the greatest threat faced by the grower in recycling nutrients is the spread of disease. The nutrients used by the plant for good growth are also those required by many microorganisms. If you add to the solution the or-

TABLE XI

Nutrient Deficiency Symptoms in Tomato

Element	Symptom description
Nitrogen	Plants are light green (lack chlorophyll); younger leaves may remain green longer
Potassium	Older leaves develop symptoms first and become chlorotic (i.e., lose their green color) and soon develop scattered dead spots
Phosphorous	Leaves are dark green; purple pigmentation may develop; growth rate slowed and the plants appear stunted
Calcium	Shoot tip growth slows and root tips may die; young leaves exhibit scattered dead spots; these leaves are generally small with twisted tips
Manganese	Leaves become chlorotic but the veins remain green (interveinal chlorosis); dead spots develop on the leaves with some leaves falling from the plant
Magnesium	Older leaves develop interveinal chlorosis; leaf margins may curl
Iron	Interveinal chlorosis, similar to with magnesium deficiency except on the younger leaves; edges and the tips of leaves may die

Source: H. M. Resh. (1989). "Hydroponic Food Production." Woodbridge Press, Santa Barbara, CA.

ganic material from plant decay and exudation, you have created a media for the growth of many organisms. Today no cost-effective and totally satisfactory resterilization system exists. However, methods such as ultrafiltration, ultrasonics, heat treatment, UV irradiation, and ozone treatment have been tried, with the latter two showing the most promise.

III. Tomato Cropping Systems

Greenhouse tomatoes are typically produced on multiple-trussed vertical vines. In these systems, plant densities of about 10,000–12,000 plants/acre are common. Plants are placed in double rows 40–45 cm apart with plants 30–35 cm apart within the row. Usually the plants are staggered in adjacent rows. Tomatoes can be trained vertically by clamping to a string hung from a wire stretched across the greenhouse. Tomatoes are always pruned to a single stem, with lateral branches being constantly removed. When the plants start setting fruit on the third cluster, it is beneficial to start removing the lower leaves to improve aeration and remove possible material for disease organisms to infect. Also the fruit will not set without pollination. In the greenhouse this is accomplished either by mechanical vibration of the flower cluster or by bringing bees into the greenhouse.

In the United States and Canada, tomato production follows a two-crop pattern. The spring crop is seeded between December 1 and January 15 and harvested starting in late April through July. The fall crop is seeded between July 1 and 15 with a harvest window commencing in October and ending in late December. Primarily because of low light levels, the yields in the fall are up to 50% less than those in the spring. Crop production ceases during the low-light winter months, as the old crop is terminated and new plants take their place.

Market demands place a premium on the continuous and predictable production of quality fruit. However, under constantly changing environmental conditions, continuous and predictable production of tomato fruit is difficult to accomplish. When uniform fruit quality is desired, this task becomes even more difficult to achieve.

Continuity of production during the winter months is important because the potential financial returns are highest at this time. Winter tomato production is expensive, however, and low light intensities combined with short days drastically reduce crop performance and quality. Supplementing the naturally available light with artificial light will alleviate some of these problems but supplemental lighting is expensive. Therefore, utilizing this resource to achieve the maximum benefit with a minimal investment is an important consideration. Adding supplemental light to a vertically grown tomato crop (the traditional cultural method) has two disadvantages: (1) light uniformity is difficult to maintain and (2) it is impossible to tailor the supplemental light schedule to a specific stage of crop development. Because many stages of plant growth and development occur simultaneously, light can not be used judiciously to achieve a specific growth effect.

A single-cluster tomato production system is capable of continuous tomato production. This system is not limited by the disadvantages inherent to vertical axis cropping systems when supplemental lighting is used. The basic components of the Rutgers version of the single-cluster production system include single-cluster tomato plants, transportable benches (tables upon which plants are grown and transported), high-pressure sodium lights, and a crop management strategy based on a plant growth model.

In this system the tomato plant is pruned to a single flower cluster and architectured by soft pinching the apical meristem one leaf above the cluster. High plant populations, 43,000 plants/acre compared to more conventional densities, are used to ensure maximum yield and to enhance crop uniformity. The high plant population concentrates crop maturity into a narrow time period, or production window. Sequential cropping of discrete groups of plants on a staggered time schedule results in continuous production. Transportable tables increase space utilization and predispose the crop to further automation and improved labor efficiency by facilitating the flow of materials in and out of the production house.

Tomatoes are one of the least automated of the greenhouse crops. Commercial mechanization of the conventional vertical axis tomato crop has been limited to systems where the machinery has been adapted to the crop. The single-cluster production system adapts the tomato crop to existing machinery and market requirements by modifying cultural practices such as plant density and plant architecture, as well as operational practices such as crop accessibility, handling, and scheduling. Thus, precision seeders, potting machines, soil mixers, pot fillers, and pot transfer mechanisms that place pots on movable benches, conventionally used for small pot crop production (e.g., poinsettia

or mum production), can be applied to the tomato crop. The single-cluster tomato crop, like the pot crop, offers a high degree of uniformity and is small, compact, and easy to handle.

The concept of growing single-cluster tomatoes for the purpose of reducing labor and developing a factorylike production scheme is the aim of the Rutgers single-cluster production system. By applying the information presented here for the control of tomato

TABLE XII
Greenhouse Cost Accounting

Overhead	Utilities	Wages and salaries	Direct costs
Depreciation	Heating fuel	General	Seeds
Interest	Telephone	FICA	Pots
Repairs	Electricity	Unemployment insurance	Media
Taxes	Water		Fertilizer
Insurance		Workmen's compensation	Tags
Advertising			Others
Office expenses			
Professional fee			
Truck expense			
Equipment rental			
Dues			
Bad debts			
Miscellaneous			

Buildings and utilities	Equipment
Land	Heating system—Piping
Site grading and roads	Boilers—gas, 2
Site services, utilities	Boiler controls
Service building, structure	Heating system—installation
Service building, internal	Supplemental lighting
Greenhouse—structure	Supplemental lighting
Greenhouse—installation	Electrical—internal
Concrete paths	Electrical—service
Contingency—10%	Shade system/thermal blankets
	Blackout curtains
	Air handling
	Carbon dioxide system
	Crop support system
	Growing system
	Nutrient system
	Computer controls
	Vehicles, tools, etc.
	Grading and packaging equipment

Source: R. Brumfeld, P. Nelson, A. Coutu, D. Willits, and R. Sowell. (1981). "Overhead Costs of Greenhouse Firms Differentiated by Size of Firm and Market Channel." Technical Bulletin 269. North Carolina Agricultural Research Service, Raleigh.

growth by environmental manipulation it seems possible that a plant factory production system could become a reality for tomatoes.

IV. Economic Considerations

In many cases, greenhouse producers of tomatoes owe their success or failure to the managerial choices they make as opposed to the technical choices. As we have seen, the technical choices of which temperature, light level, or growing media to use are complicated. The same can be said for the managerial choices. Greenhouse managers need to know their fixed "overhead" costs and their costs of production to effectively analyze alternative possibilities, implement choices, and evaluate courses of action.

No attempt will be made here to provide a methodology for a detailed economic analysis or feasibility of a greenhouse tomato business. Table XII provides the reader with a general idea of what must be considered when computing the profitability of a tomato greenhouse production business.

Bibliography

Atherton, J. G., and Rudich, J. (1986). "The Tomato Crop." Chapman & Hall, New York.

Brumfield, R., Nelson, P., Coutu, A., Willits, D., and Sowell, R. (1981). "Overhead Costs of Greenhouse Firms Differentiated by Size of Firm and Market Channel." Technical Bulletin 269. North Carolina Agricultural Research Service, Raleigh.

Hayashi, M., Kano, A., and Goto, E. (1992). "Transplant Production Systems." International Society of Horticultural Science, Wageningen, Netherlands.

McAvoy, R., and Janes, H. (1991). Environmental control of a single-cluster greenhouse tomato crop. *HortTechnology* **1**, 110–114.

McAvoy, R., Janes, H., and Giacomelli, G. (1989). Development of a plant factory model. *Acta Horticulturae* **248**, 85–94.

Preece, J. E., and Read, P. E. (1993). "The Biology of Horticulture." John Wiley & Sons, New York.

Resh, H. M. (1989). "Hydroponic Food Production." Woodbridge Press, Santa Barbara, CA.

Transgenic Animals

DAVID B. BERKOWITZ, *Food and Drug Administration, Rockville*

Glossary

Cloning Process of isolating and reproducing the DNA carrying a gene's nucleic acid sequence

Gene Sequence of DNA that specifies a unit of function, including the structural information for the gene product as well as the regulatory sequences controlling expression

Gene expression Production of the product of a gene; genes exert their effect through products, usually proteins; without expression, the organism would look as though the gene were not present

Genetic recombination Classically, the reassortment of genetic traits during formation of the gametes in sexual reproduction; for example, crosses between hornless black cattle and horned red cattle might produce the new combination of traits, hornless red animals; genes can now be recombined chemically in a process referred to as recombinant DNA techniques or "genetic engineering"

Genome Entire genetic complement of an organism

Transgene Gene introduced into an organism using recombinant DNA techniques

Transgenic animals are animals with a gene or a genetic sequence produced using recombinant-DNA techniques. The gene may be in somatic tissues only or may become part of the germ line. Transgenic animals are useful for numerous scientific purposes including the study of development, physiology, genetics, and human diseases. Agriculturally, they show promise for enhancing animal productivity and food quality.

I. Introduction

A. Definition of Transgenic Animal

It is now possible to introduce virtually any desired genetic sequence into the genome of an animal. The introduced sequence or transgene becomes part of the germ line, and the recipients of such sequences are called transgenic animals. Genes can also be introduced into somatic tissues where they may or may not be integrated into the genome. Such animals are also considered transgenic, although the transgene would not be transmitted to progeny.

Recombinant DNA techniques or "genetic engineering" make the transfer of genes across traditional species lines possible. Gene transfers can be made between animal species or from the plant kingdom into the animal kingdom, or a totally synthetic gene can be introduced into an animal. However, transgenic does not necessarily imply that the transgene is from a different genus.

B. How Transgenic Animals Are Made

In animals, gene transfer is accomplished by cloning the desired gene, usually followed by injection of the cloned DNA into a fertilized ovum or zygote. This is illustrated in Fig. 1. The round structure shown in the center of the figure is a fertilized swine ovum. The large pipette at the right is attached to a vacuum line to hold the ovum in place. The thin pipette inserted at the left of the ovum contains a solution of the cloned gene and is injecting copies of the gene into a pronucleus of the ovum. Both the paternal and maternal pronuclei are seen in the center of the ovum. The paternal and maternal genetic material will coalesce, and in a small percentage of the cases, a copy of the cloned gene will become a part of the animal's genome. Genes integrated into the genome usually replicate whenever the chromosome replicates, be-

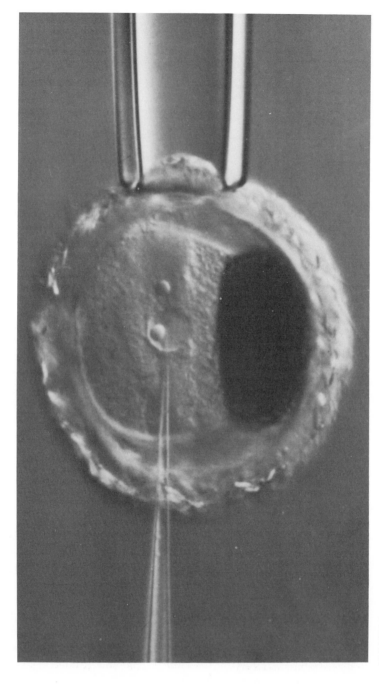

FIGURE 1 A fertilized swine ovum (zygote). The zygote has been centrifuged to make the maternal and paternal pronuclei visible for injection. The dark material separated by centrifugation is on the bottom of the zygote. [The picture was taken by R. E. Hammer and R. L. Brinster. Reproduced with permission from R. E. Hammer, V. G. Pursel, C. E. Rexroad, Jr., R. J. Wall, D. J. Bolt, K. M. Ebert, R. J. Palmiter, and R. L. Brinster. (1985). *Nature* **315**, 680–683.]

having as any other gene in the animal. In most cases the injected gene does not integrate into the recipient genome and is probably degraded. For this and other reasons, not more than 1 to 5% of the mouse zygotes injected develop into transgenic animals. The production of transgenic agricultural animals is even less efficient, ranging from 0.1 to about 0.5% of the injected zygotes.

C. Uses of Transgenic Animals

The applications of transgenesis are many, ranging from the use of short-unique DNA sequences as identity markers in animal lines, to the introduction of transgenes expected to result in more efficient animal productivity as measured by a reduction in the feed to gain ratio or in faster growth. Agricultural productivity may be enhanced by introducing genes for disease resistance or for the extension of the ecological range. For example, the ecological range may be extended into colder water for some species of fish. Many species of fish produce antifreeze proteins that lower their freezing points, allowing the fish to survive in colder water, but the introduction of antifreeze protein genes into additional fish species will allow these fishes to extend their ecological ranges. Nutritional enhancements may be possible by the introduction of genes causing, e.g., increased proportions of unsaturated fatty acids or decreased quantities of total fat. The agricultural applications of transgenesis are discussed in more detail below.

Transgenesis has a wide range of medical applications. Several of the traditional agricultural species are being used as "pharm animals" to produce drugs. Because some therapeutic agents are naturally occurring proteins or polypeptides, scientists can link the genes for these drugs to a regulatory sequence specifying expression in a specific tissue such as the mammary gland. The milk then becomes a source of a large quantity of drug which is relatively easy to isolate. The safety advantage is even more important than the simplified isolation. The harvesting of drugs from human tissue inherently brings with it the danger of transmitting human diseases through the drug. The transmission of AIDS to children receiving blood-clotting factors isolated from human serum is an example. The isolation of human proteins from transgenic animals makes the transmission of human infections far less likely. Transgenesis will also be used to produce animal tissues and organs suitable for transplantation to humans. Human organs for transplantation are in very short supply, so the objec-

tive is to genetically alter the animal tissue to reduce or eliminate rejection reactions, increasing the availability of tissues and organs suitable for transplantation. As with the drugs discussed above, this would also reduce the possibility of disease transmission from transplants.

Transgenic animals are proving to be very useful as models of human diseases. The "Harvard mouse," the first transgenic animal to be patented, is missing a tumor suppressor gene and develops tumors. The mouse is useful for studying cancer. A second Harvard mouse has recently been patented and is useful for studying benign prostatic hypertrophy, a common disease in older males. The mouse carries a growth factor gene with a controlling region assuring that the gene is expressed only in the prostate. This will be useful for detecting carcinogens and for studying treatments for prostatic hypertrophy.

In principle, once a gene for any hereditary human disease is identified, animal models can be generated by introducing the defective gene into an animal or simply by using gene targeting (see below) to disrupt the normal gene. The recipient animal is selected on the basis of a compromise between the ease of experimentation and the physiological similarity to humans for the purpose of studying the progression of and potential treatments for the disease. For instance, a gene for sickle cell anemia has been introduced into a mouse, and the mouse line is now being used to compare alternative treatments for the anemia. Two potential treatments are being evaluated. One is to coat the red cells with a chemical that helps them slip through blood clots. The other is to induce the expression of the fetal hemoglobin gene, a gene usually turned off after birth. Fetal hemoglobin could carry oxygen and dilute out the sickle hemoglobin. Transgenic animal models will be useful for comparing the effectiveness of treatments.

In addition to treating diseases, transgenesis also offers opportunities for preventing disease. Scientists are attempting to introduce transgenes that would prevent parasites from entering or maturing in intermediate hosts, thus interrupting the life cycle of the parasites. World wide, malaria kills about a million children a year. Insecticides are becoming less effective against the mosquito, the intermediate host, so transgenesis may offer an important alternative for controlling the disease by preventing pathogen production by the mosquito. Similar experiments are being conducted on snails, intermediate hosts for schistosomiasis.

II. The Production of Transgenic Animals

The introduction of a new gene into an animal requires a large amount of the gene in pure form. This is achieved by cloning, the process of isolating and culturing a gene to produce the needed quantity in pure form. A brief overview of some pertinent principles of molecular biology and cloning follows. The objective is to explain some basic principles with only enough technical details to make the concepts clear. Additional details can be found in the materials referenced.

A. Molecular Biology Background

The sequence of nucleotide bases in DNA contains the genetic information. Each position in the DNA is occupied by one of four bases, adenine (A), guanine (G), cytosine (C), or thymine (T), and each is chemically linked to the previous and next base in the strand by sugar–phosphate bridges. (see gene segment in Fig. 2.) The two strands of the DNA double helix are held together by hydrogen bonds between the bases. The geometry of the hydrogen-bonding groups in the bases is such that adenine always pairs with thymine, and guanine with cytosine, so the base sequence of the initial strand automatically determines the sequence of the complementary strand.

Most genes code for proteins, and proteins are uniquely determined by their amino acid sequences. Each sequence of three DNA bases codes for an amino acid, so the sequence of nucleotide bases in DNA dictates the amino acid sequence in proteins. Some three-base sequences determine the punctuation, coding for starting or terminating the formation of the protein chain.

DNA is not "translated" into protein directly, but first produces a messenger ribonucleic acid (mRNA) which leaves the nucleus of the cell and enters the cytoplasm where translation takes place. The mRNA has the same sequence as the coding strand of DNA, but uracil (U) replaces T. The formation of mRNA is called transcription. The reading of the messenger RNA three bases at a time, translation, produces the protein specified by the gene. Gene expression refers to the production of the gene product from the gene. The rate of production of protein is regulated at the transcription, translation, and post-translational levels, but the rate of transcription is a direct assessment of the control of expression at the gene (DNA) level.

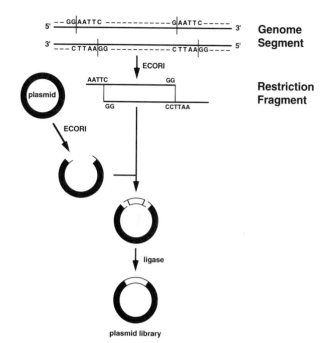

FIGURE 2 The genome segment at the top of the figure shows a DNA double helix with its two complementary strands. The two strands are held together by hydrogen bonds between the complementary base pairs. The nucleic acid bases are designated only near the restriction sites at the ends of the segment, but extend through and beyond the hypothetical segment shown. The representative restriction fragment would result from digestion of the genome with a restriction enzyme called *Eco*R1. *Eco*RI recognizes and cuts only between the G and the A of the sequence GAATTC of the DNA strand. Because the sequence cut is palindromic, the bases in the free single-stranded ends complement one another, so the ends can pair by hydrogen bonding. Such single-stranded ends are called "sticky" ends. Sticky ends allow the DNA fragments to be reassembled with themselves or with DNA from other sources cut by the same restriction enzyme. After the fragments are assembled, a ligase is used to reform the covalent bonds cut by the restriction enzymes. The sticky ends can pair with the ends of other fragments or can wrap around and form a closed circle. The joints can be made covalent by a ligase. Bacterial plasmids are covalently closed circular DNA fragments that are able to replicate autonomously in the bacterial cell. When the plasmid is opened with *Eco*R1, the sticky ends bond with genome fragments forming closed plasmids, each containing a genome fragment. After treatment with a ligase, the modified plasmids can be transferred back into *E.coli* by transfection and grown in large amounts. Colonies of bacteria carrying the plasmid with the gene of interest can be isolated by various selective techniques.

B. Cloning

Cloning is the process of isolating and reproducing copies of the DNA carrying a gene's nucleic acid sequence. The gene must be cloned so that the transgene is a major component of the DNA injected into the zygote. Cloning is possible because of two kinds of enzymes that act on DNA, restriction enzymes and ligases. Restriction enzymes cut DNA strands at specific sequences. Many cut at palindromic sequences, producing uneven ends, as shown in Fig. 2 for a restriction enzyme called *Eco*RI. "Sticky ends" allow the DNA fragments to be reassembled with themselves or with DNA from other sources cut by the same restriction enzyme. After the fragments are assembled and held by base pairing, a ligase is used to reform the covalent bonds cut by the restriction enzymes. This combination of restriction enzymes and ligases makes it possible to disassemble a genome and reassemble selected DNA fragments as desired.

To clone a mammalian gene, the DNA representing the entire genome of the animal can be isolated from the other cellular constituents and cut into restriction fragments. (Fig. 2.) Many restriction fragments of varying lengths would be produced by the restriction enzyme. Ideally, each segment of the genome would be represented in the restriction fragment mixture. The fragment carrying the gene to be cloned can be replicated using a plasmid that grows in the common bacterium, *Escherichia coli* (*E.coli*). Plasmids are circular pieces of DNA which are able to replicate in *E.coli* independently of the chromosome. Each *E.coli* cell can have hundreds of copies of the plasmid per *E.coli* chromosome. The plasmid can easily be separated from the chromosome and can be cleaved with the restriction enzymes. The resulting sticky ends can form base pairs with the sticky ends of the animal genome fragments produced by the same restriction enzyme (Fig. 2). After ligation, the result is a group of modified plasmids still able to replicate in *E.coli*, but each plasmid carries a different segment of the animal genome. The collection of plasmids can be introduced into and grown in *E.coli*, increasing the number of copies of each of the animal chromosomal fragments. The collection of plasmids is referred to as a gene library. Many bacterial colonies must be tested to retrieve from the library at least one colony carrying the plasmid with the gene to be cloned.

The frequency of plasmids in the library carrying the desired gene is low. If each plasmid carries a piece of DNA about the size of one gene, and there are 100,000 genes in the animal representing only 10% of the DNA (90% of mammalian DNA has no known function), one would have to test *at least* a million plasmids to find one carrying the gene being sought. This can be done by plating the bacteria carrying the plasmids onto petri plates so individual colonies can be examined. Each colony contains progeny from a single parental bacterium carrying identical plasmid,

i.e., all of the plasmids in a single bacterial cell are identical, so each colony represents a single plasmid. Rapid techniques are available to screen colonies a plate-full at a time by looking for DNA that anneals to a radioactive or other suitably labeled probe carrying a DNA sequence complementary to the gene. The selection is usually designed so that the desired colonies are a different color or are otherwise clearly distinguishable from the overwhelming number of background colonies. When a colony carrying the gene is found, it can be grown in culture, the plasmid DNA isolated, and the gene removed from the plasmid with the restriction enzyme, and separated from the remaining plasmid DNA. The result is a relatively large quantity of the desired gene in pure form. This DNA can be used to produce a transgenic animal.

C. Introduction of the Transgene

At present, embryo injection (Fig. 1) is widely used for introducing DNA into fertilized ova, but other alternatives offer advantages. In chickens the fertilized ova are not readily available because the shelled embryo emerges at a much later stage of development. Retroviruses have been used to introduce DNA into chicken embryos because these viruses infect many of the embryonic cells and integrate into the host genome carrying the transgene. Like the plasmid discussed above, retroviruses can be modified to carry transgenes. Retroviruses integrate at nearly random single chromosomal sites and insert a single copy of the transgene. Retroviruses might be more widely used in agricultural animals, but the size of the DNA they can carry is relatively small and there are concerns about the possible reversion of the inactivated retrovirus producing infective virus particles which may infect other animals. Although such events are extremely rare, the use of retroviruses in food animals has not been widely pursued.

The introduction of recombinant DNA into ova as a hitchhiker stuck to the outside of spermatozoa has not been reproducible in mammals, but does show promise in fish. Fish sperm were incubated with transgene DNA and added to suspensions of eggs. The DNA was incorporated into the genome of about 30% of the treated eggs. The authors of this study confirmed integration into the genome by demonstrating transmission of the transgene from some of the fish through two generations. This technique is particularly easy in fish because the eggs are normally fertilized externally. The technique will also be useful in land animals if reproducible methodology can be found.

The introduction of transgenes through embryonic stem cells offers major advantages. Embryonic stem cells are undifferentiated cells removed from very young embryos at a stage called the blastocyst. Undifferentiated means the cells are able to give rise to a complete embryo, i.e., they are totipotent. The stem cells are treated with the transgene DNA and propagated in tissue culture. Single transgenic cells from the culture can be implanted back into young embryos by micromanipulation resulting in transgenic animals with mosaic patterns of cells because only the cells derived from the reimplanted cells carry the transgene. Studies show that the micromanipulation required to inject embryonic stem cells treated with DNA into a blastocyst can be eliminated by adding the treated stem cells to morula-stage embryonic cells in culture. The stem cells attach to the outside of the morula, but as development continues, they become part of the inner cell mass from which the embryo proper develops. This method simplifies the technique by eliminating the need to manipulate blastocyst-stage embryos, which are more difficult to handle. Both techniques produce mosaic animals, but germ line cells are frequently transgenic, so fully transgenic animals can be obtained from subsequent generations.

Other techniques applicable to cell cultures can be used with embryonic stem cells. The bulk techniques used to introduce DNA into cells in culture can be used to introduce DNA into stem cells. These include the use of a DNA calcium phosphate precipitate or DEAE-dextran for presenting the DNA to the cells for uptake or electroporation, the use of electric currents. Genes can also be introduced into cells ballistically. Small particles coated with DNA are propelled from special jets by air pressure or by electropropulsion and shot into cells. This technique has been widely used in plants, and the process has been patented for use in animals.

Cell selection can be used to target a transgene to any locus in the recipient genome, a process called *gene targeting*. Cells with the transgene integrated at a desired site on the chromosome can be selected by designing the vector with a "reporter gene," which is expressed only by cells in which the desired insertion event has occurred. Thus, it is possible to select cells with specific recipient genes that have been interrupted by transgene insertion. These specifically selected "knockouts" can be used to determine the function of a known genetic locus. Genes of the recipient can also be replaced by homologous transgenes carrying small changes to study the effect of minimal changes such as single base changes on gene function. Knockouts and replacements are contributing heavily to the understanding of developmental and physiological processes.

Embryonic stem cells provide an avenue for the introduction of yeast artificial chromosomes (YACs) into animal germ lines, permitting the introduction of very large pieces of transgene DNA. In the plasmid cloning described above, the size of the DNA insert has an upper limit of about 10,000 base pairs. YACs can carry pieces of DNA over a million base pairs in length. This is an important capability because some genes and their regulatory regions are very diffuse, and transferring the entire region may be important to achieve appropriate expression. YACs contain genetic elements that allow them to be replicated in yeast as another yeast chromosome, hence their name. YAC DNA can be separated from the rest of the yeast DNA and injected into zygotes as above, but the largest pieces of DNA are difficult to handle and are transferred by directly fusing yeast cells containing many copies of the YAC with embryonic stem cells. Very large pieces of DNA are incorporated into the embryonic stem cells and may be transferred to progeny when the stem cells give rise to the germ line cells.

Surprisingly, genes can be expressed after the direct hypodermic injection of DNA into somatic tissues. DNA coding for an enzyme was expressed in mouse muscle cells surrounding the injection site. Expression of the enzyme persisted for at least 30 days after injection. When the messenger RNA for the same enzyme was injected, enzyme activity peaked at 18 hr and fell to about 3% of the peak level by 60 hr. Although the RNA had a short half-life, the DNA persisted in the cell and was expressed, but was not integrated into the chromosome. DNA has also been inserted into somatic tissues by particle bombardment technology. In this experiment DNA was coated on the surface of tiny gold beads so that 10,000 copies of the gene were present on each particle. The particles were accelerated by electromotive force into liver, skin, and muscle, each of which showed significant expression of the gene.

Direct injection techniques hold great promise for vaccines. To vaccinate, the DNA coding for a viral protein can be injected into a muscle. The muscle cells take up the DNA and produce the viral protein which is recognized as foreign and stimulates an immune response. There are special advantages for vaccines against influenza, because the influenza surface proteins change rapidly as a result of mutations enabling viruses to escape the antibodies. The influenza virus nucleoproteins do not change, but the nucleoproteins are not exposed on the viral surface and are not accessible to antibodies. DNA injection results in the intracellular production of the nucleoprotein, and this stimulates a cellular immune response to the virus. The foreign intracellular proteins stimulate the response to infection by a subclass of white blood cells called the cytotoxic T cells. Since most influenza viruses have the same nucleoproteins, a nucleoprotein vaccine should protect against infection by a heterologous virus, i.e., a virus with a different surface protein. Although the mechanism is somewhat speculative, protection against a challenge by a heterologous influenza virus has been demonstrated in mice. Another advantage of DNA vaccines is their greater temperature stability. Whole cell vaccines and proteins are more temperature sensitive than DNA.

Intravenously injected DNA is also expressed in tissues. The DNA was presented in liposomes, artificial membrane vesicles, to promote the entry of DNA into cells. After intravenous injection into mice, the gene was expressed in many tissues, including heart, lung, liver, lymph nodes, and others. Expression continued for at least 9 weeks. DNA linked to molecules that bind specific cell receptors can be directed to specific tissues. These somatic cell techniques may be particularly useful as a different approach to growth promotion in animals. The introduction of a transgene during a late stage of growth rather than at the embryonic stage may be less likely to cause the kinds of health problems seen in the transgenic pigs (see below). This technology opens a new avenue to long-acting therapeutics.

D. The Control of Gene Expression

The introduction of a transgene is of no value unless the gene is expressed (except for knockouts). Once integration of the gene has been established, expression is determined by measuring the amount of specific messenger RNA or more directly by measuring the amount of gene product formed. Gene expression is regulated at the transcriptional, translational, and post-translational levels, but the discussion here is limited to regulation of the production of mRNA. The regulation of gene expression is biologically critical. All the tissues of the body, e.g., muscle, and liver, contain the same genetic information. Differences in the genes expressed in each tissue are what distinguish one tissue from another. The tissue distinctions are

made during embryological development as the various tissues differentiate. Once differentiation has taken place, the pattern of expression usually remains constant, although levels of expressed genes change in response to physiological changes. For example, when glucose is present in the diet, insulin is released, and insulin turns off the production of a critical enzyme responsible for the formation of glucose from amino acids, phosphoenolpyruvate carboxykinase (PEPCK). Many enzyme levels change in response to metabolic shifts. In general, rapid changes are accomplished by activating preexisting enzymes by covalent changes or by structural changes induced by small molecules. The slower hour-to-hour changes are accomplished by changing the level of gene expression. Physiological balance or homeostasis is labyrinthine, and the regulation of gene expression is an important part of the homeostatic system.

The complexity of transcription control is illustrated by two types of regulatory regions, promoters and enhancers. Promoters are located just in front of the beginning of the coding sequence of the structural genes, and contain the binding site on the DNA for the RNA polymerase. Promoters are located just in front of the beginning of the coding sequence of the structural genes and contain the binding site on the DNA for the RNA polymerase. Promoters also have binding sites for *trans*-acting proteins produced elsewhere in the genome that are essential for the activation of transcription. *Trans*-acting proteins, also called transcription factors, frequently activate transcription only in the presence of hormones, growth factors, or other inducers. For example, the growth hormone promoter is activated by thyroxine. These kinds of interhormonal interactions are essential for maintaining the endocrinological balance. The metallothionein promoter is turned on only in the presence of zinc ion or other heavy metals and has been used to make transgenic animals with growth hormone levels that can be elevated by feeding zinc ion.

Enhancers also bind transcription factors, but may be located within the gene, or much farther from the gene than promoters either in front of or beyond the gene. Enhancers activate gene expression and are also responsible for tissue-specific expression. They have been used to direct the expression of genes producing therapeutic agents to the mammary glands in transgenic animals.

Two kinds of control regions possibly related to higher-order chromosome structure are important for transgene expression. Transgenic founder animals carrying identical transgenes vary widely in the levels of transgene expression. Transgenes integrate by non-homologous recombination at random sites in the chromosome, frequently in tandem arrays (i.e., multiple repeats of the sequence). Differences in levels of expression do not correlate with the number of gene copies in the tandem arrays and have been ascribed to the position of integration in the genome. Locus control regions (LCRs) and matrix attachment regions (MARs) stimulate the transcription of transgenes, making transcription independent of the position of transgene insertion and proportional to the number of gene copies. The LCRs, which are specific to the family of β globin genes, contain multiple binding sites for general and specific transcription factors and improve tissue specificity. MARs, contain the sites at which the nuclear matrix or scaffold proteins bind to the chromosomes. Both MARs and LCRs may stabilize the open form of the chromosome making it available to *trans*-acting factors essential for efficient position-independent transcription. For example, when the whey acidic protein gene, a milk protein gene, was introduced into mice, the level of expression varied with the site of integration and did not behave as the endogenous gene through the lactation cycle and in response to hormones. When the same sequence was introduced adjacent to a MAR, expression became position independent of the site of integration and, in most lines, more closely paralleled the expression of the endogenous gene through the lactation cycle. Whatever the mechanisms, LCRs and MARs are likely to be useful for controlling gene expression in transgenic animals.

III. Agricultural Applications of Transgenesis

The agricultural applications of transgenesis in animals were stimulated by the appearance of the twice-normal-size transgenic mouse on the cover of *Nature* (*London*) in 1982 (Fig. 3). The picture excited the imagination of animal scientists, because it proved that a growth hormone gene from one species, a rat, could be transferred to another species, a mouse, and produce the expected phenotypic change in the animal. It seemed that growth hormone and other genes could be transferred to farm animals to improve productivity. Many growth hormone genes have been transferred into swine and sheep, but unfortunately the animals that expressed the genes displayed one or more sequelae which precluded their use as productive

agricultural animals. They displayed pathological conditions which occur naturally, but were of greater frequency and intensity in the transgenic animals. The pathology included lameness, gastric ulcers, kidney disease, and infertility. The requirement for general good health in productive animals apparently limits the physiological phenotypic extremes attainable from either classical selective breeding or from transgenesis. The expression of a transgene must be tightly controlled to maintain the animal within a physiologically acceptable range.

Data from injected growth hormone indicate that in some animals milk production is increased, the meat is leaner, and the feed efficiency is enhanced. A well-regulated growth hormone transgene could be beneficial, but attempts to regulate the gene have not been successful. In some attempts the gene was linked to a metallothionein promoter, a promoter that turns expression of the gene on in response to elevated levels of zinc ion. Because the effects of growth hormone are less deleterious during the later stages of growth, the idea was to add zinc to the feed in a later stage of growth and reap the benefits without the undesirable effects. This worked well in mice, but pigs and sheep were less responsive to the metallothionein promoter. A few experiments have been done with other components of the growth hormone system, growth hormone-releasing factor (GRF) and insulin-like growth factor-1 (IGF-1). GRF is made in the hypothalamus and stimulates the release of growth hormone from the pituitary. The human GRF gene expressed in pigs did not stimulate growth hormone levels, probably because three amino acids were cleaved from the amino-terminal end of the GRF. In sheep, growth hormone levels were increased and resulted in the same effects as growth hormone transgenes. IGF-1 is produced in liver and other tissues in response to growth hormone and is responsible for many of the hormone's effects. Unfortunately, not enough data are available to make any conclusions about the effects of IGF-1 transgene in food animals.

Naturally occurring mutations cause "double-muscled" animals with, as the name implies, nearly twice the normal levels of muscle. These are somewhat like what the animals growth hormone might ideally produce, but because the increased muscling begins during embryonic development, the large fetus causes delivery problems. Unless the increased muscle development can be delayed until after birth, these natural mutations will have little commercial value.

Transgenesis in fish shows great promise. Growth hormone genes have been transferred into about 10

FIGURE 3 Shows two sibling male mice. The mouse on the left carries a rat growth hormone gene fused to a metallothionein control region. The mouse with the transgene weighs 44 g. The control sibling weights 29 g. [The photograph was taken by R. L. Brinster. Reproduced with permission from Palmiter, R. L. Brinster, R. E. Hammer, M. E. Trumbauer, M. G. Rosenfeld, N. G. Birnberg, and R. M. Evans. (1982). *Nature* **300,** 611–615.]

different species of fish. A salmon growth hormone gene linked to an antifreeze protein promoter produced transgenic fish that were six times larger than the control population at 26 months of age. Information is not yet available on the transmissibility of the gene or on the general and reproductive health of the fish. Nevertheless, the initial data are promising, and experiments with fish are far easier and less expensive than work with farm animals.

In farm animals, enhancers specifying gene expression in specific tissue have been useful. For example, pharmaceutical proteins such as clotting factors and tissue plasminogen activator can be produced at very high concentrations in milk. Directed expression can also be used to improve feed utilization. The expression of the gene for the enzyme cellulase was directed to the pancreas in mice. The result was mice secreting cellulase into the intestine along with the normal complement of digestive enzymes. Monogastric animals do not normally produce cellulase and are unable to digest cellulose in plant materials. With cellulase in the digestive juices, the mice will make more efficient use of plant feeds because they will be able to digest the cellulose component. The cellulase transgene might also improve the feed efficiency of swine. Ruminants are naturally able to digest cellulose because of microorganisms in the rumen that contain cellulase.

Targeting gene expression to specific tissues will also be used to change the composition of milk itself. Increasing the casein content of milk would improve its use for the production of cheese. According to a 1990 estimate, increasing the casein content by 20% could save the dairy industry 190 million dollars. Because human milk has long been the gold standard for infant formula, producers are attempting to make cow's milk more like human milk. Cow's milk contains very low concentrations of the protein lactoferrin compared to the amount present in human milk. By introducing a human lactoferrin gene into cows with its expression directed to the udder, the cow's milk will be more human like. Milk from such herds could be used to produce infant formula.

An Australian group is attempting to enhance wool production by increasing the level of the amino acid cysteine, which is limiting for wool production. They are introducing into sheep genes for bacterial enzymes for the biosynthesis of cysteine. In mammals cysteine is synthesized from the amino acid methionine which is required in the diet. Bacteria synthesize cysteine from serine, an endogenously synthesized readily available amino acid. By transferring the two necessary enzymes from bacteria into sheep, cysteine will be increased and may increase wool production.

Scientists are also examining a number ways to improve disease resistance in farm animals. One method is to insert transgenes coding for viral coat proteins into the germ line. Presumably these coat proteins occupy the viral receptors on the cell surface where the virus normally attaches to the cell preventing the attachment of real viruses. This has been somewhat successful in preventing some diseases in chickens.

Strategies for disease resistance have evolved with animals, as exemplified by interferons and the mouse Mx1 gene. In mice, the expression of a gene called Mx1 is induced by viral infection or by interferon. Expression of the gene produces resistance to infection by influenza virus. The mouse Mx1 gene linked to the influenza-sensitive promoter has been transferred into pigs. The pigs have not yet been challenged with virus to test immunity to influenza.

Because interferon prevents viral infections, scientists have considered inducing disease resistance by introducing an interferon gene that is constitutively expressed, (i.e., expressed in the absence of a specific inducer). Unfortunately, interferon is too toxic to be compatible with constitutive expression. However, in the mouse, human interferon is less toxic, and transgenic mice expressing a human interferon gene were resistant to infection by the pseudorabies virus. This suggests that the toxicity of β interferon can be controlled by amino acid sequence changes, and this would be agriculturally useful if human or interferons with other amino acid changes work in swine.

The use of transgenesis for herd improvements has not progressed as rapidly as one might have imagined in the mid 1980s. This is for a number of reasons, one

of which is that selective breeding remains a powerful competitor. Even after a transgenic animal with useful characteristics is produced, it will still have to be bred to expand the line and to be certain the trait is stably expressed in its new background. Domestic animals are far more heterozygous than mouse lines, so animal-to-animal differences can be large. If a trait can be enhanced by selective breeding, transgenesis is not likely to be competitive. [See ANIMAL BREEDING AND GENETICS.]

The cost of producing transgenic animals is high. The cost of a single transgenic cow was estimated at one-half million dollars in 1991. The costs are associated with the husbanding of the animals, including the ova donors and animals synchronized in the estrus cycle as recipients for the injected zygotes. Because integration of the transgene is random in each zygote, many animals must be produced to find at least one expressing the gene at the right level. The costs for cows are especially high because they are uniparous. However, costs are less for sheep which frequently twin and still less for pigs which average about 10 offspring per litter.

Technological developments are rapidly overcoming some of these obstacles. Gene targeting and the use of MARs or LCRs are likely to reduce the variability with integration site. Bovine ova can be removed from cows at slaughter and matured *in vitro*, greatly reducing the number of animals that have to be kept on hand to maintain the supply of ova. The ability to produce somatic cell transgenics may turn out to be far easier than producing and selecting germ line transgenics. The introduction of DNA intravenously may be as convenient as using a long-acting drug, in this case with the period of activity measurable in days or weeks rather than hours.

IV. Food Safety of Transgenic Animals

The effect of transgenesis on food safety is an important consideration, because most agricultural animals contribute to the food supply. The benchmark for the evaluation of the food safety of transgenic animals is the food safety of traditionally bred animals. Selective breeding for desirable traits has been used for centuries and is not known to have produced unsafe lines of animals. This discussion of food safety focuses on those facets of transgenesis that distinguish it from traditional breeding. Three unique features of the technology are relevant, the transgene itself, the transgene product, and secondary effects arising as a result of the integration of the transgene into the genome of the animal. The transgene DNA sequence is not likely to be of concern unless it is infectious. The DNA of all the animals and plants we eat is ingested and digested with impunity. Even human DNA from the cells of the nasopharynx and the digestive tract is digested with the food. Hazards would only result from the DNA if the transgene were infectious and could replicate and infect cells in the gastrointestinal track or elsewhere in the body.

The transgene product can be thought of as a drug, and the food safety of the flesh evaluated as it would be for an animal treated with the drug. The primary questions would concern the toxicity of the protein and the concentration of the protein in edible tissues. As with drugs, secondary effects of the gene product must also be considered. Most proteins are not orally active, but some gene products increase the levels of other animal components such as steroids which are orally active. Because the function of the gene product is known before the gene is selected for transfer, the physiological systems affected are likely to be known, and the secondary effects can be evaluated. The transfer of a gene from a known allergenic organism into another organism is possible with recombinant technology because of the ability to transfer genes across species lines. Unless it can be shown that the gene transferred from a known allergenic source does not code for the allergen, consumers must be informed that the allergen may be present in an unsuspected food. The potential allergenicity of proteins new in the food supply might be predicted by structural similarities to known allergens, but the science is not developed well enough to be highly predictive.

The effects of the integration of the transgene are the most difficult feature of transgenesis to evaluate. Because transgenes integrate into the genome nearly randomly by nonhomologous recombination, they can integrate into the middle of a host gene stopping its expression (a knockout) or into a gene in a way that increases or decreases its level of expression by putting it under the control of the transgene promoter. Because these events are random, the consequences are not predictable. However, similar events do occur spontaneously from deletions, inversions, insertions, and point mutations during normal reproduction, and yet unsafe lines of animals from safe parental lines have not been described. Unlike plants, the common food animals do not produce substances that are toxic to humans in the food, but innocuous to the animal. Increases in orally active substances such as steroids are likely to be reflected in the health of the animal. Only changes in vitamin levels or other nutritional parameters are apt to go unnoticed if affected, but this is also true of traditionally bred animals. At the present stage of technological development, the safety considerations for transgenic animals are similar to those for traditionally bred animals or animals administered drugs.

Bibliography

Berkowitz, D. B. (1993). The food safety of transgenic animals: Implications from traditional breeding. *J. Anim. Sci.* **71** (Suppl. 3), 43–46.

Boyd, A. L., and Samid, D. (1993). The molecular biology of transgenic animals. *J. Anim. Sci.* **71** (Suppl. 3), 1–9.

Chen, T. T., and Powers, D. A. (1990). Transgenic Fish. *Trends in Biotechnol.* **8**, 209–215.

Grosveld, F., and Kollias, G. (1992). "Transgenic Animals." Academic Press, New York.

Pursel, V. G., and Rexroad, C. E., Jr. (1993). Status of research with transgenic farm animals. *J. Anim. Sci.,* **71** (Suppl. 3), 10–19.

Smithies, O. (1993). Animal models of human genetic diseases. *Trends in Genet.* **9**, 112–116.

Wall, R. J., and Seidel, G. E.. (1992). Transgenic farm animals—A critical analysis. *Theriogenology* **38**, 337–357.

Watson, J. D., Gilman, M., Witkowski, J., and Zoller, M. (1992). "Recombinant DNA," 2nd Ed., Freeman, New York.

Transposable Elements in Plants

PETER A. PETERSON, *Iowa State University*

Glossary

Autonomous element Transposable element with all the functions necessary to self-excise and reinsert at new sites (see Fig. 5A)

Autonomous mutability Mutability that is controlled at the locus, and does not need a second factor

Chromosome breakage Breakage induced by a transposable element; in the *Ac–Ds* system, it occurs at a special double *Ds* (see Fig. 2C)

Reporter allele Gene with a defective transposable element insert that responds to an active element (see Fig. 2A)

Tagging (gene) Using a cloned element probe to identify and isolate a gene with a transposable element insert for molecular studies

Target site duplication (TSD) Duplicate of a host sequence induced on insertion of a transposable element at a genome site (see Fig. 2A)

Terminal inverted repeats (TIR) Sequence at the terminal ends of the element that have a characteristic number of nucleotides that identifies a system (see Fig. 4)

Terminal motifs Series of characteristic sequences related to the TIR and extending on each end of transposable elements (see Fig. 5A)

Transposable element (TE)/transposon DNA segment containing functions that induce excision and transposition

Transposase Protein product of a transposon that induces excision

Transposition Movement of an element from one site on the chromosome to a new site

Variegation Chimeric sectors on plant parts

Transposable elements are DNA segments with a distinct structure and function(s) that allow them to transpose throughout the genome. Their phenotypic expression is derived from the insertion of these elements into genes whose functions are often interrupted, that is, a null phenotype. This can be followed by the excision of the transposon out of the gene, which allows the functioning of the gene and often leads to a wild-type phenotypic expression. This insertion followed by excision results in variegation. This variegation is a distinctive type representing a return of function of the gene and can be seen in all plant tissues where this gene is phenotypically observed to function. Forms of this variegation are illustrated in Fig. 1.

I. Phenotypes, Variegation, and Components

Originally identified in the 1800s as "eversporting" varieties and reported by early biologists, including Charles Darwin, H. Lecoq, and T. A. Knight, this type of variegation was finally elucidated when Barbara McClintock observed and then described a two-unit interaction that caused the breakage of chromosomes. From this original observation, the components of this two-unit interaction were then found to be the same components controlling the variegation of numerous genes. By relating the breakage phenomenon and the variegation phenotype, it was finally determined to be caused by these same units. In fol-

FIGURE 1 Varied variegation: (A) kernels of *Zea mays, a2m;* (B) *Petunia hybrida, am1* allele; (C) *Dahlia,* horticultural variety; (D) *Glycine max, Ym-18.* [From P. A. Peterson. (1987). Mobile elements in plants. *CRC Crit. Rev. Plant Sci.* **6,** 105–208.]

lowing the genetics of these units causing breakage, McClintock observed that they changed position. This was confirmed by the demonstration of the transposition of the breakage phenomenon, through genetic means, from one position of the chromosome to another, and finally the movement of these elements into numerous genes leading to variegation. It was therefore readily acceptable to conclude that the variegation of genes was related to the breakage phenomenon and that these units causing variegation were mobile. With these observations, transposable elements were introduced into the genetic literature in the early 1950s.

A. Origin

Most of the variegated genes found by McClintock arose out of strains of genetic material with chromosomes that included an inverse duplication of the short arm of chromosome 9 in maize and, with the resulting crossovers, that underwent cycles of chromosome bridges and breakage, followed by fusion of the broken ends. It is hypothesized that this breakage of the bridged chromosomes represented a stress condition affecting genome physiology that induced unknown effects that caused the mobility of these elements. Most likely, active transposable elements were already present in the genome but the stress conditions

enhanced the mobility. This does not imply that the original transposable element arose under these conditions, in that the stress did not cause the origin of the elements themselves. Following the induction of the breakage of chromosomes, a condition was generated by the breakage activity that induced active elements already present in the genome to become mobile and by this mobility become inserted into genes, causing the variegation. In addition to this stress induced by the breakage phenomenon, variegated phenotypes appeared following irradiation such as in the Bikini atom bomb tests. Subsequent tests showed that these phenotypes were cases of mobile element inserts. Yet variegated phenotypes have been present in horticultural plants for centuries. Their pervasiveness in plant types was likely enhanced by horticulturists who selected them for their esthetic value as did native American Indians among their corn cultures. What conditions promoted their presence in these cultivars are unknown, but over a period of time, variable environmental changes could have been responsible. However, their initial origin and their entry into the genomes of plants is still a mystery. The homology of their structure and critical sequences across plant species and genera implies an ancient origin or a case of horizontal transfer. [*See* PLANT GENETIC ENHANCEMENT.]

B. Components

1. Autonomous Mutability

From early studies at the beginning of genetic investigations on transposable elements, two kinds of hereditary control of variegation were known that eventually led to the description of two kinds of elements. From genetic studies, it could be seen that when the transmission of a variegating gene was inherited as a unit (i.e., the gene in question when outcrossed was always inherited with the mutability), this indicated that the active component causing the variegation was located at the gene. This represented an "autonomous mutable locus." In current dialogue, this autonomous unit at the gene in question is the autonomous element. Carrying this further, it is apparent that the autonomous element has all the functions with the capacity to cause its own excision and reinsertion at a new site.

2. Two-Unit Mutability

The second type of variegation required two units. It could be determined genetically that the active element was inherited independently of the gene showing variegation. This variegating gene included a receptor element (receptive to transactive signals from the autonomous element, now identified as a defective element) that responded to the transactive functions of an active element located elsewhere. In later molecular studies, this receptor element was found to be similar to the active element but was deficient in a critical component of the active element (the autonomous element), lacking the necessary functions to self-excise, though it did include most of the structural integrity of the element that allowed it to respond to the active element by excising and transposing to another site.

Further study determined that these defective elements arose from deletions of important components of the active element. Their structures are identical except for variable missing parts that are necessary for inducing excisions and resulting in transposition. This will be described in the molecular description of elements. Thus the two kinds of variegation control, namely, autonomous vs two-component, represent the original element and a derivative defective type.

II. Genetic Determination and Resolution

A. Systems

With the establishment of these two-component systems, the defective form (the receptor) became available as a "reporter" allele. When a new unstable allele is discovered in a genetic study, it could be tested for its relationship to a previously described system in a genetic cross. This is illustrated in the following illustration whereby the reporter allele could be a *Ds* (dissociator of the *Ac–Ds* system) that responds by breaking the chromosome (phenotypically, the loss of genetic markers), and the new variegation (**Var**) could come from a native population. Other reporter alleles are indicated in Fig. 2A.

- The *Ac* element is the autonomous element.
- The *Ds* element is the nonautonomous element that responds to the autonomous element by excising, transposing, and inserting at a new site.
- Thus, *C Ds* is the reporter line for any *Ac*.
- A cross of *C Ds* × *c Ac* results in loss of *C* and is expressed as *C* to *c* variegation.

The cross must include a recessive *c* to expose the loss of *C* in the *C Ds* arrangement.

- **Var** is a new uncharacterized mutable phenotype.

- The unknown variegation (**Var**), if found in a commercial line, would be *c* **Var**.
- The question is whether **Var** is related to *Ac*.
- The *C Ds* line is crossed by *c* **Var**.
- If there is no variegation of *C* to *c*, **Var** is unrelated to *Ac*.
- If variegation results, **Var** is either related to *Ac* or **Var** is carrying *Ac* in the line, but is not the cause of **Var** variegation.
- A direct correlation of *Ac* effect and **Var** expression in successive crosses would prove the relation of **Var** to the *Ac* system, that is, **Var** expression is always correlated with *Ac* activity in an independent test.

Thus when a new form of variegation is uncovered, the variegation is crossed to the numerous and available transposable element system's reporter alleles (Fig. 2A). The particular selection of reporter allele depends on the genetic makeup of the line where the new variegation is found. These reporter alleles are listed in Fig. 2A. As a consequence, nine systems have been identified; however, there are, subcomponents of these systems that do not show reciprocity of activity to the response to this active transposable element. These are illustrated in Fig. 2B. Other elements have not been genetically defined. For example, the multitude and diversity of *cin* elements have not been followed genetically, and other undefined and uncharacterized inserts have been uncovered as genes have been isolated. Their identity as transposable element inserts is derived from a characteristic terminal inverted repeat (TIR) and target site duplication (TSD).

B. Specificity of Systems

As new variegation was found and tested against reporter alleles, a positive interaction indicated the same system [Fig. 2B(A)]. When a test was negative, mutable alleles fell into different families of elements, which indicated that there was a specificity of the autonomous element on the reporter allele. This specificity awaited molecular findings for an explanation. There was a genetic clue: the specificity of interaction with the specific autonomous element was related to the autonomous element that previously "visited" the locus. Prior to the molecular findings, a critical question was: How was the gene "contaminated" by the "visit." Transposable element families evolve such that reciprocity in interaction is absent [Fig. 2B(B)]. Further changes in a reporter allele occur when a "helper" element is needed with an active *En* element for transposition to occur ([Fig. 2B(C)]. In this latter

A **Transposable Element Systems**

Au*	a-dt	Ds	I/dSpm	Ds1	'r-R #2	r-cu	Mu1-Mu8	mut	mrh	rbg	rcy
Dt	+										
Ac/Mp		+		+							
En/Spm			+								
Uq				+							
Fcu					+	+					
Spf					+						
Mu1R							+				+
Mut								+			
Mrh									+		
Bg										+	
Cy							+				+

Non-autonomous (Reporter alleles) span the columns a-dt through rcy.

+ = responds as mutability; absence of + indicates no response.

* = Au = Autonomous element

B Regulator-Receptor Interactions

		Receptor	
	Standard	1	2
A	Reg1	+	-
	Reg2	-	+
	Uq case (Others)		
B	Reg1	+	+
	Reg2	-	+
	Helper Case (*Med*)		
C	Reg1 alone	+	-
	Med alone	-	-
	Reg1 + *Med*	+	+

C

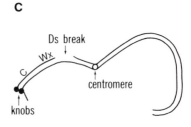

FIGURE 2 (A) Transposable element systems. Regulatory elements are specific in their activation (+) of receptor elements. There are three cases of overlap in activity: *Ac* activates all *Ds*'s, but *Uq* activates only *Ds1*; *Fcu* activates *rcu* and *R-r#2*, but *Spf* is limited to *R-r#2*; *Cy* and *Mu1R* appear to have homologous activity. (B) Types of exceptions to standardized transposable element systems. Case A: Reg 1 = *Ac*; Reg 2 = *En*. Rec 1 = *Ds* allele such as *wx-m7*; Rec 2 = an *I*-containing allele such as *a1-m(r)*. Case B: Reg 1 = *Ac*; Reg 2 = *Uq*. Rec 1 = a standard *Ds* allele; Rec 2 = a *Ds1* allele (*wx-m1*). (Distinguishes *Ac* from *Uq*.) Case C: Reg 1 = *En*. Rec 1 = *wx-m8*; Rec 2 = *c2-m881058Y*. (Distinguishes the two different Receptors and uncovers Mediator.) The basis for the specificity of systems: + = mutability; − = no mutability; *Med* = Mediator. Case A represents two different unrelated systems. When one autonomous element transactivates a reporter allele, one would expect all autonomous elements acting on related reporter alleles to be a part of the same system. But as seen in Case B, there is no reciprocity. The same holds for Case C. This may relate to the evolution of transposable element systems. (C) The *Ds* on chromosome 9. [Modified from P. A. Peterson. (1993). Transposable elements in maize: Their role in creating plant genetic variability. *Adv. Agron.* **51,** 79–124.]

case, a chimeric reporter allele incorporated some genomic sequences from the host genome.

C. Transposition

1. Genetics

The genetics of transposition was first revealed by McClintock in following the *Ds* unit that was in a specific position on chromosome 9 in maize. McClintock had originally identified this as the *Ds* locus, and specifically as a "weakened point" in the chromosome (i.e., this point in the chromosome readily dissociated). The breakage phenomenon observed in the original *Ds* position demanded that all the genes distal to the *waxy* gene (Fig. 2C) were lost owing to chromosome breakage. Subsequently, this breakage phenomenon included only the *C* locus, which was distal to *waxy*. Because the original breakage phenomenon position and the second position (near *C*) were dependent on the presence of *Ac*, it was concluded these were related events and that the *Ds* locus had moved from a position proximal (toward the centromere) to *waxy* to a position proximal to the *C* locus (Fig. 2C). In a further discovery, the *C* locus became mutable and because it responded to *Ac,* it could be concluded that this same unit (*Ds*) was involved in mutability. The origin of the variegated *c* allele indicated a further movement of the *Ds* element.

The movement of these *Ds*'s deemed to have come from transposition could also be explained by the origination of units already present at a chromosome site that respond to *Ac* without the necessity of invoking a transposition phenomenon. This was finally settled by the study of variegated pericarp in the origin of twin sectors (Fig. 3A), which represented unambiguous evidence for transposition.

2. Mechanism

Plant transposable elements transpose via a conservative mechanism whereby the movement of the element by excision from a donor site is followed by reinsertion at a recipient site via a so-called "cut-and-paste" method. Variegated pericarp and the associated origin of twin sectors represented unambiguous evidence for transposition (Fig. 3A). The pericarp locus (*P*) conditions a dominant red coloration of the pericarp that envelopes the kernel and, thus, the aleurone. Unstable pericarp represents the change of a colorless form of pericarp to a colored form and the resulting variegation is featured as longitudinal stripes from the base of the kernel to the crown involving numerous sectors. (Fig. 3A). R. A. Brink and his students, fol-

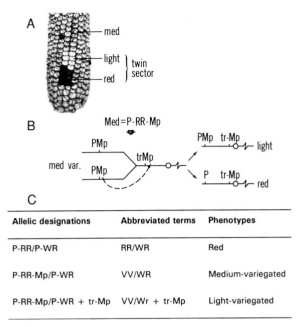

FIGURE 3 (A) Mutable pericarp with medium, light, and red phenotypes. (B) Mechanism of transposition via replicating chromosome. (C) Allelic designation of mutable pericarp. [Modified from P. A. Peterson. (1987). Mobile elements in plants. *CRC Crit. Rev. Plant Sci.* **6**, 105-208.]

Allelic designations	Abbreviated terms	Phenotypes
P-RR/P-WR	RR/WR	Red
P-RR-Mp/P-WR	VV/WR	Medium-variegated
P-RR-Mp/P-WR + tr-Mp	VV/Wr + tr-Mp	Light-variegated

lowing R. A. Emerson's early work on variegated pericarp, were able to demonstrate that one pattern of pericarp variegation, namely, a medium type, often changed to a light type and this change was proven to be caused by the inclusion of a transposed element (*trMp*) that reduced the variegation of the original mutable pericarp to a light type of variegation. The element at the *P* locus was designated *Mp* for modulator of pericarp and the final designation was *P-Mp(P-RR-Mp)* (variegated cob and pericarp) for the *P-vv* allele (Fig. 3C). The excision of *Mp* from *P-Mp* results in a red coloration of the maize cob and pericarp. This appeared as large sectors on the ear because this was pericarp variegation. Also appearing on the ear and covering several kernels were light variegated sectors that in a later analysis were shown to be the original *P-Mp* plus a transposed *Mp (trMp)* in the same clonal sector. The genetic studies readily showed that *trMp* was inherited in a linked or independent position from the *P* locus. This *Mp* was eventually shown to be homologous in structure and function to *Ac* (Fig. 2A).

The question remained regarding the origin and resulting insertion of the transposed *Mp*. The fortunate observation of twinsectors of red coloration that was twinned with a light variegated coloration (Fig. 3A) was the clue needed to unravel the basis of the origin and reinsertion of the transposed *Mp*. It became apparent that the *P* allele arising from *P-vv* resulted in a red sector. Coincident with that was a twin light variegated sector. A single event was the basis of the twins, the origin of the *P* allele red sector, coincident with the origin of the light variegated sector (Fig. 3A). The subsequent finding that *trMp* was located at the identical chromosome sites in both sectors—the gametes arising from the red sector and those arising from the light sector—confirmed the single-event hypothesis. The excision of one *Mp* from one *P-vv* allele was now located at two sites, one that included the *P*-containing chromosome yielding a red sector and the other on the sister *P-vv*-containing chromosome yielding a light phenotype. This transposition event was shown to arise by excision from a replicated strand to an unreplicated strand during chromosome replication. This is illustrated in Fig. 3B, showing *trMp* replicating at the new site. It could readily be concluded that the change in variegation pattern (medium to red and to light) was associated with the transposition of an element. This is an unambiguous demonstration of transposition, namely, a "loss and gain" observation. The allelic designations associated with these phenotypes are shown in Fig. 3C.

3. Localized Transposition Site

Transposing elements have a high affinity to reinsert at nearby chromosome sites. This is amply demonstrated with the *Ac/Mp* element and with the *En* element. The explanation for this has not been clarified, but the mechanism, as illustrated in Section II,C,2, suggests that there is an affinity for replicated strands and an excision from an unreplicated strand. This was questioned by later studies with the *En* element where the most apparent type of transposition is from a replicated strand to another replicated strand. This differs from the case with the *P* element. However, the twin spots were a phenotypic assay for transposition and this demanded that the element must transpose from an unreplicated strand to one that is replicated in order to provide the expression for the twin sectors. An explanation for this transposition to nearby sites was provided by the *Antirrhinum* studies of Coen and his group, whereby a model was suggested that the normal transposition involves a physical association between the donor and the recipient sites. This also implies that a transposed element is not floating free of any attachment in moving from a donor to a recipient site. According to the Coen model, there is a preferential insertion to recipient sites that are spatially in proximity to the donor site

that shows some homology (e.g., a small duplication) to allow an exchange. And if a chromosome condition (i.e., a replication mode) was also necessary, the same chromosome would offer a more receptive site for insertion. The inability to find a free-floating element in molecular studies supports this model's assumptions as well as the numerous studies that have demonstrated transposition to nearby sites.

III. Molecular Description

A. Structure

Following the genetic discoveries of systems and the mechanism of transposition, as well as the specificity of systems, the elucidation of the *Ac* transposable element and its derivatives dissipated the mysteries regarding these genetic features. This came initially from studies of the autonomously mutable *wx-m9* and its derivative. The initial studies with the *wx-m9* allele made it possible to compare the active element at the *wx-m9* locus with the *wx-m9* receptor allele, which was a derivative nonfunctioning element. By making a comparison of the DNA sequence and structure of the two alleles, it was possible to clarify how an autonomous element could give rise to a two-element system. This also illustrated how the *waxy* allele first "visited" by the autonomous element left behind a "signal" that allowed it to respond only to that particular element. It was found that the autonomous *Ac* element was approximately 4500 nucleotides long (Fig. 4).

When the *wx-844* allele was isolated in an isolation plot, it was then possible to describe the *En/Spm* element. This element is 8.3 kb in length and also contains a definitive structure. By examining the full-size sequence of the element and comparing it to the recovered cDNA, it was shown that there were 11 exons and 2 open-reading frames (Fig. 5A). In addition, the definitive TIRs on the ends of the element and the identifying sequences in the host chromosome, the TSD, were characterized. As opposed to the case with *Ac*, where the TIRs were 11 in *Ac*, there were 13 in *En/Spm* and the TSD was 8 in *Ac* and 3 in *En/Spm* (Fig. 4).

The structure of the transposable element had a further identifiable structure (Fig. 5B). With the *En/Spm*, in addition to the characterized TSD and TIR, there were a series of common motifs (12 and 13 bp) in the terminal 200 base pairs of the element. The later studies showed that these common motifs were

Element		Plant	(kb)	Terminal inverted repeat (bp)	Duplication of target site
Ds1	nAu	*Zea mays* L.	0.405	11	8
Ac1	Au	*Zea mays* L.	4.563	11	8
En1	Au	*Zea mays* L.	8.287	13	3
Spm-18	nAu	*Zea mays* L.	2.241	13	3
Mu1-Mu8	nAu	*Zea mays* L.		+200	9
Bg	Au	*Zea mays* L.	4.869	5	8
rbg	nAu	*Zea mays* L.		5	8
rcy:Mu7	nAu	*Zea mays* L.	2.2	+200	9
Mu R1		*Zea mays* L.	4.0	+220	9
Tam1	Au	*Antirrhinum*	17.	13	3
Tam2	nAu	*Antirrhinum*	varies	13	3

FIGURE 4 Molecular characteristics of some examples of transposable elements. Au, autonomous; nAu, nonautonomous.

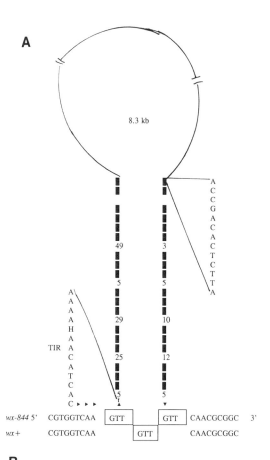

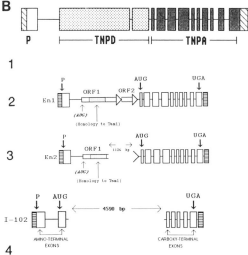

FIGURE 5 (A) Molecular description of the *En/Spm* transposable element in maize. This 8237-bp element is characterized by a host target site duplication (GTT) and a 13-bp terminal inverted repeat. The long terminal (200+ bp) that incudes common motifs is variable in length on each end (the dark dashes) and these are interrupted by variable segments that represent gaps between the common motifs. (B) Part (1): TNPA, TNPD *En/Spm* structure. Part (2): The *En/Spm* ORFs and exon distribution. Part (3): *En2* has a deletion of ORF2 and part of ORF1. Part (4): The *I-102[a1-m(r)]* allele has a gross deletion of 4590 bp. [Modified from P. A. Peterson. (1993). Transposable elements in maize: Their role in creating plant genetic variability. *Adv. Agron.* **51**, 79–124.]

in a defined orientation (head to head or tail to tail) and this was very important in maximizing excision efficiency.

Previous genetic studies showed that there were two functions of *En/Spm* with identifiable phenotypic effects. These included a *Mutator* function and a *Suppressor* function. Very early in the description of the element, two transcripts could be identified in Northern blots—a heavy-staining 2.5-kb band and a light-staining 6.0-kb band. With the aid of certain mutants that had an impaired *M* function, it could be determined that the 11 exons were associated with the *S* function. With the various mutants it was possible to show that the *Suppressor* function was allied to the 11 exons. The *Mutator* function was assigned to the two open-reading frames. A further definition of the open-reading frames showed that the ORF1 was most important in the full capacity of the *Mutator* function. The middle segment of ORF1 was also allied with considerable homology to the *Mutator* function of the *Antirrhinum* transposon.

Because of the uncertainty of how the residual *En*'s were contributing to some of the functions leading to the phenotypes, investigators found it important to make transgenic plants with tobacco with each of the components of the transposon. This included transgenics with the 11-exon unit (the *Suppressor* component TNPA in Fig. 5A) and transgenics with the two open-reading frames (the *Mutator* component TNPD in Fig. 5A). When each of the transgenics was individually grown, no excisions occurred. When the transgenics were combined in a cross, they showed transposition. This confirmed the genetic studies illustrating the *Mutator* expression functioning only with the *Suppressor* activity. The use of mutants and derivatives made it possible to identify the two transcripts to *En* structure. From these sequences the two proteins, TNPA and TNPD, could be identified (Fig. 5B).

A model was presented based on these studies showing that the most effective excision was made possible by the correct orientation of the terminal 200-bp motifs (Fig. 5A). The model showed that the *Suppressor* protein (TNPA) enveloped the terminal 200 bases and was attached to them like a zipper and that the *Mutator* function (TNPD) was then able to cut out the element following this very rigid alignment. Of course, the TIRs without the transposase are not in proximity to each other and the *Sp* protein must bring them together to begin the proper alignment. This was necessary to have the full TIRs cut in a manner so that they would be transposed intact to the site.

1. Footprints

First, the second TSD (Fig. 5A) represents additional nucleotides in the genome, which becomes a resource for changes in genome sequences. In most studies of transposable elements in plants, the excision process from the host TSD is rarely perfect, which results in recognizable footprints that are a clue that a transposon has been excised from the site. These footprints are recognized from the duplications that occur in the insertion of the element at a given site, which is illustrated with an example from the *En/Spm* element with the TGA TGA sequence or in the *Ac* system with a CATGATGC CATGATGC sequence. This duplication occurs with the insertion of the element and becomes a resource for alteration following the excision of the element. This alteration occurs during the excision process whereby free DNA strands are subject to endonuclease degradation and some new nucleotide sequences are generated. The latter was first demonstrated with the *Adh1* locus in maize and a number of revertant types that identified alterations following an excision. These alterations result in changed sequences that lead to altered proteins, some of which can be recognized phenotypi-

cally. Some include frameshift changes and the addition of nucleotides, which of course result in new phenotypes, and others include changes that result in additional amino acids, leading to altered proteins and some with a deficiency of other amino acids. With this correlation between change of nucleotide sequence and protein performance, it is surprising that often no phenotypic alteration is observed. In other cases, the alterations are phenotypically evident. The *Mu1* element generates gross deletions upon excision. It is likely that the absence of phenotypic alteration in some excisions may indicate that the change has little effect on protein performance because of the protein domain that is affected. These footprint changes have also been important in indicating the different components of the protein.

IV. Methylation Effects

It is often observed that the elements become quiescent (inactive). Furthermore, a number of inactive elements that reside in the genome become activated. This quiescence has been ascribed to methylation. Genetic inactivation of the *En/Spm* element is correlated with the sequences surrounding the element's transcription initiation site. Not only does methylation occur, but it occurs at different times in the reproductive cycle of the plant, and it increases during vegetative growth development of the male and female inflorescences and thus is transmissible. It was further shown that the susceptibility of the element to be methylated and to subsequently change during development correlates with the element's phase of activity. Thus, genetic stability associated with the spread of the methylation of the element's transcription initiation site leads to an inactive phase for the element. It was concluded that the methylation of residues within specific regions of the element is significant in maintaining the inactive phase of the element and thus leads to the regulation of the expression of the element during plant development.

The heritability of these methylation problems in several studies strengthens the universality of this in causing the quiescence of elements. Furthermore, the element maintains its inactive phase over several generations of selection. Thus this epigenetic mechanism is significant in dampening the effect of the element in populations. It appears that the unstable form of the element is programmable, which is heritable during the developmental cycle. An inactive element does change to an active one and this was found to be promoted by exposure to an active one. Or in some cases, gametes originating from tillers of plants lead to a heritable reactivation of the element. Further studies showed that the correlation of the element's genetic activity and its transcription activity was related to the methylation of C residues at the transcription site of the element.

When a reporter is introduced into a commercial corn variety or inbred, sectors of mutability are often observed and, if pursued, active elements are identified. Though these elements have not been verified as arising from methylation-suppressed elements, it can be assumed that their quiescence was so related. Even though such studies have not been pursued with many reporter alleles, it is very likely that the maize genome does carry such suppressed elements. On the other hand, when successive generations of corn populations are followed in a search of active mobile elements, elements that are active e.g., *Mrh;* see Fig. 2A) in early generations become extinguished in activity in later generations, further supporting the dampening effect on elements imposed by the genome.

V. Effects on Gene Expression

A. Phenotypic Changes

From early genetic studies, a number of derivatives of transposon-containing genes showed altered phenotypes, which indicated that the transposon induced heritable changes at the gene. This was explained in later studies by the residual "footprints" that leave the TSD duplications changed, yielding an altered reading frame leading to an altered protein.

One of the first studies that uncovered altered phenotypes was the *Dt* affect on the *A* locus that included an *a1-dt* allele. A number of revertants were uncovered and they could be distinguished. Though the majority were of the standard type that included the confirmed red color pericarp and thereby identical to the original *A1* allele, two exceptions to the majority showed different pericarp coloration. Furthermore, there was a different level of dominance. This was the first case of heritable alterations induced by a transposon effect on a locus.

Of course there is a bias in the lack of definition of the other 27 reversions that did not show any alteration. Probably, given more extensive and sensitive enzyme tests than are now possible, further alterations in the protein could be established. With the computerized simulated studies with proteins with altered amino acid distribution and content, different charges and domain effects could readily be identified.

B. Enzyme Changes

The footprints from the *Adh-1* locus harboring a transposon showed differences. There were reduced levels of mRNA in Northern blots of the *Ds*-induced change of the *Adh-1F* and *Fn335* alleles. It is likely that the position of the insert was important in affecting this phenotype in view of the positioning of it at the start of transcription and the processing of the dehydrogenase message. Altered thermostability of other alleles also could be shown. These same kinds of events affected the *wx-m8* allele. The derivatives would show altered amino acid content, which would yield altered proteins. Probably the most significant changes were found with the enzyme color series in maize. This is also true with the transposon-induced derivatives of the *Antirrhinum* series as well as the *petunia* mutability.

In one study in maize it was found that the *C1-S* allele differs from the standard *CI* allele or *C1* allele by a change in box 2 of the promoter. There is a possibility that this alteration was caused by a transposon as there is a typical 5-bp transposon-induced footprint in the vicinity of this 3-bp change in box 2. The latter results in an overexpression of the *C1* allele.

Other studies, such as a change in the promoter of the *Niv-53::Tam-1* mutant, also gave alterations. In four derived mutant lines, the *Tam-1* element was deleted, leaving altered flanking sequences of the chalcone synthase promoter. In one case, the TATA box of the chalcone gene was removed and this resulted in an extremely low expression of the gene, which mandated a new initiation site for gene transcription. Other mutants were overexpressed and others showed lower levels of expression.

Combining the presence of footprints and the phenotypic changes, it is quite evident that transposons are significant in altering protein structure and function. This is clearly evident whether it affects promoters or the structural component of the gene.

VI. Pervasiveness in Populations

A. Determination

With the available reporter alleles, it was possible to canvas populations for the presence of active transposable elements. This was first examined in the Iowa

Stiff-Stalk Synthetic (BSSS) maize population. It was surprising to find that the *Uq* element was most significant throughout all the improved BSSS populations. It was further found that there was a founder line that harbored an active *Uq* element that pervaded the whole population in subsequent selection programs. Later studies showed that the different programs were significant in the spread of the element throughout the population. In some lines, it became a major component of a population, whereas in other lines it was practically eliminated. The *Mrh* element was also found in high frequency throughout the populations.

It was also questioned how only the *Uq* element, which is homologous to *Ac,* could become pervasive. The *Uq* element may be a dampened-down element as it is limited in its activity, whereas *Ac* would be too excessive in its gross effects on genes.

Other elements are present in the maize genome, and certainly the *cin* and *tourist* elements are present in very high frequency in an extremely heterogeneous form. What effect this has on the genome is not known because only a few genes have been uncovered that harbor these elements, though *cin* has been identified in the corn progenitor teosinte.

B. Origin from Quiescent States

If a reporter allele is available in a series of lines, a frequent observation is that of small spots or sectors of spots. This would indicate that the reporter allele is responding to an active element and that the active element is changing from a quiescent to an active state. This was first seen with the *Uq* element in a survey of maize populations. A further search uncovered germinals of the *Uq* element and these were found to be diverse. This observation, coupled with the methylation of elements mentioned earlier, indicates that there are active elements in the methylated state and the demethylation is commonly occurring. Although there has not been a grand survey of these elements with reporter alleles in these populations, this has now been found with the *Uq* and the *Mrh* elements, which would indicate that the elements are maintained in a quiescent state under these methylation conditions and then they become fully active. And, if a condition becomes significant in changing the physiology of the genome, this would enhance the activation of these elements.

Transposable elements are also found in the maize progenitor teosinte. These elements in teosinte have characteristics of transposable elements and have not been studied in terms of their activity, but they do have the characteristics of transposable elements with reference to TIRs and TSDs.

VII. Plant Types Other Than Maize

Though the most intensive molecular studies have been with the two elements in maize, namely, *Ac* and *En/Spm,* the *Mu* element has also been analyzed. In other plants, such as soybeans and *Antirrhinum,* there have also been extensive molecular studies. What is generally true is that the elements in these other plants have the same general structure and, in the case of *Antirrhinum,* a homologous transposase sequence as in maize.

The *Antirrhinum* studies have been very significant in providing resource tools to analyze gene structure and function. The numerous derivative types arising from the transposon effect at a locus have given researchers adequate alleles to follow flower organ development and the interaction of the gene domains leading to flower development. Other studies with the *Tam-1* of *Antirrhinum* have elucidated the paramutability phenomenon. When Stable White *niv-44* is crossed with *Tam-1,* a large proportion of the F_1 progeny are *pale* on these and are *pale* in subsequent selfings. The heritable expression of mutability is similar to that in the maize paramutability studies.

Not many other mutability patterns of plant types have been followed except for the mutable alleles from *Petunia hybrida* and *Antirrhinum majus.* The *petunia* unstables follow the maize unstables in showing both autonomous and two-element interactions for control of mutability. Transposition patterns have been followed in the genetics of *petunia.* The *petunia* studies, as well as *Antirrhinum* studies, further strengthen the universality of transposons in a wide assortment of plants and also demonstrate that there is a universality in the structural components of the transposons. Similarly, the transposons found in soybeans and the candystripe locus in sorghum further support the prevalence of transposons among many plants.

VIII. Exploiting Transposons

A. Tagging

In addition to the evolutionary role of transposons in generating variability and their possible role in commercial line development, the other area of intensive study has been the use of transposons in tagging genes, which is the source of most of the genes that have been studied in maize. This has been most useful with the *Mu, Ac,* and *En/Spm* elements. Many researchers have exploited the *Mu* element in both general studies and the tagging process. Without the use of transposons in tagging, the studies with maize genes would have been seriously hampered. From this process, gene structure has been elucidated as well as the network of interactions, for example, as in the anthocyanin pathway, in demonstrating the kinds of interaction that take place in many of these plants. This tagging process was first exploited in *Drosophila* with the *P* elements, but it was intensively used in the maize plants. Their ready availability in maize lines has made their use very common. Further, these transposons have been put into transgenic plants and have been used in tagging in *Arabidopsis,* tobacco, tomato, and other plants. This process has probably been the most utilitarian aspect of transposons.

B. Protein Structure

Protein structure has been previously alluded to. In the study of the transposon-induced *C1* mutants in maize, two features of the acidic domain, helicity and charge, were investigated. Some mutants (*pale*-colored aleurone) caused the interruption of the helix and the introduction of one positive charge, whereas in another mutant the charge is reduced by a factor of seven though the phenotype is maintained (*pale*). It could be concluded that the ability to form an alpha helix in the *C1* protein is more important than the charge distribution within the domain. Thus the expression of the proteins could be visualized by changes induced by transposons in causing footprint changes, which are effective in causing the final phenotype change. Work will continue to progress in this area because of the numerous sites where the transposon insert can be found in a gene. With the current simulation studies of amino acid changes related to protein configuration, this will be a more generally used process in protein studies.

Bibliography

Bennetzen, J. L., Springer, P. S., Cresse, A. D., and Hendrickx, M. (1993). Specificity and regulation of the *Mutator* transposable element system in maize. *Crit. Rev. Plant Sci.* **12(1/2),**57–95.

Fedoroff, N. V. (1989). Maize transposable elements. *In* "Mobile DNA" (D. E. Berg and M. M. Howe, eds.), pp. 375–411. American Society for Microbiology Washington, D.C.

Gierl, A., Saedler, H., and Peterson, P. A. (1989). Maize transposable elements. *Annu. Rev. Genet.* **23,** 71–85.

Peterson, P. A. (1987). Mobile elements in plants. *CRC Crit. Rev. Plant Sci.* **6,** 105–208.

Peterson, P. A. (1993). Transposable elements in maize: Their role in creating plant genetic variability. *Adv. Agron.* **51,** 79–124.

Tropical and Subtropical Fruit

CHRISTOPHER MENZEL, *Queensland Department of Primary Industries, Nambour*

Glossary

Mediterranean Areas with cool wet winters and hot dry summers; days in summer are above 30°C for several weeks and water use exceeding 250 mm month^{-1}

Subtropical Areas with winter minima of 5°–10°C and summer maximums of 30°–35°C; frosts may limit tropical fruit production even at low elevation and rainfall is generally greatest in summer and least in winter or spring

Tropical Lowland areas with mean temperatures above 25°C for most of the year or 8°–10°C cooler at higher elevations up to 2500 m; frost may limit tropical fruit production above 1600 m and rainfall may be continuous or there may be one or two distinct wet seasons

Tropical and subtropical fruit play a major role in the diet of many people and can be found as part of subsistence agriculture, as part of market gardens, and more recently in extensive private and corporate plantations. Fruit were traditionally sold in local markets and eaten fresh or cooked. However, in recent years many of these industries have developed large processing and export components which generate significant income.

I. Tropical and Subtropical Fruit Production

The major tropical and subtropical fruit are citrus (73 Mt), banana (71 Mt), mango (15.7 Mt), pineapple (9.7 Mt), papaya (4.4 Mt), and avocado (1.5 Mt). Citrus include a diverse range of fruit with orange accounting for about 70% of the production. Other major species are mandarin (12%), lemon and lime (9%), and grapefruit and pummelo (6%). There are no separate statistics for the last two mentioned groups, but it is estimated that 90% of the total production comes from lemons, while grapefruit also dominates over pummelo. [*See* CITRUS FRUITS.]

Tropical and subtropical fruit are grown over a wide range of environments from about 45° N to 35° S latitude. The climates are generally warm moist tropical, subtropical, or Mediterranean (Fig.1). In true tropical lowland areas, mean temperatures are above 25°C for most of the year. Some fruit species can also be grown at higher elevation in the tropics up to 2500 m where mean temperatures are about 8°–10°C lower. There may be continuous rainfall or one or two distinct wet seasons. Subtropical areas generally have winter minimums of 5°–10°C and maximums in summer of 30°–35°C, depending on elevation and distance from coastal influences. The occurrence and frequency of frosts may limit tropical fruit production in these locations. Rainfall is generally greatest in summer and least in winter or spring. Mediterranean climates have cool wet winters and hot dry summers with day temperatures in summer of more than 30°C for several weeks and water use exceeding 250 mm month^{-1}.

Tropical fruit can be separated into different groups according to their pattern of growth and flowering. Citrus, mango, and avocado are multiple-branching trees with cyclic shoot growth, axillary (citrus) or

A

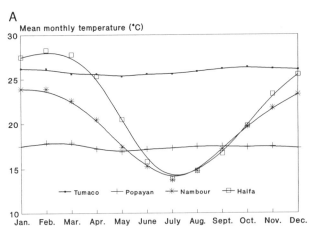

B

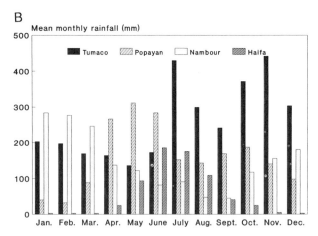

FIGURE 1 Average (a) mean monthly temperature and (b) rainfall in different tropical and subtropical fruit growing areas: Tumaco, Colombia (Lat. 2° N and 4 m elev.); Popayan, Colombia (Lat. 2° N and 1789 m elev.); Nambour, Australia (Lat. 27° S and 29 m elev.); and Haifa, Israel (Lat. 33° N and 10 m elev.). Months are southern hemisphere equivalents.

terminal flowering, and low average yields of <25–30 t ha^{-1}. Vegetative growth often competes with reproductive growth and a low proportion of dry matter is diverted to the fruit. Best yields occur when growth is limited to certain times of the year. Flowering generally occurs after a period of temperatures below 25°C and/or moisture stress. In contrast, the other major fruit species are single-stemmed with continuous leaf initiation at least until flower induction which is either terminal (banana and pineapple) or axillary (papaya). Yields are high and usually greater than 40–140 t ha^{-1}. Since there is no competition between reproductive and vegetative growth, yield is often proportional to the amount of leaf area. A high proportion of dry matter is allocated to the fruit and best yields occur when vegetative growth is encouraged. Flowering is generally not induced by cool or dry weather.

II. Citrus

A. Origin, Distribution, and Commercial Importance

Citrus includes many species and hybrids from the family Rutaceae. Most species originated in Southeast Asia and the Pacific, particularly from China and India to New Caledonia. The only exception is the grapefruit from the West Indies. The most important species are

Citrus sinensis—sweet orange
Citrus aurantium—sour orange
Citrus reticulata—mandarin
Citrus limon—lemon
Citrus aurantifolia—lime
Citrus x paradisi—grapefruit
Citrus maxima—pummelo

In official estimates, oranges are the most important citrus followed by mandarin, lemons and limes, and lastly grapefruit and pummelo. Citrus have a long history in Southeast Asia with unofficial records indicating cultivation in China for possibly 4000 years. They are now widely grown throughout the tropics and subtropics approximately between 44° N and 35° S with production of more than 1.0 Mt in the United States, Mexico, Brazil, Argentina, China, Japan, India, Iran, Pakistan, Egypt, Turkey, Greece, Morocco, Italy, and Spain. Citrus is the most widely grown tropical fruit and significant volumes of fresh and processed products are traded.

B. Botanical Relations and Cultivars

The taxonomy of citrus is complex with many species, hybrids, and cultivars. Many of the species are polyembryonic.

C. Description of Plant (Fig. 2)

Citrus are usually small trees armed with single axillary spines. Leaves are generally thin, dark glossy green with a strong aroma when crushed. Flowers are generally borne singularly and are mostly bisexual. Fruit are berries with green, yellow, or orange skin, thick leathery rind, and a yellow, orange, or red inner layer consisting of several segments filled

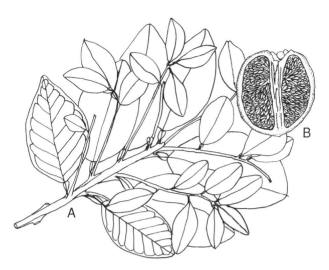

FIGURE 2 *Citrus sinensis* (sweet orange cultivar Washington Navel). (A) Vegetative shoot (× 1/2). (B) Fruit in longitudinal section (× 1/2). [Redrawn by Cathie Menzel with permission from Purseglove, J. W. (1968). "Tropical Crops—Dicotleydons," Fig. 83, p. 515. Copyright © 1968 by Longman Group U.K., Harlow, U.K.]

with pulp vessels. These vessels are firm or soft, filled with sweet, acid, or very acid juice with or without distinct oil droplets. Fruit usually have many small to large seeds, although some cultivars are seedless.

D. Growth and Development

Most *Citrus* are polyembryonic with seedlings true to type since the zygotic embryo is usually suppressed. There are some exceptions including the pummelo (*C. maxima*) which are monoembryonic. In subtropical areas with distinct dry or cool winters, the trees usually flush vegetatively in spring and again in summer. Flowers are normally borne on the spring flushes. In warm humid areas, flushing may be more or less continuous and flowering and hence fruiting occur over much of the year. Fruit set is generally very high, but is accompanied soon after by one or more periods of abscission. Fruit mature after 7 to 8 months. Depending on tree vigour, trees may follow a cycle of "on" and "off" years. Yields may be so heavy in some species that part of or the whole tree dies.

E. Ecological Adaptation

Citrus are grown in tropical areas up to an elevation of 2100 m with no distinct cold period (days below 20°C) and one or more extended wet seasons; subtropical areas with cool dry winters and warm wet summers; and in Mediterranean areas with cool wet winters and dry hot summers. Cropping occurs

throughout the year in the tropics but is normally restricted to late summer, autumn, or winter in the other climatic zones. Fruit also mature 1 to 2 months earlier in the tropics. Cultivars selected for one area do not generally perform as well in other locations. A dry period promotes floral induction in some species, although water requirements generally increase from flowering and fruit set to fruit filling. Estimates of crop water use indicate 100 mm is required during a cool month and 250 mm during a hot month.

F. Uses of the Fruit

Citrus have mainly been used as fresh fruit, but substantial quantities are now processed into juice, jams, dairy products, and sweets. There are very large industries based on the export of frozen orange concentrate particularly from South America. The fruit can be used for flavoring many dishes and segments or pieces canned. Citrus are also good sources of pectin, citric acid, and essential oils.

III. Banana

A. Origin, Distribution, and Commercial Importance

Bananas (*Musa* spp.) are thought to have originated in Southeast Asia, possibly in the area between Malaysia, Indonesia, and Papua New Guinea. However, their exact origin is not known and there is much confusion on the ancestry of modern bananas. Cultivated bananas were reported to be first taken to Europe in the 10th century and later to West Africa and South America. Banana now dominates tropical fruit production, along with citrus, and ranges from shifting cultivation, home gardens to extensive corporate plantings. In the tropics they are usually grown at elevations below 1600 m. Countries producing more than 2.0 Mt of *Musa* are Rwanda, Tanzania, Uganda, Zaire, Brazil, Colombia, Ecuador, India, Indonesia, and the Philippines. Many of these countries produce more plantain (cooking banana) than banana, although overall, about two-thirds of the world's production of *Musa* comes from banana. Bananas, notably Cavendish cultivars (AAA group), are important as an export earner for several countries including the Philippines, Malaysia, Honduras, Panama, West Indies, Colombia, and Ecuador. Cultivars for export need a long green life before ripening begins. [*See* BANANAS.]

B. Botanical Relations and Cultivars

Banana generally refers to a number of species and hybrids of *Musa* in the family Musaceae. Most edible species of banana are *Musa acuminata* or hybrids between *M. acuminata* and *M. balbisiana*, although no edible forms of the latter species have been found. There are various diploids, triploids, and tetraploids containing different proportions of *M. acuminata* (A) and *M. balbisiana* (B) such as AA, AAA, AAAA, and hybrids AB, AAB, ABB, and ABBB. There are also other species of *Musa* which are economically important as ornamentals or good sources of fiber.

C. Description of Plant (Fig. 3)

The banana plant is a large herbaceous evergreen monocotyledon from 2 to 9 m tall with a thick succulent pseudostem which comprises a series of overlapping leaf sheaths tightly wrapped around each other to form a rigid bundle 20–25 cm in diameter. New leaves originate from the growing point at the top of the underground rhizome and grow up through the center of the pseudostem. Leaves are from 2 to 4 m long and 60 to 100 cm wide and green. Juvenile leaves of many cultivars have maroon patches on the upper surface and are red-purple underneath. A major exception is the ABB group which is devoid of purple pigments. The inflorescence is a terminal spike produced from the tip of the stem after about 25–50 leaves have appeared. The inflorescence is initially a large tight, long-oval purplish bud (not in the ABB

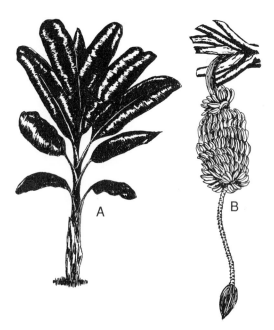

FIGURE 3 *Musa* AAB group cv. Mysore (banana). (A) Young plant (× 1/30). (B) Fruit bunch (× 1/10). [Redrawn by Cathie Menzel with permission from Purseglove, J. W. (1968). "Tropical Crops—Monocotyledons 2," Fig. 25, p. 359. Copyright © 1972 by Longman Group U.K., Harlow, U.K.]

group) which later opens to reveal slim nectar-rich flowers covered by thick waxy bracts. There are female flowers at the proximal end and male flowers at the distal end of the inflorescence. Young fruit are initially slender green fingers. The flower bracts are soon shed and fully grown fruit in each cluster become a "hand" of bananas. Mature fruit are green, yellow, or red, from 6 to 35 cm long and 2 to 5 cm wide, and range greatly in shape from oblong, cylindrical, and blunt to triangular, curved, and hornlike. When fruit are ripe, flesh is white, yellow, or red-yellow, firm or soft, and moist or dry. Plantains are normally dry even when ripe. Flavor is mild, sweet, or subacid. Cultivated varieties do not generally have seeds.

D. Growth and Development

Under optimum conditions, vegetative growth is rapid with about one leaf emerging every week. The size of successive leaves increases to a maximum shortly before flowering, when about 30 leaves have been produced. The inflorescence normally emerges 8 to 9 months after planting, longer in the cool subtropics or at higher elevation in the tropics. Fruit are normally harvested 3 to 5 months after flower opening. Side shoots or suckers emerge from buds on the rhizome initially forming a good rhizome and root system and then significant leaf production after flowering of the mother plant. Productivity can be maintained for 10 years or more in some situations before yields start to decline.

E. Ecological Adaptation

Within the latitudes of 30° N and 30° S where bananas are exploited there is a great range in environmental conditions. Growth is best in the warm humid lowland tropics with mean temperatures above 25°–27°C, but growth slows at lower temperatures and there is a longer production cycle. Most cultivars stop growing at mean temperatures below 13°C. Bananas are shallow-rooted and are very sensitive to water deficits. Yields are highest in locations with high average rainfall of 200 mm month^{-1} unless frequent irrigation is available. Yields also tend to be highest in locations with high average humidity but not associated with extended cloud cover. In subtropical areas, lower rainfall in winter is less of a concern, since growth is much slower than in summer.

F. Uses of the Fruit

Ripe bananas can be eaten fresh by themselves or used in fruit salads, mashed and used in dairy or bread products, or even frozen or dried. They can be sliced and cooked whole as a savory or dessert. Plantains or cooking bananas feature strongly in the diets of many people in the tropics and subtropics. They are not suitable for eating out of hand but must be fried or baked whole or mixed with other foods such as coconut milk. They are sometimes mashed or used in soups and stews. Plantains can also be processed into flour.

IV. Mango

A. Origin, Distribution, and Commercial Importance

The mango, *Mangifera indica*, from the family Anacardiaceae is native to Asia. There is a primary center of origin in the Indo-Burma region of South Asia and a secondary center in Southeast Asia. The other economically important member of this family is the cashew. Mango has a long history in India where it has been reported to have been grown for several thousand years. It was distributed to eastern Asia in 400–500 B.C. and to east Africa and the Americas by the end of the 18th century. The mango is now widely grown in the tropics below 600 m and in the subtropics from garden trees to small and large commercial plantings. Fruit are very popular when available. India produces 9.5 Mt, about 60% of the world's crop. Other important producers with more than 0.5 Mt each are Pakistan, Thailand, and Mexico.

The volume of world trade in fresh mango in 1985 was about 90,000 t but is increasing rapidly. The major markets are Hong Kong, Singapore, Japan, the United States and Europe. Thailand and the Philippines are important suppliers into Asian markets. Significant quantities of processed mango are also exported especially from India, which accounts for about 60% of the 30,000 t.

B. Botanical Relations and Cultivars

There are hundreds of cultivars and much confusion about their names even in India. Selection for high quality has been carried out in India for thousands of years, although clonal propagation has only been available for 400 years. Many hybrids have been developed in India and Florida over the past 20 years with better fruit color, thicker flesh, superior flavor, and more regular production. Most of the Indian cultivars are monoembryonic forming seeds with a single zygotic embryo with the seedling not true to type. Southeast Asian cultivars are generally polyembryonic forming seeds with several adventitious embryos in the nucellar tissues, which are true to type as the zygotic embryo is normally suppressed. In some countries, smooth-fleshed cultivars are grown for the fresh market and other more fibrous cultivars for processing.

C. Description of the Plant (Fig. 4)

The mango is a large erect evergreen tree up to 30–40 m high in old specimens. The leaves are borne in rosettes at the tips of branches and are initially yellow, pink, or red becoming dark-green and glossy above and lighter underneath. Mature leaves are 8–40 cm long and 2–10 cm wide. Up to 4000 small green-yellow flowers are borne on terminal panicles. The panicles have a variable proportion of male and hermaphrodite flowers depending on the cultivar and temperature. Fruit vary significantly in size, shape, and color and may be round, oval, or kidney-shaped and up to 4 kg, although normally 300–800 g. The skin is leathery, thick, and dark-green, yellow, or-

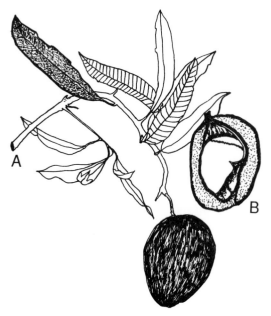

FIGURE 4 *Mangifera indica* (mango). (A) Shoot with fruit (× 1/3). (B) Fruit in longitudinal section (× 1/2). [Redrawn by Cathie Menzel with permission from Purseglove, J. W. (1968). "Tropical Crops—Dicotleydons," Fig. 2, p. 27. Copyright © 1968 by Longman Group U.K., Harlow, U.K.]

ange, or red and the flesh pale yellow to deep orange, smooth or fibrous, acid, sweet, musky and overpowering, or bland. The better flavored attractive cultivars are highly sought after in the market place.

D. Growth and Development

In mature trees, up to four leaf flushes may occur each year depending on environmental conditions, tree management, and crop load, although not all the terminal branches may flush at any one time. Many cultivars will not flower successfully if branches have flushed recently. Panicle and flower development are very rapid, normally taking no more than 30–40 days especially with day temperatures above 25°–30°C. Fruit set is rather poor with less than 1% of hermaphrodite flowers carrying a fruit to harvest even with good disease and insect control. Fruit ripen after 3 to 5 months. Biennial bearing is a problem in many cultivars especially if tree management is poor or if cool weather follows soon after harvest.

E. Ecological Adaptation

Mango is grown in a wide range of environments where temperatures and moisture supply vary considerably. It performs best in climates with dry periods

during flowering and fruit ontogeny and rain in summer after harvest. New growth is killed by light frost which limits plantings to coastal areas in cool subtropical locations. Vegetative growth is promoted by warm temperature of 25°–30°C and good moisture supply. Cool winters below 20°C are reported to induce flowering in subtropical areas, although in the tropics moisture stress is thought to be responsible. Cool nights below 12°C around flowering reduce pollination and induce the production of small unmarketable fruit. Rainfall ranges from 750 to 2500 mm year^{-1} in most mango areas. Although mango is reported to survive drought conditions, the effects of moisture stress on fruit production are not fully understood. Water stress during early fruit development increases fruit drop. Stress later during fruit maturation delays dry matter accumulation and leads to ripening abnormalities.

F. Uses of the Fruit

Mangos are generally used as fresh fruit either by themselves or in fruit salads, although significant quantities are processed into canned fruit or used in nectars, juices, jellies, dairy products, and sweets. They can also be successfully dried. Mangos are usually eaten when fully ripe, but are popular as green fruit in parts of Southeast Asia. There is also a large market for mango pickles or chutney (atchar), and in some plantations mangos are harvested green exclusively for pickling.

V. Pineapple

A. Origin, Distribution, and Commercial Importance

The pineapple, *Ananas comosus*, is the most important edible member of the family Bromeliaceae which has over 2000 species, mostly epiphytic and many attractive and economically important ornamentals. It is native to tropical South America, possibly in the area between southern Brazil and Paraguay, where it was domesticated long before the arrival of the Spanish. It was introduced to Southeast Asia in the 1500s and soon after to much of the tropical world. Pineapples are now widely grown up to 30° latitude with production of at least 0.5 Mt in the United States, Mexico, Brazil, China, Indonesia, the Philippines, and Thailand. Processing is very important with about half the world's pineapple production processed.

The pineapple is now one of the leading commercial fruit crops of the tropics with significant exports of canned and fresh product. The volume of canned fruit is about 0.7 Mt year^{-1}. The major suppliers are the Philippines, Thailand, Taiwan, South Africa, Malaysia, and more recently Indonesia. Canned pineapple juice exports are even more important, but there are no reliable figures available. Fresh fruit trade is about 0.5 Mt annually. Leading players in the fresh pineapple trade are Taiwan, the Philippines, Puerto Rico, Mexico, Brazil, Guinea, Ivory Coast, South Africa, and Martinique.

B. Botanical Relations and Cultivars

Pineapple cultivars vary greatly in yield and fruit weight as well as color and flavor of the flesh. The main commercial varieties can be grouped into four types. The Cayenne group grown mostly in Asia, Kenya, and the United States has leaves with spines only at the base and top and cylindrical fruit weighing about 2.5 kg with pale yellow to yellow flesh. The Queen group mainly grown in Australia and South Africa has spiny leaves and fruit weighing 0.9–1.3 kg with crisp golden flesh. Queen types are also low in acid and high in sugar. The Red Spanish group is mainly grown in Central and South America and Malaysia and has characteristics intermediate between those of Cayenne and Queen. Perolera is another important group. While it is grown commercially only in South America, its main use has been as a parent in breeding programs. Various hybrids between the other groups are also exploited commercially.

C. Description of the Plant (Fig. 5)

The pineapple is a perennial or biennial herb usually about 0.5–1.5 m in height, although occasionally taller. Plants have a short stocky stem and a rosette of waxy tough leaves 0.5–1.0 m long. The inflorescence is short with up to 200 bluish-purple sessile flowers each subtended by a pointed bract. After flowering, individual fruit join together to form a conical-shaped compound juicy fleshy fruit up to 20–30 cm long. The skin is tough, waxy, and dark-green, yellow, or orange-yellow when the fruit is ripe and the flesh white to yellow, juicy and acid, subacid, sweet, or bland depending on cultivar, season, and maturity. Fruit are normally seedless due to self-incompatibility unless the flowers have been cross-pollinated by hand with pollen from a different group.

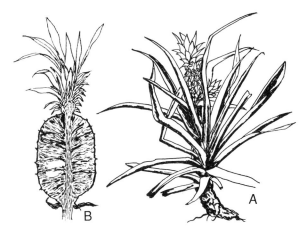

FIGURE 5 *Ananas comosus* (pineapple). (A) Plant with a young fruit ($\times$ 1/10). (B) Fruit in longitudinal section ($\times$ 1/4). [Redrawn by Cathie Menzel with permission from Purseglove, J. W. (1972). "Tropical Crops—Monocotyledons 1," Fig. 10, p. 83. Copyright © 1972 by Longman Group U.K., Harlow, U.K.]

There are generally no natural pollinators in most countries that grow pineapples.

D. Growth and Development

Pineapples are normally propagated by crowns which are removed prior to processing or by vegetative shoots which arise from the base of the fruit as it develops (slips) or from the base of the plant (suckers).

Plants can produce up to one leaf per week under ideal conditions. After floral induction the stem elongates and enlarges near the growing point and forms a tight cluster of flowers. The stem continues to grow at its apex and forms a crown of compact leaves. The first flower opens about 50 days after induction and anthesis continues for 20–40 days. Planting to harvest takes about 15–18 months in tropical areas and 20–23 months in subtropical area with a distinct cool season. One or more ratoon crops can be produced from suckers at the base of the plant thus reducing planting costs and shortening the production cycle.

E. Ecological Adaptation

The pineapple is generally grown at low elevations from 0° to 30° latitude when day temperatures range from 20°–35°C, although some commercial plantings are found up to 2300 m in the tropics. The crop cycle is shorter in the lowland tropics, while in cool areas fruit may be too acid for the fresh market for much of the year or be unmarketable due to discoloration of the flesh (endogenous browning). Sugar levels are less important for processed fruit as they can be readily adjusted in the factory. In hot dry area there can be problems with sunburn of fruit. The plant is also sensitive to frost although it will tolerate cool nights for a short period. Pineapples are tolerant to intermittent drought but are susceptible to root rots. They are grown in areas with rainfall from 650 to 3800 mm year^{-1}. This rainfall should ideally be spread throughout the year, since most plantations are not irrigated. In cooler subtropical areas, winter rainfall becomes less important because lower average temperatures markedly reduce growth rates.

F. Uses of the Fruit

Pineapples are often used fresh particularly in tropical fruit salads. They can also be processed into juice, jams, yoghurt, ice cream, or sweets. A significant proportion of the crop is usually canned into slices, cubes, or crush. Fruit slices can also be successfully dried.

VI. Papaya

A. Origin, Distribution, and Commercial Importance

Papaya, *Carica papaya,* is a member of the family Caricaceae native to tropical South America possibly in the area between Mexico and Central America. It was brought to the Caribbean and Southeast Asia during the 16th century by Spanish explorers and quickly spread to India, Oceania, and Africa. Production of more than 0.2 Mt occurs in Brazil, Mexico, Zaire, Thailand, Indonesia, and India.

The fruit are delicate, are easily bruised, and succumb to pre- and postharvest diseases, and therefore lag behind other species such as citrus, banana, and pineapple especially in export markets. Processing is also less developed. Much of the crop is grown in home gardens which are not included in official estimates of production. The tree is also susceptible to a wide range of preharvest pests and diseases which reduce fruit quality and the life of a planting. Often orchards bear well for only 2 to 3 years. The short life of plantations reduces average yields and increases growing costs. One advantage is that the tree is fast growing and bears early. Papaya can thus be interplanted as a temporary crop in orchards with slower growing longer-lived fruit trees such as mango. There

can, however, be problems with spray management in mixed plantings.

B. Botanical Relations and Cultivars

There is much variation in the size, shape, and quality of fruit and productivity even in commercial orchards because of outcrossing which gives highly variable seedling populations. Fruit from hermaphrodite or bisexual flowers are usually cylindrical or pyriform with a small seed cavity and thick firm flesh which transports well. In contrast, fruit from female flowers are nearly round or oval-shaped with thin flesh. Some industries have used hand pollination to maintain a selected strain particularly when material from overseas has been incorporated. Care must be taken to avoid cross-pollination from inferior local material. Significant breeding efforts have been made in Hawaii, Australia, Taiwan, Thailand, Malaysia, and the Philippines. Firm flesh and resistance to soft rots have been important considerations in these breeding programs.

C. Description of the Plant (Fig. 6)

Papaya is a fast growing herb-like tree reaching up to 2–10 m in vigorous 3- to 5-year-old specimens. It is usually unbranched unless the growing point is injured. The stem is hollow, green, or deep purple with a thick base. The leaves emerge directly from

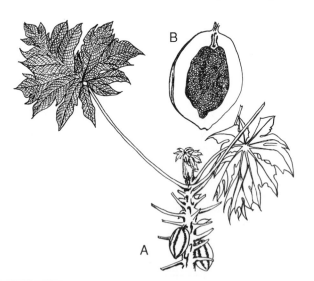

FIGURE 6 *Carica papaya* (papaya). (A) Top of a female plant (× 1/8). (B) Fruit in longitudinal section (× 1/5). [Redrawn by Cathie Menzel with permission from Purseglove, J. W. (1968). "Tropical Crops—Dicotleydons," Fig. 5, p. 47. Copyright © 1968 by Longman Group U.K., Harlow, U.K.]

the upper part of the stem with the petiole up to a meter long and the leaf blade deeply divided into 5–11 main segments usually about 25–75 cm in diameter. Both the stem and leaves contain a milky latex. The flowers are fleshy, waxy, and fragrant and have five petals. Some plants bear only female or hermaphrodite flowers, others only male flowers (dioecious plants). There may also be monoecious plants bearing both male and female flowers. Fruit are melon like, oval to nearly round, 7–50 cm long, weigh up to 9–10 kg, although normally 1–3 kg. The skin is waxy and thin, but tough. When the fruit is green it is rich in white latex. Ripe fruit have a light to deep yellow skin with soft yellow, orange, pink, or red flesh. There are numerous small black seeds coated with a transparent gel attached to the flesh by white fibrous tissue.

D. Growth and Development

Papayas are normally grown from seed. Cuttings are sometimes exploited and have high early yields but are susceptible to wind damage. With controlled pollination the ratio of offspring in seedling populations is predictable: a female × male cross gives 50% female and 50% male; female × hermaphrodite gives 50% female and 50% hermaphrodite; while hermaphrodite × male gives one-third female, one-third hermaphrodite, and one-third male. Growers normally plant three to five seedlings per site and thin out plants once they have flowered. If a hermaphrodite planting is desired, only the vigorous hermaphrodite plants are retained. For female plantings, a ratio of 1 male:10 females is essential for satisfactory production. There are a few industries partly based on clonal propagation by cuttings or tissue culture.

Seedling growth is initially rapid particularly under warm moist conditions with up to two leaves appearing each week. Once fruiting commences, the rate of stem extension and leaf initiation slows. Yield is related to the number of flowering nodes and the size of the supporting leaf area.

E. Ecological Adaptation

Papayas grow in tropical and subtropical locations up to 32° latitude, where day temperatures range from 20° to 35°C. In the tropics, they are normally found up to 1600 m elevation, above which killing frosts may occur. Frost also restricts production generally to coastal areas in subtropical locations. Fruiting is related to new growth; hence, maximum yields are

recorded in the warm tropics. In the cool subtropics both leaf and fruit growth are reduced and the production cycle is extended. Cool weather also reduces the sugar and flavor components of the fruit. Quality is superior in the tropics. Even distribution of rain of at least 1200–1500 mm year^{-1} is required for optimum production, unless irrigation is available. Cycles of dry and cool weather followed by warm wet weather which encourage rapid growth have been associated with dieback or decline in subtropical Australia.

F. Uses of the Fruit

Fresh papayas are generally eaten with orange, lemon, or lime juice or used in fruit salads. They are a favorite breakfast in many cultures. Papaya can be used in drinks, jams, candies, and crystallized fruit. Chunks are used in canned fruit salads, but do not retain the texture and flavor of fresh fruit. Firm fruit can also be baked. In some areas, papaya is grown in sizeable plantations for the extraction of papain, an enzyme collected from the latex of green fruit which has several uses in the food, beverage, and pharmaceutical industries.

VII. Avocado

A. Origin, Distribution, and Commercial Importance

The avocado, *Persea americana,* from the family Lauraceae is believed to have originated in Central America, possibly in the area between Mexico, Guatemala, and Honduras. It was cultivated in much of central and northern South America long before the arrival of Europeans. Avocado was initially sent to the West Indies in the late 1600s and quickly spread to the rest of South America and then to Asia and Africa. It is now found growing from the tropical lowlands to cool subtropical areas, many Mediterranean zones, and even in some temperate locations. Major producers with more than 0.1 Mt are Mexico, the United States, Dominican Republic, and Brazil. It is less popular in Southeast Asia, Oceania, and Africa.

Significant quantities of fresh fruit are exported from Israel, Spain, South Africa, and the United States into the U.K., France, and other E.C. countries. Demand for fruit is steadily increasing especially in Europe.

B. Botanical Relations and Cultivars

Three races are generally distinguished in order of increasing tropical adaptation: Mexican, Guatemalan, and West Indian. West Indian types contain less oil in the fruit (3–10% vs 10–30% for the other groups) and are generally considered inferior in taste and quality, lacking the true "nutty" flavour of the other groups. They also have a leathery, pliable skin, and smooth flesh. However, the West Indian types are more salt tolerant. Guatemalan races have thin to very thick skin and granular flesh. The Mexican group has thin soft skin which clings to the flesh. The races hybridize readily and hence a range of cultivars adapted to cool, dry Mediterranean climates up to warm moist tropical lowland conditions are available. Various hybrids are now commercialized and clonally propagated. The major export cultivars are Hass and Fuerte.

C. Description of the Plant (Fig. 7)

Avocado may be an erect or spreading evergreen tree up to 18–20 m tall with thick sturdy branches and a large trunk. The leaves are dark-green and glossy on the upper surface and whitish on the underside, and usually about 5–40 cm long. Those of the Mexican race have a strong aniseed smell when crushed. The small pale green-yellow flowers are borne on short panicles on terminal branches. The fruit are pear-shaped or nearly round up to 20–35 cm long and 15 cm wide. The skin may be thick or thin, smooth or rough, cling to or easily separate from the flesh, and range from yellow-green to maroon, purple, and black. Fruit weigh up to 1 kg but usually 300–500 g.

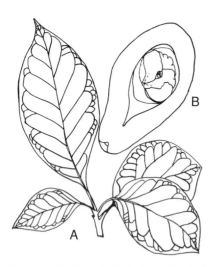

FIGURE 7 *Persea americana* (avocado). (A) Leafy shoot (× 1/2). (B) Fruit in longitudinal section (× 1/2). [Redrawn by Cathie Menzel with permission from Purseglove, J. W. (1968). "Tropical Crops—Dicotyledons," Fig. 29, p. 195. Copyright © 1968 by Longman Group U.K., Harlow, U.K.]

The flesh is yellow-green, buttery and nutty, sometimes granular, or watery and bland. The size of the ivory seed and hence flesh recovery varies greatly with the cultivar.

D. Growth and Development

Leaf growth in mature trees generally occurs in synchronized flushes promoted by warm temperatures of 25°–30°C and good moisture supply. Leaves have a short life normally less than one year. Trees usually have vegetative flushes in spring and summer in the subtropics with floral induction occurring at the end of the summer flush and fruit set concurrent with the spring flush in indeterminate flowering branches. In determinate branches, shoot growth ends with flowering. In tropical locations, flushing is more frequent and floral induction can occur several times during any dormant nonflushing period. Floral development is rapid with induction to anthesis normally taking 8 to 10 weeks, less in tropical climates. Anthesis takes 2 to 3 weeks in warm areas and 2 to 3 months in the cool subtropics. Fruit set is normally very heavy but two periods of abscission occur in late spring and summer. In subtropical locations especially at elevation, fruit set can be very poor in early cultivars flowering during cool weather in spring. The interplay between the growth flushes with production is complex. Young flushes compete strongly with the developing fruitlets but high rates of carbon assimilation and hence a sizeable leaf area are required to fill the fruit. Avocados take 6–12 months to mature and are a heavy drain on the tree due to the high oil content of the fruit. Ripening only commences once fruit are harvested and thus a single block of one cultivar in an orchard can be successfully marketed over several weeks. Fruit take 7 to 10 days to ripen at room temperature. Ripening can be delayed for several weeks with storage at 7°C.

E. Ecological Adaptation

The original avocado tree was adapted to the rainforests of the humid tropics and subtropics of Central America. Commercial production, however, has now spread to many other environments. West Indian types yield best in pantropical areas with days of 28°–36°C and high humidity especially around anthesis. Trees may be damaged at 1°–2°C. The Guatemalan races originating at higher elevation in Central America are successful in cooler areas such as coastal California. The Mexican races are the most cold tolerant and will survive short periods below freezing. Day temperatures of 25°–30°C and high humidity are optimum. The Mexican races were the source of many of the earlier commercial varieties in the main avocado growing areas of California, although about 90% of production is now based on Hass (Guatemalan). Other important cultivars are Pinkerton (mainly Guatemalan) and Reed (Guatemalan). Californian avocados are mostly grafted onto Mexican rootstocks.

Avocado cannot survive excessive soil moisture or even temporary water-logging especially when under pressure from root rot, *Phytopthora cinnamomi*. Hence, sites with poor drainage are best avoided for commercial production. Water supply is particularly critical during the flowering and fruit set period and up to the summer drop. Trees are sensitive to excess salts. Water quality should be checked before planting.

F. Uses of the Fruit

The fruit has a long history in the diet of Central Americans, being mainly used as an uncooked savory mixed with herbs and spices, but can also be used to enhance the presentation and consumption of many foods. More recently the oil has been used in cosmetics and soaps, but is generally too expensive to be used as a cooking oil.

Bibliography

Bose, T. K., and Mitra, S. K. (1990). "Fruits: Tropical and Subtropical." Naya Prokash, Calcutta Six, India.

Morton, J. F. (1987). "Fruits of Warm Climates." Creative Resources Systems Incorporated, Winterville, NC.

Nagy, S., and Shaw, R. E. (1980). "Tropical and Subtropical Fruits: Composition, Properties and Uses." AVI, Westport, CT.

Page, P. E. (1984). "Tropical Tree Fruits for Australia." Queensland Department of Primary Industries, Brisbane.

Samson, J. A. (1980). "Tropical Fruits." Longman, London.

Verheij, E. W. M., and Coronel, R. E. (1991). "Plant Resources of South-East Asia," Vol. 2. Edible fruits and nuts. Pudoc, Wageningen.

Tropical Grasslands

W. D. PITMAN, *University of Florida*

Glossary

Community Assemblage of organisms occupying a common environment and interacting with each other
Formation Major unit of vegetation representing the natural potential of an area under the ultimate control of climate; tropical grasslands and tropical rain forests are examples
Herbaceous Nonwoody
Herbivory Process of feeding on plant herbage
Landscape Ecological unit, such as a watershed or drainage basin, typically consisting of different communities or even formations which do not function independent of each other
Pastoralist Individual who derives his living from grasslands through grazing livestock; this term is typically applied to those living in close contact with the grassland ecosystem, such as the pastoral nomads
Rangeland Those portions of the grassland formations which are managed as natural ecosystems: that is, using ecological principles rather than agronomic approaches
Savanna Grassland with scattered trees or shrubs, in a distinctly seasonal climate of alternating wet and dry periods; the term savanna has been used for a number of different plant communities and landscapes with various specific definitions in the literature
Succession Process of change within communities which eventually leads to a somewhat stable but dynamic community capable of maintaining itself under the prevailing conditions

Tropical Grasslands are defined by vegetation type and either location or climate. Tropical grasslands may be defined as plant communities dominated by grasses (plants of the family Gramineae) in the tropics. Thus, by definition, tropical grasslands occur in the tropics, the zone between the Tropic of Cancer ($23\frac{1}{2}°$ N) and the Tropic of Capricorn ($23\frac{1}{2}°$ S). Grasslands at higher latitudes are excluded. Grasslands at high elevations within the tropics, such as the temperate and alpine grasslands of the Andes mountains in Peru, are considered tropical grasslands based on this definition. Alternatively, tropical grasslands may be defined as plant communities dominated by grasses in regions with tropical climates (and may even be extended to regions with subtropical climates that support grassland communities characteristic of the tropics). In this case, the high elevation areas within the tropics which are subjected to temperate or alpine climates are excluded. The areas with tropical (and subtropical) climates, which typically extend to higher latitudes in coastal zones, are included. The choice of definition depends on the purpose. For geographical purposes, the former definition could often be more useful. For agricultural purposes, the latter definition would often be most useful.

I. Description

Tropical grasslands include the native grass formations which comprise the tropical rangelands and much smaller areas of planted pasture along with naturally occurring secondary grasslands including those composed of aggressive, weedy grass species which are often abandoned and considered waste lands. As with other grasslands of the world, a number of plant families in addition to the Gramineae are typically included in the plant communities of tropical grasslands. As with other grasslands, the majority of these nongrass plants are herbaceous species. In contrast to the temperate grasslands, which are characterized by the absence of trees on the extensive plains and prairies, tropical grasslands are typified by a landscape of grass with scattered trees. In fact, tropical grasslands include a range in vegetation types from grasslands with essentially no woody plants through the complete continuum of increased woodiness to woodland conditions where an overstory canopy of woody plants prevents development of a continuous grass cover.

Tropical grasslands which occur in climates of distinct seasonal rainfall and include characteristic woody species are commonly called savannas. In some cases, competition for limited moisture maintains the balance between grasses and woody species, with the extensive fibrous roots of grasses at an advantage with limited shallow moisture and woody plants benefiting from deep moisture. Fire, either natural or anthropogenic, often limits development of woody plants and maintains the grass dominance. Such savannas occur over a wide range of rainfall conditions and geographic locations. The plant species present differ with both the moisture conditions and location. Under high rainfall conditions, extremely tall-growing grasses such as bamboo (subfamily Bambuseae) and elephantgrass (*Pennisetum purpureum*) can form dense grass stands with interspersed remnant trees where the natural forest has been disturbed. As rainfall decreases, grasses of shorter stature dominate with height of associated trees also less. Density of the grass stand becomes less under semi-arid conditions with shrubs comprising the woody component of these drier grasslands. The short, sparse grasses where tropical grasslands merge with deserts may appear similar to the temperate short-grass prairie or steppe. Tropical grasslands in similar rainfall zones have a similar general appearance regardless of location. However, species of both the grasses which dominate these grasslands and the associated trees differ with somewhat similar appearing but distinct species in the extensive tropical grasslands of South America, Africa, and Australia.

II. Distribution

Tropical grasslands occur naturally in the zone between the tropical forests and warm deserts. The largest expanse of tropical grassland occurs in Africa. This grassland extends across West Africa from the Sahara Desert southward to the Congo forest region and eastward to the Ethiopian Highlands. It then extends around the eastern extent of the Congo forest region near Lake Victoria and across southern Africa to the Kalahari Desert. Within this grassland region are considerable areas of woodland, particularly an expansive region between the tall-grass savanna just south of the Congo and the short-grass savanna immediately north of the Kalahari. Much of this African grassland includes areas where cultivated fields, woodlands, and grassland form a mosaic pattern across the landscape. Additional extensive tropical grasslands occur in western Madagascar.

Extensive grassland regions also occur both north and south of the Amazon forest of South America. Tropical grasslands also occur in Australia between the northern tropical forest and the central desert. Additional natural tropical grasslands occur in tropical Asia including the Indian subcontinent, often as relatively small areas within forested and cultivated landscapes. Grasslands are also found interspersed within forested and cultivated landscapes in Central America. As in Africa, the South American and Australian grasslands border both tropical forest and other woodland zones. These other woodlands differ from forest in that, despite dominance by woody species, a closed upper tree canopy does not develop to exclude herbaceous species including shade-tolerant grasses. Thus, there is not a distinct separation between these tropical woodlands and grasslands, and the dominance of either woody plants or grasses, especially in the transition zone, is often determined by factors other than climate and soil, such as fire and biotic effects.

Only a portion of the existing tropical grassland area (estimated to total around 30 million km^2) is generally considered to represent the potential plant community. This has been suggested to include the rainfall zone of about 200 to 600 mm across Africa below the Sahara and edaphically determined grasslands of distinct wet and/or dry conditions in Africa and South America. The existence of a tropical grassland climate has been disputed. Perhaps gradations of forest to woodland to shrubland and finally desert represent the vegetation potential of tropical climates, with occurrence of stable grasslands dependent upon edaphic, biotic, fire, or other constraints to development of woody plants.

Subtropical grasslands are found between the Australian central desert and the east coast, east of the

Kalahari Desert in southern Africa, in the western portion of southern Madagascar, east of the Andes in southern South America, in India, and in North America extending from northeastern Mexico into the southern-most portion of Texas with an isolated area in the Florida peninsula.

In the subtropics and at higher elevations in the tropics where a distinct cool season occurs, rainfall primarily restricted to the cool season favors woody, deep-rooted plants over the warm-season grasses so that a zone of grassland between forest and desert does not occur without prior disturbance of the woody plants. In such environments, the advantage of efficient water uptake by fibrous-rooted grasses is lost because they are often dormant when moisture is available. In these situations, the natural vegetation in the intermediate zone is typically brush comprised of decreasing density of thorny shrubs of decreasing height as rainfall decreases from the woodland zone to desert.

III. Additional Characteristics

In addition to the expected intermediate annual rainfall levels between those of tropical rainforests and deserts, seasonal rainfall distribution is characteristic of tropical grasslands. A distinct dry season is a key aspect of fire-induced grasslands. In extreme instances, moisture conditions can alternate from flood to essentially complete loss of moisture available within the rooting zone of herbaceous plants on an annual basis. This distribution, more than average annual amount, is a major factor in determining the range of natural grasslands in the tropics. Soils, as they affect moisture conditions and plant root growth, also are determining factors in the occurrence of natural grasslands. Unfavorable soil chemistry and low fertility characterize extensive tropical grasslands, especially in South America, but whether these limitations or anthropogenic effects ultimately restrict woody species in humid environments is still not certain.

The transition from grassland to desert on a regional scale corresponds closely with decreasing rainfall. On a smaller scale within the transition zone, soil and herbivory are important factors. In such arid and semi-arid climates, saline and sodic soils limit many grassland species and enhance the effects of moisture limitations. Excessive herbivory in arid and semiarid climates contributes to loss of herbaceous vegetation and can contribute to the conversion of grassland to desert.

At the other extreme, moisture limitations to the growth of woody species can be determinants of the extension of natural grasslands into the more humid tropical region. Again, other factors including soil, geomorphology, rainfall distribution, and herbivory contribute to the determination of the stable vegetation. As annual rainfall amount increases, extent of moisture limitations during the dry season may be a limiting factor to development of woody vegetation. Soil factors such as low nutrient status, low pH, high aluminum levels, and impediments of deep root development can also limit woody vegetation and contribute to the range of tropical grasslands. Effects of herbivory depend on which plants are defoliated, as well as the frequency, intensity, and season of defoliation. The more commonly observed effect is a seasonal overutilization of herbaceous vegetation contributing to the opportunity for establishment of woody species in grassland ecosystems which receive sufficient moisture to support woody plants. An opposite effect in the transition zone between grassland and forest or woodland is provided by fire. Burning, when sufficient fuel is provided by herbaceous vegetation, can prevent establishment of woody species and maintain the grassland vegetation.

IV. Anthropogenic Influences

From an ecological viewpoint, it is of considerable interest to distinguish between the zones of potential grassland and those of other formations. The current range of these grasslands has been greatly affected by man. Grasslands have been lost to desertification due to attempts at cultivation and overgrazing in the more arid grasslands. Similar activities of man have degraded grasslands in higher rainfall regions as erosion and brush encroachment have resulted from overgrazing and inappropriate cultivation attempts. On the other hand, clearing of forest and burning maintain grasslands in areas where forest naturally occurred. It is difficult to separate anthropogenic effects from natural development in some situations where grazing and cultivation have occurred over extended historical periods. It is even more difficult to distinguish between the natural fire-maintained savannas and some of the fire-maintained savannas that are due to man. [See DESERTIFICATION OF DRYLANDS.]

Some of the anthropogenic grasslands are readily distinguishable from the natural vegetation which characterizes grassland formations. Such secondary grasslands, those developing on sites following disturbance of the stable vegetation, can occur naturally or in response to activities of man. The natural secondary grasslands typically possess the characteristic of great diversity of plant species and succession, or change in plant populations over time, toward a diverse, dynamic but stable vegetation formation. Some disturbed sites in humid to subhumid zones from tropical Asia to subtropical America may be dominated by dense, persistent monocultures of the weedy grass *Imperata cyclindrica*. Activities of man have spread this grass and provided opportunities for its establishment and dominance by disturbing existing vegetation. On slightly drier sites where productive grasslands have been continuously overgrazed by man's excessive concentration of livestock, the grazing tolerant grass *Bothriochloa pertusa* has formed a dense monoculture of rather low productivity in various tropical locations. Although such grassland areas are atypical, these examples illustrate how unintended responses to man's activities can sometimes result in stands of less desirable species for either livestock production or environmental quality. Such degraded sites offer opportunities for grassland improvement to benefit agricultural productivity or other uses, and these opportunities occur in some areas where such improvement is of greatest urgency.

Wherever tropical grasslands occur, it is unlikely that the current extent corresponds with the area of potential grassland as determined by climatic and edaphic conditions. Most of the humid tropical grasslands are anthropogenic in nature. Such areas as the tall-grass savannas which occur at abrupt boundaries with tropical forests are for the most part anthropogenic due to the effects of such activities as shifting cultivation, harvest of trees, and repeated burning which restrict redevelopment of forest or woodland communities.

Considerable evidence indicates that grasslands previously extended into present desert regions. While climatic change may be associated to a degree, it is evident that disturbance of grasslands by continued overgrazing and attempts at cultivation on sites with inadequate moisture have contributed to, or at least accelerated, the rate of desertification in some regions. In addition to loss of arid grasslands to environmental degradation, in the more humid extent of the tropical grassland zone, extensive areas have been converted to cropland.

V. Productivity

Productivity can be considered in the sense of primary production, that is the conversion of solar energy into biomass by plants through the process of photosynthesis. This primary production over the extent of tropical grasslands is determined on a broad scale by moisture. In the more humid range of tropical grasslands, extremely high production potentials extend up to $2 \, kg/m^2$ of dry herbage annually under the most favorable conditions. On the other extreme, only a few grams of biomass per square meter may be produced in dry years in the drier extension of tropical grasslands. Along with average annual amount of moisture, fluctuations from year to year, distribution within the year, and soil factors affecting moisture retention and availability to plants affect the botanical composition of grasslands. This botanical composition, affected by previous moisture regime, affects potential productivity. Moisture at a given time affects the attainment of this previously set potential productivity.

Within moisture regimes, soil factors, especially fertility, further determine production potential. Tropical soils in areas of high rainfall are often highly leached, resulting in low fertility with associated chemical imbalances. Extensive grasslands in tropical South America are limited in productivity due to highly leached, infertile soils. [*See* SOIL FERTILITY.]

Another major determinant of productivity is degree of defoliation during the growing season. Newly expanded grass leaves in the upper canopy are the primary site of photosynthesis. As grass leaves age, they senesce and become less efficient in the use of solar energy for plant growth. The upper, young leaves are typically the most palatable and nutritious to grazing animals, and these leaves are normally removed first when a grassland is subjected to grazing. Thus, grazing can restrict primary production to levels below the climatic and edaphic potential. In some specific situations grazing has been found to increase grass production through a stimulation of rapid regrowth. Repeated overgrazing or selective grazing among plant species can change the botanical composition and/or plant density and reduce the future potential productivity.

Another aspect of grassland productivity is the support or production of grazing animals. The world's major grasslands are important areas of livestock production. Tropical grasslands on fertile soils in humid regions may support up to three to four mature cows per hectare during the growing season. The less productive grasslands in dry regions may require up to 10 hectares to support one cow for an even shorter growing season. Thus, ranching and even more intensive enterprises of livestock farming, involving annual forage crops for seasonal use, have developed in humid grassland regions. In arid grasslands, the ancient nomadic systems and rather recently expanded transhuminance are still major means of utilizing the resource for domestic livestock production in some regions.

In Africa, primary production of grasslands is much more efficiently harvested by native wildlife populations than it typically is by domestic livestock. Two to three times as much animal biomass as typically produced by domestic livestock is suggested as the potential for native wildlife populations in some grasslands. This is associated with the specialized diets of the diverse native herbivores with various herbs, forbs, and woody species consumed resulting in efficient harvest of the total grassland production. Domestic livestock generally consume selected grasses and associated plant species. [See TROPICAL PASTURE DEVELOPMENT.]

VI. The Tropical Grasses

In general, tropical grasslands are characterized by grasses of the subfamily Panicoideae in contrast to temperate grasslands where species of the subfamily Festucoideae predominate. At high elevations in the tropics, grassland areas above the tree line are often similar to temperate grasslands and consist primarily of Festucoid species. Occurrence of the Panicoid grass, *Pennisetum clandestinum* (kikuyu grass), along with Festucoid species is characteristic of the high-elevation grasslands of Africa. These high-elevation grasslands represent only a very small portion of the area of grasslands in the tropics, with an extended range in the Andes of South America and isolated peaks in East Africa and the Pacific islands.

While the subfamily Panicoideae predominates in tropical grasslands, the subfamily Eragrostoideae also provides a substantial portion of the tropical grassland species. In addition to genera such as *Cynodon* and *Chloris* which occur throughout a range of tropical rainfall zones, the number of species of Eragrostoideae and their dominance increase with increasing aridity. This increase in dominance of Eragrostoideae with increasing aridity occurs in tropical, subtropical, and warm temperate regions.

Both the Panicoideae and Eragrostoideae subfamilies are characterized by photosynthesis involving the C-4 photosynthetic pathway in contrast to the C-3 photosynthetic pathway of the Festucoideae. Four-carbon compounds, malic and aspartic acids, are the initial products of the C-4 photosynthetic pathway in contrast to the three-carbon phosphoglyceric acid

from the C-3 photosynthetic pathway. Additional anatomical and physiological differences between plants with these contrasting processes of photosynthesis contribute to substantially higher potential dry matter production for C-4 plants than for C-3 plants in warm climates which receive high levels of solar radiation.

Within the more humid tropical grasslands, where the subfamily Panicoideae predominates, the tribes Paniceae and Andropogoneae are of special significance. Some individual species of the tribe Paniceae are particularly aggressive with high growth potentials and high nutrient requirements. These include species of the genera *Brachiaria, Digitaria, Melinis, Panicum, Paspalum, Pennisetum,* and *Setaria,* which are often among the early colonizers of disturbed sites. As soil fertility decreases, which is characteristic of some tropical regions and especially of eroded and leached sites arising from disturbed woodlands and abandoned fields, species of the tribe Andropogeneae begin to increase. These grasses, including species of *Andropogon, Bothriochloa, Dichantium, Hemarthria, Heteropogon, Hyparrhenia, Schizachyrium, Sorghum, Themeda,* and *Tripsacum,* are typically efficient in the use of soil nitrogen. Thus, while they are not generally as productive on fertile sites as the Paniceae species, they may be more productive or at least more stable on infertile sites. The slower growth rates, which often correspond with increased cell wall production, combine with efficient nitrogen use, which often provides low herbage nitrogen concentrations, to produce a less digestible, lower protein herbage at plant maturity. Thus, mature grasses of the tribe Andropogoneae in the humid tropics are often of lower forage quality than those of the tribe Paniceae. These characteristics of tropical grasses, which reflect soil fertility, are major determinants of the nutritive value of these grasslands for grazing animals.

VII. Use and Management

The major use of tropical grasslands throughout the world is for the production of domestic livestock. The natural diversity typical of tropical grasslands provides sources of food and cover for a great variety of wildlife in the various regions of the world. Considerable areas in Africa are devoted primarily to provision for wildlife populations.

Management of natural grassland typically involves lower inputs than required for planted pastures. Fire is often a key aspect of this extensive management, with burning used to control woody plants, remove old herbage growth, and stimulate new regrowth.

Development of watering facilities for livestock is often a key aspect in the improvement of grassland utilization especially in drier areas or during the dry season. Manipulation of grazing through control of livestock is often the primary means of extensive grassland management. Such intensive practices as grass planting, fertilization, irrigation, and pest control are generally not viable options on the natural grasslands of the tropics due to economic and ecological constraints. Exceptions include the control of woody plants with hand labor, selective herbicides, or mechanical means in specific situations.

Approaches to the manipulation of grazing livestock to produce grassland improvement on temperate rangelands have been evaluated for much of this century. Similar evaluations of responses to grazing on tropical grasslands are much more recent and less conclusive. On the native tall-grass prairie of temperate North America, effects of grazing can be rather reliably predicted. The season of grazing, length of the grazing period, and length of time protected from grazing, along with grazing pressure and mix of the animal species (cattle, sheep, and/or goats) can affect both productivity and botanical composition of these grasslands. The specific plants which are favored with various grazing schemes are somewhat predictable, since the grazing selectivity of livestock and responses of individual plants to grazing have been extensively studied on the North American prairie. [See RANGELAND GRAZING; RANGELAND PLANTS.]

A perhaps unique and fortuitous phenomenon of the North American tall-grass prairie facilitated early approaches to grazing management. The stable grassland community is comprised of productive, palatable grasses, characterized by upright growth with growing points elevated relatively early in the development process. This morphology and palatability contribute to vulnerability of these grasses to stand loss from heavy grazing pressure. Thus, under excessive utilization, less palatable and generally less productive grasses increase, and the value of the rangeland for livestock grazing decreases. Further continuation of excessive grazing then leads to extensive loss of most of the palatable grasses, resulting in a sparse cover of grasses, invasion by weedy plants, increased soil erosion, and low levels of herbage and livestock production. Simple surveys of the vegetation over time allow trends in botanical composition, resulting from the combination of grazing and environmental conditions, to be detected. Thus, undesirable trends in condition of this rangeland can be detected, and appropriate modifications in grazing (stocking rate, season

and frequency of use, livestock species, etc.) can be made to favor the desired grasses. [See RANGELAND MANAGEMENT AND PLANNING.]

Similar approaches to grazing management of tropical grasslands have been widely promoted in the past. They have generally not been successful. A number of factors are involved. A large part of the current tropical grasslands exist where the stable vegetation formation, without manipulation by man, is woodland or forest. Regardless of grazing management, some control of woody plants will be required to maintain grassland on many of these woodland and forest sites. Also, the grasses which comprise the stable plant community on low-fertility tropical soils are not necessarily the most nutritious or palatable plants. With release of nutrients from burning and/or in animal waste from initial heavy grazing, they also may not be the most productive. Thus, the stable plant community may not be the most desirable for high herbage production or nutritive value. However, short-term benefits of the more productive, higher quality grasses may lead to a degraded condition for a much longer time if undesirable plants subsequently proliferate as nutrients are lost to leaching, erosion, and volatilization. Since many of the grasses which dominate the stable plant communities in these tropical grasslands are poor seed producers and seedling vigor of these grasses is often not good, recovery of degraded tropical grasslands even with the most favorable grazing system may not occur within the time constraints required for management decisions. Extensive areas of tropical grasslands in arid and semiarid regions which have been subjected to long periods of grazing and repeated droughts are now dominated by annual plants rather than the more stable perennial grasses. Current utilization of these grasslands often emphasizes the efficient harvest of available herbage by grazing livestock rather than emphasizing the plant community and soil stability. Such emphasis on obtaining available, immediate benefits must be evaluated in comparison with any potential opportunities for improved ecosystem stability.

Grazing management approaches for tropical grasslands need to be enhanced. Critical considerations include the invasion of woody plants, the lack of palatability and limited productivity and nutritive value of the stable plant community on many infertile tropical grasslands, the lack of information on population dynamics of many communities, and the lack of predictability of rainfall in most tropical grasslands. Certainly the importance of infrequent combinations of events, such as appropriate rain in one season for seed production of a desirable plant followed by favorable conditions for germination and establishment in a subsequent season, must be considered in grasslands with erratic rainfall patterns. Also, especially in semiarid regions, the long-term nature of any improvements in vegetation in comparison with the potential for rapid deterioration (in such situations as excessive grazing pressure during extended drought) must be recognized. Such hazards to stability of these grasslands suggest that plans must be developed and implemented to adjust grazing pressure as drought conditions are recognized before excessive damage to the plant community has occurred. Reduction of herd size prior to the most adverse effects of severe drought, rather than initial short-term supplemental feeding of livestock, may be the least damaging alternative in many situations. Some basis for the required anticipation of continuing drought to trigger implementation of drought management strategies may be provided by further improvement of recent efforts to model regional climatological patterns.

Livestock needs must receive continuing consideration, with seasonal supplementation of minerals and protein often essential for economical livestock production. Effects of such supplements on the total grassland-based livestock production system must be considered. Also the extreme seasonality of herbage production, often further complicated by erratic rainfall, and the rapid decrease in forage quality with plant maturity are tremendous constraints on the productivity of livestock in tropical grasslands. These constraints often result in low levels of both reproduction of mature animals and the growth and maturity of young animals. Substantially lower livestock production from tropical grasslands than that typical of temperate livestock production systems is currently the case. A small portion of the tropical grasslands consists of planted pastures. Some of these pastures, especially in more humid areas, are intensively managed with livestock production levels similar to those of the temperate grasslands.

Rather short-term economic conditions and/or livestock needs rather than continuing productivity or stability of the grassland are sometimes primary considerations in management of some tropical grasslands. Social and political factors limit the options available for use and management of tropical grasslands in other situations. Nonetheless, productive, stable tropical grasslands and associated livestock enterprises are currently maintained across the range of tropical grassland environments, especially where rather conservative grazing pressures are maintained

to provide surplus herbage as a buffer during droughts.

VIII. Current Environmental Concerns

Public awareness of potential and present global environmental problems has recently increased the sensitivity of governments and industry to some of the long-term consequences of decisions regarding tropical grasslands. Desertification in arid and semiarid regions can be accelerated, especially during extended drought conditions over several years, by developments intended to improve commercial production or even living conditions for people under marginal conditions. Drilling of water wells to allow greater utilization of such grasslands has been suggested to allow degradation of these areas through overgrazing which might not otherwise have been possible due to lack of available water for livestock. Likewise, improvements in animal health, which are not accompanied by use or marketing of the increased animal numbers, can lead to herd increases in good years and subsequent excessive overgrazing in dry years. Introduction of such technology to new areas must be accompanied by continuing educational efforts to reduce the opportunity for undesirable consequences. Often the choice may be between the maintenance of a slight buffer of a few cows by people living under precarious subsistance conditions versus avoiding the possibility of continuing grassland deterioration if rain does not occur soon.

A continuing increase in human populations in semiarid grassland regions during recent years is increasing pressure on productivity and sustainability of these systems. Livestock numbers have been increased in some extremely fragile environments to sustain the increased human populations. The extreme variability in herbage production from year to year and the recurring nature of droughts suggest that alternatives and strategies beyond those available to individual pastoralists must be provided for stability of these environments.

At the other end of the moisture extreme, grasslands are maintained on lands capable of producing forest, thus contributing to deforestation or at least preventing or slowing reforestation. Grasslands typically are relegated to lands which are unsuited for other higher value uses largely due to various adverse soil conditions. Deforestation is generally for purposes other than grassland development, although once depleted of nutrients and perhaps even topsoil, secondary grasslands often develop. These may develop or persist primarily through the assistance of man utilizing livestock and burning. Again, economic decisions, sometimes at the subsistence level, may require contrast of immediate benefits with potential future consequences.

Additional environmental modifications involving the natural grasslands, which are generally less dramatic than desertification and deforestation include decreases in food and habitat available for wildlife and the change from natural to managed environments as livestock production increases in intensity. Such changes are generally necessary for increases in livestock productivity and sometimes for economic survival of livestock production enterprises. Appropriate consideration of the additional ecological, recreational, and esthetic values of tropical grasslands will be provided as economic values are placed on these alternative uses and values.

A continuing dilemma in management of most tropical grasslands contrasts the need for high stocking rates to efficiently harvest herbage production during wet seasons of the year and during favorable years, while the herbage is of high nutritive value, with the need to maintain (or at least avoid starvation of) livestock during the dry season and sometimes even for periods of years of drought. While stocking rates may currently be marginally higher than appropriate in some areas, decreased livestock productivity rather than excessive environmental degradation is often the recurring effect of such marginally high stocking rates. However, throughout the tropical rangeland areas where recurring drought is a factor, stocking rates are typically high enough to make livestock systems and their grassland resource quite vulnerable to degradation from extended drought. This hazard suggests that alternative plans for grazing livestock during drought are imperative and must be developed on both individual and regional levels.

Bibliography

Heitschmidt, R. K., and Stuth, J. W. (eds.) (1991). "Grazing Management: An Ecological Perspective." Timber Press, Portland, OR.

Holechek, J. L., Pieper, R. D., and Herbel, C. H. (1989). "Range Management Principles and Practices." Prentice Hall, Englewood Cliffs, NJ.

Joss, P. J., Lynch, P. W., and Williams, O. B. (1986). "Rangelands: A Resource under Siege." Australian Academy of Science, Canberra.

Long, S. P., Jones, M. B., and Roberts, M. J. (eds.) (1992). "Primary Productivity of Grass Ecosystems of the Tropics and Sub-tropics." Chapman and Hall, London.

National Research Council (1990). "The Improvement of Tropical and Subtropical Rangelands." National Academy Press, Washington, DC.

Vallentine, J. F. (1989). "Range Development and Improvements," 3rd ed. Academic Press, San Diego.

Vallentine, J. F. (1990). "Grazing Management." Academic Press, San Diego.

Tropical Pasture Development

W. D. PITMAN, *University of Florida*

Glossary

Forage Portions of herbaceous and woody plants, other than harvested grain, which can be consumed by ungulates

Forage quality Value of particular forage for maintenance and productivity of specific classes of ungulates encompassing the concentration and availability of the various nutrients, potential intake of the forage, and any associated antiquality factors

Germplasm Genetic resources including both naturally occurring species and ecotypes and unique genotypes derived from genetic manipulation

Grazing pressure In general terms, the impact of grazing on plants or plant communities; in a more specific sense, the number of animal units per amount of available forage at a specific time

Herbage Above-ground biomass of herbaceous plants

Legume Member of the plant family Leguminosae (Fabaceae)

Monoculture Cultivation or production of a single crop or plant species on an area to the exclusion of other potential crops or species

Sowing Process of planting seed

Vegetative propagation Increase (spread or establishment) of plants by means other than seed, typically involving either rhizomes or stolons

Tropical pasture development is the deliberate alteration of existing plant communities involving the introduction of selected tropical forage plants to enhance the value of a site primarily for the production of forage for grazing animals. Fencing for control of grazing livestock and development of water sources are also integral aspects of pasture development.

I. Purpose and Scope

The purpose of pasture development in most instances is to increase both productivity and profit potential of domestic livestock enterprises. On a broader regional or national scale, the purpose of tropical pasture development is often to enhance the economy through increased productivity, to increase availability of milk or meat to improve human diets, and/or to restructure degraded landscapes into productive, stable environments.

Agronomic requirements for establishment and management of tropical forage plants involve similar principles over the range of their area of adaptation; thus, tropical pasture development extends to the subtropical and semi-arid environments where tropical pasture species are adapted. Pasture development typically occurs on sites which are not suitable for more intensive uses such as crop production. Social and political structures which do not provide opportunities for individual land managers to benefit from grassland improvement or even maintenance of existing grasslands are often limitations to tropical pasture development and contributing factors to the deterioration of grasslands. [*See* RANGELAND GRASS IMPROVEMENT; RANGELAND GRAZING; TROPICAL GRASSLANDS.]

There are substantial contrasts between approaches appropriate for development of tropical pastures in some regions and those typically used for temperate pastures. While the high degree of success with temperate pasture development suggests that it could provide a model for the less extensively studied tropical counterpart, several factors must be considered. Temperate pasture development has succeeded through the selection and breeding of a very small number of grass and legume species which are primarily suited to humid environments. While development of cultivars for specific environments has been a critical aspect of this success, continuing modification of the environment to fit the plants is also an integral part of temperate pasture technology. This modification often includes the annual or more frequent application of fertilizers, drainage of wet areas, irrigation of dry areas, and regular application of herbicides and sometimes even other pesticides. Also, complete reestablishment of the pasture system after a few years is sometimes necessary. While such intensive systems may be appropriate in some situations, tropical pastures often must be inexpensive to establish, be even less expensive to maintain, and be sustainable for decades rather than just years. Costs of failures are often measured in ecological terms rather than simply in economic terms.

II. Climatic and Edaphic Considerations

Tropical climates which provide uniform availability of adequate amounts of moisture can support continuous growth of the most vigorously growing tropical forage plants. Such climates provide opportunity for the highest levels of herbage production. Such moist tropical climates also are generally suitable for the production of many other crops including high-value tree crops, food crops for human consumption, and forestry. Thus, despite the tremendous potential productivity of tropical grass pastures in moist climates, pasture development is often not the highest use of these resources. Most of the land in moist climates which is available for the development of tropical pastures has limited value for many other uses due to constraints such as steep slopes, poor drainage, poor soil structure, shallow or stony soils, low fertility, or other soil chemical imbalances. Limitations such as inadequate drainage and low fertility typically restrict the range of suitable forage plant species and their potential productivity but not the use of these lands for pasture development.

The characteristic seasonal distribution of rainfall in the zones between equatorial regions and the subtropics greatly affects the potential agricultural uses of land. Where rain occurs over a long enough period to produce crops, such crop production typically receives priority over pasture development. Where soil fertility is rapidly depleted by crop production, pasture may be a secondary use or pastures may comprise long-term components in crop rotation systems. Where other edaphic conditions limit production of crops, they also are often limitations to the establishment of tropical pastures. However, once established, pastures of adapted species may be quite productive and sustainable under appropriate management even on steep slopes, wet sites, soils of poor tilth, etc.

As total amount of annual rainfall or length of the rainy season becomes inadequate for crop production, pasture often becomes the potential use of highest value. However, rainfall in such environments is often unpredictable as well as low in annual amount. Even though pastures of selected species may have considerably higher herbage production potentials than the existing natural vegetation, establishment of introduced pasture plants involves high risk of stand failure in the more adverse environments. When the existing vegetation is disturbed to provide a seedbed for enhanced opportunity of establishment by sown species, potential for soil erosion and invasion of undesirable plants as well as economic loss are greatly increased in erratic-rainfall environments.

Selection of forage plants adapted to, or tolerant of, adverse soil factors is the most promising approach for overcoming such limitations to tropical pasture development. Although some advances have been made toward development of cultivars suited to specific adversities, a wealth of diverse tropical germplasm is available for further progress. Intensive pasture management involving substantial inputs to overcome soil limitations is not necessarily an inappropriate approach to tropical pasture development. Especially in humid environments, such an approach can provide highly productive livestock systems. However, over extensive areas of the tropics and subtropics, such systems are difficult to sustain within current restraints. [See FORAGES.]

III. Tropical Grasses

Grass cultivars currently available for tropical pasture development possess some rather distinctive characteristics, which affect both their practical use and potential improvement. Many of the productive, aggressive tropical grass cultivars do not produce seed or at least do not produce seed in sufficient quantities for establishment of pastures by sowing seed. Extensive pasture areas have been established from stem cuttings of tropical grass cultivars of the genera *Cynodon, Digitaria,* and *Hemarthria.* Such vegetative propagation of these stoloniferous grasses typically provides more aggressive, competitive stand establishment than that obtained with sowing of seed of seed-propagated species. Vegetative propagation maintains genetic integrity of cultivars, but it also can result in lack of genetic variability so that extensive areas planted to monocultures of one superior cultivar are vulnerable to rapid, extensive damage from insects and diseases. Either low-cost labor or high levels of mechanization have proven to provide particularly suitable conditions for successful planting of extensive areas by vegetative means.

While limited seed production has precluded sowing of seed of some species of the genera mentioned above, sufficient seed production typically occurs to allow genetic improvement of germplasm through plant breeding approaches. Additional tropical grasses which are excellent seed producers have provided distinct challenges to the use of plant breeding for genetic improvement. Several tropical grass species which have been widely used in pasture improvement are capable of apomictic reproduction. This method of reproduction involves structures commonly utilized in sexual reproduction but without actual fusion of male and female gametes. Thus, attempts at crossing plants, which reproduce apomictically, produce uniform progeny identical to the female parent. Apomictic seed production is more common in the tribes Paniceae and Andropogoneae than in other grass tribes. Identification of sexually reproducing plants of some apomictic species has allowed genetic improvement to be made by utilizing sexually reproducing female parents and selection of superior apomictic progeny to secure the genetic advances into new uniform cultivars. Exclusive planting of a superior individual apomictic cultivar, as with vegetatively propagated cultivars, can produce extensive grasslands which do not possess the genetic diversity to adjust readily to plant pests. The various mechanisms of apomixis (apospory is typical of species of *Panicum, Paspalum,* and *Cenchrus* of the subfamily Panicoideae, while diplospory is the form identified in the genus *Eragrostis* of the subfamily Eragrostoideae) and extent of obligate and facultative expression of the trait complicate the process of tropical grass improvement. In some cases, considerable basic cytogenetic investigation is required for advancement of genetic improve-

ment and development of improved cultivars of apomictic species.

On the other hand, tropical pasture grasses which reproduce sexually and produce adequate seed quantities for sowing pastures are not without disadvantages. Even perennial grasses, especially those which do not form dense canopies or spread aggressively by rhizomes or stolons, typically are continually being renewed by development of new seedlings within the stand. Highly heterogeneous cultivars and especially those composed of composited germplasm can experience change in pasture composition over a period of years in response to natural selection pressure or grazing conditions. Genotypes which differ in palatability can be composited into a single cultivar which may readily be transformed into a sward dominated by the least palatable genotype within a few years of grazing.

Grasses for tropical pasture development should be both productive and sustainable. The large number of diverse and often adverse environments represented and the requirement for plant persistence with minimal inputs have resulted in the consideration of a very large number of plant species for potential use in tropical pasture development. Tropical grass cultivars are largely from the subfamily Panicoideae, tribe Paniceae. Additional cultivars have also been developed from individual genera of the subfamily Eragrostoideae, tribe Chlorideae. The aggressive characteristics of some weedy and invading species have contributed to development of cultivars of these species able to meet the need for rapid establishment. High levels of herbage production are also characteristic of these aggressive grasses. As with temperate grass cultivars, the aggressive tropical grass cultivars are often dependent upon high levels of soil fertility for productivity and stand survival. Thus, declining productivity and eventual stand loss have been problems with tropical pasture development where regular fertilization has not been a viable management option.

Increased emphasis on sustainability indicates that species of the grass subfamily Panicoideae, tribe Andropogoneae should receive further attention. While use of *Andropogon gayanus* on infertile South American sites has apparently been successful, efforts with species of *Schizachyrium* and *Tripsacum* have reflected the characteristic limitations of this tribe in seed production and quality. Cultivars of the genus *Hemarthria* possess herbage nitrogen concentrations low enough to require protein supplementation for optimal performance of some classes of livestock even during the growing season. This is characteristic of the nitrogen use efficiency of the tribe. Thus, present Paniceae and Chlorideae cultivars with aggressive establishment and herbage production qualities and limitations in sustainability contrast with the potentially more sustainable tribe Andropogoneae which is typified by limitations in establishment and forage quality.

The major tropical grass cultivars are primarily of African genera, including *Brachiaria*, *Cenchrus*, *Chloris*, *Cynodon*, *Digitaria*, *Melinis*, *Panicum*, *Pennisetum*, and *Setaria*. In general, these grasses are tolerant of grazing, as would be expected from development under the most intense grazing conditions of any tropical environment. They are also generally aggressive and productive, partially due to recent intentional selection for these qualities, but perhaps also due to development under marginal conditions where recurring forest disturbance and nutrient release provided selection pressure for such aggressive colonization of new areas. The genus *Paspalum*, which has contributed primarily in the subtropics and warm temperate regions, is the most widely used tropical American grass genus. Even cultivars adapted to infertile South American sites have primarily been developed from African species such as *Andropogon gayanus* and *Hemarthria altissima*.

IV. Tropical Legumes

A potential solution to the dilemma of maintaining adequate nitrogen levels to sustain the Paniceae and Chlorideae grass cultivars is through biological nitrogen fixation of associated legumes, which has received considerable attention over the past 30 years. Tropical legumes are widespread in the American tropics, where soil fertility in many situations has been low and provided a competitive advantage to the legumes. Even though of tropical origin and adaptation, tropical legumes utilize the C-3 photosynthetic pathway typical of temperate grasses and legumes. Thus, in warm, fertile, high-sunlight tropical environments, the tropical legumes are at a competitive disadvantage to the tropical grasses with the more efficient and productive C-4 photosynthetic pathway. Various characteristics of individual tropical legumes, such as climbing growth habit, adaptation to shade, and an extended period of growth after growth of grasses has been slowed at initiation of the dry season, help to offset this growth advantage of the grasses under pasture conditions. Early efforts to select legumes primarily for establishment ability and high yields resulted in development of some cultivars that require specialized management for sustained stands. Recent tropical legume cultivars with increased tolerance of grazing include some that are less palatable than the grasses and others with morphological characteristics such as woody stems or prostrate growth under grazing. However, combinations of grasses and legumes for sustainable, productive, low-input tropical pastures have not been developed for most situations.

The great diversity of tropical legumes possessing desirable characteristics for pasture use indicates that advancements, though amazingly elusive in the past, should still be expected. In environments with distinctly unfavorable conditions occurring on a seasonal basis, efforts to develop legume cultivars should capitalize on the natural plant strategies for avoiding such conditions. Thus, the annual legumes should receive greater attention in drastic environments where perennials do not reliably survive an adverse season. Annual legumes also have potential in drier environments where grass growth is not so dense and competitive that seedlings are adversely affected by the grass stand during establishment. Pastures based on annual legumes are particularly vulnerable to erratic rainfall early in the growing season and excessive grazing late in the season when seed is produced. This vulnerability can be partially overcome by hard-seeded legumes which can provide supplies of seed for several years from a single good seed-production year.

As rainfall increases to support a more dense grass stand and the dry season is mild enough to allow survival of perennial legumes, the advantages of annual legumes are greatly diminished compared with their disadvantages. However, the importance of seed production, hard-seededness, and establishment of new legume seedlings is not diminished greatly. Many of the herbaceous perennial legumes are rather short lived. Although complete stand establishment is not required each year, stand stability does require a continuous process of new seedling development to offset plant mortality of most species. While hard-seededness is an advantage to legumes in established pastures, it is often a trait which must be overcome, at least partially, for acceptable establishment with sowing of new pastures. Seed scarification is a requirement for acceptable germination of some, though not all, tropical legumes. Additional similar characteristics of seed-propagated legumes (and grasses) which are advantages for existing stands and disadvantages for plant domestication are indeterminate flowering and seed shattering. For harvest of seed crops, uniform development and seed retention are highly beneficial to harvest of high proportions of the seed produced. Thus, the degree of domestication desired with forage plants often is a compromise between the natural advantages of existing traits and the requirements for economical seed production and initial establishment of new pastures.

The woody legumes, such as the genera *Acacia*, *Albizia*, *Calliandra*, *Desmanthus*, *Gliricidia*, *Leucaena*, and *Sesbania*, have recently been recognized as potentially possessing ecological advantages for use in tropical environments which are capable of supporting woodland plant communities. These legumes may provide sustainable systems where their deep roots utilize moisture supplies that would otherwise favor invasion of pastures by other woody plants. They could also sustain the cycling of nutrients from greater depth and store nutrients more effectively than either the grasses or the herbaceous legumes. While much of the attention has been focused on agroforestry and associated production of food crops, many of the woody legumes have potential value as pasture plants or at least as fodder crops. In addition to development of sufficiently aggressive and adapted genotypes for successful use, particular caution must be used not to introduce excessively competitive types since brush problems in many grasslands are presented by shrub legume species.

Most of the genera providing cultivars of the herbaceous tropical legumes such as *Aeschynomene*, *Centrosema*, *Desmodium*, *Macroptilium*, and *Stylosanthes* are of American origin. However, Asia and Africa also have been sources of important tropical legumes, including the genera *Alysicarpus*, *Neonotonia*, and *Vigna*. Tropical legume cultivars of American origin are primarily from low-fertility, leached soils with limited grazing pressure. Rather recent cultivars of *Desmodium* from Asian germplasm and *Vigna* from African origin indicate that despite large numbers of species and considerable diversity in American legumes, grazing tolerance may be more widely available from sources with a history of grazing pressure. Thus, current limitations to persistence of tropical legumes may be overcome by use of herbaceous legumes with morphological adaptations which allow them to partially escape excessive defoliation or by use of woody legumes which produce at least some foliage beyond grazing or browsing height. Both these and other means of escaping and/or tolerating the effects of grazing defoliation will likely be necessary to provide suitable legumes for the many diverse tropical environments.

Unlike the tropical grasses which generally are adapted over rather broad areas encompassing ranges in moisture and soil conditions, the tropical legumes respond to very subtle environmental differences. Often only slight changes in slope, soil texture, fertility, moisture, and especially plant competition make the difference between aggressive growth and complete loss of tropical legume stands. With a few individual species, such as those of the genus *Lotononis*, the requirement for a specific rhizobial inoculant can be a primary factor. However, for most tropical legumes, such rhizobial specificity is not a factor as it typically is with temperate legumes. Thus, narrow ranges of adaptation of tropical forage legumes may be a characteristic which necessitates the development of cultivars of a large number of different species and perhaps even the use of mixtures of legume species.

V. Germplasm Development

While recognition of the potential of tree and shrub legumes is perhaps the most recent major advance in tropical pasture development, the use of improved tropical forages in general is more recent than that of temperate forages and much more recent than efforts to improve the major food crops. Thus, experience with other crops indicates that tremendous potential exists for genetic improvement of tropical forage plants. However, the asset of tremendous quantities of highly diverse germplasm, which provides the opportunity for rapid progress with genetic manipulation, is also the reason not to immediately and extensively pursue the genetic manipulation of individual germplasm for numerous specific improvements. While in a few situations this may be the appropriate approach, in most tropical environments the available germplasm with potential value has not been sufficiently evaluated to even identify the most suited species. This is particularly the case for the tropical legumes. [See PLANT GENETIC RESOURCES; PLANT GENETIC RESOURCE CONSERVATION AND UTILIZATION.]

Timely efforts to obtain and store extensive collections of germplasm of tropical forage plants have been made during the past 15 years. Australian pasture scientists were leaders in both the early development of tropical forage technology and the recent collection and storage of existing germplasm. They were joined on a large scale in germplasm collection and storage by the system of international agricultural research centers with leadership from Centro Internacional de Agricultura Tropical (CIAT) in Cali, Colombia. This location especially facilitated the collection of tropical legumes which are more widespread and diverse in the American tropics than anywhere else. This accumulation of germplasm has far outpaced efforts to characterize the germplasm and determine the potential of various available genotypes in various environments. Considerable advancement in tropical forage development will likely result from identification and use of the superior germplasm currently available.

VI. Economic and Ecological Constraints

Costs, potential returns, and risk of failure require a combined evaluation of aspects of economics and ecology of tropical pasture development. Costs and risks of site deterioration increase with the degree of modification of the existing vegetation. Simply introducing seed of a desired species into existing vegetation, referred to in Australia as augmenting native pasture, minimizes cost with perhaps a rather high risk of failure. In environments with predictable rainfall patterns, risk of establishment failure can often be progressively reduced with increasing degrees of seedbed preparation at increasing cost. However, in environments with erratic rainfall, risk of stand failure may not be reduced enough to justify the increased cost and risk of site deterioration accompanying intensive seedbed preparation.

While sustainability of tropical pastures is critical, inputs to enhance stand life or even replace degraded pastures may not be unreasonable for high value uses such as milk production and fattening of slaughter animals on sites not subjected to excessive degradation from periodic cultivation. Such high return uses of tropical pastures, and even less intensive uses in particular economic circumstances, may result in advantages for nitrogen fertilization of grass pastures over grass–legume mixtures. The response of grass to nitrogen fertilization in humid and subhumid environments is often more predictable and productive than dependence on legumes for nitrogen. As intensity of management and production potential decrease, the advantages of legume technology over nitrogen fertilizer generally increase.

Invasion of planted pastures by other plants is an essentially universal phenomenon. Pasture deterioration of some extent results. Intensively managed pastures may be routinely subjected to treatment with selective herbicides or mechanical defoliation to control invading broadleaf weeds or woody species.

Hand labor and fire are also frequently used options for control of woody plants. Fewer options are available for control of weedy grasses in introduced grass pastures. Options available for control of broadleaf weeds and woody plants are reduced when legumes are components of the pasture, since many herbicides which control these weeds also damage the pasture legumes. Since the pasture legumes are differentially affected by fire, knowledge of the response of a particular legume cultivar to fire is a critical factor in deciding among options for controlling woody plants. In the long term, development of pasture cultivars better suited to specific environments, which are both productive and capable of competing with invading species, provide the preferred option. Appropriate extent of herbage utilization and use of key periods of deferment from grazing may also increase the competitive ability of introduced pasture plants.

VII. Animal Needs versus Available Herbage

Early during the season of active plant growth, the herbage available in tropical pastures is generally at its highest nutritive value for ruminant livestock. Young leaves are generally the plant parts highest in protein and digestibility. As herbage accumulates during the growing season, the proportion of older plant tissue increases while both digestibility and protein concentration decrease. Morphological development also produces increasing proportions of stem, which is typically lower in forage quality than are leaves. In addition to the biological fixation of atmospheric nitrogen into forms available for plant use, pasture legumes are typically higher in protein than the grass available for grazing through most of the year. Thus, selected pasture legumes provide potential to enhance quality of diets of grazing animals, often increasing intake of the lower quality grass and further enhancing animal performance even beyond that due to the nutrients contained in the legume herbage itself.

As the characteristic dry season in the tropics and cool temperatures or frosts in the subtropics decrease or even terminate plant growth, the nutritional value of the remaining herbage often deteriorates rapidly. A large portion of the gains made by grazing animals during the growing season are lost during the dry season in many tropical environments. Selection of forage plants for ability to retain green leaves, a characteristic of some deep-rooted legumes, or simply to retain higher forage quality into the dry season provides potential for improvement of animal production. Protection of such herbage from utilization until the appropriate season becomes a management consideration. This concept can be extended to simply reserving areas of existing grassland for dry-season use so that minimal supplementation and available roughage may prevent excessive weight losses by grazing livestock. Despite the higher forage quality of many tropical legumes, on infertile tropical soils some legumes are not heavily utilized while the grasses are actively growing. Such legumes provide naturally deferred herbage for dry-season use.

Grazing management strategies can be developed beyond simple deferment of grazing for later use to complex grazing systems which address additional concerns. Rapid rotation systems have been promoted for enhancement of pasture utilization and increases in carrying capacity. Increased herbage utilization in such systems can sometimes be attained without decreases in individual animal performance, as typically occurs on continuously grazed grasslands, because cattle are moved through the rotation rapidly so that regrowth of essentially all pasture plants is young and nutritious when grazed and cattle remain on a pasture only for a short time. Intensive grazing systems can also be developed primarily from the perspective of providing near maximum individual animal performance, especially during the growing season. These systems differ from the rapid rotation systems just mentioned primarily in extent of grazing pressure. These latter systems often utilize short grazing periods and light stocking rates to maintain relatively high availability of high-quality forage. In some pasture types, cattle utilize primarily the upper leaf canopy. Periods between grazing cycles are also short to allow grazing of regrowth while forage quality is still high. Livestock responses to such systems are greatest with young growing animals or in milk production systems. However, production responses from such intensive systems are primarily restricted to the growing season; thus, these systems do not contribute directly during periods of greatest nutrient deficit (such as extended dry seasons).

The use of stored herbage such as hay and silage for dry-season feeding has not been widely used in the tropics. As intensification of tropical livestock production systems increases, use of such technologies to provide quality dry-season feed will perhaps increase. Potential production of selected tropical grasses in favorable environments with such systems is tremendous. Where grassland based livestock sys-

tems are integrated with crop production enterprises, considerable dry-season feed for livestock can be derived from crop residues and even production of annual herbage crops for dry-season grazing or feeding. By-products of the processing of tropical crops provide another dry-season feed source for grassland livestock production. The nutritive value and methods of most efficient utilization of many of these tropical crop by-products have not been thoroughly evaluated, even though the available by-products are commonly used to some extent.

VIII. Additional Pasture Management Considerations

Grazing systems may be developed around the needs of the pasture plants rather than, or in addition to, the consideration of livestock needs. In some situations, requirements of plants for maintenance and productivity are not adequately addressed by prevailing grazing management. Highly palatable plants, especially when grown in mixed stands with less palatable species, may require periods of deferment from grazing for survival. These deferment periods may be satisfied simply by rotational grazing providing regular recurring opportunities for regrowth. In other instances, the season of deferment from grazing may be critical. Appropriate seasons of deferment from grazing can allow heavily grazed plants to regain vigor immediately prior to stress periods. Plants may respond to such deferment by storage of energy for subsequent use, by increased seed production, or through immediate increase in plant size and even vegetative propagation. Annual legumes, as components of perennial grass pastures, may require reduced grazing pressure during the season of seed production, while benefiting from heavier utilization of the associated grass during the period of legume establishment.

Nonstructural carbohydrates and other labile plant compounds can be mobilized and used in plant growth. These components, primarily total nonstructural carbohydrates, have been extensively used to evaluate effects of defoliation on vigor and regrowth potential of temperate forage plants. The high rates of photosynthesis of tropical grasses and less than complete leaf removal by grazing defoliation suggest that stored energy may seldom be a controlling factor in the grazing management of tropical grasses. However, even with the tropical grasses, initiation of new leaves following complete defoliation is dependent upon existing energy sources. Thus, plant vigor at onset of the dry season or at the first frost in the subtropics can be critical to survival of some plants. This becomes even more critical in erratic environments where intermittent light rain or warm temperatures permit repeated leaf initiation with subsequent defoliation. Thus, while stored energy may not be a factor in growth of most tropical forage plants during the season of active growth, energy available for leaf initiation following complete defoliation by drought or frost can be critical in some situations.

IX. Global and Societal Concerns

The growing problem of desertification and its effects on pastoral societies and beyond suggest that technological developments to restore stable and productive vegetation should be a priority in arid and semi-arid grassland research. Identification of sites with greatest potential for revegetation could provide enhanced opportunities for successful small-scale plantings. Innovative means of site enhancement for plant establishment and selection of plants with superior establishment ability for use as pioneer species may be critical for greater success. Refinement of the prediction of global weather patterns and enhanced understanding of the processes of natural revegetation during favorable years may allow reseeding at times with greatest opportunity for success. Such intensive practices as site modification and planting may be used on a limited scale along with strategies to enhance opportunity for further spread and colonization on these extensive, minimally productive grasslands.

While tropical pastures are generally less intensively managed than most other agricultural lands (that is, they typically receive lower input levels), potential effects of chemical fertilizers and pesticides on the total ecosystem must be considered. Less stringent or even complete lack of government regulations regarding the use of hazardous chemicals in many tropical locations necessitates a greater individual responsibility in use of such materials.

Seedbed preparation with subsequent stand failure provides opportunity for soil erosion and site deterioration. Inappropriate choice of pasture species may result in short-term stand life followed by site deterioration. Relatively low-cost land in many tropical locations can be a considerable incentive to investment and development despite high risk. In-

creased availability of information regarding appropriate levels of development for specific sites, suitable species for sustainable use, and risks involved could reduce the failures and resulting environmental damage due to inappropriate approaches to tropical pasture development.

Concerns exist in some affluent, highly developed societies that livestock may be detrimental to the environment. Livestock production does typically result in changes in ecosystems. Often increasing improvements for livestock production result in decreasing suitability for many wildlife species. Additional concerns include the release of carbon into the atmosphere, from storage in high quantities in forest biomass, as humid pasture development occurs. Recent information indicates that carbon storage in forest, although greater than in grassland, may not be as much greater as previously thought, since grassland has been found to have a much higher proportion of below-ground biomass than forest typically has. Agriculturalists must be more aware of opportunities to minimize adverse effects of pasture development on other values and uses of land. However, the immediate needs of local people must be recognized, and appropriate compensation for alternative uses of existing and potential pasturelands may serve all interests. Continuing increases in population require increases in food production. Since tropical grasslands are the least intensively managed terrestrial food production resource, they may provide the most responsive opportunity for increased food production during the next decade or two. Thus, the tremendous opportunity for increased production of livestock to meet human nutritional needs through pasture development in many tropical regions must be carefully evaluated with due consideration to the environmental and economic costs and risks.

Bibliography

Crowder, L. V., and Chheda, H. R. (1982). "Tropical Grassland Husbandry." Longman Group Ltd., Burnt Mill, UK.

Humphreys, L. R. (1987). "Tropical Pastures and Fodder Crops." Longman Scientific and Technical, Essex, UK.

Humphreys, L. R. (1991). "Tropical Pasture Utilization." Cambridge Univ. Press, Cambridge, UK.

Humphreys, L. R., and Riveros, F. (1986). "Tropical Pasture Seed Production," revised. FAO, Rome.

Kretschmer, A. E., Jr., and Pitman, W. D. (1994). Tropical and subtropical forages. In "Forages, the Science of Grassland Agriculture" (R. F. Barnes, D. A. Miller, and

C. J. Nelson, eds.), 5th ed., chapt. 23. Iowa State Univ. Press, Ames, IA.

Mannetje, L., and Jones, R. M. (1992). "Plant Resources of South-East Asia." Purdoc Science, Wageningen, The Netherlands.

Marten, G. C., Matches, A. G., Barnes, R. F., Brougham, R. W., Clements, R. J., and Sheath, G. W. (1989). "Persistence of Forage Legumes." American Society of Agronomy, Madison, WI.

Minson, D. J. (1990). "Forage in Ruminant Nutrition." Academic Press, San Diego.

Skerman, P. J., Cameron, D. G., and Riveros, F. (1988). "Tropical Forage Legumes," 2nd ed. FAO, Rome.

Skerman, P. J., and Riveros, F. (1990). "Tropical Grasses." FAO, Rome.

Whiteman, P. C. (1980). "Tropical Pasture Science." Oxford Univ. Press, New York.

Tropical Rain Forests: Hydrology and Climate

A. JOHANNES DOLMAN, *DLO-Winand Staring Center, the Netherlands*

JOHN H. C. GASH, *Institute of Hydrology, United Kingdom*

Glossary

Albedo Ratio of reflected solar radiation to the incoming solar radiation, both integrated over all wavelengths in solar radiation

Atmospheric humidity deficit Difference between the concentration of water vapor in the air at air temperature, which is saturated with water vapor, and the actual concentration of water vapor in the atmosphere

Conductance Reciprocal of resistance

GCM General circulation model, a numerical computer model which predicts the state and movement of the atmosphere over the entire globe

Interception loss Rainfall which is intercepted by a plant canopy and evaporated directly back into the atmosphere without reaching the soil during rainfall and shortly after

Runoff Transport of water from a catchment

Stomata Small openings in the leaves of plants through which water vapor escapes and carbon dioxide is taken up

Surface, or bulk stomatal, resistance Total effect of all the individual stomatal resistances, considered to occur at one level in the canopy

Transpiration Process by which water, which is taken up by plants through the roots, is evaporated into the atmosphere through the stomatal openings on their leaves

Tropical rain forest is the climax vegetation of the humid tropics. This forest is at least partly evergreen and is typified by a dense, diverse canopy which is continuous from the ground surface to 30 m or higher and which completely covers the ground (Fig. 1). The forest grows in areas with an average annual rainfall greater than about 1500 mm and where the annual dry season is short or nonexistent. Although forests in these areas of the tropics are commonly called rain forest, moist tropical forest is a more appropriate scientific description. Annual evaporation is between 1000 and 1500 mm and comprises a transpiration component and evaporation of rainfall intercepted by the canopy. The atmospheric moisture generated by these processes interacts with the weather systems to maintain the humid, tropical climate.

I. The Hydrological Cycle

Most of the rain falling on the forest canopy is intercepted by the leaves (Fig. 2), the remainder falls through gaps directly to the ground. When the canopy is saturated, most of the water then drips to the ground to replenish the soil moisture store. Similarly, some water reaches the ground by flowing down the outside of the branches and trunks of the trees. Some of the water intercepted by the canopy evaporates directly back to the atmosphere; water which reaches the soil may be returned later through the roots and leaves (transpiration) or may percolate down to deeper layers, eventually contributing via throughflow to the river discharge. In undisturbed forest, Hortonian overland flow from the surface is generally not observed.

Clouds are formed by moist air rising to a level where the air temperature is sufficiently cold to cause the water vapor to condense. Rain then forms when the cloud droplets coalesce. The actual rainfall depends on the amount of precipitable moisture and the speed at which the rising air reaches the condensation

FIGURE 1 Photograph of tropical rain forest in Reserva Jaru, J Paraná, Rondonia, Amazonia (Photo by J. H. C. Gash.).

level. The amount of precipitable moisture is determined by both the evaporation from the surface and the large scale weather patterns, importing moisture into a region. For instance, for the Amazon basin it is estimated that 50 to 60% of the precipitation originates from water which was evaporated by the forest. The remaining 40 to 50% of the moisture is transported inland from the ocean by the Northern Hemisphere trade winds (Fig. 3). The rain forests in the Amazon thus play an essential role in maintaining the wet, humid climate on which they are dependent. [*See* METEOROLOGY.]

II. Interception of Rainfall

The canopy of a tropical forest has a large leaf area which intercepts most of the rainfall falling on to it. The aerodynamically rough forest surface generates a highly turbulent air flow which provides an efficient mechanism for transferring water vapor from the wet leaves to the atmosphere; this results in high evaporation rates during and after rainfall. Estimates of this interception loss are usually obtained by measuring the rain reaching the ground surface (throughfall)

with a set of rainfall gauges randomly placed beneath the canopy. This presents a measurement problem in rain forest where the interception loss is a small difference between two large numbers: rainfall and throughfall. The problem is exacerbated by the heterogeneity of the forest canopy which gives great spatial variability in throughfall. As a result there have been few reliable studies of interception loss from tropical forest, but those that there have been show that some 10 to 15% of the rainfall is evaporated in this way, i.e., for a rainfall of 2000 mm, 200 to 300 mm are evaporated directly, without reaching the soil. In temperate forest interception losses of 30% are more common, but storms in the tropics are generally of high intensity and short duration, giving little time for evaporation during storms. In addition the tropical forest canopy appears to shed water easily, many species having shiny leaves with drip points. A saturated canopy holds the equivalent of only about 0.7 mm of rainfall, which is evaporated at the end of a storm. In contrast to forest, agricultural crops and pasture are less aerodynamically rough, have lower evaporation rates during storms, and consequently have low interception losses. One of the immediate effects of deforestation is to remove this component from the water

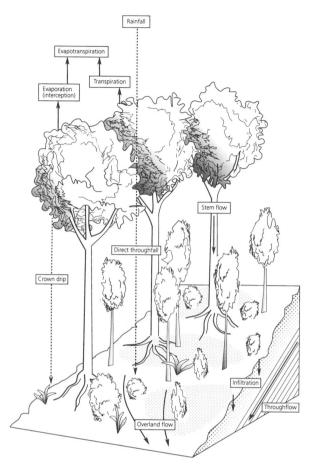

FIGURE 2 The hydrological cycle in a tropical rain forest. [Redrawn with permission from Bruijnzeel, L. A. (1990). "Hydrology of Moist Tropical Forests and Effects of Conversion: A State of Knowledge Review." Unesco, Paris and Free University Amsterdam.]

FIGURE 3 Schematic diagram of the water cycle in the Amazon basin. E is total evaporation (interception and transpiration), P is precipitation, F_i represents the amount of moisture entering the region, F_o represents the amount of moisture leaving the region, and R is the river flow of the Amazon into the Atlantic Ocean. The fluxes, denoted by arrows, are in units of 10^{12} m^3 year^{-1}. [Redrawn with permission of Kluwer Academic Publishers from Salati, E., and Nobre, C. A. (1991). Possible climatic impacts of tropical deforestation. *Clim. Change* **19**, 177–196.]

balance. This puts more water in the soil, but less water into the atmosphere. [*See* MICROCLIMATE.]

III. Transpiration

Transpiration is the process whereby water is taken up from the soil by the root system, transported through the trunk and evaporated through the stomata in the leaves. A typical value for lowland tropical forest is 1000 mm per year, while transpiration from montane forest is usually lower, but more variable. Transpiration can be estimated by micrometeorological techniques which measure water vapor as it moves through the turbulent atmospheric boundary layer above the forest. These techniques give measurements at a time scale of an hour or less which is useful for interpreting the response of the vegetation to environmental controls. Longer term extrapolation of these

results can be obtained by running a well-calibrated micrometeorological model for the required time scale. It is likely that this combination of physically based modeling and measurement provides a good estimate for the long-term water balance of tropical forest. When this technique was applied to a tropical rain forest in central Amazonia it gave an estimated 1020 mm per year being lost to the soil through transpiration. This can be compared with estimates of transpiration for a typical mid-latitude forest of around 300–350 mm per year. In the Amazon study 90% of the incoming radiant energy was used to evaporate about 50% of the precipitation back to the atmosphere.

IV. Runoff

Water, which reaches the soil layer and which is not used by the roots for transpiration, fills up the unsaturated moisture reservoir and percolates into the saturated zone, eventually leaving the forest as runoff, or riverflow. Due to the highly permeable soils, quick runoff (Hortonian overland flow) is hardly ever observed in undisturbed forest. Runoff generation in general and for tropical forest in particular is poorly understood. It is difficult to generalize individual catchment or water balance studies, as total runoff depends on the interplay between precipitation, soil hydraulic characteristics, and land morphology. For the Amazon basin as a whole it is estimated that 40% of the incoming precipitation leaves the basin as river discharge.

V. Micrometeorology of Tropical Rain Forest

Tropical rain forests are generally taller than comparable temperate forests and contain a far greater variety of tree species. Like temperate forest they are dense, extensive, and perennial. These aspects largely determine the interaction of the forest with the atmosphere.

The deep canopy and extensive leaf area of tropical rain forest are very efficient at capturing the incoming solar radiation. The leaf area of a forest canopy (Fig. 4), and the spectral properties, shape, size, and orientation of the leaves all affect the transmission and reflection of radiation through and from the canopy. The albedo (the proportion of the solar radiation which is reflected) of tropical rain forest is low—about 12% with sometimes a slight seasonal variation in the range 1–3%. In contrast, albedo values for tropical grass or tropical savannah are much higher, typically in the range 18–25%. Deforestation may result in a decrease of the amount of energy absorbed by the surface of up to 10%. The dense tropical rain forest canopy also results in only a small amount of radiation reaching the soil surface. Typically 2–5% of the radiation at the top of the canopy reaches the ground. In total, the combined effect of reflection and transmission results in a capture of about 85% of the incoming solar radiation by the forest canopy.

The tropical forest, because of its height and amount of leaf area, exerts a relatively large drag on the air. This results in an environment just above the forest which is markedly more turbulent than that over grass. The air at the top of the canopy is therefore well mixed and the temperature of the vegetation at the top of the canopy is close to air temperature. Compared to the climate above short vegetation the climate above the forest changes relatively little during the day and has a lower maximum and higher minimum temperature. At the forest floor the air is significantly decoupled from above, with lower temperatures and higher humidities than those above. This gives high relative humidities, which combined with the low windspeeds give the forest its characteristic humid climate.

From the inside of the substomatal cavity, where the air is saturated with water vapor, the water escapes through the stomatal opening by molecular diffusion (Fig. 5). The diffusion through the stomatal opening presents a resistance—in analogy with Ohm's law—to water vapor transport which is called the stomatal resistance. The bulk integrated, stomatal resistance is the surface resistance of the forest. Values for maximum stomatal conductance (the reciprocal of resistance) of leaves vary by a factor seven, depending on species and position of the leaves in the

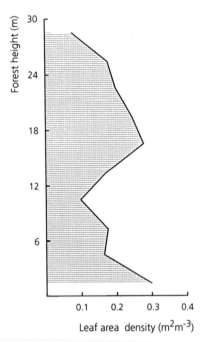

FIGURE 4 Distribution of leaf area density with height for a terra firme rain forest near Manaus, Amazonia. [Redrawn with permission from McWilliam *et al.* (1993). Leaf area index and above ground biomass of terra firme rain forest and adjacent clearing in Amazonia. *Funct. Ecol.* **7**, 312–317.]

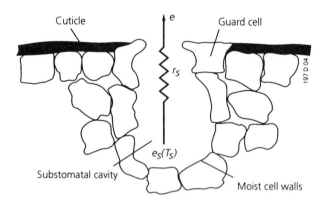

FIGURE 5 Schematic diagram of the molecular diffusion process of water through the stomatal aperture of dry leaves. Air inside the stomatal cavity is saturated (e_s (T_s) is saturated water vapor pressure at the temperature of the leaf and the water vapor diffuses through the stomatal opening to the atmosphere at water vapor pressure, e, against a stomatal resistance, r_s. [Redrawn with permission from Shuttleworth, W. J. (1988). Evaporation models in Hydrology. *In* "Land Surface Evaporation, Measurement and Parameterization" (T. J. Schmugge and J-C André, eds.). Springer-Verlag, New York.]

canopy. Tall, emergent trees have higher conductances than vegetation close to the ground. The diurnal pattern of the conductances also depends on the position of the leaf in the canopy. In the upper part of the canopy the daily maximum of conductance appears in the mid-morning, while the maximum becomes less pronounced deeper down in the canopy. At the forest floor the daily variation is virtually absent. Stomatal conductance usually increases with solar radiation and decreases with atmospheric humidity deficit. The fact that both the microclimate and the stomatal conductance vary within the canopy makes it difficult to use a single value to calculate evaporation. Adequate schemes, to integrate the effect of variation through the canopy, or multilayer evaporation models are necessary to calculate evaporation from a knowledge of stomatal conductance and weather.

The bulk stomatal or surface conductance of a rain forest can be obtained by inverting an evaporation equation such as the Penman–Monteith equation. Very few studies have had the data to do this. For the Amazon forest near Manaus a maximum value of conductance of 20.8 mm sec^{-1} was found from evaporation measurements obtained by the eddy correlation technique. Although the surface conductance shows a diurnal response to solar radiation, temperature, and humidity deficit, a clear response to soil moisture deficit has not yet been observed. This is a result of the deep roots being able to access a sufficiently large amount of soil water to continue transpiration through dry periods lasting up to at least several weeks. The common conception of rain forest trees having only a dense mat of roots close to the surface is not correct. They do have this—mainly for extracting nutrients—but they also have deep roots going at least 4–5 m into the soil enabling them to survive periods without rain.

VI. Effects of Deforestation

Understanding of the effects of deforestation on climate and hydrology can be obtained by analyzing observational records or by using numerical general circulation models (GCMs) of the atmosphere to predict the hydrological and climatological response to a hypothetical deforestation. Observation evidence for a relationship between rainfall and deforestation is scarce, due to the difficulties in obtaining reliable long-term records and the inherent variability of rainfall. There is a wealth of circumstantial evidence pointing to decreased rainfall as a result of deforesta-

tion, but, unfortunately, most of these studies do not meet the standard of scientific scrutiny. So-called paired catchment experiments in the humid tropics have shown that removal of forests may increase water yield by up to 800 mm per year. The highest increases are found 1 year after treatment (i.e., deforestation, logging). The response after the first year depends on the type of vegetation which establishes itself after deforestation and the extent of canopy closure. Evidence from controlled experiments also suggests that the largest increases in streamflow occur with the delayed flow component, which is most marked in the dry season. Evidence relating increased storm flow to logging practices is still controversial. This is partly caused by the fact that experimental basins do not necessarily reflect current logging practices.

GCMs attempt to model the three-dimensional patterns of rainfall, temperature, windspeed, and humidity of the earth's atmosphere. Using GCMs has the advantage that insights can be obtained in the interaction between the land surface and the atmosphere. The GCMs are based on physical laws, and sensitivity studies with these models allow identification of critical parameters in the surface energy and water budgets. Unfortunately, predictions with GCMs are limited by the resolution of the model grid, typically several hundreds of kilometers, the physical parameterizations used, and the specification of the input parameters. GCM experiments have improved the description of the forest atmosphere interaction by incorporation of more physically realistic models for the forest and the replacement vegetation.

To predict the impact of deforestation on climate and hydrology a control run is made with the surface parameterizations describing the existing tropical rain forest. In experiments the land surface parameters have been derived from measurements of evaporation, heat, and momentum flux obtained by micrometeorological techniques (Fig. 6). The "control" is then compared with observations so as to assess its capability to represent the current climate accurately. For the deforestation run, the forest is replaced by another vegetation (tropical grass or savannah) and the results compared with the "control" run.

In Fig. 7 the changes in rainfall and surface temperature are shown for an Amazon deforestation experiment. Most GCM experiments have predicted that deforestation leads to a reduction in rainfall. This reduction in rainfall is caused by both a reduction in evaporation and changes in atmospheric circulation pattern for the deforestation run. The reduction in

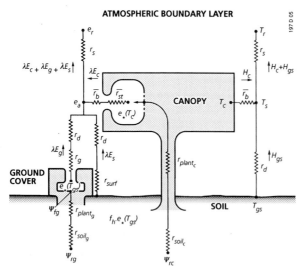

FIGURE 6 Schematic diagram of a land surface model (SiB) used in general circulation models. The transfer pathways for latent, λE, and sensible heat flux, H, are shown on the left and right side of the diagram, respectively. Fluxes are proportional to differences in temperature, T, water vapor pressure, e (e_* is saturated water vapor pressure), or water potential, ψ, divided by the appropriate resistance, r. The subscript r refers to reference height, a to canopy space, b to canopy element boundary layer, g to ground, l to leaf, d to air space between canopy and ground, c to canopy, s to soil, and st to stomatal. Resistances are shown in terms of an analogous electrical circuit. [Redrawn with permission of the American Meteorological Society from Sellers, P. J., Mintz, Y., Sud, Y. C., and Dalcher, A. (1986). A simple biosphere model (SiB) for use within general circulation models. *J. Atmos. Sci.* **43**, 505–531.]

evaporation is a result of differences in albedo, aerodynamic roughness, rooting depth, and interception storage between the forest and the replacement vegetation. Increased albedo leads to less solar radiation and less energy being available for evaporation. Aerodynamic roughness will have an effect on evaporation only when the canopy is wet (in dry conditions the surface resistance dominates the transfer process). However the aerodynamic roughness is also an important parameter in determining the large-scale circulation patterns. The rooting depth specifies the amount of soil moisture available to the vegetation for transpiration. Deforestation is usually accompanied by changes in soil properties and the newly established vegetation cannot access water as deep in the soil as the forest. It is however extremely difficult to estimate the exact value of rooting depth to be used in land surface models, as this quantity is hard to measure. The interception storage capacity of a forest is reduced when the area is deforested. This combined with a reduced aerodynamic roughness leads to a decrease in the amount of water lost by the new vegetation through evaporation of intercepted water.

Changes in atmospheric circulation as a result of deforestation are consequences of highly complex interactions and vary both spatially and temporally. Although the area-average result of deforestation is often a reduction in rainfall, the spatial patterns can be highly variable with even local increases in rainfall in certain regions. Figure 7 predicts that the impact

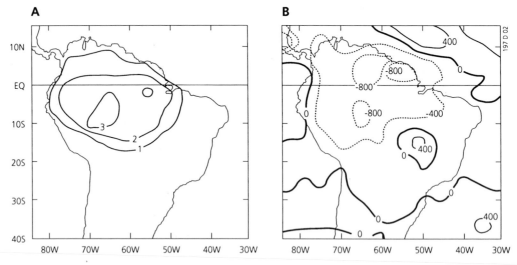

FIGURE 7 Differences between the 12-month means (January–December) of deforestation and control (intact forest) of a GCM experiment. The differences are shown as deforested minus control. (A) Surface temperature (K), (B) Precipitation (mm). [Redrawn with permission of the American Meteorological Society from Nobre *et al.* (1991). Amazonian deforestation and regional climate change. *J. Clin.* **4**, 957–988.]

of deforestation may also be felt in regions far outside the deforested area and this is clearly of importance for agriculture in the neighboring, low rainfall, savannah regions. An increase in surface temperature as observed in most studies is consistent with a reduction in evaporation (less cooling at the surface).

An important question relating to possible changes in climate following deforestation is whether the new climate would favor a vegetation different than that of tropical rain forests, for instance, tropical savannah. As one of the results of deforestation may be more prolonged dry seasons, it is likely that soil moisture plays an important role in determining what type of vegetation may be established after deforestation. For the Amazon basin it was calculated that to a significant extent topical deforestation would be irreversible, i.e., the resulting soil moisture conditions would favor another vegetation type, savannah (called cerrado), in the Southern part of the Amazonia.

The results discussed so far relate mainly to the effect of deforestation of the Amazon basin. Although this is the world's single largest tract of tropical rain forest, it is relevant to ask what the effects of deforestation in Asia and Africa might be. It is likely that the microclimatic effects of deforestation will also happen in these continents, but that the decrease in rainfall is less likely, especially for South East Asia, where rainfall patterns are dominated by large-scale features and the surface temperatures of the oceans. In Equatorial Africa large-scale deforestation may be accompanied by reduction in rainfall similar to those found in Amazonia. Both in South America and Africa these effects may sometimes be masked by variations caused by external effects such as that resulting from changes in the surface temperatures of the Pacific and Atlantic Oceans.

VII. Conclusion

The tropical rain forest presents a unique biome, both in terms of species composition and in microclimate.

Substantial advances in our understanding of the hydrology and climatology of these forests have been gained in the past 2 decades. Parallel development in measurement techniques and numerical modeling has increased our knowledge of the role of rain forest in the regional and global climate. However our knowledge and understanding of the interaction between this important biome and the climate is still meager. Because of their size and equatorial position the rain forests of the world are a major heat and moisture source for the global circulation of the atmosphere. The potential regional and global impacts of large-scale deforestation in the tropics require concerted international efforts both to improve our understanding of this biome and to safeguard its future against large-scale devastation.

Bibliography

Bonell, M., Hufschmidt, M. M., and Gladwell, J. S. (eds.) (1993). "Hydrology and Water Management in the Humid Tropics." Cambridge Univ. Press, Cambridge, Mass.

Bruijnzeel, L. A. (1990). "Hydrology of Moist Tropical Forests and Effects of Conversion: A State of Knowledge Review." Unesco, Paris, and Free University, Amsterdam.

Dolman, A. J., Gash, J. H. C., Roberts, J. M., and Shuttleworth, W. J. (1992). Stomatal and surface conductance of tropical rainforest. *Agric. For. Meteorol.* **54,** 303–318.

Lean, J., and Rowntree, P. A. (1993). GCM simulation of the impact of Amazonian deforestation on climate using an improved canopy representation. *Q. J. R. Meteorol. Soc.* **119,** 509–530.

Myers, N. (ed.) (1991). Tropical rainforests and climate. *In* "Climatic Change," Vol 19, Nos. 1 and 2. Kluwer Academic, Dordrecht.

Nobre, C. A., Sellers, P. J., and Shukla, J. (1991). Amazonian deforestation and regional climate change. *J. Clim.* **4,** 957–988.

Shuttleworth, W. J. (1988). Evaporation from Amazonian rainforest. *Proc. R. Soc. London B,* **233,** 321–346.

Turfgrasses

ROBERT C. SHEARMAN, *University of Nebraska*

Glossary

Artificial turf Synthetic surface (i.e., carpet-like) that simulates a turf

Cool-season turfgrasses Turfgrasses (e.g., Kentucky bluegrass, creeping bentgrass, and tall fescue) that grow most actively in the spring and fall

Mowing height Height of cut above the soil surface; a fundamental practice of turfgrass culture

Turf Closely mowed ground cover, usually comprised of grasses

Turfgrass blend Turfgrass community involving a combination of two or more cultivars of a species

Turfgrass community Composite of individual turfgrass plants that are mutually interactive with their environment

Turfgrass culture Composite of primary and secondary cultural practices involved in growing turfgrasses for their intended purpose, such as lawn, golf course greens, sports turf, or other purposes

Turfgrass mixture Turfgrass community comprised of two or more species

Turfgrass quality Assessment of uniformity, density, texture, growth habit, smoothness, and color of a turf

Warm-season turfgrasses Turfgrasses (e.g., bermudagrass, zoysiagrass, and buffalograss) that grow best in the warm portions of the year; they are usually dormant during the winter and their adaptation is limited by low-temperature injury

Turfgrasses are an integral part of our daily lives. Turfs provide aesthetic and functional value to our landscapes. They contribute to our psychological, physical, and environmental well-being. The cool, clean, and pleasing green environment turfs provide make a pleasant place for work and leisure, but turfs provide more than aesthetics. Turfs dissipate heat, reduce glare, abate noise, minimize soil erosion, eliminate dust and mud, enhance air quality, and contribute to increased property value. Many outdoor recreational and sports activities, such as baseball, croquet, football, golf, lawn bowling, rugby, soccer, softball, and volleyball use turf as their functional surface. Turfs serve as a safety factor on highway rights-of-way, airfields, and correctional facility surrounds.

I. Turfgrass Industry

The turfgrass industry is broader and more complex than first perceived by the casual observer. It involves individuals and organizations sharing a common interest in the production, maintenance, and use of green spaces for aesthetic and functional purposes. In the United States, a number of surveys have contributed to the better understanding of the size and scope of the turfgrass industry in various states. This information has been used to estimate the overall value of the turfgrass maintenance industry in the United States as contributing $25 to 30 billion annually to the economy. However, the true value of the industry comes from the contributions of all types of green areas to quality of life.

Grasses and gardens are found in biblical reference. Lawns were a part of Persian and Arabian gardens, and the Romans adapted the Persian garden concept to their culture. Medieval English literature makes reference to lawns, which were mixtures of low-growing grasses and wildflowers. During the 16th and 17th centuries, lawns became more common in cities located in Great Britain and northern Europe.

Encyclopedia of Agricultural Science, Volume 4 Copyright © 1994 by Academic Press, Inc. All rights of reproduction in any form reserved.

Many cities had a common green area that served as a meeting place for civic and leisure activities.

There is some uncertainty about when the care of turfgrass facilities or the manufacture of specific products for turfgrass maintenance began. It has been advocated that the turfgrass equipment manufacturing industry began when Edwin Budding invented and patented the reel-type lawn mower in 1830. Others felt it began in 1618, when the feathered golf ball was invented. Regardless of this uncertainty, golf course development and maintenance has set the historic baseline for the turfgrass industry.

Technological advances for the turfgrass industry have been largely due to development, distribution, and service of products for the maintenance of golf courses. In recent years, maintenance of residential and commercial lawns has had the most growth of any segment of the industry and has had considerable influence on products manufactured to support its needs. Sports fields use both natural and artificial turf surfaces. Artificial turf evolved as a development of the plastics industry. It is commonly used on sports fields, such as indoor and intensively used facilities. Maintenance of natural turf sports fields has become more technical as extremely expensive and multi-use facilities have incorporated the use of natural turfs into their systems. Management of sports turf is a growing part of the turfgrass industry. Millions of individuals worldwide participate in sports and recreational activities, such as softball and soccer, that involve turfgrass surfaces.

II. Turfgrasses

A basic understanding of turfgrasses and the turfgrass plant is needed to ensure their proper maintenance, culture, and use. The geographic distribution and use of turfgrasses are influenced by the species adaptation to temperature and precipitation patterns. Turfgrasses that originated and continue to persist in a particular region are called native species, while those that are introduced to a region and become permanently established are called adapted or naturalized species. Turfgrass species commonly used today evolved from relatively few locations, but have become widely distributed throughout the world. In most cases, the turfgrasses are not native, but are adapted species.

A. Cool-Season Species

Turfgrass species with growth optimums at soil temperatures of 15 to 24° C are called cool-season turf-

grasses. Most of these species had their origin in northern Europe and were forest margin species. These grasses are used widely throughout the cool-humid, cool-subhumid, and cool-semiarid portions of the world.

Cool-season turfgrasses grow best in the spring and fall, and their growth and development slows considerably during the summer. There are over 20 species included in this category of turfgrasses (Table I), but only 7 of these species are used extensively as turfs.

Kentucky bluegrass is the most widely grown cool-season turfgrass. It is adapted to a wide climatic region. Kentucky bluegrass forms a dense, medium

TABLE I

Cool-Season (A) and Warm-Season (B) Grass Species Commonly Used as Turfs throughout the World

	A. Cool-season species
Kentucky bluegrass	*Poa pratensis* L.
Canada bluegrass	*P. compressa* L.
Annual bluegrass	*P. annua* var. *annua* L.
	P. annua var. *reptans* (Hausskn.) Timm.
Creeping bentgrass	*Agrostis palustris* Huds.
Colonial bentgrass	*A. tenuis* Sibth.
Velvet bentgrass	*A. canina* L.
Redtop	*A. alba* L.
Red fescue	*Festuca rubra* L.
Chewings fescue	*F. rubra* var. *commutata* Gaud.
Sheep fescue	*F. ovina* L.
Hard fescue	*F. ovina* var. *duriscula* (L.) Koch
Tall fescue	*F. arundinacea* Schreb
Annual ryegrass	*Lolium multiflorum* Lam.
Perennial ryegrass	*L. perenne* L.
Smooth bromegrass	*Bromus inermis* Leyss.
Fairway crested wheatgrass	*Agropyron cristatum* (L.) Gaertn.
Alkaligrass	*Puccinellis distans* (L.) Parl.
	B. Warm-season species
Common bermudagrass	*Cynodon dactylon* (L.) Pers.
F$_1$ hybrid bermudagrass	*C. d.* x *C. transvaalensis* Burtt-Davy
Korean lawngrass	*Zoysia japonica* Steud.
Manilagrass	*Z. matrella* (L.) Merr.
Mascarenegrass	*Z. tenuifolia* Willd.
St. Augustinegrass	*Stenotaphrum secundatum* (Walt.) Kuntze
Centipedegrass	*Eremochloa ophiuroides* (Munro.) Hack.
Carpetgrass	*Axonopus affinis* Chase
Bahiagrass	*Paspalum notatum* Flugge.
Kikuyugrass	*Pennisetum clandestinum* Hochst. ex Chiov.
Buffalograss	*Buchloe dactyloides* (Nutt.) Engelm.
Blue Grama	*Bouteloua gracilis* (H.B.K.) Lag. ex Steud.
Seashore Paspalum	*Paspalum vaginatum* Swartz.

textured, high-quality turf when grown in open sunlight. It is variable in texture, color, shoot density, growth habit, disease resistance, adaptation, and cultural practice requirements. It is this variability that leads to its widespread acceptance and use. Periods of drought and high temperature stress can seriously damage Kentucky bluegrass stands by impairing growth and development. Damage is particularly bad when the turf is not adequately hardened to withstand such environmental stress. A properly conditioned Kentucky bluegrass turf can survive an extended drought and recover by initiating growth from crown tissues and nodes located on rhizomes. Kentucky bluegrass is widely used for medium- to high-maintenance lawns, sports fields, parks, golf course fairways and tees, and cemeteries. It is often planted as a blend or as a mixture.

Annual bluegrass is a complex species, which is comprised of annual and short-lived, perennial biotypes. It is about equally accepted as a weed or turfgrass species. It is rarely included as a component of turfgrass seed mixtures. It often invades and becomes a dominant component of closely mowed, intensely fertilized, and frequently irrigated turfs. It forms a fine-textured, dense turf of high quality under proper soil, environmental, and cultural conditions. It grows well in compacted soils, but is highly susceptible to high- and low-temperature stress.

Creeping red, Chewings, sheep, and hard are fine-leaved fescues that form a dense, uniform turf. The fine-leaved fescues have very fine, almost needle-like leaves. They should not be confused with the turf-type tall fescues. Red fescue and Chewings fescue are the most commonly used of these species. They are often used in seed mixtures with Kentucky bluegrass to enhance shade adaptation. As a group, they are best adapted to well-drained, infertile soils. They are not tolerant of high temperatures, but they are very drought resistant.

Tall fescue has undergone considerable improvement in recent years with the development of turf-type cultivars. Prior to their development, the species would have been described as forming a course textured, low-density, bunch-type turf. Recent cultivar releases are darker green and finer textured than the older, forage-type cultivars. Tall fescue is very tolerant of high temperatures and is quite drought resistant. It is also very wear tolerant, but lacks tolerance to compacted soil conditions.

Perennial ryegrass is a bunch-type grass with medium texture and medium to high shoot density. It is similar to Kentucky bluegrass in appearance and is often included in seed mixtures with it. Perennial ryegrass has the most rapid seedling establishment rate of any of the cool-season turfgrasses. It is often included in seed mixtures when rapid establishment is needed. Perennial ryegrasses have excellent wear resistance and are highly tolerant of compacted soil conditions. They are very drought avoidant due to their ability to form a deep, extensive root system, but they are only moderately drought tolerant due to their bunch-type growth. Perennial ryegrasses require medium to high intensity of culture to maintain desired turfgrass quality.

Creeping bentgrass is used primarily for golf greens, tees, and fairways, but is also used for bowling greens, grassed tennis courts, and crochet turfs. It forms a very fine-textured, high-quality turf that tolerates close mowing. It is a long-lived perennial with excellent low-temperature hardiness. Creeping bentgrass tolerates a wide range of soil types and conditions, but prefers fertile, slightly acid, fine-textured soils. It is susceptible to a number of turfgrass diseases and requires careful management to maintain a quality turf.

Several other bentgrass species are used in specific turf situations. Velvet bentgrass forms a very fine-textured, high-quality turf under close mowing. It is not as aggressive as creeping bentgrass, but it is suited for golf or bowling greens, croquet turfs, and elite lawns. Colonial bentgrass is similar to creeping bentgrass except it is not a vigorous, creeping type. It is often used in mixtures with other cool-season turfgrass species for fairways, tees, and fine textured lawns. Redtop forms an open turf of low shoot density. It was once widely used in turfgrass mixtures, but is now considered to be a weed in quality turfs.

Other cool-season turfgrass species, such as annual ryegrass, alkaligrass, and fairway crested wheatgrass are used to meet special needs. Annual ryegrass is used in low-cost turfgrass mixtures, for temporary turfs, and as species in overseeding dormant warm-season turfs. 'Fults' alkaligrass was selected for use on sites where alkaline soils limit growth. Fairway crested wheatgrass is well-adapted to cool, semi-arid regions. It has excellent drought resistance and is used for revegetation of low rainfall sites.

B. Warm-Season Species

Turfgrass species with growth optimums at soil temperatures of 27 to 35° C are called warm-season turfgrasses. Warm-season turfgrasses are used throughout the warm-humid, subhumid, semiarid, and arid regions of the world. They grow best during the warm summer months and generally cease growth and become dormant with the onset of winter. In some cases, dormant warm-season species are sprayed with a colorant to maintain a green appearance, or are overseeded with cool-season species to provide improved appearance, playing conditions, and use.

Thirteen warm-season turfgrass species are commonly used as turfs in their zones of adaptation (Table I). These species have widespread centers of origin, which can be traced to Africa, Asia, or South America. Buffalograss and blue grama grass are native to the Great Plains of North America. The distribution and use of warm-season turfgrasses is strongly influenced by the species' ability to tolerate suboptimal temperatures. Warm-season turfgrasses do not grow well in regions that commonly have early fall or late spring freezes or regions with severe winters.

Relative comparisons between warm- and cool-season turfgrasses reveal that warm-season species are more heat, drought, and traffic tolerant than cool-season species. Warm-season turfgrasses have deeper, more extensive root systems than cool season. Cool-season turfgrasses are more low-temperature tolerant and are less likely to discolor and become dormant than their warm-season counterparts. Cool-season species are most commonly established from seed, while warm-season turfgrasses are often established from sod, sprigs, or plugs. Since these are relative comparisons, it is important to note that exceptions to these characteristics do occur in both species.

Common bermudagrass is found throughout most of the tropical, subtropical, and warm-humid regions of the world. It has a vigorous and aggressive growth habit, spreading both by stolons and rhizomes. It forms a dense turf, but not as fine and dense as that of the F_1 hybrid or improved bermudagrasses. Both species form dense sods, with deep, extensive root systems. Bermudagrasses are quite variable in color, shoot density, leaf texture, and adaptation. Species and cultivars differ in their adaptation to low temperatures. Bermudagrass discolors and becomes dormant under low temperatures and high light intensity conditions. Bermudagrasses with low-temperature hardiness and adaptation to cooler regions become dormant more quickly than those that are considered to be less hardy.

Bermudagrasses are widely used for medium- to high-maintenance turfgrass areas, such as lawns, parks, sports turfs, fairways, tees, and greens. Common bermudagrass is used in low-maintenance areas, like roadsides and utility turfs. Bermudagrasses tolerate close mowing and require medium- to high-intensity culture. They are very tolerant of intense traffic, especially when they are actively growing. The bermudagrasses have poor shade tolerance.

The zoysiagrasses are found predominantly in the warm-humid and transition regions of the world. There are three species that are commonly used for turfs (Table I). These species are native to the tropical portions of eastern Asia. Zoysiagrasses form dense, low-growing turfs of high quality. They spread by rhizomes and stolons, form a tight sod, but have a slow establishment rate. The stems and leaves of zoysia species are stiff and fibrous. They have excellent wear tolerance, but their slow growth rate results in a poor recuperative rate after injury.

The three zoysiagrass species differ in their characteristics and adaptation. Korean lawngrass is the most cold tolerant of the three species, while mascarenegrass is the least tolerant. Mascarenegrass has a growth habit that is more diminutive and slower than the other species. Zoysiagrasses are more shade tolerant than most warm-season turfgrasses. Manilagrass is more shade tolerant than the other species. Zoysiagrasses are used in high-quality lawns, golf course tees and fairways, sports turfs, and general grounds. Mascarenegrass is used for golf and bowling greens in some areas of the world. Zoysiagrasses require low to medium intensity of culture, once they are well-established.

Buffalograss is a warm-season turfgrass that is native to the Great Plains region of North America. It was one of the primary species of the shortgrass prairies. Pioneers settling on the Great Plains used sod of this species to construct their sod homes. Buffalograss is well-adapted to warm, semiarid, and subhumid areas. Prior to the increased use of irrigation on turfgrass sites, buffalograss was the most commonly used warm-season species in the semiarid area. Its use declined, with increased use of irrigated bermudagrass for high-quality turfs. However, in the mid 1980s, development of turf-type buffalograsses renewed interest in their use. Two vegetatively propagated, turf-type cultivars of buffalograss have recently been released, and seeded cultivars are soon to be released. Turf-type buffalograsses spread by stolons to form a dense, fine-textured turf, similar in appearance to improved bermudagrasses. Buffalograss has excellent drought resistance, but has poor shade tolerance. Buffalograss requires a low intensity of culture. It is adapted for use on lawns, golf course fairways and roughs, and general turfgrass sites.

St. Augustinegrass is a warm-season grass that is native to the West Indies. It forms a coarse-textured, low-growing turf that spreads by stolons. It has a vigorous, spreading growth habit, with a medium establishment rate. It is less tolerant of traffic than either bermudagrass or zoysiagrass, but it recovers well from wear injury. St. Augustinegrass has poor low-temperature tolerance. It has a high water use rate and only fair drought resistance. St. Augustinegrass has the best shade tolerance of the warm-season turfgrasses. St. Augustinegrass requires medium- to low-intensity management and is used in lawns and general turfgrass areas in warm-humid regions. It is generally not used on sports turfs or other intensely trafficked areas.

Bahiagrass, centipedegrass, carpetgrass and kikuyugrass are other warm-season turfgrass species that are used on a limited basis or for very specific turf conditions. Bahiagrass is well suited for growth in warm-humid regions, and turfs receiving low-intensity culture. It is used extensively on roadsides in the southern part of the United States. Centipedegrass is native to southern China. It spreads by short, thick stolons and forms a relatively dense turf. Centipedegrass requires similar intensity of culture as bahiagrass. It is best suited for use on lawns and low traffic sites. It is adapted to coastal areas in the warmer parts of the warm-humid regions of the world. Carpetgrass is native to south Central America. It forms a coarse, low-growing turf. It has very poor low-temperature tolerance. Carpetgrass requires a low intensity of culture and is used for lawns and other turf sites that receive minimal traffic. Kikuyugrass is native to east Africa and is used for lawns and golf course fairways and roughs. It has a very aggressive growth habit, spreading by rhizomes and stolons. It can become an undesirable, weed species, when it contaminates a quality turf. Kikuyugrass is very traffic tolerant, but has poor low-temperature tolerance. Its use is limited to the warmer parts of the warm-humid regions of the world.

C. Turfgrass Communities

It is important to have an understanding of turfgrasses and their adaptation. Only adapted turfgrass species will supply a quality, permanent turf. Before establishing a turf, consideration should be given to selecting species and cultivars that are suited to the climate, environment, use, and intensity of culture where they will be used. Turfgrass stands are communities of plants that change composition in response to these conditions.

Communities may be monostands or polystands. Monostands are comprised of a single cultivar of a species. A monostand is limited in its ability to change in response to changing conditions. Polystands are comprised of two or more species, cultivars, or both. A stand with two or more species is termed a mixture, while those comprised of two or more cultivars are called blends. Mixtures and blends provide turfgrass communities with a wider genetic base and better adaptation to changing environment, use, and culture than monostands. Mixtures and blends enhance the potential for maintaining turfgrass quality by minimizing pest problems which increase with time.

III. Turfgrass Establishment

Turfgrasses play an important role in minimizing soil loss from wind and water erosion. This is particularly true during their establishment phase. The longer the establishment period, the greater the potential for wind and water erosion. Poor establishment may also result in a thin, open turf that is easily invaded by weeds. The establishment phase is important to the final turfgrass quality and its long-term maintenance. Turfgrasses can be established vegetatively or from seed. In either case, proper soil preparation, weed control, fertilizing, watering, and post-seed germination or planting care are needed.

A. Seeding

Seeding is the most common means used for turfgrass establishment, especially for cool-season turfgrass species. Proper steps should be followed to successfully establish a turf, ensure rapid stand development, enhance soil stabilization, and attain desired turfgrass quality. These steps include controlling weeds that may persist after establishment; grading the soil to ensure proper surface and subsurface drainage; modifying soil with organic matter, lime, or sand as needed; fertilizing based on soil test recommendations; and finalizing soil preparation for a firm seedbed. Advanced planning is required for proper timing and coordination of these procedures. The same preparation steps are required whether the turf is seeded or vegetatively established.

Successful establishment from seed requires selecting an adapted turfgrass mixture or blend; using quality seed; planting at the proper rate, date, and time;

ensuring good seed soil contact; using proper mulching procedures; and following appropriate postgermination care. Seed can be spread by broadcast and drill-type spreaders or by hydroseeding. Hydroseeding involves disbursing seed and a cellulose fiber mulch with a pressurized stream of water. Unlike drill seeding, hydroseeding does not ensure good seed soil contact. It is best used in regions with uniform rainfall during the establishment phase.

B. Vegetative

Turfgrasses can be established vegetatively by sprigging, stolonizing, plugging, or sodding. Planting turfgrass stolons, rhizomes, or both in shallow furrows or spaced holes is called sprigging. Sprigs are covered to a depth of 15 to 25 mm, and the soil is firmed to enhance contact with the vegetative materials. Sprigging requires less plant material than stolonizing. Improved bermudagrasses are often established vegetatively by sprigging. Stolonizing involves broadcasting stolons over a prepared soilbed, covering them with topdressing, and rolling to ensure good soil contact with the stolons. Stolons can also be applied by hydroplanting, which is basically the same procedure used for hydroseeding. Creeping bentgrass and improved bermudagrasses are sometimes established by stolonizing. Plugging describes the use of small sod pieces to establish a turf. Plugs have a better survival rate, but a poorer establishment rate, than either sprigging or stolonizing. Zoysiagrass, St. Augustinegrass, and buffalograss are often established from plugs.

Harvesting mature turf, including roots, stolons, rhizomes, and soil, and transplanting it to a new site is termed sodding. Sod provides a rapid method of establishment. Sodded turfs are essentially ready for immediate use. Soil preparation for sodding is similar to the procedures used for seeding a turf. Kentucky bluegrass and bermudagrass are turfgrass species that are widely used in the sod industry.

IV. Turfgrass Cultural Practices

A. Primary Cultural Practices

Mowing, fertilizing, and irrigating are primary cultural practices that directly affect leaf, shoot, and root growth and the overall turfgrass quality and performance.

Mowing is fundamental to all turfgrass culture. Turfgrasses species and cultivars differ in their ability to tolerate close mowing. Turfgrasses with spreading, low-growth habits tend to tolerate lower cutting heights than those with erect growth habits. Creeping bentgrass and annual bluegrass can tolerate mowing heights of less than 6 mm. Tall fescue, bahiagrass, and St. Augustinegrass prefer mowing heights of 38 to 76 mm. Turfgrasses have an optimum mowing height range. As the mowing height is lowered below the optimum, tolerance to environmental stress, such as high temperature and drought, decreases.

Mowing frequency influences turfgrass quality, stress tolerance, and function. Golf course greens are mowed close and frequently to enhance their quality and playability. It is not uncommon to mow a creeping bentgrass green five to seven times per week at 3.5 to 4.0 mm. Frequent mowing reduces vertical elongation of the turfgrass leaves and shoots, increases shoot density, and reduces water use rate by enhancing canopy resistance. Mowing frequency should be dictated by the growth rate of the turfgrass. Rapid-growing turfs require frequent mowing. It is generally recommended that no more than one-third of the turfgrass topgrowth be removed with any mowing. For example, a Kentucky bluegrass turf maintained at 50 mm should be mowed when it reaches a height of 75 mm. It is not necessary to remove clippings on home lawns and general turfgrass sites if the appropriate mowing frequency is maintained. Turfgrass clippings contribute very little to thatch accumulation, but do recycle nitrogen, phosphorus, potassium, and other plant nutrients as they decompose in the turfgrass canopy. Clippings are removed from a turf, like golf course greens, if they disrupt its function.

Rotary and reel-type mowers are the most common turfgrass mowers. Rotary mowers cut with a horizontal blade that is rotating at a high speed. Rotary mowers are used extensively on home lawns and general turfgrass areas. Reel mowers provide the highest quality of cut. They cut with a scissor-like action. The reel catches the turfgrass leaf blades and brings them in contact with a sharp, cutting edge called the bedknife. Reel mowers are commonly used on golf course and sports turfs, where a high-quality of cut is desired. Mower operation and mowing patterns also influence turfgrass quality. It is recommended to change direction with each mowing. Changing mowing patterns minimizes compaction stress and reduces turfgrass grain development. Mowers should be kept sharp and in good operating condition.

Turfgrasses require adequate nutrition to perform up to its potential. Turfgrass nutrition influences growth rate, leaf area, depth, and extent of rooting and water use of turfs. Turfgrasses derive most of their nutrients from the soil, but supplemental fertilization is typically needed since soils are often deficient in one or more of the essential elements needed for turfgrass growth and development. Turfgrass fertilization should be based on soil test recommendations. Nitrogen, phosphorus, potassium, calcium, magnesium, and sulfur are required in relatively large amounts, while micronutrients, such as iron, manganese, zinc, copper, molybdenum, boron, and chloride, are needed in trace amounts (e.g., mg liter^{-1}). Turfgrasses are quite responsive to nitrogen, in terms of color and growth rate. This responsiveness can lead to problems, since excess nitrogen fertilization encourages topgrowth at the expense of root growth and reduces turfgrass stress tolerance.

It is important to meet and not exceed the nutritional needs of turfgrasses. Nutrient requirements vary by species and cultivar, length of growing season, intensity of culture, and use. Nutrient availability is influenced by a number of factors, such as soil texture, organic matter content, soil reaction, soil microorganisms, and soil moisture. A thorough understanding of these factors and their interactions is needed to develop an adequate nutritional program and select the appropriate fertilizer materials to meet the nutritional needs of the turfgrass plant.

In many areas, natural precipitation must be supplemented with irrigation to provide desired turfgrass quality and function. Irrigation should be supplied as the plant needs water. Some soil drying between irrigations is desirable. Irrigating too frequently can result in reduced turfgrass vigor and quality. Turfgrass species and cultivars vary in their water use rates. St. Augustinegrass and tall fescue can use in excess of 12 mm of water per day. Buffalograss, zoysiagrass, bermudagrass, and Kentucky bluegrass have shown promise for water conservation through reduced water use rates. Turfgrass water use rates can be altered by changes in environment, soil water content, cultural practices, and pest damage.

The turfgrass irrigation industry is relatively new, when compared to the field crops industry. Its evolution to automated, underground system with a high degree of sophistication has been fairly rapid. Permanent, underground systems are preferred for most turfgrass sites. These systems do not disrupt the mowing, function, and appearance of the site. Sod production requires the use of aboveground systems due to sod harvest concerns. It is important to consider the type of irrigation system, quantity and quality of water available, source of water, and frequency of irrigation, as well as the turfgrass species and cultivars, soil type, topography, length of growing season, intensity of culture, and use, before initiating an irrigation program. Turfgrasses should be irrigated based on their water use rates and not on a set schedule. It is best to irrigate in the early morning (0400 to 0800 hr), when evaporation rates are low and wind does not disrupt irrigation pattern uniformity.

B. Secondary Cultural Practices

Soil cultivation, topdressing, thatch removal, and vertical mowing or grooming are cultural practices that are employed on an as needed basis. They play an important role in maintaining turfgrass quality and function. Secondary cultural practices are often interactive with primary practices in influencing the overall quality of the turf.

Turfgrass soil cultivation includes the practices of coring, slicing, and spiking. These practices are used to minimize the negative effects of soil compaction, improve soil aeration, and enhance water infiltration rates. Coring is the most commonly used practice. Turf sites, that receive intense traffic or are grown on high clay content soils require annual coring to maintain a quality turf. Slicing and spiking are used mostly on golf and bowling greens, or sports turf, since they can be practiced more frequently than coring and with minimal disruption to the playing surface.

Topdressing is the distribution of a light layer of prepared soil medium over a turfgrass area. Topdressing is most commonly practiced on golf course greens, bowling greens, and sports turfs to smooth the playing surface, reduce thatch, cover sprigs and stolons in establishment, modify soil, and provide winter protection. The topdressing material should match the underlying soil medium as closely as feasible. Frequency of topdressing is dictated by the growth rate of the turf and the need to maintain a smooth, uniform playing surface.

Thatch is a tightly intermingled layer of living and dead plant material located between the soil surface and the turfgrass canopy. It has detrimental effects on turfgrass quality and performance, when it accumulates to excessive amounts. On home lawns an accumulation of 13 mm or more is considered to be excessive. Some problems associated with excess thatch accumulation include reduced heat, cold, and drought resistance; reduced wear tolerance; increased disease and insect problems; susceptibility to scalping injury and localized dry spots; and loss of playing surface uniformity due to foot printing effects. Thatch is best controlled through sound cultural practices and approaches that encourage biological breakdown. Topdressing and core cultivation are beneficial cultural practices used to manage thatch accumulation. Power raking helps reduce thatch when it accumulates to excessive levels.

Vertical mowing is used for thatch removal (e.g., power raking), renovation, and overseeding and control of turfgrass grain in golf course and bowling greens. Vertical mowing is also referred to as grooming, particularly when used on golf greens to enhance putting surface uniformity.

C. Pest Management

Insects, diseases, weeds, nematodes, and certain vertebrate pests can cause considerable damage to turfs and reduce turfgrass quality and function. Use of adapted turfgrass species and sound cultural practice systems favor the competitive advantage of the turf over pests and reduces their ability to influence stand quality and composition. Weeds disrupt the uniformity of turfgrass stands. Their appearance in a turf is often an indicator of poor cultural practices, unfavorable environmental conditions, disease, insect damage, or a combination of these factors.

Pests may inevitably become a part of the turfgrass ecosystem with time. Keeping these pests below damaging levels becomes a part of management through the use of cultural practices, pesticides, and biological controls in a systems approach. There is a growing interest in the use of integrated pest management approaches to reduce the negative impacts of pests on turfgrass quality and function. Knowing the turfgrasses being grown and their potential pest problems and understanding the biological and environmental factors that influence both the turf and pests are essential approaches in preventing pests from reaching unacceptable levels. [See INTEGRATED PEST MANAGEMENT.]

V. Future Trends and Developments

Turfgrasses have been commercially recognized since before World War II, but the industry's growth and development accelerated after the war. This growth has continued into the nineties. It is estimated that the turfgrass industry contributes in excess of $25 to 30 billion annually to the United States economy. The growth of the turfgrass industry in the United States is due to societal demands, increased leisure time, and greater discretionary income. These trends are continuing and are increasing on a worldwide basis. There is particular interest in the game of golf, with a growing number of golf courses being developed in European and Asian-Rim countries.

The turfgrass industry in the United States is undergoing change. Golf course development has been relatively stable since the early seventies, but demand for the game continues to exceed the development of new facilities. The lawn care service experienced tremendous growth and development through the late sixties and mid seventies, but this growth seems to have peaked in recent years. Sports turf maintenance is a growing segment of the industry at the present time. Environmental concerns are paramount throughout the industry. There is an increasing emphasis on the use of integrated pest management and water and energy conservation practices. These trends are likely to continue for the near future.

Bibliography

Beard, J. B. (1973). "Turfgrass Science and Culture." Prentice-Hall, Englewood Cliffs, NJ.

Beard, J. B. (1982). "Turfgrass Management for Golf Courses." The United States Golf Assoc., Burgess, Minneapolis, MN.

Carrow, R. N., Shearman, R. C., and Watson, J. R. (1990). "Turfgrass." In "Irrigation of Agricultural Crops" (B. A. Stewart, and D. R. Nielson, eds.). Agronomy Monograph No. 30. Am. Soc. Agronomy Madison, WI.

Turgeon, A. J. (1991). " Turfgrass Management." Third Ed. Prentice-Hall, Inc. Englewood Cliffs, NJ.

Waddington, D. V., Carrow, R. N., and Shearman, R. C. (eds.) (1992). "Turfgrass." Agronomy Monograph No. 32. Am. Soc. Agronomy Madison, WI.

U.S. Department of Agriculture: A National System of Agricultural Research

JOHN PATRICK JORDAN, DAVID R. MACKENZIE,
U.S. Department of Agriculture
PATRICIA BRAZEEL LEWIS, *Rutgers University*

Glossary

Biotechnology Set of tools (including techniques of recombinant DNA, tissue culture, gene transfer, embryo manipulation, and bioprocess engineering) that allows scientists to understand and manipulate life processes at the molecular level

Cooperative agreement Research contract between USDA and other entities for research supported financially by both parties for their mutual benefit

Formula funding Appropriated by Congress, administered by USDA, and distributed to the states based on the state's portion of the United State's rural and farm population; state matching of formula funding on a dollar-for-dollar basis is required; the Hatch Act program funding the state agricultural experiment stations and the McIntire-Stennis Cooperative Forestry Research Program are two of the formula-funded programs

Gene mapping Determination of the relative locations of genes on a chromosome

Genetic engineering Steps required for identifying, isolating, and transferring a desired gene from one organism to another; commonly involves transfer from one species to another

Genome Complete genetic code for any individual organism; the genetic sum of its DNA

Intellectual property Products developed through intellectual rather than manufacturing processes; it includes novel conceptual, physical, or compositional processes resulting in unique products that may be patented or copyrighted (e.g., Unique plants, animals, and microbes developed through the use of genetic engineering; computer programs; musical compositions; and books and manuscripts)

Peer review Review of research proposals in a particular scientific area by a panel of experts in that area; for example, a project requesting federal funding is "peer reviewed" and recommended by a scientific panel prior to the awarding of any funds

Precommercial Refers to the late stages in the research process prior to the development of any potential commercial application

Special research grants Funds appropriated by Congress and distributed by USDA to experiment stations or other research institutions for specific research projects at specific locations

Strategic planning derived from the military use of the word "strategy," it includes the definition of mission and objectives—how the company or public institution sees its purpose and where it wants to go—and determination of the best means to achieve those goals at a broad level

Value-added Economic idea that traces the final value of purchased goods and services to see where the value was created or increased; in a primary industry such as agriculture, added value often comes from processing harvested products (e.g., converting corn into ethyl alcohol fuel; using starch from potatoes to make biodegradable plastics)

For more than 100 years, the U.S. Department of Agriculture (USDA) has been the initiator, the incubator, and the launch pad for a national system of agricultural research and development. The reason is simple. It takes cooperation to address the complex problems of real life. The USDA research programs, both those conducted by Department employees (in-house researchers) and those done outside the Department (extramural researchers), are part of a complex mosaic that together with other federal, university, and private research programs form a national system of agricultural research and development that cooperatively addresses problems in the areas of agriculture production, food, fiber, fuel, and protection of the environment. The strength of the U.S. agricultural research system lies in the tight, productive cooperation among government, the universities, and industry, according to a Washington Post editorial in 1992. The editorial noted that over the past century, this combined effort has led to possibly "the most successful research and development program in the country's history."

I. Background of USDA-Supported Research

The development of publicly supported agricultural research is an exciting and successful chapter in U.S. history. No other area of state–federal relations has been more effectively integrated over the years. Historians note that the forces of policy and research joined program development in making agriculture one of the most productive sectors in the country.

A. Land-Grant Colleges Created

There have been several key actions that set the stage for the creation of land-grant colleges. By the time the Constitutional Convention convened in Philadelphia in 1787, there had been colleges and seminaries dedicated to classical studies for more than 150 years. But it was not until the 1840s when Jonathan Baldwin Turner of Illinois proposed establishing colleges dedicated to agriculture and the mechanic arts that the idea of applying academic science to the resolution of real world problems was born. This was a new concept in education. [See EDUCATION: UNDERGRADUATE AND GRADUATE UNIVERSITY.]

Despite a raging Civil War, this proposal eventually was passed by both Houses of Congress and signed into law by President Abraham Lincoln on July 2, 1862. The law became known as the Land Grant Act of 1862 or the First Morrill Act, named for U.S. Representative Justin Smith Morrill of Vermont.

To finance this endeavor, the Act provided for the sale of public land. The money from the sales was invested as an endowment to finance the establishment of at least one college in each state to teach agriculture and mechanic arts without abandoning other scientific and classical studies. This combination of liberal arts and practical education became known as the land-grant college ideal.

B. Congress Creates Agriculture Department

Concomitantly with the establishment of land-grant colleges, Congress established a government agency to look after the interests of farmers. This idea had been a persistent one since George Washington's days as president. But Congress turned down Washington's proposal and even when it finally established the U.S. Department of Agriculture in 1862, the new department was not given cabinet status. That came after a later battle. The department's original mission was to educate and investigate in areas connected with agriculture. [See GOVERNMENT AGRICULTURAL POLICY, UNITED STATES.]

Today, USDA, as a cabinet-level department, not only operates federal research laboratories while supporting university-based research, but also operates two of the country's largest social service programs. It administers the nation's largest public recreation program through the Forest Service and the gigantic food stamp and commodity programs.

In the 1860s, Americans were undergoing a period of intellectual awakening that advanced the cause of education, particularly practical education for an agrarian, but rapidly industrializing young country. And together the newly created land-grant universities and the Department of Agriculture met the demand with vigor.

C. Historically Black Land-Grant Colleges Created

With time it became clear that in some states some Americans were excluded from the land-grant institutions. Justin Smith Morrill, author of the First Morrill Act and by then a senator, set about correcting that oversight. Although allowing for dual educational systems that separated institutions on the basis of race, the Morrill Act of 1890 provided the basis for a second set of land-grant institutions later referred to as the historically black land-grant institutions or the 1890 institutions.

This Second Morrill Act codified the principles of the first piece of legislation, but added the principle of equal access to all citizens. The 1890 institutions joined by Tuskegee University turned out to principally serve the African American students of the South and the East.

D. Agricultural Experiment Station System Created

The idea of institutions of higher learning dedicated to meeting the needs of the common man was an excellent idea, unique to this country, but it was not nearly enough. The country needed institutions that engaged in the genesis of new knowledge, and transmitted that knowledge to every community in America. This need led to the establishment of state agricultural experiment stations (SAES). The first two were established in the states of Connecticut and California in 1875, to be eventually followed by stations in all other states and territories in subsequent years. The stations were dedicated to helping the farmers, ranchers, homesteaders, and citizens in general make the best use of food, fiber, fuel, and forest resources, and to increase land productivity in producing such resources. [See AGRICULTURAL EXPERIMENT STATIONS.]

Individual stations were a good idea, but an organized national system was needed. U.S. Representative William H. Hatch of Missouri, then chairman of the House Agriculture Committee, authored an act in 1887 to establish in conjunction with the land-grant colleges and universities, a national system of federated yet independent state agricultural experiment stations. This action created a system of national funding for these stations.

E. USDA Creates Agency to Work with the States

In 1888, USDA created an office to fulfill federal obligations under the Hatch Act. Although it has undergone several reorganizations, today that office works closely with a system of 59 experiment stations in the 50 states and several U.S. territories. This agency administers USDA's extramural research grants programs for research carried out by non-USDA scientists. It also works with non-land-grant colleges and universities as well as private industry.

F. Cooperative Extension Service Created

Over the years, disciplines of home economics, forestry, veterinary medicine, and many other areas have become integral parts of the experiment station system. But the new knowledge did not do much good sitting on a shelf. It had to be transmitted to the people who could use it. This need led to the idea of literally placing an extension of the land-grant university in every county in the United States. That idea was codified in the Smith–Lever Act of 1914 which created the Cooperative Extension Service system. The program is a cooperative effort of states, counties, and the USDA. [See COOPERATIVE EXTENSION SERVICE.]

Unfortunately, the 1890 Institutions essentially were left out of the original funding for research and extension. It was not until the 1960s that a meager amount of funds was allocated for their use. This support for the 1890 Institutions was strengthened by the passage of the Evans–Allen Act, which for the first time brought significant amounts of money to the 1890 research programs. The program was further strengthened in Farm Bills passed by Congress beginning in 1977.

II. Organizations and Missions

There are a number of organizations focusing on agricultural research including private laboratories operated by endowments, grants, or other funding mechanisms; USDA laboratories; non-USDA federal laboratories; and the laboratories of universities and industry. One of the most important tasks in developing a national system of agricultural research is matching these organizations and missions to the identified needs. This is discussed further in Section II.E.

A. USDA Laboratories

While USDA has for more than a hundred years been in the business of supporting university-based research, it also has been operating its own research facilities.

By directly engaging in research through these "in-house" laboratories, research studies can be conducted that address national and regional issues, including those responding to the needs of the USDA regulatory agencies such as the Food Safety Inspection Service and the Animal and Plant Health Inspection Service.

This plural system allows enormous flexibility in addressing multiple agricultural needs.

B. University Laboratories

The second form of research supported by USDA involves university-based laboratories engaged in a Federal–State partnership research effort. In this arrangement, federal funding for research from USDA is generally matched with state appropriations to support agricultural research at state agricultural experiment stations, forestry schools, veterinary colleges, and home economics colleges, located mostly at the nation's land-grant universities, as well as the 1890 institutions. The USDA administers these extramural research grants programs.

With this arrangement, another dimension—the state perspective—is added to the national system for agricultural research. Together, these efforts promote national, regional, and state perspectives within the national research system while also creating a direct affiliation of the research system with undergraduate and graduate education.

Scholars of research administration point out that this research–education hybrid is virtually unique to the U.S. system, and is one of the primary reasons American agricultural technology has been so productive.

C. Private Laboratories

USDA laboratories and the Federal–State research partnership are not the only players in the success of agricultural production. Private laboratories also conduct research, either directly within corporations or through sponsorship from diverse sources of funding (e.g., philanthropic foundations, grants, and contracts for research).

A notable example of private laboratories is the Boyce Thompson Research Institute in Ithaca, New York, which operates as an independent, private research laboratory funded through an endowment and external grants.

Other private laboratories include those major corporations conducting proprietary-interest research (e.g., Monsanto, DuPont, Pioneer Seed Co.). These private laboratories also sometimes engage in cooperative research with USDA laboratories and university-based laboratories.

D. Non-USDA Federal Laboratories

In addition to USDA laboratories, other federal laboratories make significant contributions to the body of knowledge in agricultural science. The Environmental Protection Agency, the Department of Interior, and the Department of Energy are federal agencies with laboratories conducting research with agricultural applications. Other federal sponsors of research relating to agriculture include institutions such as the National Science Foundation, the National Institutes of Health, and the Agency for International Development. These federal agencies provide grants to research scientists to conduct research both directly and indirectly related to agriculture.

E. Cooperative Planning

With so many different agricultural research partners, one of the great challenges of agriculture administration is matching activities to institutional mission. There is the constant need to guard against duplication and redundancy so that resources are not wasted. There also is a need to maintain constant vigil to make sure that knowledge gaps do not appear through inattention to emerging problems.

Consequently, communication among the research system's components is paramount in identifying strategic issues and developing plans appropriate to individual missions, resources, and need. Some of the oversight for this is provided at the federal level through the National Science and Technology Council, which is administered through the White House's Office of Science and Technology Policy. This council uses working groups to identify new areas of research and to provide government-wide initiatives for areas in need of additional national emphasis.

At the nonfederal institutional level, considerable attention is focused on policy coordination through the Experiment Station Committee on Organization and Policy (ESCOP), an arm of the National Association of State Universities and Land-Grant Colleges. The ESCOP planning and budget process annually addresses program priorities and funding needs, all in collaboration with the U.S. Department of Agriculture.

Individual USDA agencies also engage in strategic planning and priority setting. The intramural research arm of the USDA is noted for its elaborate, 6-year, rolling plan and the heavy involvement of its National Program Staff in coordinating the agency's research activities at multiple levels. As a consequence, policy, budgets, and programs are continuously reviewed within and between agencies, across agencies, and within regions to derive appropriate plans.

F. Stakeholders Get a Voice in Agricultural Policy

As a countercheck to this system, the Department of Agriculture uses the Joint Council on Food and Agricultural Sciences and the Users Advisory Board to gather information from the "stakeholders" in agricultural research to assure that real world priorities and needs are being met and that resources are allocated appropriately. Recently the USDA established the Agricultural Science and Technology Review Board authorized in the 1990 Farm Bill to provide further guidance to the Department's setting of the research agenda. Additional checks are provided through review of Regional Research plans and allocations by the Committee of Nine, an advisory body established through the Research and Marketing Act of 1946 to recommend regional projects worthy of receiving funding. USDA also uses scientific peer-review panels to assure the quality of the science being proposed by individual investigators.

As a consequence of this constant oversight, the Department of Agriculture can assure Congress and the public of the quality of research programs and that resources are being directed to real needs.

III. USDA Research Programs

USDA-supported research programs seek to provide technology appropriate to the entire spectrum of production and use of food, fiber, and feed. For this reason, USDA's research programs focus on:

- Plant and animal systems of interest to production agriculture
- Human use of the products of agriculture
- Appropriate use of natural resources and the protection of the environment as it relates to agriculture
- New products and processes for the harvested products of agriculture in ways that would enhance value-added and utilization
- Economics of markets, trade, and policy to provide an economically stable and profitable agricultural system

Each of these areas of investigation are studied, in varying degrees, by in-house USDA laboratories and university-based laboratories in the Federal–State partnership.

A. Plant Systems Program

The continuous improvement of crop and forest species for agricultural production requires a basic under-

standing of the biology of the plants, the opportunities for the application of new knowledge, and problem-solving research that can deal with site-specific problems such as crop weeds, insect pests and diseases, climate variables, and differences in crop productivity attributed to soil.

Of primary interest in today's agricultural research agenda is the application of the new tools of molecular biology to understanding of the plant genome structure and to develop the tools to precisely move genetic traits between species through use of genetic engineering. Genomic mapping and genetic engineering offer new approaches to complement more conventional research methods intended for the improvement and cultivation of agriculturally important plants. As a consequence, the spectrum of USDA-sponsored plant system research activities ranges from fundamental studies at the molecular level to very applied problem solving at the farm level.

B. Animal Systems Program

Animal agriculture will continue to be an important component of U.S. agricultural production. However, the interests of consumers and the nature of the problems of animal production systems continue to evolve, as food preferences shift and knowledge is gained by consumers on desirable dietary habits.

Considerable research attention is now being focused on the application of the tools of biotechnology to animal improvement and well-being. Fundamental research investigations into genetic transformation systems, the use of hormones to regulate growth, and the genetic engineering of animal vaccines to control animal disease are some examples of today's animal science research that is looking to better provide for consumer needs and animal production requirements. Physical resources for conducting such research include facilities at SAES and major USDA laboratories that have specialized animal research facilities.

C. Nutrition, Diet, and Health Program

The consumption and use of the products of agriculture directly affect the nutritional status of the consuming public. The growing American interest in fitness and proper dietary practices has emerged as a defining force in the marketplace and in daily individual behavior. To meet these consumer expectations, agricultural research is devoting considerable attention to human nutrition and to diet and health relationships to better serve public expectations.

The quantity and quality of food consumed, the presence or absence of contaminants, postharvest treatments, and the preparation of foods are some of the types of research supported by the Department of Agriculture through its five human nutrition laboratories and the Federal–State partnership. The spectrum of these research activities extends from fundamental investigations to very practical studies aimed at bringing the frontiers of science to solutions of real problems.

D. Natural Resources and the Environment Program

The Department of Agriculture's research interests include stewardship of natural resources and protection of the environment. Research into the sustainability of agricultural production systems, the management of forests, and the maintenance of water, soil, and air quality are all aspects of USDA-supported agricultural research.

E. New Products and Processes Program

USDA is also interested in research that would place higher value on harvested products through manufacturing and processing to make new or altered products. The production of biodegradable polymers from cornstarch, pulp paper made from kenaf, the development of biofuels, and similar advanced technologies continue to receive concerted research attention from USDA.

F. Markets, Trade, and Policy Program

The development of agricultural product markets (both domestic and international), the fostering of trade, and the impact of policies that affect U.S. competitiveness in a global economy are also topics researched by USDA through its extended network. These research activities are considered important components in establishing U.S. agricultural product competitiveness.

IV. USDA Funding Mechanisms

USDA funds outside research in several different ways. The base funded programs are those programs funded by Congress for state experiment station and land-grant university support. These programs include the Hatch Act Programs, the McIntire–Stennis

Cooperative Forestry program, the Evans–Allen program for the 1890 institutions, and a program of animal health and disease research. These programs use federal dollars, in combination with state funding, to create a basic level of support for programs addressing state and local needs. They allow for start-up research efforts by new scientists as well as for collaborative regional research ventures. Funding for several of these programs is distributed on a formula basis tied to the state's rural and farm population.

Targeted special grants programs are aimed at specific research problems in a given part of the country, while competitively awarded grants fund the best agricultural science as judged by peer review, regardless of institution, location, or specific area of scientific investigation.

USDA, particularly the in-house research programs, also uses cooperative agreements to support both science and scientists in mutually advantageous arrangements with universities or other institutions.

V. Reporting Accomplishments

USDA maintains a number of public information programs aimed at informing both the users of agricultural science information and the consumers of agricultural products about the scientific breakthroughs generated through its in-house laboratories and through its extramural grants programs. The university system also reports research accomplishments on a regular basis.

Publications, audio and videotape programs, and other methods are used to provide information to specific groups as well as the news media. In addition, USDA maintains a number of online computer databases that provide information directly to subscribing groups. The Computerized Information Delivery Service (CID) operated by the USDA Office of Government and Public Affairs delivers more than a million lines of data monthly directly to subscribers ranging from news media outlets to state farm bureaus, private corporations, consumer groups and other online database services. The Research Results Database, available through the USDA Cooperative Extension Service, provides monthly updates on recent research results from the Agricultural Research Service and the Economic Research Service.

One of the largest research databases is the Current Research Information System (CRIS), maintained by the Cooperative State Research Service. The system maintains information on more than 30,000 ongoing and recently completed agricultural and forestry research projects in the United States. The research described in the database includes projects conducted or sponsored by USDA's research agencies, the state agricultural experiment stations, state forestry schools, land-grant colleges of 1890, U.S. schools of veterinary medicine, and participants in the Department's competitive grants program. Data are available through direct retrieval services to scientists at CRIS-participating institutions and to the public through commercial online files. Information on latest advances in USDA research is available through TEKTRAN (Technology Transfer Automated Retrieval System). This system was especially designed for direct access to research discoveries by agribusiness firms.

VI. Program Planning for the Future

USDA's vision for the future takes into account the need to constantly involve the stakeholder. For agriculture, the stakeholders represent different sectors, ranging from farm and ranch communities to the consumers of both raw and processed agricultural products. There also are a number of agricultural service sectors that provide input into agricultural production. These views represent a critical perspective necessary for developing USDA's agricultural research agenda.

Each sector has its own perspective, particular needs, and priorities. Involving these "users" in the planning process provides a mechanism for continual adjustment in the USDA's research program.

In addition to sampling the stakeholders' perspective, considerable communication is needed with the USDA's partners in other federal agencies to help select the priorities. The Department does this through a variety of mechanisms, including interagency committees, scientific meetings, and dialogue with professional societies to provide needed communications.

VII. System Effectiveness

From its origins as a minor agency advocating science and progress for farmers in 1862, the USDA grew to cabinet level status surrounded by an extensive network of state and county agricultural program professionals. Farmers at the grassroots level pressured for cabinet status because the early work of

USDA in partnership with the land grant colleges and state agricultural experiment stations, plus the growing importance of international trade, helped transform the agricultural sector.

Over the past 100 years, the farm population has continued to decline as a percentage of the general population. This means that farm interests must continue to be reconciled with the interests of an increasingly urbanized nation. These alliances often mean that new partners do not necessarily understand agriculture's historic, public sector mission.

In addition, the agricultural establishment has added significantly to its social agenda, but the resulting new alliances between traditional farm interests and the new partners who have gained a voice in agricultural policy are often shaky. Competition is often fierce for scarce federal dollars among environmentalists, consumers, the poor, retailers, agribusiness, farmers, university and federal researchers, commodity groups, and others.

On the road to modernization, farm politics has defied broader traditions of limited government in an essentially laissez-faire, or market-oriented, economy by calling for interventionist public policy. But successes in agricultural development have often been matched by a harsh measure of failure. Problems of commodity surplus occur and with them low prices persistently return to drive less successful producers from the sector leading to loud cries from farm policy critics.

Now, some critics charge, the system of organization originally needed to reach and establish direct relationships with farmers creates problems in transacting new business. The reason, according to Theodore Schultz, Nobel Laureate in economics, is the large number of intertwined agricultural organizations crisscrossing America from the most remote county seat to Washington, DC. Each layer, he said, adds costs and regulation to the action of doing business.

A 1991 General Accounting Office (GAO) report to the Secretary of Agriculture seems to back up some of Dr. Schultz's assessment. That report said, "USDA's organizational structure—essentially unchanged since the 1930s—is not responsive to the new challenges facing the Department."

Among the primary challenges of the 1990s is the development of new industrial uses for traditional agricultural products, many analysts say. Turning corn into fuel and potato starch into plastic substitutes are just the beginning. But critics charge those new challenges will not be met unless there are corresponding changes in rules, policies, practices, procedures, and organization.

Some changes seem inevitable. Even before the GAO report was released, USDA had embarked on an internal review of its organization and structure. The results of that assessment and other assessments probably will bring many changes in the 1990s. Although the public agricultural enterprise has been enormously successful in the past, critics charge that it also must become a more equal partner with industry in the development of new ideas. For every dollar spent in the laboratory on research, it takes 10 dollars to develop the research, and 100 dollars to bring production of the product on line. Since these preproduction tasks can take 10 to 15 years to complete, a private–public partnership is essential, advocates charge.

Some advocates for agricultural policy changes say one of the biggest needs is for an institutional means of splitting the costs of product development between government and the private sector, especially non-farm, small businesses. A second major factor is the number of regulatory agencies scrutinizing each product before it goes on the market. And finally, there must be a complete assessment of the degree of consumer and environmental risk that can be associated with any product.

The variety of funding mechanisms, the cooperative planning efforts by USDA, and the working relationships between various public and private laboratories including in-house USDA laboratories, university laboratories, and private and non-USDA federal laboratories seem to offer real solutions to those scientific and policy dilemmas.

A. Policy Changes Affecting Research

The emerging national recognition that public and private research in the United States have functioned differently has led to the conclusion that public institutions, such as the USDA and universities, should be patenting living material to be licensed to private industry. The intention of such patents would be to provide better linkage between the public and private sector agricultural research communities, and thus meet one of the stated objectives of U.S. agricultural research: to get research results into use.

In the past, a distinction was made between precommercial and commercial agricultural research. Public laboratories primarily focused on precommercial investigations, allowing any scientific discoveries to then "transfer" to private entities for commercial development. This process of "technol-

ogy transfer" has now come under question as the United States reexamines its competitive standing in global trade.

The previous open system of public research provides no assurance that primarily U.S. companies will necessarily benefit from the research paid for by American tax dollars. Increasingly, public institutions may focus on areas leading to commercial development. The Patent and Trademark Act of 1980 gave universities the rights to inventions developed under federal grants and contracts. Federal scientists also are able to secure patents for government-sponsored work.

Recent legal decisions giving "inventors" the right to patent living organisms also have caused complications. Prospects for patenting plants and animals has caused some institutions (e.g., universities) to move conceptually closer to commercial applications. The patenting of living material limits access for other scientists. As a result, the sharing of information and biological materials may be disrupted. This is a major concern for much of the scientific community, which remains uneasy over the scientific consequences of these ethical and legal choices regarding patenting plants and animals.

B. USDA's Role

The USDA will undoubtedly play a major role in establishing the final balance between an open scientific system in the public sector and the intended benefits of patenting living material. This process will likely take place through discussions among the stakeholder sectors, the scientific community, the private sector, and other science-related disciplines that contribute to agriculture's research effort (e.g., ecology, human medicine, biological sciences). The final resolution should represent a combination of choices that will provide societal benefits that outweigh the negative consequences.

In the dynamics of an ever-evolving system of agricultural science, USDA will play a central role as a direct participant and as a facilitator of actions by other institutions. Each of the partners in this national agricultural research system will contribute equally to the cornucopia that feeds not only Americans, but also a considerable portion of the world.

Bibliography

Browne, W. P., O'Connell, P., McLaughlin, E. W., and Handy, C. (1992). "Overcoming Obstacles to Change in American Agriculture." Unpublished paper, U.S. Department of Agriculture.

Kerr, N. A. (1987). "The Legacy: A Centennial History of the State Agricultural Experiment Stations 1887–1987." University of Missouri Agricultural Experiment Station, Columbia.

Experiment Station Committee on Organization and Policy (1990). "Report of the Planning and Budget Subcommittee. Research Agenda for the 1990s: A Strategic Plan for The State Agricultural Experiment Stations." Texas Agricultural Experiment Station, College Station, TX.

Experiment Station Committee on Organization and Policy and the Cooperative State Research Service, U.S. Department of Agriculture (1989). Proceedings of a Symposium on Agricultural Research: Meeting the Challenge of the 1990s. Washington, DC, June 13–16.

General Accounting Office (1991). Report to the Secretary of Agriculture. U.S. Department of Agriculture Improved Management of Cross-Cutting Issues in Agriculture. GAO/Rced-91-41. General Accounting Office, Washington, DC. March 1991.

National Academy of Science (1990). Board on Agriculture Report. Investing in Research: A Proposal to Strengthen the Agricultural, Food, and Environment System. National Academy Press, Washington, DC.

Office of Technology Assessment, Congress of the United States (1991). OTA Report. Federally Funded Research: Decisions for a Decade. Government Printing Office, Washington, DC, May 1991.

U.S. Department of Agriculture (1986). Yearbook of Agriculture, 1986. Government Printing Office, Washington, DC.

U.S. Department of Agriculture (1992). Yearbook of Agriculture, 1992. Government Printing Office, Washington, DC.

Washington Post (1992). Editorial, August 16, 1992.

U.S. Farms: Changing Size and Structure

DAVID A. LINS, *University of Illinois*

Glossary

Farm Establishment that sells or would normally sell $1000 or more of agricultural products annually

Net cash farm income Receipts from sales of agricultural products plus government payments received less cash costs of production

Net worth Total assets minus total liabilities, also sometimes called "equity"

Off-farm income Income generated by farm operators or their family members in activities which are not related to the production of agricultural products

Return on assets (ROA) Net farm income plus interest expenses minus a charge for unpaid labor, all divided by total farm assets; it is a percentage return to assets used in agriculture

Return on equity (ROE) Net farm income minus a charge for unpaid labor divided by total farm net worth or equity; it is a percentage return to the money invested by owners of agricultural assets

Vertical integration Process of combining two or more stages of production under the control of a single firm

Change has been an important feature of U.S. farms since the days of the homesteaders. As the West was settled, farm numbers expanded rapidly while in recent decades the number of farms has plummeted and farm size has increased. Ownership patterns also continue to change, although private ownership of land has remained a guiding principal. The financial performance of farm firms has also changed over time and new patterns continue to emerge. Nowhere is change in agriculture more evident than in the growing integration of production, marketing, and distribution of agricultural products. This article focuses on the changing nature of U.S. agriculture and explores possible future directions in farm size and structure.

I. Changes in Farm Size and Number of Farms

The U.S. Department of Agriculture currently defines a farm as a place that sells $1000 or more of agricultural products annually. From 1975 through 1990, more than 375,000 farms went out of business with most of the land and other assets being absorbed into larger farms (Table I). Although this decline in the number of farms is significant, the rate of decline is much lower than in earlier years. Land in farms is also decreasing, but at a slower pace than the number of farms—the net result is an increase in average size of farms.

In addition to an increase in acreage, many farms have increased the volume of output through improved production practices and more intensive operations. Another way of measuring farm sizes is through the volume of annual sales or "economic classes" (Table II). The two largest economic classes (gross sales of over $100,000 per year) account for less than 15% of the farms, but nearly 50% of the land farmed. On the other end of the spectrum, the two smallest economic classes (gross sales of less than $5000 per year) account for about 40% of the farms, but less than 7% of the land farmed. Over time, there has been a growing proportion of farms in the larger economic classes. However, part of that trend is due to inflation in prices, since economic classes have not

TABLE I

Farms: Number, Land in Farms, and Average Size of Farm, United States, 1975–1990

Year	Farms[a] (number)	Land in farms (1000 acres)	Average size of farm (acres)
1975	2,521,420	1,059,420	420
1976	2,497,270	1,054,075	422
1977	2,455,830	1,047,785	427
1978	2,436,250	1,044,790	429
1979	2,437,300	1,042,015	428
1980	2,439,510	1,038,885	426
1981	2,439,920	1,034,190	424
1982	2,406,550	1,027,795	427
1983	2,378,620	1,023,425	430
1984	2,333,810	1,017,803	436
1985	2,292,530	1,012,073	441
1986	2,249,820	1,005,333	447
1987	2,212,960	998,923	451
1988	2,197,140	994,543	453
1989	2,170,520	991,153	457
1990[b]	2,143,150	987,721	461

Source: U.S. Department of Agriculture (1991). "Agricultural Statistics, 1990." Washington, DC.
[a] A farm is an establishment that as of June 1 sold or would normally have sold $1000 or more of agricultural products during the year.
[b] Preliminary.

TABLE III

Gross Cash Income from Farm Sources, by Major Component, 1945–1990

	Farm marketings[a]			Percentage of total	
Year	Livestock	Crops	Total	Livestock	Crops
1945	12,008	9,655	21,663	55.4	44.6
1950	16,105	12,356	28,461	56.6	43.4
1955	15,967	13,523	29,490	54.1	45.9
1960	18,989	15,023	34,012	55.8	44.2
1965	21,886	17,479	39,365	55.6	44.4
1970	29,532	20,977	50,509	58.5	41.5
1975	43,089	45,813	88,902	48.5	51.5
1980	67,991	71,746	139,737	48.7	51.3
1985	69,822	74,293	144,114	48.4	51.6
1990	89,623	80,364	169,987	52.7	47.3

[a] Forest products are included in farm marketings prior to 1978.

been adjusted to maintain a constant purchasing power. [*See* PRODUCTION ECONOMICS.]

Changes in the location and type of agricultural production are also common although the balance between livestock and crop production has remained fairly stable over time (Table III). Since 1945, livestock and livestock products have continued to ac-

count for approximately 50% of total farm marketings. While there has been some shift in consumer preferences away from beef toward turkey and broilers, sales of livestock as a percentage of total farm sales have not changed much since 1945. The geographic location of various production activities, particularly for some types of livestock, has shifted over time.

The distribution of crop and livestock farms by enterprise type and net cash income, is shown in Table IV. The most common farm type is red meat, but income per farm is much higher on most other farm types. A relatively high percentage of farms in the red meat category are small part-time cattle farms.

A myriad of social, political, and economic forces have generated changes in the number and size of

TABLE II

Percentage of Farms, Land in Farms, and Average Size, by Economic Class, United States, June 1, 1985 and 1990

	Percentage of total				Average size of farms	
	Farms		Land		1985	1990[a]
Economic class Gross value of sales	1985(%)	1990[a] (%)	1985 (%)	1990[a] (%)	(acres)	(acres)
$1,000–$2,499	25.1	22.2	3.8	3.0	67	62
$2,500–$4,999	14.3	13.7	3.6	3.1	112	104
$5,000–$9,999	11.8	11.7	4.6	4.1	176	162
$10,000–$19,999	10.7	11.1	6.8	6.3	283	262
$20,000–$39,999	10.1	12.1	9.4	10.8	417	411
$40,000–$99,999	14.2	14.4	24.3	23.2	760	743
$100,000–$249,999	9.7	10.0	25.5	26.0	1,172	1,198
$250,000	4.1	4.8	22.0	23.5	2,419	2,256
Total	100.0	100.0	100.0	100.0	446	461

Source: U.S. Department of Agriculture (1991). "Agricultural Statistics, 1990." Washington, DC.
[a] Preliminary.

TABLE IV

Distribution of Farms by Enterprise Type and Net Cash Income, 1990

Farm type[a]	Number of farms (thousands)	Net cash income (billion dollars)
Crops		
Cash grain	426	17.1
Tobacco	87	0.8
Cotton	24	3.9
Fruit, vegetables	108	10.7
Livestock		
Red meat	993	15.1
Poultry and eggs	38	5.7
Dairy	169	6.8

Source: Agricultural Income and Finance: Situation and Outlook Report, AFO-45, ERS-USDA, May 1992.
[a] Farm types are defined as those with 50% or more of total value of production accounted for by a specific commodity or commodity group.

TABLE V

Index of Farm Labor Productivity per Hour, Selected Years (1967 = 100)

Year	Index
1938	20
1944	25
1949	33
1954	43
1959	62
1964	83
1969	112
1974	132
1979	198
1984	212
1989	259

farms. Some of the more important factors affecting the number and size of farms are government farm programs, growth in labor-saving technology, and relative incomes of farm versus nonfarm residents. A later section on financial performance will address the issue of relative incomes more fully.

U. S. government farm and food policies have generally attempted to balance public concerns over an adequate and stable supply of high-quality, reasonably priced food with concerns of incomes for agricultural producers. While there is considerable debate over the long-term effects of commodity price support programs, most analysts agree that such efforts have slowed the adjustment process in agriculture. This has resulted in more farms and smaller farms than would likely exist in the absence of such price support programs. [See CROP SUBSIDIES; GOVERNMENT AGRICULTURAL POLICY, UNITED STATES.]

Disaster assistance and credit programs of the Federal government have also been used to assist financially distressed producers. Again, the long-term effect appears to be one of slowing the transition to fewer and larger farms.

One of the primary reasons for a movement to fewer and larger farms has been the tremendous growth in new technology which is often capital intensive, but labor-saving. Productivity per worker has grown sharply (Table V) and capital employed in agriculture has expanded, while the number of farms has declined. Many factors contribute to this growth in technology including publicly supported research and outreach activities which have made

adoption of new technologies virtually mandatory for firm survival. [See ENERGY UTILIZATION; LABOR.]

While the above mentioned factors will continue to influence the number and size of farms, other factors may be particularly influential in determining the future directions in the number and size of farms. First, there now appears to be a concerted effort to reduce the large subsidies associated with agricultural production in many of the developed countries of the world. This movement toward lower subsidies in agriculture will create a strong impetus toward "survival of the fittest." The lowest cost/highest profit farms have tended to be larger scale operations. Thus, the trend to fewer and larger farms is likely to continue.

A second factor influencing the future size and structure of agriculture is the aging farm population. The average age of farmers has steadily increased in recent years creating considerable concern over who will serve as the next generation of farmers. As the older generation of farmers retire or scale back their operations, the potential for consolidating farms into larger more efficient units will likely increase. [See RURAL SOCIOLOGY.]

Changing consumers preferences, both in terms of choice of geographic areas in which to live and in terms of food consumption patterns, will also influence the size and type of farms. Economic diversification, better communications systems, and improved road systems all contribute to increased financial viability for small part-time farms that rely heavily on off-farm incomes. Changes in consumption patterns, primarily resulting from health concerns, have already created a shift among livestock products and increased the demand for fruits and vegetables. Further changes of this nature can be expected as the population of the United States grows older, and in the process becomes more concerned with healthful diets.

II. Farm Structure and Ownership

There is some concern that U.S. agriculture is being taken over by large-scale corporate farms and that such actions are likely to lead to higher food prices. To explore this issue, it is useful to examine how the ownership and structure of U.S. agriculture have changed over time and how they might continue to evolve in the future.

Table VI illustrates the proportion of farms, acreage, and gross sales by type of organization. As shown in Table VI, sole proprietors account for 87% of all farms, 65% of the acres farmed, and 56% of the total farm sales. Partnerships are the second most common form of business organization accounting for 10% of all farms. Corporations account for only 3% of all farms, but most of these are family-held corporations. Nonfamily farm corporations account for less than 0.5% of all farms, but they do account for 6% of gross sales. Notice also that nonfamily farm corporations tend to rent a much smaller proportion of the land they operate than do family owned businesses.

It is evident from Table VI that rented land is a very significant component of the operation of many farms. Table VII identifies the amount of land in farms and the proportion which is rented. From 1940 through 1964, the proportion of land rented tended to decline; since 1969 the proportion of rented land has tended to increase. Overall, the percentage of land rented has not changed dramatically in the last 40 years. What has changed significantly is the proportion of "tenant operated farms," defined as farms in which the operator farms only land rented from others. While nearly 39% of all farmers in 1940 rented all of the land they operated, this fell to only 11.5% by 1987. This is due in part to the demise of sharecrop farmers in the south and because farm operators have become more interested and more able to own at least some portion of the land they operate.

To evaluate the future changes in farm ownership patterns, it is useful to examine recent data on who is buying and who is selling farmland (Table VIII). While significant regional variation is apparent, the majority of buyers for all farmland are owner-operators. Nonfarmer buyers are also important and in some regions account for over 50% of the purchases. The majority of sellers of farmland tend to be active farmers who either remain in farming after the sale or retire. Note that nonfarmers are also significant sellers of farmland, but in recent years they have purchased more than they have sold. These nonfarmer owners then contribute to the amount of land which is offered for rent.

In examining the patterns of landownership and use, it is important to recognize that from 1940 until 1980, farmland values increased virtually every year. And during the decade of the 1970s, farmland value increases exceeded the rate of inflation by a substantial margin. This history of capital gains generated considerable incentive for the ownership of land and may explain, at least in part, the reasons for the significant decline in tenant operated farms during this time period.

The crash in farmland values during the early to mid-1980s starkly reminded owners that farmland can also decrease in value. The decrease in land values, combined with more modest rates of capital gains after the mid-1980s, has significantly altered the eco-

TABLE VI

Selected Farm Characteristics by Type of Organization, 1987

Farm organization type	Proportion of total (%)			Average farm		Proportion of land leased (%)
	Farms	Acres	Sales	Sales ($1000)	Size (acres)	
Sole proprietor	87	65	56	42	347	43
Partnership	10	16	17	117	768	49
Corporation						
Family	3	11	20	437	1743	43
Nonfamily	<$\frac{1}{2}$	1	6	1341	2167	33
Institutional[a]	<$\frac{1}{2}$	7	1	107	5396	13

Source: Olaf Kula and Denise Rodgers, "Farmland Ownerhsip and Renting in the United States, 1987," ERS-USDA, AGES 9130, June 1991.
[a] Institutional includes cooperatives, estates or trusts, prison farms, grazing associations, Indian reservations, or institutions **run** by a government or religious entity.

TABLE VII

Land Rented by Tenants and Part Owners, 1940–1987

Year	Land in farms	Land rented by operators (million acres)			Proportion of land leased (%)	Tenant operators (%)
		Tenants	Part owners	Total		
1940	1,165.1	313.2	155.9	459.1	44.0	38.8
1945	1,141.6	251.6	178.9	430.5	37.7	31.7
1950	1,161.4	212.2	196.2	408.4	35.2	26.9
1954	1,158.2	192.6	212.3	404.9	34.9	24.4
1959	1,123.0	166.8	234.1	400.9	35.7	20.5
1964	1,110.2	144.9	248.1	393.0	35.4	17.1
1969	1,063.3	137.6	241.8	379.4	35.7	12.9
1974	1,017.0	122.3	258.4	380.7	37.4	11.3
1978	1,029.7	124.1	285.3	406.3	39.4	12.7
1982	986.2	113.6	269.9	383.5	38.9	11.6
1987	964.5	126.9	275.4	402.3	41.7	11.5

Source: Olaf Kula and Denise Rodgers, "Farmland Ownerhsip and Renting in the United States, 1987," ERS-USDA, AGES 9130, June 1991.

nomics of land ownership. Many farmers today believe that returns from the rental of land may equal or exceed the returns from owning land, especially if debt financing is required to acquire land. Consequently, equity ownership of land, particularly from nonfarmers and institutional investors has become more popular in recent times. The net effect should be an increase in the nonfarm ownership of farmland combined with a higher proportion of farmland being rented by farm operators.

III. Farm Financial Performance by Size and Structure

The financial position and performance of farms vary greatly by size and structure. Past changes and future directions in size and structure are dictated in large part by financial performance. If large farms generate more operator income and greater returns on equity capital, then changes in direction of larger farms are likely to continue. Likewise, if corporate farms can generate a better financial performance than sole proprietorships, movement toward corporate farming is likely to occur. In this section, the financial performance of farms is examined with the underlying objective of trying to discern how that may impact future changes in the size and structure of farms.

Table IX illustrates the balance sheet for farms classified by the value of annual sales. For the largest size farms (over $1 million in annual sales) total farm assets average nearly $5.3 million with a net worth of over $4.1 million. In contrast, farms with less than $20,000

in annual sales have an average of $229,000 of assets and a net worth of $209,000. Notice that the debt-to-asset ratio tends to rise as size of farm increases.

Estimates of net cash farm income for farms classified by annual sales show that farms in the largest size category averaged well over $1 million in net cash income while farms in the lowest size category had a negative net cash income on average (Table X). Net cash farm incomes vary widely by size of farm and generalizations about low income in agriculture are often too simplistic to be of much value in assessing how the sector is likely to change in the future.

Off-farm income is also an important source of income for farm families, often accounting for more of their total income than farm sources (Table XI). In recent years, the lowest off-farm income was achieved by farms in the middle size sales class while the farms in the smallest size sales class had the largest off-farm income. Thus, economic forces are creating two divergent types of farm firms: large farms which rely almost totally on farm sources of income, and small part-time farms which rely almost entirely on off-farm income.

Overall, financial performance of the farm sector can also be judged in the context of rates of return on assets (ROA) and return on equity (ROE) (Table XII). ROA measures a percentage return to all capital invested in agriculture—the capital provided by the owners as well as the capital provided by lenders. ROE measures a percentage return only to the equity that owners have invested in the business. Ideally, ROE should exceed ROA so that borrowed funds are generating a return higher than the interest cost

TABLE VIII

Farmland Buyers and Sellers, 1989–1991

Buyer

Percentage of value[a]

Region	Tenant			Owner-operator[a]			Retired farmer			Nonfarmer		
	1989	1990	1991	1989	1990	1991	1989	1990	1991	1989	1990	1991
Northeast	5	9	10	39	31	53	1	1	1	55	59	36
Lake States	17	20	23	60	58	60	2	2	2	22	20	15
Corn Belt	10	11	10	53	60	59	2	★a	2	35	27	29
Northern Plains	13	15	12	71	75	72	4	1	1	11	10	15
Appalachia	5	6	6	51	46	46	1	★	1	43	47	47
Southeast	1	1	2	59	64	79	1	★	★	39	35	19
Delta States	7	7	13	41	39	40	2	1	2	50	53	45
Southern Plains	10	9	11	49	61	54	1	1	3	40	29	32
Mountain	7	7	11	61	52	52	1	★	★	31	40	37
Pacific	13	5	3	71	79	76	1	1	2	16	16	19
48 States	8	8	9	54	60	62	1	1	1	37	31	28

Seller

Percentage of value

Region	Estate			Active farm operator who						Retired farmer			Nonfarmer/nonfarm business		
				Remained in farming			Retired or quit								
	1989	1990	1991	1989	1990	1991	1989	1990	1991	1989	1990	1991	1989	1990	1991
Northeast	8	9	14	31	17	26	25	34	25	13	15	19	23	25	16
Lake States	13	16	18	16	15	17	27	18	18	13	17	21	31	34	26
Corn Belt	31	32	33	16	17	15	14	12	12	10	11	12	29	28	28
Northern Plains	26	30	30	21	15	13	13	16	17	15	13	19	25	26	21
Appalachia	27	18	25	20	18	26	17	22	17	10	12	11	26	30	21
Southeast	13	5	14	51	55	56	16	14	9	6	4	5	15	22	16
Delta States	11	12	14	30	18	31	12	23	13	4	6	9	43	41	33
Southern Plains	24	16	24	25	33	21	14	20	17	7	8	10	30	23	28
Mountain	5	8	7	46	24	34	15	14	17	7	5	9	27	49	33
Pacific	6	4	9	41	57	33	21	21	18	11	4	4	21	14	36
48 States	18	15	20	29	32	28	17	18	15	10	9	11	26	26	26

Source: "Agricultural Resources: Situation and Outlook Report." AR-22, June 1991, ERS-USDA.

[a] ★, less than 0.5%.

on those borrowed funds. ROE did exceed ROA throughout the decade of the 1970s (Table XII). During the decade of the 1980s, however, ROA exceeded ROE in most years. This relatively poor financial performance of the farm sector is likely to force continued adjustments and changes in the sector. Farms with the poorest financial performance will continue to be forced out, while the more successful farms will likely absorb the assets into larger, more efficient, and more profitable units.

IV. Emerging Trends in Size and Structure of Farms

Change will continue to shape the size and structure of U.S. farms. Several emerging trends are likely to play a major role in this process. In this section, four interrelated trends are identified and their potential impact on the size and structure of farms is explored.

A. Vertical Integration

Vertical integration is the process whereby various stages of production are brought under the control of a single entity or a closely linked group of entities. It now appears likely that vertical integration will continue to grow and expand in agriculture.

There are already numerous examples of vertical integration within the agricultural sector. For example, some large cattle feeding operations now have slaughtering plants as a part of their combined operations. Some fruit and vegetable packing and canning

TABLE IX

Farm Sector Balance Sheet (Including Operator Households), by Value of Sales Class, December 31, 1990

Item	$1,000,000 and over	$500,000 to $999,999	$250,000 to $499,999	$100,000 to $249,999	$40,000 to $99,999	$20,000 to $39,999	Less than $20,000
				Million dollars			
Total							
Farm assets	82,105	62,546	89,878	195,463	175,160	103,312	287,694
Real estate	50,586	40,047	57,611	132,787	122,249	75,176	224,123
Livestock and poultry	13,404	5,458	7,047	13,473	11,539	6,287	11,884
Machinery and motor vehicles	6,884	5,345	9,460	21,391	18,605	9,339	20,677
Crops stored[a]	2,109	2,320	3,798	7,373	3,633	1,340	1,852
Purchased inputs	446	415	509	708	415	136	213
Household goods	3,335	2,640	3,798	8,755	8,060	4,957	14,777
Investments in cooperatives	3,429	4,811	5,171	5,945	4,286	1,548	2,461
Other financial	1,912	1,510	2,482	5,032	6,374	4,529	11,708
Debt	17,280	12,956	18,750	33,425	25,437	11,618	25,601
Real estate[b]	5,587	5,974	8,855	17,586	14,054	7,479	18,863
Nonreal estate	11,693	6,982	9,895	15,839	11,383	4,139	6,738
Equity	64,825	49,590	71,128	162,038	149,723	91,694	262,093
				Percentage			
Debt-to-asset ratio	21.0	20.7	20.9	17.1	14.5	11.2	8.9
				Thousand dollars			
Per farm:							
Farm assets	5,296	2,291	1,400	913	572	399	229
Real estate	3,263	1,467	897	620	399	290	179
Livestock and poultry	865	200	110	63	38	24	9
Machinery and motor vehicles	444	196	147	100	61	36	16
Crops stored[a]	136	85	59	34	12	5	1
Purchased inputs	29	15	8	3	1	1	0
Household goods	215	97	59	41	26	19	12
Investments in cooperatives	221	176	81	28	14	6	2
Other financial	123	55	39	24	21	17	9
Debt	1,115	474	292	156	83	45	20
Real estate[b]	360	219	138	82	46	29	15
Nonreal estate	754	256	154	74	37	16	5
Equity	4,182	1,816	1,108	757	489	354	209

Source: Economic Indicators of the Farm Sector, National Financial Summary, 1990, ECIFS 10-1, ERS-USDA, November 1991.
[a] Non-CCC crops held on farms plus value above loan rate for crops held under CCC.
[b] Includes CCC storage and drying facilities loans.

TABLE X

Number of Farms, and Net Cash Farm Income, by Value of Sales Class, 1990

Item	$1,000,000 and over	$500,000 to $999,999	$250,000 to $499,999	$100,000 to $249,999	$40,000 to $29,999	$20,000 to $39,999	Less than $20,000
	Thousands						
Number of farms	16	27	64	214	306	259	1,254
	Million dollars						
Total:							
Gross cash income	57,496	21,234	25,779	39,370	24,047	9,000	9,051
Cash receipts from marketings	56,231	19,872	23,125	34,830	21,004	7,759	7,166
Direct Government payment commodities	2,760	3,145	5,288	9,115	5,250	1,794	1,008
Price-support-only commodities	5,634	3,801	5,737	11,456	7,229	2,030	1,329
Nonsupported commodities	47,837	12,926	12,100	14,259	8,525	3,934	4,829
Government payments	436	985	2,130	3,222	1,760	524	241
Farm-related income	829	377	525	1,318	1,283	717	1,644
Cash expenses	38,203	13,780	15,617	24,306	16,119	6,619	9,515
Net cash income	19,293	7,454	10,163	15,064	7,928	2,381	−464
	Dollars						
Per farm operation[a]							
Gross cash income	3,708,945	777,624	401,468	183,937	78,565	34,749	7,216
Cash receipts from marketings	3,627,349	727,763	360,125	162,726	68,623	29,958	5,713
Direct Government payment commodities	178,029	115,158	82,351	42,585	17,151	6,928	804
Price-support-only commodities	363,458	139,212	89,344	53,523	23,619	7,840	1,059
Nonsupported commodities	3,085,862	473,393	188,430	66,618	27,853	15,191	3,850
Government payments	28,096	36,056	33,174	15,055	5,749	2,024	192
Farm-related income	53,501	13,804	8,168	6,156	4,193	2,767	1,311
Cash expenses	2,464,395	504,645	243,201	113,559	52,664	25,557	7,586
Net cash income	1,244,550	272,978	158,267	70,378	25,901	9,192	−370

Source: Economic Indicators of the Farm Sector, National Financial Summary, 1990, ECIFS 10-1, ERS-USDA, November 1991.
[a] Farm operations may have several households sharing in the earnings of the business (for example, partners or shareholders in farm corporations). The number of households per farm tends to increase as farm sales increase.

plants now own a significant portion of the land used to supply their raw materials. Other examples can also be cited.

The primary objective of vertical integration is to assure a more uniform supply of products and a more tightly controlled quality of final products. To the extent that vertical integration succeeds in accomplishing these objectives, the integrated firm may face significant cost advantages over those firms who separate the various stages of production.

TABLE XI

Off-farm Cash Income of the Principal Farm Operator and Family, by Value of Sales Class

Year	$1,000,000 and over	$500,000 to $999,999	$250,000 to $499,999	$100,000 to $249,999	$40,000 to $29,999	$20,000 to $39,999	Less than $20,000
	Million dollars						
Total							
1990	441	708	1,774	3,873	7,754	8,266	44,159
	Dollars						
Per family							
1990	28,472	25,916	27,629	18,096	25,335	31,916	35,206

Source: Economic Indicators of the Farm Sector, National Financial Summary, 1990, ECIFS 10-1, ERS-USDA, November 1991.

TABLE XII

Rates of Return on Farm Assets and Equity (Excluding Operator Households), 1970–1990[a]

Year	Rates of return on farm assets			Rates of return on farm equity		
	Current income	Real capital gains	Total	Current income	Real capital gains	Total
			Percentage			
1970	3.0	−0.6	2.3	2.2	0.2	2.4
1971	3.0	2.9	5.9	2.3	4.4	6.7
1972	4.2	7.5	11.7	3.7	9.8	13.6
1973	7.7	10.2	17.9	7.9	13.8	21.6
1974	4.5	−2.1	2.4	4.0	−0.9	3.1
1975	3.6	7.5	11.1	2.8	10.2	13.0
1976	2.1	9.7	11.8	1.0	12.5	13.5
1977	1.8	3.6	5.4	0.5	5.5	6.0
1978	2.4	8.5	10.9	1.2	11.7	12.9
1979	2.5	4.9	7.4	1.2	7.6	8.8
1980	1.2	−0.5	0.7	−0.6	1.3	0.7
1981	2.3	−8.0	−5.7	0.4	−8.0	−7.6
1982	2.2	−8.0	−5.8	0.0	−8.6	−8.6
1983	1.3	−2.6	−1.2	−1.1	−2.2	−3.3
1984	3.0	−12.9	−9.9	0.9	−15.4	−14.5
1985	3.6	−12.3	−8.7	1.9	−15.0	−13.1
1986	3.8	−7.6	−3.8	2.1	−9.1	−6.9
1987	4.8	2.8	7.6	3.6	4.6	8.2
1988	4.5	1.3	5.8	3.3	2.4	5.7
1989	5.5	−2.3	3.2	4.5	−1.9	2.6
1990	5.2	−2.6	2.5	4.2	−2.2	2.0

Source: Economic Indicators of the Farm Sector, National Financial Summary, 1990, ECIFS 10-1, ERS-USDA, November 1991.

[a] Rates of return are estimated using the current cost (market value) of assets and equity, not historic cost.

Vertical integration normally requires fairly large-scale operations to generate economically viable units. For example, a small-scale hog operation cannot effectively start its own feed manufacturing or meat processing facilities. Consequently, a move toward vertically integrated production is likely to bring with it a move to fewer and larger farms. These integrated units are also likely to involve more partnerships and corporate forms of business. These units are also very profit oriented and are thus unlikely to remain in low profit ventures simply to maintain a "way of life."

B. Contract Production

Closely related to vertical integration, contract production involves legal linkages between producers and either input supply or, more commonly, processing or distribution firms. Unlike vertical integration, ownership of the various stages of production remains with separate parties.

The variety of production contracts now being offered to agricultural producers is so numerous and varied that it is not easy to give a simple yet comprehensive classification scheme. However, the method of classifying contracts developed by Mighell and Jones almost 30 years ago is still quite useful.[1] They divided production contracts into three basic categories:

(1) Market-specification contracts
(2) Production-management contracts
(3) Resource-providing contracts.

The characteristics of these types of production contracts are further explained in Table XIII. Many of the contracts offered in grain and specialty crops are market-specification contracts. Contracts for vegetables and seed production tend to be oriented toward production-management contracts with some taking on the characteristics of resource-providing contracts. Contracts for livestock production tend to be resource-providing contracts or production-

[1]Mighell, Ronald L. and Lawrence A. Jones. *Vertical Coordination in Agriculture*. Agriculture Economics Report No. 19. Washington, D.C.: Economic Research Service, USDA. 1963

TABLE XIII
Characteristics of Agricultural Production Contracts

	Types of contractual arrangements		
Characteristics	Market-specification	Production-management	Resource-providing
Involvement by contracting firm	Low	Medium	High
Level of producer's independence	High	Medium	Low
Contractor ownership of inputs or resources	None	Some	Many
Quality standard	Medium	High	High
Contracting firm's management input	Low	Medium	High
Contracting firm's ownership of final product	No	Possibly	Majority of the time
Marketing channel for producer	Guaranteed	Same	Same
Pricing of products	Fixed price specified in contract or tied to open market prices plus a premium	Fixed price is normally specified in the contract	Ownership often retained by contractor so payment is for services rendered not for the commodity
Overall producer risk	High	Medium	Low
Overall contractor risk	Low	Medium	High

Adapted from Coaldrake, K. (1992). "Contractual Arrangements in the Production of High-Value Crops in East Central Illinois: Contract Types, Producer Characteristics and Producer Attitudes." University of Illinois.

management contracts with relatively few being market-specification type contracts.

Contract production is certainly not new to agriculture. Examples of contract production abound in seed, vegetables, fruit, and broilers. Less common has been contract production in hogs, cattle, and various types of food and feed grains. However, as farms have become larger and more specialized, profit margins have narrowed. These lower profits margins on larger-scale units have left producers highly vulnerable to changes in yields and commodity prices. In response, a growing number of producers have found contract production a desirable alternative. Livestock production, especially in hogs, now appears to be headed more and more toward contract production. In contrast, feed and food grains have not yet seen dramatic increases in the use of contract production. Yet these firms face risks similar to those of livestock producers. Continued movement in the direction of contract production seems likely.

The trend toward contract production has interesting ramifications on the size and structure of farms. Farms producing under contract often face much different risks than those who operate in the open market. The primary source of risk for contracting producers is the financial stability of the integrator providing the contract. In some cases, the integrator will offer some form of loan guarantee to lenders providing loans to producers under contract. The net effect is an ability on the part of the contracting producer to undertake a larger size operation than would be the case without the contract. The use of contract production appears to have relatively minor impacts on farm organizational structure. Most farms entering into such contracts are sole proprietors. The ability to contract may generate a larger scale of operation and thereby create a stronger incentive for partnership arrangements with children or other related parties.

Production and marketing coordination are often provided through the efforts of producer cooperatives and bargaining associations. These efforts at production-marketing coordination are particularly strong in dairy, and fruit and vegetable production. Other agricultural products may become more closely linked to this process as the benefits of a coordinated production-marketing strategy become more clearly documented and demonstrated.

C. Debt vs Equity Capital

Capital used in agriculture can be broken into two major classes; debt capital provided by lenders, and equity capital provided by owners. One can further distinguish equity capital according to whether it is provided by owner-operators or whether it is provided by "external" sources. One of the emerging trends in agriculture is the growing importance of "external" equity capital for the ownership of farmland. External equity capital has been attracted to farmland in recent years for two major reasons: the high cost of borrowed funds relative to the expected returns from land, and the attractiveness of returns on farmland relative to other investment options.

Owners of farmland obtain returns from two sources, income returns and capital gains (losses). The later returns are realized only when the land is sold. Information in Table XII revealed that the income return to farm assets is relatively low. But if one owns the land and rents it out, it is not uncommon to obtain cash rents in the range of 4–6% per year. If one combines this with inflationary expectations for farmland values which are now in the range of 2–4% by most estimates, the total return to the ownership of land is expected to be 6–10% annually. However, the cost of borrowing money to buy land is in the range of 8–10% creating little economic incentive for farm operators to borrow money to buy land.

However, people who inherit land from relatives, or investors who have substantial assets to invest may find an 8–10% return relatively attractive in today's financial environment. Consequently, investment in farmland that is equity financed may appear to be a relatively sound investment. The net result of these economic circumstances should propel the farm sector toward more absentee ownership of land, and consequently a higher proportion of rented land than in the past.

D. Agricultural Trade Liberalization and Export Subsidies

The current efforts to liberalize trade is most evident in the current negotiations being conducted under the auspices of the General Agreement on Tariffs and Trade (GATT). The GATT negotiations have the goal of reducing trade distorting tariffs and subsidies on agricultural commodities. Many of the developed nations including the United States, the European Community, and Japan support agricultural prices through a complex set of tariffs, import restrictions, and export subsidies. In contrast, many developing nations use implicit or explicit export taxes to set their agricultural prices well below world market-clearing levels. The net effect is overproduction in developed countries and too little production in developing economies. [See TARIFFS AND TRADE.]

While GATT negotiations have encountered many roadblocks, the efforts to lower subsidies and encourage agricultural trade are clearly receiving considerable attention. To the extent that such trade liberalization policies occur, domestic producers could face stiff competition from foreign sources. Reduced price supports could result in a further loss of some of the less efficient producers and could easily speed the change in types of products which are produced.

Other examples of movements toward liberalized trade include the Canada–U.S. Trade Agreement (CUSTA) and the North American Free Trade Agreement (NAFTA) which is currently being negotiated. The impact of such trade agreements will vary by type of farm and by geographic location. However, the net effect will be to require firms to compete on a more global scale. Production activities in which the United States has a comparative advantage will flourish, while protected segments of agriculture may diminish.

V. Summary and Conclusions

Change has continually reshaped the size and structure of U.S. farms. In earlier decades, this change was driven by the availability of land as the nation expanded westward. This period entailed a rather substantial growth in the number and size of farms.

Changes in production technologies, beginning as early as the decade of the 1920s, started to alter the economics of farm production. Larger more efficient production units began to replace the smaller less efficient operations. Smaller and less efficient farms began to rely on off-farm income as a more important source of livelihood. These changes created a more dichotomous agricultural structure: large efficient farms that obtain most of their income from farming operations, and small part-time farms that obtain most of their income from off-farm sources.

The size and structure of farms will continue to change in the future. However, these changes will likely be driven by a somewhat different set of forces than existed in the past. One form of change has involved a greater linkage of the various stages of agricultural production. Continued movement toward vertically integrated and/or contract production is likely to significantly alter the structure of agriculture. Likewise, a growing commitment to liberalization of agricultural trade and the subsequent reduction of agricultural subsidies is likely to create forces for change that are linked to a global economy. On balance, it appears that these emerging trends will create an economic climate conducive to fewer, larger, and more efficient farming operations. At the same time, these forces should continue to generate an abundant supply of food at reasonable prices.

Bibliography

Economic Research Service, USDA (May 1992). "Agricultural Income and Finance: Situation and Outlook Report." AFO-45, Washington, DC.

Economic Research Service, USDA (November 1991). "Economic Indicators of the Farm Sector, National Financial Summary, 1990." ECIFS, 10-1, Washington, DC.

Kula, O., and Rodgers, D. (June 1991). "Farmland Ownership and Renting in the United States, 1987." ERS/USDA, AGES 9130, Washington, DC.

Office of Technology Assessment (March 1986). "Technology, Public Policy, and the Changing Structure of American Agriculture." Washington, DC.

U.S. Department of Agriculture (1991). "Agricultural Statistics, 1990." Washington, DC.

Viticulture

RONALD S. JACKSON, *Brandon University, Manitoba, Canada*

Glossary

Bearing wood Sections of cane possessing the buds that produce the fruit-bearing shoots
Cane Mature portion of a shoot
Cordon Branches from the grapevine trunk, usually horizontally positioned
Coulure Physiological disorder showing excessive fruit drop shortly after pollination
Inflorescence Flower cluster and associated supporting structures
Isotherm (annual) Line connecting locations on a map possessing the same average yearly temperature
Rootstock Cultivar to which most commercial grapevine varieties are grafted to provide the root system
Scion Shoot- and fruit-bearing portion of a grafted grapevine
Training system Form of the shoot system developed to position the fruit for optimal fruit yield and quality
Véraison Period when the fruit begins to lose its green coloration and commences its last growth phase

Viticulture deals with the cultivation of wine, table, and raisin grapes. Because each use involves its own set of desirable fruit characteristics, it is uncommon for individual cultivars to be grown for more than one purpose. Vineyard climate and soil characteristics impose limits on cultivar suitability, as much as cultivar choice places limits on site appropriateness. Viticultural practices that can influence cultivar–site compatibility involve training system and rootstock use as well as the type and degree of fertilization, irrigation, and disease/pest management. Harvest method and timing depend primarily on cultivar characteristics and grape use.

I. Introduction

When and where humans first began to cultivate grapes will probably never be known. Absence of a common root word for grape in Indo-European languages suggests that the discovery of grape edibility occurred independently throughout Europe. The ancestral range of the European grape (*Vitis vinifera*) extended around the Mediterranean coast, westward from Algeria around to Syria, up into central Europe, and east to between the Black and Caspian seas. Most researchers believe that the origin of viticulture occurred within the Anatolian region of northern Turkey or adjacent Transcaucasia. This zone includes the regions in which the distribution of wild *V. vinifera* grapevines most closely approaches the origins of Western agriculture in the Near East.

Current evidence suggests that grapes and viticulture were introduced to Palestine and Egypt from the Caucasus about 4000 B.C. Beginning about 1000 B.C., grape culture spread throughout most of the Mediterranean Basin; spread continued into central Europe during the Roman period. Viticulture subsequently spread into Asia and finally throughout much of the world in the past few centuries.

Most commercial viticulture is restricted to regions located between the 10 and 20°C annual isotherms in the Northern and Southern Hemispheres. Where local conditions or vineyard practices compensate, viticulture is possible in warmer subtropical regions and in colder temperate zones. In moist subtropical regions, disease problems become increasingly limiting and severe pruning is required to promote bud burst for continued growth. In cold regions, winter survival may require the whole shoot system to be laid on the ground for burial each fall.

II. Economic Importance

Grapes are the world's most important fleshy fruit crop. Global production in 1992 was about 60.6 million metric tons. In comparison, global production of oranges, bananas, and apples, according to data from the United Nations Food and Agriculture Organization (FAO), was 57, 49.6, and 43.1 million metric tons, respectively. Although viticulture has spread around the globe, the main centers of grape culture remain in Mediterranean Europe (Tables I and II). About 68% of the world's vineyard hectarage occurs in Europe, of which 40% of the world total is located in Spain, Italy, and France. Global grape usage varies considerably from region to region and country to country (Tables I and II). For example, most French grapes are used in wine production whereas most Turkish grapes are grown for raisin production or for use as a fresh fruit crop.

III. Grape Species and Cultivars

The most important grapevine species is *V. vinifera*, the dominant or only grapevine species grown in most of the world, with the exception of the Pacific north-

western and eastern regions of North America, Brazil, Uruguay, Japan, and northern China. In the latter regions, most vines are cultivars of or hybrids between two or more North American *Vitis* species (American hybrids) or complex hybrids between North American species and *V. vinifera* (French–American hybrids). In American hybrids, the primary species involved are *V. labrusca*, *V. aestivalis*, *V. riparia*, and *V. cinerea*, whereas in French–American hybrids the main North American species are *V. rupestris*, *V. riparia*, and *V. aestivalis*. The latter species were used as sources of disease and pest resistance. Several newer *V. vinifera* hybrids are being produced using *V. amurensis* from Manchuria to provide cold tolerance, and using several species native to the southern United States, Mexico, Central America, and southern China to enhance adaptation to warm humid climates. In the southeastern regions of the United States, most cultivars are derivatives of *V. rotundifolia*, the muscadine grape.

North American *Vitis* species have been used almost exclusively in the development of rootstocks for grafting *V. vinifera* cultivars. Rootstocks can (1) provide resistance or tolerance to various root pests, including phylloxera and nematodes, as well as to several soilborne viral pathogens; (2) donate increased tolerance to high-calcium soils, salt, and drought; and (3) regulate vegetative vigor. Grapevines in most commercial viticultural regions must be grafted onto appropriate rootstocks.

There are about 15,000 named grape varieties, most of which are wine grapes, reflecting the major use of the fruit. The most widely grown cultivars are a few varieties grown extensively in Spain, the former Soviet Union, and South America. Because wines from these cultivars are rarely seen in world channels, and typically do not carry a varietal designation, the names

TABLE I

World Regional Statistics for Vineyard Coverage and Total Grape, Wine, Table Grape, and Raisin Production in 1992[a]

Region	Vineyard area		Total grape production		Wine production		Table grapes		Raisins	
	10^3 ha	%	10^6 kg	%	10^6 liter	%	10^6 kg	%	10^6 kg	%
Africa	351	4.2	2732	4.5	1148	3.8	649	7.8	46	4.5
Americas	784	9.5	10,278	17.0	4064	13.5	1664	20.0	338	32.6
Asia	1407	17.1	9402	15.5	483	1.6	1782	21.4	489	47.2
Europe	5626	68.3	37,132	61.3	23,857	79.4	4142	49.7	81	7.8
Oceania	67	0.8	1041	1.7	500	1.7	94	1.1	82	7.9
Total	8235		60,585		30,050		8330		1036	

[a] Data from Tinlot and Rousseau (1993). The state of vitiviniculture in the world and the statistical information in 1992. *Bulletin de l'Office Internationale de la Vigne et du Vin* **66**, 861–943.

TABLE II

Top 10 Countries in Vineyard Coverage and Total Grape, Wine, Table Grape, and Raisin Production in 1992[a]

Country	Vineyard area		Country	Total grape production		Country	Wine production		Country	Table grapes		Country	Raisins	
	10^3 ha	%		10^6 kg	%		10^6 liter	%		10^6 kg	%		10^6 kg	%
Spain	1360	16.5	Italy	10,178	16.8	Italy	6869	22.8	Turkey	1766	22.2	Turkey	350	33.8
Italy	1008	12.2	France	8514	14.1	USSR (ex)	6540	21.8	United States	1012	12.1	United States	298	28.7
France	950	11.5	United States	5490	9.1	Turkey	3704	12.3	Australia	921	11.1	Australia	82	7.9
USSR (ex)	813	9.9	Spain	5356	8.8	Chili	1800	6.0	Greece	689	8.3	Greece	78	7.5
Turkey	580	7.0	USSR (ex)	4545	7.5	United States	1562	5.2	Iran	572	6.9	Iran	55	5.3
Portugal	371	4.5	Turkey	3450	5.7	Spain	1435	4.8	Afghanistan	407	4.9	Afghanistan	45	4.4
United States	301	3.7	Argentina	2127	3.5	Brazil	1340	4.5	South Africa	261	3.1	South Africa	44	4.2
Romania	252	3.1	Germany	1735	2.9	Algeria	1000	3.3	Chile	257	3.1	Chile	17	1.6
Iran	232	2.8	Portugal	1650	2.7	Japan	755	2.5	Mexico	252	3.0	Mexico	17	1.6
Argentina	209	2.5	South Africa	1406	2.3	Greece	750	2.5	Syria	206	2.4	Syria	15	1.4

[a] Data from Tinlot and Rousseau (1993). The state of vitiviniculture in the world and the statistical information in 1992. *Bulletin de l'Office Internationale de la Vigne et du Vir* **66**, 861–943.

of these cultivars are unfamiliar to most wine consumers. Examples are Airen, Rkátsiteli, Trebbiano, Garnacha, Carignan, and País (Criolla). In contrast, most well-known grapevine cultivars constitute only a small fraction of the vines grown, even in the country of origin. The comparatively small vineyard area given over to famous cultivars partially reflects the more demanding conditions required to develop their unique varietal character. Some of the most highly prized wine cultivars are Cabernet Sauvignon, Chardonnay, Pinot noir, Riesling and Syrah (Shiraz).

For wine grapes, it is desirable to have relatively small berries, providing a high skin-surface to juice-volume ratio. The skin and the immediately underlying tissues possess the pigments of red grapes and most varietally distinctive aroma compounds. It is also preferable that the internal tissues of the fruit hydrolyze during ripening. This process greatly eases juice extraction and limits the development of pectin-induced cloudiness in wine. High sugar contents (22–25%) and comparatively acidic juice (pH 3.1–3.5, 0.55–0.85 g/liter titratable acidity) are desirable at maturity. Better cultivars possess a distinctive subtle aroma sufficient to generate but not mask the development of a complex wine fragrance.

Table grapes are thought to be the most ancient of grapevine cultivars because of their extensive accumulation of mutations. Most table grape varieties are unpigmented (produce no anthocyanins), partially to completely seedless, large fruited, low in acidity (0.3–0.6 g/liter), and moderate in sugar accumulation (18–20%). Additional desirable traits include retention of a pulpy flesh and the ability to be stored for several months (to extend the shipping period of the crop). Most long-established table grape varieties are thought to have originated in central Asia or the Near East, and are adapted to hot arid climates. Several hundred table grape varieties are grown worldwide. Some of the more important cultivars are Almeria, Calmeria, Dattier, Emperor, Malaga, Perlette, Ribier (Alphonse Lavallée), Flame Tokay, and Thompson Seedless (Sultana).

Theoretically, any cultivar can be used for raisin production; in practice, only a few are. Thompson Seedless (Sultana) is the most extensively used cultivar in almost every raisin-producing region of the globe. However, Muscat of Alexandria is the dominant raisin cultivar in a few countries. For currant production, Black Corinth (Zante Currant) is grown almost exclusively.

IV. Yearly Growth Cycle

Initiation of grapevine growth in the spring commences when conditions permit sufficient physiological activity for the sap to flow. This occurs when temperatures warm, vine cells have lost their cold acclimation, and exposure to cold has reversed bud dormancy. The impending reactivation often is indicated by sap bleeding from the cut ends of last year's growth. The rate of bud swelling and cell growth depends on the ambient temperature. Although this is a varietal trait, most cultivars show rapid resumption of growth when the average daily temperature reaches about 10°C.

Reactivation of growth tends to begin in the most terminal buds and to progress downward. Reactivation initially involves the dissolution of the callose inclusions that plug the sieve cells in the fall. Subsequently, the vascular cambium becomes active, producing new xylem and phloem cells internal and external to the cambium, respectively.

As buds swell, cells in the primary (main) bud of the overwintering compound bud begin to grow and divide. The elongating embryonic shoot and enlarging leaves force the bud scales apart. The two embryonic inflorescences typically found in each fertile (flower-bearing) bud also recommence their development. The other two buds (secondary and tertiary) of the overwintering bud usually remain inactive. Only when the primary bud is killed or severely damaged does the secondary bud become active. Tertiary buds may develop and burst if both primary and secondary buds are killed.

Once reactivated, shoot growth rapidly reaches its maximum within a few weeks. Subsequently, shoot growth slows and essentially stops about 100 days after bud burst. Unlike most temperate perennial plants, grapevines do not show determinate growth, that is, the formation of terminal dormant buds at the shoot apex. If considerable vegetative growth occurs throughout the summer, it typically results from lateral bud activation. All leaves produce compound buds at the leaf base, where the petiole joins the shoot (axil). The newly formed compound bud possesses four buds, the outermost and most mature of which is called the lateral bud. If the lateral bud becomes active and produces a shoot (called a lateral), the bud does so in the season of its production. The inner three buds (primary, secondary, and tertiary) remain dormant, and potentially become active only in subsequent years. Compound buds formed in the leaf axils of lateral shoots may become active and produce a third set of vegetative shoots in a single season. Each shoot system has the potential to produce its own fruit crop.

The potential of grapevines to produce three shoot systems in any one season provides the plant with an incredible ability to adjust to changing environmental conditions and stresses. Limiting this vegetative potential is one of the major tasks of the grape grower. The energy of the vine needs to be shifted from continued vegetative growth toward increased production of fully ripened fruit, preparing the plant for winter, and sustaining long-term vine health. Excessive vegetative growth draws nutrients away from developing buds and produces shading that reduces inflorescence initiation for the subsequent season's crop. Continued shoot and leaf production also limits nutrient availability for berry development. In addition, late vegetative growth and shading retard bud and cane maturation, and can result in increased winter injury. Finally, because most shoot growth is removed (pruned) at the end of the season, excessive shoot production can result in the associated loss of considerable stored nutrients and can retard subsequent canopy production.

The initiation of significant root growth in the spring usually starts when shoot growth has begun to slow. Root extension usually reaches its maximum and starts to decline between flowering and the last phase of berry development. In some regions, a second root growth period occurs in the fall.

As the shoot extends and the leaves unfold, the embryonic inflorescences begin to elongate and the flowers mature. Typically, two inflorescences are produced per shoot, located opposite the third and fourth, fourth and fifth, or fifth and sixth leaves. Flowering generally occurs when the average daily temperature approaches 20°C. Self-pollination usually results when the fused petals (calyptra) separate from the base of the flower, shaking pollen from the anthers onto the stigma. Warm sunny conditions encourage the rapid flowering and fertilization that promote uniform fruit ripening. Pollination is essential for fruit initiation, even in "seedless" varieties. In seeded cultivars, the number of seeds per berry (maximum 4) influences the size of the fruit. Typically, one fertilized seed per berry is necessary to produce the hormones required to maintain fruit development. Dehiscence of fruit with few or no fertile seeds (shatter) occurs shortly after flowering. The sensitivity of some cultivars to excessive shatter is called *coulure*. In seedless varieties, timing of seed abortion influences the maximum size of the fruit. Spraying with natural or artificial plant hormones can compensate for a deficiency and promote increased fruit size.

Induction of the two inflorescences typically found in fertile buds for the subsequent year's fruit production is separated by several weeks. The induction and initial differentiation of their development typically occur, respectively, during blooming and the initial phase of fruit enlargement of the current year's crop.

Berry development is commonly divided into four phases. Phase I refers to the initial growth period during which most cell division occurs. Phase II is a less well defined period during which fruit enlargement is minimal and most seed development occurs. Phase III is the second berry growth period, when most increase in fruit size results from cell enlargement, especially in the flesh. The initiation of Phase III is termed *véraison*. From this point onward, the berry begins to take on its mature coloration and shows marked sugar accumulation, its acidity declines, and varietal flavors are generated. Transport of water and inorganic nutrients from the xylem and subsequently water, inorganic, and organic nutrients from the phloem eventually ceases. By the end of Phase III, all vascular connections with the fruit are broken or sealed. In Phase IV, postmaturation changes include continued fruit softening and acidity decline, degradation or modification of aromatic compounds, and progressive drying.

Because climate and soil conditions can significantly influence grapevine growth and berry maturation, most vineyard activities are designed to diminish undesirable effects and promote favorable influences. Assuming that water, nutrient, pest, and pathogen stresses are adequately controlled, the primary factors affecting fruit ripening are the solar and temperature conditions around the vine and fruit. In cooler regions, maximal exposure of the fruit to the sun is usually preferred, whereas in hot arid climates, some shading of the fruit is usually beneficial.

Solar radiation has both direct and indirect effects on berry development. Because berry photosynthesis is limited and occurs only during the pre-*véraison* periods, the primary direct effect of sun exposure is through its greater proportion of red and ultraviolet radiation. In contrast, shade light has a higher proportion of blue wavelengths, because of the absorption of red and ultraviolet radiation by the leaf canopy, and the blue enrichment of skylight. The higher proportion of red radiation in direct-beam sunlight can enhance the activation of certain enzymes such as those promoting malic acid respiration. Direct sun exposure is also important in the development of mature berry coloration, aroma development, and sugar accumulation. Ultraviolet radiation favors cuticular development of the fruit and leaves, and thus tends to reduce disease incidence. Indirectly, solar radiation causes fruit heating and enhances the rate and extent of the decline in fruit acidity. In addition, heating enhances transpiration and the accumulation of nutrients transported in the xylem and phloem. Sun and wind exposure also speed the drying of fruit and leaf surfaces, thus limiting infection by a wide range of pathogens.

V. Vineyard Site Selection

Selection of a vineyard site and appropriate cultivars involves both site–cultivar compatibility and anticipated financial returns. The most widely used indicator of site–cultivar suitability is the heat summation (degree–day) system developed by Winkler and Amerine for California. In most locations, however, heat summation data must be complemented with relevant soil and vineyard climate details. Important modifying meso- and microclimatic conditions include factors such as minimum winter temperatures, frequency of early fall and late spring frosts, relative humidity, solar exposure, and soil drainage. The more closely regional conditions approach the limits of a proposed cultivar's climatic suitability, the more significant become the meso- and microclimatic factors of the site. For example, sloped vineyard sites become progressively more valuable the higher the latitude. Slopes can increase solar exposure, especially valuable in the spring and fall; can enhance drainage, permitting earlier soil warming and vine activation; and can direct cool air away from the vines, potentially extending the frost-free growing season by several weeks. A porous rocky soil can be valuable in rapid soil warming during the day and heat radiation to the vines during the night. Dark soils can further increase the absorption of solar radiation and moderate the microclimate around the vines.

In dry climates, where irrigation water is unavailable or prohibited, deep soils may permit grape culture by letting roots reach deep sources of groundwater. In certain regions such as the sherry region of Spain, development of a hard, noncracking, chalk crust in the summer can limit water evaporation from the soil. Soil texture can also significantly influence the upward capillary movement of water in the soil, supplying surface roots with moisture under dry conditions.

VI. Vineyard Establishment

Establishment of a vineyard involves even more capital investment than is usually required to start an orchard of equivalent size. In comparison, however, fruit production approaches typical values sooner in vineyards. Commercial production is often reached within 4–5 yr on fertile soils, whereas on drier low-nutrient hillside sites standard yields may not be reached for 6–7 yr. No crop is produced for the first 3 yr and production is usually prevented by inflorescence removal until the fourth year. The first 3-yr growth is directed to establishing the grapevine's woody structures and initiating its training system.

The planting of new vineyards, or the insertion of replacement vines, normally involves the use of grafted cuttings. Young vines are obtained by grafting short cane sections or buds from the desired scion variety onto a rootstock possessing appropriate resistance and agronomic traits. Choosing the appropriate rootstock or combination of rootstocks for a vineyard is crucial, since an error at this point may require uprooting and replanting years in advance of the usual productive life-span of a grapevine (40–50 yr).

Rootstock canes may be induced to root before or after grafting the scion, depending on the ease with which rooting occurs. All buds are removed from the rootstock cane before grafting the scion. It is important that the cambial tissues of the scion and rootstock be contiguous and protected from drying. In several countries, grafted vines are produced by specialist nurseries and are purchased on contract for direct planting in the vineyard.

The type and degree of preparatory vineyard work depends on whether the location is virgin land or has been previously cultivated. For a new vineyard, deep tilling may be essential to ensure good drainage. Depending on whether irrigation is necessary, and the type to be installed, laying pipes or ground leveling may be necessary, and is preferably performed before planting. If the field is contaminated with noxious weeds, nematodes, or other soil-inhabiting pests, use of eradicative herbicides or soil sterilization is easier and safer before planting.

In planting, it is crucial to provide adequate water to promote early root system development and to ease root penetration into the surrounding soil. Soil penetration is further facilitated if the hole has loose, uneven, angled sides and is backfilled with soil of the same type and texture as the vineyard. Both features reduce the likelihood of root growth being confined within the planting hole. Plastic mulches are useful in promoting early and extensive root growth as well as controlling weed growth around the young grapevines.

During the first season, vegetative growth is permitted to develop essentially at will. Watering usually is stopped after the end of July to slow vegetative growth and to promote cane maturation. In late fall or winter, after leaf drop, the vine may be pruned back to the strongest shoot. The latter is tied upright to a stake to become the trunk of the developing grapevine. This cane may be pruned back to the four most mature buds. During the second year, pruning is conducted consistent with the training system desired. The third year's growth further establishes the training system and initiates the inflorescences for the subsequent year's crop. Grapevine productivity usually reaches its maximum within 7–10 yr.

VII. Training Systems and Pruning

Probably several hundred named training systems exist worldwide, with new forms continually being developed and older systems being refined. Each system attempts to direct most of the vine's energy into producing mature fruit and maintaining the long-term health of the vine. Most systems have developed in particular regions in response to the prevailing climate and soil conditions and the needs of local grape cultivars. Newer systems such as the Geneva Double Curtain (GDC), Lyre (U), Ruakura Twin Two Tier (RT2T), and Scott Henry Trellis (SH) are divided-canopy systems. In other words, the shoots coming from a variously branched cordon system are positioned to minimize leaf and fruit shading. Thus, the training system provides conditions that can direct the potentially excessive vigor of strong, healthy vines into increased yield and improved fruit quality. Vines freed from systemic viral and bacterial pathogens, on moist fertile soil, with weed, fungal, and other pest problems adequately regulated tend to be excessively vigorous when traditional training systems are employed. The latter often were developed for vines unknowingly infested with several systemic pathogens and were cultivated on relatively poor soils under dryland conditions. These conditions, associated with severe pruning, restricted vine growth and promoted fruit maturity.

Canopy division physically separates and directs the larger number of primary shoots adequately supported by strong vines to maximize solar exposure. The increased number of grape clusters produced places an early nutrient drain on the vine, limiting the activation of lateral shoots. Physical placement of the shoots over a wide area minimizes canopy and fruit shading. Limited shading and a more open canopy speed drying of the foliage and fruit, help minimize disease incidence, and facilitate the application of chemical sprays if required.

Training systems are often classified relative to the length of the bearing wood retained at the end of the growing season. Short canes with two to four buds are called spurs, whereas longer sections possessing upward of 12 buds are termed canes. Most training systems also may be grouped as head trained, with bearing wood arising from a central crown (head), or cordon trained, with bearing wood located along one or more branches of the trunk (cordons). Training systems also may be grouped based on shoot positioning (vertically upright or downward, pendulous, or horizontal), canopy height (low, standard, or high), or trunk number. Several trunks may be developed per vine when the incidence of crown gall is high.

An old but expensive system of regulating vine vigor, still popular in some parts of Europe, is high density planting. This method involves some 4000–5000 vines/ha, in contrast to the 1100 to 1600 vines/ha common outside Europe. High density planting limits root extension, while promoting early grapevine productivity, increased yield per hectare, and full fruit maturation. Modern divided-canopy systems achieve many of the same goals (increased yield of high quality fruit) at lower initial costs. Purchasing grafted vines is one of the major expenses of establishing a vineyard. Modern training systems also use wide row spacing, and thus are compatible with most currently used vineyard equipment in the New World.

Because of shifts in consumer demand, it may be desirable to convert some or all of an existing vineyard to another variety. Grafting over is much less expensive and more rapid than tearing out the existing vines and replanting. In grafting over, the head of the grapevine is removed and several canes or buds of the desired scion variety are grafted onto the trunk. The shoots derived from the grafted scion are trained into the new fruiting portion of the vine. Nearly full productivity may be reestablished within about 2 yr. [*See* PLANT PROPAGATION.]

Between leaf fall and the start of growth in the spring, most of the shoot growth (~90%) is pruned away. Pruning has several purposes. One of the primary functions is to regulate fruit production by removing excess fertile buds. Thus, depending on the capacity of the vine, a cultivar-specific number of buds is retained. By judicious selection of the bearing wood, the grape grower can both direct the initial growth of the shoots and choose their position on the vine. Both features are important in providing the shoots with the best solar exposure for growth and fruit ripening. Pruning is also essential to maintaining the training system.

In the majority of training systems, it is important to neither overprune nor underprune. Overpruning tends to promote lateral bud activation, berry shading, and delayed fruit ripening. Underpruning can result in excessive fruit production, delayed maturation, and poor berry quality. In a few years, however, unpruned vines may adjust by producing smaller grape clusters on thin shoots, whose extremities self-dehisce. Consequently, fruit quality improves to the point where it approximates that of many of the better training systems. This observation has led to the development of the minimal-pruning training system. In minimal pruning, the vine is initially trained to a bilateral cordon, after which pruning is primarily limited to skirting (the removal of shoots that trail down to the ground). Minimal pruning provides considerable cost savings while producing increased yields of good quality fruit that is easily harvested mechanically. Minimal pruning has proven popular in many of the drier regions of Australia.

Most pruning is conducted in the late fall or winter months, because choosing the cane wood and counting the number of buds to retain is easier when the vine is defoliated. However, in some situations additional summer pruning is desirable. Removing various lengths of shoot growth is termed trimming. Trimming the terminal few centimeters of the growing shoots during flowering can enhance fruit set in varieties sensitive to *coulure*. Later removal of longer shoot segments may be employed in windy climates to produce more sturdy shoots, to limit excessive leaf and fruit shading, or to ease movement of machinery through the vineyard. However, trimming must be done judiciously since it can induce lateral bud activation, producing a carbohydrate drain that can retard fruit ripening and cane maturation.

Other forms of summer pruning include flower- and fruit-cluster thinning. These procedures may be used to limit yield when more fertile buds survive the winter than expected. In cold climatic regions it is usual to leave more buds than "ideal," in the expectation that a portion will not survive the winter.

An increasingly popular summer pruning technique is basal leaf removal, which involves removing the leaves adjacent to, and immediately above and below, fruit clusters. This method improves the light and humidity microclimate around the berry cluster, and thus promotes fruit quality and health. Basal leaf removal also permits the more efficient application of pest control chemicals.

VIII. Fertilization

Grapevines are one of the few major crops with modest yearly nutrient demands. This characteristic partially explains why viticulture historically could be relegated to poor hillside soils, or vines trained up trees on the edges of fields and roadsides. The deeply penetrating root system of grapevines allowed them to gain access to water and nutrients beyond the reach of annual food crops.

The potential of the vine to obtain nutrients deep in the soil, and the extensive storage of nutrients in the woody structures of the vine, severely complicates assessing the value of most fertilizer applications. This problem is important since excess fertilization is economically wasteful, can lead to groundwater pollution, and can disrupt the uptake of other nutrients. For example, grapes are seldom deficient in phosphorus and its addition can interfere with potassium uptake. Although most inorganic nutrients are nontoxic at higher than typical soil concentrations, increasing the availability of several micronutrients such as boron and zinc rapidly leads to toxicity.

Many factors affect nutrient availability and uptake by the vine, most of which are not readily influenced by the grape grower. Where the soil is relatively low in organic content, adjustment of the pH upward or downward may be achieved by the addition of crushed limestone or elemental sulfur, respectively. Alternatively, rootstocks able to derive the requisite inorganic nutrients from acidic or alkaline soil may be employed.

Where soils are deficient in particular nutrients, optimal application requires their addition at appropriate rates and times, and in appropriate manners. For example, addition of ammonia should be conducted sufficiently in advance of peak nitrogen-demand by the grapevine, providing time for soil bacteria to convert the ammonia nitrogen into the more readily absorbed and mobile nitrate form. Because most positively charged mineral nutrients such as potassium do not migrate effectively through the soil, it is important for effective uptake that they be applied throughout the root zone. For micronutrients, deficiency often can be treated by foliar application.

After being out of favor for many years, the use of manures has received renewed interest. In addition to the slow release of inorganic nutrients, manures liberate organic chelators that help retain inorganic nutrients in readily available forms. Chelators and other humic components of manure also promote the development and maintenance of the soil's aggregate structure and friability. The latter features improve soil porosity, facilitating water and air penetration, and minimize soil erosion.

IX. Irrigation

In some regions, notably Europe, irrigation is prohibited for wine grapes. Although excessive irrigation can result in increased yield and reduced fruit quality, proper application can regulate vine vigor and promote fruit ripening and quality. In addition, in many semiarid and arid regions, viticulture would not be commercially viable without irrigation.

Grapevines are particularly sensitive to water stress in the first few weeks following flowering. Water stress during this period can result in permanent restriction in maximum fruit size. Although normally undesirable, restricting berry enlargement by limiting water availability has occasionally been done to avoid fruit-cluster compactness and to diminish the incidence of Botrytis bunch rot. Early water stress also can negatively affect inflorescence induction and fruit set. After *véraison*, limited water deficit can be beneficial in restricting additional vegetative growth, promoting cane maturation, and enhancing berry ripening. When water deficiency develops slowly, the vine often temporarily counteracts its effects by increasing root growth, decreasing root osmotic potential (to favor water uptake), and modifying stomatal response (to reduce water loss by transpiration).

Because the physiological effects of water stress may last for several days following the restoration of turgor, prediction of the development of a water deficit is important in timing irrigation. Recently, the use of hand-held infrared thermometers has become popular in assessing impending water stress. As water stress develops, stomatal closure results in a sharp rise in leaf temperature above ambient temperature, as the cooling effect of transpiration decreases.

Three main irrigation techniques are used in viticulture: furrow, sprinkler, and drip systems. Their respective use depends partially on the cost, availability, and quality of the water, and on installation cost, vineyard topography, and auxiliary uses. [*See* IRRIGATION ENGINEERING: FARM PRACTICES, METHODS, AND SYSTEMS; WATER: CONTROL AND USE.]

Where water is inexpensive and of ample supply, the relatively inefficient use of water by furrow irrigation may not be an important factor. Furrow irrigation has the lowest installation cost of any irrigation system, but is applicable only on relatively level terrain. Care must be used on heavy soils, where disruption of soil aggregate structure results in clay particle migration, plugging of soil pores, and decreasing infiltration rates.

In cooler regions, where protection from late-spring or early-fall frosts is frequently necessary, sprinkler irrigation has a distinct advantage. Under frost conditions, the release of heat as irrigation water freezes on the vine limits the formation of ice crystals in plant tissues. Sprinkling must be continued until atmospheric conditions warm sufficiently to melt the ice coating. Otherwise, heat to melt the ice is extracted from vine tissues and frost damage can develop. Sprinkler irrigation has less tendency to disrupt the soil's aggregate structure because nozzle opening and application rates can be chosen to limit soil puddling. When the salt content of the water is higher than ideal, irrigation may need to be limited to evenings or cloudy days to minimize toxic salt build-up on the fruit and foliage due to evaporation.

Although sprinkler irrigation is suitable for sloped terrain, drip irrigation is often preferred. Drip irrigation has many advantages including maximal efficiency of water use, opportunity to apply fertilizer and nematicides jointly, avoidance of erosion and soil compaction, restricted growth of all but drought-tolerant weeds, and applicability on shallow soils or terrain where saline water is close to the soil surface. However, because root production occurs predominantly around the emitters, water stress can develop rapidly if water is not applied frequently.

X. Pest Control

Two trends are currently changing established means of disease, pest, and weed control. One is organic viticulture, in which use of synthetic chemicals is restricted or prohibited. The other trend is integrated pest management (IPM), in which control measures for all diseases, pests, and weeds of a crop are integrated and coordinated. [*See* INTEGRATED PEST MANAGEMENT.]

In organic viticulture, several grape pests can be adequately controlled by predatory or parasitic agents, but their use often requires maintaining overwintering sites for the biological control agent(s). However, control of other pests and pathogens often requires elemental or inorganic chemical pesticides such as sulfur or copper sulfate, respectively; organic chemicals such as soaps and oils; or biologically generated toxins such as that produced by the bacterium *Bacillus thuringiensis*. Use of organic fertilizers such as manure can indirectly aid disease and pest control by slowing nutrient release to the vine and minimizing the production of succulent tissues favored by most pests and pathogens.

IPM has become increasingly popular as a means of preserving and increasing the effectiveness of chemical control measures in the face of growing pest and pathogen resistance, and opposition to pesticide use by environmentalists and governments. IPM may employ all the methods used in organic viticulture but does not exclude the use of synthetic control agents.

Viticulture provides one of the oldest and best examples of biological control, the use of resistant rootstocks in regulating the ravages of the phylloxera root louse (*Daktulosphaira vitifoliae*). Without grafting to a resistant rootstock, culture of *V. vinifera* varieties would be essentially impossible in most parts of the world. Although biological controls have proven less applicable in the control of fungal, bacterial, viral, and weed problems, detailed knowledge of the biology of these agents can increase the efficiency and reduce the number of applications of chemical control agents. [*See* PEST MANAGEMENT, BIOLOGICAL CONTROL.]

Breeding was used most extensively in the late 1800s to incorporate resistance to various pests and diseases, and gave rise to the French–American hybrids. However, changes in fruit flavor limited their acceptance, especially in Europe, where laws have been passed to restrict or prohibit their cultivation. Thus, developing new resistant varieties is not a priority item in most countries, although rootstock development continues, since they do not alter the flavor characteristics of the scion cultivar.

Cultural controls include factors such as minimizing dusty conditions for spider mite control, basal leaf removal for limiting Botrytis bunch rot, and ap-

propriate timing of suitable levels of ammonia fertilizer to reduce the production of sensitive succulent tissues. [*See* PEST MANAGEMENT, CULTURAL CONTROL.]

The efficiency of chemical control agents can be increased by the application of several new concepts and technical advances. These include avoiding the mixing of incompatible compounds, preferential use of nonspecific chemical agents (to which pest resistance develops slowly), restricted use of curative agents (to which resistance may develop quickly), alternate use of different chemical agents (to limit specific pesticide/fungicide build-up and reduce the likelihood of resistance development), use of climatic conditions in disease forecasting (to minimize unnecessary chemical applications), and use of nozzles with an appropriately narrow range of droplet sizes (to reduce drift and improve effective impact and surface coverage). [*See* PEST MANAGEMENT, CHEMICAL CONTROL.]

The incidence and importance of particular diseases and pests varies from year to year and region to region. For example, downy mildew (*Plasmopara viticola*) is a minor problem in much of California, but a major pathogen in the more humid parts of North America and most of Europe. In contrast, powdery mildew (*Uncinula necator*) and Botrytis bunch rot (*Botrytis cinerea*) are important pathogens in almost every viticultural region. Powdery mildew often is more serious in drier years, whereas bunch rot is especially prominent during wet years.

Most viral diseases such as fanleaf degeneration and leafroll are globally serious problems. Their almost universal distribution may be due to the widespread dispersal of unknowingly infected rootstock in the control of phylloxera. The most widely dispersed of bacterial grapevine pathogens is *Agrobacterium tumefaciens*, the causal agent of crown gall. This pathogen is particularly damaging in cool climatic regions.

The major roundworm pathogens of grapevines are the root-knot nematodes (*Meloidogyne* spp.) and dagger nematodes (*Xiphinema* spp.). The latter are important vectors of the grapevine fanleaf virus. Major insect pests include several types of leafhoppers and various tortricid moths (e.g., several grape berry moths, the omnivorous leafroll, and the orange tortrix). Several spider mites also can cause considerable damage.

The major air pollutant causing serious grapevine damage is ozone. Severe physiological disorders in certain regions, and with particular cultivars, are *coulure* (inflorescence necrosis) and *dessèchement de la rafle* (bunch-stem necrosis). The most notable nutrient deficiency syndrome, especially on calcareous (alkaline) soils, is iron chlorosis.

XI. Harvesting

Selecting the harvest date is one of the most critical decisions in the viticultural calendar. This choice establishes the maximum quality of the fruit and the wine potentially made from it. Correspondingly, there is much concern in correctly predicting the optimal date of fruit maturity. Before the availability of analytical chemical indicators, color, texture, and taste were the only means of assessing grape ripeness. Currently, measurement of the sugar content or the sugar–acid ratio is the primary means by which grape maturity is assessed and the projected harvest date set.

For wine grapes, additional indicators of maturity may include the measurement of selected phenolic compounds such as anthocyanins, or aroma constituents and their precursors. The more the chemical nature of a grape's varietal aroma is known, the more useful its measurement may become in determining the optimal harvest date for wine grapes. Where permitted, adjustment of the sugar and acid content of the juice or wine is easier, and meets with more consumer acceptance, than artificial adjustment of the aroma. Aroma adjustment is permissible only in selected fortified wines (e.g., vermouth or marsala) or in wine-based beverages such as wine coolers. Examples of grape components potentially or actually being used in determining grape harvest are monoterpenes, methoxypyrazines, and norisoprenoid precursors.

Choice between manual and mechanical harvesting often depends as much on grape use, variety, and training system as on labor cost and availability. Topography, notably steep slopes, or vineyard layout, such as narrow rows, may require manual harvesting. In addition, use as table grapes or in the production of certain wines (white sparkling wines from red grapes) essentially makes manual harvesting obligatory. Where other conditions permit, varietal suitability and training system are the main nonmonetary factors affecting the choice of manual versus mechanical harvesting. Varietal suitability for mechanical harvesting depends on the ease with which individual grapes or clusters separate from the vine, and the resistance of the skin to rupture during separation. The fruit clusters of cultivars such as Cabernet Sauvignon and Flora separate easily, with little fruit rupture, whereas the clusters of other varieties such as Zinfandel and Muscat Canelli separate with difficulty and show medium to heavy juice release.

Where applicable, mechanical harvesting has several distinct benefits, notably picking speed and continuous operation under most climatic conditions. With cultivars suitable for mechanical harvesting, differentiation is rarely possible between wines made from grapes harvested mechanically or manually from similar vines.

Harvesting machines usually detach the fruit by shaking the vine trunk, by striking the shoots, or by a combination of both actions. Their effectiveness depends primarily on the training system and on how close or distant the fruit is from the trunk. Shaker types are generally better with spur pruned vines, whereas striker types are more effective with cane pruned vines.

Bibliography

Coombe, B., and Dry, P. (1988,1992). "Viticulture," Vols. 1 and 2. Winetitles, Adelaide, Australia.
Flaherty, D. L., Christensen, L. P., Lanini, W. T., Marois, J. J., Phillips, P. A., and Wilson, L. T. (1992). "Grape Pest Management," 2d Ed., Publ. No. 3343. Division of Agriculture and Natural Resources, University of California, Oakland.
Gladstone, J. (1992). "Viticulture and Environment." Winetitles, Adelaide, Australia.
Howell, G. S. (1987). *Vitis* rootstocks. In "Rootstocks for Fruit Crops" (R. C. Rom and R. F. Carlson, eds.), pp. 451-472. Wiley, New York.
Jackson, R. S. (1994). "Wine Science. Principles and Applications." Academic Press, San Diego.
Mullins, M. G., Bouquet, A., and Williams, L. E. (1992). "Biology of the Grapevine." Cambridge University Press, Cambridge.
Petrucci, V. E., Clary, C. D., and O'Brien, M. (1983). Grape harvesting systems. In "Principles and Practices for Harvesting and Handling Fruits and Nuts" (M. O'Brien, B. F. Cargill, and R. B. Fridley, eds.), pp. 525-574. AVI, Westport, Connecticut.
Smart, R. E., and Robinson, M. (1991). "Sunlight into Wine. A Handbook for Winegrape Canopy Management." Winetitles, Adelaide, Australia.
Williams, L. E., and Matthews, M. A. (1990). Grapevines. In "Irrigation of Agricultural Crops" (B. A. Stewart and D. R. Nielsen, eds.), Agronomy Series Monograph #30, pp. 1019–1055. American Society of Agronomy, Madison, Wisconsin.
Winkler, A. J., Cook, J. A., Kliewer, W. M., and Lider, L. A. (1974). "General Viticulture." University of California Press, Berkeley.

Waste Management Engineering

WILLIAM F. RITTER, *University of Delaware*

Glossary

Aeration Process forcing intimate contact between air and a liquid by one or more of the following methods: spraying the liquid in the air, bubbling air through the liquid, and agitating the liquid to promote absorption of oxygen through the air–liquid interface

Agricultural wastes Wastes normally associated with the production and processing of food and fiber on farms, feedlots, ranches, ranges, and forests that may include animal manure, crop residues, and dead animals; also agricultural chemicals and their residues and containers, which may contribute contaminants to surface and subsurface water

Biochemical oxygen demand (BOD) Quantity of oxygen used in the biochemical oxidation of organic matter in a specified time and at a specified temperature and conditions; normally 5 days at 20°C unless otherwise stated

Biological wastewater treatment Forms of wastewater treatment in which bacterial or biochemical action is managed to stabilize or oxidize the unstable organic matter present; oxidation ditches, aerated lagoons, aerobic lagoons, anaerobic lagoons, anaerobic digesters, and aerobic digesters are examples

Chemical oxygen demand (COD) Measure of the oxygen-consuming capacity of inorganic and organic matter present in water or wastewater, expressed as the amount of oxygen consumed by a chemical oxidant in a specified test; it does not differentiate between stable and unstable organic matter and thus does not necessarily correlate with biochemical oxygen demand

Digestion Usually refers to the breakdown of organic matter in a water solution or suspension into simpler or more biologically stable compounds, or both; in anaerobic digestion, organic matter may be decomposed to soluble organic acids or alcohols and subsequently converted to gases such as methane and carbon dioxide

Effluent Wastewater or other liquid treated or untreated that is discharged

Manure Fecal and urinary excretion of livestock and poultry, often referred to as livestock waste; this material may contain bedding, spilled feed, water, or soil, as well as wastes not associated with livestock excreta, such as milking center wastewater, contaminated milk, hair, feathers, or other debris

Solids content (1) Sum of the dissolved and suspended constituents in water or wastewater; (2) residue remaining after a sample of water, wastewater, or semisolid material is evaporated and the residue is dried at a specified temperature (usually 103°C for 24 hr); usually stated in milligrams per liter or percent solids

Waste management as related to agricultural sciences deals with the collection, transport, storage, treatment, and disposal or reuse of wastes associated with livestock and poultry production systems. It also encompasses the management, treatment, and disposal or reuse of wastewater, sludge, and solids generated from the processing of raw agricultural products, namely, fruits, vegetables, meat, poultry, fish, and dairy products. Selection of waste management systems is based on economics, engineering, public reactions, and regulations. Federal, state, and local regulations attempt to minimize or eliminate pollution through the development of waste management system by owners and operators.

TABLE I
Fresh Manure Production and Characteristics per 1000-kg Live Animal Mass per Day

Parameter		Units	Dairy 640 kg	Beef 360 kg	Veal 91 kg	Swine 61 kg	Sheep 27 kg	Goat 64 kg	Horse 450 kg	Layer 1.8 kg	Broiler 0.9 kg	Turkey 6.8 kg	Duck 1.4 kg
											Typical live animal masses		
Total manure	mean	kg	86	58	62	84	40	41	51	64	85	47	110
	std deviation		17	17	24	24	11	8.6	7.2	19	13	13	**[a]
Urine	mean	kg	26	18	**	39	15	**	10	**	**	**	**
	std deviation		4.3	4.2	**	4.8	3.6	**	0.74	**	**	**	**
Density	mean	kg/m³	990	1000	1000	990	1000	1000	1000	970	1000	1000	**
	std deviation		63	75	**	24	64	**	93	39	**	**	**
Total solids	mean	kg	12	8.5	5.2	11	11	13	15	16	22	12	31
	std deviation		2.7	2.6	2.1	6.3	3.5	1.0	4.4	4.3	1.4	3.4	15
Volatile solids	mean	kg	10	7.2	2.3	8.5	9.2	**	10	12	17	9.1	19
	std deviation		0.79	0.57	**	0.66	0.31	**	3.7	0.84	1.2	1.3	**
Biochemical oxygen demand, 5 day	mean	kg	1.6	1.6	1.7	3.1	1.2	**	1.7	3.3	**	2.1	4.5
	std deviation		0.48	0.75	**	0.72	0.47	**	0.23	0.91	**	0.46	**
Chemical oxygen demand	mean	kg	11	7.8	5.3	8.4	11	**	**	11	16	9.3	27
	std deviation		2.4	2.7	**	3.7	2.5	**	**	2.7	1.8	1.2	**
pH	mean		7.0	7.0	8.1	7.5	**	**	7.2	6.9	**	**	**
	std deviation		0.45	0.34	**	0.57	**	**	**	0.56	**	**	**
Total Kjeldahl nitrogen	mean	kg	0.45	0.34	0.27	0.52	0.42	0.45	0.30	0.84	1.1	0.62	1.5
	std deviation		0.096	0.073	0.045	0.21	0.11	0.12	0.063	0.22	0.24	0.13	0.54
Ammonia nitrogen	mean	kg	0.079	0.086	0.12	0.29	**	**	**	0.21	**	0.080	**
	std deviation		0.083	0.052	0.016	0.10	**	**	**	0.18	**	0.018	**
Total phosphorus	mean	kg	0.094	0.092	0.066	0.18	0.087	0.11	0.071	0.30	0.30	0.23	0.54
	std deviation		0.024	0.027	0.011	0.10	0.030	0.016	0.026	0.081	0.053	0.093	0.21
Ortho phosphorus	mean	kg	0.061	**	**	0.12	0.032	0.019	0.019	0.092	**	**	0.25
	std deviation		0.0058	**	**	**	0.014	**	0.0071	0.016	**	**	**
Potassium	mean	kg	0.29	0.21	0.28	0.29	0.32	0.31	0.25	0.30	0.40	0.24	0.71
	std deviation		0.094	0.061	0.10	0.16	0.11	0.14	0.091	0.072	0.064	0.080	0.34

[a] **, No data available.

I. Waste Characteristics

A. Livestock Manure Characteristics

Livestock manure production and characteristics are important in the planning, design, and operation of livestock waste management systems. The descriptive data in Table I for livestock manure are drawn from a wide base of published information. When site-specific data or actual sample analyses can be performed, those data should be used for the planning, design, and operation of livestock waste management systems in lieu of the data in Table I. [See ANIMAL WASTE MANAGEMENT.]

B. Food Processing Wastewater Characteristics

Food processing can result in considerable quantities of solid waste and wastewater. Many of the wastes can be used in by-product recovery procedures. Solid waste from food processing may contain a high percentage of raw product and may exhibit characteristics of the raw product. Wastewater, on the other hand, is a dilute material that may contain low concentrations of some of the components of the raw product.

Dairy food processing waste characteristics are presented in Table II, and meat and vegetable wastewater characteristics are presented in Tables III and IV. The characteristics of solid fruit and vegetable wastes are presented in Table V. [See DAIRY PROCESSING AND PRODUCTS; MEAT PROCESSING.]

TABLE II
Dairy Food Processing Wastewater Characteristics

Product/operation	Wastewater	
	Mass (kg/kg milk processed)	BOD$_5$ (kg/1000 kg milk received)
Bulk milk handling	6.1	1.0
Milk processing	4.9	5.2
Butter	4.85	1.46
Cheese	2.06	1.8
Condensed milk	1.85	4.5
Milk powder	2.8	3.9
Milk, ice cream, and cottage cheese	2.52	6.37
Cottage cheese	6.0	34.0
Ice cream	2.8	5.76
Milk and cottage cheese	1.84	3.47
Mixed products	1.8	2.5

II. Livestock Waste Management

A livestock waste management system may consist of collection, storage, treatment, transfer, and utilization.

A. Collection

Collection refers to the initial capture and gathering of the waste from the point of origin or deposition to a collection point. Livestock and poultry manure collection often depends on the degree of freedom that is allowed the animal. If animals are allowed to move freely in a given space, the manure will be deposited randomly. Components of manure collection may include paved alleys, gutters, and slotted floors, as well as associated mechanical and hydraulic equipment to transfer the manure to storage.

Alleys are paved areas where the animals walk and may have a solid floor or a slotted floor. On slotted floors, animal hoofs work the manure through the slots into the alleys below. Paved alleys are used for beef, swine, and dairy and may be used below caged layers in poultry operations. The manure is collected by flushing or scraping the alleys. Mechanical scrapers are propeled by an electrical driver attached by cables or chains, and tractor scrapers are used in irregular-shaped alleys and open areas where mechanical scrapers cannot function properly. A tractor scraper can be a blade attached to either the front or rear end of a tractor or a skid-steer tractor that has a front-mounted bucket. Scrape alley widths generally vary from 2.5 to 4.3 m for dairy and beef and from 1.0 to 2.5 m for poultry and swine.

Alleys can also be cleaned by flushing. Slope is critical and generally varies from 1.25 to 5%. The length and width are also important factors in flush alleys, which should generally be less than 60 m long and vary in width from 1.0 to 3.0 m depending on the animal type. A number of mechanisms are used for flushing alleys, the most common being the emptying of large tanks of water or the use of high-volume pumps.

Gutters are narrow trenches used to collect animal wastes and are employed in confinement stall or stanchion dairy barns and in some swine facilities. Deep, narrow gutters with Y, U, V, or rectangular cross-sectional shapes that drain by gravity may be used in swine facilities. Narrow gutters can also be cleaned by flushing. Scrape gutters are frequently used in

TABLE III

Meat Processing Wastewater Characteristics

Component	Units	Red meat			Poultry[a]	Broiler[b]
		Slaughter	Packing	Processing[a]		
Volume	Liters/1000 kg[c]	406	610	737	1458	
Moisture	%					95.0
TS	% w.b.					4.9
	kg/1000 kg[c]	4.7	8.7	2.7	6.0	
VS	kg/1000 kg[c]					4.30
FS	kg/1000 kg[c]					0.65
BOD$_5$	kg/1000 kg[c]	5.8	12.1	5.7	8.5	
N	kg/1000 kg[c]					0.30
P	kg/1000 kg[c]					0.084
K	kg/1000 kg[c]					0.012

[a] Quantities per 1000-kg product.
[b] All values % w.b.
[c] Per 1000-kg live mass killed.

confined-stall dairy barns. The gutters are 41 to 61 cm wide and 30 to 41 cm deep with no bottom slope.

B. Storage

Storage is the temporary containment of the waste. The length of storage depends on the weather, crop, growing season, equipment availability, soil, soil conditions, labor requirements, and management flexibility. Manure can be stored as a solid, semisolid, slurry, or liquid.

Waste storage structures can be used for manure that will stack and can be handled by equipment designed for solid manure. The structures can be open or roofed to control excess moisture. Seepage and runoff must be controlled from open stacks. The structures often have wooden, reinforced concrete, or concrete block sidewalls. In some instances, manure may be stored in open stacks in fields. The amount of bedding material often dictates whether or not manure can be handled as a solid.

Waste storage ponds can be used to store solid and semisolid manure. They are earthen impoundments used to retain manure, bedding, and runoff liquid. The manure will likely be removed as a liquid unless precipitation is low or a means of draining the liquid is available. The ponds may have to be lined with compacted clay soil or artificial liners to prevent seepage and groundwater contamination.

Liquid and slurry manure can be stored in waste storage ponds or in aboveground or belowground tanks. Earthen storage is generally the least expensive type of storage. Storage ponds are generally rectangular but may be circular or any other shape that is practical. Manure storage tanks can be constructed of metal, concrete, or wood. Belowground tanks can be loaded using slotted floors, push–off ramps, gravity pipes, gutters, or pumps. Aboveground tanks are typically loaded by a pump moving the manure from a reception pit. Tank loading can be from the top or bottom of the tank. Waste storage ponds must provide not only volume to store wastewater and manure, but also storage capacity for normal precipita-

TABLE IV

Vegetable Processing Wastewater Characteristics

Component	Units	Cut bean	French style bean	Pea	Potato	Tomato
TS	kg/1000 kg[a]	15	43	39	53[b]	134
VS	kg/1000 kg[a]	9	29	20	50[b]	
FS	kg/1000 kg[a]	6	14	19	3[b]	
COD	kg/1000 kg[a]	14	35	37	71[c]	96
BOD$_5$	kg/1000 kg[a]	7	17	21	32	55

[a] kg/1000-kg raw product.
[b] Total suspended solids.
[c] Percentage of TSS.

TABLE V
Fruit and Vegetable Solid Waste Characteristics (Percent Wet Mass Basis)

Fruit/vegetable	Moisture content	Total solids	Volatile solids	Fixed solids	N	P	K
Banana, fresh	84.0	16.0	13.9	2.1	0.53		
Broccoli, leaf	86.5	13.5			0.30		
Cabbage, leaf	90.4	9.6	8.6	1.0	0.14	0.034	
Cabbage, core	89.7	10.3			0.38		
Carrot, top	84.0	16.0	13.6	2.4	0.42	0.03	
Carrot, root	87.4	12.6	11.3	1.3	0.25	0.04	
Cassava, root	67.6	32.4	31.1	1.3	1.68	0.039	
Corn, sweet, top	79.8	20.2	19.0	1.2	0.67		
Kale, top	88.4	11.6	9.7	1.9	0.22	0.06	
Lettuce, top	94.6	5.4	4.5	0.9	0.05	0.027	
Onion, top, mature	8.6	91.4	84.7	6.7	1.37	0.02	
Orange, flesh	87.2	12.8	12.2	0.6	0.26		
Orange, pulp	84.0	16.0	15.0	1.0	0.24		
Parsnip, root	76.3	23.7			0.47		
Potato, top, mature	12.8	87.2	71.5	15.7	1.22		
Potato, top, tuber					1.60	0.25	1.9
Pumpkin, flesh	91.3	8.7	7.9	0.8	0.12	0.037	
Rhubarb, leaf	88.6	11.4			0.20		
Rutabaga, top	90.0	10.0			0.35		
Rutabaga, root	89.5	10.5			0.20		
Spinach, stems	93.5	6.5			0.065		
Tomato, fresh	94.2	5.8	5.2	0.6	0.15	0.03	0.30
Tomato, solid waste	88.9	11.1	10.2	0.9	0.22	0.044	0.089
Turnip, top	92.2	7.8			0.20		
Turnip, root	91.1				0.34		

tion and runoff (less evaporation) during the storage period. Storage volume requirements for tanks are the same as those for ponds except that in most cases outside runoff is excluded from the waste storage tanks because of the relative high cost of storage.

C. Treatment

Treatment is any function that reduces the pollution potential of the waste, including physical, chemical, and biological treatment. It also includes activities that are classified as pretreatment, such as the separation of solids. Treatment methods used for agricultural wastes include the use of lagoons, oxidation ditches, and composting; these processes reduce nutrients, destroy pathogens, and reduce solids.

Anaerobic lagoons are widely used to treat animal wastes and are designed on the basis of the volatile solids loading rate. The rate of solids decomposition is a function of temperature, therefore the design loading rate varies from one location to another. Lagoons should be constructed to avoid leakage and potential groundwater pollution. If an anaerobic lagoon is managed and designed properly it will reduce animal waste odors. Anaerobic lagoons generally range in depth from 2 to 6 m.

Aerobic lagoons can be used if minimizing odors is critical. These lagoons operate within a depth range of 0.6 to 1.5 m to allow for the oxygen entrainment that is necessary for the aerobic bacteria. Aerobic lagoons are designed on the basis of the biochemical oxygen demand added per day and they should never be overloaded or they will become anaerobic. Surface area requirements are much larger for aerobic lagoons than for anaerobic lagoons.

Aerated lagoons operate aerobically and are dependent on mechanical aeration to supply the oxygen to treat the waste and minimize odors. This type of lagoon combines the small surface area feature of an anaerobic lagoon and the relative odor-free operation of an aerobic lagoon. The main disadvantages of aerated lagoons are the energy requirements and cost to operate the mechanical aerators and the high level of management required. Surface aerators that float on the surface of the lagoon or diffused-air systems may be used, the former being generally more economical to operate.

Oxidation ditches may be used for treating animal wastes in situations where there is not sufficient space available for a lagoon and odors are critical. The shallow, continuous ditch generally has an oval layout. It has a special aerator spanning the channel, and the action of the aerator moves the liquid waste around the channel and keeps the solids in suspension. Oxidation ditches can be expensive to operate and take considerable management.

Composting is the aerobic biological decomposition of organic matter, usually in solid and semi-solid form. Generally organic waste is mixed with other ingredients such as straw, wood chips, or corn cobs in a prescribed manner to accelerate the process. It converts an organic waste into a stable organic product by converting nitrogen from the unstable ammonia form to a more stable organic form. The end result is a product that is safer to use than raw organic material. Composting also reduces the bulk of organic material, improves its handling properties, reduces odor, fly, and other vector problems, and can destroy weed seeds and pathogens. The three basic methods of composting are windrow, static pile, and in-vessel.

The windrow method involves the arranging of compost mix in long, narrow piles or windrows. To maintain aerobic conditions, the compost mixture must be periodically turned. The minimum turning frequency varies from 2 to 10 days depending on the type of mix, volume, and ambient temperature. As the compost ages, the frequency of turning is reduced. Windrows are generally 1.2 to 1.8 m deep and 1.8 to 3.0 m wide.

The static pile method consists of mixing the compost material and then stacking the mix on perforated plastic pipe through which air is drawn or forced. The compost mixture height generally ranges from 2.4 to 4.6 m and the width is usually twice the depth.

The in-vessel composting process involves placing the compost in a container where it is continuously or periodically stirred. It is not as popular as the windrow or static pile methods, primarily due to cost and greater mechanical complexity.

Manure contains products that can be reclaimed by mechanical separation for feed or bedding. Solids in dairy manure can be removed and processed for use as a bedding material. Mechanical separators are also used to remove solids to reduce the volatile (organic) solids loading and in some cases the required volumes of storage facilities and of lagoons. Screens and centrifuges are commonly used to separate solids; screens are statically inclined or in continuous motion to aid in separation. Solids must be processed before they can be used for feed or bedding. If they are intended for bedding, the material should be composted or dried; if the solids are used for feed, they may need to be mixed with other feed ingredients and ensiled.

In many instances it is beneficial to remove manure, solids, and soil from the runoff from livestock operations. The most common device to accomplish this is the settling basin, which is a shallow pond designed for low velocities and the accumulation of solids. It is positioned between the wastewater source and storage or treatment facilities.

D. Transfer

Transfer refers to the movement and transportation of the waste throughout the system, including the transfer of waste from the collection point to the storage facility, to the treatment facility, and to the utilization site. The waste may require transfer as a solid, liquid, or slurry depending on the total solids concentration.

Liquid and slurry manure can be moved by gravity if sufficient elevation differences are present. For slurry manure a minimum of 1.2 m elevation is required between the top of the collection pit and the surface of the manure in storage. Gravity-flow slurry manure systems typically use 46- to 76-cm-diameter pipe.

Manure scraped from open lots can be loaded into manure spreaders or storage or treatment facilities using push-off ramps or docks. A ramp is a paved structure leading to a manure storage that can be level or inclined, whereas a dock is a level ramp that projects into the storage or treatment facilities.

Either displacement or centrifugal pumps are used to transport or agitate manure. Piston and air-pressure transfer displacement pumps are used for transferring manure, whereas diaphragm and progressive cavity displacement pumps are used for agitating, transferring, and irrigating manure, as are centrifugal pumps.

E. Utilization

Utilization is the function for which the manure and wastewater (effluent) is used for a beneficial purpose. The typical method is to apply animal manure to cropland, pasture, and hayland as a source of nutrients for plant growth and of organic matter to improve soil tilth. Manure and wastewater should be applied at rates at which the nutrient requirements of the crop are met. In many instances, nitrogen is the element that is used to determine the amount of manure to be applied. When nitrogen is used as the limiting nutrient, excessive phosphorus will be applied for most crops and manures. Today there is concern for the buildup of excessive phosphorus levels in soils where manure is applied. In some areas or watersheds, phosphorus is beginning to be used as the limiting nutrient for manure application.

Manure may also be utilized for energy. Liquid manure confined in an airtight vessel decomposes and produces methane, carbon dioxide, hydrogen sulfide, and water vapor as gaseous by-products in a process known as anaerobic digestion. Biogas, the product of anaerobic digestion, is typically composed of 55 to 65% methane, 35 to 45% carbon dioxide, and traces of ammonia and hydrogen sulfide. Biogas can be burned in boilers to produce hot water, in engines to power electrical generators, and in absorption coolers to produce refrigeration. The hydrogen sulfide present in biogas may cause the gas to have an odor similar to that of rotten eggs. Hydrogen sulfide mixed with water vapor can form sulfuric acid, which is highly corrosive. The most frequent problem with anaerobic digestion is related to the economical use of the biogas.

III. Food Processing Waste Management

The food processing industry has three possibilities for treating their wastewaters: (1) they may be treated separately in an industrial wastewater treatment plant; (2) raw wastewaters may be discharged to a municipal treatment plant for complete treatment; or (3) the wastewater may be pretreated at the site prior to discharge to a municipal wastewater treatment plant. Treated wastewater may be disposed of by stream discharge or applied to land. Federal and state regulations determine the minimum level of effluent quality that must be obtained for stream discharge and land application.

A. Pretreatment

Most food processing plants that discharge to municipal wastewater treatment plants use some form of pretreatment. Pretreatment processes may include both physical and chemical treatment processes, including screening, sedimentation, flotation, and flocculation.

Screening is one of the initial pretreatment steps in waste treatment and four types of screens are commonly used in the food processing industry. The most common screens are 840–420 microns, and fine screens (less than 74 microns) can also be used. The most common type of screen is the static screen, fol-

lowed by the vibrating or oscillating screen; other types are the rotary drum screen, tangential screen, and rotating drum centrifugal screen. Selection of the type of screen to use will depend on initial cost, operating and maintenance costs, space required, hydraulic capacity, and percentage of solids captured.

The sedimentation process is used to remove settleable organic and inorganic solids suspended in the influent. Sedimentation tanks or clarifiers, as they are sometimes called, are rectangular or circular. Solids are removed by gravity or by skimming in the case of floatables. Wastewater moves through the sedimentation tank very slowly, giving the settleable solids an opportunity to sink to the bottom of the tank. Sedimentation tanks should be at least 3.0 m deep.

Dissolved-air flotation is a treatment process that removes suspended solids in the form of floating sludge. Air flotation involves the atmospheric pressurizing of the wastewater stream and the injection of air into the stream. Then as this mixture is released into an open tank, the air releases from the bulk fluid as small bubbles. The removal of suspended solids depends on the attachment of fine air bubbles to each suspended solid particle. These bubbles improve the buoyancy of the suspended particle, causing it to float to the surface where it is removed by mechanical means. Air flotation has an advantage over gravity sedimentation when used for the removal of oils, fine particulate matter, and fat, which are not readily amenable to sedimentation. Dissolved-air flotation is particularly useful in the treatment of poultry and meat packing or processing wastewater.

In some cases difficulties are encountered in the removal of suspended solids because of the size and density of the particles. To aid in the removal of these suspended solids, flocculating agents are used, which help to physically entrap the suspended particles through electrostatic interactions and adsorption. The entrapment results in the formation of larger and more dense particles that become amenable to sedimentation. Flocculating agents commonly used are lime, ferric chloride, ferrous sulfate, aluminum sulfate, and organic polymers. Organic polymers are generally used in conjunction with inorganic flocculating agents.

B. Biological Treatment

Biological treatment systems are "living" systems that rely on mixed biological cultures to break down waste organics and remove organic matter from solution. Biological treatment is the most important step in wastewater treatment. Generally sedimentation will only remove 35 to 50% of the BOD. Activated sludge, trickling filters, rotating biological contactors, and lagoons are common aerobic biological treatment processes used in the food processing industry. Some emerging technologies that have recently been used in the food processing industry include sequencing batch reactors and fluidized beds. Some anaerobic treatment processes are also used to treat food processing wastewater, and these may be used in combination with aerobic processes.

The activated sludge system is a process in which a mixture of wastewater and activated sludge is combined, agitated, and aerated. The activated sludge is a floc of biologically active material composed of viable microorganisms and suspended solids that have been developed from defined agitated and aeration conditions. The mixture of activated sludge solids and raw wastewater is referred to as the mixed liquor suspended solids. After a specific aeration time, the mixed liquor suspended solids enter a settling basin, where the solids are allowed to settle out and returned to the head of the aeration tank. Excess solids are removed from the settling basin as sludge and thickened and treated. Air or oxygen is supplied to the activated sludge process by mechanical means. There are a number of variations of the activated sludge process. Common processes used in the food processing industry are conventional activated sludge, contact stabilization extended aeration, and the oxidation ditch. Use of sequencing batch reactors in which aeration and settling are done in the same tank is a new modification of the activated sludge process.

In comparison to the activated sludge process, other forms of biological treatment use contact surfaces containing fixed biological material that extracts the pollutants from the wastewater stream. Common surface contact systems are trickling filters, rotating biological contactors, fluidized beds, and biofilter activated sludge processes.

In the trickling filter system, wastewater is distributed over a bed of media. Modern trickling filters use synthetic media whereas older trickling filters have crushed rock. Wastewater flows through the media to which the microorganisms are attached. As the biomass builds up on the media, at some point it will be sloughed off from the surface and fall to the bottom of the bed, where it is carried with the wastewater to a settling tank, where it is settled out and returned to the head of the system and settled out in a primary clarifier. Trickling filter depths may range anywhere from 1.5 to 6.1 m.

In the rotating biological contactor, the organic waste is extracted from the waste stream by biota film attached to rotating contact surface disks. The disks are usually 3.7 m in diameter and made of lightweight plastic. Approximately half of the disk is immersed in a trough containing the wastewater. The disk rotates slowly to allow proper film contact with the wastewater, and brings an adsorbed film of wastewater into the air where the film absorbs the available oxygen. The adsorbed biota film continues to grow and is ultimately sloughed off by the shear force of the rotating disc. The sloughed solids flow out with the treated wastewater to a final settling tank, where they are settled out. The rotating biological contactor discs will generally be placed in a series.

In a fluidized bed reactor, the wastewater to be treated passes upward through a bed of fine-granulated material, such as sand, at sufficient velocity to suspend the media. The reactor requires relatively little space to operate. The biofilter activated sludge process has a trickling filter followed by an aeration tank. Return activated sludge is recycled to the trickling filter.

One of the most common treatment processes in the food processing industry is the use of lagoons, which are relatively maintenance free and generally located in rural areas where land is available. The types of aerobic systems used are aerated lagoons, tertiary ponds, and facultative stabilization ponds. The latter depends on a symbiosis relationship within the aquatic ecosystem and on wind disturbances for physical incorporation of dissolved oxygen into the water. Generally the upper depths of the pond are aerobic whereas the bottom of the pond is anaerobic. The design depth varies from 1.0 to 2.0 m.

Tertiary ponds are less than 1 m in depth and have a low BOD loading. The principal use of a tertiary pond is to reduce the residual BOD and suspended solids in the wastewater that has been treated by another biological system such as activated sludge or trickling filter. The tertiary pond is also used to remove nitrogen and phosphorus from the wastewater. They are also referred to as polishing ponds.

The aerated lagoon incorporates the use of mechanical agitation and aeration to provide a complete-mixing aerated aquatic environment. These lagoons are commonly aerated with floating or platform-mounted mechanical aeration units. Aerated lagoons are generally 2.4 to 3.7 m deep.

The number and type of anaerobic treatment systems being used in the food processing industry have grown rapidly since the late 1970s and early 1980s. Prior to that, only anaerobic lagoons and a few anaerobic contact process systems were used.

Anaerobic lagoons are generally single celled and are the oldest and most frequently used anaerobic technology in the food processing industry. They generally range from 3.0 to 6.0 m deep and have anaerobic conditions throughout the lagoon because of the relatively high BOD loading rate. They are used primarily in the meat and poultry industries. A more recent development involves placing synthetic covers over anaerobic lagoons, for covered lagoons have higher BOD removal rates, and odors and biogas are captured.

The anaerobic contact process is analogous to the aerobic activated sludge process and relies on a completely mixed reactor to maximize biomass and food contact. The key components of the contact process are the completely mixed reactor, the biomass degassing unit, and the solids separation device. Settled solids are returned from the clarifier to the mixed reactor. The anaerobic contact process has been applied to meat processing wastewaters since the late 1950s.

Two new technologies that are being used are the upflow anaerobic sludge blanket (UASB) process and the anaerobic filter. The UASB process employs a single reactor containing a bed of active granular anaerobic sludge covered by a blanket of flocculent, less dense sludge. Influent wastewater is evenly distributed beneath the bed and flows upward through the two zones of biomass, each 1 to 2 m in depth. A three-phase separator is employed at the top of the reactor to separate biogas and solids from the liquid.

Anaerobic filters employ fixed media within a reactor to support the development of high concentrations of active biomass. Media can range from rock to pall rings to reticulated polystyrene. The systems can be operated in either the upflow or downflow mode.

C. Disinfection

The purpose of disinfection of any wastewater is to protect the public health from the spread of disease by controlling the point-source discharge. The practice of disinfection is carried out where wastewater treated for feces has been treated and discharged to a stream. Some state regulatory agencies require all point-source discharges to be disinfected. The methods use chlorine, ozone, and ultraviolet light, with chlorination being the most widely used disinfection practice.

D. Sludge Treatment and Disposal

Sludge from biological treatment processes and from the pretreatment processes of sedimentation and dissolved-air flotation must be stabilized. In some cases sludge is thickened before it is stabilized to increase the solids content. Sludge may be thickened by sedimentation or dissolved-air flotation.

Sludge is stabilized before ultimate disposal to stabilize and reduce the solids and reduce odors. The most common methods of stabilization are anaerobic digestion and aerobic digestion, the former consisting of two distinct stages that occur simultaneously in a digester. The first stage consists of hydrolysis of the high-molecular-weight organic compounds and conversion to organic acids by acid-forming bacteria; the second stage is gasification of the organic acids to methane and carbon dioxide by the methane-forming bacteria. Anaerobic digesters are closed structures with either floating or fixed roof covers. The digesters may be one or two stage.

Aerobic digesters are operated under aerobic conditions. Sludge is aerated in open basins for an aeration time of 10 to 20 days. Organic solids reduction can run as high as 40%.

Sludge can be further stabilized after digestion by composting. The objectives of composting are to biologically stabilize the organics, destroy pathogenic organisms, and reduce the volume of the sludge. The optimum moisture content for a compost mixture is 50 to 60%. Dewatered sludge is mixed with either an organic amendment like dried manure, straw, or sawdust or a recoverable bulking agent like wood chips. Composting may be performed in an enclosed vessel, where the compost mixture is slowly agitated, or in windrows or static piles with forced aeration. The windrows have to be turned periodically.

After sludge is aerobically or anaerobically digested it may be dewatered if it is not to be applied to land as a liquid. Digested sludge may be dewatered with open sand drying beds or by vacuum filtration, pressure filtration, or centrifugation. Pressure filtration dewatering is done using either a belt filter press or a plate-and-frame filter press. Vacuum filters require considerable energy so they are being replaced by belt filter presses, which are more economical to operate and produce a drier sludge cake. Modern sand drying beds have paved areas with watertight walls sloping to drainage trenches filled with a coarse sand bed supported on a gravel filter with a perforated pipe underdrain. Sludge is applied to a depth of 30 cm or more and may be pumped from the digester. Supernatant (sludge liquid) is drawn off after the solids settle and the solids are left to dry. The solids are removed from the drying fed by a front-end loader.

Sludges may be disposed of on land or in landfills, or may be incinerated. Sludges are applied to cropland, forestland, or disturbed lands undergoing land

TABLE VI

Comparison of Design Features of Alternative Land Treatment Systems

Feature	Slow rate (type 1)	Slow rate (type 2)	Rapid infiltration	Overland flow
Application techniques	Sprinkler or surface	Sprinkler or surface	Usually surface	Sprinkler or surface
Annual hydraulic-loading rate, meters/year	1.7–6.1	0.6–2.0	6.1–91.5	7.3–56.7
Minimum preapplication treatment provided	Primary sedimentation	Primary sedimentation	Primary sedimentation	Screening
Disposition of applied wastewater	Evapotranspiration and percolation	Evapotranspiration and percolation	Mainly percolation	Surface runoff and evaporation with some percolation
Need for vegetation	Required	Required	Optional	Required

reclamation. Composted sludges may be used as a potting soil medium or sold as a soil amendment.

E. Land Application

Land treatment methods can be classified into three main groups: slow rate, rapid infiltration, and overland flow. These alternatives differ considerably with respect to both treatment objectives and site characteristics. Comparison of design features for the different types of land treatment systems is presented in Table VI.

The slow rate system is the most widely used treatment process. Wastewater is applied to vegetated land by sprinkler irrigation or by surface irrigation methods such as graded border or furrow irrigation. The water applied is either consumed through evapotranspiration or percolates vertically or horizontally through the soil profile where treatment occurs. There are typically two types of slow rate systems. The system listed as type 1 in Table VI generally has a higher hydraulic loading rate. Its design objective is wastewater treatment and the limiting design parameter is usually soil permeability or constituent loading. The type 2 system has the design objective of water reuse through crop production or landscape irrigation.

Rapid infiltration systems have relatively high application rates compared to those of slow rate systems. Wastewater is applied on an intermittent schedule usually to shallow infiltration or spreading basins. In some cases high-rate sprinklers are used. Vegetation is not used in infiltration basins but is required with high-rate sprinklers. In a rapid infiltration system the wastewater that is applied may be allowed to recharge groundwater and help augment water supplies or prevent saltwater intrusion or may be recovered using underdrains or pumped withdrawal. The treatment potential of rapid infiltration systems is somewhat less than that of slow rate systems.

Overland flow systems utilize the vegetative cover as a treatment component and consist of a series of graded slopes and terraces. Slopes are generally 2 to 5% and the length of the slopes may be from 46 to 76 m. Wastewater is applied at the top of the slope or approximately one-third of the distance down the slope by high-pressure sprinklers, low-pressure sprays, or surface methods such as gated pipe. The amount of the waste water lost will depend on the time of year and local climate. In many systems, over 60% of the applied water is collected as runoff on an annual basis.

Bibliography

Overcash, M. R., Humenik, F. J., and Miner, J. R. (1983). "Livestock Waste Management," Vols. I and II. CRC Press, Boca Raton, FL.

Tchobanoglous, G., and Burton, F. L. (1991). "Wastewater Engineering: Treatment, Disposal, and Reuse," 3rd ed. McGraw–Hill, New York.

Totzke, D. E. (1990). Anaerobic treatment technology: Poised for the 1990's. *In* "1990 Food Industry Environmental Conference Processing, Nov. 12–14, 1990, Atlanta, GA," pp. 460–470. Georgia Tech. Research Institute, Atlanta, GA.

U.S. Department of Agriculture. (1992). "Agricultural Waste Management Field Manual." Soil Conservation Service, Washington, D.C.

Viessman, W., and Hammer, M. J. (1993). "Water Supply and Pollution Control," 5th ed. Harper Collins College Publishers, New York.

Water: Control and Use

J. P. RILEY, W. R. WALKER, *Utah State University*

Glossary

Aquifer Water-bearing formation beneath the land surface that provides a good water reservoir; a formation, group of formations, or part of a formation that contains sufficient permeable material to be capable of yielding significant quantities of water to wells and springs

Ground water That part of the subsurface water that is in the saturated zone or, more generally, all water which occurs below the land surface as distinct from surface water

Hectare Metric unit of area equal to 10,000 square meters (approximately 2.5 acres)

Hydrologic cycle Continuous process whereby water which falls as precipitation from the atmosphere evaporates from land and water surfaces and, after condensation in the atmosphere, is deposited again on earth as precipitation

Permeable Condition of a geologic material that renders it capable of transmitting a significant quantity of water without impairment of the structure of the geologic material

Surface subsidence Lowering of the land surface above a ground water aquifer resulting from a consolidation of the aquifer material produced by dewatering all or part of the aquifer by pumping or other drainage procedures

Surface water All fresh water which occurs on the earth's surface, including overland flow, stream and river flows, lakes, and surface ponds and reservoirs

Tonne Metric unit of weight equal to 1000 kilograms (approximately 2200 pounds)

Water demand Quantity of water required during a particular time interval for a particular use or purpose

Water is essential to life, growth, and reproduction. On a global scale, water is the energy regulator of the heat budget of the earth. Without the evaporation of water, life on earth would be impossible. As an energy carrier, it makes possible water power, steam power, and space heating. It is a pervasive solvent for such diverse processes as industrial production and for the use of soil nutrients by plants. Water is essential for plant photosynthesis and for all animal life, including human. Finally, water provides a means of transport—for navigation, for drainage canals, for recreation, and for waste water. Accordingly, provision of an adequate supply of water is a major goal throughout the world.

I. Introduction

This article deals with the problem of matching the water demands of society to available water supplies. For the globe as a whole, there are adequate supplies of water. However, the temporal and spatial distributions of these supplies frequently do not match with the demands of society. In many places water shortages limit agricultural production, industrial output, and the capacity to support increasing populations. To the extent possible demands for water are met by the development of control systems which consist of physical facilities to collect, store, and redistribute water in accordance with the spatial and temporal requirements of society. [*See* WATER RESOURCES.]

Redistribution of water requires that changes be brought about in the naturally occurring physical system. These changes often deplete both the quantity and quality of the water in parts of the natural hydrologic system and thus produce negative impacts. It is important that these potential negative impacts be carefully evaluated, and to the extent possible, mitigated, for all water resource development projects.

A. The Global Supply of Water

Of the vast quantities of water on the earth—about 1.4 billion cubic kilometers—97.4% is in the oceans. The remaining 2.6%—about 36 million cubic kilometers—is fresh water, and of this, 77% is found in polar icecaps, icebergs, and glaciers. Nearly 90% of the remaining fresh water is found in ground water. The rest of the fresh water is found in rivers, lakes, animals and plants, and the atmosphere. It is clear that the usable water on the land surfaces of the earth (often termed the renewal water supply), on which most terrestrial life and our entire economy are dependent, constitutes only a minute fraction of the total water of the earth. However, this tiny fraction of the world's water is vital to life on the planet, and humans depend on it for such uses as water supply, food, transportation, and recreation.

B. The Distribution of the Global Supply

As stated above, for the globe as a whole, there is no shortage of water. However, the distribution of the global supply in both the spatial and temporal dimensions is often not consistent with needs as evidenced by the fact that there are severe shortages of water, as well as severe floods, in many parts of the world. Strong natural and manmade factors combine to reduce the water available to specific regions and localities in the right amount, at the right time, and of the required quality.

The most important natural force involved in the distribution of water on the Earth's surface is the dynamic character of the biosphere. Part of the water supply is in a continuous process of change from the solid (snow and ice) and liquid forms to the vapor state and then back again as precipitation. This part of the supply evaporates from water and land surfaces and, after condensation in the atmosphere, is deposited again on earth. Through the precipitation process, evaporation and runoff water from land and water surfaces are replaced as fresh water. This circulation pattern is termed the *hydrologic cycle*. It is, in effect, a gigantic still.

C. Surface and Ground Water Supplies

Water for use by humans is drawn from two sources—surface water and ground water. Surface water is found in streams, rivers, reservoirs, and lakes. Ground water is drawn from aquifers or underground reservoirs. For the globe as a whole, and in most localities, surface water is at present the most important source. In the United States, for example, about 80% of the water used (exclusive of hydropower generation) is withdrawn from surface water. However, ground water is a major source in many parts of the world. The great Ogallala aquifer in the United States is the largest known aquifer in the world, and it supplies water to large parts of the Midwest, particularly to Colorado, Kansas, Nebraska, New Mexico, Oklahoma, and Texas. Other large aquifers are found in India, China, Iraq, Syria, Russia, and Egypt. [*See* GROUND WATER.]

Much of the water in aquifers is millions of years old, and less than 1% of the water content of aquifers is replenished each year. When ground water withdrawals exceed replenishments, the aquifer is said to be "mined." In many parts of the world today, ground water that has accumulated over millions of years is being rapidly mined to meet demands resulting from population growth and expanded energy and agricultural uses.

When ground water levels recede because of overdraft, increased energy and capital equipment are needed to meet demands. Eventually the costs of lifting water can exceed the benefits, and the existing uses, such as for irrigation, have to be abandoned. This situation has already come about in many regions of Texas and Arizona. Clearly, there can be environmental and energy benefits to pumping aquifers at the same rate as the annual recharge instead of mining ground water. It should be emphasized that sustained ground water mining can cause aquifer consolidation and thus a permanent loss of aquifer storage capacity and surface subsidence.

II. Water Control

A. Water Distribution Systems

As previously stated, human activity is an important element affecting the global distribution of water. Some human actions affect the distribution of water adversely. For example, floods are a scourge that continue to plague many parts of the world, particularly poor countries that lack the resources and infrastructure to cope with them. Often floods downstream are caused by human activity upstream. A well-known example is the upstream deforestation in Nepal and India that causes downstream flooding in Bangladesh.

Other human activities degrade the quality of water. The pollution of important rivers and streams in the United States by municipal and industrial wastes during the first half of this century is an obvious case in point.

However, many human activities affect the supply of water constructively. An immense set of manmade physical facilities exists to increase the local supply of water, to control potentially destructive forces, and to enhance the quality of water. An example is the Central Utah Project, which collects water from the streams on the south slopes of the Uintah mountain range, stores it in reservoirs, and transports it through the Wasatch mountain range to be used for irrigation, for municipal and industrial purposes, and to generate electrical energy. Another important example is the huge multipurpose project involving the waters of the Nile River in Egypt. These physical facilities are the components of local and regional supply systems—reservoirs, wells, pumps, pipelines, aqueducts, and canals. The human resources include farmers, technicians, engineers, and managers. The institutional resources include corporations, financial institutions, a framework of customs, laws, agreements, operating rules, governmental agencies, nongovernmental organizations, and educational institutions. These facilities and institutions convert the raw water in streams and aquifers into a developed resource—water that can be supplied for either withdrawal or for instream uses on a reliable basis.

B. Agricultural Distribution Systems

Once water has been controlled by a dam, diversion, or ground water well, it can be conveyed and distributed to croplands for use. If this distribution is well planned, designed, operated, and maintained, it will deliver water at a rate, frequency, and duration that optimize crop production. If it is not, it will limit crop production, exacerbate waterlogging problems, and degrade the quality of nearby streams, lakes, reservoirs, and/or ground water basins. [*See* IRRIGATION ENGINEERING: FARM PRACTICES, METHODS, AND SYSTEMS.]

The distribution system begins at the *headworks,* which are structures or combinations of structures located near the controlled source of water which withdraw water into the distribution system. Headworks consist of intake structures, screens and debris-removal devices, and water-measurement structures. From the headworks water flows through the *conveyance network* toward *turnouts* where it is delivered to irrigators. The *conveyance network* is composed of ca-

nals or pipelines. Control and management of water in the conveyance network requires a large number of structures to regulate water levels and flow, dissipate energy, and monitor flow rates. Conveyance networks generally branch into successively smaller canals and/or pipes to direct the water over an area where crops are being grown. It is common to name the various canal or pipeline branches in order to describe the component of the distribution system to which one is referring. For example, the terms "main canal," "branch canal," "distributary canal," and "minor canal" are used to represent first-, second-, third-, and fourth-order canal segments. The main canal supplies water to the branch canal which in turn supplies the distributary, and so on.

The structural elements of the distribution system are visible and important because they determine the cost of the system and how it will impact the environment around it. However, the most important aspect of distribution systems is how they are operated, because this determines how well these systems meet their goals of providing irrigation water at a rate, frequency, and duration that will optimize crop production. The operation of a distribution system is defined by restrictions on the water supply (such as water rights), the nature of the agency actually responsible for operating the system (government or private organization), and how irrigators use water at the farm level (growing rice as opposed to growing wheat, for example). Most often the operation of the distribution system can be classified as *demand, rotation,* or *continuous flow.* A demand-based operation is controlled by the needs of the croplands which are communicated to the distribution system operators by the irrigators. Rotation systems are more structured and allocate time among the irrigators according to relatively fixed rules for sharing the water. Continuous flow occurs when the water supply is not regulated but is delivered to the irrigators continually. The choice of operating scheme has tremendous impact on the use of water at the farm level. Demand systems are flexible and productive but are harder to achieve and thus require a greater level of skill and training. Rotation and continuous flow schemes are simpler to operate but at the same time provide a less useful water supply at the farm where it is used.

III. Uses of Water

A. Offstream Uses

Offstream uses include domestic and commercial consumption, manufacturing, agriculture, energy production (primarily cooling and water for steam-powered generation of electricity), and the minerals industry. Total global consumptive demand for off-stream uses is expected to continue to rise. Rural consumptive demand for domestic uses is expected to remain fairly constant at less than 2% of the total whereas urban consumptive requirements for domestic purposes are expected to rise slightly but remain at approximately 13% of the total. Industrial requirements, at 15% of the total, approximately equal domestic uses.

A full 70% of all offstream water is used for irrigation. This water is vitally important to the maintenance and expansion of agricultural production. The major focus of this article is on the functions of irrigation and on the problems facing the use of water for agricultural production.

B. Instream Uses

This form of water use is often referred to as instream-flow needs; that is, the amount of water flowing through a natural stream channel needed to sustain instream values at acceptable levels. Values of instream flow relate to uses made of water in the stream channel, including fish and wildlife population maintenance, outdoor recreation activities, navigation, hydroelectric generation, pollution control, conveyance to downstream points of diversion, and ecosystem maintenance (including freshwater requirements of estuaries, riparian vegetation, and flood-plain wetlands). Streamflow sufficient to meet all of these requirements establishes the acceptable level for instream-flow uses. Understandably, at a given location in a particular stream system, only certain uses may be applicable.

C. Growth of the Demand for Water

During the 20th century the demand for water has increased rapidly for two reasons. First, population growth alone has generated additional needs for water. Second, per capita demand has risen with global economic growth and urbanization. As a consequence, "global water use doubled between 1940 and 1980, and is expected to double again by the year 2000. Two thirds of the projected use will go into agriculture. Yet 20 countries with 40 percent of the world's population already suffer water shortage." (Postel, 1984).

This increase in consumption, leading in many countries to competition for the scarce resource, is a major factor generating needs for effective water management. The shortages lead to competition and confrontation not only internally but between countries as well.

D. Focus on the Agricultural Uses of Water

1. Food Production Using Irrigated Agriculture

Water is the major limiting factor for agricultural production worldwide. Crops require and transpire massive amounts of water. For example, a corn crop that produces 6500 kg of grain per hectare will take up and transpire about 4.2 million liters of water during the growing season. Irrigated crop production requires large quantities of water. For instance, the production of 1 kg of the following food and fiber products under irrigation requires on the average: 1400 liters for corn, 1900 liters for sugar, 4700 liters for rice, and 17,000 liters for cotton. The amount of water required to produce 1 kg of grain-fed meat ranges from 4200 to 8300 liters when the water requirement for irrigated grain is included.

The use of water by crops is the prime reason that agriculture returns a relatively small portion of the water applied in irrigation. Approximately 60% of the water applied in irrigation is consumed and does not return to streams for reuse. In contrast, only about 5% of the water pumped for public supplies is consumed.

Irrigation has been used to increase agricultural production since the dawn of agriculture. However, until about the beginning of the 19th century, irrigation systems were small, and most eventually failed because they did not provide for salinity control. The estimated area of irrigated land in the world in 1880 was about 8 million hectares (Gulhate, 1958). This figure reached about 40 million hectares by 1900. As experience was gained in planning, constructing, and operating irrigation projects, the global irrigated area expanded rapidly. By 1985, of the approximately 1.5 billion hectares of cultivated land in the world, about 271 million hectares, or 18%, were irrigated (Worldwatch Institute, 1987, p. 125).

Irrigation produces special pollution problems when stream water is degraded by the addition of salts in returning drainage waters. For example, when irrigation water is withdrawn from the Colorado River in the Grand Valley at Grand Junction, Colorado, and later returned to the river, an estimated 18 tonnes per hectare of salts are leached from the irrigated land and added to the river water. At times during the summer, the Red River in Texas and Oklahoma is more saline than seawater, mainly due to irrigation use and normal evaporation.

Whereas the overall contribution of irrigation to agricultural production is clear, the precise contribution varies widely around the world. Irrigation may be applied to the desert, where rainfall rarely occurs, such as in Egypt or southern Iraq. It may replace or supplement rainfall agriculture, as in dry-farming regions of the United States; it may make possible multiple-cropping in areas where only single-cropping is otherwise possible because of wet and dry seasons, as in Bengal or Senegal; or it may serve as insurance against damaging, short-term droughts, as in the eastern United States. The uses of irrigation include sporadic spreading of meager spring flood waters in the deserts of the Middle East, sprouting a thin crop of wheat, and carefully controlled, optimal applications under the sophisticated technology used in the southwestern United States. [*See* DRYLAND FARMING.]

2. Irrigation Systems

When water is diverted through a turnout from the distribution system it enters the control of the on-farm component of agriculture, or the *irrigation system*. There are three basic types of irrigation systems: (1) surface irrigation systems, (2) sprinkle irrigation systems, and (3) drip irrigation systems. Each of these has many configurations. Surface irrigation, for example, is often described by the terms "furrow irrigation," "border irrigation," or "basin irrigation." Sprinkle irrigation has individual members like "center-pivots," "side-roll" or "wheel-line," "big gun," and others. Drip irrigation is also known as "trickle irrigation" and has special configurations as do surface and sprinkle irrigation systems.

Surface irrigation systems distribute water over a field using gravity. Flow is introduced to the field at one point, then moves over the land surface, wetting the soil as it progresses. Surface irrigation has been practiced for thousands of years and today comprises more than 90% of irrigation worldwide. Some countries, such as the United States, have about 55% surface irrigation and some, such as Israel, have very little, but these are exceptions rather than rules. Surface irrigation is relatively inexpensive to implement, but unless care is given to proper design and management, application efficiencies will be as low as 40 to 50%. Modern land-leveling equipment and computerized design methodologies have helped to implement surface irrigation systems with efficiencies as high as 90%. The major advantages of surface irriga-

tion include low cost, low energy requirements, and, where water is plentiful, low irrigator skill. The major disadvantages include potentially low efficiencies and the land leveling requirement.

Sprinkle irrigation systems distribute water using an orifice to convert pipeline pressure into the kinetic energy of a jet issuing from the orifice. As the jet emerges from the orifice, it breaks into individual droplets. Under ideal conditions, the droplets would be distributed uniformly over an area around the orifice. In practice, however, it is impossible to construct an orifice which achieves perfect uniformity, and the droplet patterns of several sprinklers are overlapped to approximate uniform coverage. Sprinkle irrigation systems are recommended and used on practically all types of soil, topography, and crops. It is a flexible and efficient system of irrigation. The main disadvantages of sprinkle systems are that they have a high initial cost, they typically use substantially more energy than surface irrigation, they are accompanied by higher evaporation losses, and they require more maintenance than surface irrigation systems. Land leveling is not required and application efficiencies of 60% are common. Unlike surface and drip systems, sprinkle systems may be used for other reasons, such as temperature control, evaporative waste disposal, and seed germination.

Drip irrigation systems also use an orifice to convert pipeline pressure into the kinetic energy of orifice discharge, but do so differently. In a drip irrigation system the orifice is designed to dissipate nearly all of the kinetic energy in the flow so that when it emerges from the orifice it moves slowly. Drip systems, therefore, irrigate a small area around each orifice, which is generally called an emitter. Drip systems usually irrigate widely spaced or row crops where an individual pipeline can be located nearby to provide one or more emitters to each plant. The slow flows and the individual plant locations give drip irrigation very precise water control which translates into application efficiencies of 90% or greater. Since only a small surface area is wetted, evaporation losses are negligible. Drip systems apply irrigation water to crops much more often than either surface or sprinkle systems. This high-frequency irrigation regime has been shown to increase crop yields. The disadvantages of drip systems include high cost, the necessity of water supply filtration and treatment, and in some cases, the buildup of salts in the soils. Drip irrigation does not represent a large percentage of irrigation worldwide, but it is an important technology for special applications.

IV. Water Management

In many parts of the world, the food supply depends upon extensive irrigation development. For example, on the Indian subcontinent, which has one-fifth of the population of the world, water supply seriously limits agricultural production on 65% of the arable land and prevents year-round production on an additional 29%. The Green Revolution, while providing a potential for important food supply increases, cannot reach that potential without substantial and sustained improvement in the management of available water and soil resources, especially in arid and subhumid areas. These regions comprise approximately one-sixth of the total land surface and a substantially greater portion of the world's potential for agricultural production. Virtually all irrigated or potentially irrigable portions of the globe face serious management problems involving water, soil, and crop production systems.

A. Water Management Needs

A number of powerful factors act to force conscious management of water resources throughout the world. These factors operate in all societies, political systems, and stages of development. The political and administrative adaptations designed to deal with them vary widely, but the fundamental forces do not differ.

Often there is not enough water to meet unlimited competing demands, and means of mediating among the various potential uses must be devised. The kinds of uses typically continue to increase, and means of meeting these new needs must be found. The management needs include flood mitigation, land drainage, sewer systems, culvert design, water supply, irrigation, hydroelectric power generation, and navigation. Demands on a single water source may include withdrawals for use on irrigated land, in factories, or in towns and cities; falling water for hydropower; impoundments for recreational lakes or for flood control; flow of streams for carrying wastes or for navigation; and maintenance of wetlands for waterfowl. If upstream users discharge large quantities of wastes into a river, the supply of usable water available to downstream users is diminished. In some withdrawal uses (such as hydropower generation), most of the water is returned to the stream in good condition. In others, notably irrigation, much of the water is lost through consumptive use, and the returning drainage waters usually carry increased salt levels.

Each of these uses has its peculiar requirements in terms of quantity, quality, location, and timing, and these often conflict. Water resource development projects—canals, wells, dams, impoundments, pumps, and so forth—generally require large capital investments, and it takes time to construct them. Years elapse between authorization, planning, and construction to operation. Additionally, the installations are durable and thus "freeze" the pattern of water management of a region for generations, influencing rates of economic growth, levels of health, and amenities of living. Taking an intelligent long view is an important aspect of successful water management.

Until fairly recently the major concern was to develop the physical, economic, and institutional control procedures necessary to make water available for a specific purpose. Now, however, water systems generally involve multiple-purpose projects. In addition, it is necessary to manage water resources in the context of the total environment. Thus, water resource planning and management need to be integrated with comprehensive planning and management plans for entire river basins or regions.

Water management is further complicated by the fact that the problem is seldom one of simply how much water but rather of how much water of a particular quality is acceptable or needed for a given use at a given time. Pollution is a prime example of the problem of quality. Pollution reduces the utility of water for municipal and irrigation purposes and threatens aesthetic values.

B. Administrative Structures for Management

Because of the powerful competing interests involved, administrative structures have been developed to control the distribution of water. The formalities and complexities of these structures vary widely, depending upon need and cultural background. For some projects, typically the smaller ones, the administrative mechanisms can be quite informal and simple. However, for large and extensive projects, such as those which exist in California, complex administrative structures for managing water resources are necessary.

In the more complex systems, there are water-source controllers, producers of water, transmitters of water, users of water, and reclaimers of water. The first three levels are usually, but not always, institutions. Users frequently are individual farmers. Reclaimers may be individuals, but because there are aspects of reclamation that can be controlled only by community action, this function generally is most satisfactorily implemented by an institution with adequate control authority.

The authority to make decisions in such complex systems is virtually always decentralized. Each management level usually has its own authority for decision making, subject to physical, legal, and indirect social constraints of the public at large and of other interacting levels. Such a structure is a hierarchical multilevel decision-making system with multiple goals and objectives that are often not commensurable. Each level is optimized at the stage at which it occurs in the system, subject to constraints imposed by both higher and lower decision-making levels. Ideally, all levels are then subjected to an overall analysis for optimality of the trade-offs among various compatible and noncompatible objectives at all levels. Efficient and effective water resource management can be achieved only by considering all facets—engineering, social, political, and economic. Sometimes this situation exists, but often it does not.

C. Special Management Needs for Irrigated Agriculture

The basic elements of irrigation water management systems consist of (1) water supplies, including storage and distribution works; (2) crop production subsystems as they are affected by irrigation, leaching, and drainage; (3) underlying ground water storage areas that interact with the crop production system; and (4) social and institutional subsystems within which production is accomplished, resources are made available, and various levels of policy are established and implemented. These processes are strongly interrelated. They constituite a dynamic and continuous system, with each component of the system influencing, and, in turn, being influenced by, other components. Applying irrigation water to a field, for example, might satisfy the soil moisture requirements of the crop, but failure to recognize the need for drainage might lead to establishment of an undesirably high water table and/or salinity conditions within the soil profile.

As is true of all water management, effective irrigation water management systems must be designed and operated to fit within a broad social–political–biological environment. For instance, in the early days of irrigation in the western United States, physical facilities were built to transport water to the land, but the failure to recognize the need for effective social–political–economical institutions at the user level resulted in the bankruptcy and collapse of many of these early developments.

V. Conclusions

Water is controlled and regulated to serve a wide variety of purposes including flood mitigation, irrigation, supplies for culinary and industrial purposes, transportation, the generation of electrical energy, wildlife preservation and culture, aesthetics, and recreation. Flood detention reservoirs, storm drains, and dikes are examples of the types of structures used to control water so that it will not cause excessive damage to property, public inconvenience, or loss of life. Irrigation projects, hydroelectric power dams, municipal water supply works, and navigation improvements are examples of the use of water for beneficial purposes.

Because of its important role in global food production and because it uses a large proportion of our available fresh water supplies, irrigation is given special consideration in this article. Irrigation is the application of water to soil to supplement deficient rainfall to provide adequate water for plant growth. It has been practiced for centuries. Some of the works built in the Nile River Valley around 3000 B.C. still play an important part in Egyptian agricultural production. However, as the need for food continues to escalate and other conflicting uses enter the picture more strongly, there is an ever-increasing need for the efficient control and use of irrigation water.

As human demands on available land and water resources have increased, there has been a corresponding increase in the need to more carefully control and regulate the use of these resources. Physical facilities must be planned and implemented in the context of multiple, dynamic, and often conflicting social needs and demands. Included in these processes are the complex and increasing environmental issues and concerns. Thus, both well-designed physical facilities and effective management institutions and policies are essential to the efficient control and use of the earth's limited supply of available fresh water.

Bibliography

American Society of Civil Engineers. (1991). "Management, Operation and Maintenance of Irrigation and Drainage Systems."

Baumgartner, A., and Reichel, E. (1975). "The World Water Balance—Mean Annual Global Continental and Maritime Precipitation, Evaporation, and Runoff." Elsevier, New York.

Gulhati, N. D. (1958). Worldwide view of irrigation developments. *Proc. Am. Soc. Civil Engineering,* Paper 1751.

Hubbert, M. K. (1940). The theory of ground water motion. *J. Geol.* **48,** 785–944.

Hubbert, M. K. (1974). World potential and developed water power capacity. *Water Resources Bull.* **10,** 17–29.

Ivovitch, M. I. (1973). World water balance by continent. *EOS* **54,** 19.

James, L. J. (1988). "Principles of Farm Irrigation System Design." Wiley. New York, N Y.

Keller, J. and Bliesner, R. D. (1991). "Sprinkle and Trickle Irrigation." Van Nostrand–Reinhold, Princeton, NJ.

Kidd, C. V. and Pimentel, D. eds. (1992). "Integrated Resource Management: Agroforestry for Development." Academic Press, New York, N Y.

Labye, Y., Olson, M. A., Galand, A., and Tsiourtis, N. (1988). Design and optimization of irrigation distribution networks. FAO Irrigation and Drainage Paper 44, Rome, Italy.

Linsley, R. K., Franzini, J. B., Freyberg, D. L., and Tchobanoglous, G. (1992). "Water-Resources Engineering." 4th ed. McGraw-Hill, , New York, NY.

McGuinnes, C. L. (1952). "The water situation in the United States with special reference to ground water." *Geol. Sur. Cir.* **114**(8), 127.

Postel, (1984). *In* "Earth '88: Changing Geographic Perspectives." National Geographic Society, Washington, DC.

President's Science Advisory Committee. (1967). The world food problem, Vol. II. Report of the Panel on the World Food Supply, The White House, Washington, DC.

Smith, R. A., and Alexander, R. B. (1983). A statistical summary of data from the U.S. Geological Survey's National Water Quality Networks. U.S. Geological Survey Open File Report 83-533.

Solley, W. B., Chase, E. B., and Mann, W. B., IV. (1983). Estimated use of water in the United States in 1980. *U.S. Geol. Surv. Circ.* **1001,** 55.

U.S. Department of the Interior, Bureau of Reclamation. (1974). Design of small canal structures. Engineering and Research Center, Denver, CO.

U.S. Environmental Protection Agency. (1983). Conveyance, treatment, and control of municipal wastewater, combined sewer overflows, and stormwater runoff. The 1982 Needs Survey. Office of Water Program Operation, Washington, DC.

U.S. Geological Survey. (1984). "National water summary 1983—Hydrologic events and issues. Water Supply Paper 2250. U.S. Government Printing Office, Washington, DC.

Walker, W. R., and Skogerboe, G. V. (1987). "Surface Irrigation—Theory and Practice." Prentice-Hall, Englewood Cliffs, NJ.

Worldwatch Institute. (1987). "State of the World, 1987." Norton, New York, NY.

Worldwatch Institute. (1988). "State of the World, 1988." Norton, New York, NY.

Worldwatch Institute. 1989. "State of the World, 1989." Norton, New York, NY.

Young, L. L. (1964). Summary of developed and potential water power of the United States and other countries of the world, 1955–1962. *U.S. Geol. Surv. Circ.* **483,** 38p.

Water Resources

SUN F. SHIH, *University of Florida*

Glossary

Application satellites Satellite-based sensor systems being used in water resources are primarily two basic types. (1) *Earth resources satellites* include the Landsat (USA), SPOT (French), Meteor-priroda (USSR), ERS-1 (European), and J-ERS-1 (Japan). The Landsat remote-sensing system was first launched in 1972 and has been applied widely around the world for studying water resources. The type of sensor, band designation, spatial sensitivity range, and spatial resolution used in the Landsat system are listed in Table I. As Table I shows, the existing Landsat system has two important sensors, i.e., thematic mapper (TM) and multispectral scanner (MSS). Recently, the SPOT system has also been used. The SPOT has high-resolution visible (HRV) imagery which includes three bands (0.5–0.6, 0.6–0.7, and 0.78–0.9 μm) with 20-m resolution color mode, and 10-m resolution panchromatic mode (0.51–0.73 μm). (2) *Weather satellites* include NOAA-TIROS (USA), GOES (U.S.), Meteor-2 (USSR), Meteosat (European), GMS (Japan), and Feng-Yun (China). Most weather satellites include both visible and thermal infrared sensors.

Geographic information system (GIS) Computer system designed specifically to manage large volumes of geocoded spatial data derived from a variety of sources. The capabilities of a GIS system are to accept input data; to serve as a clearinghouse for data; to store, retrieve, manipulate, analyze, overlay, and display these data based on the requirements of the user; and to create both tabular and cartographic output which reflect these requirements.

Ground-penetrating radar Radar system, which currently operates in the frequency range of 80 MHz to 1 GHz, has been designed specifically to penetrate earthen materials. It radiates repetitive, short-duration, electromagnetic pulses into the soil from a broad-band-width antenna. Towing the antenna along the ground produces a continuous profile of subsurface conditions on the graphic recorder.

Land use/land cover Land use/land cover information has always been and continues to be an important element in the integration, planning, and management of water resources, agricultural resources, land resources, environment protection, economy, and landscape. A land-use classification system used by the United States Geological Survey (USGS) emphasizes remote sensing as the primary data source. This classification system as shown in Table II represents only the more generalized first and second classification levels. The approach to land use/land cover classification is "resource oriented," providing greater flexibility when separating data into distinguishable classes.

Remote sensing Gathering of information about an object without using an instrument in physical contact with the object. Humans' ears, eyes, and nose are typical natural sensors with limited capabilities. Today, based on scientific research and development, the remote-sensing techniques are being developed into ground-based, airplane-based, and satellite-based sensor systems.

Satellite image processing Satellite-sensed images

TABLE I

Comparisons of Type of Sensor, Band Designation, Spectral Sensitivity Range, and Spatial Resolution Used in Landsat Remote Sensing Systems

Type of sensor (1)	Band (NASA designation) (2)	Spectral sensitivity range		Spatial resolution (m) (5)
		Wavelength (μm) (3)	Color (4)	
(a) Landsat 1 and 2[a]				
RBV[b]	Band 1	0.475–0.575	Blue-green	76
	Band 2	0.580–0.680	Yellow-red	76
	Band 3	0.690–0.830	Red-infrared	76
MSS[c]	Band 4	0.5–0.6	Green	76
	Band 5	0.6–0.7	Red	76
	Band 6	0.7–0.8	Near infrared	76
	Band 7	0.8–1.1	Near infrared	76
(b) Landsat 3[a]				
RBV[b]	Two cameras	0.505–0.750	(Panchromatic)	40
MSS[c]	Band 4	0.5–0.6	Green	76
	Band 5	0.6–0.7	Red	76
	Band 6	0.7–0.8	Near infrared	76
	Band 7	0.8–1.1	Near infrared	76
	Band 8	10.4–12.6	Thermal infrared	234
(c) Landsat 4 and 5[a]				
TM[d]	Band 1	0.45–0.52	Blue	30
	Band 2	0.53–0.61	Green	30
	Band 3	0.62–0.69	Red	30
	Band 4	0.78–0.91	Near infrared	30
	Band 5	1.57–1.78	Intermediate infrared	30
	Band 6	10.42–11.66	Thermal infrared	120
	Band 7	2.08–2.35	Mid infrared	30
MSS[c]	Band 1	0.5–0.6	Green	76
	Band 2	0.6–0.7	Red	76
	Band 3	0.7–0.8	Near infrared	76
	Band 4	0.8–1.1	Near infrared	76

[a] Launch dates: Landsat 1: 7/23/72, operation ended 1/6/78. Landsat 2: 1/22/75, operation ended 2/25/82. Landsat 3: 3/5/78, operation ended 3/31/83. Landsat 4: 7/16/82. Landsat 5: 3/1/84.
[b] Return beam vidicon camera.
[c] Multispectral scanner.
[d] Thematic mapper.

provide data to the computer which are digitally compatible with computer software developed for interpreting physical meaning on the earth surface. A public domain computerized image processing program used in the United States is the Earth Resources Laboratory Application Software (ELAS). ELAS is a software package designed and maintained by the National Aeronautical and Space Administration (NASA) to provide analysis and processing capabilities that enable the construction and manipulation of various geographical data files.

Water resources rank among the most important renewable natural resources on the earth in all of their three phases (i.e., liquid, solid, or vapor), and are one of the most fundamental requirements for agricultural production. The water resources most available for use in agriculture are derived from precipitation (i.e., rainfall and snowfall), rivers, lakes, reservoirs, and groundwater. Water resources research for agriculture concentrates on the collection of sufficient basic hydrologic cycle-related data for better planning and management of these re-

TABLE II

Land Use/Land Cover Classification System for Use with Remote Sensor Data by the United States Geological Survey

Level I	Level II	
1. Urban or built-up land	11	Residential
	12	Commercial and services
	13	Industrial
	14	Transportation, communications, and utilities
	15	Industrial and commercial complexes
	16	Mixed urban or built-up land
	17	Other urban or built-up land
2. Agricultural land	21	Cropland and pasture
	22	Orchards, groves, vineyards, nurseries, and ornamental horticultural areas
	23	Confined feeding operations
	24	Other agricultural land
3. Rangeland	31	Herbaceous rangeland
	32	Shrub and brush rangeland
	33	Mixed rangeland
4. Forest land	41	Deciduous forest land
	42	Evergreen forest land
	43	Mixed forest land
5. Water	51	Streams and canals
	52	Lakes
	53	Reservoirs
	54	Bays and estuaries
6. Wetland	61	Forested wetland
	62	Nonforested wetland
7. Barren land	71	Dry salt flats
	72	Beaches
	73	Sandy areas other than beaches
	74	Bare exposed rock
	75	Strip mines, quarries, and gravel pits
	76	Transitional areas
	77	Mixed barren land
8. Tundra	81	Shrub and brush tundra
	82	Herbaceous tundra
	83	Bare ground tundra
	84	Wet tundra
	85	Mixed tundra
9. Perennial snow or ice	91	Perennial snowfields
	92	Glaciers

sources for agricultural production on a sustainable basis.

I. Hydrologic Cycle

The endless recirculation of water in the atmosphere–hydrosphere–lithosphere is known as the hydrologic cycle. The cycle is the principal mechanism governing the distribution of water over the earth, balancing flows between the sea, the continent, and the atmosphere. The principal factor driving this endless recirculation is solar activity which controls the thermal regime of the earth and the atmosphere circulation. The hydrologic cycle can be studied according to the particular scale of reference, i.e., global scale, basin scale, etc. From the agricultural point of view, the basin-scale hydrologic cycle is emphasized. The basin-scale cycle is considered to be a continuous circulation of water from water vapor to precipitation, stream flow, lakes, reservoirs, soil moisture, groundwater, and out of basin transfer, to the return to water vapor through evaporation and transpiration. Within a basin, the dynamics of the hydrologic processes are governed mainly by the temporal and spatial characteristics of inputs and outputs, the land use/land cover conditions, the slopes, the soils, the underlying geology, and the implementations of irrigation and drainage.

II. Land-Use Classification

A. Conventional Techniques

In general, the conventional land-use classification methods have relied on ground observation and aerial photography, resulting United States Department of Agriculture–Soil Conservation Service (USDA-SCS) soil surveys, USGS topographic maps, USGS land use/land cover maps, and other such resources. The USGS standard topographic quadrangle maps cover 7.5 min of latitude and longitude and are published at the scale of 1 : 24,000. These maps show man-made features, water features, road classifications, urban areas, U.S. land lines, and woodland. The smallest mapping unit of the USGS land use/land cover maps for urban, water, mines, quarries, gravel pits, and certain agricultural land is four hectares in contrast to 16 hectares for the other categories. [*See* LAND USE PLANNING IN AGRICULTURE; SOIL AND LAND USE SURVEYS.]

B. Satellite Methods

The land use/land cover classification based on satellite images can be accomplished by two general methodologies. One method is a supervised classification technique in which the operator classifies an area of pixels (picture elements, i.e., sensor spatial resolutions) that belong to one or more specific categories of land use/land cover. The computer then uses one of many classifying algorithms to group pixels of similar spectral response. The other classification method is an unsupervised classification technique. In this method, the satellite images are loaded into the computer as mentioned in the supervised classification technique. The operator then determines how many different classes are desirable and the computer classifies each pixel into one of the statistically created classes. The computer uses a sophisticated set of algorithms to determine which pixel belongs to which class. The different classes are then related to individual land use/land cover complex represented by a color which can be viewed on the computer monitor. The location and spatial pattern are noted and compared with quadrangle maps and through extensive ground-truthing. Finally, the established classes are grouped into similar land uses to form the desired classes which can be stored in a GIS database.

III. Precipitation

A. Rainfall Estimation

1. Conventional Methods

The primary conventional method used in rainfall estimation is the raingauge measurement. The large spatial and temporal variability of rainfall distribution requires a dense raingauge network if acceptable accuracy of rainfall estimation is to be achieved. However, there is a nonlinear relationship between the increase in number of gauges and the improvement in accuracy, and the improvement is mainly for reducing the temporal variation. A dense network is also costly to maintain and operate. Furthermore, measurement of rainfall by gauges is affected in particular by the interrelated factors of topography, site, wind, and gauge design. The gauge catch may be representative of a small or large area depending upon rainfall event, slope, aspect, elevation, and location in relation to hills and ridges. Because of these inherent limitations of the raingauge design for rainfall measurements, point data could contain ambiguities producing an increase in uncertainty of regional estimates. [*See* METEOROLOGY.]

2. Remote-Sensing Methods

a. Cloud-Indexing Approach Using satellite-based visible and thermal-infrared data to characterize the cloud type or temperature for correlation with rainfall via empirical relationships is the basic concept of the cloud-indexing approach. This approach is time-independent, identifies different types of rain clouds, and estimates the rainfall from the number and duration of clouds.

b. Thresholding Approach This approach is based on satellite derived temperature thresholding and cloud brightness to identify potential rain clouds. This approach considers all clouds with low upper surface temperatures to be rain clouds.

c. Life-History Approach This approach is based on the premises that significant rainfall comes mostly from convective clouds, and that convective clouds can be distinguished from other clouds in satellite images. This approach is time-dependent and considers the rates of change in individual convective clouds or in clusters of convective clouds.

d. Pattern-Classification Approach This approach uses a statistical pattern-classification technique to assign rainfall to one of several classes according to such parameters as coldest cloud-top temperature, average cloud-top temperature, and average cloud-top temperature difference between two consecutive images.

e. Integration Approach This approach correlates a small-coverage (e.g., raingauge), high-resolution sensor with a large-coverage (e.g., satellite), low-resolution sensor, and then uses the large-coverage sensor to estimate the regional rainfall in a given area which is not covered by the small-coverage sensor.

f. Microwave Radiometry Microwave techniques offer a great potential for measuring rainfall because at some microwave frequencies clouds are essentially transparent, and the measured microwave radiation is directly related to the presence of rain drops themselves. Microwave radiometry or passive microwave techniques react to rain in two fundamental ways: by emission/absorption and by scattering.

g. Radar Raindrop and snow crystals can cause a backscatter of radio waves that could be detected through radar. Thus, attempts have been made to transform radar echoes into quantitative rainfall measurements using a reflectivity method. One important step involved in this method is to properly choose the parameters used in the radar reflectivity factor (Z)–rainfall rate (R) relation which is usually called a Z–R relation equation. This relation involves two calibration parameters called a and b which vary with rainfall types, seasonal vegetation condition, and the site of interest.

h. Lightning Flashes Rainfall has been thought to play a major role in separating the electric charge in thunderstorms, and in initiating lightning discharge. A state-of-the-art lightning detective network, the National Lightning Detection Network (NLDN), has operated with full coverage of the contiguous United States since 1989. The NLDN provides lightning flash occurrence time, location, polarity, stroke count, and regional amplitude in near real-time. These lightning flashes are being used to predict storm movement and rainfall rate.

B. Effective Rainfall

Effective rainfall is defined as a rainfall which is temporarily stored on the soil surface or in the soil without causing runoff or seepage to the groundwater. Effective rainfall is an important factor used to estimate the agricultural watershed runoff, the supplemental irrigation requirement, and the quantity of drainage. Since the water-table depth is inversely related to the soil moisture content along the soil profile above the water table, a deeper water table indicates a lower moisture content in the soil. That in turn, can increase the effective rainfall. A study of effective rainfall shows that about 3.4 cm of rainfall is stored in an organic soil for each 100 cm increment of water-table depth.

C. Snow Measurement

1. Conventional Methods

A popular technique of snow measurement is to measure 24-hr snowfall with a ruler, and to estimate the precipitation amount based on the assumption of the 10% of snow volume, i.e., using 10 cm of snow as equivalent to 1 cm of water. The snow gauge is also often used. Either ruler or snow-gauge measurements are made at several points to estimate snow cover.

2. Remote-Sensing Methods

a. γ Radiation Method This method takes advantage of the natural emission of low level γ radiation from the soil. An aircraft passes over the same flight line before and after snow cover and measures the attenuation resulting from the snow layer which is empirically related to an average snow water equivalent for the site.

b. Visible/Near Infrared Method Snow can readily be identified and mapped with the visible bands of satellite imagery because of its high reflectance in comparison to non-snow-covered areas. Generally this means selecting data from the National Oceanic and Atmospheric Administration (NOAA) weather satellite Advanced Very High Resolution Radiometer (AVHRR) visible band, Landsat MSS bands 4 or 5, SPOT, or Landsat TM bands 2 and 4. The contrast between clouds and snow is greater in the near infrared (i.e., Landsat TM Band 5) and this serves as a useful discriminator between clouds and snow.

c. Thermal Infrared Method Thermal data can be useful for helping identify snow/nonsnow boundaries and discriminating between clouds and snow with the NOAA weather satellite AVHRR data.

d. Radar The technique of using radar to measure snowfall is similar to the one used in rainfall measurement except that the calibration parameters are chosen differently.

IV. Soil Moisture Monitoring

A. Conventional Approaches

Soil moisture content information is an important parameter for studying soil water movement, evapotranspiration, irrigation scheduling, crop water stress, crop management, and hydrologic modeling. Conventional methods of measuring soil moisture content include tensiometer, neutron probes, gravimetric soil sampling, soil lysimetry, chemical method, and soil electrical resistance. These methods provide data for a point rather than large-scale areal measurements and are time consuming. An alternative technique for measuring soil moisture content for large-scale areas needs to be developed. [*See* SOIL-WATER RELATIONSHIPS.]

B. Remote-Sensing Approaches

1. Visible/Near Infrared Method

In general, wet surfaces have less reflectance values in both visible and near infrared than do dry surfaces.

However, the reflected solar radiation is dependent not only upon the soil moisture condition but also on confounding factors such as organic matter, structure, roughness, texture, mineral content, illumination geometry, angle of incidence, color, and plant cover. In other words, it is possible to develop a unique relationship between spectral reflectance and soil moisture for a specific site where the confounding factors are known or can be balanced out.

2. Mid-Infrared Method

Mid-infrared (MIR) reflectance is inversely related to the surface soil moisture content. Thus, the MIR data of the Landsat TM band 7 can be used to assess regional soil moisture conditions. This high-resolution assessment (i.e., 30 m) of regional soil moisture information would result in more efficient direction of ground-based investigators to areas with the most extreme (wet or dry) conditions.

3. Thermal Infrared Method

The thermal infrared (TIR) method is based on the observation that soil surface temperature is primarily dependent upon the thermal inertia of the soil. The thermal inertia, in turn, is dependent upon both the thermal conductivity and volumetric heat capacity. The inertia is an indication of soil resistance to the diurnal surface temperature fluctuation. A soil with a high thermal inertia (due to a high soil moisture content) will have a lower diurnal range of surface temperature. Temperature-based soil moisture estimation has been based on the use of temperature information collected in the form of TIR data using ground-based devices, airborne instruments, or satellites. The applicability of the ground-based and airborne TIR instruments has been limited to relatively small (field) scales of operation using either diurnal (maximum–minimum) temperature difference or surface–air temperature difference techniques. Although the weather satellites can provide half-hourly (GOES satellite) or several times daily (TIROS satellite) coverage of a large area, their applicability to soil moisture estimation is limited by the low spatial resolution (1–8 km) of their TIR imagery. However, the current Landsat satellites (4 and 5) have a TIR data band in the TM sensor (i.e., band 6) system which has a high (120 m) resolution. This single daily surface temperature data set from the Landsat TIR imagery can provide useful information for periodic (8 to 16 days) monitoring of the spatial distribution of soil moisture conditions mainly because the daytime temperature is inversely related to the soil moisture content. Therefore, Landsat TM TIR data have significant potential for the detection of the soil moisture condition of various land-use categories. The results might be implemented in such ways as land-use evaluation, land-use planning, preplanting soil moisture mapping, drought area assessment, and drainage zone identification.

4. Microwave Sensing Method

Both passive (radiometric) and active (radar) microwave systems can be used to measure soil moisture. The theoretical basis of this microwave sensing method consists of the dielectric properties of a soil, which are highly correlated with the soil moisture content.

V. Evapotranspiration Estimation

A. Conventional Approaches

Evapotranspiration (ET) is an important process in both hydrologic cycle and agricultural watershed management. Numerous techniques can be used to estimate ET using conventional approaches, such as mass (water vapor) transfer, energy budget, water budget, groundwater fluctuations, evaporation pan, empirical formulae, and combination (of energy budget and mass transfer) methods. Most of these are based on the relationship between free-water evaporation (or the transpiration of a freely transpiring crop surface) and the climatological parameters, mainly net radiation flux, temperature, wind speed, and relative humidity of the air. A variety of techniques have been developed partly in response to the availability or lack of certain data for ET estimation. Factors such as data availability, the intended use, and the time scale required by the problem must be considered when choosing the ET calculation technique. The combination method is known as the Penman method, which is superior to most empirical methods for ET estimation. However, the Penman method requires a variety of climatological data, such as maximum and minimum air temperatures, relative humidity, solar radiation, and wind speed. If some of these data are not available, alternative methods must be used for ET estimation. In choosing an alternative technique, one should minimize the input climatological data as much as possible without affecting the accuracy of estimation, so that the multicollinearity problem among the data can be eliminated and the data availability can be improved. [See IRRIGATION ENGINEERING, EVAPOTRANSPIRATION.]

B. Data-Short Environment

ET estimates are not available for certain parts of the world, because some basic climatological data and water budget data are not available for use in conventional methods. One alternative is to adopt the available ET estimates directly from other areas where crop and climatic conditions are similar. An approach used to diagnose the similarity between two areas is the Koppen climate classification which is based on the vegetation zones, temperature, rainfall, and seasonal characteristics. This alternative ET estimation method is good for an area lacking reliable climatic data. Another alternative is to generate synthetic climatic data to be used in conventional approaches of ET estimation. This alternative method is useful for an area that has some climatic data available that can be used as a basis for data generation.

C. Water-Use Efficiency Index

A water-use efficiency index (WUEI) is defined as the additional crop yield per unit ET. The WUEI can be grouped into high, medium, and low categories. High WUEI values indicate that less water is used for producing per unit of additional crop yield. For dry-biomass production, the WUEI varies from greater than 35 kg ha^{-1}/mm for the high category, to between 15 and 35 kg ha^{-1}/mm for the medium category, and to less than 15 kg ha^{-1}/mm for low category. For grain production, the WUEI is about 5 kg ha^{-1}/mm less than that for dry-biomass production in each category. The C$_4$ plants (i.e., plants whose first carbon compound in photosynthesis consists of a four-carbon atom chain) are mostly classified into the high WUEI category and C$_3$ plants (i.e., plants whose first carbon compound in photosynthesis is composed of a three-carbon atom chain) into the medium and low WUEI categories. If a regional crop yield is known, the WUEI information can be used to estimate regional ET. This WUEI information can be used as a potential tool to develop criteria of water allocation for crop production.

D. Remote-Sensing Approach

Remote-sensing techniques cannot measure evaporation or ET directly. However, remotely sensed data support methods for extending empirical relationships based on either vegetation mapping or climatic factors (such as temperature and solar radiation) which are used in ET estimation. The Landsat MSS data have been used to map the littoral zone vegetation of lakes to adjust the effective surface area to account for ET and improve the total water budget computation of lakes. Water surface temperature has been measured using the TIROS satellite data to estimate the lake surface evaporation. Estimates of the net radiation from GOES satellite data can be used to estimate ET. The resulting moisture flux is then used to develop a water balance model for predicting crop yields.

VI. Groundwater

A. Water Table Investigation

Water table information, as a part of the shallow groundwater aquifer, is important to monitor roots reaching the capillary fringe of the water table, changes in vegetation types and pattern, potential ET, effective rainfall, soil moisture, irrigation, drainage, and runoff. The established approach for measuring water table depth has been the observation of water levels in monitor wells. This method is reliable and provides detailed information about the water table at a specific location. However, most investigations require groundwater information over the entire region of interest, with data indicating both depth and distribution of the water table. Unless sufficient monitor wells are installed, necessary information on regional water table depth is incomplete and interpretations must be inferred from a limited number of widely spaced observation wells. Errors often arise as a result of the incompleteness of sampling. Alternative approaches using state-of-the-art geophysical techniques are available. Many of these techniques provide continuous spatial measurements that can improve water table interpretations significantly and help alleviate some of the problems inherent in point-sampling methods. Though still in the developmental phase, the ground-penetrating radar (GPR) is designed specifically as a readily available tool for shallow, subsurface site investigations. In earthen materials, the GPR has provided continuous data of subsurface conditions from depths of less than 1 m to more than 30 m. Landsat MSS data bands 4, 5, and 7 have also been used in conjunction with aerial photographs to assess perched water tables. Furthermore, aerial photograph interpretation and satellite data analysis can provide the location of aquifers from surface features which should precede ground surveys and fieldwork. Temperature difference techniques as mentioned in the soil moisture section can also be used to infer or identify shallow groundwater and springs or seeps. Synthetic aperture radar (SAR) and side-looking radar (SLAR) data have a great potential for groundwater exploration, especially in arid and hyperarid regions. [*See* GROUND WATER.]

B. Flowing Well Assessment

The artesian wells flowing uncontrolled in many parts of the world have caused a serious saline-contamination problem. Locating these wells by ground search is made difficult by the urbanized or reforested condition of former agricultural land. Both ground-based color infrared (GCIR) and aerial color infrared (ACIR) photographs taken for analysis of the spectral reflectance of land-surface features can provide information for detection of flowing wells. Both GCIR and ACIR showed similar patterns of spectral reflectance for the same component class of land-surface features. Well-site soil has a higher spectral reflectance than similar soil not associated with a well. Well water has a higher spectral reflectance than natural pond. Most vegetation types have differences in spectral reflectance magnitude. The scatter diagram of green and red channels of spectral reflectance video-digitized from ACIR photography appears to be useful for classifying land-cover types and distinguishing flowing well sites. Both Landsat and SPOT satellite data have been used to identify former agricultural land and providing clues for well assessment.

VII. Agricultural Water Quality

A. Water Quality Determination

Remote sensing has an important role in water quality evaluation and management strategy. Sources of pollution are often easy to identify, especially when there are pipes or open channels discharging into a lake or river. Nonpoint source pollution can perhaps be evaluated best by remote sensing. Monitoring large areas on a frequent basis can only be achieved economically with remote-sensing techniques. In the meantime, remote sensing is limited primarily to surface measurements of turbidity, suspended sediment, chlorophyll, eutrophication, and temperature. However, these characteristics of water quality can be used

as indicators of more specific pollution problems. Because the intensity and wavelength of reflected light are modified by the volume of water and its contaminants, an empirical relationship can be established between the reflectance measurements and certain water quality variables.

B. Wetland Assessment

Wetlands are of interest to water resource management as a natural vegetation filter for improving water quality in fresh water marshes. The studies have emphasized the form of nutrient uptake by wetland plants, detention time of water in the wetland, and best-management practices. Landsat data have been used to make estimates of wetlands water volumes on a monthly basis by combining depth/stage relationships with surface water area. The scatter diagram of band 4 and band 5 from Landsat MSS data can be used most efficiently to identify the wetland. An additional aspect of wetlands management involves the extent of dredging, lagoons, drainage, and other man-induced changes that have an impact on the natural environment. Remote sensing is well suited to monitor these changes and to make preliminary estimates of the environmental impact. The temporal aspect of Landsat and SPOT data allows changes to be observed over time and, in some cases, predevelopment baseline data to be obtained from earlier satellite scenes. [*See* WETLANDS AND RIPARIAN AREAS: ECONOMICS AND POLICY.]

VIII. Irrigation

A. Irrigation in Water Resources

In general, irrigation can be defined as the quantity of water released from an external source to adequately wet the crop root zone. Water source availability varies with space and time, and different crop root zones also have spatial and temporal characteristics which are extremely difficult to measure by conventional methods, such as ground-survey, but this information is very important to water resources planning and management. The alternative of using remote sensing in groundwater assessment, mentioned above, can be also used to assess surface water source, crop identification, and crop spatial coverage. [*See* IRRIGATION ENGINEERING: FARM PRACTICES, METHODS, AND SYSTEMS.]

B. Surface Water Source Assessment

1. Water Surface

Since land/water contrast is very strong in the near infrared band, Landsat and SPOT data can be used to delineate the water surface area from the surrounding land. As an example, the density slicing from Landsat MSS band 7 (i.e., near infrared) and the scatter diagram of bands 5 and 7 can be used to assess the water-surface area.

2. Water Volume

A technique is being developed to use a number of Landsat data sets covering the lakes of interest to correspond with a wide range of known lake stages. An average water surface area between two stages can be derived from the Landsat data. The change in lake volume is estimated from the change in stages multiplied by the corresponding average water surface.

3. Water Depth

Two methods have been used to remotely estimate the water depth of a lake. The first method is based on the measured water depth at control points as the dependent variable and satellite data as independent variables used to develop a regression model for water-depth estimation for areas other than the control points. The second method is based on a concept of the major vegetation associations in the littoral zone of a lake which are linked to elevation through the hydroperiod. The littoral zone vegetation map which can be derived from the satellite data is used to estimate ground elevation. The water depth is then estimated based on the deviation between the recorded lake water stage and the satellite-derived ground elevation.

C. Crop Identification

Most vegetation types have their own pattern of spectral response in the range from 0.36 to 1.11 μm. However, a general pattern of spectral response for live vegetation has a minimum response of approximately 0.68 μm, and three peaks occurring around the regions of 0.54–0.56, 0.75–0.90, and 0.95–1.05 μm. These peak regions could be applied to design satellite-based crop identification systems. As an example, the first peak of spectral response falls within the Landsat MSS band 4 and TM band 2; the second and third peaks fall within MSS band 7 and TM band 4. Therefore, the scatter diagrams of band 4 versus band 7 in MSS and band 2 versus band 4 in TM could be used for crop identification. Furthermore, the effect of a citrus canopy on SPOT image spectral response has been studied. Researchers found that the red and green bands are highly correlated with the citrus canopy. Therefore, it will be advantageous to include data from these two bands in any agricultural land-use classification scheme in areas where citrus crops are significant.

D. Crop Spatial Coverage

An irrigated crop has a higher spectral response in the near infrared region than the nonirrigated crop. The integration of historical satellite data with a GIS can provide not only the spatial distribution of irrigated crop coverage changes but also the expansion of agriculture into previously uncultivated areas.

IX. Drainage

A. Drainage in Water Resources

Agricultural drainage refers to the removal of excess field water which interferes with land forming, land preparation, tillage, crop growth, fertilizer application, weed control, insect and disease problems, field cultivation, and harvest operations. In general, this drained water typically has a water quality problem caused by improper insecticide, herbicide, and fertilizer applications. This field drainage water can influence regional water resources planning and management. Two major problem areas involved in agricultural drainage are identification of areas with drainage problems and the design of adequate systems for the drainage of excess field water. In some localities drainage problems are difficult to identify using the conventional ground-survey method. The alternative of using remote-sensing technique should be considered. Drainage-basin parameters such as physiographic features, topographic maps, vegetation state, drainage density, and drainage pattern are important information to have not only for designing a new drainage system but also for evaluating the existing drainage system. Using conventional ground-survey methods to obtain these basin parameters is expensive and difficult. The possibility of utilizing remotely sensed data should be encouraged. Furthermore, inadequate drainage is associated with and contributes to the severity of saline accumulation conditions which interfere with the growth of most crops.

Again, assessment of saline-affected areas is difficult to accomplish by conventional ground-survey methods. Therefore, the possibility of using remote-sensing technique should be investigated. [*See* SOIL DRAINAGE.]

B. Drainage Problem Identification

1. Perched Water Table

The Landsat and SPOT data in conjunction with aerial photographs can provide a potential methodology for identifying perched water tables.

2. Soil Color

The saline-affected area offer depicts a snowy halo of salt on top of the soil due to the evaporation of surface or near-surface water from perched water-table accumulation. The organic matter accumulated under a poorly drained condition also can cause a darker soil color than that under a well drained condition. These contrasts of soil colors can be identified using satellite visible images.

3. Plant Response

For tree crops growing in poorly drained soil, the first symptom is light green or yellow leaves which are sparser and smaller than normal. Defoliation follows, leaving a bare, dead framework of branches. These plant-response symptoms can be detected by visible and infrared images from the Landsat and SPOT satellites.

4. Drainage-Water Collection

The satellite data can be used to evaluate the seasonal variation of drainage water accumulation which can provide a clue for identifying some drainage problems. As an example, in Saudi Arabia, there is an old concept that the collected drainage water remains in lakes to evaporate during the whole year. However, the Landsat data showed that the drainage water flows to the sea in the winter season and diminishes during the summer season.

C. Drainage-Basin Parameters

1. Physiographic Features

The usual physiographic features such as basin shape, circularity, and stream orders can be discerned by satellite images.

2. Topographic Maps

Recent use of SPOT imagery and its stereographic capabilities have demonstrated its potential in topographic mapping.

3. Vegetation State

Vegetation state is an important parameter to be considered in drainage studies. The satellite visible red band is good for separating vegetation types and for delineating nonvegetated areas.

4. Drainage Density

The drainage density is defined as a ratio between the length of each channel segment in a basin and the drainage area of the basin. Both segment length and drainage area of the basin can be estimated through the use of Landsat and SPOT data.

5. Drainage Pattern

The drainage pattern which includes drainage network, stream length, and the location of ponds and lakes is readily obtained from satellite imagery. The visible red band is best for showing channel networks. The SLAR can penetrate the dense vegetation and produce an image that depicts drainage patterns.

D. Salinity Assessment

Satellite data have been used to detect saline soils with high water tables. It has been found that satellite data can be used to determine whether a soil is undergoing a salinization or a desalinization process. Recently, the GPR has been used to delineate the saline-affected area.

X. Agricultural Runoff Prediction

A. Conventional Method

The impact of land use changes on the basinwide runoff is of interest to many water resources planners and managers. There is a conventional technique called the USDA-SCS curve number method which is widely used to estimate the peak discharge for a drainage basin. This method utilizes an important parameter called runoff curve number (CN). The CN is an index of runoff potential and is a function of soil type, the land-use condition, and the antecedent soil moisture. Thus, recently this method has been used as an index to assess the land-use change effect on basinwide runoff for three reasons. First, the soil type within a basin does not effectively change with time. Second, the antecedent soil moisture affected by weather conditions is assumed to be stable for long-term average conditions. Third, the basinwide runoff is a summation of subbasin runoffs and the maximum potential difference between rainfall and runoff is linearly related to the CN. Therefore, the basinwide runoff index could be estimated from a weighted CN which can be obtained from either the overall land-use classification or from the subbasins. Thus, the prime variable in the basinwide runoff index estimation is land-use change with time. In addition, a hydrologic soil grouping established by the SCS labels soils as A, B, C, and D. These groups are determined by infiltration rate and soil permeability. Group A soils are well drained, coarse sandy soils having the lowest runoff potential. Group D soils consist of heavy clays, are the most poorly drained, and have the highest runoff potential. Groups B and C are ranked approximately between these extremes. These soil hydrologic groups in combination with the land use/land cover information are used to select the appropriate CN from a chart. In the past CNs have been calculated using a wealth of ground-survey land use/land cover information. However, as mentioned above in the land-use classification, the land-use change data gathered by the conventional method are expensive and difficult. An alternative to be investigated is the use of satellite imagery to assess land-use changes.

B. Remote-Sensing Method

The role of remote sensing in runoff predictions is generally to provide a source of input data or as an aid to estimating equation coefficients and model parameters. There are three general areas where remote-sensing data are currently being used as input data for a runoff investigation. First, these remotely sensed data are very useful for obtaining information on watershed geometry, drainage network, and other map-type information. Second, remote sensors produce input data for an investigation of empirical flood peaks, annual runoff, or low flow equations. These two applications use satellite imagery in the same way that aerial photography has been used. Third, runoff models (e.g., SCS curve number method) that are based on a land-use component have been modified to use land-use classes from satellite image classification.

Bibliography

Engman, E. T., and Gurney, R. J. (1991). "Remote Sensing in Hydrology." Chapman and Hall, New York, NY.

Shih, S. F. (1987). Using crop yield and evapotranspiration relations for regional water requirement estimation. *Water Resources Bull.* **23**(3), 435–442.

Shih, S. F., and Chen, E. Y. (1987). Using GOES thermal infrared data to map freeze zones for citrus and consequences for water management. *Water Resources Res.* **23**(4), 737–743.

Shih, S. F. (1988). Satellite data and geographical information system for land use classification. *J. Irrigation Drainage Eng. Am. Soc. Civil Engineers* **114**(3), 505–519.

Shih, S. F. (1990). Satellite data and geographic information system for rainfall estimation. *J. Irrigation Drainage Eng. Am. Soc. Civil Engineers* **116**(3), 319–331.

Shih, S. F., and Jordan, J. D. (1990). Remote sensing application to well monitoring. *J. Irrigation Drainage Eng. Am. Soc. Civil Engineers* **116**(4), 497–507.

Shih, S. F., and Cheng, K. S. (1991). Evapotranspiration estimation for data-short environment. *J. Irrigation Drainage Eng. Am. Soc. Civil Engineers* **117**(1), 107–122.

Shih, S. F., and Jordan, J. D. (1992). Landsat mid-infrared data and GIS in regional surface soil moisture assessment. *Water Resources Bull.* **28**(4), 713–719.

Shih, S. F., and Jordan, J. D. (1993). Use of Landsat thermal infrared data and GIS in soil moisture assessment. *J. Irrigation Drainage Eng. Am. Soc. Civil Engineers* **119**(5), 868–879.

Xin, J. N., and Shih, S. F. (1991). NOAA polar-orbiting satellite APT data in lake evaporation estimation. *J. Irrigation Drainage Eng. Am. Soc. Civil Engineers* **117**(4), 547–557.

Weed Science

STEPHEN O. DUKE, *USDA-Agricultural Research Service, Mississippi*

Glossary

Allelopathy Production of phytotoxins or chemical growth retardants by a plant which stunts the growth of or kills competing plants

Biocontrol Use of other organisms (e.g., microbes, insects, or nematodes) to manage weeds

Competition Reduction of a plant's supply of some necessary factor for growth and survival by another plant

Herbicide mode of action Physiological and biochemical mechanism through which a herbicide inhibits growth or kills a plant

Herbicide-resistant crop Crop made resistant to a herbicide through biotechnological methods

Interference Negative interactions between two plant species (generally a crop and a weed); interference consists of both competition and/or allelopathy

Mycoherbicide Fungal plant pathogen used to manage weeds

Safener Compound used to protect a crop from herbicides

Weed Plant in a place and at a time when it is unwanted by humankind

Weed science is the scientific study of all aspects of weeds and their management. It is an eclectic discipline that incorporates expertise from many other sciences, including botany, chemistry, biochemistry, agronomy, plant physiology, plant pathology, plant genetics, soil science, ecology, and economics. A large proportion of weed science research has dealt with the science of herbicides; their synthesis, their use, their physiological and biochemical modes of actions, and their behavior in the environment.

I. Background and Economics

Weeds are ubiquitous and continually changing pests in agricultural and other settings. Before the 20th century, when most of humankind were subsistence farmers, people dealt with weeds primarily through brute force. They used labor-intensive, mechanical methods such as hoeing, hand pulling, and cultivation with animal-drawn implements. Cultural methods, such as rotating crops or selecting a competitive crop variety, were also useful in reducing weed pressures. The origin of weed science as a separate scientific discipline can be traced to the need for less labor-intensive methods of weed management with the movement from agrarian to metropolitan societies in developed countries.

Before World War II, there were agronomists and other scientists who specialized in weeds and their management; however, weed science did not exist as a separate discipline. The discovery of modern herbicides during World War II and the advent of their commercial availability after the war spurred the organization of weed control specialists to formalize weed science as specific scientific discipline. Just as plant pathologists and entomologists are driven primarily by the need to control and manage plant pathogens and insects that are agricultural pests, the ultimate objective of most weed science research is to reduce the costs, environmental damage, and toxicological effects of weeds through improved management strategies and methods.

Weeds cause multibillion dollar economic losses every year; perhaps $20 to $30 billion in the United States alone. To determine the entire cost of weeds, the costs of control measures and the economic damage of uncontrolled weeds must be computed. Furthermore, weeds poison people, pets, and livestock, reduce the esthetic value of property, provide alternate hosts for undesirable insects and plant pathogens, block waterways and irrigation channels, and adversely affect water quality in aquaculture and recreational pursuits. No part of our food or natural fiber supply is immune from the negative effects of weeds. The need for cost-effective and environmentally safe weed management is great, and the need increases in developed and developing countries as the farm labor supply shrinks.

II. Weed Biology and Ecology

A. Biological and Physiological Attributes of Weeds

At first glance, weeds and crops appear to be quite similar. They are both usually fast-growing, determinate higher plants. Weed scientists have attempted to discover the biological and physiological traits which might distinguish particularly troublesome weeds from crops and other plants. Several generalizations can be made. First, weeds often grow better than crops under stressful environments such as drought, flooding, low light, or temperature extremes. Thus, most weeds are at a competitive advantage over crops under such conditions. Second, unlike most other noncrop plant species, the life cycle, biology, and physiology of weeds is usually well-adapted to areas of disturbance, such as tilled fields, lawns, and ditches. Third, most of the major weeds in agricultural ecosystems are reproductively prolific by either seed production and/or asexual means (tubers, rhizomes, stolons, etc.). There are many exceptions to various aspects of these generalizations because of the diverse and changing ecological niches that can be filled by weeds in agricultural and other settings. For example, parasitic weeds such as dodder (*Cuscuta* spp.) and witchweed (*Striga* spp.) are most successful under environmental conditions that normally favor the crop. However, they are similar to other weeds in that they are reproductively prolific.

Unlike crops, weeds are not introduced into the environment by planting at the beginning of favorable growing conditions. Therefore, in most climates, weeds must persist in the environment during unfavorable conditions (e.g., winter or dry seasons). Annual weeds overcome unfavorable climate with dormant seeds, and perennial weeds use a variety of strategies, including dormant seeds, buds, rhizomes, tubers, etc. Whether annual or perennial, these hardy propagules must have precise regulation of dormancy so that loss of dormancy does not occur at unfavorable times or places. For example, seedlings from very small weed seeds will not survive if the seed germinates at a soil depth too great for the seedling to emerge. Therefore, weed propagules are particularly well equipped to sense both quantity and quality of light, temperature, atmospheric gases, and other environmental signals for breaking dormancy at the proper time, in the appropriate microenvironment.

In cultivated crops, the weed seed bank is an important determinant of weed populations. When weeds are not effectively controlled, high numbers of weed seed are produced and cultivated into the soil. In many weed species, the seed can remain dormant for many years. Every year, cultivation brings a certain fraction of seed from the seed bank close enough to the soil surface to be exposed to dormancy-breaking conditions. Thus, one year of poor weed control can result in weed problems for years into the future.

In most cases, crops have had poisonous secondary compounds bred out of them. For example, the wild species from which tomatoes and potatoes originated have high levels of poisonous alkaloids. In many cases, weeds contain high levels of exotic, poisonous compounds. Although the exact function of most of these compounds is unknown, the majority of evidence indicates that they play a vital role in protection of weeds from pathogens, insects, nematodes, and herbivores. It is common to find very healthy weeds in fields of crops that have been ravaged by one or more microbial or animal pests. Thus, in the absence of insecticides, nematocides, and fungicides, weeds are usually more secure from these pests than the crop.

Significant physiological or biochemical differences between crops and weeds can be the basis for herbicide design. If an important biochemical site is more important to the weed than the crop, it may be an ideal herbicide target. However, there are no sites that are common to all weeds, but not to crops. There are herbicides that attack biochemical sites in monocots that are resistant in dicots (e.g., the aryloxyphenoxy propionates), and there are those to which dicots are extremely susceptible, but have little effect on monocots (e.g., 2,4-D). Many highly successful weeds have C_4 carbon fixation, whereas only a handful of crops have this type of carbon assimilation. However, despite significant effort, this site has not been successfully exploited by the herbicide industry.

B. Weed–Crop Interference

The density of weeds in a field required to reduce crop yield can be surprisingly small. This is partly because weeds are generally good competitors for water, light, and nutrients. Furthermore, in addition to reducing abiotic sustenance that the crop could use, weeds also can introduce undesirable, new factors to the field such as allelochemicals. Some weed species produce sufficiently phytotoxic allelochemicals to stunt the growth of competing plant species, including both the crop and other weeds. Such effects are often subtle and difficult to prove.

Understanding the effects of different levels of interference is important in determining potential crop losses and economic thresholds of weeds. The economic threshold can be defined as the weed density at which the economic loss justifies the expense of a weed management option (e.g., cultivation or a herbicide treatment). The decision is complicated by the fact that even a few weeds left in a field will generate large numbers of weed seed or other propagules that may cause problems in future crops. Thus, present and future interference must be predicted for the most effective weed management decisions. Furthermore, the effect of weeds on the quality of harvested crops is an almost unstudied aspect of weed science that should be understood in order to accurately determine economic thresholds.

C. Population Genetics and Ecology of Weeds

Compared to major crops and even some wild plants with no significant economic value, little is known of the genetics of weeds which cause the greatest economic damage. Within a given geographic area, the gene pool of most weed species is generally more varied than that of crops. Considering the weed's enormous reproductive capacity, this may give the weed population an advantage under a range of environmental and biotic stresses. For example, more than 200 weed species have evolved resistance to one or more herbicides. In some cases, resistance becomes predominant within three or four generations of weeds exposed to the herbicide. Some species become resistant to certain herbicides across wide, geographi-

cally isolated areas, demonstrating that these species are predisposed to become resistant to particular herbicides. For example horseweed (*Conyza* spp.) has become resistant to paraquat in the British isles, Israel, North America, Europe, Japan, and Australia. The interactions of plant biochemistry, physiology, and genetics which predispose certain species to become resistant to particular herbicides are not understood in any of the numerous examples of this phenomenon. Similarly, when biocontrol methods of weed control become more widely utilized, the population genetics of target weeds will play an important role in determining how soon resistance will occur.

The success of a weed species in any environment is due to a myriad of factors. In agricultural ecosystems consisting of a crop monoculture and associated weeds, predicting the success of particular weed species or understanding the shifts in predominant weed species is difficult. Factors such as competitive ability, stress tolerance, genetic diversity, reproductive modes, and susceptibility to weed management techniques all play roles. How these factors compare to the crop and competing weed species determines the success of a weed. The large number of weed species, each with wide but varying genetic diversity, insures that successful weed management agents or strategies are generally only temporary, lasting until a new weed species fills the voided agroecosystem niche or until the managed weed evolves to cope with the management system.

III. Nonchemical Methods of Weed Management

A. Cultural Methods

Before the advent of herbicides, cultural methods were the only techniques available for weed management. Weeds can be managed by manual cultivation (e.g., hoeing or pulling), by animal-drawn cultivators, or by mechanized means. Manual cultivation is not severely limited by weather conditions, is highly precise, and does not require skilled labor. However, in most of the developed world it is too expensive for economic agricultural production of agronomic crops. Mechanized cultivation for weed management is much more cost-effective. It may be made before, during, and/or after crop development. Problems associated with mechanized cultivation include soil compaction by heavy farm equipment, soil loss from wind and water, inability to cultivate during long wet periods, and highly efficient transportation of weed propagules to microenvironments suitable for dormancy loss and seedling establishment. [*See* PEST MANAGEMENT, CULTURAL CONTROL.]

In lawns and fields, mowing can effectively manage or eliminate unwanted vegetation of many weed species. Mechanical mowing or cutting with larger implements can be used to reduce understory weedy brush and vegetation from orchards, pastures, and other locations.

There is currently a trend to minimize cultivation in order to conserve soil and fossil fuel. Mulches are a cultural alternative to cultivation. In agronomic crops, only plant mulches are economically feasible. Cover vegetation used as mulch may be living or dead during crop production. For example, in temperate zones, winter ryegrass may be sown after crop harvest. In the Spring, it is generally killed with a herbicide before or during crop planting. Effective planting into untilled soil usually requires specialized equipment. Since no tillage is used, no new weed propagules are brought to the soil surface, and the dense mulch of living or dead vegetation suppresses or prevents the establishment of weeds from the propagules that might exist on the soil surface. Furthermore, survival of weed propagules on the soil surface, where they are exposed to climatic extremes and herbivorous animals, is significantly less than that in the soil. Some mulch species have allelopathic effects upon certain weeds, further enhancing their weed-suppressing activity.

In high value crops, such as many horticultural crops, plastic mulches have been used to economically suppress weeds. Plastic mulches suppress weeds by several mechanisms, including (1) providing a mechanical barrier; (2) preventing access to proper light quantity and/or quality; (3) creation of an unsuitable gaseous environment for seedling establishment; (4) enhancement of weed pathogen activity; and (5) raising the temperature to levels that kill weeds. Light transmittance (both quantity and quality), gas permeability, and mechanical strength of the mulche influence each of these mechanisms. The latter mechanism is termed solarization and is considered the most important means of weed suppression by plastic mulches.

The geometry of planting can greatly influence weed management. For example, when crop rows are planted closer together and/or more crop plants are planted per unit area, the crop will more rapidly compete effectively with weeds for sunlight than in widely spaced rows. Crops planted in elevated rows (ridges) can be cultivated (ridge tillage) more effectively under some circumstances.

Crop rotation generally aids in reducing weed problems. The weeds associated with different crops differ due to many factors. Thus, crop rotation reduces the soil seed bank of particular weed species during the years that a crop with which the weeds are incompatible is grown.

Fire can be used to manage weeds. Burning crop stubble after harvesting can reduce weed populations and destroy seed of some weed species. However, this method is illegal in some U.S. states. Hand-held or mechanized devices for directing flames to weeds have been used successfully in some settings for weed control. Electrocution of weeds with tractor-mounted electrodes has been researched, but not adopted commercially.

B. Biocontrol

Weeds have natural insect, pathogen, nematode, and herbivore pests, just as do crops. Those organisms that are specific for weeds can be turned against them. This approach can be divided into "classical" and "inundative" biocontrol methods. The classical approach is to introduce an exotic weed pathogen or insect that will propagate itself within the environment after it is unleashed. This strategy has been most successful when insects from outside the range of the weed are released. In cases in which the weed has not evolved defenses to the insect or pathogen and the biocontrol agent has no local enemies, there is an enhanced chance of success with this method. The classical approach is particularly appealing in settings in which the use of herbicides is prohibited by either economics or environmental concerns. For example, the *Opuntia* spp. cactus, a particularly onerous weed in the rangelands of Australia, was effectively removed as a significant problem by the introduction of the *Cactoblastus* moth. There have been similar successes with the classical approach in the rangelands and waterways of the United States. The classical approach has generally been a public sector effort, in that once the biocontrol agent is released, it is self-propagating and there is no opportunity for repeat sales of the biocontrol product. This approach is generally too slow for use in annual crops in which weeds must be rapidly and uniformly suppressed. [*See* PEST MANAGEMENT, BIOLOGICAL CONTROL.]

The inundative approach involves augmentation of the population of a natural enemy of a weed to numbers that can effectively manage it. Because these are indigenous organisms, they generally have natural enemies and the target weed has some tolerance to them. Thus, they usually dissipate with time, requiring reapplication every year. Microbial biocontrol agents lend themselves to this method, in that they can be produced, stored, and applied to weeds, much like chemicals. Three commercial mycoherbicides have been marketed in North America and several others are under development (Table I). Mycoherbicides may be applied as either mycelial preparations to the soil or spores to the soil or foliage.

The most common limitations to inundative microbial biocontrol agents are cost, short shelf-life, unpredictable efficacy, limited host range, and requirements for specialized application equipment. Although more than 200 potential mycoherbicides have been discovered, only four are commercially available, and there is little prospect that many more will be become available in the next decade. Further research on microbe strain selection and manipulation, storage formulation and stabilization, application formulation, application technology, and host range manipulation will be required before microbial herbicides can be expected to play a significant role in weed control.

Grazing and foraging animals (e.g., goats, geese, and pigs) have sometimes been useful in the biocontrol of weeds. Goats, in particular, will remove much of the unwanted vegetation from cattle and sheep pastures. In Australia, rotating sheep with wheat is an important component of weed control in both wheat and pasture. Pigs have been used to remove the tubers and rhizomes of perennial weeds from agricultural land.

IV. Herbicides and Their Use in Weed Management

A. Herbicides and Their Modes of Action

Since the first synthetic, organic herbicide, 2,4-D, was introduced commercially after World War II, thousands of herbicides have been patented and hundreds have been marketed. The herbicide market is highly competitive, with continual improvements in selectivity, safety, and efficacy. The approval, registration, and use of herbicides is a highly regulated activity. The most desirable selectivity is for the herbicide to have no effect on crops, with a useful level of phytotoxicity on all of the major weeds in those crops. There is a trend toward development of herbicides with more biological activity per unit mass. These low use-rate compounds generally have one very specific molecular site of action that is unique to plants. [See HERBICIDES AND HERBICIDE RESISTANCE; PEST MANAGEMENT, CHEMICAL CONTROL.]

Herbicides can be classed by chemical family or by their mode of action (Table II). It has become increasingly important to understand the biochemical mechanism of herbicides. This information can be important in predicting toxicological effects, in designing more effective and selective herbicides, and in producing herbicide-resistant crops by biotechnology (see later).

There are thousands of potential biochemical sites in plants that could be targeted by a herbicide. Several million compounds have probably been screened for herbicidal activity, and, of these, several hundred have been commercialized, although many of these products are no longer on the market. The molecular sites of action of the majority of commercialized herbicides are known. Less than 20 molecular sites of action are represented. Thus, of the thousands of potential sites of action, only a small fraction are represented by commercially successful herbicides. This may be because only a few sites of action have the unique characteristics required for a good herbicide target or because organic chemists who have synthesized the majority of the compounds screened by the herbicide industry have generated a less diverse spectrum of

TABLE I

Mycoherbicides That Have Been Commercially Available during the Past Decade or Have Been or Are under Development

Organism	Trade name	Target weed
Commercially available		
Colletotrichum gloeosporiodes[a]	Collego	Northern jointvetch (Aeschynomene virginica)
Phytopthora palmivora	DeVine	Stranglervine (Morrenia odorata)
Colletotrichum gloeosporiodes	Luboa-2	Dodder (Cuscuta spp.)
Colletotrichum gloeosporoides	Biomal	Round-leaved mallow (Malva pusilla)
Under development		
Alternaria cassiae	Casst	Sicklepod (Cassia obtusifolia)
Colletotrichum truncatum	Coltru	Hemp sesbania (Sesbania exaltata)
Colletotrichum coccodes	Velgo	Velvetleaf (Abutilon theophrasti)

[a] Different strains of C. gloeosporoides have distinctly different host specificities.

TABLE II

Modes of Action of Several Major Herbicide Classes

Mode of action (molecular site)	Chemical class of herbicide	U.S. tradename examples of herbicide class	Decade of first introduction
Auxin-type activity			
Site of action unknown	Phenoxypropanoic acids	2,4-D	1940s
Inhibition of amino acid synthesis			
Acetolactate synthase	Sulfonylureas	Glean	1980s
	Imidazolines	Scepter	1980s
Enolpyruvylshikimate phosphate synthase	Glyphosate	Roundup	1970s
Glutamate synthase	Glufosinate	Ignite	1990s
Inhibition of carotenoid biosynthesis			
Phytoene desaturase	Pyridazinones	Zorial	1970s
Exact site unknown	Isoxalidinones	Command	1980s
Inhibition of photosystem II			
D-1, quinone-binding protein	Triazines	Atrazine	1950s
	Nitriles	Buctril	1960s
	Substituted ureas	Lorox	1950s
	Anilides	Stam	1960s
Interference with microtubules			
Tubulin	Dinitroanilines	Treflan	1960s
Exact site unknown	Dithiopyr	Dimension	1990s
Inhibition of porphyrin synthesis			
Protoporphyrinogen oxidase	p-Nitrodiphenyl ethers	Blazer	1960s
Inhibition of lipid synthesis			
Acetyl CoA carboxylase	Cyclohexanediones	Poast	1980s
	Aryloxyphenoxypropanoates	Hoelon	1970s
Unknown	Acetanilides	Lasso	1960s
Inhibition of folate synthesis			
Dihydropteroate synthase	Asulam	Asulox	1960s
Inhibition of cellulose synthesis			
Exact molecular site unknown	Dichlobenil	Casoron	1960s
Generation of superoxide radical			
Photosystem I	Dipyridiliums	Gramoxone	1960s

compounds than required to discover other effective sites of action. This question remains to be answered.

Although most successful herbicides are the result of random screening of compounds for herbicidal activity, this discovery strategy is in a state of rapidly diminishing returns. Two new strategies are becoming more important: biorational design and using natural phytotoxins as templates for new herbicides. Biorational design is the process of targeting a specific molecular target in the weed. For example, inhibitors of a particular enzyme in the weed can be designed, based on detailed knowledge of the enzyme structure, substrate(s), product(s), and/or cofactors. Success of this strategy is partially dependent on adequate knowledge of the physiology and biochemistry of the weed. Natural phytotoxins offer new and unusual chemicals with proven herbicidal activity. Using these chemicals without modification or as templates for structure–activity manipulations that might improve their characteristics has become an important herbicide discovery strategy.

B. Herbicide Use

By unit mass, herbicides constitute 60 to 70% of all pesticides used in agriculture. In developed countries, more than 90% of the land on which all major crops are grown is treated with a herbicide at least yearly. Thus, herbicides have become the major tool for weed management in agriculture.

Herbicides are applied in several different ways. Before or during planting of a crop, they can be applied directly onto or incorporated into the soil. These practices can alleviate weed pressure during establishment of the crop stand. Later, herbicides can be applied directly over the emerged crop or between crop rows if the crop is susceptible to the herbicide (postemergence application). Postmergence applications can be made with many different types of spray systems (hand-held, tractor-mounted, or aircraft-mounted) or by rubbing the herbicide onto the weed foliage from a wax bar or rope wick impregnated with herbicide. Herbicides can also be applied in irrigation water (chemigation). In areas of high weed pressure, more than one of these methods, each with a different herbicide, is generally utilized.

In many situations, herbicides are sprayed in mixtures of two or more pesticides in order to minimize the number of trips over the field with mechanized or aerial spray equipment. Other herbicides or pesticides can decrease or increase the activity of a herbicide, depending on many factors. Without knowledge of potential interactions, either in the mixing tank or on or in the plant, tank mixing pesticides can result in poor performance of agrochemicals. Marketing premixed combinations of compatible or synergistic herbicides is a growing trend.

Formulation of herbicides can also strongly influence their weed-killing capacity. Adjuvants used with herbicides generally increase droplet spreading and decrease the rate of droplet drying on leaf surfaces. These effects, as well as others, have been implicated in their improvement of herbicide activity. The proper formulation for a herbicide is a function of the target weed species, the age of the weed, the herbicide, and climatic conditions. Not enough is known of how these factors interact in order to custom formulate a herbicide for a particular set of conditions. Such optimal formulations could greatly reduce the amount of herbicide needed for effective weed management.

Chemical safeners are used with some crops to protect them from herbicides that ordinarily could not be used with the crop. Most safeners act by enhancing the metabolic degradation of the herbicide in the crop. In almost all cases in which crops are naturally tolerant to a herbicide, the crop is tolerant through rapid metabolic degradation of the herbicide rather than due to resistance at the molecular target site.

In some cases, reduced tillage results in increased dependency on herbicides. Without tillage, herbicides can be the major alternative for weed management. Even with vegetative mulches grown during the fallow season, herbicides are often used to kill the mulch vegetation before or during planting of the crop.

C. Herbicide Resistance

Resistance to herbicides has evolved more slowly than insect resistance to insecticides for several reasons. These include the relatively long generation time of weeds, the long-lived soil seed bank, and the often intermittent nature of the selection pressure. Nevertheless, more than 200 weed species have evolved resistance to various herbicides and the problem is growing geometrically. In some cases the weed is

resistant only to the herbicides that have been used on the fields in which it originated. In other cases, resistance extends to other herbicides with the same mechanism of action, even though the weed population may not have been exposed to these herbicides (cross-resistance). Occasionally, resistance is found to an array of herbicides with diverse mechanisms of action (multiple resistance). If the weed population has been exposed to all of these herbicides, multiple resistance can be the result of multiple mechanisms of resistance. If not, enhanced capacity to degrade or sequester a wide range of xenobiotics may explain multiple resistance.

D. Environmental and Toxicological Aspects of Herbicide Use

In developed countries, the largest volume of pesticides introduced into the environment is comprised of herbicides. Furthermore, many of these compounds are placed directly into the soil where they are readily mobile. It is not surprising that herbicides and herbicide breakdown products represent a major fraction of pesticides and pesticide-related compounds found in groundwater. Postemergence, foliarly applied herbicides can be leached into soil or into surface water. Herbicide sprays (particularly aerially applied) can drift onto nontarget crops and into nonagricultural areas (recreational, residential, etc.). Volatile herbicides become part of the atmosphere until sufficiently degraded. Any herbicide used in agriculture has the potential to contaminate food (either human or for animal feed) in the applied form and/or as degradation products. Considering the large amount of herbicides used worldwide, the potential for environmental contamination is significant if use restrictions are not carefully followed. The toxicological and environmental effects of current levels of contamination are a point of controversy.

Herbicide registration (approval for commercial use) and directions for use are highly regulated in the United States and most other developed countries. In general, the trend is toward more stringent registration and use restrictions. Tolerance levels (allowable concentrations) in food and water are set by the U.S. Environmental Protection Agency (EPA) for each herbicide. An allowable daily intake is also set for each herbicide and its degradation products. These levels are based on toxicology data, with a large safety factor built in. Nevertheless, large amounts of herbicides are used, and improving analytical capacities are making it possible to detect minute quantities of herbicides in our food and water. These previously undetectable levels of herbicides cause concern in some quarters, even though they are well below safety standards established by EPA.

Herbicide residues consumed by the average person in food and water are thought by many scientists to constitute a small fraction of the carcinogens in the food and water supply. At any level, probably only a small fraction of herbicides and their residues are carcinogenic. Other carcinogens–such as natural pesticides from plants, compounds from smoked, charred, or seared foods; toxins from spoilage microbes, nitrates, nitrites, and nitrosamines, and ethanol–are thought by many to play a more important role in disease development in humans. However, this is a controversial area in which absolute proof of cause and effect is extremely difficult.

Most of the data available indicate that herbicide residues have no direct long-lasting effects upon soil microflora. Vegetation changes caused by the herbicide are more influential in indirectly affecting soil biotica.

Current trends in herbicide use and regulation will mitigate future environmental effects of herbicide use. Most newer herbicides registered are low-rate use compounds that are less mobile in soil. Furthermore, they generally have short environmental half-lives. Some older, higher use rate herbicides will soon disappear from the market because of competition and/or increased regulatory pressures.

V. Weed Science in Integrated Pest Management

Like all ecosystems, agroecosystems are comprised of various biotic and abiotic components involved in complex interactions. Integrated pest management may be defined as pest management strategies which are designed with some knowledge of these interactions in order to minimize cost, both economic and environmental. [See INTEGRATED PEST MANAGEMENT.]

For example, rotation of crops is helpful in control of all crop pests because long-standing monocultures allow the buildup of populations of nematodes, weeds, insects, and pathogens that are injurious to the crop. Consideration of the effects of pesticides on nontarget organisms is important in integrated pest management. For example, herbicides can significantly influence susceptibility of crops to plant patho-

gens. In some cases, the crops are made more resistant to pathogens and in others their resistance is reduced. For example, glyphosate has been found to increase the susceptibility of some plant species to certain pathogens under some conditions by blocking the plant's biosynthetic machinery which produces antimicrobial compounds.

Weeds can be alternate hosts for crop-damaging nematodes or insects. Conversely, weeds can be hosts or habitats for beneficial insects. Little is known of such relationships and their role in crop production.

VI. Future Trends in Weed Management

A. Biotechnology and Weed Management

All crops are naturally resistant to some herbicides. However, they are not always resistant to herbicides that could offer valuable weed management tools for the crops. Plant breeders have spent little effort in developing cultivars resistant to new herbicides because of limited variability in crop germplasm and the possibility that, after a long and laborious breeding effort, the herbicide will disappear from the ever-changing herbicide market. With modern biotechnology, any crop can be made resistant to any herbicide relatively quickly.

The methodology has consisted primarily of cell selection or gene transfer techniques. Treating crop cell cultures with herbicides to select for natural mutations conferring resistance has resulted in several herbicide-resistant crops. This method does not require a biochemical knowledge of mode of action or degradation of the herbicide. An alternative method is genetic modification of the crop by genetic engineering. Foreign genes can confer herbicide resistance by introducing resistant sites of action or enzymes that degrade the herbicide. Examples of each method are provided in Table III. An example of a herbicide-resistant crop is depicted in Fig. 1.

Controversy exists regarding the environmental impact of herbicide-resistant crops produced by biotechnology. However, in most cases the herbicides to which these crops are being developed offer more environmentally benign choices than currently exist. Furthermore, they will provide management options to farmers that can be used with reduced tillage and no-tillage agriculture, thus, conserving soil and fuel. They also offer one of the few hopes for coping with

TABLE III

Herbicide-Resistant Crops Available or Currently under Development

Herbicide	Crop	Method[a]	Strategy[b]
Atrazine	Canola	M	Site
Bialaphos	Soybean, corn	B	Degrade
Cyclohexanediones	Corn	C	Site
Bromoxynil	Tobacco, cotton, potato	B	Degrade
Glufosinate	Tobacco, sweet potato, tomato, sugarbeet, oilseed rape, alfalfa corn, poplar	B	Degrade
Glyphosate	Poplar, soybean, tomato cotton, flax, sugarbeet	B	Site
Imidazolinones	Canola	M	Unknown
	Corn	C	Site
Sulfonylureas	Tobacco, corn, cotton	B	Site
	Canola	C	Site
2,4-D	Tobacco	B	Degrade
	Cotton	B	Degrade

Note: Partial listing of research and development of herbicide-resistant crops by industry.

[a] B, gene transfer by biotechnology; M, microspore mutagenesis and selection; C, cell selection.

[b] Site, site of action; Degrade, enzyme(s) for degradation of herbicide.

parasitic weeds which drastically reduce crop yields in Africa. [*See* PLANT BIOTECHNOLOGY: FOOD SAFETY AND ENVIRONMENTAL ISSUES.]

Genetic modification of microbial weed control agents by biotechnology could solve some of the problems in development of effective microbial herbicides. Such manipulation could allow the development of mycoherbicides and bacterial herbicides with more desirable host ranges and improve virulence. However, without proper safeguards, such modified plant pathogens could cause harm to crops or other important plant species.

Ultimately, molecular biology will be used to make crops more competitive with weeds. However, this will be a difficult task in that competitive ability is a complex, multigenic trait, and imparting certain aspects of competitiveness may conflict with other desirable traits such as crop yield.

B. Weed Management in Organic Farming

Organically-grown foods are generally defined as foods produced without using synthetic fertilizers or pesticides. This eliminates the use of synthetic herbicides for weed management, leaving only natural herbicides, biocontrol, and cultural methods for weed control.

FIGURE 1 The response of a nonselected line (left) and two corn lines (middle and right) selected for resistance to sethoxydim, a grassy weed herbicide, at 0.44 kg sethoxydim/ha. These plants were regenerated from sethoxydim-resistant or nonselected callus cultures. The photographs were taken approximately 10 days after treatment with the herbicide. (Courtesy of David A. Somers, Department of Agronomy and Plant Genetics, University of Minnesota.)

Natural compounds are intrinsically no more safe than synthetic ones. The most potent toxins known are natural compounds. Nevertheless, by some definitions, organic foods can be produced with the use of natural toxins as pesticides. Two toxicologically safe natural compounds, bialaphos and phosphinothricin, are commercially available as herbicides. Bialaphos is a fermentation product of *Streptomyces viridochromogenes* that is effective on a broad spectrum of weeds. It is currently available only in Japan and other Asian markets. To be herbicidally effective, bialaphos must be broken down in the plant to phosphinothricin. Phosphinothricin is synthetically produced and sold throughout most of the world as the herbicide glufosinate. Although synthesized glufosinate is chemically identical to the natural product phosphinothricin, it might not be considered as a component of organic farming by organic farming purists.

C. New Technology and Weed Management

Empirical models or "expert systems" are under development as aids for farmers in making decisions affecting weed management. With the paper data input (e.g., weed species, weed density, weed and crop development stage, climatic conditions, expected price of the harvested crop, and herbicide prices) the computer model produces a range of weed control options with estimated return on the investment. When perfected, such management tools will allow maximal efficiency and minimal environment impact of weed management actions.

Only a small amount of herbicides sprayed into the environment reach target weed species. This is due to a number of factors, including drift of spray particles away from the target and the fact that the spray equipment cannot differentiate between target species and other plant species or bare ground. Spray equipment has been recently developed which will differentiate between vegetation and bare ground, spraying only when vegetation is detected. If a field is 25% covered by weeds before planting, this spray system can potentially reduce the amount of herbicide needed by 75%. This equipment can be used to treat weeds between crop rows with nonselective herbicides or to spray all of the vegetation in a field with crops that are resistant to the herbicide.

It is technically feasible for a miniature television camera to capture the image of a plant, for a computer to analyze the image and identify the species, and for the computor to actuate a spray system to treat identified weeds with the appropriate herbicide. Such a system could greatly increase weed management efficiency and safety by greatly reducing the amount of herbicide needed for a high level of weed control. The low speed, insufficient reliability, and high cost of such a system would be unacceptable at present. However, rapid advances in electronics and engineering will probably make such a system practical within the next decade.

D. Potential Impacts of Global Climate and Atmospheric Changes on Weed Management

Global climate change will affect agriculture, as crop production is intrinsically linked to climate. As mentioned earlier, weeds generally tolerate climatic stress better than the crops with which they associate themselves. In some geographic areas, climatic change in the form of increased drought stress, ultraviolet radiation, and temperatures will give weeds an advantage over crops. Air pollution (SO_2, ozone, etc.) is harmful to both crops and weeds. Little is known of relative tolerance of crops and associated weeds to these stresses. [See AIR POLLUTION: PLANT GROWTH AND PRODUCTIVITY.]

The carbon dioxide enrichment of the atmosphere that has occurred during the past century enhances the growth of all plants. However, it favors C_3 plants (generally dicots) more than C_4 plants (generally monocots such as grasses). This trend should favor many dicot weeds (e.g., velvetleaf) over C_4 monocot crops such as corn. Conversely, C_4 weeds in C_3 crops (e.g., johnsongrass in soybeans) should become less competitive.

As climate and the atmosphere change, shifts in predominant weed species and/or ecotypes of species can be expected. Just as there are varieties of most major crops that can be grown in a wide range of climates, there are weed species that are most adapted to each climate. In some areas there have been profound changes in the weed species with certain crops during this century. These changes can be linked to use of certain herbicides in some cases; however, in others, there is no clear reason for the shift in vegetation. Whether the climate or atmospheric changes that have already occurred are involved is unknown.

E. Weed Control in a More Stringent Regulatory Environment

In most countries the toxicological and environmental regulations governing pesticides are becoming increasingly stringent. This is leading to safer herbicides, but is escalating costs of commercializing new products. Fewer companies are engaging in herbicide development and fewer new herbicides are being introduced. In the United States, older pesticides that were registered for use at a time when regulatory requirements were less strict are in the process of being re-registered, using current regulatory requirements. This process will lead to the loss of availability of many older herbicides.

In major crops, there is little likelihood that these trends will drastically impact chemical weed control in the next decade. However, they have already greatly limited the availability of inexpensive chemical weed control in minor crops, many of which are horticultural crops. The herbicide industry can no longer afford the cost of registration or re-registration of some herbicides for many minor crops. Weed control in such crops is now generally much more expensive than in major agronomic crops.

Bibliography

Ashton, F. M., and Monaco, T. J. (1991). "Weed Science." Wiley-Interscience, New York.

Baker, N. R., and Percival, M. P. (eds.) (1991). "Topics in Photosynthesis," Vol. 10. Elsevier, London.

Caseley, J. C., Cussans, G. W., and Atkin, R. K. (eds.) (1991). "Herbicide Resistance in Weeds and Crops." Butterworth-Heinemann, Oxford.

Cobb, A. (1992). "Herbicides and Plant Physiology." Chapman and Hall, London.

Devine, M. D., Duke, S. O., and Fedtke, C. (1993). "Physiology of Herbicide Action." Prentice Hall, Englewood Cliffs, NJ.

Duke, S. O. (ed.) (1985). "Weed Physiology," Vols. I and II. CRC Press, Boca Raton, FL.

Duke, S. O. (ed.) (1993). "Pest Control Agents and Technologies with Reduced Environmental Impact." American Chemical Society, Washington, DC.

Duke, S. O., Holt, J. S., Hess, F. D., and Christy, A. L. (1991). "Herbicide-Resistant Crops." Comments from CAST, no. 1991-1, Council for Agricultural Science and Technology, Ames, IA.

McWhorter, C. G., and Gebhardt, M. R. (1988). "Methods of Applying Herbicides." Weed Science Society of America, Champaign, IL.

Radosevich, S. R., and Holt, J. S. (1984). "Weed Ecology." Wiley-Interscience, New York.

Wetlands and Riparian Areas: Economics and Policy

RALPH E. HEIMLICH, *USDA-Economic Research Service*

Glossary

Circular 39 wetlands Classification developed by the U.S. Fish and Wildlife Service in 1954 that distinguishes between coastal and inland areas of fresh and saline wetlands, deriving 20 wetland types on the basis of water depth and vegetation within these four broad categories

Cowardin system wetlands Named after its developer, this classification includes both wetlands and deepwater habitats grouped in a hierarchical structure on the basis of hydrologic, geomorphologic, chemical, and biological factors; five major systems (marine, estuarine, riverine, lacustrine, and palustrine) form the first level in the hierarchy, further subdivided into subsystems based on the degree of inundation and dominance of vegetative types

Externalities Unavoidable joint product of an economic production process that may produce goods or evils, enjoyed by, or inflicted on, society at large

Farmed wetlands Wetlands that have been cleared, drained, or otherwise manipulated to make cropping possible, but still meet jurisdictional wetland definitions

Hydric soils Soils that are saturated, flooded, or ponded long enough during the growing season to develop anaerobic conditions that favor the growth and regeneration of hydrophytic vegetation; hydromorphology characteristic of hydric soils includes development of gray mottles or matrix, organic streaking, and manganese or iron oxide nodules or concretions

Hydrophytic vegetation Vegetation that is adapted for growth in saturated soil conditions; biologists divide hydrophytic vegetation into several classes, including obligate, facultative-wet, and facultative species that always, primarily, or equally often appear in wetlands

Jurisdictional wetland Wetlands defined and delineated according to one or another of Agency or Interagency Manuals for Identification and Delineation of Wetlands issued in 1987, 1989, or 1991 for the purpose of administering Section 404 of the Clean Water Act or the so-called swampbuster provision of the 1985 Food Security Act

Wetlands farmed under natural conditions Open wetland that dries out adequately in normal years to plant and harvest a crop

Wetlands and riparian areas are areas intermediate between land and water. Since 1977, the Federal government has used a three-part definition involving hydric soils, hydrophytic vegetation, and hydrology. According to the U.S. Army Corps of Engineers (COE), which administers Section 404, wetlands are "areas that are inundated or saturated by surface or ground water at a frequency and duration sufficient to support, and that under normal circumstances do support, a prevalence of vegetation typically adapted for life in saturated soil conditions." The phrase "under normal circumstances" has been interpreted to mean that an area with wetland hydrology and hydric soils is still a wetland, even when adapted vegetation has been removed to make areas suitable for farming. Delineating wetlands has been controversial because of conflicts between landowners who want to use and develop these areas and environmentalists who want to preserve them.

I. Definition and Delineation

Controversy over wetland definitions has a long history, paralleled by evolving views on the need for government regulation of wetlands. Farmland does not correspond with the general public's image of wetlands, but may be treated as wetlands by the two programs that most directly affect private landowners: The Clean Water Act's (CWA) Section 404 permit program and the Food Security Act's (FSA) swampbuster provision. The U.S. Fish and Wildlife Service (FWS) developed the first federally applied wetland delineation method that considered vegetation and hydrology in 1979. In 1987, USDA, COE, and EPA developed manuals using a three-part wetland definition that considered soils, vegetation, and hydrology for their programs.

Concern that important wetlands were not covered under Section 404 and that all four Federal agencies with wetland programs were using different wetland delineation procedures led to development of the Federal Interagency Manual for Identification and Delineation of Wetlands in 1989. While some critics of the 1989 manual claimed that it expanded the area under Section 404 jurisdiction, there is no clear evidence that an expansion occurred because the area defined as wetland under varying definitions has never been estimated.

Before 1989, COE did not consider areas previously cleared for crop production as wetlands subject to permit requirements. The 1989 Manual delineated as wetland farm fields that had hydric soil if they had sufficient wetland hydrology to support hydrophytic vegetation if left undisturbed. COE reinterpreted the "normal circumstances" language of their definition to include situations where wetland vegetation, including trees, had been cleared for agricultural production. The 1989 manual also delineated as wetlands land whose soils are saturated within 18 in. of the surface for only 7 days during the growing season. These interpretations created problems with a variety of drier altered, artificial, or managed wetlands, and were at odds with the general public's image of a wetland.

An impression that wetland area had been expanded could have resulted from maps of hydric soils used to show areas that could potentially be wetlands. Presence of hydric soils is definite evidence that an area developed under saturated conditions. However, drainage for farming or other development alters the hydrology of a site with hydric soils, removing it

from any wetland delineation. The 1989 manual required that an area have hydric soils and wetland hydrology.

A backlash against the 1989 manual developed as areas previously not considered wetlands became subject to permit requirements. Attacks by a coalition of farm, development, and utility company interests resulted in legislation introduced in the House to reform wetland regulation by changing the 1989 definition. Under this pressure, a revised wetland delineation manual was proposed in August 1991. Important differences between the 1989 and 1991 manuals are outlined in Table I. The 1991 manual requires that all three criteria be present at least some time in the year in order for a site to be a wetland. How many days and to what degree a site must be flooded to be a wetland are particular points of difference between the 1989 and 1991 manuals. Indicators of wetland hydrology are restricted and secondary indicators require corroborating evidence. There are differences in the way the growing season is defined in the two manuals, as well as differences in the methods that can be used to determine presence of hydrophytic vegetation. Special procedures are outlined for sites that have been disturbed, including farmed wetlands. Other procedures are used for "difficult-to-identify" wetlands that focus on which of the three criteria is difficult to determine. Finally, because of the growing controversy, the 1991 manual got far greater public notice and public comment than the 1989 manual.

Field tests of the 1991 and 1989 manuals by Federal, joint Federal and State, and State field teams under a variety of conditions indicated that 30 to 80% of land delineated as wetlands in the 1989 manual were excluded by the 1991 manual. Areas that would have been excluded include cottonwood and willow wetlands in riparian areas of the Rocky Mountains and Southwest, most bogs in the Northeast and Midwest, and many prairie potholes in the Dakotas. Also excluded would be high coastal marsh along the Pacific coast, some of the Florida Everglades in the National Park and remaining on private land, and as much as 80% of the Great Dismal Swamp in Virginia and North Carolina.

By January 1992, the 1991 delineation manual received more than 80,000 formal comments. Attempts to revise the manual to account for the diverging views bogged down. Funding for a National Academy of Science (NAS) study of the delineation question was included in EPA appropriations in 1993 that delayed any decision on delineation for 18 months. In the interim, COE and EPA have returned to use

TABLE I

Comparison of 1989 and 1991 Wetland Delineation Manuals

Item	1989 Manual	1991 Manual
Evidence of three parameters: hydric soils, hydrophytic vegetation, and wetland hydrology	Hydrology could be assumed from vegetation and soils; vegetation could be assumed from soils and hydrology	Independent indicators of all three required unless site is disturbed or a playa lake, prairie pothole, vernal pool, pocosin, or other special wetland
Duration of inundation or saturation	Seven or more days during the growing season	Inundated 15 or more consecutive days or saturated to the surface 21 or more consecutive days during the growing season
Depth of soil saturation	Saturated within 6–18 in. of the surface, depending on soil type	Saturated to the surface as indicated by water that can be squeezed from surface soil
Acceptable indicators	Lists strong and weak indicators of hydrology, including presence of hydric soils	Lists primary and secondary indicators of hydrology; only primary indicators can be used without corroborative information; eliminates presence of hydric soil as an indicator of hydrology
Definition of growing season	Based on growing season maps delineated by soil temperature regimes	Based on local weather data indicating 3 weeks before last spring killing frost and 3 weeks after last fall killing frost
Hydrophytic vegetation criterion	Under normal circumstances, based on composition or a prevalence frequency analysis	Under normal circumstances, based only on a prevalence frequency analysis
Public input	Notice and public comment rulemaking not required	Formally proposed in the *Federal Register*; public comment not required, but solicited

of the 1987 delineation manual. President Clinton's August 1993 wetland policy statement affirmed use of the 1987 delineation manual pending completion of the NAS study. The President's statement also gave USDA responsibility for all wetland delineation on agricultural lands, but details about how this arrangement will be worked out within existing COE and EPA authorities remain to be specified. USDA never formally adopted the 1989 manual and is still running the swampbuster program under regulations first issued in 1987.

II. Current Extent

A. Wetlands

While no estimates of wetland extent using jurisdictional definitions have been made, various estimates and inventories using scientific definitions have been made over the years. According to the 1987 National Resources Inventory (NRI) there were 83.2 million acres of rural nonfederal wetlands in 1982. These are wetlands defined by the older Cowardin wetland definition based primarily on hydrology and used by the FWS. This definition excludes many acres of farmed wetlands included in current jurisdictional definitions. Eighty-three percent of nonfederal wetlands inventoried were privately owned, with the remainder in State (13%) and local (2%) government ownership or on Indian tribal lands (2%). "Wetland" is neither a land use nor a land cover, but a condition prevailing in many rural land uses. More than half of all nonfederal wetlands were forested. The second largest land cover category (20.9%) was "other lands," a residual category. About 17% of wetlands were in pasture and range. Only 5.6% of wetlands was in crops. Not inventoried in the NRI were an estimated 12.5 million acres of wetlands on Federal land, excluding Alaska.

Both farmed wetlands and wetlands farmed under natural conditions, as well as undisturbed natural wetlands, are subject to swampbuster provisions. Cropland on hydric soil that was once wetland but had been converted before 1985 is termed "prior converted" wetland and is exempt from swampbuster provisions. An example of farmed wetland is cleared bottomland fields in the lower Mississippi alluvial plain that flood over winter but are dry in time for spring plantings of soybeans or other crops. An example of wetlands farmed under natural conditions is the prairie potholes of the Northern Plains, shallow depressions of glacial origin that collect snowmelt and spring runoff but are dry enough to plant wheat in most years. A landowner cannot further drain or otherwise alter the hydrology of these wetlands to plant a crop without losing farm program benefits. Farmed wetlands and wetlands farmed under natural conditions are not pristine natural ecosystems, but they do continue to perform valuable natural functions. For example, prairie pothole wetlands provide important waterfowl feeding and nesting areas and bottomland wetlands provide waterfowl wintering areas and nursery areas for fish and invertebrates which fish feed upon.

There is no reliable estimate of the total farmland acreage subject to swampbuster and Section 404, but available data indicate some realistic limits. All 83.2 million acres of wetland inventoried in the NRI is subject to swampbuster provisions, but only 7% (5.7 million acres) was rated by USDA Soil Conservation Service technicians as having high or medium potential for conversion to cropland and thus has some likelihood of creating a violation. In addition to land inventoried as wetland, 53 million acres of nonwetland cropland on hydric soils can be identified from the NRI. More than half of this land (30 million acres) had no drainage. Half of that (17.9 million acres) needed drainage or other conservation practices for improved crop production. The remaining land was drained to some degree, but 4.5 million acres was not adequately drained for best crop production. These 53 million acres of cropland converted prior to 1985 are excluded from swampbuster provisions and COE agreed to exempt them from Section 404 permit requirements in 1990, a decision confirmed by regulation as part of President Clinton's wetland plan in 1993 (Table II).

When the 1989 interagency delineation manual was first introduced, some COE field staff did not distinguish between prior converted wetlands, farmed wetlands, and wetlands farmed under natural conditions. Complaints from farmers prompted the COE leadership to clarify the manual's three-part definition, stressing that a site ". . . effectively and legally drained to the extent that it no longer meets the regulatory wetlands hydrology criteria . . ." is not subject to Section 404. Staff were cautioned not to determine hydrology solely on hydric soil characteristics. In a memorandum issued in July 1990, the COE reiterated that normal practices are exempt from Section 404 (see below). Note, however, that substantial changes in land use, either to a more intensive agricultural use or to a developed use, are not considered normal practice. Coincident with President Clinton's wetland policy statement in 1993, the COE and EPA formalized guidance exempting 53 million acres of prior converted agricultural land from Section 404 jurisdiction. These actions completed a movement toward more consistent Federal wetland policy because both swampbuster and Section 404 were now using very similar wetland definitions.

Normal Farming Activities Are Exempt
from Section 404 Permit Requirements of the Clean Water Act

Certain activities conducted by farmers in agricultural wetlands are exempt from Section 404 requirements, and do not require notification or application to the Corps of Engineers for a Section 404 permit. These include:

Plowing	Harvesting
Seeding	Cultivating

These activities can be conducted on prior converted wetlands, farmed wetlands, and unaltered wetlands under natural conditions. The activities must be part of an ongoing farming operation, and cannot be associated with bringing a wetland into agricultural production or converting an agricultural wetland to a nonwetland use.

Other activities are exempt, providing woody vegetation is not removed and existing drainage is not modified. These include:

Drainage system maintenance	Cropping hay or
	pastured wetland fields
Construction of	Maintenance of
Farm ponds	Farm ponds
Irrigation ditches	Irrigation ditches
Farm roads	Farm roads

Specific exemptions were developed for troublesome, locally occurring practices, such as construction of rice levees in crop rotations.

B. Riparian Areas

Riparian areas are transition zones between aquatic and upland ecosystems with several characteristics

TABLE II

Wetlands and Hydric Cropland, United States, 1982

	Thousand acres	Percentage of wetlands
Rural, nonfederal wetlands	83,212	100
Potential for cropland	78,516	94
No conversion potential	42,639	51
Unlikely and other	30,177	36
High or medium potential	5700	7
Cropland	4696	6
		Percentage of hydric cropland
Cropland on hydric soil	53,137	100
Not drained	30,244	57
Needs drainage for farming	17,888	34
Drained	22,892	34
Not adequately drained	4468	8

Source: 1982 and 1987 National Resources Inventories.

that distinguish them from adjacent uplands. Natural riparian vegetation is adapted to high soil moisture. Riparian areas require high water tables or periodic flooding to maintain their natural vegetation. There is also a high degree of exchange between the aquatic and terrestrial systems: flooding from the streams brings nutrients to the terrestrial vegetation, while debris from the terrestrial vegetation is a food source for aquatic species. Riparian areas are generally more productive than upland areas, producing more biomass and maintaining a greater diversity of plant and animal species. Vegetative productivity and diversity make riparian areas excellent habitat for fish and wildlife species, and highly valued for livestock grazing.

Because of their proximity to water, riparian areas have been attractive sites for agricultural, residential, commercial, and industrial development. As a result, they have undergone dramatic alterations from their original state. Loss and alteration of riparian areas have occurred because of dam construction, channelization, and agricultural development. Livestock grazing is a major factor impacting many riparian areas.

While riparian areas serve important agricultural and ecological functions, there are surprisingly little data available describing their extent and location. The term "riparian" is used in several different contexts, ranging from all land in the flood plain to specific woodland habitats along streambanks. The term "riparian" has no official or regulatory meaning. One useful definition of riparian areas is land within the 100-year flood plain plus land along natural streambanks as riparian land. Data on land use or vegetation

within riparian areas, which is of key importance for assessing agricultural and wildlife values, are less available than information on total area. Based on potential vegetation types, the original extent of riparian forest ecosystems has been estimated at 67 million acres. Including narrower cold water stream valleys and intermittent streams, increases the original extent to a range of 75 to 100 million acres, of which only 23 million acres remained in forested riparian ecosystems, excluding Alaska, by 1970. The 1977 and 1982 NRI inventories, respectively, estimated 52 million acres and 55 million acres of nonfederal, forested, flood prone land. However, much of this land is in pine plantations and other altered forest habitats. As much as 70–90% of all original forested riparian ecosystems in the United States have been eliminated through land use change.

1. Federal Riparian Land

Data on federally owned riparian land are sparse and of dubious reliability. Of the 175 million acres of public land in the Bureau of Land Management's (BLM) coterminous jurisdiction in 1985, only 903,000 acres (0.5%) was estimated to be riparian land. Riparian acreage increased 73% from 523,000 acres in 1977, when these estimates were first published, but had been as high as 941,000 acres in 1984. These changes are possibly due to changing floodplain definitions and reflect improvements in BLM reporting procedures. Over the same period, estimated miles of fishable streams remained relatively constant at about 20,000 miles. Oregon has the largest amount of BLM riparian area and the most stream miles, but Montana and Wyoming have riparian acreages almost as large, with proportionally fewer stream miles.

The Forest Service controls 187 million acres in the National Forest System. Of this, it is estimated that 2.3 million acres are riparian lands and wetlands, with 84,000 miles of fisheries streams. Only 65,000 acres of BLM riparian habitat was being managed in fiscal year 1977, and more than 440,000 acres were identified as being in unsatisfactory condition. Little information beyond these bare statistics is available for federally owned riparian areas. While public land managers have been working to improve conditions on many sections of federal riparian rangeland, successful projects represent only a small portion of such land in poor condition.

2. Nonfederal Riparian Land

A total of 56 million acres of frequently flooded land, a useful proxy for riparian land, was estimated in the 1982 NRI. Lands with a flooding class of "frequent" are defined as having more than a 50% chance of flooding in any year, or more than 50 times in 100 years. Almost 92% of rural nonfederal riparian lands were privately owned, while about 7% were controlled by state and local governments. Private riparian areas were predominantly forested (46%) with the remainder about equally divided between cropland, pasture and rangeland, and other uses. About 60% of state-owned riparian areas were in other nonagricultural uses, with the remainder split between forest

and agricultural covers. Eighty% of Indian-owned riparian areas were rangeland or barren.

Agricultural uses accounted for almost 40% of rural nonfederal riparian land in 1982 (Table III). Almost all cropland was used for crop production. Livestock grazing accounted for 86% of pasture land and 94% of range in riparian zones. Most of the remainder was idle, but 2% was used for wildlife or recreation purposes, mostly in state or local government ownership. Wood production was the principal use for 94% of forested riparian areas, but only part of this was actively managed for timber production. Almost 3% of forested riparian areas were set aside for wilderness, wildlife, or recreation uses. The cover on more than 1 million acres of other nonagricultural land in riparian areas that was designated for wildlife and recreation uses cannot be determined from the NRI categories, but may also have been in natural or relatively undisturbed vegetation. Overall, protected uses such as state or locally controlled wildlife sanctuaries, wilderness areas, and recreation areas made up 4% of rural nonfederal riparian zones.

Developed uses were a small (less than one percent) part of riparian areas, but most developed uses in flood prone and natural streambank areas were excluded from the NRI because they were located in urban areas. Land that was idle or whose use could not be determined constituted 15% of rural nonfederal riparian area, reflecting the residual nature of much riparian land.

TABLE III

Land Cover and Land Use of Rural Nonfederal Riparian Areas, United States, 1982

Land use	Crop land	Pasture land	Range land	Forest land	Other land[a]	Total
			Thousand acres			
Agriculture	7753	6108	7026	699	0	21,586
Crops	7680	0	0	0	0	7680
Grazing	73	6108	7026	699	0	13,906
Wood production	0	0	0	23,563	0	23,563
Developed uses[a]	3	31	5	9	115	162
Wild areas[b]	19	123	178	728	1196	2,244
Idle[c]	251	804	270	129	7022	8476
Total[d]	8033	7067	7480	25,127	8333	56,040

Source: 1982 National Resources Inventory.

[a] Includes residential, commercial, industrial, institutional, transmission, waste disposal, transportation, military, and research uses.
[b] Includes designated wilderness, designated wildlife, designated wildlife study, and designated recreation uses.
[c] Includes idle land and land for which no use could be determined.
[d] Detail may not add to totals due to rounding.

3. Riparian Wetlands

Riparian areas are sometimes treated as synonymous with wetlands, particularly in arid parts of the West. While there is overlap, riparian areas are more extensive than riparian wetlands. Riparian wetlands are listed among the 10 most critical wetland problem areas by the U.S. Fish and Wildlife Service. Threats to these wetland systems include conversion to cropland, overgrazing, dam construction, and groundwater pumping that lowers water tables and drys up riparian wetland areas.

The 1982 NRI inventoried 144,000 nonfederal acres identified as riverine wetland systems across the United States, almost all of which are included within riparian land (Table IV). Riparian lands accounted for about 37% of rural nonfederal wetlands inventoried in the 1982 NRI. In addition to the riverine wetlands, almost all estuarine wetlands, about one-third of palustrine (upland) wetlands and 1/10th of lacustrine (lake shore) wetlands were located in riparian zones. However, 48% of frequently flooded lands were not wetlands as classified by the FWS's Cowardin system. Thus, a substantial upland component of riparian areas should be considered for management in addition to that area classed as wetland.

Eighty percent of the wetland riparian area was classed palustrine, a slightly smaller proportion than for all wetlands. More than 60% of all wetlands in riparian zones were forested and this land cover accounted for about three-fourths of riparian palustrine wetlands. Most of the other wetland types, including riverine wetlands, were inventoried in other nonagricultural land covers. For example, land cover on all riverine wetlands was barren land in the "other" category. Only about 20% of riparian pasture and range-land was wetland, classed predominantly as palustrine.

III. Wetland Values

Perceived values of wetlands in North America have increased rapidly over the past two decades. Intrinsic wetland characteristics were often unrecognized or undervalued relative to values from conversion of wetlands to other land uses. For most of our history, we did not appreciate the benefits produced by wetlands because we did not understand enough ecology, biology, and hydrology. Our forefathers perceived only disease, foul odors, and wild animals in swamps and marshes and sought to "reclaim" them. Scientists today, recognizing how many different species and functions depend on wetlands, strive to increase our awareness of their ecological and environmental importance. Wetlands are the site of processes that produce social values: fish and wildlife values, like spawning areas for fish and duck breeding habitat; ecological services, like water quality improvement and flood peak storage; and economic values, including marketable commodities, like furs or wild rice, and nonmarket goods, like recreation (Table V).

The table below illustrates some of the bioeconomic linkages found in wetlands. To start, a wetland generates a function that produces a good or supports a service. Techniques are needed for estimating the economic value of wetland services which account for complex bioeconomic linkages. For example, the wetland may be a physical medium for tree growth that supports a service, such as commercial tree harvest. That service has an economic value, in this case

TABLE IV

Land Cover and Wetland Status of Rural Nonfederal Riparian Areas, United States, 1982

Land use	Crop land	Pasture land	Range land	Forest land	Other land[a]	Total
			Thousand acres			
Not wetland	7255	5372	6120	7475	1160	27,382
Palustrine	779	1694	979	17,652	1839	22,942
Estuarine	0	0	381	0	5005	5386
Lacustrine	0	0	0	0	173	173
Riverine	0	0	0	0	136	136
Marine	0	0	0	0	21	21
Subtotal	799	1694	1360	17,652	7173	28,658
Total[b]	8033	7067	7480	25,127	8333	56,040

Source: 1982 National Resources Inventory.

[a] Detail may not add to totals due to rounding.

TABLE V
Illustrative Wetland Functions and Estimated Values

Function	State and wetland type	Value per acre
		Dollars per acre
Fish and wildlife		
Mammal/reptile	Louisiana coastal	12
Fish/shellfish	Louisiana coastal	32–66
Waterfowl	Massachusetts coastal marsh	167
General	Michigan coastal marshes	843
Ecological services		
Sediment accretion	Georgia river	3
Flood control	Massachusetts river	362
Water quality	Georgia river	1108
Waste assimilation	Virginia tidal marsh	6225
Life support	Georgia river	10,333
Market services		
Fish production	Virginia tidal marsh	269
Timber production	Georgia river	1605
Aquaculture	Virginia tidal marsh	872–2241
Nonmarket services		
Education/research	Louisiana coastal	6
Waterfowl hunting	Mississippi bottomlands	12–17
Recreation	Massachusetts river	38
Recreation	Louisiana coastal wetlands	45
Recreation	Florida estuary	76
Historic and archeological	Louisiana coastal	323

the net value of the timber. Foresters can model and value linkages between site characteristics and tree growth, determining the types of trees that will grow on a site and the associated boardfeet of timber that can be produced. Next, the good or service must be valued in economic terms. Forest economists use market valuation techniques which consider commercial prices of timber, transportation costs, production costs, and other factors to estimate the net economic value of the timber produced.

Wetland	Forestry	Fisheries	Recreation
Function	Tree habitat	Fish habitat	Wildlife habitat
Service	Commercial timber harvest	Commercial fish harvest	Recreational waterfowl harvest
Value	Net economic value of timber	Net economic value of commercial fish	Net economic value of hunting success

In the example of commercial fishing, the linkages are less clear, particularly the relationship between

fish habitat and commercial fish harvest. A wetland area functions as a nursery ground for young fish, and as a medium for further growth. The tonnage of fish and shellfish that can be harvested in an estuary, or offshore from the estuary, is related to this wetland habitat function, among other things. The economic value linkage is the relationship of the commercial fish harvest to the net value of the commercial fish species. That is, once the tonnage harvested is known, an economist can combine dock prices with estimates of production and harvesting costs to estimate the net economic value of the harvest.

Finally, the linkages that are least clear are those involving nonmarket valuation. For example, the wetland function could be wildlife habitat that provides a service of recreational waterfowl bag for hunters. Estimating the relationship between wildlife habitat and waterfowl bag is an extremely complicated process. The economic valuation linkage is the relationship between recreational waterfowl bag and the net economic value of hunting success. Nonmarket valuation techniques, such as the contingent valuation method, the travel cost method, or hedonic pricing, can be used to establish the linkage between the service and wetland values. The relationships between wildlife, wildlife populations, waterfowl bag, and economic values involve biological, recreational, sociological, and economic considerations.

While some of the values illustrated in Table V are impressive, most of them have been arrived at by economists using nonmarket valuation techniques. Even the market goods, such as fish production, timber production, and aquaculture, are not generally produced directly in the wetland, but indirectly because the wetland exists. Wetlands are typical of an economic phenomenon called externalities. Services produced by a wetland, such as wildlife habitat and flood control, are available to everyone in its vicinity, regardless of such concepts as property rights. But wetlands give least to their legal owner. The paradox of prodigious wetland output is that the wetland owner has very little ability to charge others for the services the wetland produces. The owner cannot gain from the wetland except by destroying it to accommodate some other use of the land.

IV. Wetland Conversion for Agriculture

A. Trends in Wetland Conversion

Despite controversy over wetland delineation, several sets of more or less reliable data provide insight into overall trends. The earliest wetland inventories treated all wetlands the same, describing them with such terms as "swamp and overflowed lands." These terms were adequate when the object of the inventories was to quantify how much land was unfit for crop production without drainage efforts. As wildlife management became an object of wetland inventories, a management-based classification was adopted by the FWS and published in their Circular 39. For the National Wetland Status and Trends Analysis, FWS commissioned the Cowardin system, a new classification system designed to capture ecologically important differences and segregate dissimilar wildlife habitats that are geographically separated. Neither of the systems used for management or scientific wetland inventories precisely matches any of the jurisdictional wetland definitions used in regulatory programs. Thus, there is no accurate, comprehensive accounting of wetlands subject to Section 404 or the swampbuster provisions.

The FWS estimates that in 1780 there were 392 million acres of wetlands in what now constitute the 50 United States, and 221 million acres of wetlands

in the lower 48 States. By 1980, only 274 million acres remained, with only 104 million acres in the lower 48 States. This amounts to a 53% loss over 200 years, or an average annual loss of 585,000 acres.

USDA conducted drainage inventories to identify lands suitable for drainage and assess the agricultural potential of remaining wetlands. In 1906, 79 million swampland acres (excluding Alaska) were thought to have farm potential, but two-thirds of this was not fit for cultivation unless drained and cleared. A more comprehensive inventory in 1919 showed 91.5 million acres unfit for crops without drainage, but judged that only 75 million acres could ever be developed for agriculture. The American Society of Agricultural Engineers conducted a similar drainage survey in 1946–1948 that identified 97 million acres of wet, swampy, or overflow lands. However, they judged only 20 million acres could be drained for farming at reasonable cost. A related 1948 estimate by the Soil Conservation Service showed 20.7 million acres physically feasible to drain and develop for agriculture.

The FWS, cooperating with State fish and game departments, conducted the inventory published as Circular 39 in 1954. For the first time, this inventory focused on managing wetlands, rather than eliminating them. It counted a total of 74.4 million acres in the 20 wetland types listed in Circular 39. The National Wetland Status and Trends Analysis was conducted by the FWS in 1979 to not only identify current wetlands according to the Cowardin system, but estimate changes from the mid-1950s to the mid-1970s. Using aerial photographic techniques on 3629 4-square mile units, this study estimated a drop in public and private wetland acreage of 13.8 million acres, from 108.1 to 99.0 million acres in the lower 48 States. The most recent FWS estimates show a 2.6 million acre drop in wetlands in the lower 48 States, from 105.9 million acres in the mid-1970s to 103.3 million acres by the mid-1980s. The mid-1970s estimate was adjusted up from the previous study because of better classification on improved color infrared aerial photography.

USDA's Soil Conservation Service conducted the 1958 Conservation Needs Inventory, which identified 73.5 million acres of rural, nonfederal land needing treatment for excess water. More than 80% of this land was cropland. Some 172.5 million acres were judged to have drainage problems. Similar statistical spatial sampling methods were used in the 1975 Potential Cropland Survey to record 21.4 million acres of high and medium potential cropland suffering from wetness, but only 181,300 acres were identified as wetland types 3–20 in the Circular 39 classification. The 1977 NRI identified 41.5 million acres of wetland types 3–20. The 1982 NRI inventoried all rural, non-federal wetlands according to both the older Circular 39 and later Cowardin classifications. It found 78.4 million acres of wetlands. The 1987 NRI reclassified some of the sample points originally visited in 1982 to increase 1982 rural nonfederal wetlands to 83.2 million acres. A loss of 1.2 million acres was estimated to occur between 1982 and 1987, resulting in only 82 million wetland acres by the latter date.

Average annual rates of wetland conversion have generally been falling since the first reliable scientific wetland inventories were taken in the mid-1950s (Table VI). FWS estimated the net rate of wetland conversion between the mid-1950s and mid-1970s at 455,000 acres per year, mostly from inland (palustrine) wetlands. Eighty-seven percent of the 13.8 million acres of wetlands converted were to agricultural uses and 8% were to urban uses. A more recent study by FWS using similar methods records a decline in average wetland conversion to 288,900 acres per year for the mid-1970s to mid-1980s. Conversions to agricultural use accounted for a smaller 56% of average annual losses. However, much of the 41% converted to other uses was cleared and drained, possibly intended for agricultural use, but had not yet been put to an identifiable use at the end of the period. Urban uses were 3% of losses. Based on changes at NRI sample points between 1982 and 1987, the rate of conversion dropped to 130,800 acres per year. Agriculture accounted for 38% of wetlands converted. A specific inventory of wetland NRI points done in 1991 provided an estimate of 107,750 acres of wetland lost annually between 1987 and 1991, of which agricultural conversion accounted for only 27%.

B. Economics of Conversion for Agriculture

Agricultural conversion has historically been a far more widespread cause of wetland conversion than urban uses. Factors that affect the economics of agricultural wetland conversion are technology, effective crop prices, farm program considerations, tax effects, and land values. Technological change can alter the profitability of wetland conversion by reducing the cost of conversion. An example is the introduction of plastic subsurface drain tile continuously installed using drainage plows. Technological advances such as continuous corrugated plastic tubing, improved manufacturing methods and materials, advances in field installation techniques and machinery,

TABLE VI

Extent and Changes in Wetlands, 1954 to 1991

	National Wetland Status and Trends[a]					National Resources Inventory[b]			
	1954	1954–1974	1974	1974–1983	1983	1982	1982–1987	1987	1987–1991
					Million acres				
Wetlands inventoried	108.1		105.9 (99.0)		103.3 (78.4)	83.2		82.0	
Average Annual				Thousand acres per year					
Net change[c]		455.0		288.9			124.0		na
Conversion to									
Agriculture		600.0		237.5			50.0		29.3
Urban/development		55.0		14.1			56.0		58.3
Other		35.0		171.7			24.8		20.3
Total		690.0		423.2			130.8		107.8
				Percentage of total conversion					
Conversion to									
Agriculture		87		56			38		27
Urban/development		8		3			43		54
Other		5		41			19		19
Total		100		100			100		100

Sources: [a] U.S. Fish and Wildlife Service, National Wetland Status and Trends Analysis, mid-1950s to mid-1970s and mid-1970s to mid-1980s. Excludes Alaska and Hawaii. The 1974 wetland extent was increased because of better photo interpretation using color infrared photography not available earlier. [b] Soil Conservation Service, USDA, National Resources Inventories, 1982, 1987, and 1991 Wetlands Update. Includes only rural, nonfederal land. Excludes Alaska. Wetland extent not estimated in 1991.
[c] Conversion of wetland to nonwetland uses, plus increases in wetlands due to restoration, abandonment and flooding.

and improvements in design and engineering, such as laser guidance, reduced the real cost of surface drainage from a high of $225 per acre in 1900 to $140 per acre in 1985 (1985 constant dollars). Subsurface drainage costs have declined more dramatically, halving between 1965 and 1985 to a cost of $415 per acre.

The principal way in which the agricultural business cycle affects wetland conversion economics is through the effective price of the commodity being produced. When market prices for commodities increase, as they did during the 1970s and early 1980s, gross revenues and net returns from crop production increase. If these conditions are expected to prevail for a sufficiently long period of time, if increases in crop production along the intensive margin (i.e., greater use of nonland inputs), and if other opportunities to develop new cropland at lower cost are limited or exhausted, producers will favorably consider investments in wetland conversion. Regardless of any wetland protection policies, much of the incentive for new wetland conversion was undercut in the mid-1980s as crop prices fell and other tax and subsidy incentives were eliminated.

In agriculture, no less than other economic sectors, income tax treatment of investments and expenses affects their profitability. Before the 1986 tax reform act, wetland conversion investments were favored in the Internal Revenue Code in a number of ways. First, expenses for land clearing, drainage, and land shaping could be deducted from farm income. Deducting these expenses instead of capitalizing them decreases the taxable basis of the improved land, resulting in larger capital gains when the land is sold. Deductions were also available for depreciation of machinery used in wetland conversion under the accelerated cost recovery system and for interest payments on debt financing conversion investments. An investment tax credit equal to 10% of the depreciable investments associated with conversion was also available. Finally, up to 60% of long-term capital gains realized from the sale of improved farmland could be excluded from ordinary income and taxed at preferential capital gains rates. In addition to farm income, all of these tax reducing provisions were available to shelter nonfarm income and could easily be applied to incomes of passive investors. The effect of these provisions was to reduce the cost of wetland conversion, providing an artificial incentive for further conversion activity.

Prior to 1985, U.S. farm price and income support programs were another important factor in wetland conversion economics in two ways. Before market prices for crops rose in the mid-1970s and after they fell in the mid-1980s, loan rates and target prices in the farm programs set effective prices for commodities higher than prevailing market prices. Basic eligibility for price and income support programs is determined by crop acreage bases and voluntary compliance with farm program set aside provisions designed to control supplies of crops produced. The producer's payment is based on the crop acreage base, less the set aside requirement, times the program yield, times the deficiency payment. Converting wetlands and other kinds of land for crop production in high-price periods insures a higher gross subsidy in low-price years when the programs operate. Further, to the extent that converted wetlands are not completely drained, these may be the least productive croplands that can be idled to meet set aside requirements. Thus, U.S. price and income support programs created an artificial incentive to convert wetlands, as well as other land.

The final economic factor in wetland conversion is land values. The income theory of value says that the value of land or any productive asset equals the capitalized net present value of the expected stream of earnings possible with that asset. In the case of farmland, current values should be no greater than expected net returns from farming. However, there is a degree of speculation in all asset valuation because of differing expectations of future changes in prices, costs, or other factors affecting returns. Because of the rapid increase in farm prices during the 1970s, expectations of continued price increases caused farmland values to exceed values based on current net returns. Such "speculative bubbles" affect investment decisions, including the decision to convert wetlands, and inevitably burst. High expectations concerning eventual values of cropland converted from wetlands in the later 1970s were subsequently shown to be ill conceived as supply responded and commodity prices dropped. Many wetlands converted to agriculture during this period have since been abandoned.

C. Profitability of Conversion

The economics of wetland conversion are identical to any other economic investment. The rational decision to undertake drainage, dredging, filling, or other physical means of conversion depends on the expected stream of future revenues, including any increase in revenues that can be earned on the converted wetland, minus the cost of conversion and the expected stream of future production costs, all discounted to present value terms. If the expected revenues exceed the expected costs, and the percentage return on assets invested in the conversion exceeds that of alternative investment opportunities, the rational person would convert the wetland.

There are a number of ways in which converting a wetland can be profitable for a landowner. Some wetlands are attractive sites relative to alternative sites and produce higher revenues because the wetland confers some particularly desirable feature on the land. Examples include access to recreational waters in the case of marina development and the great natural fertility of bottomland soils that are continuously enriched by fresh deposits of silt.

Other wetlands are a nuisance that increases the cost of production unless converted. An example is prairie pothole wetlands within farm fields that require more turns for machinery and form point rows and dead rows that cannot be planted or harvested. Wetlands within fields can also restrict machinery choices to smaller, lighter, less economical sizes. Another example is isolated wetlands in housing developments that reduce the number of buildable lots, increasing the cost of each remaining lot.

Still other wetlands are converted incidental to economic activity. Flood control measures may not be intended to convert wetlands at all, but can restrict the cyclical inundation that naturally occurs in bottomland hardwood wetlands. Construction of dugouts as catchments for irrigation water, a common practice for center pivot irrigation in Nebraska, can lower water tables and incidentally destroy adjacent wetlands.

Finally, some wetlands are converted for the investment or speculative gain to be had. This accrues from the difference between raw land costs for unconverted wetlands and developed values for buildable or farmable land, including conversion costs. This difference can often provide enough motive for much wetland conversion.

Changes in economic conditions alone between the mid-1970s and late 1980s have made much, if not all, agricultural drainage unprofitable. Reduced prices for agricultural commodities and increased prices for crop inputs have squeezed profits, generally making investments in wetland conversion less desirable. The effects of the swampbuster and income tax reform provisions over the past decade generally reduced wetland conversion profitability. These reforms, combined with reduced profitability due to market conditions, made almost all agricultural wetland conversion unprofitable in the late 1980s and early 1990s. As long as agricultural commodity prices remain low

and dependence on farm program participation to supplement farm incomes remains, there will be little economic incentive for agricultural wetland conversion. There may still be incentives for enhanced drainage on farmed wetlands and the motivation for eliminating "nuisance" wetlands remains, as long as swampbuster sanctions can be avoided. [*See* PRICES.]

V. Policy Development

A. What is "No Net Loss?"

The goal of "no net loss" of wetlands came to prominence in then-Vice-President Bush's election campaign as part of his promise to be the "environmental President." President Bush never backed away from that goal, and President Clinton's wetland plan promises to embrace "no net loss" through a new Executive Order. The origin of the "no net loss" goal goes back to FWS's mission to protect waterfowl, and to certain private initiatives, such as Ducks Unlimited work to conserve and restore waterfowl habitat. As early as 1954, FWS associated waterfowl conservation with wetland habitat. The National Wetland Priority Conservation Plan, required under the Emergency Wetland Resources Act of 1986, emphasizes conserving and restoring wetlands. The North American Waterfowl Management Plan, a joint agreement and treaty between the United States and Canada, also calls for restoring former waterfowl habitat. The North American Wetlands Conservation Act establishes a Wetland Trust Fund, authorizes appropriations of $15 million annually over 1991–1994, and establishes the North American Wetlands Conservation Council to approve wetland restoration projects. Another step on the road to "no net loss" occurred in North Dakota. The Garrison Diversion project was the subject of a compromise between the State of North Dakota, the COE, and environmental groups that had been delaying the project. These parties agreed to a reduced project if North Dakota, among other conditions, adopted a "no net loss" of wetlands program.

The direct antecedent of "no net loss" at the Federal level was the National Wetland Policy Forum. Quoting from their report:

> Although calling for a stable and eventually increasing inventory of wetlands, the goal does not imply that individual wetlands will in every instance be untouchable or that the no-net-loss standard should be applied on an individual permit basis—only that the nation's overall wetlands base reach equilibrium between losses and gains

in the short run and increase in the long term. The public must share with the private sector the cost of restoring and creating wetlands to achieve this goal.

The "no net loss" goal means restricting landowners' property rights to protect a continued stream of public goods from the resources. A fundamental issue raised by a no net loss policy is the appropriate balance between the regulatory and compensatory measures. The public believes fundamental property rights are important and also values the public goods produced by natural resources in private ownership. Society needs to balance these conflicting values and choose between or combine regulation and compensation to achieve that balance.

There is also an issue of conservation versus restoration. Should society put relatively more effort into conserving existing wetland resources than restoring wetlands that have previously been converted? On a pure efficiency basis, conservation avoids adding the cost of restoration on top of the original costs of converting the wetland. The National Wetland Policy Forum and President Bush stated that conservation will not be enough. Unavoidable wetlands losses will occur for overriding public purposes. How do we make up for those unavoidable losses? The only way is some form of a wetland restoration or creation program. In the United States, wetland conservation and restoration have been accomplished voluntarily, in response to a growing array of positive incentives provided by conservation programs, and under requirements of regulatory and quasi-regulatory programs. Policies affecting agricultural wetlands have been evolving for more than 200 years.

B. Evolution of Agricultural Wetland Policy

For the first 200 years of U.S. history, the Federal Government approved of and assisted with wetland drainage to further public health and economic development goals. Between 1849 and 1860, the Swampland Acts granted 64.9 million acres of wetlands to 15 States. Grants were made on the condition that proceeds of wetlands sold to individuals be used for reclamation projects. For the first 70 years of this century, USDA had a policy of direct financial and technical assistance to the farm community for wetland drainage. Flood control, navigation, stream channelization, and highway projects also contributed to agricultural drainage by providing drainage outlets. While Federal aid was not solely responsible for wetland drainage, it did provide positive economic incentives.

Most direct incentives ended in the 1970s for a variety of reasons, culminating in Executive Order 11990 issued in 1977. This ordered agencies of the Federal Government to ". . . minimize the destruction, loss or degradation of wetlands . . ." and to ". . . avoid direct and indirect support of new construction in wetlands wherever there is a practicable alternative . . ." Indirect Federal assistance for wetland conversion in agriculture was eliminated by the so-called "swampbuster" provision of the 1985 FSA and changes in the 1986 Tax Reform Act. The swampbuster provision was a quasi-regulatory policy that made a farm operator ineligible for price support payments, farm storage facility loans, crop insurance, disaster payments, and insured or guaranteed loans for any year in which an annual crop was planted on converted wetlands. Tax reform restricted or eliminated many provisions that indirectly subsidized agricultural wetland conversion. Among these were deductions for land clearing expenses, deductions for soil and water conservation expenses, and preferential treatment of capital gains, including capital gains realized from draining wetlands.

Further changes to agricultural wetland policy were also included in the 1990 Food, Agriculture, Conservation, and Trade Act (FACTA). One important change closed a loophole in the swampbuster provision. After 1985, producers who converted a wetland and planted an agricultural commodity lost farm program benefits on their entire operation. However, eligibility for benefits was retained for any year in which no crop requiring annual tillage was planted despite wetland destruction. The 1990 FACTA expands the swampbuster "trigger" to include conversion of a wetland to make production possible. Converting a wetland to make production possible invokes loss of benefits and benefits cannot be restored until the converted wetland is restored.

In return for this change, commodity interests obtained some concessions on swampbuster. The minimal effect clause, which exempts conversions that are determined to have minimal effect on the hydrological and biological properties of the wetland, was expanded to allow mitigation. Mitigation is the term for wetland restoration or creation at another site to replace wetlands lost to development. In the changes to swampbuster, a farmer can drain a wetland without losing farm program benefits if another prior converted wetland somewhere else on the farm or in the local area is restored.

Farm groups also convinced Congress to change the so-called "drop dead" penalty in the swampbuster provision. The previous penalty meant loss of all farm program benefits, even for small wetland conversions. The new graduated penalty provision allows an operator to violate swampbuster once in 10 years if the wetland is restored and if the conversion occurred in good faith. The penalty ranges from $750 to $10,000, depending on the severity of wetland destruction. While substantial, these fines are less than farm program benefits which may run to several hundred thousand dollars. The operator remains ineligible for farm program benefits until the converted wetland is either restored or mitigated.

Agricultural wetland policy has turned from subsidizing conversion of wetlands for agricultural use to elimination of direct and indirect subsidies for conversion. The next step in the evolution of policy is toward positive incentives for wetland protection and restoration, some of which were passed in the 1990 FACTA.

C. Federal Wetland Regulation

Historically, Congress created financial incentives in agricultural programs to compensate farmers for changes in the bundle of property rights that they can exercise on their land. Some view the swampbuster provision as regulatory. In fact, it is a condition on receipt of benefits in a voluntary program, albeit one that many farmers view as necessary to their economic survival. Many States have wetland regulations that limit what can be done to drain or alter these lands. The only Federal program regulating wetland conversion was and remains Section 404 dredge and fill permit requirements enacted in the 1972 Federal Pollution Control Act amendments. Section 404 evolved to deal primarily with marine and estuarine wetlands associated with navigable waters. The COE administers Section 404 with oversight by EPA. Section 404 permits are justified under the legal authority to limit discharge of dredge and fill material into navigable waters. This justification is derived from a long-recognized Federal jurisdiction over navigation. However, Section 404's bark is worse than its bite. In 1990, of more than 15,000 individual permits, 67% were approved, 30% were withdrawn by applicants or processed as general permits, and only 3%, or 500 permits, were denied. An estimated 75,000 activities were also allowed under one of 37 COE regional or nationwide general permits, including most agricultural activities.

In the past, drainage was excluded from Section 404 requirements. Thus, the program has not affected agriculture to any extent because most on-farm con-

version involves drainage rather than dredge and fill. In addition, "Normal agricultural and silvicultural practices . . . ," such as maintenance of drainage ditches and levees, have been exempt from Section 404 permit requirements. Section 404 regulations exempt most routine agricultural practices. Between 1972 and 1987, these exemptions and a general reluctance by the COE to treat land cleared for agricultural production as wetlands meant that Section 404 had little impact on agriculture except where extensive new conversion was occurring.

However, after the "no net loss" goal and the 1989 manual, opposition to more aggressive field implementation of Federal wetlands policies by farmers, developers, and small landholders was being expressed to Congress and at higher levels in the Bush Administration. An EPA/COE regulatory guidance letter and more recent regulations issued in 1993 further exempted farmland converted prior to 1985, consistent with the scope of USDA's swampbuster program. Nevertheless, changes in levees, dikes, and drainage on a larger amount of farmland still classified as wetlands and previously ignored now come under Section 404's purview. Most normal agricultural activities are allowed to continue under 404 scrutiny, but conversion of wetlands to agricultural use and conversion of wetlands used for agricultural production to more developed uses requires a Section 404 permit.

None of these efforts to moderate the new policies occurred soon enough or went far enough to head off rapidly coalescing opposition. Bolstered by successful cases in the Claims Court of the United States and the prospect of a conservative majority in the Supreme Court, property rights interests targeted wetland regulation as an opening wedge in rolling back all kinds of regulation designed to promote the general welfare, unless compensation is provided to landowners. Wetland regulation was attacked as a "taking" without compensation, proscribed under the Fifth Amendment to the Constitution.

Representatives Hayes and Ridge introduced regulatory reform legislation which addressed wetland delineation, differential regulatory responses for different categories of wetlands, and compensation for wetlands most severely regulated. Environmentalists responded with the Edwards Bill (Table VII). After protracted internal bickering, the Bush Administration responded with a plan for accelerated regulatory reform issued on August 9, 1991, followed shortly by the proposed 1991 interagency wetland delineation manual, a substantial revision of the 1989 manual.

Little progress was made in implementing the Bush plan prior to the 1992 Presidential election.

The Clinton Administration moved quickly, designating an interagency task force led by the new White House Office on Environmental Policy to craft their own wetland regulatory reform package. On August 24, 1993, the Administration released a plan that proposed the following. First, the Clinton Administration promised to embrace the 1988 National Wetland Policy Forum's goal of no net loss of wetlands by issuing an Executive Order. Second, the fairness, flexibility, and speed of the Section 404 permit process would be increased by establishing a 90-day deadline for most permit issuances, issuing guidance to subject less valuable wetlands with less vigorous permit review for small projects and limited impacts, and establishing an administrative appeals process for COE permit decisions. Third, differences over wetland delineation were resolved by confirming use of the 1987 delineation manual pending completion and review of the NAS study, giving USDA's Soil Conservation Service lead responsibility for identifying wetlands on agricultural land, and exempting 53 million acres of prior converted cropland from both swampbuster and Section 404 requirements. Additional wetland protection was promised by closing a loophole that allowed wetland destruction through drainage and excavation that did not involve dredge and fill. Incentives were promised for State, tribal, and local governments to engage in watershed planning to avoid conflicts between wetland protection and development. Finally, the Administration promised to support wetland restoration by increasing funding for USDA Wetland Reserve Program (WRP), supporting voluntary, nonregulatory restoration programs, and endorsing use of mitigation banks.

The Clinton wetland plan consists of a mix of immediate and long-term administrative actions and legislative proposals. The COE and EPA issued final regulations exempting prior converted cropland and extending the scope of regulated activities to include drainage and excavation, required as part of the settlement of a successful lawsuit by the National Wildlife Federation. They also issued regulatory guidance on flexibility in permit review and joined with USDA and Interior on a statement of principles regarding wetland delineation on agricultural lands. A new Executive Order embracing the no net loss goal, administrative appeals, permit deadlines, and mitigation banking will require further work. Much of the Administration's plan is encompassed in Senate Bill 1304, introduced by Senators Baucus and Chafee as part of work on reauthorization of the Clean Water Act and incorporated into Senate Bill 1114.

Agencies dealing with wetlands are more optimistic that problems surrounding Federal wetland protection have been successfully addressed by the Clinton Administration's plan than at any time in the recent past. After stymieing progress on Clean Water Act reauthorization in the 102nd Congress, compromises also seem within reach in the 103rd Congress.

D. Positive Conservation Programs

While regulatory and quasi-regulatory agricultural wetland protection policies were evolving, there were programs designed to give positive incentives to conserve wetlands on private lands. USDA's Water Bank program was authorized in 1970 and amended a decade later. In return for annual per-acre payments, landowners agree not to burn, drain, fill or otherwise destroy the character of enrolled wetland areas for 10 years. Additional cost-sharing payments are available for installation of conservation practices designed to maintain vegetative cover, control erosion, improve habitat, conserve surface water, or manage bottomland hardwoods.

Agreements have been effected in 15 states, but the program has concentrated in the Prairie Pothole region. Some 4,400 agreements have been contracted covering almost 500,000 acres of land at an average rental cost of $15 per acre. Only one-third of the land under Water Bank agreements is wetland, while the remaining two-thirds is adjacent upland area on which agricultural use is restricted to protect wetland values, such as waterfowl nesting.

In 1989, Conservation Reserve Program (CRP) eligibility was expanded to include wetland that had been cropped for at least 2 years between 1981 and 1985, but had not been drained. About 410,000 acres were enrolled in 1989, most in the Prairie Pothole region of North Dakota, South Dakota, and Minnesota.

Under the Small Wetland Acquisition program, FWS can either purchase a wetland and the surrounding upland acreage outright, or enter into a permanent easement agreement restricting wetland use. Compensation is made on a one-time basis with the payment varying according to land values in the immediate area and the development potential of the wetlands. Permanent easements on about 126,000 acres of wetlands and adjacent areas included in National Waterfowl Production Areas and refuges be-

TABLE VII

Comparison of Congressional and Administration Wetland Regulatory Reform Proposals

Item	H.R. 1330 Hayes/Ridge	H.R. 350 Edwards	S. 1304 Baucus/Chafee	Bush August 9, 1991, Plan	Clinton August 24, 1993, Plan
Delineation	Requires all three indicators; surface saturation for 21 days. Delays any revision of manuals until completion of NAS study.	Requires consistency with a NAS study of 1989 and 1991 manuals under EPA.	Wetlands are defined in the act using the COE definition, including isolated wetlands. Continues use of 1987 Manual until completion of NAS study.	Proposed 1991 manual in response to public comments on 1989 manual.	Urges Congress to define waters of the U.S. and wetlands, including isolated wetlands. Continues use of 1987 Manual until completion of NAS study.
Categorization	Three Classes: A, Critical B, Significant C, Limited or marginal.	None	Under wetlands and watershed management planning, provides for assessment of functions and relative value of wetlands within management units and categorization of activities according to adverse effects.	Limited number based on function, value, scarcity; favored nationwide a priori mapping of "high," "medium," and "low" value wetlands with differential regulatory response.	Opposes a priori categorization; Issued 404(b)(1) guideline flexibility guidance, development of wetlands functional assessment tools, encourages advance planning, and regionalized general permits.
Regulatory response	A, Generally denied permits B, Sequencing applies considering six specific factors; permits generally issued within 6 months C, No permit required.	No permit if there is a practical alternative with less environmental impact; fast track minor permits within 60 days; reduce paperwork and delays.	Issued within 90 days unless a NEPA or ESA impact statement is required, a Federal or State Governor requests a delay, or COE and the applicant agree more time is needed; EPA must determine restrictions on discharges within 180 days after a permit is issued; establishes administrative appeals procedure by landowner or third party.	Six-month approval; sequencing for highest category; general permits for low-value; mitigation required.	COE regulations to be revised within 1 year requiring permit decision within 90 days, except where NEPA or ESA impacts; Administrative appeal process required for permit denials, but not by third party.
Regulatory scope	Expands to include drainage, channelization and excavation; exempts normal ag practices, man-made wetlands, activities under approved State plan; prior converted cropland is in Type C.	Expands to prohibit discharge of pollutants or other alteration of navigable waters, including draining, dredging, channelization, flooding, clearing vegetation, obstructions, and other water diversions; exempts normal ag practices, man-made wetlands; requires rule on prior converted cropland.	Expands to include draining, mechanized land clearing, ditching, channelization, or other excavation; exempts an expanded list of normal ag practices, man-made wetlands.	Supports legislation to expand to drainage and other activities; exempts man-made wetlands, normal ag practices, prior converted cropland.	Issued final regulations expanding "discharge of dredged materials" to excavation activities, including ditching, channelization, and mechanized land clearing and nontraditional use of pilings; exempts normal ag practices, prior converted cropland, and man-made wetlands.
State program assumption	Specifies conditions for State programs; COE must respond or approve within 1 year; States may develop management plans; COE must approve within 60 days.	None	EPA grants for State conservation plans; allows State general permits, but not unless part of a wetlands and watershed management plan after 1996.	Encourages flexibility for State 404-level protection, including wetlands adjacent to navigable waters	Provides technical and financial assistance for State/Tribal/Local assumption and programmatic general permits; encourages CWA funding for wetland and watershed planning.

General permits	Allows general permits with reporting and mitigation	Clarifies general permit program and requires reporting of effects	Encourages use of State, regional, or nationwide permits when impacts on wetlands are minimal and not cumulative; Expands programmatic general permits for existing State/Tribal/Regional/Local programs if part of a wetlands and watershed management plan; and to USDA's Swampbuster program; limited to 5 years with review.	Encourages use of State general permits	Requires COE guidance on State/Tribal/Regional/Local programmatic general permits; regionalizes existing general permit on isolated and headwater wetlands.
Mitigation banking and restoration	COE must establish a bank in each State; includes restoration, enhancement, preservation, or creation.	Establishes restoration pilot project	Requires COE/EPA rules within 1 year; mitigation restricted to advance restoration.	Requires mitigation banking proposal related to categories	Requires COE guidance on concurrent mitigation requirements and COE/EPA guidance on mitigation banking; encourages banking and requests legislation to fund banks using CWA State Revolving Fund monies.
Coordination	"Unified" in COE	Interagency agreements	Requires coordination with USDA; Exempts prior converted cropland and nontidal drainage and irrigation ditches; swampbuster programmatic general permit.	Requires guidance for better Federal coordination.	Gives USDA responsibility for delineation and mitigation on ag lands; Continues expedited review and resolution of concerns under 1992 4/4(q) MOA.
Watershed management planning	States may develop management plans; exemptions for activities under approved State plan.	None	Establishes State and substate wetlands and watershed managment units, management entities, plan development requirements, and approval process; provides funding, expedited permit review, mitigation banking, and programmatic general permit incentives for planning; grants for State wetland conservation and restoration plans.	Encourages management plans as part of categorization and wetland mitigation banking.	Request CWA amendment to authorize development of integrated wetlands and watershed planning; endorses State/Tribal wetland conservation plans; provides greater integration with 4/4 permit review.
Compensation	Type A wetland owners eligible	Provides for tax deductions for diminution in value for compatible, nondegrading uses of wetlands; directs establishment of Wetlands Stewardship Trust to receive such donations of property easements.	None	None	None; encourages 404 operation to avoid "takings."

tween 1981 and 1988 averaged $279 per acre, while purchases averaged $800 per acre.

An agricultural wetland reserve was established as part of the 1990 FACTA. The Act called for restoration of one million acres of cropland to wetlands. The WRP requires permanent or long-term easements with the landowner to restrict agricultural use of restored wetland. Eligibility extends to existing cropped wetlands, restorable wetlands, other non-cropped wetlands (such as Water Bank lands), riparian corridors, and critical wildlife habitat. Adjacent cropland that may be used as a buffer zone or is functionally related to the restored wetland is also eligible. Economic uses of the restored wetlands can be included in the restoration plan that will help reduce the cost of acquiring easements, if those uses are not incompatible with the basic objective of preserving the wetland. Costs of such a reserve are to include the easement value, which cannot exceed the market value of the land, and restoration cost sharing for the actual restoration of up to 100% for permanent easements. A total of 55.6 million acres of cropland converted from former wetlands is eligible for WRP, which should make the 1-million acre target easy to achieve.

Initial WRP enrollments in 1992 were restricted to nine pilot states. Owners of more than 462,000 acres expressed interest in WRP and almost 250,000 acres were offered for enrollment by producers, from which USDA selected 49,888 acres at a cost for easements and restoration of $46.4 million. Despite the large response to the pilot WRP program, Congress provided no additional funding toward the 1 million acre goal in FY 1993, prompting fears that the program would not be pursued. However, $67 million was provided for 1994 to enroll an additional 75,000 acres. In addition, money from the $60 million provided for emergency flood relief in the Midwest can be used to enroll land in WRP when the cost of rebuilding levees and ditches is too great. President Clinton's 1995 budget contains $283 million for WRP.

A more comprehensive wetland restoration effort is envisioned in the 1992 report of an NAS panel on restoration of aquatic ecosystems. Considering the scientific and technical feasibility of wetland restoration, the NAS panel recommended an ambitious goal of restoring wetlands at a rate that offsets future losses and results in a net gain of 10 million acres of wetlands by 2010, an amount equal to 10% of losses since 1780. The report contains numerous recommendations to implement this goal, including an interagency, intergovernmental planning process for a national aquatic ecosystem restoration strategy, a unified agency to carry out the plan, enhancement of existing Federal programs to facilitate restoration, and establishment of a National Aquatic Ecosystem Restoration Trust Fund.

A final source of increased wetland restoration is the mitigation banking provision in the 1990 Intermodal Surface Transportation Efficiency Act (ISTEA). While State highway departments previously established mitigation banks to compensate for unavoidable wetland conversion in the path of new highways, this provision is the first to allow Federal highway monies to fund mitigation banks early in the design phase. If carefully implemented, this provision will let wetlands be restored, created, or enhanced long in advance to more than offset projected losses, resulting in net gains of wetland acreage, often on former agricultural land. Specific wetland restoration projects, like the dechannelization of Florida's Kissimmee River, are also included in new authorities of the COE contained in the Water Resources Development Act of 1990.

Bibliography

The Conservation Foundation (1988). "Protecting America's Wetlands: An Action Agenda. The Final Report of the National Wetlands Policy Forum." Washington, DC.

Dahl, T. E., and Johnson, C. E. (1990). "Status and Trends of Wetlands in the Conterminous United States, Mid-1970's to Mid-1980's." U.S. Department of the Interior, Fish and Wildlife Service, Washington, DC.

Heimlich, R. E., and Langner, L. L. (1986). "Swampbusting: Wetland Conversion and Farm Programs," AER-551. U.S. Department of Agriculture, Economic Research Service, Washington, DC.

Kusler, J. (1992). Wetlands delineation: An issue of science or politics? *Environment* **34**(2), 7–37.

National Research Council (1992). "Restoration of Aquatic Ecosystems: Science, Technology, and Public Policy." Water Science and Technology Board, Commission on Geosciences, Environment, and Resources, Washington, DC.

Office of Technology Assessment (1984). "Wetlands: Their Use and Regulation," OTA-O-206. U. S. Congress, Washington, DC.

Wheat Breeding and Genetics

P. S. BAENZIGER, B. MORENO-SEVILLA, Y. YEN, L. OBERTHUR, V. GUSTAFSON
University of Nebraska

Glossary

Cultivar Currently or previously cultivated (commercially grown) variety

F_n F is an abbreviation for filial generation which is any generation after the parent generation and "n" is the number of generations after the parent generation (e.g., F_2 is the second generation after the parent generation)

Genome Basic (monoploid) set of chromosomes in a progenitor species; polyploid species have multiple genomes

Genotype Total genetic constitution of an organism

Phenotype Total observable characteristics of an organism

Wheat breeding can be described as human-made evolution of wheat to serve humanity. Wheat breeding is both the science and art of genetically improving wheat by creating genetic variation, inbreeding to create variants, selection of superior variants, and evaluating the selections under natural conditions. Its goal is new cultivars that are superior to existing cultivars for at least one important trait.

I. The Biology and Uses of Wheat

The genetics and breeding of any crop are determined by its biology. Cultivated wheats are predominantly two species, namely, bread or common wheat (*Triticum aestivum* L.) and durum wheat (*T. durum* L.). Common wheat is the more predominant wheat and is classified by its physical characteristics and end uses. Hard common wheats are used to make breads and rolls. Soft common wheats are used to make cookies, cakes, and crackers. Durum wheat is used mainly to make pasta and semolina products. Hard, soft, and durum wheats can be harvested for forage and their straw used for animal feed or bedding. Hence, wheat can be developed for sophisticated baking processes or for total biomass as is required in a productive forage crop. [See WHEAT PROCESSING AND UTILIZATION.]

Both cultivated wheat species are allopolyploids. Common wheat is a hexaploid ($2n = 6x = 42$ chromosomes) and has three genomes (designated AABBDD). Durum wheat is a tetraploid ($2n = 4x = 28$ chromosomes) and has two genomes (designated AABB). Diploid ($2n = 2x = 14$ chromosomes) *Triticum* relatives are rarely grown commercially.

Hexaploid and tetraploid wheats evolved by two evolutionary processes. The original progenitor species is not known, but was a diploid. By divergent evolution, it evolved into numerous diploid species including *T. monococcum*, *T. tauschii*, barley (*Hordeum vulgare*), and rye (*Secale cereale*). The second evolutionary process was convergent evolution in which by natural hybridization and spontaneous chromosome doubling, polyploid species were formed. For example, *T. monococcum* (the A genome donor) hybridized with an unknown *Triticum* species (the B genome donor) to form *T. dicoccoides,* the progenitor of durum wheat, genomic constitution AABB. A second hybridization occurred between *T. dicoccoides* and *T. tauschii* (the D genome donor) to form common wheat, genomic constitution AABBDD

The two evolutionary processes have two notable effects. First, divergent evolution greatly increased the genetic diversity within wheat and its relatives. As discussed later, genetic diversity is critical for plant breeding. Also, the effective use of genetic diversity has made wheat the most widely grown cereal in the world and it has the highest total grain production. Second, convergent evolution greatly increased genetic redundancy (having multiple genes code for similar proteins or nucleic acid polymers that are involved in a process) within wheat. As discussed later, genetic redundancy allows chromosomal manipulations and breeding strategies that are not possible in diploid crops. [*See* EVOLUTION OF DOMESTICATED PLANTS.]

Both common and durum wheat are naturally self-pollinating. Two other propagation mechanisms are common in plants, cross-pollination and asexual reproduction. The mechanism of reproduction is important because it largely determines the breeding methods that are used. In self-pollinated crops, it is often difficult to make a cross between two different plants, but it is very easy to allow the plants to inbreed by selfing. Self-pollinated crops are usually marketed as pure-lines (synonymous with inbred line). In cross-pollinated crops (e.g., corn), it is very easy to make a cross, but then can be very laborious to inbreed the progeny. Cross-pollinated crops are usually marketed as hybrids or open pollinated populations or synthetics (the parents are selected and allowed to random mate, the progeny seed is sold as the synthetic). There are many forms of asexual reproduction including fragmentation (e.g., cuttings, tubers) and apomixis, but all are a form of cloning (making an identical copy of the original plant). In cloning, it is difficult to introduce new traits, but it is very easy to maintain the existing plant and its traits.

II. Phases of a Wheat Breeding Program

All breeding programs have five main phases: (1) defining the problem and setting the objective, (2) identifying and incorporating useful genetic variation, (3) inbreeding and selection among the resultant variants, (4) evaluation of selected elite lines, and (5) cultivar release. Every phase is critical to the overall success of the breeding effort. Wheat is grown in widely differing environments with different diseases and insect pests and has a multitude of uses. Hence, identifying the problem and setting the objective is the starting point for all wheat breeding efforts. If done poorly, the breeding effort will inevitably be unsuc-

cessful. With the diversity of wheat growing environments and uses, it should be of little surprise that the germplasm used, breeding methods, and release procedures will also differ greatly. [*See* CULTIVAR DEVELOPMENT; PLANT GENETIC ENHANCEMENT.]

III. Identifying and Incorporating Useful Germplasm

Once the breeding objective is determined, the next step is to find germplasm that has the trait of interest and determine how it is inherited. For our purposes, inheritance can be defined as how closely do the progeny resemble the parents. There are three types of phenotypic traits. Traits that have discrete classes are known as qualitative traits. Examples of qualitative traits include seed color and most disease and pest resistances. Qualitative traits are controlled by relatively few major genes (genes that have distinguishable effects). Traits without distinct classes, but having continuous variation, are known as quantitative traits. Examples of a quantitative trait are grain and forage yield. Quantitative traits are controlled by many genes, have cumulative (but not distinguishable) effects that are often greatly modified by the environment. The final class of traits are those that resemble quantitative traits in that they exhibit continuous variation but in this case the variation is due to the environment and not due to genetics. For these traits there is no useful genetic variation or all of the known genetic variation has already been used to improve wheat. An example of a trait with little useful genetic variation is resistance to wheat streak mosaic virus. An example of a trait where most or all of the genetic variation has already been used to improve wheat is winterhardiness, the ability of winter wheat to survive the winter. After initial gains in winterhardiness, little progress has been made. Fortunately, the last group of traits is rare. Where there is no useful genetic variation or all of the genetic variation has been previously used, wheat breeding will be ineffective. [*See* PLANT GENETIC RESOURCES; PLANT GENETIC RESOURCE CONSERVATION AND UTILIZATION.]

In wheat, the main method of introducing genetic variation is by sexual hybridization (crossing two or more different genotypes). Because wheat is naturally self-pollinated, the female plant is hand emasculated and subsequently fertilized by pollen from the male plant. Most crosses are between pure-lines (S × T, where S and T are pure-lines, the cross is known as a single cross) or between the F_1s of pure-lines [(S × T) × U, where U is also a pure-line, the cross is known as a three-way cross; or (S × T) × (U × V) where V is also a pure-line, the cross is known as a four-way or double cross]. When pure-lines are crossed, all the gametes from S will be identical to each other, as will the gametes from T. Hence, each F_1 seed of the single cross should be genetically identical. If the pure-lines are not completely pure (how this can occur will be discussed later), care must be taken to cross a number of random plants within S to a number of lines within T to accurately represent S and T. The situation becomes considerably more complex in three-way and double crosses. Using the three-way cross as an example, the gametes from (S × T) will segregate for the traits that S and T differ. The gametes from U should all be identical. Hence, to accurately represent the three-way cross, (S × T) × U, enough three-way cross F_1 seed should be made to represent the variation between S and T. Obviously, even more F_1 seed is required in double crosses where the seed must represent the variation between S and T, and between U and V, and with the cross combination. For this reason, most wheat breeders use single or three-way crosses.

With the relatively recent discoveries of genetic male sterility and of chemicals that cause male sterility by damaging the pollen in wheat anthers, it is possible to develop in wheat populations similar to those in cross-pollinated crops. However, neither genetically or chemically induced male sterility is widely used and it remains to be seen if population improvement will be successful in wheat.

If sexual hybridization is the predominant method of increasing genetic variation within breeding populations, the critical question is how to select parents having the desired traits. There are three important gene pools available to wheat breeders. The most important and commonly used gene pool includes lines from the breeding program or from other breeding programs in areas of similar climate, diseases, insects, and with similar end use. This gene pool will include wheat lines from neighboring areas, but will also include lines from similar climatic regions that may be separated by large distances. For example, the wheats of Turkey and the countries to its north have provided the genetic foundation for wheat in the U. S. Great Plains. Even today, wheats are exchanged and readily used in breeding programs in both regions. The reason for concentrating on this gene pool is that plant breeding requires the accumulation of many genes for adaptation, disease and pest

resistance, and end use quality. By crossing lines that have similar traits or characteristics, the likelihood is increased that many of the important genes are already identical or similar between the two lines; hence, there will be less segregation among the progeny. While it may sound contradictory to make a cross to increase the genetic variation within a breeding population and then use as parents lines that may have many genes in common, the difficult task facing wheat breeders is to improve wheat for some traits without reducing the value of the other traits. This goal requires building upon the already accumulated base of beneficial genes. Also if there is too much variation within the breeding population, it becomes very difficult to identify superior lines among average lines. Except for very specific traits, wheat breeders have always made more progress by crossing good lines to good lines than by crossing good lines to poor lines. In the latter crosses the genetic variation may be greater, but the population mean is lower so that the resulting selected lines are generally poorer.

The second major gene pool is those lines that are adapted to other regions, have disease or insect resistances that may not be necessary to meet the breeding objective, or have different end use quality. These lines are highly improved lines, but would be considered as being partially adapted or unadapted to the targeted area for the breeding objective. However, these lines will probably still have some genes in common with the adapted germplasm; hence, while introducing more genetic variation than if only lines from the first gene pool were used, the total variation often will still be manageable. The population mean will be reduced, but the increased variation may allow the selection of superior lines. To effectively use this gene pool, three-way or multiple crosses are almost exclusively used. The line from the secondary gene pool will be crossed to an adapted parent and then crossed to the same adapted parent or to another adapted parent. In this way, the three-way cross will have three-fourths of its genes from the adapted wheats and only one-fourth from an unadapted or poor quality parent. Additional crosses to adapted wheats may be needed to increase the proportion of adapted genes in the progeny of the cross.

The final gene pool includes the progenitor species of wheat and their relatives. Because common and durum wheat are polyploids and many of the progenitor species and their relatives are diploids or polyploids that include genomes not found in cultivated wheat, few applied plant breeders work directly with this gene pool. However, wheat cytogeneticists, scientists highly skilled in chromosome and genome analysis, have made tremendous contributions to wheat improvement by transferring genes from the wild relatives and incorporating them into cultivated wheat. Usually the transferred genes control qualitative traits because of the difficulties involved in identifying and maintaining the genetic expression of the trait in crosses. Fortunately, because wheat is a polyploid, it is able to temporarily tolerate under the appropriate conditions, aneuploidy (chromosome loss or gain) and genome loss or gain. Once the gene has been incorporated into wheat (usually through repetitive crosses of the wheat relative and its cross progeny to adapted wheat parents), breeders can manipulate the trait as they would any other trait in wheat.

Occasionally, increasing genetic variation by inducing mutations has been attempted, though with only moderate success. Mutation breeding is more difficult in wheat than in other crops because wheat is a polyploid; hence, there are multiple copies of many important genes. Also some traits are controlled by gene families consisting of multiple genes closely linked together. A mutation in one of the genes will not affect the linked genes or genes at other loci, and hence may not affect the plant phenotype. [See PLANT GENE MAPPING; TRANSPOSABLE ELEMENTS IN PLANTS.]

IV. Inbreeding and Selection

Once the objective has been determined and the cross made, wheat breeders must choose which inbreeding and selection system (often referred to as breeding method) they will use. Inbreeding is important because it leads to homozygous (pure) lines from a heterozygous cross. Selection is important because only a very few of the homozygous lines will be superior and must be selected. The great majority of lines will be inferior and will need to be discarded.

There are two types of selection: natural selection and artificial selection. Natural selection is done by "nature" and plants that are not adapted to the growing environment perform poorly and may be lost from the population. Every wheat breeder chooses the selection nursery site to have an environment that will increase the beneficial and minimize the negative aspects of natural selection. For example in winter wheat breeding, it is common that the selection nursery be in an environment that will cause winter-tender lines to die. Artificial selection is selection done by the wheat breeder. An example of artificial selection

is the breeder selecting for plant maturity. Again the wheat breeder will choose a selection nursery site that increases his or her ability to select. However, artificial selection is more time and labor consuming than natural selection; hence, wheat breeders try to use natural selection to rid their populations of poor plant types (culling selection) and artificial selection to choose the better plant types (positive selection).

The common breeding methods for wheat are: (1) mass selection, (2) pure-line breeding, (3) pedigree breeding, (4) bulk breeding, (5) single seed descent or doubled haploid breeding (the two methods have similar objectives and will be discussed together), and (6) backcross breeding. Each inbreeding and selection method is described in great detail in the references given in the bibliography at the end of this article. In general, the breeding methods differ in how the population inbreeds and how selection is done. In this brief description of wheat breeding, the general outline of each breeding method will be given. The differences between the methods will be discussed to illustrate why one breeding method is chosen over another one. However, it must be recognized that in the hands of a skilled wheat breeder, every breeding method can successfully lead to new wheat cultivars. Finally, it is rare that any breeding method is used in its pure form. In practice, the advantages of different breeding methods often are combined.

The mass selection method was commonly used when wheat was first introduced into a new area. The procedure involves growing a population of wheat and selecting a large number of plants that are phenotypically similar (conversely, discarding a small number of plants that are phenotypically dissimilar from the majority of plants). The mass selected population is very similar to the original population with the exception of the plants that were removed and usually requires less field testing to verify its performance which should be very similar to that of the original population. One of the best examples of mass selection was the introduction of Turkey wheat from Turkey and Crimea to the Great Plains. Off-type plants were discarded and the Great Plains Turkey wheat was formed. As wheat is grown widely in the world, the importance of introduced cultivars that are improved by mass selection has lessened.

Mass selection currently is used when a popular cultivar is grown in an area on the edge of its adaptation zone. For example, Siouxland, a popular winter wheat cultivar developed in Nebraska, was grown in Texas. However, in Texas, Siouxland was discovered to have two plant types; one requiring a short vernalization period and one requiring a longer vernalization period. In Nebraska, the winters are sufficiently long that both types would vernalize. However, in the milder winters of Texas, occasionally only the plant type requiring a shorter vernalization period would vernalize. The Texas wheat breeders selected, using mass selection, the plant types needing a short vernalization period and released Siouxland 89 which was better adapted to Texas growing conditions than the original Siouxland. Probably the greatest use of mass selection is to remove variants (off-type plants) from a released cultivar, thus maintaining its purity.

A second breeding method is the pure-line breeding method. In this method, a number of individual plants were selected from an introduced cultivar. The progeny of the individual plants are grown in rows and the best rows selected. Finally the best rows would be grown in replicated yield trials to determine which selection is best. As opposed to mass selection which maintains many of the attributes of the original population, a pure-line derived from an introduced cultivar is derived from a single plant, and hence can be different from the cultivar. Pure-lines require field testing to verify their performance. As mentioned previously, the importance of introduced cultivars has lessened and with it the importance of the pure-line breeding method. It is currently used as an alternative to mass selection for improving an existing cultivar. As will be discussed later, many modern cultivars are heterogeneous (variable) for some traits. To improve the uniformity of the cultivar, plant breeders can use either mass selection or pure-line breeding methods depending upon whether they wish to keep some of or remove the heterogeneity.

Both mass selection and pure-line breeding involve selection within existing populations, usually cultivars. However, populations must be created for new breeding progress to occur. Four breeding methods (pedigree, bulk, single seed descent and doubled haploidy, and backcrossing) begin with the progeny of a cross (the new population). The four methods differ predominantly on the type of selection and when it occurs, though backcrossing involves a different crossing procedure.

In the pedigree method, the wheat breeder selects plants in the F_2 populations and the progeny (the next generation) of that plant are grown in a progeny row (the progeny row is also known as a "family"). In the next generation, plants again are selected from the better progeny rows and their seed is planted the following season as progeny rows. This process (select plants, plant seed as progeny rows, and select

best plants in best rows) of artificial and natural selection continues until there is little segregation within the progeny row and selection must be made solely among rows. The amount of segregation within a row depends upon how many generations of inbreeding have occurred and how successful the breeder has been in selecting for phenotypic uniformity. Usually five to six generations of selfing and selection are needed to obtain uniform lines. In every selected line there will be some heterozygosity which with further inbreeding will become heterogeneity within the line. The earlier selection ends, the greater the heterozygosity and eventual heterogeneity. Because selection occurs every season and careful records must be taken on the selected progeny rows and the plants, the pedigree method is resource and labor intensive. The main advantage of the method is the information obtained by consecutive selection and notetaking. The progeny row will indicate the genetic basis of the traits that are being selected.

Also in nature, it is rare that all of the traits that a breeder wishes to observe occur in the same season. For example, many diseases require high humidity or rain for infection. However, selection for drought tolerance requires low humidity and low rainfall. Hence, it would be very difficult to select for disease resistance and drought tolerance concurrently using the same breeding site. Of course the wheat breeder could separate the seed and plant the progeny in disease- and drought-prone environments, but this would double the size of the breeding nurseries and be even more labor and resource intensive. If one main breeding nursery is used for selection, it is possible that during the course of a cultivar selection at that site, that some seasons may be suitable for high disease infection allowing selection for resistance while other seasons may be suitable for selecting for drought tolerance. Cumulatively the wheat breeder can determine a cultivar's disease resistance and drought tolerance. The pedigree method is still very common today for wheat breeding, though it was probably more popular when wheat breeding was less mechanized and more labor intensive.

In the bulk breeding method, the wheat breeder plants the progeny of a cross in bulk at the selection nursery. The bulk is harvested and a portion of the bulk seed is planted the following year. This process (planting and harvesting as a bulk) is repeated until the population is considered to contain a mixture of predominantly homozygous lines. While the plants are growing in a bulk, natural selection and plant to plant competition occur which are normally beneficial. When semi-dwarf wheats (the green revolution wheats) were first developed there was a concern with the bulk breeding methods that the tall wheat progeny of a tall wheat × semi-dwarf wheat cross would be more competitive and shade the semi-dwarf progeny. While this may occur, the relatively few generations of planting and harvesting as a bulk did not eliminate semi-dwarf plants from the population. Hence, wheat breeders were able to select semi-dwarf wheats from the population even if they were at a lower percentage than might have been expected if no selection or competition occurred. As in the pedigree breeding method, the number of generations of selfing it requires to obtain a mixture of predominantly homozygous plants depends on the number of genes segregating in the cross and the desired level of phenotypic uniformity. Usually five to six generations of selfing are considered ample. The key to the bulk breeding method is that wheat plants are self-pollinated so even plants that grow near each other generally do not outcross (less than 6% and usually less than 1%). When the population consists of predominantly homozygous plants, the wheat breeder selects the plants and sows their progeny as progeny rows. Selection is usually done among rows as the parent plants were predominantly homozygous so there should be little variation within the row. If variation within the progeny row is found, the breeder can discard the row or select plants within the row and plant new progeny rows which should be more uniform. The main differences between the bulk and pedigree breeding methods are (1) the bulk relies almost exclusively on natural selection in the early generations of selfing, and (2) the bulk requires very little record keeping (simply the parents of the cross and the generation of selfing). With the ease of plot planting and mechanical harvest, the bulk method is very popular, particularly in winter wheat breeding where there is usually only one generation per year.

Single seed descent and doubled haploidy are very similar to each other, but very different from the other breeding methods. Single seed descent and doubled haploidy both attempt to rapidly inbreed without natural or artificial selection. Single seed descent breeding is done by starting with a large number of F_2 plants and harvesting a single seed from each plant. The seed is planted and at maturity again a single seed is harvested from the plant. This process (harvesting and planting single seed from each plant) continues until plants that are predominantly homozygous are developed (usually five to six generations of selfing). In this procedure, no selection is normally done,

though the original F_2 plants may be selected for important qualitative traits before beginning the process.

In doubled haploid breeding, the gamete from a heterozygous plant is manipulated to form a haploid plant. In wheat, the most common method is anther culture. In anther culture, the anthers of a wheat plant are cultured on media that allow the immature pollen grain (known as a microspore) to form a haploid plant. The chromosomes of the haploid plant are doubled spontaneously or through the use of chemicals such as colchicine which inhibit spindle formation. The doubled haploid plant is completely homozygous and a pure-line. In both single seed descent and doubled haploid breeding the seed from the predominantly or totally homozygous plants are harvested and grown in progeny rows. The selection will be among rows as there will be very little within-row variation.

The advantage of both single seed descent and doubled haploid breeding is the speed with which homozygous lines are developed. Because there is little or no selection, plants can be grown in unrepresentative conditions such as greenhouses or growth chambers. By using these growing environments, single seed descent can produce predominantly homozygous spring wheat lines within 2 years (six generations; approximately 4 months per generation). Winter wheats are more difficult to use in single seed descent because they require vernalization which adds an additional 6 weeks per generation. Doubled haploids can produce homozygous lines within a year. As the doubled haploid process is completed in one generation, it is less sensitive to vernalization requirements and more attractive to winter wheat breeders. Though selection is critical to successful wheat breeding, the ability to produce lines in the absence of selection can also be beneficial. Large international wheat breeding efforts, such as those at the international centers, have the responsibility of breeding for diverse ecogeographic areas. The main breeding center may not represent the targeted areas elsewhere in the world; hence, it would be better to develop lines without selection than to develop lines that were selected in a nontargeted area.

The final breeding method is known as backcross breeding method and in many ways is one type of a crossing procedure. Backcross breeding is used when an adapted wheat cultivar needs to be improved in one or a few traits. After a germplasm line is identified that has the desired trait or traits, the germplasm line (known as the donor parent) is crossed to the adapted parent (known as the recurrent parent). The F_1 seed is planted and the plants are crossed again to the recurrent parent to produce backcross seed. The crossing process continues where the cross progeny are crossed to the recurrent parent. The cross progeny are screened for the trait or traits and only those having the trait or traits are used in the following crosses. This procedure maintains the trait(s) of interest while gradually removing the other traits of the donor parent. The end result of the backcross breeding method is an improved cultivar that is very similar to the recurrent parent but with the extra desired trait or traits from the donor parent. Backcrossing is one of the most predictable breeding methods. This is both an advantage and a disadvantage. The advantage is the predictability which is unusual in plant breeding. The disadvantage is the conservative nature of the procedure in that it often requires five to six cross generations, screening at most backcross generations, and at the end of the process the desired trait may be linked to a deleterious trait or the recurrent parent may no longer be an important cultivar due to more recent releases. One of the reasons why there is little improvement for wheat streak mosaic virus resistance is that the genes incorporated from wild wheat relatives are linked to deleterious genes that reduce the yield or quality of the crop more than the disease. Backcrossing is used extensively when the donor parent is from the unadapted or wild relative gene pool. It is also extensively used when a breakthrough in yield is made and additional traits must be added to incrementally improve the wheat cultivar.

Wheat breeders chose their breeding method by their breeding objective. For example if only one or a few traits need improvement, backcrossing can be used. If a number of traits need to be improved and labor is inexpensive, then the pedigree method may be chosen. If a number of traits need to be improved, labor is expensive, but mechanical planters and harvesters are available, the bulk method may be chosen. When working with crosses involving very high yielding lines where early generation selection may be ineffective, then it may be better to rapidly inbreed using single seed descent or doubled haploidy and then select among the pure lines.

As mentioned previously, it is rare that a single breeding method is used exclusively in the development of a wheat cultivar. For example, a spring wheat breeder may make a cross and then use the pedigree breeding method for two or three generations to select for easily measured traits (for example maturity, disease or insect resistance, plant height). More difficult to measure traits are more challenging to select for

in early generations. Hence, a spring wheat breeder may advance the selected lines by single seed descent for two generations during the off season (the season when the crop is normally not grown in the field in his or her target area) and then evaluate the homozygous lines for these traits (yield, end use quality) in the following breeding season. By using both the pedigree and single seed descent method, the wheat breeder was able to select the major genes early in the program, rapidly move through the generations where selection would be less effective, and then thoroughly evaluate the homozygous lines. In winter wheat, the breeder might grow his F_2 and F_3 generations in bulk at a location that usually has a harsh winter, thus letting nature kill the winter tender types. It is best to use natural selection for winter survival because it is very difficult to simulate a harsh winter in a controlled environment. Also, every winter is different; hence, multiple selection environments are preferred. Winterhardiness is controlled by recessive genes; hence, selection can quickly and effectively remove the winter-tender types. The breeder may then use pedigree selection for one or two additional generations to select for major genes.

In this brief discussion of inbreeding and selection methods, the traits being selected have not been discussed in detail. There is a pattern or hierarchy to selection. In early generations, wheat breeders select for traits that are highly heritable and distinguishable. The traits would include disease and insect resistances, plant height and morphology, plant maturity, and plant growth habit (spring or winter for winter wheat, winter survival). Due to the number of lines in a typical wheat breeding program, most of the early generation selections are done visually in environments that have high incidences, naturally or with artificial inoculation, of diseases or insects, etc., that allow the breeder to select the plants having the traits of interest. In the early generations, a wheat breeder may have 2,000,000 or more plants and can select among 40,000 to 100,000 progeny rows.

As inbreeding increases and the lines become more homozygous, the breeder is able to better see what the finished cultivar could be. At this time, the wheat breeder has many fewer lines and begins to select for quantitative traits or traits that are difficult or expensive to assay. Obviously the most important quantitative trait is grain yield or for areas where wheat is used as a forage, forage yield. However, other important traits include end-use quality and other grain characteristics. In addition, many qualitative traits are modified by minor genes that are most easily selected in later generations. Wheat breeders would select first for grain yield and once they have selected the acceptable group of lines, would then begin the evaluation for end-use quality which is a more expensive and limiting assay.

Selection for end-use quality is extremely important for wheat being used as a food grain. Each end use has its own characteristics and needs, and hence its own selection techniques. The techniques will vary with the amount of seed available, the number of lines that need to be tested, and the importance of the lines. For example, in hard wheats used for bread, the first quality test could be determining protein content to eliminate lines that are too low in protein (less than 12.5%) to produce a good loaf of bread. Thousands of lines can be assayed inexpensively for protein content. As the number of lines are reduced, the lines could be rated using a mixograph which measures some of the bread dough properties and estimates protein quality (as opposed to protein quantity). The mixograph assay requires 10 g of flour; hence, each sample must be micromilled before it can be assayed. As the micromilling and mixograph assay both require more time and grain than the protein content assay, they are usually done only on more advanced lines. After further selection, fewer advanced lines will be milled and baked into loaves of bread. For this rating procedure, often 1000 g of grain is needed and two loaves are baked. Most breeding programs do not have 1000 g of grain of breeding lines until later generations and would usually evaluate by baking a loaf of bread only for 100–200 highly selected lines. As a line is considered for release, it may be evaluated by commercial millers and bakers to see how it performs in their various baking processes. Often fewer than 20 lines per year are evaluated commercially prior to release as commercial wheat cultivars.

Similar to the hierarchy of end-use quality assays, there is one for most other traits. For example, in early generations it may be easy to artificially inoculate wheat plants for leaf (*Puccinia recondita*), stripe (*P. striiformis*), or stem (*P. graminis*) rust which can be readily evaluated visually. In later generations when there are fewer lines, diseases that are more difficult to evaluate, such as root rots or some viral diseases, may be undertaken.

From the above description, it should be clear that most wheat breeding programs begin with literally thousands of lines. By selection, the lines are gradually reduced to very few that may be released. In the initial stages of selection, most lines are selected visually or by using very inexpensive and quick assays. As the number of lines are reduced and more is known about them, more complicated and expensive assays are used (i.e., replicated yield trials, disease and insect screening, end-use quality). The very best breeding programs may release one new cultivar a year.

V. Evaluation

The final process of selection is extensive evaluation of promising experimental lines. The purpose of evaluation nurseries is to determine the areas of adaptation of a new line. Wheat is the most widely grown crop in the world and it is important that producers know where new cultivars should and should not be grown. Hence, the evaluation nurseries should represent the diverse growing conditions that may be found within the region for which the wheat breeding program is attempting to produce new cultivars. As opposed to selection nurseries which attempt to magnify differences among lines so as to make selection easier, evaluation nurseries attempt to very accurately and precisely determine how a line will perform under normal conditions.

The evaluation trials will involve replicated field trials and often complex statistics to determine which lines are similar and which are different. The nurseries will use standard procedures or those that are believed to be possible in the future for land preparation, planting, and harvesting. As it is unlikely that all of the possible environments will be represented in one year, wheat breeders often collaborate in testing advanced lines in regional or international yield trials. For example, wheat experimental lines developed in Texas may be tested in Nebraska to more fully evaluate their winterhardiness or lines developed in Nebraska may be tested in Kansas where there is greater incidence of soil borne viruses and leaf rust than in Nebraska.

By the time an experimental line is released, it is not unusual for it to be evaluated for more than 6 years in multiple locations in a region and have data from over 100 replicated breeding trials. Even with all of these data, it is common for new information to be obtained after the cultivar is released.

VI. The Decision to Release a Wheat Cultivar

The general practice for determining whether an experimental line should be released is that it must be superior to already released cultivars for at least one important trait. Often the superiority is for yield as that is the primary determinant of crop value. However, improved disease or insect resistance or superior stress tolerance or end-use quality also may be the deciding factors for releasing a cultivar.

In some countries, particularly European countries, there are national cultivar release boards that determine if an experimental line should be released. This is often based on national yield trials and end-use quality evaluation. In the United States, the main wheat breeding programs are at land-grant universities and commercial companies. The land-grant universities have generally accepted procedures for cultivar release and each university will decide if an experimental line developed by the university should be released. For commercial breeding programs, the decision to release a cultivar will be made jointly by their research and marketing teams. There is no national wheat board in the United States that determines if an experimental line can be released as a cultivar.

As there are great differences among countries for release procedures, there are also widely differing laws regulating the sale and shipment of seed. The strictest laws for seed sales are in Europe where most wheat breeders are affiliated with commercial companies and where new seed is purchased annually by the growers. In the United States, wheat cultivars may be protected by the Plant Variety Protection Act. This law is important because it allows the wheat breeder and his or her breeding institution to require that the seed be sold by name and as a class of certified seed. The certified seed classes are foundation, registered, and certified seed.

VII. Wheat Seed in the Marketplace

Grain is the common term for wheat seed that is sold for making products or feeding to animals. The term wheat seed is usually used only for seed that will be planted. When a wheat breeder determines that an advanced line has potential to be released as a cultivar, he or she begins increasing the seed. This seed is known as breeders seed and is usually less than 100 kg. Breeder seed should be the purest seed. The breeder seed is used to produce foundation seed. Foundation seed is the purest commercial seed and is used to produce registered seed. Registered seed is used to produce certified seed which is the commonly sold seed purchased by the farmer. Each

time the seed is planted, between 40 and 60 times more seed is harvested. Hence, from the 100 kg of breeder seed, 4000 to 6000 kg of foundation seed can be produced which in turn can produce 160,000 to 360,000 kg of registered seed which in turn can produce 6,400,000 to 21,600,000 kg of certified seed. The 21,600,000 kg of seed took 4 years to produce and will plant between 200,000 and 400,000 ha which would represent 15 to 30% of the wheat hectarage in Nebraska. Hence, not only does it take 7 or more years to develop a spring wheat cultivar and 10 to 12 years to develop a winter wheat cultivar, it takes 4 years to produce enough seed to have a commercial impact. To shorten this time, most breeders increase a number of lines every year in hopes that one will be eventually released.

VIII. The Future of Wheat Breeding

As described, wheat breeding has five phases: defining an objective, identifying and incorporating useful genetic variation, inbreeding and selecting among the variants, evaluating the selected lines, and releasing a new cultivar. New technologies will change wheat breeding if they can affect one of these five processes. Genetic engineering, the transfer of a gene(s) from one organism to another or the same organism without having sexual hybridization, has the potential to greatly expand the germplasm available to wheat breeders. Literally the complete biosphere becomes the gene pool for wheat breeding. Similarly, the ability to modify genes, change how they are regulated, or change the amount of product they make will expand the gene pool.

Selection will be aided by improved genetic assays such as restriction fragment length polymorphisms or isozymes that are tightly linked to the genes of interest. Already, a very quick isozyme assay is used to identify a resistance gene for a root rotting fungus. Testing plants for resistance to the fungus is very imprecise as well as being very time and labor consuming. Selection will also be aided by improved statistical techniques to determine differences and similarities among lines and by better abilities to store and retrieve previous information. Statistics is one of the foundations of plant breeding and improved computers and software will greatly improve breeding efficiency. The already mentioned doubled haploid methods have promise in speeding the inbreeding process. However, evaluation procedures and the decision process to release a cultivar will probably not change. To determine how an advanced line performs in a region, it must be adequately tested in that region before it can be released as a new cultivar.

Bibliography

Allen, R. E. (1987). Wheat. *In* "Principles of Crop Development" (W. R. Fehr, ed.), Vol. 2. Iowa State Univ. Press. Ames, IA.

Baenziger, P. S., and Peterson, C. J. (1992). Genetic variation: Its origin and use for breeding self-pollinated spe-cies. *In* "Plant Breeding in the 1990s" (T. M. Stalker and J. P. Murphy, eds.). C A B International. Wallingford, England.

Fehr, W. R. (1987). "Principles of Crop Development," Vol. 1. Iowa State Univ. Press. Ames, IA.

Feldman, M. (1976). Wheats. *In* "Evolution of Crop Plants" (N. W. Simmonds, ed.). Longman, New York.

Heyne, E. G. (ed.) (1987). "Wheat and Wheat Improvement." American Society of Agronomy, Madison, WI.

Jensen, N. F. (1988). "Plant Breeding Methodology." Wiley, New York.

Wheat Processing and Utilization

Y. POMERANZ, *Washington State University*

Glossary

Breadmaking Conversion of wheat flour into yeast-leavened bread in a straight dough, sponge and dough, or liquid fermentation process

Extrusion process Process of conversion of cereal products into pasta, instant and infant foods, breakfast foods, pet foods, feeds, and cereals for industrial uses

Flour fractionation Separation of wheat flour into protein-rich and starch-rich fractions by air-classification following pin milling

Industrial products Use of cereal grains or their fractions into materials for chemical base materials, modified products, or energy sources

Wheat milling Process of converting wheat into milled products: flour, shorts, bran, and germ

This article reviews various aspects of wheat processing and utilization: Included are wheat milling (roller milling; selection, blending, and cleaning; conditioning; breaking, sieving, and purification; reduction milling; flour grades and yields, and fractionation); breadmaking (the role of flour; additives and fermentation); soft wheat products (cookies and crackers; cakes; and doughnuts); extrusion products (pasta and extrusion cooking); and industrial uses.

I. Wheat Milling

Most harvested wheat is processed for food. The main use of wheat for food is the manufacture of flour for making bread, biscuits, pastry products, and semolina and farina for alimentary pastes. A small portion is converted into breakfast cereals. Industrial uses of wheat include the manufacture of malt, potable spirits, starch, gluten, pastes, and core binders. Some wheat flour (mainly low-grade clears) is used to manufacture wheat starch as a by-product of viable (functionally in bread making) gluten. The gluten is used to supplement flour proteins in specialty baked goods (hamburger buns, hot-dog buns, hearth-type breads, specialty breads, etc.) and as a raw material for the manufacture of monosodium glutamate, which is used to accentuate the flavors of foods. Some low-grade flours are used in the manufacture of pastes for bookbinding and paper hanging, in the manufacture of plywood adhesives, and in iron foundries as a core binder in the preparation of molds for castings.

In wheat and flour technology, the term "quality" denotes the suitability of the material for some particular end use. It has no reference to nutritional attributes. Thus, the high-protein hard wheat flour is of good bread-making quality but is inferior to soft wheat flours for chemically leavened products such as biscuits, cakes, and pastry.

The miller desires a wheat that mills easily and gives a high flour yield. Wheat kernels should be plump and uniformly large for ready separation of foreign materials without undue loss of millable wheat. The wheat should produce a high yield of flour with maximum and clean separation from the bran and germ without excessive consumption of power. [*See* WHEAT GENETICS AND BREEDING.]

A. Roller Milling—General

In the production of white flour, the objective is to separate the starchy endosperm of the grain from the bran and germ. The separated endosperm is pulverized. A partial separation of the starchy endosperm

Encyclopedia of Agricultural Science, Volume 4   Copyright © 1994 by Academic Press, Inc.   All rights of reproduction in any form reserved.

is possible because its physical properties differ from those of the fibrous pericarp and oily germ. Bran is tough because of its high fiber content, but the starchy endosperm is friable. The germ, because of its high oil content, flakes when passed between smooth rolls. In addition, the particles from various parts of the wheat kernel differ in density. This makes their separation possible by using air currents. The differences in friability of the bran and the starchy endosperm are enhanced by wheat conditioning, which involves adding water before wheat is milled. The addition of water toughens the bran and mellows the endosperm. The milling process comprises a gradual reduction in particle size, first between corrugated break rolls and later between smooth reduction rolls. The separation is empirical and not quantitative. The milling process results in the production of many streams of flour and offals that can be combined in different ways to produce different grades of flour.

Wheat flour production involves wheat selection and blending, cleaning, conditioning, breaking, bolting or sieving, purification, reduction, and treatment (bleaching, enrichment, supplementation). An outline of the wheat milling process is shown in Fig. 1.

B. Selection, Blending, and Cleaning

The miller must produce a flour with definite characteristics and meet certain specifications for a particular market. The most critical requirement is maintaining a uniform product from a product (wheat) that may show a wide range of characteristics and composition. Consequently, selection of wheats and binning according to quality for proper blending are essential phases of modern milling.

Wheat contains many impurities that can be removed by specialized machines. Preliminary cleaning involves the use of sieves, air blasts, and disc separators. This is followed by dry scouring in which the wheat is forced against a perforated iron casting by beaters fixed to a rapidly revolving drum. This removes foreign materials in the crease of the kernel and in the brush hairs. A few mills are equipped with washers in which the wheat is scrubbed under a flowing stream of water.

C. Conditioning

In this process water is added and allowed to stand for up to 24 hr to secure maximum toughening of the bran with optimum mellowing of the starchy endosperm. The quantity of added water increases with decreasing moisture content of the wheat, with increasing vitreousness, and with increasing plumpness. Generally, hard wheats are tempered to 15–16% moisture and soft wheats to 14–15% moisture. In the customary conditioning, the wheat is scoured again, after it has been held in the tempering bins for several hours. A second small addition of 0.5% water is made about 20–60 min before the wheat goes to the rolls.

D. Breaking

The first part of the grinding process is carried out on corrugated rolls (break rolls), usually 24–30 in. long and 9 in. in diameter. Each stand has two pairs of rolls, which turn in opposite directions at a differential speed of about 2.5:1. In the first break rolls there are usually 10–12 corrugations per inch. This number increases to 26–28 corrugations on the fifth break roll. The first break rolls are spaced so that the wheat is crushed and only a small quantity of white flour is produced. After sieving, the coarsest material is conveyed to the second break rolls. The second break rolls are set a little closer than the first break rolls so that the material is crushed finer and more endosperm particles are released. This process of grinding and sifting is repeated up to six times. The material going to each succeeding break contains less and less endosperm.

E. Sieving and Purification

After each grinding step, the crushed material is conveyed to a sifter fitted with a series of sloping sieves. The process results in separation of three classes of material: (1) coarse fragments, which are fed to the next break until only bran remains; (2) flour, or fine particles, which pass through the finest (flour) sieve; and (3) intermediate granular particles, which are called middlings.

The middlings consist of fragments of endosperm, small pieces of bran, and released embryos. The bran-rich material is removed from the middlings in purifiers. Purifiers also produce a further classification of middlings according to size and complete the work of the sifters. An upward air current through the sieve draws off light material to dust collectors and holds bran particles on the surface of the moving middlings so that they drift over to the tail of the sieve.

F. Reduction

The purified and classified middlings are gradually pulverized to flour between smooth reduction rolls,

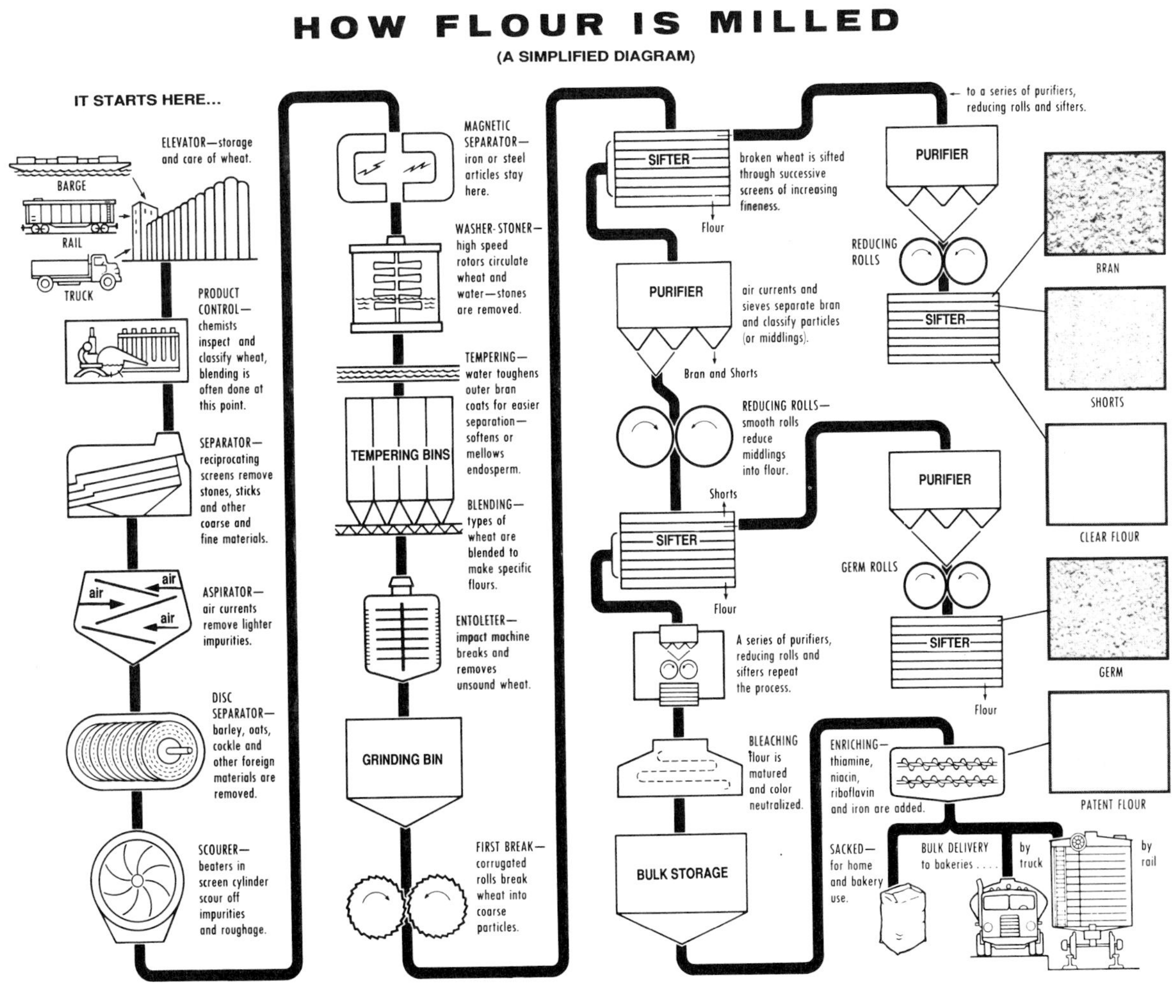

HOW FLOUR IS MILLED

(A SIMPLIFIED DIAGRAM)

IT STARTS HERE...

ELEVATOR—storage and care of wheat.

BARGE
RAIL
TRUCK

PRODUCT CONTROL—chemists inspect and classify wheat, blending is often done at this point.

SEPARATOR—reciprocating screens remove stones, sticks and other coarse and fine materials.

ASPIRATOR—air currents remove lighter impurities.

DISC SEPARATOR—barley, oats, cockle and other foreign materials are removed.

SCOURER—beaters in screen cylinder scour off impurities and roughage.

MAGNETIC SEPARATOR—iron or steel articles stay here.

WASHER-STONER—high speed rotors circulate wheat and water—stones are removed.

TEMPERING—water toughens outer bran coats for easier separation—softens or mellows endosperm.

TEMPERING BINS

BLENDING—types of wheat are blended to make specific flours.

ENTOLETER—impact machine breaks and removes unsound wheat.

GRINDING BIN

FIRST BREAK—corrugated rolls break wheat into coarse particles.

SIFTER

Flour

broken wheat is sifted through successive screens of increasing fineness.

PURIFIER

air currents and sieves separate bran and classify particles (or middlings).

Bran and Shorts

REDUCING ROLLS—smooth rolls reduce middlings into flour.

Shorts

SIFTER

Flour

A series of purifiers, reducing rolls and sifters repeat the process.

BLEACHING flour is matured and color neutralized.

BULK STORAGE

to a series of purifiers, reducing rolls and sifters.

PURIFIER

REDUCING ROLLS

SIFTER

PURIFIER

GERM ROLLS

SIFTER

Flour

ENRICHING—thiamine, niacin, riboflavin and iron are added.

SACKED—for home and bakery use.

BULK DELIVERY to bakeries .... by truck   by rail

BRAN

SHORTS

CLEAR FLOUR

GERM

PATENT FLOUR

FIGURE 1 Milling process of flour. (*Source:* Wheat Flour Institute, Chicago.)

which revolve at a differential of about 1.5:1. The space between the rolls is adjusted to the granulation of the middlings. The endosperm fragments passing through the rolls are reduced to finer middlings and flour. The remaining fibrous fragments of bran are flaked or flattened. After each reduction step, the resulting stock is sifted. These steps are repeated until most of the endosperm has been converted to flour and most of the bran has been removed as offal by the reduction sifters.

The embryos are largely released by the break system and appear as lemon-yellow particles in some of the coarser middling streams. The embryos are separated as flakes during sieving. Germ may be separated by gravity also. Previously, all the germ was mixed with the shorts as feed. Some special uses of germ in foods and as a source of pharmaceuticals have been developed.

G. Flour Grades and Yields of Mill Products

Each grinding and sieving operation produces flour. With each successive reduction, the flour contains more pulverized bran and germ. The flour from the last reduction, called "red dog," is dark in color and high in components originating from the bran and germ, such as ash, fiber, pentosans, lipids, sugars, and vitamins. Such flour is mostly sold as feed flour.

In a large mill there may be 30 or more streams that vary widely in composition. If all the streams are combined, the product is called straight flour. A straight flour extraction means, generally, a 75% flour, because wheat milling yields about 75% white flour and about 25% feed products. Frequently, the white streams are taken off and sold separately as patent flours; the remaining streams, which contain some bran and germ, are called clear flours. A diagram of flours and milled feed products is given in Fig. 2.

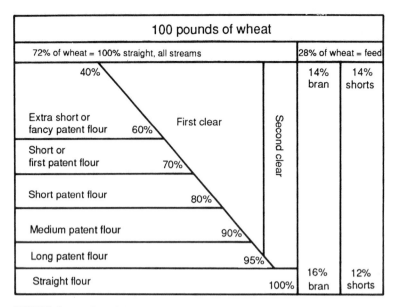

FIGURE 2 Grades of flour (*Source:* C. O. Swanson, Kansas State University, Manhattan, KS.)

Some lighter, clear flours are used in blends with rye and/or whole wheat flours in the production of specialty breads. The darker grades of clear flours are used in the manufacture of gluten, starch, monosodium glutamate, and pet foods.

The plump wheat grain consists of about 83% endosperm, 15% bran, and 2.5% germ. These three structures are not separated completely, however, in the milling process. The yield of total flour ranges from 72 to 75%, and the flour contains little bran and germ. In ordinary milling processes only about 0.25% of the germ is recovered. Bran ranges from 12 to 16% of the wheat milled. The remaining by-products are shorts.

H. Flour Fractionation

Wheat flour produced by conventional roller milling contains particles of different sizes (from 1 to 150 μm) (Fig. 3). The flour can be ground, pin-milled to avoid excessive starch damage, to fine particles in which the protein is freed from the starch. The pin-milled flour is then passed through an air classifier. A fine fraction, made up of particles about 40 μm and smaller, is removed and passed through a second air classifier. Particles of about 20 μm and smaller are separated; they comprise about 10% of the original flour and contain up to about twice the protein of the unfractionated flour. This high-protein flour is used to fortify low-protein bread flours or for enrichment in the production of specialty baked goods. A compa-rable fraction containing about half the protein content of the unfractionated flour is also obtainable.

I. Soft Wheat Milling

Soft wheats are milled by the method of gradual reduction, similar to the method for milling hard bread wheats. Patent flours containing 7–9% protein, milled from soft red winter wheats, are suitable for chemically leavened biscuits and hot breads. Mixtures of soft wheats are used to make flours for use in cookie and cake making; such flours usually contain 8% protein or less and are milled to very short patents (about 30%). Treatment with heavy dosages of chlorine lower the pH to about 5.1–5.3, weaken the gluten, and facilitate the production of short pastry.

J. Durum Wheat Milling

In durum milling, the objective is the production of a maximum yield of highly purified semolina. Durum wheat milling involves cleaning and conditioning of the grain, light grinding, and extensive purification. The cleaning, breaking, sizing, and purifying systems are much more elaborate and extensive than in flour mills. On the other hand, the reduction system is shorter in durum mills, because the primary product is removed and finished in the granular condition. The break system is extensive to permit lighter and more gradual grinding than in flour mills. Durum wheat of good milling quality normally yields about 62% semolina, 16% clear flour, and 22% feeds.

HOW FLOUR IS FRACTIONATED

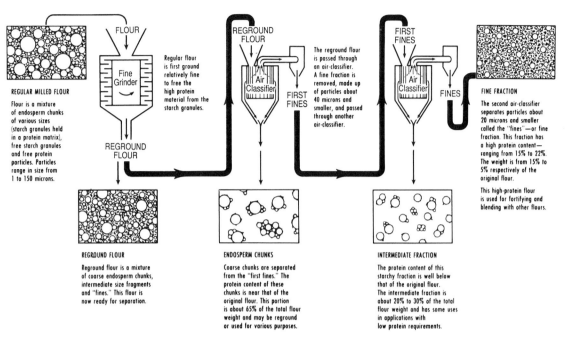

FIGURE 3 How flour is fractionated. (*Source:* Wheat Flour Institute, Chicago.)

Proximate chemical composition of a commercial mill mix of hard red spring wheat and its principal milled products is given in Table I. Table II shows the average nutritional value of 100-g milled products in West Germany.

II. Breadmaking

The production of baked goods comprises the following steps: (1) preparation of raw materials (selection, preparation, and scaling of ingredients); (2) dough formation and development; (3) dough processing (fermentation and leavening, dividing, molding, and shaping); (4) baking; and (5) manufacture to finish products (including measures to retain quality, slicing, packaging, sterilization, etc.).

A. Flour

Although bread has been produced from meals and flours milled from most cereal grains, the type of bread accepted by the customer in the Western world is normally prepared from wheat meal or flour or

from wheat-type meals or flours. Flour used in bread making is generally milled from common (or so-called vulgare) wheat. Flour from durum wheat is used in some parts of the world (mainly the Middle East) to make flat bread. In the Western world, durum is used mainly to make semolina for pasta production. Bread-making quality of a flour depends on the quality and quantity of the flour proteins. Proteins of flours milled from common wheat possess the unique and distinctive property of forming gluten when wetted and mixed with water. It is gluten formation, rather than any distinctive nutritive property, that gives wheat its prominence in the diet.

When water is added to wheat flour and mixed, the water-insoluble proteins hydrate and form gluten, a complex and coherent mass in which starch, added yeast, and other dough components are imbedded. Thus, the gluten is, in reality, the skeleton or framework of wheat-flour dough and is responsible for gas retention, which makes production of light leavened products possible. [*See* FOOD BIOCHEMISTRY: PROTEINS, ENZYMES, AND ENZYME INHIBITORS.]

On the basis of their suitability to produce yeast-leavened bread, wheats and flours are classified

TABLE I

Proximate Chemical Composition[a] of a Commercial Mill Mix of Hard Red Spring Wheat and Its Principal Mill Products

Product	Proportion of wheat (%)	Protein[b] (%)	Fat (%)	Ash (%)	Starch (%)	Pentosans (%)	Total sugars[c] (%)
Wheat	100.0	15.3	1.9	1.85	53.0	5.2	2.6
Patent flour	65.3	14.2	0.9	0.42	66.7	1.6	1.2
First-clear flour	5.2	15.2	1.4	0.65	63.1	2.0	1.4
Second-clear flour	3.2	18.1	2.4	1.41	56.3	2.6	2.1
Red dog flour	1.3	18.5	3.8	2.71	41.4	4.5	4.6
Shorts	8.4	18.5	5.2	5.00	19.3	13.8	6.7
Bran	16.4	16.7	4.6	6.50	11.7	18.1	5.5
Germ	0.2	30.9	12.6	4.30	10.0	3.7	16.6

Source: USDA mimeographed publication ACE-189 (1942).

[a] 13.5% moisture basis.
[b] Nitrogen × 5.7.
[c] Expressed as glucose.

broadly into two groups, strong and weak. Strong flours contain a relatively high percentage of proteins that form a tenacious, elastic gluten of good gas-retaining properties and are capable of being baked into well-risen, shapely loaves that possess good crumb grain and texture. They require considerable water to make a dough of proper consistency to give a high yield of bread. The doughs have good handling properties and are not critical in their mixing and fermentation requirements. They yield good bread over a wide range of baking conditions and have good fermentation tolerance.

In contrast, weak flours have a relatively low protein content and form weak gluten of low elasticity and poor gas-retaining properties. They have relatively low water-absorbing capacity, yield doughs of inferior handling quality, and have mixing and fermentation requirements that render them more likely to fail in baking. Weak flours require less mixing

and fermentation than strong flours to give optimum baking results.

B. Other Ingredients

The amount of water added during dough mixing depends on water absorption of the flour, the method and equipment used to make and process the dough, and the characteristics desired in the baked bread. Water is added to bind dough ingredients into a coherent mass, to dissolve certain ingredients (i.e., sugars, soluble proteins, and pentosans), for development of yeast and/or sour dough microorganisms, and for leavening action at the baking stage.

Salt is added (about 1.5% of flour weight) for taste and to improve dough handling. Salt slows down water imbibition and swelling of flour proteins, shortens the gluten, reduces dough extensibility, and improves gas retention, bread crumb grain, and slicing

TABLE II

Average Nutritional Value of 100-g Milled Products

Milled product and type	Main nutrients (g)			Energy		Minerals/mg				Vitamins		
	Proteins	Fat	Carbohydrates	Calories (kcal)	Joules (kJ)	K	Ca	P	Fe	B$_1$ (μg)	B$_2$ (μg)	Niacin (mg)
Wheat flour, 550	10.6	1.1	74.0	348	1480	126	16	95	1.1	110	80	0.5
Wheat flour, 1050	12.1	1.8	71.2	349	1485	203	14	232	2.8	330	100	2.0
Wheat meal, 1700	12.1	2.1	69.4	345	1465	290	41	372	3.3	360	170	5.0
Rye flour, 997	7.4	1.1	75.6	342	1453	240	31	180	2.3	190	110	0.8
Rye meal, 1800	10.8	1.5	70.1	337	1432	439	23	362	3.3	300	140	2.9

Reproduced with permission (courtesy, AID, Ministry of Nutrition, Agriculture, and Forestry, Bonn, 1977).

properties. The amount of yeast is about 2% (flour basis) in regular white bread; for rolls, larger amounts of yeast are used. Bakers' yeast ferments the available sugars (in flour or added) to yield carbon dioxide (and alcohol) to provide light, porous, yeast-leavened products.

Bread can be produced from flour, water, salt, and yeast and/or sour dough. Optional ingredients include fats or oils, sugars, milk powder or mixtures of vegetable (i.e., soy flour) proteins and whey proteins, oxidants, enzymic supplements, dough conditioners, dough softeners, and others.

Figure 4 compares the loaf volumes of breads made from good- and poor-quality wheat flours and very lean to optimized formulations.

C. Fermentation

Bread-making processes can be divided into those that depend on biological and those that depend on mechanical dough development. In processes that employ a biological dough development in production of wheat breads, the effect of yeast development is critical. The main biological processes include the following.

Straight dough. The dough is prepared by incorporating all ingredients in a single stage, and fermentation is carried out in bulk.

Sponge and dough process. Bread dough is prepared in two stages (see Fig. 5).

Liquid ferment process. A liquid ferment contains the essential ingredients for yeast growth (with or without wheat flour) and after fermentation constitutes all or part of the dough liquor.

In processes employing mechanical dough development, traditional bulk fermentation can be replaced by intense mechanical energy input to a dough.

III. Soft Wheat Products

Low extraction, low protein soft wheat flours are uniquely suited for the production of cookies (biscuits), most cakes, wafers, cake doughnuts, and similar baked products.

A. Cookies and Crackers

A high ratio of spread to thickness (W/T) is used as criterion of adequacy of cookie flour. Whereas weak, low-protein soft wheat flours have a W/T ratio of 8.5–10.0, strong, high-protein, hard wheat flours

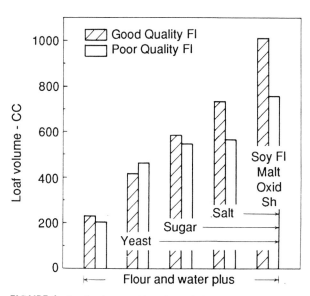

FIGURE 4 Loaf volumes of breads made from good- and poor-quality wheat flours (100 g) and very lean to optimized formulations (including soy flour and additive for oxidation of sulfhydryl-SH-groups). [From Finney, K. F. (1978). *In* "Cereals 78: Better Nutrition for World's Millions." (Y. Pomeranz, ed.). Am. Assoc. Cereal Chemists, St. Paul, MN.]

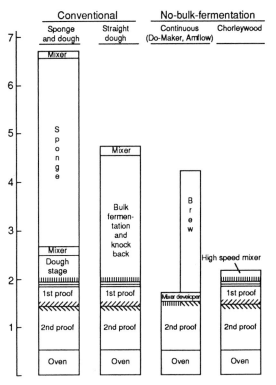

FIGURE 5 Comparison of processing stages and times for two conventional and two no-bulk-fermentation bread-making methods [From Tipples, K. H. (1967). *Bakers Digest* **41(3)**, 18–20.]

have a ratio of 6.5–8.0. The main types of cookies, depending on their production methods, are wire cut, rotary, and deposit.

B. Cakes

Most cakes are prepared from batters rather than doughs. The distinguishing differences between the two are summarized in Table III. High-quality cakes should have a large volume, fine grain, and a moist, tender crumb. The flour used for their production is milled from low-protein soft wheats. Chlorine treatment makes it possible to produce sponge cakes with more even crumb texture, increased volume, and greater symmetry. Chlorinated flours are used in layer, genoese, yellow, madeira, and fruit cakes made with greater proportions of sugar and liquor (so-called "high-ratio" cakes).

C. Doughnuts

Production of cake doughnuts is one of the most critical baking processes. The cake doughnut is the only item produced in the bakery that does not have some mechanical means of forming the dough piece into the desired product. The fluid–viscous batter is deposited into the frying fat. It depends on the flow and characteristics of this batter in the fluid medium to flow, fry and set in the desired size and shape.

In general, a doughnut mix contains 55–65% flour (mix weight basis) of 9–10% protein to yield the proper tenderness–structuring profile. Sugar in the

range of 22–30% is added to sweeten, tenderize, aid moisture retention, accelerate crust formation, and effect spreading in the fryer. Some shortening, 3–9%, is also included to aid tenderness, increase shelf life, and lubricate the protein structure for proper flour performance. Dried egg yolks (0.5–3.0%) provide richness and tenderness, and 3–5% nonfat milk solids act as a binder and structure builder and contribute to crust color, shelf life, gas retention, and "crowning." Leaveners (1.75–3%) are usually blends of fast-acting sodium pyrophosphate and slower-acting sodium aluminum phosphate, monocalcium phosphate, and sodium bicarbonate. Sometimes, glucono-δ-lactone may be used.

IV. Extrusion Products

Cereals can be processed into foods by extrusion. Regular extrusion is used primarily for the production of alimentary pastes. More recently, high-temperature, short-time (HTST) extrusion is used to produce instant and infant foods, expanded pet foods, feeds, and cereals for industrial uses.

A. Pasta

The basic raw material for the production of high-quality pasta products is semolina from durum wheat. Hard durum wheat has a tough, horny endosperm. Semolina from durum wheat requires less water to form a dough and produces a translucent pasta product of acceptable cooking and eating properties. A variety of pasta products can, however, be manufactured from a wide range of wheats milled to various granulations.

Commercial semolina should pass through a U.S. No. 20 sieve and should contain a maximum of 3% flour (passing through a No. 100 sieve). A uniform fine particle size is specified. According to FDA standards of identity, egg noodles and egg spaghetti must contain 5.5% egg solids, by weight, in the final product. Optional ingredients (in specific maximum amounts) include seasonings, enrichment (minerals and vitamins), soy flour and soy protein, vegetables, and gluten. In commercial practice, alimentary pastes are formed by extrusion on large automatic machines (capacities up to 1500 lb per hour) that perform several operations. Material flow in the processing of pasta products is depicted in Fig. 6. Water is added (along with other ingredients) to make a stiff dough with

TABLE III
Distinguishing Characteristics of Doughs and Batters

Characteristics	Dough	Batter
Basic ingredients in recipe	Flour, sugar, fat	Sugar, eggs, fat, flour
Processing	Kneading, mixing	Beating, stirring, mixing, short heating
Raising	Biological, chemical, physical	Chemical, physical
Factors affecting binding of water or consistency	Wheat gluten, pentosans, damaged starch, swelling agents	Eggs, fat, sugar, damaged starch, and in part wheat gluten and swelling agents
Consistency	Elastic to plastic	Foamy, soft-plastic, pastelike to semifluid

Source: Menger and Bretschneider, 1972.

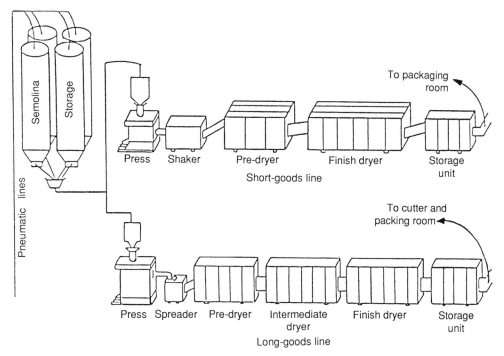

FIGURE 6 Material flow in the processing of pasta products. [From Fraase, R. G., Walsh, D. E., and Anderson, D. E. (1974). An analysis of the economic feasibility of processing pasta products in North Dakota. Station Bull. ND Agric. Ept. No. 496.]

about 31% water. The dough is forced under pressure through dies of an extrusion auger.

Pasta products marketed in Europe and the western hemisphere include spaghetti—small diameter, solid rods; macaroni—hollow tubes; noodles—flat strips or extruded oval strips; and miscellaneous products—cut by revolving or blade cutters. The various pasta shapes are illustrated in Fig. 7.

B. Extrusion Cooking

An extrusion cooker may be considered as a continuous reactor capable of simultaneous transporting, mixing, shearing, and forming of food materials under elevated temperature and pressure at short resistance times.

The basic components of an HTST extrusion cooking system include (1) continuous, uniform, and controlled feeding of processing materials to the extruder; (2) equipment to precondition the materials with steam at controlled temperatures; (3) uniform application of steam and/or water; (4) an extrusion assembly for process materials; (5) temperature control during the whole process; (6) control of residence time in the extruder to optimize temperature, shear, and agitation; (7) control of exudate shape and size; and (8) availability of equipment to dry, cool, size, and

treat the product through the addition of flavors, vitamins, fats, etc. A typical arrangement is shown in Fig. 8. Extrusion can be used for production of foods, feeds (e.g., pet foods, fish feed, and gelatinized cereals for ruminants), and products for industrial purposes (e.g., pregelatinized or modified starches and flours). The extruded foods include breakfast cereals and snacks; fortified cereal extrudates; instant or quick-cooking noodles or pasta; alimentary pastes from non-wheat flours; crackers, wafers, crisp-bread products; extruded flour for baking; and miscellaneous foods.

V. Industrial Uses

Traditionally, cereals are considered food and feed grains. However, large and widespread production beyond the demands of the principal markets have encouraged exploration of industrial uses of cereals. Cereal grains, milled products, and by-products of milling are finding increasing use in a variety of nonfood applications.

About 1 ton of wheat straw is produced along with 1 ton of wheat grain. Total production of straw pulp on a worldwide basis is about 14 million metric tons. By using better collection methods, the straw potential could be increased to 1 billion metric tons. Only

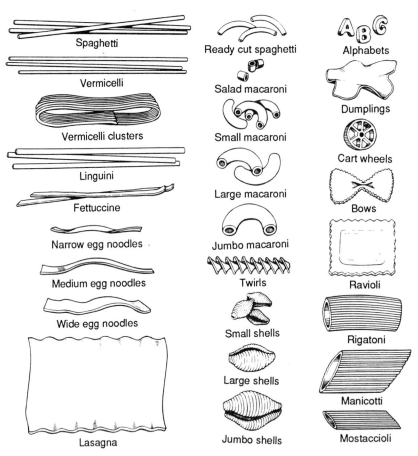

FIGURE 7 Pasta products. (Courtesy of Conagra Co. Ltd., Omaha, NE.)

10% of the world's straw used for pulp production would be about 30 million tons of pulp. Residues and by-products of cereals are excellent sources of furfural, a basic raw material in many industrial technologies.

Cereal biomass can be pyrolyzed to produce sugar, olefinic compounds, charcoal, and gaseous fuel. Carbohydrates can be hydrolyzed to fermentable sugars to make ethanol and then converted into ethylene and butadiene. Biomass can be digested by anaerobic bacteria to produce methane. Biomass can be reacted with carbon monoxide, using heat, pressure, and a catalyst to produce an oil. Lignin can be used to make phenol in benzene production.

Cereal polymers (carbohydrates and proteins) can be converted into monomers, which can provide the raw material and flexibility as basic raw materials. Equally promising are novel uses of undegraded polymers.

Most industrial uses of cereals depend on the properties of the main component, starch, which ranks in many developed countries as a major industrial chemical. Raw materials and technology exist for basing a portion of the chemical industry on four fermentation products: ethanol, isopropanol, *n*-butanol, and 2,3-butanediol. Industrial uses constitute an economic market for grain ethanol, in which the product is competitive with ethanol derived from petroleum and natural-gas liquids.

Wheat or low-grade wheat flours can be separated into many products that find wide applications.

Wheat flours. In paper sizing and coating; as adhesive or laminating mixtures in corrugated box boards, paper bonding, plywood industry, decorative woods and veneers, detergent formulations.

Starch. In paper sizing and coating, fiber or textile finishing, printing mixtures, paper bonding, adhesives, plywood industry, alcohol production.

Gluten. In paper manufacture, surface-active agents, adhesives, monosodium glutamate and glutamic acid, edible and/or soluble packaging fabrics, coatings, gums, sausage casings.

Wheat germ. In production of antibiotics, vitamins, pharmaceuticals, skin conditioners.

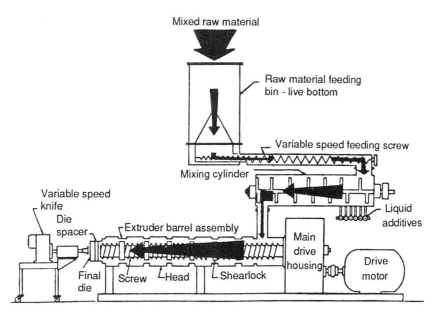

FIGURE 8 Typical arrangement of line bin feeder, preconditioner, HTST extrusion cooker. (Courtesy of Wenger Mfg. Co., Inc., Sabetha, KS; from Smith and Ben-Gera, 1980.)

Wheat bran. In production of furfural, in the production and/or carriers of enzymes, antibiotics, and vitamins.

Residues remaining after the harvest of crops have been proposed as an energy source. Wheat cropping typically produces 2.5 tons of residue per acre. The benefits are limited by high energy costs to collect, transport, and process the residues. The energy to collect 1 ton of wheat straw is 50,500 kcal.

The conversion of glucose to ethanol is represented by the formula:

$$C_6H_{12}O_6 \rightarrow 2C_2H_5OH + 2CO_2.$$

180 g	92 g
673 kcal	655 kcal
12.88 lb	1 gal (84,356 BTU)

The production of alcohol as a source of fuel has been the subject of many investigations. Some surveys concluded that ethanol production uses more energy than it produces. Differences of opinion on the energy balance derive mainly from variations in interpretation.

The result depends strongly on assumptions about use of crop residues for fuel and the rating of gasohol (a 90:10 mixture of fuel and alcohol). In terms of total nonrenewable energy, gasohol is close to the energy break-even point. On the other hand, in terms of petroleum or petroleum suitable energy, "gasohol" is an energy producer, as most energy inputs into the process can be supplied by nonpetroleum sources like coal.

Bibliography

Matz, S. A. (1991). "The Chemistry and Technology of Cereals as Food and Feed," 2nd ed. Van Nostrand Reinhold, New York.

Morton, I. D. (ed.) (1987). "Cereals in a European Context." VCH, New York.

Pomeranz, Y. (ed.) (1972–1990). "Advances in Cereal Science and Technology," 10 Vols. Am. Assoc. Cereal Chem., St. Paul, MN.

Pomeranz, Y. (1987). "Modern Cereal Science and Technology. VCH, New York. [Japanese Translation, PAN, Tokyo, 1989]

Pomeranz, Y. (ed.) (1988). "Wheat Chemistry and Technology," 3rd ed., 2 Vols. Am. Assoc. Cereal Chem., St. Paul, MN.

Pomeranz, Y. (ed.) (1989). "Wheat is Unique." Am. Assoc. Cereal Chem., St. Paul, MN.

Pomeranz, Y. (1991). "Functional Properties of Food Components," 2nd ed. Academic Press, San Diego, CA.

Pomeranz, Y., and Meloan, C. E. (1994). "Food Analysis: Theory and Practice," 3rd ed. Chapman and Hall, New York.

Wildlife Management

JAMES A. BAILEY, *Colorado State University*

I. Wildlife Values
II. Wildlife Biology
III. Types of Wildlife
IV. Population Dynamics
V. Management Practices
VI. Wildlife Policy and Administration

Glossary

Climax-adapted species Species adapted to, and dependent upon, habitat resources occurring within a climax biotic community

Climax biotic community Terminal, relatively stable biotic community that results from progressive development of vegetation and soils following land disturbance

Density dependent Correlated with population density, this usually applies to population characteristics, especially rates of reproduction and mortality; generally, reproduction declines and mortality increases with increased density

Density independent Not correlated with population density, especially population characteristics; in particular, weather events and sudden degradation of habitat may cause these stochastic population changes

Habitat resource Any of the food, cover, or other characteristics of a habitat that are used and needed by a wildlife population

Limiting resource Habitat resource that is inadequate, in quantity or quality, for the needs of a wildlife population; the lack of this resource thus limits the size, productivity, or quality of the population

Population density Number of animals in a population relative to the amount of available habitat, or of habitat resources

Species of developmental stages Species adapted to, and dependent upon, habitat resources occurring within temporary stages of biotic succession that follow land disturbance

Wildlife management is practiced to attain the goals of wildlife conservation, which is the wise use of wild lands, plants, and animals. Wildlife management is the art of making land produce valuable populations of wildlife in relatively natural biotic communities. Vertebrate animals are usually emphasized in wildlife management; but it is clear that maintaining suitable environments for wild vertebrates always requires some emphasis on plants and invertebrates as well.

I. Wildlife Values

Wildlife are managed to enhance their positive values to mankind and to minimize their negative values. Positive values include commercial, recreational, biotic, scientific, aesthetic, and social values. Negative values are the damages caused by wildlife to private and public properties and the costs for controlling those damages.

The commercial value of wildlife includes the value of wild animals and their parts (hides, antlers, etc.) to subsistence users and as articles for trade or sale. In addition, diverse entrepreneurs realize profits by providing equipment, lodging, food, transportation, and various services to people who pursue wildlife, usually for recreational purposes. Many rural economies depend upon subsistence and other commercial values from wildlife. The value of wildlife parts, and the value of income to wildlife-related business, may be calculated in dollars to measure commercial value of wildlife.

The recreational value of wildlife consists of the enjoyment, and the physical and mental well-being, that are realized when people hunt, fish, view, or study wildlife. This value may be measured by these recreators' "willingness to pay" for wildlife-related experiences. In countries where wildlife is a publicly owned resource, actual expenses of recreators almost

Encyclopedia of Agricultural Science, Volume 4 Copyright © 1994 by Academic Press, Inc. All rights of reproduction in any form reserved. **537**

always underestimate willingness to pay. Economists have developed indirect methods for estimating untested willingness to pay and provide a dollar-based measure of recreational value of wildlife for comparisons with other resources.

The contributions of wildlife to maintaining valuable ecosystems constitute a biotic value. Wildlife activities including predation, scavenging, seed dispersal, pollination, and soil tillage contribute to maintaining the diversity of species in ecosystems and may prevent some populations from extirpation or from becoming detrimentally large.

Populations of wild animals are used to study processes including natural selection and evolution, population dynamics, competition, epidemiology, and zoogeography. The resulting knowledge is applied to practical problems and enhances science, education, philosophy, and even religion.

The social value of wildlife consists of benefits accruing to communities. As people realize economic and other values from wildlife, they may become more satisfied, productive, and cooperative members of society. Moreover, communities offering abundant wildlife experiences will attract professionals, including doctors, lawyers, and engineers, who would otherwise practice in more developed and lucrative cities.

The aesthetic value of wildlife is most personal and diverse. It includes the contribution of wildlife to literature, music, and art, as well as the beauty in seeing or hearing wild animals. In addition, as people study and understand wildlife, their aesthetic appreciation is expanded. There is beauty that meets, not only the eye and ear, but also the educated mind.

Wildlife may create problems for mankind. They may consume or damage agricultural crops, destroy livestock, carry disease to livestock or to humans, deface or damage buildings, among other problems. Direct and indirect methods for controlling these damages may be costly. Wildlife causing such damage are labeled "overabundant".

Since wildlife values are so diverse, and may not be measured in any one scale, such as dollars, the total value of a species population, or of a wildlife community, is difficult to measure for comparing the value of wildlife management against other activities. Replacement costs may be used to measure total wildlife value. Thus, the costs of gaining control of, and managing, sufficient habitat to recreate a wildlife resource would be the total value of the wildlife resource.

II. Wildlife Biology

Successful wildlife management depends upon knowledge of the biology, especially ecology, of wildlife species.

A. Habitat Requirements, Limiting Factors

A suitable habitat is the most basic need of every wildlife species. Each species has evolved a unique set of anatomical, behavioral, and physiological adaptations that determine the habitat resources it may exploit and also will require. Moreover, the sexes and age classes of animals may exploit habitat differently, and habitat needs may vary seasonally. Consequently, habitat requirements are unique and numerous for every species. However, all species need foods including water, cover resources, and a suitable geographic distribution of these habitat resources.

Food and cover resources must be suitably juxtaposed on the landscape to allow a species to use those resources. Many species are highly mobile and may migrate seasonally, so that some habitat resources may be far apart. Other species are sedentary, requiring that their habitat resources occur within a limited area. In addition, proximity of resources may benefit a population by allowing resource exploitation with minimal energy expense or minimal exposure to predation.

While a wildlife species population will require several different habitat resources, the quality of animals, and productivity and number of animals, will usually be limited by an insufficiency of only one or a few of those resources. Most habitat resources will not be limiting. Lands containing limiting habitat resources are termed "critical areas." Impacts that diminish resources on critical areas will diminish a population over a much larger area. Also, management to improve a population's habitat must enhance those habitat resources that limit the population. Enhancement of nonlimiting resources is wasted management.

B. Biotic Succession

Vegetation, an important component of wildlife habitats, may change steadily over many years—altering habitat conditions for wildlife. This natural process of vegetative development follows each episode of land disturbance. Disturbance may be natural (fire, windstorm, flood) or human-caused (logging, land-clearing, overgrazing, prescribed fire). Following disturbance, the species composition and structure of vegetation changes until a plant community of relatively stable species composition is attained. This community is termed climax vegetation. Since wild animals depend (indirectly in the case of carnivores) upon vegetation, the species compositions of wildlife communities also change during vegetative succession toward a climax biotic community.

Wildlife that depend upon early stages of vegetative succession are "disturbance-adapted species." Maintenance of their habitat requires periodic disturbance to maintain early stages of plant succession. Wildlife dependant upon climax vegetation are "climax-adapted." Their habitats require protection from natural or human-caused disturbance. Still other wildlife species require a mixture of vegetative stages. Enhancing their habitat may require disturbance or protection, depending upon which needed stage of vegetation is most scarce at a particular time and location and therefore is limiting the species population.

C. Reproduction

Successful reproduction is critical for (1) offsetting natural mortality and maintaining wildlife populations, and (2) producing annual surpluses of those species that are harvested. Some wildlife species have adapted to their normally high rates of natural mortality by having high reproductive potentials. These species, termed r-selected (selected for a high rate of population increase), may have large litters or clutches and may breed at an early age and more than once per year. Most are small animals, such as rodents, squirrels, and most birds. Populations of r-selected species usually contain a preponderance of young animals because individuals are replaced rapidly. (There is a high turnover rate.) Populations of r-selected species may expand rapidly to utilize temporary habitats, such as those occurring following vegetation disturbance. Other wildlife species have adapted to more stable environments by having low reproductive potentials commensurate with normally low rates of natural mortality. These are termed K-selected species (selected by conditions existing when a population persists near the carrying capacity, K, of the environment). They have small litters or clutches and may breed infrequently and late in life. They are mostly large birds and mammals. Populations of K-selected species normally contain mostly old animals and are relatively stable from year to year. The categories of

r- and K-selected species are useful, but not discrete, as wildlife species exhibit a continuum from very r-selected (i.e., rabbits) to very K-selected (i.e., grizzly bears).

Reproductive success often declines as population size increases (density-dependent reproduction, where density = the number of animals per unit of habitat). Density dependence may result from competition among breeders for habitat resources or from physiological responses to stresses of crowding and competition. Reproductive success may also be influenced by density-independent factors, especially weather that may affect the availabilities of habitat resources or the survival of neonates. Density-independent factors predominately influence reproductive success in r-selected species; density-dependent factors are more important in K-selected species.

D. Mortality

Wild animals are lost from populations by starvation or malnutrition, natural or human-caused accidents, predation, exposure, diseases, and harvest by man. Mortality rates are sometimes density dependent (a greater proportion of the population dies when the population is larger). Also, density-independent mortality occurs due to stochastic events such as severe weather, outbreaks of some diseases, or sudden destruction of habitat. Predation rates may be density independent or may be either positively or negatively correlated with prey density, depending on habitat conditions and on the ratio of predator abundance to prey abundance.

Density dependence results from habitat carrying capacity. As a population increases toward the maximum number of animals that habitat resources can sustain, an increasing proportion of the population becomes vulnerable to most forms of mortality. Particularly in r-selected species, a "doomed surplus" of vulnerable animals is produced annually. Various types of mortality will interact to remove these vulnerable animals. Such mortality factors are compensatory, in that a decline (or increase) of one type of mortality will produce an increase (or decline) of other types of mortality, so that total mortality is unchanged. When harvest by man is compensatory, it is termed "replacive," in that harvest replaces, and does not add to, natural mortality. Harvest is most apt to be replacive for r-selected wildlife with high natural rates of population turnover.

For *K*-selected species, such as large mammals, human harvest may be used to limit population size and achieve high rates of (density-dependent) reproduction. Such harvest is more additive than replacive, although the intended limitation of population size may also achieve lowered rates of (density-dependent) natural mortality in the long term.

III. Types of Wildlife

A. Categories Based on Biology

Some wildlife species have evolved anatomical, physiological, and behavioral characteristics for living in unique environments. These **specialized species** are adapted, but also limited, to a narrow range of environmental conditions. They are quickly reduced or eliminated by alteration of habitat. Other wildlife are **generalized species**. They have large geographic ranges, exist in a variety of habitats, and have diverse food habits. Generalized species adapt readily to most habitat changes.

Climax-adapted species are specialized for living in climax vegetation. They are eliminated by disturbance of the climax. Other wildlife are adapted for living in the vegetation of disturbed sites. **Disturbance-adapted species** decline as vegetation develops toward climax. Management of habitat for these species is described above.

Habitat-interior species do not compete well with the many other species that live near the edges of patches of homogeneous vegetation. They only prosper deep within these patches, and large patch size is a habitat need. In contrast, **edge species** prosper with simultaneous access to the habitat resources of two or more vegetation patches. Environments with numerous, small or narrow patches of vegetation favor edge-adapted species.

Relict populations of wildlife occupy isolated, small areas of suitable habitat, often far from the main range of their species. They may be part of a local fauna and flora representing past climatic conditions. Relict populations usually are small and very sensitive to habitat change or to slight increases in mortality rates. As with all small, isolated populations, they may lose genetic diversity through random selection and may experience depressed reproduction or survival due to inbreeding.

B. Categories Based on Status or Habitat

A sharp rise in extinctions, coincident with expansion of industrialized man, is depleting the earth's biotic resources. Reversing this trend will require a system of habitat reserves in each of the planet's biotic regions. Some rare, high-profile species are legally recognized as **threatened** by, or in immediate danger of, extinction. In the United States, classification as **endangered** currently (1994) requires that a rare species be fully protected and that priority be given to its habitat needs in land management.

In contrast, some wildlife thrive in habitats created by man. These populations are **overabundant** if they damage agricultural crops and other property, kill livestock, or spread diseases to domestic animals or humans. Wildlife damage is controlled by direct reduction of offending animals, by barriers and repellents, and by manipulating habitat to remove critical needs of overabundant wildlife.

Wildlife used and enjoyed by people may be emphasized in land management. These **featured species** include those harvested for recreation or subsistence and those especially sought for viewing by recreators. The take of harvested species usually is regulated to maintain a base population and a sustained harvestable surplus. Featured species are also enhanced indirectly by habitat manipulation or habitat protection.

Generalized species, primarily, have adapted to farms and urban areas. Most **farm wildlife** depend upon limited areas of unused habitat such as windbreaks, hedgerows, roadsides, ditchbanks, and retired acres. Extensive monocultures of cropland, often treated with harmful pesticides, produce little wildlife. Likewise **urban wildlife** depend upon vegetated yards, cemeteries, semi-wild parks, and unused floodplains. In contrast, rangelands and forests sustain a greater variety of wildlife. **Rangeland wildlife** are enhanced by good range management including development of water sources, prevention of overgrazing, and protection of riparian sites. The variety of **forest wildlife** in commercial forests will depend upon the intensity of silviculture. Extensive monocultures of even-aged trees sustain few wild species. In multiple use forestry, timber harvests may be used to develop forest types, stand ages, and patch sizes that will provide habitats for many disturbance-adapted species or may optimize habitat for one or a few featured, disturbance-adapted species. [*See* FOREST ECOLOGY; RANGELAND MANAGEMENT AND PLANNING; SILVICULTURE.]

Many species of wildlife have been transplanted between continents or between major biotic regions of continents. Successful transplants are considered **exotic species**. Exotic wildlife have damaged and destroyed native floras and faunas, especially on oceanic islands and in the Australian region, which have been isolated from competition and evolution on the major continents. Elsewhere, transplants of exotic wildlife have brought failures, successes, and some problems. Of many game birds transplanted into the United States, only three persist; and only one, the ring-necked pheasant, is truly successful. In contrast, many transplants of large hooved mammals into the United States have succeeded. Many of these exotic mammals have modest ranges, as they are controlled by hunting; but the number of exotic hooved mammal species exceeds the number of native hooved mammals in the United States.

IV. Population Dynamics

A wildlife population's rate of increase, r, is determined by the component rates of reproduction, mortality, immigration, and emigration. In small populations within large, ideal habitats, r approaches the species' maximum biotic potential. As a population grows toward limits set by habitat carrying capacity, r usually declines in a density-dependent manner. However, stochastic events may cause small or large variation of r. Density dependence usually predominates in large, homeothermic wildlife in good habitats. Density independence is more common in populations of small, especially heterothermic, vertebrates and in populations in poor habitats or near the edges of their geographic ranges. Density dependence of r may be delayed (correlated with past, rather than current, density). Delayed density dependence occurs when characteristics of the population, or its environment, result from population density, but persist temporarily following a change in density. Delayed density dependence causes populations to fluctuate in alternating periods of abundance and scarcity. In a few populations, these fluctuations are regular and termed "cyclic."

Wildlife populations and habitats are monitored to (1) detect unacceptable changes in abundance, population quality, or habitat condition, and (2) evaluate the efficacies of management practices. Monitored population characteristics include reproduction, animal condition, population sex–age composition, and population size and trend. Monitored habitat characteristics include abundance, distribution, and utilization of habitat resources. Obtaining unbiased and suitably precise estimates of these characteristics requires methods and sampling procedures adapted to local

conditions. A great variety of estimation methods has been developed.

V. Management Practices

A. Habitat Management

Habitat management includes protection or manipulation of habitat, depending upon goals and upon the needs of targeted wildlife species. Knowledge of species' habitat requirements, of local limiting factors, and of successional affinities of species, cited above, is necessary for effective management. Habitat management may be used to increase or to decrease populations of targeted species. Where a small number of species is targeted, many other wildlife species will also be affected. Some will be enhanced; some reduced; and some precluded. Where biodiversity is a primary goal, management must develop and maintain a diversity of vegetation types, successional stages, and patch sizes. Where wildlife production is secondary to other land uses, such as agriculture or forestry, primary land uses may be modified or limited to sustain moderate populations of featured wildlife species.

B. Population Management

Most harvest for commercial or recreational purposes is regulated by state or federal agencies to assure maintenance of suitable base populations. Timing and length of the harvesting season, daily and seasonal limits, methods of taking, and the species, sex, or ages of animals taken may be manipulated to achieve

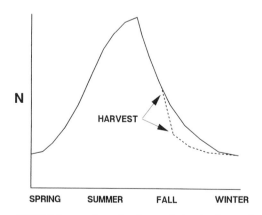

FIGURE 1 Yearly cycle of a population (N) having large recruitment and turnover annually (solid line). Harvest may be applied as replacive mortality without affecting the base population in a subsequent breeding season (dotted line).

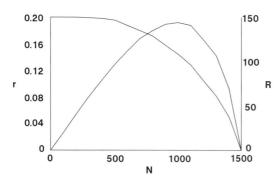

FIGURE 2 Effect of a density-dependent rate of recruitment ($r = R/N$) upon the number of animals recruited (R) to a population (N). In populations with strong density dependence, harvest may be applied as an additive mortality to maintain N at the base population producing the maximum R and maximum harvestable surplus.

harvest goals. Wildlife are also exploited to control overabundant populations.

For populations of r-selected species (usually small game), in which the determinants of r are largely density independent, there are variable but usually large annual surpluses of animals. Harvests usually are conservative, tend to be replacive mortality, and rarely affect base population size (Fig. 1). For populations in which r is more precisely density dependent (usually big game), harvests are more apt to be additive mortality and may be used to regulate base population size. With a density-dependent r, maintaining a base population somewhat below the carrying capacity of the habitat will maximize the sustained yield of animals per year (Fig. 2).

Wildlife are transplanted to establish populations in unoccupied but suitable ranges and to augment the genetic diversities of small, isolated populations. Rarely, diseases of especially valuable wildlife are controlled by capturing and vaccinating animals or by feeding or injecting drugs to control diseases or parasites.

VI. Wildlife Policy and Administration

Ownership and management of wildlife varies greatly among nations. In the United States, wildlife are the collective property of all the people. Government agencies, as public trustees, manage and protect wildlife. However, much wildlife habitat is privately owned and controlled, creating conflicts between public and private goals.

States have retained responsibilities for managing most wildlife populations within their boundaries. State agencies are highly variable, but usually include programs for regulating recreational and commercial harvests, enforcing wildlife laws, monitoring populations, monitoring and advising on impacts of land uses upon wildlife, public education, and advising landowners on habitat management and on controlling wildlife damage. Policies for most state wildlife agencies are formulated by appointed commissions. Most funding of state programs is derived from sales of hunting and fishing licenses and from taxes on purchases of hunting and fishing equipment.

Several federal agencies manage wildlife habitats on federal lands and are responsible for certain wildlife populations. In particular, threatened and endangered species, migratory waterfowl, and marine fishes and mammals are managed by the federal government, with cooperation from the states. Federal management agencies include the Fish and Wildlife Service, National Park Service, and Bureau of Indian Affairs within the Department of Interior; the Forest Service, Soil Conservation Service, and the Animal and Plant Inspection Service within the Department of Agriculture; and the National Marine Fisheries Service within the Department of Commerce.

Bibliography

Anderson, S. H. (1991). "Managing our Wildlife Resources." Prentice–Hall, NJ.
Bailey, J. A. (1984). "Principles of Wildlife Management." Wiley, New York.
Peek, J. M. (1986). "A Review of Wildlife Management." Prentice–Hall, NJ.
Robinson, W. L., and Bolen, E. G. (1984). "Wildlife Ecology and Management." Macmillan, New York.
Soule', M. E. (ed.) (1986). "Conservation Biology: The Science of Scarcity and Diversity." Sinauer Assoc., MA.

Women in Agriculture

CORNELIA BUTLER FLORA, *Virginia Polytechnic Institute and State University*

Glossary

Alienation of land Privatizing land and making it available for sale

Division of labor When productive activities are divided by the characteristics of the workers. In the social division of labor, some people produce one good or service and other people another. In the task division of labor, the production process is broken down into its component tasks, which are assigned to different types of workers

Hacienda Extensive agriculture production system

Mestizo Individual of mixed ancestry; in Latin America, often the progeny of indigenous groups with colonizers

Role Set of expectations governing the behavior of persons holding particular positions in society

Role complementarity When the activities and responsibilities of men and women work together toward common goals without hierarchical implications for the differences

W omen have always been active in agriculture. Early archeological data suggest women were the first to domesticate plants, bringing the seeds they had gathered near to their dwellings to be planted and raised on a systematic basis to ensure food supply.

Further, it is suggested that women were crucial in the domestication of animals, which in turn contributed toward creating agricultural surplus through the use of animal traction and manure to increase productivity, as well as the products of milk, fiber, and meat provided by the animals themselves. Women's actual agricultural activities have changed dramatically over time, yet women's contributions to agricultural production continue to be of importance. Increased agricultural productivity allowed for the social division of labor and more and more individuals to be freed from the demands of food production, thus creating ruling and warrior classes. Within agriculture, division of labor also occurred.

I. Traditional Division of Labor

Historical accounts of Europe, Africa, Asia, and Latin America all suggest the importance of women in agricultural production. We have evidence from drawings and farm records of women's complementary activities within the feudal system as well as in more independent farming systems and political structures.

A. Role Complementarity

Contemporary anthropological accounts also stress the role complementarity of women in traditional agriculture. In most agriculturally based households, it was crucial that everyone work, young, old, male, and female. The division of labor was based, in part, upon the physical abilities of the individuals, so that the old were spared from extremely heavy work as were the very young. In large measure what work was done by age and gender was culturally determined. What was men's work in one culture, such as, for example, the care of milk cows, was women's work in another culture. Almost always land clearing and plowing, which were viewed as heavy work, was a male-dominated activity, but there are cultures in which women engaged in these activities as well.

Roles in agriculture were learned through apprenticeship, which was often gender specific. There were women's knowledge streams and men's knowledge streams. Women, for example, would know how to choose the best seed to save over the hungry season to be planted again for the next harvest, as well as the way to care for small animals to ensure survival of the healthiest when food supply was limited. In Honduras, in an area of recurrent drought where feed is limited, the practice in hog rearing is to let shoats suckle from the sow for the first month. Natural selection occurs, and two-thirds of the shoats die. The shoats that survive the first few months then receive supplemental feed and care. Given the limited resources available, the high shoat mortality is not a problem and, in fact, helps assure that those shoats in which the family production system invests will then survive to adulthood and serve as a source of savings for the family. Animal husbandry and the local knowledge to maximize local resources is often in women's hands.

Further, women often gather herbs and medicines from forested areas. Current studies in a variety of areas suggest that women are able to identify nearly six times as many different species of indigenous plants than are men. This is an important part of maintaining genetic diversity within the biosphere. [See LABOR.]

B. Community Interdependence

In more traditional communities, much of agriculture was based on a community division of labor, not just on a family division of labor. Complicated labor exchanges were negotiated by men and by women, often with members of the same sex. Such exchanges involved direct exchanges of labor at times of particular high labor demand, as well as simple gifts, particularly of food, seed, and plant cuttings, that could be utilized to maintain agricultural productivity. Very often women were in charge of the less-formal exchange relationships that were vital in maintaining communities and protecting them from the necessity of becoming totally dependent on the sale of labor. Such informal exchanges helped maintain smallholder agricultural production.

II. Integration into the World System

A. Impacts of Changes in Labor Use

Traditional communities were based on subsistence production with very little for sale. As these communities were penetrated by world markets, the division of labor in agriculture changed dramatically. In much of the colonized world, particularly Africa and Latin America, the first impact on traditional farming systems was the removal of male labor to work in seasonal plantation agriculture. Men were needed for the sugar harvest and the banana harvest. A few women followed to provide the necessary domestic functions of food and laundry. But generally, women remained at home in charge of the subsistence production plots and animal production activities.

That disruption in traditional farming systems intensified as harvests of export crops such as coffee and cotton utilized entire families as laborers. Perhaps the most disruption to the complementary division of labor by gender occurred in those areas in Africa, Latin America, and parts of Asia where male labor was pulled into mining activities. Whereas in the seasonal plantation crops, men could return home for plowing and land clearing, when they worked in the mines they were often gone for years at a time, which left women in charge of those farming systems. Particularly, in parts of southern Africa, where strict rules regulated the movement of people across national boundaries, agriculture became an almost entirely female phenomenon.

Integration into a world economic system changed land use—from subsistence crops and those destined for domestic markets to export crops. In much of Latin America, for example, large areas of very good land had been given out as Spanish or Portuguese land grants and were farmed extensively with livestock, predominately cattle. Indigenous peoples and *mestizos* had use rights to land, on which they raised subsistence crops in exchange for the labor they provided to the *hacendado*.

B. Impacts on the Shift to Export Crops

Different areas of Latin America entered the export crop market at different times. For example, the islands of the Caribbean were settled by colonists from several nations primarily because of their prime conditions for sugar production. Those areas were almost always export oriented. As a result on those islands, particularly in the English-speaking Caribbean, women produce most of the food crops. Male labor is used for the harvest of the plantation crops, particularly sugarcane.

In other areas of Latin America, few export crops were planted until the era of land reform, beginning in the early 1960s. Most land reforms propagated during that period was intended to make land more productive, not redistribute land. Under the threat of expropriation, many large landowners shifted from extensive agricultural systems to more intensive ones, including soybeans, cotton, even more sugarcane—all crops aimed for foreign markets. As a result, local populations, who had farmed the land as part of their usufruct rights, were displaced. Many moved to the cities, whereas others moved to less-desirable highland areas where they found that the traditional practices that worked well on flat ground tended to erode badly hillside lands. Others moved to jungle and rain forest areas, with equally disastrous results.

In more marginalized hillside populations, men continued to provide labor for the export crops, although increasingly, as in places like Brazil, women have done so as well. In the new cropping systems that emerged in the fragile highland areas, there was a marked division between his crops and her crops. She raised vegetables and tree crops around the house, and he raised row crops and commercial tree crops further away from the household living area. There was also an increase in the division of labor in animal raising, varying by area. Traditionally men are in charge of large animals, which required a certain capital investment, and women maintain the production of small animals, using them for both household consumption and sale in times of economic stress.

C. Impacts of Alienation of Land

A third important trend that has affected the division of labor by gender worldwide has been the movement toward the alienation of land. In traditional agricultural communities, much land was controlled in common with village leaders assigning land use on a year by year basis. In this system, women had access to land through traditional use rights. As land became titled and later sold, it was almost always titled in the name of the man in the household rather than the man and woman. The new private plots in the reformed areas and in new colonization and transmigration areas favored men's crops. There was seldom land left for the women's gardens, which were often

vital for household nutrition and even survival. Women's collective production efforts were eliminated entirely. Often the animals that women would pasture, such as small ruminants, also were not allocated land for grazing.

These three trends have tended to break down the role complementarity previously present in traditional agricultural systems. One can no longer assume what men will do or women will do in agriculture. A lot depends on the differential factor markets by gender. For example, if there is a place where male labor pays more, the men may migrate. On the other hand, if women will work for less, often large exporters will hire primarily women to do the field work. Thus, there have been enormous shifts and breakdowns in the subsistence-oriented family and community-based agricultural production system.

III. Current Characteristics of Women in Agriculture Worldwide

Not only has there been traditional divisions of labor by gender in agricultural production, which have varied enormously over time and space, there has also been enormous variation of income streams within households. Different members of farming households have different sources of income, and those sources of income have different uses depending on the gender. In pre-World War II American agriculture, women very often had the egg and butter money earned by raising chickens or milking the cows and marketing the product in local markets.

Women's production was used either to barter for other kinds of food the family needed, such as coffee or salt at the local store, or for cash when necessary for other family necessities. Very often such cash could be used for special items of household consumption or even savings for children's schooling. Male income would be more likely to be reinvested in the farm itself.

A. Income Streams by Gender

In developing countries we find a wide variation in the intrahousehold income streams. In some areas household income is pooled. In other areas, women lend their husbands money at interest. The sale or home use of different crops is decided by different members of the family.

Income that goes directly to women in agricultural households is more likely to be used for household necessities, particularly children's food, clothing, and schooling. Men's income is often used for a variety of male bonding activities, such as drinking, that may contribute to community solidarity but not to household well-being. As a result of these different income flows, increasing a farm family's income does not equally benefit all family members. The existence of patriarchy, that is to say, the dominance of the oldest male in the household, tends to mean unequal and sometimes arbitrary distribution of income within any particular household.

B. Resource Access by Gender

The impact of unequal access to resources combined with heavy work loads for all household members can be judged by looking at the sex ratio in rural farm areas. There are generally many more men than women, despite the overall tendency of women to outnumber men as adults. Women are more likely to leave farm areas, as they feel the hard work that they put in on a farm, particularly in livestock operations such as dairy, is not worth the limited return in cash and respect that they receive. Thus, the constraints to participation in agricultural production for many women in advanced industrial societies come from a relatively high labor demand, little chance of leisure, and little control over resources for production. Although figures for many developed countries show women as major landowners, this gives a distorted picture. Women who own land are very often widows who are simply owning land as placeholders for their sons, who take on the major decision making and control of the agricultural production practices.

IV. Technology and Women

Agricultural technology has been developed to make both labor and land produce more per unit. However, most of that technology has been channeled toward men. For example, when chicken production became highly technical and market oriented, the technology was brought by the extension service to the males of the family, and women lost their source of separate incomes, although they would often do the work. Access to the credit needed to expand the chicken production in the high-technology buildings with the other high-technology inputs were aimed at men. In addition, the technical assistance that came either from the agricultural extension service or, later, the poultry integrators (large multinational corporations who purchased the chickens), was also almost entirely aimed at males. And the milk check, the chicken check, or the egg check would be written in the name of the male head of household.

In the developing world as well, technological innovation has tended to disadvantage women compared to men. The fact that women's income streams were not recognized often meant that income moved from female hands to male hands as more official marketing channels were put into place, such as milk production in the *altiplano* of Bolivia. Further, the labor that women did that gave them their income streams, such as rice hulling in parts of Africa and Asia, was, when mechanized, taken over by men, leaving women without the hard work, but also without the important income that it generated.

A number of studies in different parts of the world have shown that farm women produce as much as farm men when they have access to similar resources. This includes education, access to markets, access to credit, and access to technical assistance. New inputs and marketing channels of agriculture are gendered, and they are biased almost always toward men and away from women.

V. Gendered Patterns of Production

Despite the gendering of the factor markets necessary for production, including land, labor, and capital markets, a number of different gender patterns in agriculture have emerged and are present in different areas and in different proportions. The first is separate, different agricultural enterprises. This occurs most often in Africa but also in parts of Latin America and the Caribbean, where men will have particular crops for particular markets and women will have quite different crops with quite different markets.

The second pattern is separate, similar agricultural enterprises. For example, both may raise vegetables. In the Caribbean, men may raise vegetables for a world market, whereas women may raise vegetables for the local market. The first pattern has implications for agricultural research and extension in that there is a tendency to focus only on the crops males raise. The second pattern has implications for agricultural research and extension in that, particularly in the fruits and vegetables, those for a local market can have different characteristics than those for markets where extensive shipping is required. Thus, they will use different varieties of the same species.

A third pattern involves separate tasks within the same enterprise. This often occurs in developed countries, as well as in developing countries, where men will be in charge of plowing, women in charge of seed selection, both do planting, both do harvesting, men do tilling, and women do postharvest processing.

A fourth pattern, much less common, is shared tasks in the same enterprise. Although such ungendered task sharing is occurring in Canada, the United States, and Europe, this pattern has actually decreased as increasing stress on farm incomes has forced men and women off the farm to seek outside income. Interestingly enough, in many rural areas, women have an advantage in terms of off-farm employment. Thus, men take over many of the jobs that they once shared with their wives.

The final pattern, which is increasing in many developing countries and in certain parts of the developed world, are female-run enterprises that are both the de facto (the enterprise has a male head of household but the women actually runs it because the male is gone for all or most of the year) and the de jure female-headed enterprises (the land and resources are legally in the woman's name). De jure female farms are much less common. They tend to be present in developed countries where there is an increasing number of women choosing to engage in agriculture on their own.

VI. Implications for Agricultural Change

The recognition of the role of women in agriculture, as landowners, agricultural managers, and agricultural workers, is extremely important in understanding how agriculture will change over time. For example, women agricultural workers are very prevalent in export crops production in many developing countries, especially in harvesting and immediate postharvest processing. Women tend to be used because they are a cheaper, more docile labor force than men for a variety of reasons due to segmentation of the labor market. In many developed countries, on the other hand, male migrant laborers serve the same function and may displace female local workers.

Agricultural research will be different if it recognizes the role of women. It may change the types of crops or animal enterprises that are researched, and it might change the characteristics that are bred for or the type of farming practices that are developed, depending on recognition of the differential needs of different types of producers.

Agricultural extension would change if there was recognition of the types of agricultural work that women actually do and the fact that "trickle across" does not work. If women carry out the tasks, then women need to be directly trained to do them.

Agricultural marketing would also change if there was an awareness of what women actually do in agriculture. For example, if women do the work, agricultural marketing that allows them to receive the cash for the product would lead to increased and more efficient production. Utilizing women's groups for marketing or including women in existing agricultural marketing cooperatives as a specific policy might be very important in a number of situations.

In value-added agriculture, understanding who does what when can be extremely important. Value-added practices, such as cheesemaking in a number of areas, often takes away from what women traditionally did to earn income by mechanizing the process and turning it over to men. On the other hand, a number of artisanry or rustic development projects which have women use very traditional means to process food after it is produced may add to women's work, but not to their incomes. Thus, value-added strategies must include awareness of not only who does what, but who has control over which resources in agricultural production.

Finally, recognizing the role of women in agriculture has enormous implications for how agricultural communities are organized. It is important to recognize women's role as wage laborers and their need for the kinds of services that facilitate their participation in the labor force, such as health care and child care as well as organizing agricultural communities, particularly regarding natural resource management. It is very important to include women in natural resource management, as they often have particular interests in common property as well as in individual property.

VII. Sustainable Agriculture and Women

Sustainable agriculture contributes to the survival of farm families on the land, maintains and improves environmental quality, and maintains and improves agricultural communities and the quality of life for individuals in them, as well as in urban areas. Agriculture, as part of many watersheds, is also important for maintaining a safe water supply, as well as a safe food supply.

Sustainable agriculture often uses a wide variety of new technologies in new ways. To be successful, it must be aware of the gendered division of labor, as well as control over resources by gender. Sustainable agriculture demands a community commitment as well as an individual commitment toward social change. Local knowledge of both men and women is important in developing a more sustainable agriculture. Women's knowledge of biodiversity as well as practices that sustain the soil and maintain the water supply will be crucial in this. [See SUSTAINABLE AGRICULTURE.]

Ecofeminism states that women have a particular concern and linkage to the soil and animals and, thus, an inbred desire to sustain and protect them. Those who are antiessentialists in viewing women and the land point out that there are cultural reasons why women would be more concerned about sustainable agriculture than would men, who often have a shorter time frame in seeking profits. Certainly, we can attribute much of the degradation of land to male agricultural practices, such as the suitcase farming that went on in the western United States that helped set up the dust bowl. But this may be because men had control over the land, not because men are inherently less sustainability oriented than women.

VIII. Conclusions

Women have been, and continue to be, active in agriculture as workers, owners, and managers of both common agricultural land and individually held agricultural resources. Understanding the specificity of women's activities can help make agriculture more efficient and effective as resources are developed and targeted to the part of the population that can best use it. But because gender is a social phenomenon, it must be understood in context. There is little we can generalize about women in agriculture worldwide, except that it is important to take what they do into account.

Bibliography

Deere, C. D. (1990). "Household and Class Relations: Peasants and Landlords in Northern Peru." University of California Press, Berkeley.

Feldstein, H. S., and Poats, S. V. (eds.) (1989). "Working Together: Gender Analysis in Agriculture." Kumarian Press, West Hartford, CT.

Fink, D. (1992). "Agrarian Women: Wives and Mothers in Rural Nebraska 1880–1940." Univ. North Carolina Press, Chapel Hill.

Gladwin, C. H. (ed.) (1991). "Structural Adjustment and African Women Farmers." Univ. Florida Press, Gainesville.

Haney, W. G., and Knowles, J. B. (eds.) (1988). "Women and Farming: Changing Roles, Changing Structures." Westview Press, Boulder, CO.

Jensen, J. M. (1991). "Promise to the Land: Essays on Rural Women." Univ. New Mexico Press, Albuquerque.

Poats, S. V., Schmink, M., and Spring, A. (eds.) (1988). "Gender Issues in Farming Systems Research and Extension." Westview Press, Boulder, CO.

Wood Properties

JERROLD E. WINANDY, *USDA-Forest Service, Forest Products Laboratory,[1] Wisconsin*

I. Wood Structure
II. Physical Properties
III. Mechanical Properties
IV. Factors Affecting Properties of Wood
V. Properties and Grades of Sawn Lumber

Glossary

Allowable property Value of a property normally published for design use; allowable properties are identified with grade descriptions and standards, and they reflect the orthotropic structure of wood and anticipated end uses

Anisotropic Exhibiting different properties along different axes; in general, fibrous materials such as wood are anisotropic

Annual growth ring Layer of wood growth put on a tree during a single growing season. In the temperate zone, the annual growth rings of many species (e.g., oaks and pines) are readily distinguished because of differences in the cells formed during the early and late parts of the season; in some temperate zone species (e.g., black gum and sweetgum) and many tropical species, annual growth rings are not easily recognized

Diffuse-porous wood Certain hardwoods in which the pores tend to be uniformly sized and distributed throughout each annual ring or to decrease in size slightly and gradually toward the outer border of the ring

Earlywood Portion of the annual growth ring that is formed during the early part of the growing season; it is usually less dense and mechanically weaker than latewood

Hardwoods General botanical group of trees that has broad leaves in contrast to the conifers or soft-

woods; term has no reference to the actual hardness of the wood

Latewood Portion of the annual growth ring that is formed after the earlywood formation has ceased; it is usually denser and mechanically stronger than earlywood

Lumber Product of the saw and planing mill manufactured from a log through the process of sawing, resawing to width, passing lengthwise through a standard planing machine, and crosscutting to length

Orthotropic Having unique and independent properties in three mutually orthogonal (perpendicular) planes of symmetry; a special case of anisotropy

Ring-porous woods Group of hardwoods in which the pores are comparatively large at the beginning of each annual ring and decrease in size more or less abruptly toward the outer portion of the ring, thus forming a distinct inner zone of pores, the earlywood, and an outer zone with smaller pores, the latewood

Softwoods General botanical group of trees that in most cases has needlelike or scalelike leaves (the conifers); term has no reference to the actual hardness of the wood

Wood is an extremely versatile material with a wide range of physical and mechanical properties among the many species of wood. It is also a renewable resource with an exceptional strength-to-weight ratio. Wood is a desirable construction material because the energy requirements of wood for producing a usable end-product are much lower than those of competitive materials, such as steel, concrete, or plastic.

I. Wood Structure

A. Microstructure

The primary structural building block of wood is the tracheid or fiber cell. Cells vary from 16 to 42 μm in

[1]The Forest Products Laboratory is maintained in cooperation with the University of Wisconsin. This article was written and prepared by U.S. Government employees on official time, and it is therefore in the public domain and not subject to copyright.

diameter and from 870 to 4000 μm long. Thus, a cubic centimeter of wood could contain more than 1.5 million wood cells. When packed together they form a strong composite. Each individual wood cell is even more structurally advanced because it is actually a multilayered, filament-reinforced, closed-end tube (Fig. 1) rather than just a homogeneous-walled, nonreinforced straw. Each individual cell has four distinct cell wall layers (Primary, S_1, S_2, and S_3). Each layer is composed of a combination of three chemical polymers: cellulose, hemicellulose, and lignin (Fig. 1). The cellulose and hemicellulose are linear polysaccharides (i.e., hydrophilic multiple-sugars), and the lignin is an amorphous phenolic (i.e., a three-dimensional hydrophobic adhesive). Cellulose forms long unbranched chains, and hemicellulose forms short branched chains. Lignin encrusts and stiffens these polymers.

Because carbohydrate and phenolic components of wood are assembled in a layered tubular or cellular manner with a large cell cavity, specific gravity of wood can vary immensely. Wood excels as a viable building material because the layered tubular structure provides a large volume of voids (void volume), it has an advantageous strength-to-weight ratio, and it has other inherent advantages, such as corrosion resistance, fatigue resistance, low cost, and ease-of-modification at the job site.

B. Macrostructure

The cross-section of a tree is divided into three broad categories consisting of the bark, wood, and cambium

(Fig. 2). Bark is the outer layer and is composed of a dead outer phloem of dry corky material and a thin inner phloem of living cells. Its primary functions are protection and nutrient conduction. The thickness and appearance of bark vary substantially depending on the species and age of the tree.

Wood, or xylem, is composed of the inner sections of the trunk. The primary functions of wood are support and nutrient conduction and storage. Wood can be divided into two general classes: sapwood and heartwood. Sapwood is located next to the cambium. It functions primarily in food storage and the mechanical transport of sap. The radial thickness of sapwood is commonly 35 to 50 mm but may be 75 to 150 mm for some species. Heartwood consists of an inner core of wood cells that have changed, both chemically and physically, from the cells of the outer sapwood. The cell cavities of heartwood may also contain deposits of various materials that frequently give heartwood a much darker color. Extractive deposits formed during the conversion of living sapwood to dead heartwood often make the heartwood of some species more durable in conditions that may induce decay.

The cambium is a continuous ring of reproductive tissue located between the sapwood and the inner layer of the bark. Usually, it is 1 to 10 cells wide depending on the season. All wood and bark cells are aligned or stacked radially because each cell in a radial line originated from the same cambial cell.

1. Growth

Growth in trees is affected by the soil and environmental conditions with which the tree must exist and

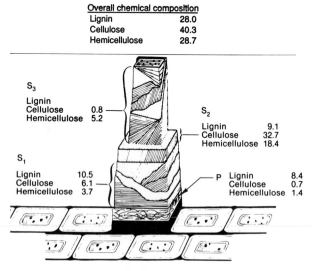

FIGURE 1 Microfibril orientation for each cell wall layer of Scotch pine with chemical composition as percentage of total weight. Cell wall layers are primary (P), S_1, S_2, and S_3.

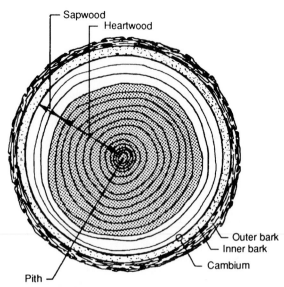

FIGURE 2 Elements of macrostructure normally visible without magnification.

contend. Growth is accomplished by cell division. As new cells form, they are pushed either to the inside to become wood cells or to the outside to become bark cells. As the diameter of the tree increases, new cells are also occasionally retained in the cambium to account for increasing cambial circumference. Also, as the tree diameter increases, additional bark cells are pushed outward, and the outer surface becomes cracked and ridged, forming the bark patterns characteristic of each species.

The type and rate of growth vary between earlywood and latewood cells. Earlywood cells have relatively large cavities and thin walls, whereas latewood cells have smaller cavities and thicker walls. Because void volume is related to density and density is related to lumber strength, latewood is sometimes used to judge the quality or strength of some species. Earlywood is lighter in weight and color, softer, and weaker than latewood; it shrinks less across the grain and more lengthwise along the grain than does latewood.

2. Growth Rings

Growth rings vary in width depending on species and site conditions. Rings formed during short or dry seasons are thinner than those formed when growing conditions are more favorable. Also, rings formed in shady conditions are usually thinner than those formed by the same species in sunny conditions. It is commonly believed that the age of a tree may be determined by counting these rings. However, this method can lead to errors because abnormal environmental conditions can cause a tree to produce multiple-growth increments or even prevent growth entirely for a period.

3. Knots

As a tree grows, branches develop laterally from the trunk. These branches produce gross deviations in the normal grain of the trunk and result in knots when the log is sawn into lumber or timber. Knots are classified in two categories: intergrown knots and encased or loose knots. Intergrown knots are formed by living branches. Encased knots occur when branches die and the wound is surrounded by the growing trunk. Knots result in grain deviations, which is significant because straight-grained wood is approximately 10 to 20 times stronger parallel to grain than perpendicular to grain. Accordingly, knot size is a major predictor of sawn-timber strength.

4. Reaction Wood

Reaction wood is the response of a tree to abnormal environmental or physical stresses associated with leaning trees and crooked limbs. It is generally believed to be an attempt by the tree to return the trunk or limbs to a more natural position. In softwoods, reaction wood is called compression wood and results in the production of wood cells rich in phenolic lignin and poor in carbohydrates. It is found on the lower side of the limb or inclined trunk and effectively results in a higher cell wall packing density and high compression strength. Many of the anatomical, chemical, physical, and mechanical properties of reaction wood differ distinctly from those of normal wood. The specific gravity of compression wood is frequently 30 to 40% greater than that of normal wood, but the tensile strength is many times lower. This is why all grading rules restrict compression wood in any form from graded softwood lumber and timber.

II. Physical Properties

Physical properties are the quantitative characteristics of wood and its behavior to external influences other than applied forces. Included here are directional properties, moisture content, dimensional stability, thermal and pyrolytic (fire) properties, density, and electrical, chemical, and decay resistance. Familiarity with physical properties is important because they can significantly influence the performance and strength of wood used in structural applications.

The physical properties of wood most relevant to structural design and performance are discussed in this section. The effects that variations in these properties have on the strength of wood are more fully discussed in Section IV.

A. Directional Properties

Wood is an orthotropic and anisotropic material. Because of the orientation of the wood fibers and the manner in which a tree increases in diameter as it grows, properties vary along three mutually perpendicular axes: longitudinal, radial, and tangential (Fig. 3). The longitudinal axis is parallel to the fiber (grain) direction, the radial axis is perpendicular to the grain direction and normal to the growth rings, and the tangential axis is perpendicular to the grain direction and tangent to the growth rings. Although most wood properties differ in each of these three axis directions, differences between the radial and tangential axes are relatively minor when compared to differences between the radial or tangential axis and the

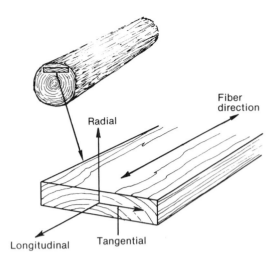

FIGURE 3 Three principal axes of wood with respect to grain direction and growth rings.

longitudinal axis. Property values tabulated for structural applications are often given only for axis directions parallel to grain (longitudinal) and perpendicular to grain (radial or tangential).

B. Moisture Content

The moisture content of wood is defined as the weight of water in wood given as a percentage of ovendry weight. In equation form, moisture content (MC) is expressed as follows:

$$MC = \frac{\text{moist weight} - \text{dry weight}}{\text{dry weight}} \times 100\%. \quad (1)$$

Water is required for the growth and development of living trees and constitutes a major portion of green wood anatomy. In living trees, moisture content depends on the species and the type of wood, and may range from approximately 25% to more than 250% (two and a half times the weight of the dry wood material). In most species, the moisture content of sapwood is higher than that of heartwood.

Water exists in wood either as bound water (in the cell wall) or free water (in the cell cavity). As bound water, it is bonded (via secondary or hydrogen bonds) within the wood cell walls. As free water, it is simply present in the cell cavities. When wood dries, most free water separates at a faster rate than bound water because of accessibility and the absence of secondary bonding. The moisture content at which the cell walls are still saturated but virtually no water exists in the cell cavities is called the fiber saturation point. The fiber saturation point usually varies between 21 and 28%.

Wood is a hygroscopic material that absorbs moisture in a humid environment and loses moisture in a dry environment. As a result, the moisture content of wood is a function of atmospheric conditions and depends on the relative humidity and temperature of the surrounding air. Under constant conditions of temperature and humidity, wood reaches an equilibrium moisture content (EMC) at which it is neither gaining nor losing moisture. The EMC represents a balance point where the wood is in equilibrium with its environment.

In structural applications, the moisture content of wood is almost always undergoing some changes as temperature and humidity conditions vary. These changes are usually gradual and short-term fluctuations that influence only the surface of the wood. The time required for wood to reach the EMC depends on the size and permeability of the member, the temperature, and the difference between the moisture content of the member and the EMC potential of that environment. Changes in moisture content cannot be entirely stopped but can be retarded by coatings or treatments applied to the wood surface.

C. Dimensional Stability

Above the fiber saturation point, wood will not shrink or swell from changes in moisture content because free water is found only in the cell cavity and is not associated within the cell walls. However, wood changes in dimension as moisture content varies below the fiber saturation point. Wood shrinks as it loses moisture below the fiber saturation point and swells as it gains moisture up to the fiber saturation point. These dimensional changes may result in splitting, checking, and warping. The phenomena of dimensional stability and EMC must be understood, recognized, and considered in good timber design.

Dimensional stability of wood is one of the few properties that significantly differs in each of the three axis directions. Dimensional changes in the longitudinal direction between the fiber saturation point and ovendry are between 0.1 and 0.2% and are of no practical significance; however, in reaction or juvenile wood, these percentages may be significantly higher. The combined effects of shrinkage in the tangential and radial axes can distort the shape of wood pieces because of the difference in shrinkage and the curvature of the annual rings (Fig. 4). Generally, tangential shrinkage (varying from 4.4 to 7.8% depending on species) is twice that of radial shrinkage (from 2.2 to 5.6%).

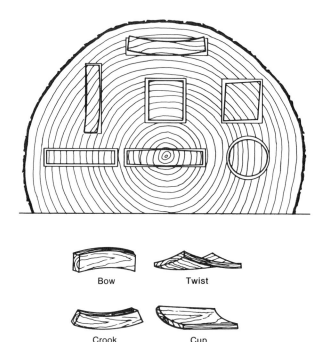

Bow

Twist

Crook

Cup

FIGURE 4 Characteristic shrinkage and distortion of wood as affected by direction of growth rings. Such distortion can result in warp, generally classified as bow, twist, crook, and cup.

D. Thermal Expansion

Thermal expansion of dry wood is positive in all directions; wood expands when heated and contracts when cooled. Wood that contains moisture reacts to temperature changes differently than dry wood.

The linear expansion coefficients of dry wood parallel to grain are generally independent of specific gravity and species and range from approximately 3×10^{-6} to 4.5×10^{-6} per °C. The linear expansion coefficients across the grain (tangential and radial) are in proportion to density and range from approximately 5 to 10 times greater than parallel to grain coefficients.

When moist wood is heated, it tends to expand because of normal thermal expansion and shrink because of moisture loss from increased temperature. Unless the initial moisture content of the wood is very low (3 to 4%), the net dimensional change on heating is negative. Wood at intermediate moisture contents of approximately 8 to 20% will expand when first heated, then gradually shrink to a volume smaller than the initial volume as moisture is lost in the heated condition.

E. Pyrolytic Properties

Under appropriate conditions, wood will undergo thermal degradation or pyrolysis. The by-products of pyrolysis may burn, and if enough heat is generated and retained by the wood, the wood can be set on fire. In the presence of a pilot flame (independent source of ignition), the minimum rate of heating necessary for ignition is of the order of 0.3 calorie per square centimeter. In the absence of a pilot flame, the minimum rate of heating necessary for ignition is of the order of 0.6 calorie per square centimeter, nearly double the rate of the pilot flame situation.

Still, heavy timber construction deserves an extremely favorable fire-insurance rating because it will generally not produce sufficient heat energy to maintain combustion unless an external heat source is present. Timber will gradually produce a char layer from the residue of wood combustion. This char acts as a thermal insulator. On heavy timbers, this char layer will eventually inhibit combustion by establishing a thermal barrier between the uncharred wood (interior to char) and the heat of the fire (exterior to char). Heavy timber is virtually self-extinguishing, but steel, which has a thermal conductivity 100 times that of wood, will absorb heat until it reaches a temperature at which it yields under structural load without actually burning.

F. Density and Specific Gravity

The density of a material is the mass per unit volume at some specified condition. For a hygroscopic material such as wood, density depends on two factors: the weight of the wood structure and moisture retained in the wood. Wood density at various moisture contents can vary significantly and must be given relative to a specific condition to have practical meaning.

Specific gravity provides a relative measure of the amount of wood substance contained in a sample of wood. It is a dimensionless ratio of the weight of an ovendry volume of wood to the weight of an identical volume of water. In research activities, specific gravity may be reported on the basis of both weight and volume ovendry. For many engineering applications, the basis for specific gravity is generally the ovendry weight and volume at a moisture content of 12%. For example, a volume of wood at some specified moisture content with a specific gravity of 0.50 would have a density of 500 kg/m^3.

G. Electrical Resistance

Wood is a good electrical insulator. However, significant variations in conductivity do exist. These variations in electrical resistance can be related to variations in grain orientation, temperature, and moisture content. The conductivity of wood in the longitudinal axis is approximately twice that in the radial or tangential axes. The electrical conductivity of wood generally doubles for each 10°C increase in temperature. Generally, variations in conductivity related to wood density and species are considered minor.

The correlation between electrical resistivity and moisture content is the basis for electrical resistance-type moisture meters that estimate moisture content by measuring the resistance of the wood between two electrodes. Moisture content meters, as these instruments are commonly called, need to be calibrated for temperature and species and are effective only for moisture content ranges of 5 to 25%. They are generally unreliable for high resistivities at moisture contents below 5 or 6%, for estimating the moisture content of green timber, or for estimating moisture content of treated timbers (most treatments alter conductivity).

H. Decay Resistance

Wood decay fungi and wood-destroying organisms require oxygen, appropriate temperature, moisture, and a food source. Wood will not decay if kept dry (moisture content less than 20%). On the other extreme, if continuously submerged in water at sufficient depths, wood will usually not decay. Whenever wood is intermediary to either of these two extremes, problems with wood decay can result. To avoid problems with decay where moisture cannot be controlled, the engineer or designer can use either naturally durable species or treated timber.

The natural durability of wood to the mechanisms and processes of deterioration is related to the anatomical characteristics and species of wood. In general, the outer zone or sapwood of all species has little resistance to deterioration and fails rapidly in adverse environments. For heartwood, natural durability depends on species. Heartwood forms as the living sapwood cells gradually die. In some species, the sugars present in the cells are converted to highly toxic extractives that are deposited in the wood cell wall. Many species produce durable heartwood, including western red cedar, redwood, and black locust; however, durability varies within a tree and between trees of a given species. To enhance durability, wood can be treated with an EPA-registered, toxic preservative chemical treatment.

I. Chemical Resistance

Wood is highly resistant to many chemicals, which gives it a significant advantage over many alternative building materials. Wood is often considered superior to alternative materials, such as concrete and steel, partly because of its resistance to mild acids (pH more than 2.0), acidic salt solutions, and corrosive agents. Generally, iron holds up better on exposure to alkaline solution than does wood, but wood can be treated with many of the common wood preservatives (e.g., creosote) to greatly enhance its performance in this respect.

Heartwood is far more durable than sapwood to chemical attack because heartwood is more resistant to penetration by liquids. Many preservative treatments, such as creosote or pentachlorophenol in heavy oil, can also significantly increase the ability of wood to resist liquid or chemical penetration, or both. Chemical solutions may induce two general types of action: normal reversible swelling by a liquid and irreversible chemical degradation. With the former, removal of the liquid will return wood to its original condition. With the latter, permanent changes occur within the wood structure from hydrolysis, oxidation, or delignification.

III. Mechanical Properties

Mechanical properties are the characteristics of a material in response to externally applied forces. They include elastic properties, which characterize resistance to deformation and distortion, and strength properties, which characterize resistance to applied loads. Mechanical property values are given in terms of stress (force per unit area) and strain (deformation resulting from the applied stress). The mechanical property values of wood are obtained from laboratory tests of lumber of straight-grained clear wood samples (without natural defects that would reduce strength, such as knots, checks, splits, etc.).

A. Elastic Properties

Elastic properties relate the resistance of a material to deformation under an applied stress to the ability of the material to regain its original dimensions when the stress is removed. For a material with ideal elastic properties loaded below the proportional (elastic) limit, all deformation is recoverable and the body returns to its original shape when the stress is removed. Wood is not ideally elastic in that some deformation from loading is not immediately recovered when the load is removed; however, residual deformations are generally recoverable over a period of time. Although technically considered a viscoelastic material, wood is usually assumed to behave as an elastic material for most engineering applications.

For an isotropic material with equal property values in all directions, elastic properties are measured by three elastic constants: modulus of elasticity (E), modulus of rigidity (G), and Poisson's ratio (μ). The following equation shows the relationship:

$$\mu_{ij} = E_k/G_{ij}, \qquad (2)$$

where i, j, and k represent the three principal axes. Because wood is orthotropic, 12 constants are required to measure elastic behavior: three moduli of elasticity, three moduli of rigidity, and six Poisson's ratios.

1. Modulus of Elasticity

Modulus of elasticity relates the stress applied along one axis to the strain occurring on the same axis. The three moduli of elasticity for wood are denoted E_L, E_R, and E_T to reflect the elastic moduli in the longitudinal, radial, and tangential directions, respectively. For example, E_L relates the stress in the longitudinal direction to the strain in the longitudinal direction.

Elastic constants vary within and between species and with moisture content and specific gravity. The only constant that has been extensively derived from test data is E_L. Other constants may be available from limited test data but are most frequently developed from material relationships or by regression equations that predict behavior as a function of density. Relative values of elastic constants for clearwood of several common wood species are given in Table I.

2. Shear Modulus

Shear modulus relates shear stress to shear strain. The three shear moduli for wood are denoted G_{LR}, G_{LT}, and G_{RT} for the longitudinal-radial, longitudinal-tangential, and radial-tangential planes, respectively. For example, G_{LR} is the modulus of rigidity based on the shear strain in the LR plane and the shear stress in the LT and RT planes. The modulus of rigidity for several wood species and for each plane are given in Table I.

3. Poisson's Ratio

Poisson's ratio relates the strain parallel to an applied stress to the accompanying strain occurring laterally. For wood, the six Poisson's ratios are denoted μ_{LR}, μ_{LT}, μ_{RL}, μ_{RT}, μ_{TL}, and μ_{TR}. The first subscript refers to the direction of applied stress; the second subscript refers to the direction of the accompanying lateral strain. For example, μ_{LR} is the Poisson's ratio for stress along the longitudinal axis and strain along the radial axis. Estimates of Poisson's ratios for several wood species and for each orientation are given in Table I.

B. Strength Properties

Strength properties are the ultimate resistance of a material to applied loads. With wood, strength varies significantly depending on species, loading condition, load duration, and a number of assorted material and environmental factors.

Because wood is anisotropic, mechanical properties also vary in the three principal axes. Property values in the longitudinal axis are generally significantly higher than those in the tangential or radial axes. Strength-related properties in the longitudinal axis are usually referred to as parallel-to-grain properties. For most engineering design purposes, simply differentiating between parallel- and perpendicular-to-grain properties is sufficient because the relative tangential and radial directions are randomized by the primary sawing process (i.e., conversion from logs to boards).

1. Compression

When a compression load is applied parallel to grain, it produces stress that deforms (shortens) wood cells along their longitudinal axis. When wood is stressed in compression parallel to grain, failure initially begins as the microfibrils begin to fold within the cell wall, thereby creating planes of weakness or instability within the cell wall. As stress in compression parallel to grain continues to increase, the wood-cells themselves fold into S shapes, forming visible wrinkles on the surface. Large deformations occur from the internal crushing of the complex cellular structure. The average strength of green clear wood specimens of Douglas-fir and loblolly pine in compression parallel to grain is approximately 26.1 and 24.2 MPa, respectively.

When a compression load is applied perpendicular to grain, it produces stress that deforms the wood cells perpendicular to their length. Once the hollow cell cavities are collapsed, wood is quite strong because no void space exists. In practice, compressive strength of wood perpendicular to grain is usually assumed to be exceeded when deformation exceeds 4% of the proportional limit stress. Using this convention, the average strength of green clear wood specimens of Douglas-fir and loblolly pine in compression perpendicular to grain is approximately 4.8 and 4.6 MPa, respectively.

Compression applied at an angle to the grain produces stresses that act both parallel and perpendicular

TABLE I

Elastic Ratios for Various Species

Species	Approximate specific gravity[a]	Approximate moisture content (percentage)	Modulus of elasticity ratio[b]		Ratio of modulus of rigidity to modulus of elasticity[c]			Poisson's ratio[d]					
			E_T/E_L	E_R/E_L	G_{LR}/E_L	G_{LT}/E_L	G_{RT}/E_L	μ_{LR}	μ_{LT}	μ_{RT}	μ_{TR}	μ_{RL}	μ_{TL}
Balsa	0.13	9	0.015	0.046	0.054	0.037	0.005	0.23	0.49	0.67	0.23	0.02	0.01
Birch, yellow	0.64	13	0.050	0.078	0.074	0.068	0.017	0.43	0.45	0.70	0.43	0.04	0.02
Douglas-fir	0.50	12	0.050	0.068	0.064	0.078	0.007	0.29	0.45	0.39	0.37	0.04	0.03
Spruce, Sitka	0.38	12	0.043	0.078	0.064	0.061	0.003	0.37	0.47	0.44	0.24	0.04	0.02
Sweetgum	0.53	11	0.050	0.115	0.089	0.061	0.021	0.32	0.40	0.68	0.31	0.04	0.02
Walnut, black	0.59	11	0.056	0.106	0.085	0.062	0.021	0.50	0.63	0.72	0.38	0.05	0.04
Yellow-poplar	0.38	11	0.043	0.092	0.075	0.069	0.011	0.32	0.39	0.70	0.33	0.03	0.02

[a] Based on ovendry weight and volume at the moisture content shown.
[b] E is modulus of elasticity; T, tangential axis; L, longitudinal axis, R, radial axis.
[c] G is modulus of rigidity.
[d] μ is Poisson's ratio.

to grain. The strength at any intermediate angle is intermediate to values of compression parallel and perpendicular to grain and is determined using Hankinson's formula.

2. Tension

Parallel to its grain, wood is very strong in tension. Failure occurs by a complex combination of two modes: cell-to-cell slippage and cell wall failure. Slippage occurs where two adjacent cells slide past one another. Cell wall failure involves rupture within the cell wall with little or no visible deformation prior to complete failure. Tensile strength parallel to grain for clear wood has been historically difficult to obtain; it is often conservatively estimated from bending test values because clear wood normally exhibits initial failure on the face stressed in tension.

In contrast to tension parallel to grain, wood is relatively weak when loaded in tension perpendicular to grain. Stresses in this direction act perpendicular to the cell lengths and produce splitting or cleavage along the grain, which can have a significant effect on structural integrity. Deformations are usually low prior to failure because of the geometry and structure of the cell wall cross-section. Strength in tension perpendicular to grain for clear green samples of Douglas-fir and loblolly pine average 2.1 and 1.8 MPa, respectively. However, because of the excessive variability associated with ultimate stress in tension perpendicular to grain, design situations that induce this stress should be avoided.

3. Bending

Flexural (bending) properties are critical. Bending stresses are induced when a material is used as a beam, such as in a floor or rafter system. The bending strength of clear Douglas-fir and loblolly pine averages 52.6 and 50.3 MPa, respectively, while the modulus of elasticity averages 10.7 and 9.7 GPa, respectively. Because tensile and compressive strengths parallel to grain are different from each other, the strength in bending is less than in tension but more than in compression.

4. Shear

When used as a beam, wood is exposed to compression stress on one surface of the beam and tensile stress on the other. This opposition of stress results in a shearing action through the section of the beam. This parallel-to-grain shearing action is termed horizontal shear. The horizontal shear strength of clear Douglas-fir and loblolly pine averages 6.2 and 5.9 MPa, respectively. Conversely, when stress is applied perpendicular to the cell length in a plane parallel to grain, this action is termed rolling shear. Rolling shear stresses produce a tendency for the wood cells to roll over one another. In general, rolling shear strength values for clear specimens average 18 to 28% of the parallel-to-grain shear values.

5. Energy Absorption Resistance

Energy absorption or shock resistance is a function of the ability of a material to quickly absorb and then dissipate energy via deformation. Wood is remarkably resilient in this respect and is often a preferred material for shock loading. Several parameters are used to describe energy absorption depending on the eventual criteria of failure considered. Work to proportional limit, work to maximum load, and work to total failure (i.e., toughness) describe the energy absorption of wood materials at progressively more severe failure criteria.

6. Fatigue

The fatigue resistance of wood is sometimes an important consideration. Wood, like many fibrous materials, is quite resistant to fatigue (i.e., the effects of repeated loading). In many crystalline metals, repeated loadings of 1 to 10 million cycles at stress levels of 10 to 15% of ultimate can induce fatigue-type failures. At comparable stress levels, the fatigue strength of wood is often several times that of most metals.

7. Hardness

Hardness represents the resistance of wood to indentation and marring. Hardness is comparatively measured by force required to embed a 11.3-mm ball one-half its diameter into the wood.

IV. Factors Affecting Properties of Wood

To this point, our discussions of wood properties have mostly been based on tests of straight-grained specimens of clear wood. Clear wood properties are important, but by no means do they totally represent the engineering performance of solid-sawn lumber, timber, or glulam (glued-laminated timber) containing knots, slope of grain, and other strength-reducing characteristics. To understand the properties of these end-use products, the user must appreciate

TABLE II

Mechanical Properties of Some Commercially Important Woods Grown in the United States[a]

Common name of species	Moisture condition	Specific gravity[b]	Static bending Modulus of rupture (MPa)	Static bending Modulus of elasticity[c] (GPa)	Static bending Work to maximum load (kJ/m³)	Impact bending[d] (m)	Compression parallel to grain[e] (MPa)	Compression perpendicular to grain[f] (MPa)	Shear parallel to grain[g] (MPa)	Tension perpendicular to grain[h] (MPa)	Side hardness-load perpendicular to grain (kN)
Hardwoods											
Ash,	Green	0.35	34.9	5.89	43.8	0.56	14.7	1.2	4.5	1.6	1.33
quaking	Dry	0.38	57.5	8.08	52.0	0.53	29.1	2.5	5.8	1.8	1.56
Cherry,	Green	0.47	54.8	8.97	87.6	0.84	24.2	2.5	7.7	3.9	2.94
black	Dry	0.50	84.2	10.20	78.1	0.74	48.7	4.7	11.6	3.8	4.23
Cottonwood,	Green	0.37	36.3	6.92	50.0	0.53	15.6	1.4	4.7	2.8	1.51
eastern	Dry	0.40	58.2	9.38	50.7	0.51	33.6	2.6	6.4	4.0	1.91
Elm,	Green	0.46	49.3	7.60	80.8	0.97	19.9	2.5	6.8	4.0	2.76
American	Dry	0.50	80.8	9.18	89.0	0.99	37.8	4.7	10.3	4.5	3.69
Hickory,	Green	0.64	75.3	10.75	162.3	1.88	31.4	5.8	0.4	—	—
shagbark	Dry	0.72	138.3	14.79	176.7	1.70	63.1	12.1	16.6	—	—
Maple Red	Green	0.49	52.7	9.52	78.1	0.81	22.5	2.7	7.9	—	3.11
	Dry	0.54	91.8	11.23	85.6	0.81	44.8	6.8	12.7	—	4.23
Sugar	Green	0.56	64.4	10.61	91.1	1.02	27.5	4.4	10.0	—	4.31
	Dry	0.63	108.2	12.53	113.0	0.99	53.6	10.1	16.0	—	6.45
Oak Northern	Green	0.56	56.8	9.24	90.4	1.12	23.6	4.2	8.3	5.1	4.45
red	Dry	0.63	97.9	12.46	99.3	1.09	46.3	6.9	12.2	5.5	5.74
White	Green	0.60	56.8	8.56	79.4	1.07	24.4	4.6	8.6	5.3	4.72
	Dry	0.68	104.1	12.19	101.3	0.94	0.9	7.3	13.7	5.5	6.05
Walnut,	Green	0.51	65.1	9.72	100.0	0.94	29.4	3.4	8.4	3.9	4.00
black	Dry	0.55	100.0	11.50	73.3	0.86	51.9	6.9	9.4	4.7	4.49
Yellow-poplar	Green	0.40	41.1	8.35	51.4	0.66	18.2	1.8	5.4	3.5	1.96
	Dry	0.42	69.2	10.82	60.3	0.61	37.9	3.4	8.1	3.7	2.40
Softwoods											
Cedar, western red	Green	0.31	35.6	6.44	34.2	0.43	19.0	1.6	5.3	1.6	1.16
	Dry	0.32	51.4	7.60	39.7	0.43	31.2	3.1	6.8	1.5	1.56
Douglas-fir,[i]	Green	0.45	52.7	10.68	52.0	0.66	25.9	2.6	6.2	2.1	2.22
coast	Dry	0.48	84.9	13.35	67.8	0.79	49.5	5.5	7.7	2.3	3.16

Fir											
Balsam	Green	0.33	37.7	8.56	32.2	0.41	18.0	1.3	4.5	1.2	1.29
	Dry	0.35	63.0	9.93	34.9	0.51	36.2	2.8	6.5	1.2	1.78
White	Green	0.37	40.4	7.94	38.3	0.56	19.9	1.9	5.2	2.1	1.51
	Dry	0.39	67.1	10.27	49.3	0.51	39.7	3.6	7.5	2.1	2.14
Hemlock,	Green	0.42	45.2	8.97	47.2	0.56	23.0	1.9	5.9	2.0	1.82
western	Dry	0.45	77.4	11.16	56.8	0.58	49.3	3.8	8.8	2.3	2.40
Larch,	Green	0.48	52.7	10.00	70.5	0.74	25.7	2.7	6.0	2.3	2.27
western	Dry	0.52	89.0	12.80	86.3	0.89	52.2	6.4	9.3	2.9	3.69
Pine											
Eastern	Green	0.34	33.6	6.78	35.6	0.43	16.7	1.5	4.7	1.7	1.29
white	Dry	0.35	58.9	8.49	46.6	0.46	32.9	3.0	6.2	2.1	1.69
Loblolly	Green	0.47	50.0	9.59	56.2	0.76	24.0	2.7	5.9	1.8	2.00
	Dry	0.51	87.6	12.26	71.2	0.76	48.8	5.4	9.5	3.2	3.07
Ponderosa	Green	0.38	34.9	6.85	35.6	0.53	16.8	1.9	4.8	2.1	1.42
	Dry	0.40	64.4	8.83	48.6	0.48	36.4	4.0	7.7	2.9	2.05
Redwood											
Old-	Green	0.38	51.4	8.08	50.7	0.53	28.8	2.9	5.5	1.8	1.82
growth	Dry	0.40	68.5	9.18	47.2	0.48	42.1	4.8	6.4	1.6	2.14
Young-	Green	0.34	40.4	6.57	39.0	0.41	21.3	1.8	6.1	2.1	1.56
growth	Dry	0.35	54.1	7.53	35.6	0.38	35.6	3.6	7.6	1.7	1.87
Spruce											
Sitka	Green	0.37	39.0	8.42	43.1	0.61	18.3	1.9	5.2	1.7	1.56
	Dry	0.40	69.8	10.75	64.4	0.64	38.4	4.0	7.9	2.5	2.27
White	Green	0.33	34.2	7.81	41.1	0.56	16.1	1.4	4.4	1.5	1.42
	Dry	0.36	64.4	9.79	52.7	0.51	35.5	2.9	6.6	2.5	2.14

[a] Results of tests on small, clear, straight-grained specimens. Values in the first line for each species are from tests of green material; those in the second line are from tests of seasoned material adjusted to a 12% moisture content.

[b] Based on weight ovendry and volume at moisture content indicated.

[c] Measured from a simply supported, center-loaded beam, on a span-depth ratio of 14/1. The modulus can be corrected for the effect of shear deflection by increasing it 10%.

[d] Height of drop causing complete failure.

[e] Maximum crushing strength.

[f] Fiber stress at proportional limit.

[g] Maximum shearing strength.

[h] Maximum tensile strength.

[i] Douglas-fir in the States of Oregon and Washington west of the summit of the Cascade Mountains.

the impacts of several anatomical and processing-related factors. The user must also appreciate the interactive nature of environmental factors. This section will attempt to briefly relate the importance of many of these factors independently and in aggregate.

A. Anatomical Factors

The mechanical properties of wood vary between species; they are often compared via species averages (Table II). However, because mechanical properties vary within a species, it is incorrect to think that all material of Species A is stronger than material of Species B if, for example, average values are 10 to 15% different.

1. Specific Gravity and Density

The property values of wood increase with increasing specific gravity (SG). While density is a measure of weight per unit volume often reported with kilograms per cubic meter, SG is a dimensionless ratio of the density of wood at a specified moisture content to the density of water. Because changes in moisture contents result in dimensional changes, SG and density should be compared at the same moisture content. Specific gravity is an index of mechanical property values of wood free from defects; the higher the SG, the higher the appropriate property value. However, SG and density values for lumber are also affected by the presence of gums, resins, and extractives, which contribute little to mechanical properties.

2. Knots

A knot is that portion of a branch that has become incorporated in the bole of the tree. The influence of a knot on mechanical properties of a wood member is due to the interruption of continuity and change in direction of wood fibers associated with a knot. The influence of a knot depends on its size, its location, its shape, its soundness, and the type of stress measured.

Most mechanical property values are lower at sections containing knots. Knots generally have a greater effect on tensile strength than on compressive strength. For this reason, knots have their greatest influence in the tension zone when exposed to bending stress. The effects of knot size, type, and location are specifically addressed by the grading rules that specify limits for each commercially marketed species–size–grade combination.

3. Slope of Grain

The mechanical properties of wood are quite sensitive to fiber and ring orientation. For example,

parallel-to-grain tensile or compressive strength property values are generally 10 to 20 times greater than those perpendicular to grain. Deviations from straight grain in a typical board are termed slope of grain or cross-grain. The terms relate the fiber direction to the edges of the piece. Any form of cross-grain can have detrimental effects on mechanical properties.

4. Juvenile Wood

During the first 5 to 20 years of growth, the immature cambial tissue produces wood cells with distinct variations in microfibril orientation throughout the important S_2 layer of the cell wall. This wood is referred to as juvenile wood. Juvenile wood exhibits excessive warpage because of anatomical differences within this S_2 layer of the cell wall. It also exhibits lower strength properties and becomes a problem within the wood industry because of the trend toward processing younger, smaller diameter trees as the larger diameter, old-growth stock becomes more difficult to obtain.

5. Creep

Wood is a viscoelastic material. Initially, it will act elastically, experiencing nearly full recovery of load-induced deformation upon stress removal. However, wood will experience nonrecoverable deformation upon extended loading. This deformation is known as creep. For example, the magnitude of additional creep-related deformation after a 10-year loading will roughly equal the initial deformation caused by that load. The rate of creep increases with increasing temperature and moisture content.

B. Environmental

1. Moisture Content

Mechanical property values of wood increase as wood dries from the fiber saturation point to 10 to 15% moisture content. For clear wood, mechanical property values continue to increase as wood dries below 10 to 15% moisture content. For lumber, studies have shown that mechanical property values reach a maximum at about 10 to 15% moisture content, then begin to decrease with decreasing moisture content below 10 to 15%. For either product, the effects of moisture content are considered to be reversible in the absence of decay.

2. Temperature

Strength and stiffness decrease when wood is heated and increase when cooled. The temperature effect is immediate and, for the most part, reversible for short heating durations. However, if wood is exposed to elevated temperatures for an extended time, strength is permanently reduced because of wood substance degradation and a corresponding loss in weight. The magnitude of these permanent effects depends on moisture content, heating medium, temperature, exposure period, and to a lesser extent, species and specimen size. As a general rule, wood should not be exposed to temperatures above 65°C. The immediate effect of temperature interacts with the effect of moisture content so that neither effect can be completely understood without consideration of the other.

3. Decay and Insect Damage

Wood is conducive to decay and insect damage in moist, warm conditions. Decay within a structure cannot be tolerated because strength is rapidly reduced in even the early stages of decay. It has been estimated that a 5% weight loss from decay can result in strength losses as high as 50%. If the warm, moist conditions required for decay cannot be controlled, then the use of naturally decay resistant wood species or chemical treatments are required to impede decay. Insects, such as termites and certain types of beetles, can be just as damaging to mechanical performance. Insect infestation can be controlled via mechanical barriers, naturally durable species, or chemical treatments.

V. Properties and Grades of Sawn Lumber

At first, the highest quality level of sawn lumber might seem desirable for all uses, and indeed it is needed for several uses. However, in most situations, such material would be prohibitively expensive and a wasteful use of our timber resource. In practice, the quality level needed for a function can be easily specified because lumber and timber are graded in an orderly system developed to serve the interests of the users and the producers.

The grading system is actually several systems, each designed for specific products. Hardwood lumber is mostly graded for remanufacture, with only small amounts graded for construction. Softwood is also graded for both remanufacture and construction, but primarily for construction.

In practice, an orderly, voluntary but circuitous system of responsibilities has evolved in the United States for the development, manufacture, and merchandising of most stress-graded lumber and timber. In general, stress-grading principles are developed from research findings and engineering concepts, often within committees and subcommittees of the American Society for Testing and Materials.

For lumber, the National Institute for Standards and Technology cooperates with producers, distributors, users, and regional grade-rules-writing agencies through the American Lumber Standard Committee (ALSC). The ALSC has assembled a voluntary softwood standard of manufacture, called the American Softwood Lumber Standard. The American Softwood Lumber Standard and its related National Grading Rule prescribe the ways in which stress-grading principles can be used to formulate grading rules for dimension lumber (nominal 2 to 4 in. thick). This lumber standard is the basis for commercially marketing structural lumber in the United States.

For timbers (more than 5 in. nominal), the National Grading Rule does not apply. Thus, each regional grade-rules-writing agency publishes grade rules for timbers following the general principles of the National Grading Rule, but each differs slightly in eventual grade requirements and names. For further specifics on the various characteristics for the individual species-grade combinations, contact the individual grade-rules-writing organizations directly. In North America, those agencies are National Lumber Grades Authority (Vancouver, BC, Canada), Northeastern Lumber Manufacturers Association (Cumberland, ME), Redwood Inspection Service (Mill Valley, CA), Southern Pine Inspection Bureau (Pensacola, FL), West Coast Lumber Inspection Bureau (Portland, OR), and Western Wood Products Association (Portland, OR). [See FOREST TREE, GENETIC IMPROVEMENT.]

Bibliography

American Society for Testing and Materials (1991). "Annual Book of Standards," Vol. D.09 Wood. Philadelphia, PA.

Forest Products Laboratory (1987). "Wood Handbook: Wood as an Engineering Material." Agric. Handb. 72. U.S. Department of Agriculture, Forest Service, Washington, DC.

Panshin, A. J., and deZeeuw, C. (1980). "Textbook of Wood Technology," 4th ed., p. 705. McGraw-Hill, New York.

U.S. Department of Commerce. (1986). American Lumber Standard PS20-70. Washington, DC.

Wool and Mohair Production
and Processing

C. J. LUPTON, *Texas A&M University*

Glossary

Fiber Unit of matter characterized by flexibility, fineness, and high ratio of length to thickness typically capable of being spun into yarn

Grade Fineness of wool and mohair fibers

Hair Usually straight, relatively brittle, and lustrous; stronger, smoother, and coarser than wool and generally lacks felting properties

Wool and mohair adjectives *grease:* fiber taken from the living sheep or Angora goat which has not been commercially scoured; *pulled:* fiber taken from the pelt of a slaughtered animal which has not been commercially scoured (synonym: slipe); *raw:* fiber in the grease, pulled, or scoured state; *recycled:* fiber that has been reclaimed from woven, knitted, or felted structures whether or not it was used by the ultimate consumer; *scoured:* fiber from which the bulk of impurities has been removed by an aqueous or solvent washing process; *virgin:* new wool fibers that have not been reclaimed from any spun, woven, knitted, braided or otherwise manufactured product

Woolen and worsted systems Two distinct systems for producing yarns with wool and mohair; woolen-spun yarns tend to be bulky with low twist and fibers lying in random directions; in contrast, worsted yarns are compact and highly twisted containing relatively long fibers that are more or less parallel to the longitudinal axis of the yarn; most short fibers are removed in a combing process

In the restricted context of this article, wool is defined as the fibrous covering of the sheep, *Ovis* species, and mohair is the fiber harvested from Angora goats, one breed within the *Capra* species. Thus, the term wool is much broader, encompassing fibers from all sheep breeds. In contrast, mohair is grown by a single breed of goat. Production and processing refer, respectively, to the quantities of fibers grown by these animals throughout the world and their conversion from a raw, agricultural commodity to a finished fabric whether it be a bolt of suit cloth or the covering material for a paint roller. In a broader sense, production encompasses all the genetic and environmental factors that influence the amount of fiber grown.

I. Origins of Domestic Sheep and Goats

A. Sheep

The domestication of sheep and goats was probably complete more than 11,000 years ago. At that time, fibers produced by wild sheep and goats bore little resemblance to modern, white finewools or mohair. Sheep were covered with coarse, medullated, colored hair with a trace of an undercoat of relatively fine, soft fibers of lighter shade. In all likelihood, the fibrous coverings of sheep and goats were probably similar in texture and appearance to many other species. Thus, it was not the fiber attributes that led to domestication but rather the convenience of accessible supplies of meat, skins, fat, bone, horn, and gut. The natural herding instincts of sheep and goats coupled with their abundance and their relatively docile nature no doubt recommended these species above all others to ancient man.

From skeletal remains, it is known that sheep had been domesticated as early as 9000 B.C. in the Zagras mountains where Iraq now borders Iran. In prehistory, people learned that wool could be felted to produce fabrics that could be tailored. They also learned to spin yarns and weave fabrics. Sometime long ago, the observation was made that imparting twist to a strand of fibers imparts strength. From this observation evolved the art and science of yarn making and subsequently fabric making by methods that include, among others, weaving and knitting. Development of the sheep fleece through selective breeding is highly correlated with the development of spinning and weaving from a craft to current industrial practices. Much of the selective breeding is totally undocumented. It is known that the coarse, colored fleeces of ancient sheep were shed once a year unlike the white, fine fleeces of modern sheep breeds. Some of the old-world breeds persisted to the present time and are represented by the Mouflon (of Corsica and Sardinia), the Bighorn Sheep (of the United States), Soay (St. Kilda, Scotland), and some of the hair breeds of India and Africa. Much of what we know about the early development of sheep has been deduced from ancient depictions of sheep in sculpture, relief, and paintings. Samples of wool fabric are available from about 1500 B.C. Some conclusions have also been drawn from ancient parchments made from sheepskin. In particular, the evolution of the sheep as a fiber producer has been followed to some degree by studying the primary and secondary follicles in the preserved skin. In ancient fleeces, the ratio of primary to secondary follicles was in the order of 1:3. Primary follicles produced coarse, medullated fibers. Secondary follicles, when active, produced fine, undercoat fibers. As sheep were selected for wool production, the ratio of primary to secondary follicles increased to 1:5 for present day medium wool sheep and as

high as 1:25 for finewool-producing merino sheep. During this period of selection, primary follicles have become smaller and secondaries somewhat larger so that in today's finewool sheep, both types of follicle are producing fibers of comparable size. Further, the density of follicles in the skin has been increased from less than 10 mm^{-2} to as much as 80 mm^{-2} in very productive finewool sheep.

Wool-containing textile remains from Roman times are quite numerous. Generally, these have been shown to be composed of finewools (in remnants of clothing), medium wools (in blankets and rugs), and wools of intermediate fineness (in hosiery and knitwear). True finewool-producing sheep are thought to have been developed first in the Middle East which was, consequently, the site of early advances in textile technology. The products of this technology were distributed throughout the Mediterranean region and beyond by Greek and Phoenician sea-going traders. Greek legend concerning the golden fleece of Colchis dates to about 700 B.C. and this has been linked to the existence of fine wool since antiquity. The Romans conquered Great Britain in 55 B.C. and introduced the craft of wool textile manufacturing there and throughout Europe. Development of this art form and the subsequent wool industry was ultimately responsible for producing much of the wealth which resulted in the acquisition of the British Empire. Romans also introduced sheep to Spain which they considered to have an ideal climate for wool production. Following the fall of the Roman Empire about 600 A.D., written European history became almost nonexistent. Only with the advent of the European Renaissance in the 13th century can the development of sheep and wool production be followed. By this time, invaders of Arab origin had brought truly finewool sheep into Spain and, following expulsion of the Islamic Moors from Spain in 1491, development of the Merino breed is quite well documented. Merinos did not leave Spain until the 18th century at which time numerous European countries became recipients of this superior wool-producing breed. In the meantime, many other distinctive sheep breeds had been developed in Europe. All of these produced wool that was coarser but invariably longer than the merinos. Nevertheless, the wool of many breeds was fine enough to make clothing. Meat from sheep, wool, and wool textiles were extremely important to European economies. Great Britain introduced fine wool sheep in its South African and Australian colonies with a view to further increasing revenues from wool. The first importation of merino sheep into Australia occurred in 1793. However, the best documented importation occurred in 1797 from South Africa. Progress in selective breeding can be assessed in terms of wool production of the sheep. During the mid 1800s, fleece weights for sheep producing 20 μm wool were around 1 kg. Today, merino sheep producing the same grade would be growing more than 5 kg per year. This increase was achieved primarily by selecting for more dense and longer fleeces.

Domesticated sheep arrived in the New World with the first Spanish explorers and settlers. Most of these sheep were of the "churra" variety though some were merinos. Early Dutch settlers probably brought the first sheep to the east coast region of the United States but the policy of the English monarchs was to suppress production in the American colonies. This single policy was undoubtedly a major contributing cause of the American Revolution. After the Revolution, a concerted effort was made to improve the quality of wool produced in the United States. Finewool rams were imported primarily from Spain and France. As the pioneers moved westward, sheep trailed along with them serving a similar purpose to their forbearers on other continents 10,000 years earlier. Sheep numbers had increased to 53 million head by 1844 and peaked in 1942 when the population was 56 million. Since that time, numbers have declined to their present level of 11.2 million, two-thirds of which are in the western states and Texas. Nationally, sheep are of minor importance compared to cattle and hogs. However, sheep are still an important part of the agricultural economy in Texas, Wyoming, California, Montana, South Dakota, and several other states mainly because these ruminants (and goats) can constitute a profitable operation on land that is too poor to support cattle alone.

B. Angora Goats

Mohair is produced by a single breed of goat, the Angora, which was named after a Turkish province. The historical origin of the breed is still something of a mystery. One theory is that Angora goats evolved in the geographic region of present-day Turkey. However, the absence of any description of this type of goat by classical Roman or Greek authors would seem to undermine such a theory. A more likely hypothesis is that Angora goats arrived in Turkey with migrating pastoral tribes during the 11th century having originated in Central Asia. Perhaps derived from wild goats of Central Asia, e.g., *Capra falconeri,* Angoras were first described in Europe by Father Belon

in 1554 after his travels through Asia Minor, including the province of Angora. Raw mohair reached Europe from Turkey in 1820. The expertise for producing pure mohair textiles was generated over time using the worsted system as a basis. As the demand for mohair increased, Angora goats were eventually released from Turkey. South Africa received its first importation in 1838 and by 1893 a major industry involving nearly 3 million goats had been established. In 1848, the first Angora goats were imported into the United States. Here, the growth of the industry was much slower than in South Africa. By 1900, less than 0.25 million Angora goats were present in the United States. With the major producers being Turkey, South Africa, and the United States in this century, mohair production has fluctuated widely, mainly as a result of fashion changes. [See GOAT PRODUCTION.]

II. Distribution of Sheep and Angora Goats throughout the World

The world population of wooled sheep in 1991 was 1160.4 million. The numbers of sheep in the major producing regions are shown in Table I. Australia leads with 166.2 million followed by the former Soviet Union (134.6 million), China (115.2 million), and New Zealand (55.2 million). During this period, the United States reported 11.2 million.

The world population of Angora goats was approximately 5.4 million in 1991. Table II shows the population and production in seven countries. South Africa is the leading producer followed closely by the United States with over 90% of the mohair production being in Texas.

III. Production and Consumption of Wool and Mohair

A. Wool

In the period 1991–1992, world wool production was 3.01 million tonnes (metric tons) greasy wool which is equivalent to approximately 1.74 million tonnes of clean wool. In general terms, this amount was composed of 52.9% merino wool, 23.3% cross-bred wool, and 23.8% carpet-type wool. Production by country is summarized in Table I. The world's largest production and the main source of apparel wools entering international trade channels is from Australia.

TABLE I

World Wooled Sheep Population and Wool Production (1990–1991)[a]

Country	Sheep population (million)	Raw wool production (1000 tonnes, greasy)	Wool production (1000 tonnes, clean equiv.)
Albania	1.6	3	1
Argentina	26.9	136	82
Australia	166.2	1066	699
Brazil	20.1	27	19
Bulgaria	7.1	26	11
Canada	0.8	2	1
Chile	5.3	20	12
China	115.2	240	120
Czechoslovakia	1.0	5	3
Falkland Islands	0.7	3	2
France	11.1	23	13
Germany	3.2	21	11
Greece	10.2	10	6
Hungary	1.9	7	3
India	40.0	35	21
Iran	34.0	32	14
Iraq	7.8	17	7
Irish Republic	9.1	17	11
Italy	10.8	14	6
Lesotho	1.5	3	1
Mongolia	14.3	20	11
Morroco	16.2	35	14
Namibia	6.7	1	1
New Zealand	55.2	305	228
Pakistan	30.2	63	26
Peru	12.3	10	7
Poland	3.9	15	8
Portugal	3.4	9	5
Romania	14.1	33	15
South Africa[b]	25.0	106	63
Former Soviet Union	134.6	471	212
Spain	24.0	42	19
Turkey	47.5	83	42
United Kingdom	43.9	72	48
United States of America	11.2	41	22
Uruguay	25.9	94	62
Yugoslavia	7.4	10	5
Other African countries[c]	126.9	111	51
Other American countries[d]	25.1	22	11
Other Asian countries[e]	51.7	68	34
Other Western European countries[f]	6.4	12	7
World total	1160.4	3330	1934

[a] *Source:* International Wool Textile Organisation.

[b] Includes estimated Bantu production.

[c] Other African countries include: Algeria, Botswana, Egypt, Ethiopia, Kenya, Libya, Mali, Mozambique, Sudan, Swaziland, Tanzania, Tunisia, Zambia, and Zimbabwe.

[d] Other American countries include: Bolivia, Columbia, Ecuador, Greenland, Mexico, Paraguay, and Venezuela.

[e] Other Asian countries include: Afghanistan, Bangladesh, Bhutan, Cyprus, Gaza, Indonesia, Israel, Jordan, Kuwait, Lebanon, Macao, Malaysia, Myanmar, Nepal, Saudi Arabia, Syria, Thailand, and Yemen.

[f] Other Western European countries include: Austria, Belgium, Denmark, Finland, Iceland, Luxembourg, Malta, Netherlands, Norway, Sweden, and Switzerland.

TABLE II

World Angora Goat Population and Mohair Production by Main Producing Countries (1991)

Country	Angora goat population (1000's)	Mohair production (greasy, mkg)
Argentina	183	0.6
Australia	183	0.6
Lesotho	152	0.5
New Zealand	91	0.3
Turkey	365	1.2
South Africa	2284	7.5
United States of America	2071	6.8
Other countries	61	0.2
Total	5390	17.7

Source: International Mohair Association and Mohair Council of America.

Australia's production fell 17% in 1991–1992 to its lowest level since 1985–1986. Reduction in sheep numbers and wool production are attributed to relatively low financial returns for wool and movement of producers to other agricultural enterprises. Wool production also fell in Argentina, Uruguay, the former Soviet Union, South Africa, and New Zealand. In contrast, wool production in China, Pakistan, the United Kingdom, and the United States was relatively static. The carry forward of unsold wool stocks into 1991–1992 from Australia, New Zealand, South Africa, Argentina, Uruguay, and the U.K. was a record 719,000 tonnes (clean equivalent).

Consumption of virgin wool is shown in Table III. Following two successive years of decline, wool consumption increased by 6% in the calendar year 1991 to about 1.63 million tonnes clean. Strong growth in consumption was noticed primarily in China (+50%) and also in South Korea (+24%), Taiwan (+139%), Italy (+13%), and the United States (+22%). For the first time on record, China became the world's largest user of wool. Consumption in the former Soviet Union and in Eastern Europe declined by 7 and 26%, respectively, probably as a result of the political turmoil in these areas. With wool becoming more competitively priced compared to synthetic fibers, wool consumption is expected to increase during the next few years. It remains to be seen if this trend will be strong enough to cause a turnaround in sheep numbers and wool production. Drought in some of the major wool growing areas and low returns in 1992 and 1993 may persuade some growers to stay out of the business permanently.

B. Mohair

In recent years, world mohair production peaked in 1988 when 25.95 million kilograms (mkg) was produced. Since that time, a reduction in world demand for mohair coupled with a prolonged drought in South Africa have resulted in a decline in production which is estimated to be 16.85 mkg in 1992. Table II shows world mohair production for the calendar year 1991. South Africa has been the major producing country since 1976. Prior to that year, the United States and South Africa alternated the lead. In 1992, the United States again became the world's leading mohair producer. In contrast, production in Turkey, the historical home of mohair, has been declining steadily for many years while the relatively small amounts of production in Argentina and Lesotho have been fairly constant. Australia and New Zealand initiated mohair production in the early 1980s, reporting 0.5 and 0.05 mkg, respectively, in 1984. Production increased for a few years and remained constant at 1.0 and 0.5 mkg between 1988 and 1990 before declining quite drastically in 1991. Accurate records of worldwide mohair consumption by country are not available. Table IV shows the countries to which U.S. mohair was exported in 1991.

Large fluctuations in the demand for mohair and consequently prices paid are accepted phenomena in the mohair business. Despite promotional efforts by the International Mohair Association (IMA), these dramatic changes in demand, production, and prices seem to be permanent fixtures because mohair is, first and foremost, a fashion fiber. When designers utilize lustrous fabrics with a brushed, hairy appearance for a particular fall or winter season, the outlook for mohair is bright. The primary challenge to the IMA and others with investments in the mohair industry is to develop products with year-round, long-term appeal. With such products, the oftimes devastating effects of cyclical demand, with production lagging 2 or 3 years behind, might be overcome.

IV. Major Wool Producing Sheep Breeds

The position of sheep among animal vertebrates is shown below:

Class	*Mammalia* (mammals, those which suckle their young)
Order	*Ungulateae* (hoofed mammals)

TABLE III

Consumption of Virgin Wool by the Wool Textile Industry at the Spinning Stage (1991)

Country	Wool consumption (1000 tonnes–clean basis)	Country	Wool consumption (1000 tonnes–clean basis)
Afghanistan	11.250	Korea (South)	60.145
Algeria	21.500	Libya	1.650
Argentina	29.535	Macao	2.000
Australia	16.871	Malaysia	1.924
Austria	6.438	Mauritius	2.236
Belgium	33.800	Mexico	6.700
Bolivia	4.940	Mongolia	9.120
Brazil	5.300	Morocco	18.250
Bulgaria	10.594	Nepal	9.200
Canada	4.707	Netherlands	4.800
Chile	6.962	New Zealand	17.066
China	250.424	Norway	2.290
Columbia	3.455	Pakistan	28.855
Czechoslovakia	16.348	Peru	4.400
Denmark	2.995	Poland	11.130
Ecuador	1.000	Portugal	14.321
Egypt	4.460	Romania	13.413
Finland	0.550	Saudi Arabia	1.400
France	23.777	South Africa	4.446
Germany	59.073	Former Soviet Union	234.900
Greece	12.435	Spain	22.887
Hong Kong	5.973	Sweden	0.413
Hungary	2.658	Switzerland	11.626
Iceland	0.498	Syria	11.500
India	33.000	Taiwan	30.399
Iran	21.722	Turkey	62.499
Iraq	4.480	United Kindgom	71.268
Irish Republic	8.168	United States	62.638
Israel	0.720	Uruguay	6.348
Italy	155.090	Venezuela	0.800
Japan	116.719	Yugoslavia	14.719
Jordon	1.000		
Kenya	1.224	Total	1621.008

Source: International Wool Textile Organisation and International Wool Secretariat.

Suborder	*Artiodactyla* (even-toed ungulates)
Section	*Pectora* (typical ruminants)
Family	*Bovidae* (hollow-horned ruminants)
Subfamily	*Caprinae* (sheep and goats)
Genus	*Ovis* (sheep)
Species	*Ovis aries* (domesticated sheep)
	Ovis ammon (Argali)
	Ovis canadensis (North American Bighorn)
	Ovis orientalis (Urial)
	Ovis laristanica (Urial)
	Ovis musimon (Moufflon)
	Ovis tragelaphus (North African Aoudad)
	Ovis vignei (Asiatic Urial)

Breeds that belong to the species *Ovis aries* number over 500 but can be categorized into five groups by the type of wool they produce. These are: fine-wool, medium-wool, long-wool, crossbred-wool, and carpet-wool type of sheep. Within species, there are also substantial variations in other traits, e.g., size and shape, color of wool, horns, and type of tail.

A breed can be defined as a group of sheep with a common origin and certain physical characteristics that are readily distinguishable. Wool characteristics of several important breeds are presented in Table V.

V. Fiber Composition and Growth

In its raw state, the keratin of sheep and Angora goat fibers is coated with variable amounts of wax and

TABLE IV
United States Exports of Greasy Mohair (1991)

Country	% of total
United Kingdom	55
India	16
Taiwan	12
Belgium	9
Italy	4
Hong Kong	1
Germany	1
Others	2

Source: Mohair Council of America, 1992.

suint which in turn are contaminated to varying degrees with dirt, plant parts, urine, feces, and other miscellaneous materials. The amounts of wax and suint are somewhat genetically controlled while the contaminants are almost totally influenced by the environment. The waxes which protect the fibers against water and sunlight damage are composed of a mixture of esters and constitute 2–30% of the weight of greasy fibers. These esters are condensation products of water-insoluble alcohols (23) and higher fatty acids (36). The complex chemical characteristics of wool wax have been described. The purified form of wool wax is known as lanolin. The term "yolk" refers to the combination of wax plus suint. By convention, suint is defined as the portion of the yolk that is soluble in cold water. It consists primarily of a mixture of potassium salts of fatty acids (C_5–C_{16}) and is present in amounts varying from 2 to 15% of the greasy fleece. Suint is composed of 30–40% inorganic matter and 60–70% organic material. Other metal ions present in suint include sodium, calcium, and magnesium. Inorganic anions present in suint ash include carbonate (primarily), chloride, sulfate, phosphate, and silicate.

Not including the 0.5% or so of inorganic material, cleansed wool and mohair have the following approximate analysis: carbon, 50%; oxygen, 22–25%; nitrogen, 16–17%; hydrogen, 7%; and sulfur, 3–4%.

The basic chemical building blocks of wool and mohair are 19 amino acids. These compounds are carried to the point of fiber synthesis in follicles in blood, at which point the amino acids are polymerized to form a complex mixture of polypeptides which is called keratin. Individual polypeptide molecules are composed of many amino acid molecules attached end to end through peptide bonds. Free amino and carboxylic acid groups at the end and along the length of these long molecules contribute to the dyeing behavior of wool and mohair. Individual molecules are

covalently attached to other polypeptide chains via disulfide bonds contained in the amino acid cystine. In addition, adjacent molecules are bonded together through ionic, hydrogen, and Van der Waals attractions. All these bond types contribute to the strength and elasticity of wool and mohair fibers. At the molecular level, polypeptide molecules are arranged in the form of α-helices. Stretching a wool or mohair fiber below the point at which it will break results in the breaking of many hydrogen and Van der Waals bonds and the helix form changes to β. When the fibers are released from extension, contraction to original length is accompanied by a return to the α-helix structure. The ability of wool and mohair textiles to return to their original dimensions after physical distortion is a direct consequence of the physical changes that can occur in the α-helix structure. At the molecular level, areas of molecular organization (crystalline regions) and disarray (amorphous regions) have been observed using X-ray techniques.

In wool and mohair fibers, the protein keratin is contained in two types of cell that constitute the microstructure. These are called cuticle and cortical cells. Cuticle cells are readily observed through the light microscope and appear as platelike scales on the fiber surface that are laid down in an overlapping fashion. Much variability exists in scale size and shape among fibers of varying diameter and between species. Nevertheless, the topography of these animal fibers is unmistakable and has never been artificially synthesized. In very fine wool fibers, individual cuticle cells overlap each other and form a complete ring around the circumference of a fiber like a stack of crowns ("coronal" arrangement). In coarser fibers, overlapping of corticle cells is still apparent but several cells circumscribe the fiber ("imbricate" arrangement). In coarse wool and mohair, cuticle cells appear to be arranged in a mosaic ("reticulate" arrangement) with minimal overlapping of individual cells being apparent. This arrangement of cuticle cells is responsible for the increased luster observed in mohair and some coarse wools (Lincoln and Leicester, for example) compared to finewools. Three distinct regions (epi-, exo-, and endocuticle) have been isolated and defined in the cuticle.

Cortical cells compose the cortex of the fiber and are much longer (80–100 μm) than they are wide (3–5 μm). These cigar-shaped cells are themselves composed of macrofibrils which in turn are made up of microfibrils. It has been postulated that the microfibrils contain 11 protofibrils and that each protofibril is composed of three polypeptide molecules

TABLE V

Breed Classification by Fiber Diameter, Wool Production, and Staple Length

	Range of average diameter (μm)	Grease fleece wt. range, ewes (kg)	Range of staple length (mm)
Finewool breeds			
Superfine Australian merino	<18	3–4	75–90
Fine Australian merino	19–20	3–5	80–100
Medium Australian merino	21–22	4–6	90–100
Strong Australian merino	23–26	5–7	100–130
Cormo	19–23	4–5.5	100–130
Rambouillet	19–24	4–7	60–100
Debouillet	18–22	4–7	75–125
Medium wool breeds			
Dorset (horned and polled)	26–32	2–3.5	75–100
Finnsheep (Finnish Landrace)	24–31	2–3.5	75–100
Hampshire	25–33	2.5–4.5	60–100
Oxford	28–34	3–4.5	75–130
Romanov	28–33	2.5–6	100–125
Ryeland	26–32	2–4	75–100
Shropshire	25–33	2–4.5	80–100
Southdown	23–29	2–3.5	50–75
Suffolk	26–35	2.5–3.5	75–100
Texel	28–33	3–4.5	70–100
Wiltshire Horn	40–80	1	20–30
Long wool breeds			
Border Leicester	30–40	4.5–6	150–250
Cheviot	26–33	2–3	75–130
Coopworth	35–39	5–7	150–250
Cotswold	33–40	5.5–7	200–300
English Leicester	37–40	5–6	150–280
Lincoln	39–48	5.5–9	250–300
Romney Marsh	32–39	4.5–8	125–220
Crossbreed wool type breeds			
Columbia	23–30	5.5–7.5	100–150
Corriedale	25–33	4.5–7	100–180
Montadale	25–30	3–5	75–125
Panama	25–30	6–7	75–125
Perendale	28–35	3–6	100–180
Polwarth	23–26	4–5.5	75–110
Polypay	24–31	3–4.5	75–125
Targhee	21–25	4.5–6.5	75–125
Carpet wool breeds			
Drysdale	35–45	5–7 (6 month)	100–150 (6 month)
Karakul	25–36	2–4.5	150–300
Navajo-Churro (Undercoat)	22–24	2–3.5	140–150
(Outercoat)	37–47	(both coats)	200–350
Scottish Blackface	28–38	2–3	250–350
Also, numerous Asiatic types including fat-tail and fat-rump sheep			

in an α-helix arrangement (Fig. 1). In the microstructure, cortical cells are differentiated by physical and chemical properties into ortho and para cells. In crimped fine wool, the *ortho* cortical cells are concentrated on the outside of each curve, para cells being on the inside. In order to accommodate this arrangement along the length of a fiber, the structure must continuously twist (Fig. 2). In coarse wool and mohair, ortho

cells tend to be surrounded by para cells. Thus, the distribution of ortho and para cells in wool and mohair is associated with the presence (or absence) and type of fiber crimp.

Crimp in wool and waviness in mohair are readily observable in the macrostructure. Using a light microscope, three distinct regions can be readily distinguished in fibers that have never been shorn and were

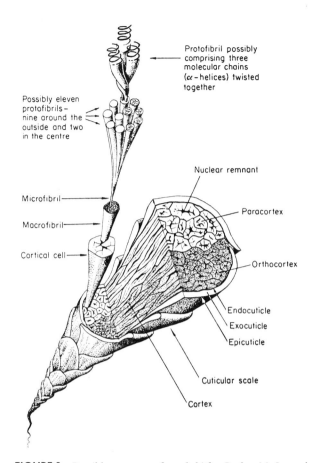

FIGURE 1 Possible structure of wool. [After Ryder, M. L., and Stephensen, S. K. (1968). "Wool Growth." Academic Press, London.]

plucked out of the skin rather than shorn. These regions are referred to as "tip," "shaft," and "root." After the first shearing, tips no longer exist. Thus, fibers shorn after the first shearing are composed entirely of shaft since the root portion is left in the animal. Even in these fibers, variations in diameter exist along the length of individual fibers, these being related to nutrition and health factors during the period of fiber production.

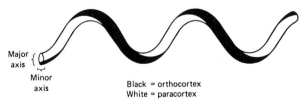

FIGURE 2 Crimped wool fiber showing typical coil formation. [Ater Botkin, M. P., Field, R. A., and Johnson, C. L. (1988). "Sheep and Wool: Science, Production, and Management." Prentice-Hall, Englewood Cliffs, NJ.]

One further component that is readily observable in the cortex of some fibers is the medulla. This portion of the fiber consists of a network of hollow, air-filled cells in which the cell walls may have collapsed to form a partially or completely hollow, strawlike fiber. Medullated fibers are common and often desirable in coarse wool but are considered a serious fault in mohair. Medullated fibers in which the medulla diameter constitutes more than 60% of the fiber diameter are termed "kemp." Kemp fibers appear not to accept dyestuff and are thus easily distinguished as white, chalky fibers in dyed fabrics. At least three types of medullation are distinguished: fragmented, interrupted, and continuous (Fig. 3).

Skin functions as a single organ although it contains cells arranged in multiple tissues (blood vessels, connective tissue, epidermis, follicle, glands, and muscle) and composing intercellular material (e.g., lymph and connective fibrous material). Since fleeces from different sheep breeds and Angora goats differ in so many respects, it follows that the dimensions and composition of fiber-producing organs in these animals also exhibit marked differences. The study of the structure of these tissues is termed, "skin histology." A simplified, three-dimensional representation of fiber-producing cells in the skin appears in Fig. 4. The various zones of the follicle concerned with the functional stages of fiber formation are shown in Fig. 5. Blood supply to the papilla provides nutrients for fiber formation. The follicle bulb is one of the most active dividing tissues in the body. The proteins that compose keratin are formed in the keratogenous zone and are keratinized in the final hardening zone. The sebaceous gland and the sweat (or suderiferous) gland excrete wax and sweat, respectively, which diffuse over the fiber surface in the pilary canal. Coarse-wooled sheep and Angora goats produce less wax than fine-wooled sheep (e.g., karakul, 2.35%; merino, 14.3–16.1%). The arrector muscle has an inactive role in sheep but may influence crimp.

Two types of follicle have been distinguished in histological studies, primary and secondary. A primary follicle is shown in Fig. 5. Secondary follicles are similar in appearance but do not have sweat glands or arrector pili muscles. The development of follicles has been studied for sheep and Angora goats. In merino sheep, follicles are distinguishable in 60-day-old fetuses. All primary follicles produce a keratinized fiber by 108–110 days of fetal development. Some secondaries produce fiber by 120–145 days of development. Post-natal development of the remaining secondary follicles is rapid concluding about 6 months

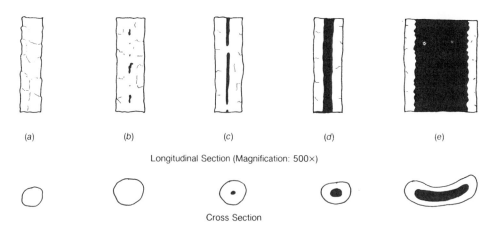

Longitudinal Section (Magnification: 500×)

Cross Section

FIGURE 3 Types and degrees of medullation in wool and mohair fibers.

after birth. The rate of development and number of secondary follicles formed during this time can be greatly affected by available nutrition. Even under optimum conditions of nutrition, a small percentage of the secondary follicles may never fully develop. In general, fibers produced by primary follicles are coarser than those produced in secondaries. The difference in average diameter between fibers produced in secondary compared to primary follicles is minimal for finewool breeds and substantial for coarse wool breeds and Angora goats.

Follicles lie at an acute angle in the skin surface. Generally groups of three primary follicles ("the trio") are associated with a specific number of secondary follicles, this number being very variable among breeds and between species. Within a breed, the ratio of secondary (S) to primary (P) follicles is somewhat variable with high S : P ratios being associated with high wool or mohair production of relatively fine fiber and vice versa.

VI. Breeding and Selection for Wool and Mohair

A. Sheep

In sheep, fleece traits are relatively high in heritability compared to reproductive and growth traits. Staple length and fiber diameter are both highly heritable (Table VI) whereas measures of fleece weight, yield, crimp, and luster fall in the medium or low to medium heritability categories. Occasionally, a black lamb occurs in a white flock. More commonly, a predominantly white lamb is born with a black spot in its fleece or on its eyelid, ear, leg, or foot. This important

fault in white finewool sheep appears to be inherited and is most commonly explained by the existence of a pair of recessive genes. Many variations in color are present in the sheep population and, with few exceptions, are due to differences in genetic makeup rather than environmental influences. Even in finewool sheep breeds, some lambs are born with hairy fleeces. The hair is usually shed before weaning. The presence of hair in the fleece, particularly in the region of the britch is a fault and is considered to be highly heritable by most sheep breeders. In Rambouillet and other finewool breeds, the appearance of wool grown on the belly is quite different from that grown elsewhere in the fleece. Belly wool is typically shorter, lower yielding, and contains different crimp than wool in the bulk of the fleece. When this type of wool extends beyond the belly, it is considered to be a fault since overall fleece weight is reduced. This trait is considered to have medium heritability. [*See* ANIMAL BREEDING AND GENETICS.]

Fleece traits correlate with each other to varying degrees. Most of the traits are positively correlated. Thus, selection for increased fleece weight is expected to also result in increased fiber length, for example.

TABLE VI

Heritability Estimates for Sheep Fleece Traits

Trait	Estimated range of heritability (%)
Grease fleece weight	30–40
Clean fleece weight	30–40
Yield of clean wool	30–40
Staple length	40–50
Fiber diameter	30–50
Crimp	20–30
Luster	20–30

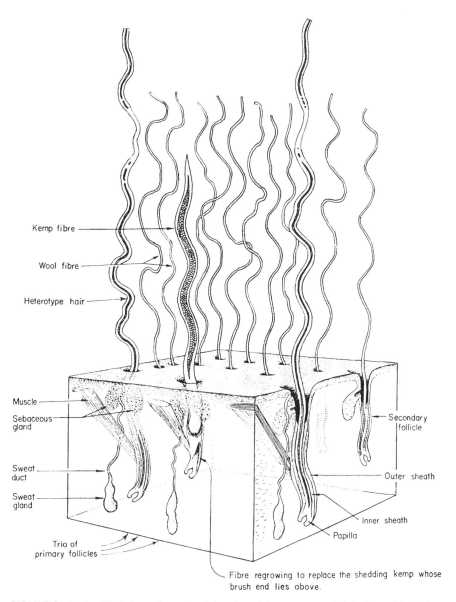

FIGURE 4 A simplified three-dimensional drawing of the structure of adult sheep skin. [After Ryder, M. L., and Stephenson, S. K. (1968). "Wool Growth." Academic Press, London.]

Unfortunately, the positive correlations of other traits with fiber diameter mean that selecting for one trait will result in an increase in average fiber diameter, this being particularly undesirable in finewool breeds. Conversely, selecting for finer wool will be expected to result in reduced fleece weight. A knowledge of correlations between fleece traits is a key factor in successful selection for more productive sheep. The situation is further complicated when traits not concerned with wool are taken into consideration, particularly in the so-called dual-purpose breeds where meat production is also a major factor. Selection for wool traits can be counterproductive for meat traits and vice versa.

Traditionally and in many flocks today, sheep are selected for wool traits using subjective methods, i.e., using the senses of sight and touch. Since objective methods are more accurate, progress can be accelerated by using measurements made with instruments. In large flocks, this may not be economically feasible so selection emphasis is placed primarily on the potential male stud animals that are subsequently used to breed many ewes. Superior young males are often identified using performance

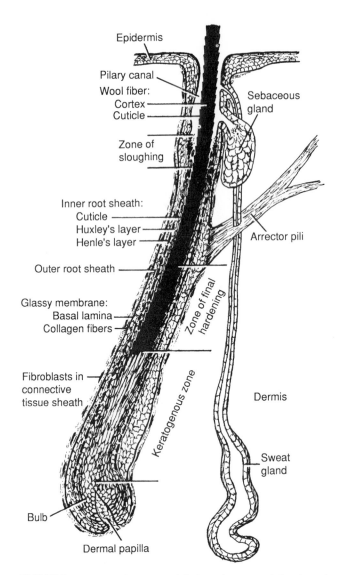

Epidermis

Pilary canal

Wool fiber:
Cortex
Cuticle

Sebaceous gland

Zone of sloughing

Inner root sheath:
Cuticle
Huxley's layer
Henle's layer

Arrector pili

Outer root sheath

Glassy membrane:
Basal lamina
Collagen fibers

Zone of final hardening

Fibroblasts in connective tissue sheath

Dermis

Keratogenous zone

Sweat gland

Bulb

Dermal papilla

FIGURE 5 Diagram of a primary follicle with a nonmedullated wool fiber. [After Chapman, R. E., and Ward, K. A. (1979). "Physiological and Environmental Limitations to Wool Growth." University of New England, Armidale.]

tests. Since wool traits are not perfectly heritable, desired changes are rarely achieved in one generation. Change in a particular trait that can be expected between generations may be predicted by multiplying selection differential by heritability. When average change in a particular trait for a ewe flock is being considered, then generation length must also be taken into account. Obviously, if ewes are being retained in a flock for 8 years, progress will be slower than if the generation interval were 3 or 4 years. Selection is not only practiced to alter or

improve traits but is necessary to maintain optimized production traits.

B. Angora Goats

Angora goats are raised primarily for their mohair. Production of meat from older animals or young cull goats is of secondary importance. Thus, the emphasis in selection is almost entirely on mohair production and quality. However, some attention must be paid to body conformation in order to retain functional, productive animals capable of surviving under harsh range conditions.

As with sheep, the amount of mohair grown in unit time is positively correlated with animal weight and fiber diameter. Selection for larger animals is desirable for several reasons. The greater skin area provides more sites for mohair production and larger size is positively associated with ease of kidding, fertility, and number of kids born and raised. However, size of goat must be balanced with fineness of mohair produced since only a small market exists for excessively coarse mohair. In addition to these factors, increased staple length, luster, style (number of twists per unit length in staple), and character (number of waves per unit length in staple) of mohair are traits assessed and selected for in Angora goats. Since medullated fibers constitute a serious fault, their presence in mohair is vigorously selected against using visual and objective techniques.

VII. Central Performance Tests

Since some meat production and wool traits are negatively correlated and since most wool and mohair traits require objective measurement for efficient selection, it is difficult for many sheep and Angora goat producers to properly identify potential stud animals. Central performance tests for sheep breeds in which wool production is important are typically conducted during the fall and winter months. Rams born the previous spring or fall are entered into these tests since testing animals that are younger than this does not give an accurate indication of future wool production or quality. Typically, body growth rate as well as wool traits are measured over a 4- to 6-month period while all the animals being tested are maintained under uniform conditions. Thus, central performance tests may be used as a basis for within- and between-flock selection of sires. Since the cost of testing animals is quite high, most cooperators in these central tests are pure breeders. However, the positive effects of the performance tests are also shared to some degree with commercial producers who purchase their replacement rams and billie goats from the pure-bred breeders.

Ranking of animals in performance tests is normally accomplished using an index equation since several traits, rather than a single trait, are being considered. For finewool, dual-purpose breeds such as the Rambouillet, the index contains such factors as daily body weight gain and final body weight in addition to the wool traits. Each trait is weighted in the index according to heritability, economic importance, and desired selection pressure.

Increased wool or mohair production may be achieved by selecting for increased fiber diameter, fiber length, and/or total number of fibers covering the body surface. This latter trait is most commonly estimated by measuring fiber density (or producing follicles per unit area) and estimating body surface area. Increases in fiber length, density, or body surface result in proportionate increases in clean wool production. Since volume is proportional to the square of fiber diameter, and weight is directly proportional to volume, it follows that doubling fiber diameter results in a fourfold increase in clean fiber production. Because of the price structure, it is not always economically advisable to increase mohair or wool production by selection for increased fiber diameter even though this is the most efficient way to do it.

The selection index equations used in the Texas Agricultural Experiment Station performance tests are as follows. For finewool rams:

Index value = 60 × [daily body weight gain in pounds] + 4 × [staple length in inches with no credit above 5.5 in.] + 4 × [12 months clean fleece weight in pounds adjusted for initial body weight] − 3 × [face cover score] − 4 × [skin fold score] with ± fiber diameter and variability points according to the following schedule. Fiber diameter on the side; −3 for each micron (μm) or fractional value above 22.9 μm and +3 for each μm or fractional value below 22.0 μm. Variability between side and britch diameter; −2.5 for each μm the britch is coarser than the side with no advantage if the britch is finer than the side wool.

For Angora billie goats the equation is

Index value = 4 × [clean fleece weight in pounds adjusted for initial weight] + 25 × [average daily body weight gain in pounds] + 0.12 × [final weight in pounds] + 3 × [straightened lock length in inches] − 1.5 × [average fiber diameter in μm] − 3 × [face cover score] + 2.5 × [character score] + 1.5 × [neck cover score].

Similar indices are being used in all the major wool and mohair production areas throughout the world to assist producers in selecting the most productive sires.

VIII. Environmental and Health Management Aspects of Fiber Production

A. Nutrition

Nutrient requirements of sheep and Angora goats are met primarily by native or improved ranges, fields, pastures, and crop residues. However, when these are not available or when it is desirable (e.g., fattening lambs for the meat market) diets are formulated and fed to support desired production levels. In the United States, excellent sources of detailed nutritional information for sheep and Angora goats are the National Research Council's (NRC) bulletins on recommended nutrient allowances. Specific information is presented on energy (total digestible nutrients, digestible energy, and metabolizable energy), crude protein, mineral, and vitamin requirements for many different categories of sheep and Angora goats. In addition, these bulletins list detailed compositions for sheep and goat feeds. These include: forages and roughages; pasture, range plants, and forages fed green; silages; energy feeds, protein, and mineral supplements. [See ANIMAL NUTRITION, RUMINANT; FEEDS AND FEEDING.]

The physical dimensions and hence the amount of wool and mohair produced by sheep and Angora goats are dependent upon the nutrition status of the animal. Generally, as the quality and quantity of available nutrition declines, fiber diameter and fiber length decrease resulting in lower wool and mohair production. The effects of short-term deficiencies in nutrition that may exist toward the end of pregnancy, when the fetus has a high demand on available nutrients, can have a substantial effect on wool fiber diameter and staple strength. The demands on a ewe during the last stages of gestation and during lactation are often so great that nutrients available for wool production become inadequate. At such times, the diameter of the fiber being produced can be reduced so dramatically as to cause a tender spot or "break" that affects the whole fleece. This defect in wool can greatly undermine its value particularly when a break exists close to the center of the staple, causing the broken halves to be too short for worsted processing. When a break occurs close to one end, this constitutes a less serious fault, but much short wool will be lost in carding and combing. The constitution of a female Angora goat (doe) is quite different from most ewes. When shortages of nutrition exist, the does tend to continue mohair production at rates close to optimal. Before fiber production is reduced significantly, the doe is more likely to abort her fetus. Hence, tender mohair, or mohair with breaks in the staple, is very unusual. It should be noted that disease and illness can also cause drastic changes in fiber diameter and production and that nutrition inadequacies are not always the cause of these problems in wool or mohair. Weak points in animal fibers are sometimes associated with radical changes in diet (e.g., from pasture to feedlot) or ingestion of poisonous plants. Even under optimal production conditions, finewool ewes raising a lamb will shear 10–20% less wool than one that is "dry." Similarly, ewes raising twin lambs will shear at least 5% less wool than ewes raising single lambs. These numbers are variable among breeds.

If a ewe or doe is undernourished during late pregnancy or lactation, there is little chance that her offspring will ever fulfill its maximum potential for fiber production. Only limited initiation and maturation of primary and secondary follicles occur in an undernourished fetus, lamb, or kid. No amount of feeding after the first few months of the animals life can correct this situation.

In relation to their size, Angora goats produce more fiber than Rambouillet sheep. Efficiency of fiber production is almost twice as high for the Angora goat compared to the Rambouillet sheep. Specific information is available in the technical literature on the effects of nutrition on wool and mohair production. There is a greater magnitude of wool data than mohair information. Nevertheless, knowing the breed (genetic background) of sheep and goats, their age and weight, conditions under which the animals are maintained, and health status and having specific knowledge of the type and quantity of food ingested, the amount and average diameter of fibers produced can be predicted with fair accuracy.

B. Flock Management

Several other aspects of environmental management influence the quality of wool and mohair production. Improperly designed feeding systems can result in fleeces contaminated with hay, pellets, and other feedstuffs. Improper pasture use results in fleeces heavily infested with plant seeds and parts. Ideally, sheep and goats are removed from contaminating pastures during the period when grass and plant seeds are falling and attempts are made to remove the objectionable plant species from the range. This is achieved by using combinations of chemical, mechanical, and fire treatments in addition to strategic grazing. Sometimes the problem of fleece contamination with vegetable matter can be avoided by heavy grazing of plants before seeds mature.

Colored fiber contamination is a serious problem in white wool and mohair. This problem can be minimized by shearing off all urine- and fecal-contaminated fibers sometime before shearing proper. This management practice, known as "tagging," is quite common in the sheep but not in the Angora goat industry. Most producers make an effort to remove colored fibers at shearing time. Connected with this issue is removal of belly fibers from the fleece. It has been shown that removal of belly wool from finewool sheep fleeces significantly reduces colored fiber counts in products made from the wool. Fibers from other animal species probably contribute to colored-fiber content of the belly wool. Separation of "belly mohair" is not a common practice in the United States.

Other fleece contaminants that the textile industry has focused on in recent years include polypropylene and branding paint. Polypropylene has many agricultural uses. Polypropylene twine is used to tie hay bales and polypropylene and polyethylene ribbon are used in the manufacture of some brands of feed sacks. Unfortunately, it finds its way into wool and mohair fleeces. With the characteristic of fibrillating when processed mechanically, it is invariably apparent in the final product where it constitutes a serious fault. Producers can eliminate the polypropylene contamination problem by removing all known sources of this contaminant from areas where sheep and goats are grazed, penned, and sheared. In some countries and locations within the United States, paint branding of sheep is required by law. To avoid permanent discoloration of the wool, producers should use only the recommended brands of "fully-scourable" paint. Failure to do so results in reduced value of the fiber.

Theoretically, shearing sheep and goats before lambing and kidding, particularly when the animals are moved indoors to give birth, results in cleaner, less contaminated fleeces. Many sheep producers are not prepared to follow this practice, mainly for environmental reasons. However, this is normal practice for Angora goats. However, shearing should be close to parturition since often the associated fever causes a temporary cessation of keratin production which manifests itself as a weak point in the fiber. The closer this weak point is to the base or tip of the fiber, the more value it will retain.

When accompanied by wind, heavy rain immediately after shearing can lead to disastrous livestock losses. High conduction heat-loss can affect animals within 30 min. The rapid chilling puts the freshly shorn animal into irreversible shock. Angora goats are more susceptible to this problem than sheep. However, it can be serious for both species. This problem can be avoided by providing shelter to animals immediately after shearing when weather conditions are unfavorable.

C. Health Management

Internal and external parasite infestation has been shown to reduce wool and mohair production. Even moderate populations of external parasites undermine the quality and appearance of wool and mohair since animals tend to entangle their fleeces as they rub to reduce skin irritation. Good managers ensure minimal infestation through regular and strategic drenching and spraying with anthelmintics and pesticides. Since animal health generally affects wool and mohair production and quality, successful managers also make conservative use of vaccines and antibiotics in their cost-effective health programs. Great variation exists among the health management practices of individual producers. On one extreme is the individual who has great concern for the well-being of the animals. At the other end of the spectrum is the producer who regards the animals simply as economic units.

Other health problems that have a direct effect on fiber quality and quantity are diseases of the skin. These can occur when the skin is damaged, e.g., at shearing or by plant-seed puncture, and becomes infected. Since treatment is not often feasible for individual animals in large flocks, the untreated infection can eventually cause death, more often through dehydration, since a very sick animal may not walk far to water. Mycotic dermatitis is an infection of fleece-zone skin that when left untreated, results in "lumpy" wool and possible death. Antibiotics can be used to treat this disease. [*See* ANIMAL DISEASES.]

Another skin disease that arises when sheep and goats remain wet for several days is caused by the bacterium *Pseudomonas aeruginosa*. Under warm, wet conditions, the bacteria multiply rapidly and give rise to a condition known as fleece rot. The wool and mohair are usually colored green/blue due to deposition of the pigment pyocyanine. This pigment is not easily scoured and constitutes a serious fault. In addition, affected fleeces smell badly and this attracts blow flies. Thus, fleece rot is often the cause of a fly strike. The larvae feed on the wet wool adjacent to the skin, causing fiber to detach. Affected animals are shorn completely and affected areas are treated with ointments, sprays, or powders.

Skin infections often result in abscesses in lymph nodes. *Caseous lymphadenitis* produces green pus in these abscesses. Although these do not usually adversely affect fiber production, their presence can cause carcasses for meat to be condemned.

Scab (scabies or mange) affects sheep and goats. Several types of minute mites are responsible for this condition. The mites live on tissue serum and cause intense itching. Thus, the wool or mohair is typically rubbed off by the irritated animal and scaly lesions appear. Affected animals become emaciated and anemic. Specific miticides are recommended by veterinarians.

IX. Physical Properties and Characterization

Fleece and fiber characteristics of white wool and mohair that are of primary importance to the worsted industry are: yield, including quantity and type of vegetable matter; average fiber diameter; average staple length; staple strength and position of break; color; and proportion of colored fibers. In the case of mohair, the proportion of medullated fiber and the amount of luster are also of primary importance. Traits of secondary importance include: variability of fiber diameter, variability of staple length; proportion of matted fibers (cots); and resistance to compression. Other value-determining characteristics include: presence/absence of weathered tips; age/breed/type; style; character; and handle. Most of these properties can be measured with instruments which makes the measurements "objective." Some properties can only be assessed using human judgment, which is "subjective" measurement. Individual batches of wool and mohair are variable in all of the properties listed. Variability exists in individual staples and even within single fibers. Thus, methods were developed to sample wool and mohair to obtain representative samples. These methods fall into two categories, core sampling and grab sampling, the latter being used when staple length must be preserved. Packages of greasy or scoured fiber are typically core-sampled with tubes measuring 2.2 cm ($\frac{7}{8}$ in.) or, in the United States, 5.1 cm (2 in.) in diameter. These samples are used to measure all the listed characteristics except for length.

Standard test methods and practices of the International Wool Textile Organisation (IWTO) and the International Mohair Association (IMA) are used throughout the world to characterize the physical properties of wool and mohair. In addition, most producing and manufacturing countries maintain their own national test methods. In the United States, these methods are under the jurisdiction of the American Society for Testing and Materials (ASTM).

Wool and mohair fibers are hygroscopic, meaning they are capable of absorbing moisture and losing it when the humidity or temperature of the surrounding atmosphere changes. Despite this property, which relies on gaseous adsorption and desorption of water vapor, the fibers themselves are measurably water repellant due to the lipophilic surface of the epicuticle. The ability of wool and mohair to retain moisture without feeling wet is responsible for many of the associated comfort properties. It also makes it necessary to specify the temperature and humidity at which fibers are tested since temperature and moisture content affect most physical properties. Standard conditions of testing for wool and mohair are 20°C and 65% RH throughout the world. When wool and mohair are equilibrated under these conditions after being "bone" dried, the fibers contain less moisture than when they are conditioned from the wet side. Convention requires, therefore, that fibers be dried prior to testing, yield testing being the exception.

The standard test methods for yield have changed little since their introduction. Basically, the methods involve scouring greasy samples in hot, soapy water followed by determination of residual grease, inorganic ash, and vegetable content of the dried and scoured fiber. Wool or mohair "base" can be calculated from these data. Various factors may be applied to the base yield to incorporate standard amounts of moisture and permitted tolerance levels of ash and grease. These methods are accurate but tedious. Near infrared reflectance spectroscopy is being investigated as a potential replacement.

After yield, average diameter is the most important value-determining factor of wool and mohair within a specific length category. Fiber diameter and length determine the fineness of yarn that can be spun from a particular batch of fibers. In fact, old subjective methods for expressing fineness of wool and mohair use a system composed of yarn sizes to indicate fiber fineness (e.g., 30's to 80's for wool and 18's to 40's for mohair). The numbers refer to the number of 560 yard hanks in one pound of the finest yarn that can be spun from that fiber. Increased speed of processing and worsted spinning are making these values obsolete and the numbers have only theoretical value now.

Internationally, microprojection techniques for determining fiber fineness and distribution (in microns = one millionth of a meter) have been the standard for many years. Although accurate, these methods are slow and tedious and have been replaced in many testing facilities by air-flow instruments. Air-flow is relatively fast and accurate but is not capable of measuring distribution of fineness. Modern technology (e.g., computers, lasers, and automatic image analysis) is currently being evaluated to provide rapid measures of these important fiber diameter traits. Staple length determines primarily which system will be used to spin the fibers, i.e., worsted, woolen, or short staple. A highly significant linear relationship exists between staple length of sound greasy fibers and average fiber length in top. This, in turn, has a major influence on spinning capabilities. Traditionally, manual means have been used to quantify length and length distribution. However, semi-automated, photoelectric methods are now available to determine this characteristic more rapidly. Staple strength is a major determinant of yarn strength. Several instruments were developed for measuring the strength of individual, greasy staples and even fibers. Current state-of-the-art instrumentation for measuring staple length and strength is the Automatic Tester for Length and Strength (ATLAS). This instrument is being used commercially to provide presale staple length and strength data for Australian wools.

The color of greasy wool and mohair is not strongly correlated with clean wool color or whiteness. Thus, wool and mohair are washed before this characteristic is determined. The presence of colored (yellow, brown, and black) fibers in white wool and mohair constitutes a serious fault and greatly undermines value since the fibers are no longer suitable for use in white or pastel textiles. Because colored fibers are usually in very low concentration and not uniformly distributed throughout accumulations of wool or mohair, testing for their presence in greasy samples does not usually produce an accurate answer. After scouring and mechanical processing, all the homogenizing that takes place up to top production provides a structure (the top) in which colored fiber content can be determined with accuracy. This is normally determined by counting the number of colored fibers in unit weight of top. Image analysis techniques are being investigated to provide an objective measurement of this undesirable trait. Because of difficulties involved in obtaining a representative sample, it is doubtful that an objective method of measuring dark fibers in greasy wool or mohair can be developed.

Visual appraisal of crimp frequency and definition in wool has been used to estimate average fiber diameter and resistance to compression. Instruments are available for more accurate determinations. Resistance to compression provides a measure of the bulkiness of wool which is very important to manufacturers of sweaters, carpets, and futons.

There is currently no objective measure of luster in wool or mohair. However, luster visually assessed in the clean portion at the greasy staple base provides a reasonable estimate of the degree of luster that will be present after scouring. Medullation, particularly in carpet wools and mohair, is an important measurable characteristic. In carpet wools, medullation is a desirable trait. In mohair, kemp fibers (medullation greater than 60% of fiber diameter) represent a serious fault. An instrument was developed for measuring total medullation in wool and mohair (the Medullameter) but it is incapable of differentiating between med (medullation less than 60% of fiber diameter) and kemp fibers, the latter being much more undesirable than the former. Thus, the basis for most medullated fiber measurements is still the projection microscope, although again, an image analysis technique is being developed to provide a faster result.

In mohair terminology, style and character of greasy staples refer to the twist (ringlets) per unit length and the number of waves per unit length, respectively. Although these traits are normally assessed subjectively, they can be painstakingly measured with a ruler. The amount of style and/or character in mohair is thought to be indicative of the length and length variability that can be obtained in top after mechanical processing. These relationships have not been quantified.

Many physical properties of wool and mohair are usually invariable and therefore, not measured routinely on individual lots. Such properties include elasticity, conductivity of heat, flammability, felting propensity, durability, softness, resistance to soiling, and drape. Keratin fibers are noted for their ability to recover from stretching, a property that is attributable to the cell structure and chemistry of the fibers. Elasticity is important for the comfort and ease of care (including shape retention and crease shedding) of garments made from wool and mohair. Wool and mohair do not readily conduct heat. Thus, when knitted or woven into clothes, the tiny pockets of air formed in the fabric structure serve to keep the body at a reasonably constant temperature in both excessively hot or cold climates. Wool and mohair do not burn readily when exposed to a flame and are self-extinguishing when the heat source is removed. Thus, wool and mohair are ideal fibers in end-uses that require flame retardance such as children's sleepwear, wallcoverings, carpets, and upholstery. The natural flame retardance of wool and mohair alone or in blends with natural and synthetic fibers can be enhanced by application of chemicals.

When subjected to intermittent pressure and heat in the presence of moisture, fabrics composed of wool mat or felt to varying degrees. This property is a direct result of the scale structure in the cuticle which gives rise to the "differential frictional effect" and which is not so apparent in the relatively smooth mohair fibers. In addition to commercial felts, felting is essential to obtain the required effect in a broad spectrum of wool fabrics ranging from minimal felting in worsted suitings to a significant amount in brushed woolen coating materials.

Wool and mohair are extremely durable. Protected from moth, chemical, and mechanical damage, textiles composed of these fibers are longlasting. The longevity of mohair upholstery pile fabrics used in public transportation is legend. Generally, the coarser the fiber, the longer the product will resist wear. Coarser fibers are normally restricted to use in carpets, upholstery, and outerwear whereas the finer, softer grades are used in garments that are worn next to the skin. Softness is particularly important in textiles composed of woolen yarns for which many users have an expectancy for comfort and softness. In such end-uses, many synthetic fibers and the coarser types of wool and mohair simply cannot perform. Unlike nylon and polyester, wool and mohair do not permit build-up of static electricity except under very dry conditions. The anti-static properties also contribute to the resistance to soiling of wool and mohair textiles. Further, the bright colors of dyed wool and mohair fabrics can easily be returned from soiled textiles by either aqueous or solvent cleaning. However, care must be taken in the case of wool to avoid matting or felting shrinkage.

The term "drape" refers to the way a fabric hangs from or around the object it is covering. Wool and mohair fabrics are considered to have excellent drape when used in a range of products from high quality suitings, to drapes, to outerwear garments. The drape and grace exhibited by wool and mohair in well-tailored suits are seldom surpassed using fabrics composed of synthetic fibers.

X. Specialty Wool and Mohair

An increased demand for colored wool has resulted from the re-emergence, growth, and popularity of handcrafts including handspinning, weaving, and knitting. Specialized markets exist throughout the world, but particularly in Europe and the United States, for properly prepared colored fleeces that exhibit the attributes desired by handspinners. More recently, a demand has also been created for naturally colored mohair. Although goat geneticists might deny the existence of a colored gene in purebred Angora goats, the fact remains that a few colored goats are born, even in tightly controlled Angora goat flocks. Thus, in the United States and Australia, small flocks of these colored Angora goats have been established and are being maintained and bred specifically for the handcraft trade. The range of available colors in mohair, which include black, brown, taupe, and gray, is far less than the broad spectrum available in wool. Besides color, other desirable features of fleeces intended for the handspinning market include adequate length (>10 cm), structural soundness of fibers (no breaks), and freedom from stains and vegetable matter defect. Fleeces coarser than 25 μm with distinct crimp and luster seem to be most popular with handspinners.

Another form of specialty wool is the so-called "superfine" wool currently being produced in Australia under the auspices of the Sharlea Society. Sheep in range flocks are selected for their ability to produce wool finer than 18 μm and longer than 85 mm. These sheep are sheared, fitted with protective coats, and kept indoors eating carefully controlled diets. The wool produced is extremely fine, clean, strong, and uniform and commands high prices at auction. About 50,000 kg were produced in 1990 with Japanese textile firms being the major buyers. This type of wool is used to produce suitings and knitwear of the highest quality. On a smaller scale, New Zealand also has enterprises with coated sheep, but in that country the sheep are maintained on pasture.

Certain breeds of sheep grow wool that is not often used in the mainstream of textiles or constitutes only a small proportion of the whole. Although these wools are not necessarily expensive, they are regarded as specialty products. Further, modern marketing methods have done much to enhance the reputation of erstwhile ordinary wools, e.g., British wools, to the point where they are now sold as specialty wools. Similar marketing methods are being practiced in countries of origin to enhance the reputations of mohair, e.g., "Texas" and "Cape" mohair. Thus, it is somewhat difficult to differentiate between a true specialty product and a good marketing ploy. The specific attributes of wool produced by different sheep breeds were discussed previously.

Historically, mohair with excellent style (i.e., ringlet staples) has been carefully hand scoured and dried to produce "hair" for dolls. Although this business is relatively small, it does exist. Only long, clean, white, lustrous staples may be used in this product.

Lastly, some of the most specialized wools come from sheep that have been selected and bred specifically for carpet-wool production. Such breeds include the Drysdale, Tukidale, Elliotdale, and Carpetmaster that produce straight, heavily medullated (>20%) wool in a range around 40 μm. These wools, though excellent in carpets, have little or no utility outside of these products and are produced primarily in New Zealand but also in the high rainfall areas of Australia.

XI. Shearing, Preparation, and Classing

Most sheep are shorn once a year thus providing wool of adequate length for processing on the worsted system. Some breeds of sheep (e.g., Drysdale) and Angora goats grow wool and mohair so fast that it is shorn at 6-month intervals and still has adequate length for worsted processing. In hot climates where high atmospheric temperatures are thought to impair lamb production, some sheep are shorn twice or even three times a year, thus producing short wool which is suitable only for processing on the woolen, cotton, or short-staple systems.

Methods of removing wool and mohair from the animals vary among countries. The shearing method that has evolved for sheep in Australia and other major wool producing countries involves maneuvering the animal through a sequence of positions in which it is comfortable but essentially immobile. In this way, the skin is kept tight while the majority of the fleece is removed in one piece using electric shears or clippers. In countries influenced by Spanish culture, including the United States, following removal of belly and some leg wool, the legs of sheep and Angora goats are tied together before the bulk of the fleece is removed. In South Africa, many Angora goats are still shorn with hand shears. Research into chemical and robotic shearing of sheep has been undertaken for years. To date, no economical shearing method has been devised to replace manpower.

Facilities for shearing sheep and goats vary considerably among and within countries. In the major wool-producing countries, most ranches, stations, and farms have permanent facilities, typically consisting of a complex arrangement of pens and a substantial building (Fig. 6) containing more pens, a shearing floor, and room to sort and package the wool or mohair. Sheep and goats in other countries, including many locations in the United States, are shorn in temporary shearing facilities or buildings that are used for other purposes during the remainder of the year. Whatever the physical plant, shearing is usually contracted by the producer since it is a highly skilled profession. Permanent damage can be done to the animal and the fibers if untrained shearers are used. In the United States, shearing facilities span the whole spectrum from tents or tarps set up on the open range, to dirt floors in the corner of barns, to customized shearing trailers, to Australian-style shearing facilities. Whatever the facilities, some precautions are usually followed before shearing and are generally the producer's responsibility. Sheep and goats are held in clean, dry pens or small pastures (traps) without feed and water for 12 hr prior to shearing. The animals are not bedded down on straw or hay since this contaminates the fibers. The producer provides enough laborers to deliver the animals to the shearers and to handle the fleeces and sheep or goats after shearing. However, many shearing companies offer a turn-key job and provide this labor, tables for skirting, skirters, classers, and wool balers. It is to the producer's advantage to organize all these details prior to the day of shearing.

Traditionally, wool and mohair were shorn and the whole fleece was placed into some kind of receptacle (e.g., a large jute bag), packaged, and sold. The different qualities or grades of fiber in a single package were not separated until it arrived at a textile mill or custom sorting facility. However, adding value to these fibrous commodities is now an objective of most wool and mohair producers in the world. Thus, wool and mohair fleeces are often skirted and classed prior to packaging and marketing. Skirting is the practice of separating all inferior fleece portions such as belly fiber, urine-stained, and fecal-contaminated fibers from the bulk of the fleece immediately after shearing (Fig. 7). The products of skirting wool are termed "skirted wool" and "skirts." There are several categories of skirts separated for their different compositions and values. The term more commonly used when applied to mohair is "preparation" but implies essentially similar treatment of the fleece. After the different components have been separated, the bulk of the fleece is classed. This means that skirted fleeces are grouped according to (visually assessed) fineness, yield, vegetable matter content and type, staple length, strength, and color. In the United States, the term "grading" means grouping fleeces according to average fiber diameter. However, some confusion exists and the terms "grading" and "classing" are used interchangeably (but incorrectly) by many people. When classing

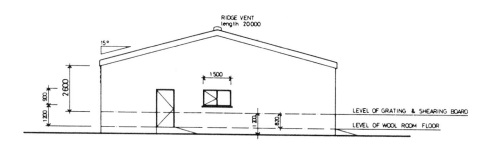

EAST ELEVATION

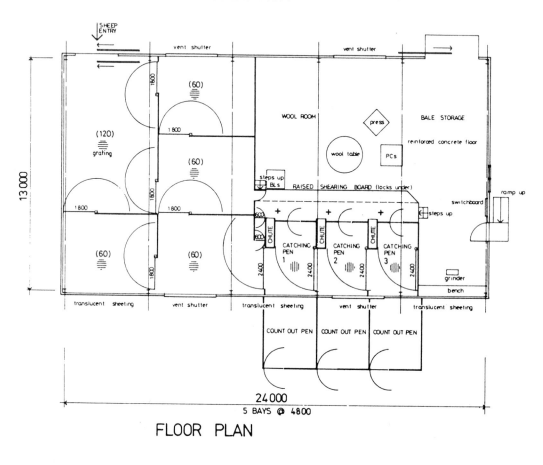

FLOOR PLAN

FIGURE 6 A three-stand Australian style shearing shed design. [Adapted from Wool Harvesting Notes, Wool Research Trust Fund, Sydney. 1982. Plan No. 4310.]

is performed at a brokerage firm or textile mill by highly trained personnel, the process is called "sorting." Long-term experience in Australia, New Zealand, and South Africa together with recent research studies and actual use in the United States, have shown that skirting and classing of wool immediately after shearing are indeed value-adding procedures for the producer. The same cannot be said for mohair, although preparation and classing are standard procedures throughout South Africa. In Texas, much of the mohair is packaged directly without skirting but simply grouping fleeces by animal age, e.g., kid, young goat, adult. Fleeces packaged in this way are known in the trade as "original bag" mohair.

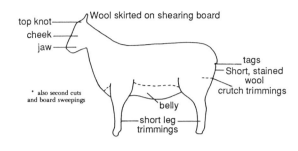

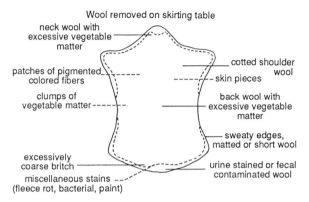

FIGURE 7 Wool skirting. [After Lupton, C. J., Pfeiffer, F. A., and Blakeman, N. E. (1989). "Optimizing the value of grease wool through preparation and marketing." *SID Res. J.* **5**, 2.]

In the major wool-producing countries, wool is packaged in bales. Fleeces placed in older types of baling machines are manually pressed through a system of mechanical levers whereas the newer versions are driven by electric or gasoline motors that hydraulically press the wool. Both systems are capable of producing bales of uniform size and weight (200 kg). Elsewhere in the world, many other forms of packaging exist. In the United States, for many years the standard form of packaging has been burlap sacks measuring between 1.8 and 2.5 m in length. These sacks are capable of being manually or mechanically packed. However, the density of the resulting package is much lower than a bale. Since wool bags are awkward to stack and cannot be efficiently packaged in shipping containers, five or six bags are typically baled together in the warehouse prior to shipment. Progressive producers and warehouses in the United States are now using Australian-style balers. In South Africa, the whole mohair clip is baled. In contrast, most of the U.S. clip is packaged in jute bags. Traditionally, baling material has also been composed of jute. However, polyethylene and polypropylene bale covers are now being used since they are considered to result in less contamination of the wool within the bale. The issue of jute versus hydrocarbon divides the wool

industry at this time since advantages and disadvantages exist for both fiber classes. Whatever the form, the outside of the package is usually inscribed with enough information to identify the source of the wool or mohair, the type or class of fiber, classer (if used), and the number of the sack or bale.

XII. Marketing of Wool and Mohair

In this context, marketing is considered to be the aggregate of functions involved in moving the fibrous raw materials from producer to textile manufacturer. Thus, method of selling is just one part of the overall marketing strategy. For both wool and mohair, broad spectra of marketing methods exist, even within a single country. It is beyond the scope of this article to cover all known marketing methods for wool and mohair. Rather, some of the simplest and some of the more innovative will be considered. In the United States, a proportion of all wool and mohair is prepared for sale simply by shearing it from the animal, packaging whole fleeces in jute bags, and transporting the bags to warehouses or cooperatives. Such packaged products, known as "original bag," are made available for inspection to buyers who purchase the fiber after making subjective assessments. In contrast, an increasing proportion of U.S. wool and mohair is skirted and classed on the farm or ranch during shearing. Bales containing single classes of wool are delivered to warehouses where they are core-sampled prior to storing. Typically, the core samples are tested for clean yield and average fiber diameter, and this information is made available to potential buyers at the time of sale. This method of marketing wool (and mohair) in discrete classes and with objective measurements is modelled on methods developed in Australia. South Africa and New Zealand also market their wool and mohair in a similar manner.

Until recently, Australia and New Zealand both used floor-price schemes in an attempt to stabilize wool prices. A period of good demand and high prices for wool was followed by overproduction and decreased demand which culminated in early 1991 in the collapse of these schemes in Australia and New Zealand, but not in South Africa. Wool and mohair in that country is still purchased by national marketing boards when auction prices fall below predetermined levels. However, the major wool-producing countries (and the United States) now have "free" markets which once again are subject to rapid fluctuations in price.

Major sectors of the Australian wool industry are the growers, brokers, buyers, testers, "dumpers," processors, and the Australian Wool Corporation (AWC). The growers raise the sheep and have them sheared by some of the 13,000 unionized shearers. Shorn wool is classed by some 35,000 registered woolclassers, the majority of whom are trained producers who prefer to class their own wool. The different lines are then packed into bales and delivered to the broker. Woolbrokers act as agents for the growers in the sale of their wool. There are about 30 brokers in Australia handling the majority of Australian wool that is sold by auction. In addition to warehousing the grower's wool, the broker obtains representative grab and core samples for display use and for testing of core and grab samples by the Australian Wool Testing Authority (AWTA). The test information is made available to buyers prior to the time of sale. The broker is also responsible for organizing and advertising auctions, conducting the financial transactions, and arranging for the physical delivery of the wool. Other optional services available to the grower include bulk classing and reclassing, blending of lots, and sampling of wool not sold under the sale by sample scheme.

Wool-buying firms purchase wool through the auction system for individual overseas mills, a variety of clients, Australian textile companies, and speculatively for their own accounts. In addition, private buyers travel the country purchasing wool directly from growers. Less than 20% of Australian wool is sold outside the auction system via private treaty.

The AWTA provides accurate, impartial testing services in an attempt to "maximize net income to the Australian wool industry by encouraging the optimum application of objective measurements by woolgrowers, brokers, buyers and processors."

The wool dumping section of the industry compresses the farm bales into more compact bales, usually just prior to shipment, thereby minimizing freight costs.

The AWC was incorporated in 1973 having responsibilities associated with marketing and domestic promotion of the Australian clip. Funds are provided by a levy on proceeds from wool sales. The AWC participates in and makes recommendations for wool research conducted by Australian and international agencies. In addition, the AWC is also charged with maintaining the quality of clip preparation. This is achieved through the operation of a voluntary, woolclasser registration scheme, a clip inspection service, and general extension work.

In Great Britain, marketing techniques are quite different. Nearly all the fleece wool is sold through the producer-operated British Wool Marketing Board (BWMB) which was established in 1950. The Board arranges for wool received from the farmer to be classed at a central location and then sells it to the trade at auction. The Board is also responsible for fleece improvement and wool preparation programs and policies and promotion of wool sales. The Board sponsors wool research and product development. Without the BWMB, the vast majority of producers selling individually could not hope to obtain full market value for their small, variable clips. The system appears to be working well since, for its type, British wool regularly commands the highest price in the world.

Each year, the government establishes a guaranteed price for British wools after consultation with the farmers' unions. The Board then estimates its marketing costs and deducts this from the overall guaranteed price. A schedule of maximum prices for all grades is then prepared and made available to producers in April, prior to shearing time. This schedule of prices reflects changes in the relative market prices of different grades from the previous year and results in the payment of an average price to all producers of a particular grade who present their wool in the recommended manner. The effect of this pricing mechanism is to eliminate short-term price fluctuations to producers while passing on long-term market differentials. When the proceeds of the Board's wool auctions exceed the amount paid to producers in any one year, the excess goes into a reserve account. When the situation is reversed, money is withdrawn from the reserve or borrowed from the government. Special arrangements are made with the government to avoid excessive accumulations of debts or credit balances.

In the United States, most wool and mohair is sold through commission warehouses, cooperatives, and wool pools. Some wool and mohair is still sold directly by producers to order buyers, independent warehouses, or representatives of textile firms. In recent years, there has been a trend in both the wool and mohair sectors for marketing organizations to band together to offer larger accumulations of classed wool and mohair matchings. For wool, the U.S. Wool Marketing Association is leading the way in innovative marketing while the U.S. Mohair Marketing Board is serving a similar role for mohair. Public auction, though popular for livestock, is not a common method of selling wool and mohair in the United States. Despite recent attempts to use this method of sale, sealed bid, direct, private treaty, and forward contract remain the predominant methods of sale.

XIII. The National Wool Act in the United States

Recognizing wool as an essential and strategic commodity, the Congress of the United States established the National Wool Act in 1954 to provide wool and mohair producers with price stability and financial incentives to keep producing and improving the quality of their products. Today, more than 125,000 families consider that raising sheep and goats is an important part of their ranching/farming operations. Since low-cost wool imports continue to threaten the livelihoods of these people and many more thousands of U.S. textile workers, the existence of the Wool Act is still of vital importance to them. The program also has a self-help aspect. Producers have the option to give up a portion of their incentive payment to fund promotional and market development programs for wool, mohair, and lamb, operations which are now coordinated by the American Sheep Industry Association (ASI) and the Mohair Council of America (MCA). The incentive program is funded by tariffs on imported wool and mohair, both raw materials and textiles. For example, in 1988, $435 million was collected in wool tariffs. Producers received $86.4 million in incentive payments and $348.6 million remained in the U.S. Treasury. The National Wool Act makes it economically possible to produce wool and mohair in the United States today. It is surprising, even to other agricultural commodity groups, that the program is able to function without any direct cost to the U.S. taxpayer. On the contrary, the mechanism put into place to fund the incentive program invariably produces excess funds available for other taxpayer-supported programs.

According to the Act, a certain price is set each marketing year to encourage increased production and improved quality. This national support level is set by the Secretary of Agriculture. A second formula based on the historical value of wool production of lambs is used to determine the average price to be paid for the weight of wool on unshorn lambs marketed. Sheep and goat raisers that participate in this program must file sales receipts at their local Agricultural Stabilization and Conservation Service office for all their wool and mohair sales within a specific calendar year. This permits calculation of a national average price

for wool and mohair. Subsequently, the national incentive levels are calculated.

For example, if the national support level is set at $1.81/lb and the actual weighted average price of U.S. wool is $0.87/lb, then the national incentive level will be 108% (i.e., $1.81 − $0.87 = $0.94; ($0.94 ÷ $0.87) × 100 = 108%). Thus, a producer selling his wool for $1.00/lb will also receive an incentive payment of $1.08 (less ASI deductions). The greater the price received for wool, the greater incentive payment, up to a limit of four times the national average price. Thus, the Act provides a real incentive for the production of more and higher quality wool. The mohair program works in a similar manner. However, the actual support level set for mohair is invariably different (and higher) than that established for wool. There is no incentive payment on unshorn Angora goats.

In 1993, the U.S. government decided to phase out this incentive program over a 3-year period. This action is expected to have a short-term negative effect on the viability of the sheep and goat industries.

XIV. Scouring

Wool and mohair in bales or baled bags are allowed to "bloom" (recover from high compression) before opening. Opening is a mechanical cleaning process in which compressed fleeces are transformed into individual staples. A significant amount of loose dirt and vegetable material is removed in this process. Wool and mohair are scoured (washed) before further mechanical processing to remove as much of the nonkeratinous material as possible with minimal entanglement of the fibers. Suint, being soluble in water, is easily removed. Wool and mohair waxes are emulsified in aqueous solutions at temperatures above the melting point of the waxes (>50°C). Traditionally, solutions of soap and sodium carbonate were used to emulsify waxes from natural fibers and to stabilize the resultant emulsions. Commercially, soaps have been replaced by more efficient nonionic detergents. Cleansing of the fibers is achieved as the fibers are raked slowly through a sequence of four to six scouring baths. Intermediate squeezing between high-pressure rollers minimizes contamination from one bath into the next. Grease levels are reduced to below 1% (typically 0.4–0.8%) in the scouring process, and residual detergent is rinsed out in the last scouring bath, this being composed of clean, warm water only. The slow action of the rakes, essential to avoid felting or matting of wool, belies the large throughput of scouring trains. Modern, 2-m-wide minibowl scouring trains are capable of cleansing more than 1400 kg of greasy wool per hour ($\equiv > 1000$ kg/hr of New Zealand crossbred wool). Mohair is less susceptible to entanglement in scouring and, since it initially contains lower levels of wax than most wools, it can be scoured at a faster rate. Waxes removed in the scouring process are reclaimed from the effluent of scouring plants. Partially refined waxes are used as industrial greases, particularly in applications where water resistance is required. Wool and mohair wax is further refined to produce lanolin which is used in cosmetics and ointments. Traditional scouring of wool and mohair is now considered to be quite wasteful in terms of energy and water usage. Modern technology has drastically reduced the amounts of water and energy required to cleanse the greasy products. An added bonus of this technology is that effluent can be treated more efficiently, thus reducing the cost of wax removal and the cost of making the effluent environmentally acceptable. A combination of high effluent treatment and shipping costs has resulted in the relocation of many scouring plants from the countries where wool and mohair are manufactured to the locations where the fibers are produced. This trend is expected to continue into the 21st century.

Only small amounts of certain types of vegetable material are removed in scouring. Further mechanical processing (carding, gilling, and combing) is necessary to remove the rest. In cases where the vegetable content is deemed too high for mechanical removal alone, the trade resorts to a process known as "carbonizing." In this process, scoured wool or mohair is impregnated with a dilute solution (6%) of sulfuric acid. The impregnated fiber is then squeezed to produce a specific uptake of acid and the fibers are then dried and subjected to temperatures around 105°C for a short time. The combined effect of heat and acid converts the cellulosic, vegetable impurities to carbon. The carbon residue is subsequently crushed and shaken out of the fibrous mass. Neutralizing the fibers in a dilute solution of sodium carbonate followed by a further rinse in a very dilute detergent solution completes the carbonizing process. The fibers are then redried. In addition to removing plant parts and other vegetable material, carbonization can reduce the strength of the wool and mohair and cause the fibers to be more brittle and harsher to the touch. Even under optimum conditions, the process causes the luster of mohair to be diminished.

A number of chemical processes can be carried out in the scouring train once the majority of dirt and grease has been removed. These include bleaching (with bisulfite or hydrogen peroxide), mothproofing, applying bacteriostatic finishes, and dyeing (including application of optical brighteners).

XV. Mechanical Processing

Fibers exiting the dryer after scouring are entangled to varying degrees. Generally, finer fibers are more matted than coarser fibers as a result of the scouring and drying processes. Typically, scoured batches of wool or mohair are blended in various methods using vast machines designed for the purpose. Blending at this stage assures homogeneity of the finished products. Blended fibers are then carded to disentangle the wool or mohair, to remove vegetable material, and produce a fiber web or sliver for further processing. In carding, fibers are essentially separated and individualized by the action of metallic card wires or clothing which are attached to the surface of large and small rotating drums. In the "woolen system" the card web is fed through a condenser in which it is split into continuous, narrow (1.2 cm) strips along its length. False twist is applied to each of the strips which are then wound onto a spool. The resulting product, know as "roving," "roping," or "slubbing," becomes the feed stock for a woolen spinning frame. In this machine, fibers in the roving are drawn out and twisted to produce the desired size (weight per unit length) and type of yarn. Woolen yarns are normally composed of relatively short fibers loosely spun to form a bulky yarn, such as those used in sweaters, tweeds, and blankets. Worsted yarns are composed of longer fibers and are uniform, smooth, lean, and relatively strong. Fabrics composed of worsted yarns such as fine dress fabrics and suitings are typically tightly woven and have extremely smooth surfaces. Worsted yarns require several more processing steps than woolen yarns. In the worsted process, fiber exiting the worsted card is condensed into a sliver. Several card slivers become the feed stock for "gilling" or "pin drafting." In these processes, multiple slivers are drawn down between two sets of rollers while the fiber movement is controlled between rows of pins. The resulting sliver is more uniform (in terms of weight per unit length) and contains fibers that are more parallel in the longitudinal direction than the feedstock. Slivers containing parallelized fibers are mechanically combed to remove short fibers (noils). The rectilinear or French comb predominates in today's worsted industry. However, circular Noble combs are still functioning in some combing plants. The resulting combed sliver is no longer uniform in terms of weight per unit length so it is subjected to at least one but usually several more gilling processes before being wound into balls prior to shipment to a worsted spinning plant. The product after combing and finisher gilling is known in the trade as "top." Top is produced by firms that call themselves top-makers or combers and is sold in the international trade to companies that refer to themselves as worsted spinners. Using pin-drafting, drawing, and/or roving machines, spinning companies attenuate top to a structure referred to as roving. Worsted roving which contains some twist then becomes feedstock for the worsted spinning frame where worsted yarns are finally produced. Ring spinning is by far the most important process used to produce worsted yarns. However, some yarns are still produced by the old flyer and cap spinning systems. New open-end and Repco spinning systems are used to produce specialty yarns. At least one further process after spinning is required to wind the yarn from the small spinning bobbins onto large packages suitable for dyeing, weaving, or knitting. Additionally, individual yarns may be twisted together to form two- (or more) ply yarns using a machine known as a twister.

XVI. Woven and Knitted Fabrics, Carpets, and Felts

Woven fabrics composed of worsted or woolen yarns are constructed on looms by interlacing yarns that intersect each other at right angles. The yarns in the longitudinal direction of the fabric are referred to as "warp" while those that run across the width are called "filling" or "weft." Typically, worsted fabrics are light and durable with individual yarns being visible. Woven worsted fabrics are stronger, smoother, and often more expensive than woolen fabrics. It is not uncommon for a finished woolen fabric to have a completely different appearance than the loom-state product. Finishing for most woven worsted fabrics entails removal of surface fiber ends to create a clear, flat finish. In contrast, finishing of woolen fabrics requires various degrees of felting and usually raising of surface hairs. These processes are described in more detail in the next section.

Weaving is the most widely used fabric construction technique. Many different interlacing patterns (weaves) exist which produce wide variation in appearance and utility. The simplest and most common design is the plain weave. Other common constructions include twill, satin, crepe, and pile (looped and cut) weaves. Many permutations exist within a particular weave type. Specific weaves can be further altered in appearance by changing yarn types and sizes and/or the number of warp and weft threads per unit area.

Most of the designs that are constructed today on complex modern looms were also conceived and constructed by early, primitive weavers. However, evolution of the loom has permitted mass production of woven fabrics of uniform, high quality. In the traditional type of loom, the shuttle carries the filling yarn through the separated warp yarns. Once in place, the filling yarn is pushed into place using a reed. At this point, the positions of the warp yarns are changed and the next weft thread is inserted. The most visible changes that have occurred in loom technology concern the method used to insert the weft thread. To produce faster and quieter looms, the shuttle has been replaced by numerous mechanisms which include the water jet, air jet, and rapier. New methods have also been devised for controlling lifting of the warp threads. These are now so sophisticated that pictures can be woven into cloth to produce tapestry effects. Some of these modern devices are interfaced to computers to facilitate changing and monitoring of the process.

Fabrics composed of wool and mohair are also constructed using the knitting process. In knitting, one or more yarns are directed into a series of interlocking loops. Hand knitting with two or more needles is in common use throughout the world. However, numerous types of knitting machines exist which are capable of producing fabric at faster rates than weaving. As with weaving, numerous designs are used, the more common being the plain, rib, and purl types which are constructed on weft knitting machines. Different knitted fabrics are constructed using the so-called warp knitting technique. Warp knitting is somewhat unique in that it was developed as a machine technique and does not have a hand-constructed counterpart. The first warp knit fabric was produced on a tricot machine. Warp knitting evolved into the fastest method of making cloth out of yarns, the most common construction being the plain tricot jersey. Other types of knits are produced on Raschel warp knitting machines which are capable of handling coarser, spun yarns. A relatively new concept in knitting technology is the so-called knit-weave technique which combines the principles of knitting and weaving to produce a unique type of fabric.

Carpets are constructed using several distinct techniques. These include weaving, tufting, fusion bonding, knitting, needling, and knotting. Some floor coverings are composed of true and needle-punched felts. Whatever the means of construction, carpets, mats, and rugs usually contain the coarser grades of wool and mohair ($>34\,\mu$m). These fibers are ideal for carpet construction due to their excellent appearance retention, abrasion resistance, resilience, anti-soiling, anti-staining, and anti-static properties. Natural flame resistance also enhances their use in institutional, aircraft, and home carpets where resistance to burning is a prerequisite. As for other textiles, nylon, polyester, acrylic, polypropylene, cotton, and rayon compete with wool and mohair for use in carpets. The approach taken by most manufacturers of wool carpets is to produce a product of very high quality. Thus, the woven Axminster and Wilton carpets made with worsted yarns, tufted carpets composed of woolen or semi-worsted yarns, and the hand-knotted, sculpted carpets made in the Orient, are esthetically and technically among the best carpets produced in the world today.

Wilton and Axminster (names of towns in England) carpets are woven on very specialized looms. Wiltons are produced on Jacquard looms capable of producing loop, cut pile, combination loop and cut pile, level, multilevel, multicolored, or solid colored carpets. Axminster looms are even more versatile and are capable of using an almost unlimited combination of colors and designs. Machine-tufted carpets, being somewhat less expensive to produce, are formed in two distinct operations. First, yarn is needled through a primary backing (composed of polypropylene, for example) to produce the tufts. Then the reverse side of the carpet is coated with a heavy latex, which after baking, holds the tufts permanently in place. Concurrently, a second backing (typically composed of jute) is attached to the primary backing and is also held in place by the latex. Since its introduction, the tufting technique has progressively permitted greater versatility. Today, tufted carpets can be constructed with cut or uncut pile (or combination effects), level or multilevel, solid or multicolored. Printing of carpets has added a further dimension to the production of color effects. Tufted carpets can be piece dyed immediately after tufting, before application of the latex. The technology (PTO) also exists to dye wool and mohair carpets continuously. Differential shades can be obtained by using yarn mixtures composed of regular and shrinkproofed wool, for example. Tufted carpets usually require brief finishing processes (steaming, brushing, and shearing, for example) to further enhance their appearance. Wool and mohair carpets constructed using other technologies represent smaller proportions of the overall carpet market. However, some of the most beautiful (and expensive) carpets constructed today are produced by artisans under relatively primitive conditions and many of these products are purchased as investment items by collectors. Being composed of wool and mohair, floorcoverings are susceptible to insect (clothes-moth larva, for example) damage and must be treated to avoid this problem.

Wool felt is arguably the world's oldest textile structure. Felt is defined (by ASTM) as a textile structure characterized by interlocking and consolidation of its constituent fibers achieved by the interaction of a suitable combination of mechanical energy, chemical action, moisture, and heat but without the use of weaving, knitting, stitching, thermal bonding, or adhesives. As the name implies, part-wool felts are composed of wool mixed with one or more synthetic, cellulosic, or other animal fiber. The combined actions of compression, heat, and moisture are used to manufacture felts starting with carded batts of fibers. The felting propensity of wool depends upon its surface structure. If the fiber scales are removed or covered, wool will not felt. Production of felts is achieved in hardening, felting, and milling machinery. Felts are produced in a broad range of thicknesses and densities. Felts from 1 to 25 mm in thickness are produced in roll form. Thicker felts (up to 76 mm) are supplied in sheets. A broad range of felt densities is available from soft (0.2 g/cm^3) to extra hard (0.7 g/cm^3). Felts are used in a very wide range of applications which are still expanding. To produce this wide range of felts, many different grades of wool (19–32 μm) and other fibers are used in the manufacturing process. The range of fiber length used is relatively narrow (2.5–5 cm). Selection of the correct wool for a particular end-use relies heavily on the skill and experience of the feltmaker. Differences in the origin, average fiber diameter, crimp, and degree of weathering can produce major differences in felting behavior.

A relatively recent innovation has been the introduction of felted yarns. The bulk of this production goes into carpets, but significant production has been used in upholstery, craft, and hand knitting to manufacture products with unique performance and appearance characteristics.

Feltlike products are also produced using weaving, knitting, stitching, bonding, and needle-punching techniques. Often, dissection is required to establish how a particular product was manufactured.

XVII. Wet Processing and Finishing

In the broadest sense, the term "finishing" refers to any process carried out on loom- or knitting machine-state fabric during its conversion into finished fabric. Some wet processes applied to fibers in loose-stock, sliver, or yarn form have marked effects on the finished fabric (e.g., dyeing) and are referred to in this section. Important components of fabric quality that are influenced in finishing include: color, cover, crease resistance, dimensional stability, drape, ease of fabrication, easy care properties, elasticity, handle, surface smoothness, and luster.

Finishing of wool and mohair fabrics usually involves at least three distinct objectives. First, the fabric is cleansed. Second, a specific finish is developed, and third, specialized textures are created. Finishing is divided into two broad categories; wet finishing and dry finishing. Dry finishing includes the drying process itself and wet finishing is typically initiated with scouring (not to be confused with scouring of the raw materials to remove grease, suint, and dirt).

When performing any wet treatment on wool or mohair, the fabrics may be processed in open width or rope form. Washing in open width is best suited to worsteds and other fabrics where a clear finish is required. When fabrics are processed in rope form, special precautions and care are taken to ensure that the positions of creases are changed often in order to avoid permanent marking of the fabric. This is very important during fabric dyeing.

Scouring removes a variety of nonfibrous materials that have been introduced inadvertently or for various reasons. These include spinning additives, warp sizes and lubricants, miscellaneous oil stains, dust, and dirt. Fabrics are scoured in open width and in rope form, the form and type of machine used having a major influence on the final fabric properties. Scouring also results in relaxation of tensions introduced during the manufacturing processes. All this is achieved by immersing and working the fabrics in hot, soft (or softened) water containing adequate soap, soda ash, and/or synthetic detergents for a specific length of time. The time, temperature, and concentrations of emulsifying agents are dependent upon type of goods, levels of impurities, and type of scouring machine.

Rinsing follows scouring to minimize the concentration of residual chemicals.

A large proportion (~99%) of wool and mohair fabrics are finished and dyed in their natural color without bleaching. However, when a bright white or a white base for pastel shades is required, bleaching becomes a necessity. The two main agents used to bleach wool are sulfur dioxide (reductive bleach) and hydrogen peroxide (oxidative bleach). Solutions of hypochlorites, so commonly used in the home to bleach cellulosics, cannot be used because they cause protein fibers to yellow and degrade. Traditionally, sulfur dioxide obtained by burning sulfur was used to treat damp fabrics overnight in a sealed container or room (stoving). The process is quite slow and the whiteness obtained is not always permanent. A yellow color develops during the lifetime of the white textile presumably due to reoxidation of the reduced pigments. Many other means have been devised to treat wool with solutions of sulfurous acid. Wool can be bleached with hydrogen peroxide at several stages of processing including loose stock, sliver, yarn, or in fabric form. Acid and mildly alkaline conditions are used to obtain the desired degree of whiteness.

Fabrics containing wool and wool/mohair blends are subjected to milling (or fulling) in order to be consolidated in both warp and weft (length and width in the case of knits) directions and to develop a fabric surface that is felted to the desired degree. Milling and scouring are often combined. As discussed previously, the ability of wool to felt is a direct consequence of its elasticity and scale structure. Two factors, moisture and compressive deformation followed by relaxation, must be present to produce felting in wool. Industrially, felting is achieved in the milling process which involves squeezing the fabric in rope form between high-pressure rollers and then into a spout, thus compressing the fabric first in two dimensions (width and thickness) followed by compression in the length direction. Milling is achieved in mildly alkaline or strongly acidic conditions in the presence of milling lubricants and detergents (or soap).

The purpose of carbonizing fabrics composed of wool and mohair is to remove vegetable matter such as burrs, seed, cotton, rayon, or jute. The principle is identical to that described for scoured fibers. Fabrics are impregnated with dilute sulfuric acid, then dried and baked (~140°C) for a short while. After baking, the fragile dehydrocellulose is removed mechanically by first crushing and then beating the cloth. Residual acid is removed by neutralizing with dilute alkali followed by copious rinsing. Specialized acidizing, neutralizing, and drying equipment is used to carbonize fabrics.

Raising is a dry finishing process for modifying the appearance and softening the handle of fabrics by increasing the number and length of surface fibers. One or both sides of fabric can be raised as in the production of blankets, fleecy fabrics, and velours. Since wool and mohair are most pliable when damp, fabrics are usually raised in a wet condition. Concentration of raising assistants, type of machinery, machine settings, and duration of process all influence the final result. A similar process can be performed on yarns to obtain brushed yarns. This is particularly common for straight and looped mohair yarns spun for the sweater trade. Traditionally, woolen fabrics were raised using natural teazles. Except for special qualities of fabric, teazles have been replaced by wire clothing in double-action raising machines, for example. Brushing and napping machines are used to obtain similar effects but to lesser degrees.

Tentering involves fastening the two edges of fabric using clips or pins to a parallel set of chains and stretching the fabric to the desired (i.e., designed) width. Relaxation in the length direction can be achieved by overfeeding the fabric onto the chains. While the fabric is held to width it is dried in the tenter oven in a continuous process. Since temperatures of 110–140°C are typical, great care is used not to overdry or singe the fabric. Mohair is particularly susceptible to overdrying, with yellowing and loss of luster being the highly visible results.

The objectives of shearing depend upon the type of fabric being considered. When a clear finish is required, shearing is used to completely remove all surface fibers (i.e., as for pool table cloth). However, shearing is also used to control the height of the fiber ends above the surface of raised fabrics (i.e., as in melton type fabrics). Shearing machinery typically consists of several sets of brushes, a shearing bed, and the shearing unit itself which has a fixed ledger blade and a rapidly rotating shearing cylinder with 14-20 helical blades.

Pressing of fabrics is required to improve the appearance and luster. Pressing also affects the handle of fabrics. Pressing is achieved through joint application of heat and pressure in the presence of moisture. Traditionally, hydraulic presses in which the fabric was pressed between smooth layers of heavy cardboard ("papers") were used in batch processes throughout the world. Modern mills are more likely to use continuous paper presses and rotary presses for higher productivity. Unfortunately, the effects obtained by pressing are not usually permanent and decatising is necessary to stabilize the luster, handle, and general appearance achieved up to this stage of finishing. Decatising, which also improves the crease resistance of wool and mohair fabrics, is achieved by winding fabric under controlled open width and tension onto a perforated decatising roller. Layers of fabrics may be separated by fabrics composed of cotton or cotton/polyester. Once on the roller, the fabric is exposed to the action of heat and water. The degree of setting obtained in the fabric is dependent upon the length of the heating period, the moisture content and temperatures of the fabric, and the cooling period on the roller. Several types of decatising machinery are in common use in the wool finishing industry. Wet decatising (boiling and crabbing) machines utilize hot water and steam. Dry decatising (autoclave and luster decatising machines) use alternating steam and vacuum cycles to apply successive hot and cold treatments resulting in high degrees of fabric set and stability. Modern machines are available to perform the decatising process continuously.

A typical finishing sequence for yarn-dyed, fancy worsted menswear suiting might include the following steps: inspect, burl (de-knot), and mend; scour and mill in rope form, crab, cool overnight on the beam; hydroextract, tenter, and dry; steam and brush reverse side; shear, once on reverse side, twice on face; rotary press; decatise for luster, final inspection.

Wool and mohair are dyed in all of the following forms: loose stock, sliver, yarn (in hanks or packages), fabrics, and garments. Specialized machinery exists for dyeing in each of these forms and in the case of fabrics, in open width and rope form, as well as batch and continuous. Discussion of these machines is beyond the scope of this article. Protein fibers can be dyed with basic, acid, direct, mordant, vat, and reactive dye classes. New developments in dyeing and wet finishing are being influenced primarily by environmental rather than cost-efficiency considerations. Thus, there is a trend to scour and dye in shorter liquor to goods ratios and to replace chlorination in shrink resist finishes with more acceptable chemical reactions. Similarly, concerns about discharge of heavy metals will result in reduced use of chrome dyeing.

Printing is another method of applying color to wool and mohair but only about 1.5% of the total world Merino production and very little mohair is printed (this compares to about 40% for cotton). Sliver and fabrics composed of wool or mohair can be printed by a variety of methods. Usually, fabrics are pretreated using an alkaline scour, crabbing, desizing, or chlorinating to render the surface more hydrophilic. Traditional print–dry–steam–develop methods of screen printing are used to achieve excellent color yields and clarity. Discharge, resist, and sublimination transfer printing have also been applied to wool fabrics.

Chlorination/resin application treatments are important for producing fully machine-washable wool textiles. These processes are typically carried out continuously with the wool in top form, although fabrics and garments can be treated. The resin employed most commonly is a water soluble, cationic polyamide–epichlorhydrin polymer (Hercosett 125). The combined effect of chlorination followed by resin treatment is to eliminate the differential frictional effect by partial destruction and coating of the fiber scales. More recently, polyurethane, silicone-based polymers, plasma, and potassium tertiary butoxide treatments have been demonstrated to produce effective shrink resistance of wool fabrics.

Wool and mohair fabrics are protected against damage by clothes-moth larvae and other insects. Numerous organic compounds have been used to make the fibers either unpalatable or poisonous to the moth grubs. The first water-soluble product commercially applied to wool for this purpose was Eulan N followed later by Mitin FF. Both of these products are chlorinated aromatics. The last important chlorphenylid-based products to be developed (Eulan WA New/U33 and Mitin LP) are no longer available. In the late 1970s, synthetic pyrethroids were developed for mothproofing. Permethrin soon became the most popular product but it is now being banned in several European countries following the realization that it is very toxic to aquatic organisms. Mitin LF is still available. Pyrethroids with lower toxicity (e.g., cycloprothrin) are likely to be used in the future. Still, the most effective way to eliminate moth damage altogether is to make the textile inaccessible to moths. Thus, wool and mohair garments should be stored in polyethylene bags or wooden chests constructed for the purpose. Of course, this is not practical for protecting upholstery, wall, or floor coverings in which case chemicals must be used. Following the realization that many respiratory problems in humans are caused by the debris left by dust mites, mite repellents are now being formulated for application to wool and mohair textiles.

With respect to flammability, wool and mohair are regarded as safe fibers. Animal fibers ignite when subject to a sufficiently powerful heat source. However, they usually do not support combustion. When the heat source is removed, wool and mohair continue to burn and smolder only for a short time. Natural protein fibers have a high ignition temperature, a high limiting oxygen index, a low heat of combustion, and a low flame temperature compared to other common textile fibers. In addition, wool and mohair do not melt and drip when ignited, unlike many synthetic fibers. However, some end-uses, e.g., textile furnishing in aircraft, require a higher degree of flame resistance than that which is naturally present. Consequently, flame-resistant finishes were developed specifically for fabrics composed of wool, mohair, and their blends with cotton and synthetic fibers. Nonpermanent finishes used solutions of borax and boric acid which had to be replaced after the fabrics were cleaned. One of the early permanent finishes was based on tetra-kis hydroxymethyl phosphonium chloride bound in a polymer produced by the reaction of urea with melamine formaldehyde. This process was expensive and was superseded by simpler and less expensive techniques based on complexes of titanium or zirconium with fluoride, citrates, or other carboxylic or hydroxy-carboxylic acids. These are applied by a variety of methods to wool and wool-rich blends. More recently, an advance in flame-retarding wool has been achieved by combining the established Zirpro process and tetrabromophthallic acid. This treatment produces very short after-flaring times in wool fabrics and provides high levels of durability to machine washing.

XVIII. End-Uses of Wool and Mohair

The suitability of wool and mohair for specific end-uses is determined primarily by average fiber diameter and length. Ranges of fiber diameter used in the main wool and mohair product categories are shown in Figs. 8, 9, and 10. The shaded areas indicate the relatively narrow range from which the bulk of products are composed. Table VII shows consumption of virgin wool in six major categories. Womenswear (outerwear, dresses, skirts, suits, trousers, coats, and jackets), other apparel, and carpets (woven and tufted) each compose 19% of total wool consumption followed in decreasing order by menswear (outerwear, suits, trousers, jackets, and coats), knitwear (adults,' men's sweaters, and women's sweaters), and other interior textiles. Generally, grades of wool used in underwear and one segment of knitwear are finer than those required for women's woven outerwear.

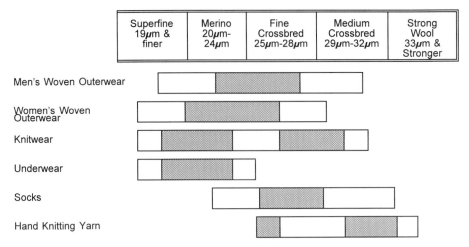

FIGURE 8 Wool diameter ranges for apparel products. [*Source:* International Wool Secretariat.]

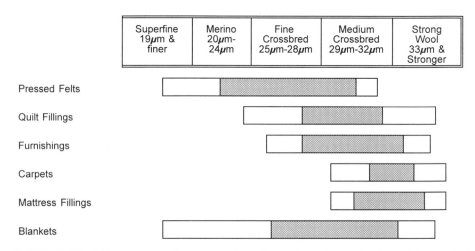

FIGURE 9 Wool diameter ranges for nonapparel products. [*Source:* International Wool Secretariat.]

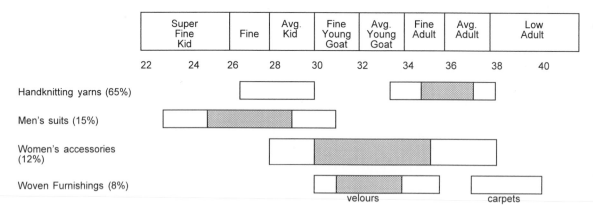

FIGURE 10 Mohair diameter ranges for major products. [*Source:* Mohair Council of America and F. Oglesby Wool and Mohair, Inc.]

TABLE VII
Consumption of Virgin Wool (%)

Apparel products		Nonapparel products	
Menswear	17	Carpets	19
Womenswear	19	Other interior textiles	10
Knitwear	16		
Other apparel	19		
Total	71	Total	29

Source: International Wool Secretariat.

Women's outerwear tends to be manufactured with finer fibers than men's outerwear and socks. The bulk of handknitting yarns are composed of even coarser fibers. Except for some blankets and felts, most nonapparel wool products are fabricated with coarser wools than apparel products.

Wool pressed felts have surpassed all other forms of textile in the number and diversity of their application. Industrially, felts are used for sealing, lubricating, wiping, filtering, polishing, and insulation against vibration. Superfine felts are used for display purposes, particularly exhibition and shop window fittings, soft toys, and in the hat trade. Thicker felts are used for saddle blankets and inner soles for boots, shoes, and waders. Use of felt in clothing has been quite small and dormant in recent times. Although wool felts have been used in floor coverings and furnishings, current use is at a low level. Versatility of felt, the resurgence of interest in natural products, and a new generation of artistic designers who are interested in working with wool felts, are all expected to result in greater acceptance and use of wool felts in the future.

Historically, mohair was used in textiles that were required to be highly durable. Thus, the stereotypical mohair product was a heavyweight, upholstery pile fabric commonly used in public transportation vehicles. Changes over time have resulted in mohair becoming regarded as a luxury fashion fiber. Consequently its use in bus and train upholstery has declined while uses in luxury items have increased. Major end-uses of mohair are listed in Fig. 10. In blends with wool, finer grades of mohair are used to produce lightweight (tropical) men's suitings. Since mohair has the capability of being dyed to very bright shades while retaining its natural luster, these attributes are used to produce attractive dress materials, shawls, stoles, plushes, astrakhans, and various types of womenswear coatings composed typically of velour fabrics but also novelty fabrics containing bouclés and worsted yarns. Mohair is also used to produce smooth, high quality linings for suits, curtains, drapes, and table coverings. A small amount of mohair is used to produce highly resilient carpets, rugs, and paint rollers.

The major use for mohair is in hand-knitting yarns in which the natural luster and brightness of mohair combined with its smooth handle, warmth, and tendency to resist dirt, creasing, and felting provide distinct advantages over synthetic fibers and even wool. The bulk of these yarns are knitted into sweaters and other ladieswear accessories. Brushed yarns and fabrics composed of adult mohair and mohair-rich blends often dominate the sweater market when it becomes fashionable.

XIX. Sheepskins

After a sheep is killed for its meat, the skin is removed at the slaughterhouse. All adhering fat and muscle tissue is removed to avoid problems in further processing. Wool may be removed from skins by fellmongering. In this process, fiber removal is achieved through bacterial action ("sweating"), or with the assistance of a depilatory agent ("painting") such as sodium sulfide. Both reactions result in slipe wool (unscoured) and pelts (dewooled skin). Scoured slipe wool is referred to as skin wool by the trade. Pelts are normally pickled in a solution containing sulfuric acid, sodium chloride, and a fungicide. Subsequently, they can be split, degreased, and eventually tanned using one of several methods, e.g., vegetable, chrome, oil, or formaldehyde. However, not all skins are handled in this manner. Soon after removal, skins can be temporarily preserved to permit export or shipping to other locations. This is achieved by drying (air or controlled) or salting. This latter process is usually achieved in a drum which is rotated to distribute sodium chloride (and other chemicals) throughout the "green" skins. Many skins are tanned with the wool intact. These woolskins are used to produce sheepskin goods.

Bibliography

Botkin, M. P., Field, R. A., and Johnson, C. L. (1988). "Sheep and Wool: Science, Production and Management." Prentice-Hall, Englewood Cliffs, NJ.
Cottle, D. J. (ed.) (1991). "Australian Sheep and Wool Handbook." Inkata Press, Melbourne.

Hunter, L. (1993). "Mohair: A Review of its Properties, Processing and Applications." CSIR Division of Textile Technology, Port Elizabeth.

Rodgers, P. (ed.) (1987). "Sheep Production Handbook." Sheep Industry Development Program, Inc., Denver.

Rogers, G. E., Reis, P. J., Ward, K. A., and Marshall, R. C. (eds.) (1989). "The Biology of Wool and Hair." Chapman and Hall, New York.

Rouette, H.-K., and Kittan, G. (1991). "Wool Fabric Finishing." Wool Development International, Ltd., Ilkley.

Ryder, M. L., and Stephenson, S. K. (1968). "Wool Growth." Academic Press, New York.

Shelton, M. (1993). "Angora Goat and Mohair Production." Mohair Council of America, San Angelo.

Stewart, R. G. (1983). "Wool Scouring and Allied Technology." Wool Research Organisation of New Zealand, Christchurch.

Van der Westhuysen, J. M., Wentzel, D., and Grobler, M. C. (1988). "Angora Goats and Mohair in South Africa," 3rd ed. Mohair Board, Port Elizabeth.

Von Bergen, W. (1963). "Wool Handbook," 3rd ed. Interscience, New York.

World Hunger and Food Security

JOHN W. MELLOR, *John Mellor Associates, Inc.*

Glossary

Developed countries Defined geographically as the countries of North America, Europe, East Asia, Australia, and a few other areas in which agriculture is highly productive but small compared to nonagriculture and incomes provide a diverse and high level of consumption

Developing countries Defined geographically as the countries of Asia, Africa, Latin America, and various islands, dominated by agriculture as a source of income and employment and in which incomes for the bulk of the population are inadequate to provide a modern level of living

Food security Assurance of adequate food for a healthy and active life

Hunger Insufficient food intake to allow an active and healthy life

Market prices Prices determined by supply and demand in freely functioning markets

Safety net Legislated and effectively administered minimum quantity of goods and services, particularly of food, made available to ensure a minimum level of living for the poor

Food security is a state in which all people are ensured adequate food for a healthy and active life. The devel-oped countries have largely achieved food security. The bulk of the countries in Africa, Asia, and Latin America have not. Market processes place the bulk of adjustments to a decline in the food supply on the poor who are consequently food insecure. Thus, in food insecure countries governments normally intervene in times of food shortage to protect the poor. Food security is achieved by a complex process of agricultural development in which the bulk of the rural people participate. Technological improvement of crop varieties (usually in combination with increased use of purchased inputs such as chemical fertilizers) is important to achieving food security, as is massive investment in roads and education. Concurrent programs for health and family planning reduce population growth rates and further enchance the per capita availability of food and other elements of improved well-being. The scientifically advanced and wealthy countries can be immensely helpful in assisting the transition of poor countries to a state of food security.

I. Introduction

The agricultural and industrial revolutions of the 18th century made it possible for nations to sufficiently improve their material well-being to ensure their people a healthy diet for an active life. Greatly increased wealth, and the participation of the entire population in producing and consuming that wealth, provided the economic margin for food security. It did so in the face of vagaries of weather, which continued to cause large fluctuations in local food production.

By the mid-point of this century, food security for the total populations had been largely achieved by the well-to-do developed countries. Now it is only destruction of economies by man-made war and civil unrest, not natural phenomena, that can bring inadequate food intake and famine to substantial numbers of the people in those nations. However, food security as the basic condition of a fair and just society still has not been achieved by countries containing a majority of mankind. Bringing food security to all is the achievable challenge of our times.

Fifty years ago, the bulk of humanity, including essentially all the people of Africa and Asia, excluding Japan, lived in a colonial regime. Even the bulk of Latin America was in a strongly dependent circumstance. Under colonialism, the conditions for gross food insecurity and for periodic famine were endemic. Major colonial powers, such as the British, developed intricate famine codes delineating the bureaucratic procedures for ameliorating the effects of famine. But the sheer existence of those codes indicates that famine was the order of the day. Famine was inevitable given the low incomes and lack of participation in development of the bulk of the population.

World War II brought the beginning of the end of colonialism, an end which came rapidly through much of Asia, and more slowly in Africa. Concurrently, those countries of Asia, Africa, and Latin America, which had not been colonies, moved to a status of much less dependence.

Coincident with the departure of colonialism, we find that famines, the most virulent manifestation of food insecurity, declined greatly in incidence and changed radically in causal force. Throughout human history, inclement weather has been a primary cause of famine. Large numbers of poor people obtaining barely sufficient food in normal weather find a lethal insufficiency when a sequence of bad years occurs.

The mechanism by which unfavorable weather caused famine varied from person to person. In some cases, it was simply a lack of production from one's own land. Lack of income and lack of food were coterminous. In other cases, decline in agricultural output directly reduced the employment and income derived by the landless from harvesting and other farm production activities. It also reduced the spending of land-owning people with consequent further reduction in employment in rural nonagricultural goods and service activities. The reduced employment and incomes of the poor, caused by lower agricultural production, would in turn lead to the contradiction of starvation concurrent with apparently adequate supplies of food.

In the postcolonial period, famines have indeed occurred, although generally at lesser intervals and with lesser severity than in the past. Postcolonial period famines have been caused, in general, not by the weather but by civil strife that not only disrupts trans-

port of food from favored areas to nonfavored areas, often by intent, but which also stands in the way of information transmittal and political mobilization to support the famine-hit areas. The massive famine in China, following the "great leap forward" of the late 1950s, was somewhat different than other modern famines. China's brutal central control of the economy and allocation of labor caused massive dislocation of food production and its distribution and control of communication hid the size of the famine from the outside world.

While it is true that modern communication and transportation and the mobilization of assistance from the high-income developed countries has virtually eliminated famine from open, peaceful countries; chronic food insecurity continues in massive proportions, through good years and bad. As countries bring an end to chronic food insecurity, they will have sufficient national income to ensure themselves against the transitory food insecurity of bad crop years.

We have described the circumstance of decolonization, of building new political and economic systems, as a time-consuming and painful process, which lays the groundwork for accelerated economic growth and the achievement of food security for all. A few countries completed those foundation-laying tasks rather quickly and have surged into middle-income status, such that the thought of famine or even of food insecurity for even small elements of their population is unthinkable. Taiwan is the striking example, but we also find Malaysia and Thailand moving quickly into that status.

It is in the next 50 years that we may expect to see the foundation-laying stage passed and countries one after another throughout Asia, and then increasingly in Africa, moving into the stage of accelerated economic growth, rising incomes, and the achievement of food security.

This article first describes the current state of food insecurity in the world, delineates a conceptual framework for processes to ensure food security, and presents programs for dealing with transitory food insecurity, as well as the basic processes for improving or removing chronic food insecurity. The article closes with discussion of the state of food security expected in the 21st century and the broad policy needs to ensure an end to food insecurity.

II. The Present Status of Food Security

Food security is seen by virtually all development oriented organizations as a major affliction. Most institutions, e.g., the World Bank, The Food and Agriculture Organization of the United Nations, the International Fund for Agricultural Development, define food security as a circumstance in which all people at all times have sufficient food to lead healthy and active lives. Such a broad, but powerful definition, conveniently divides itself into chronic aspects of food security and transitory aspects.

Chronic food insecurity describes the situation of those people who at least for significant periods of each year are food insecure on a day-to-day basis. Such food insecurity manifests itself in the significant stunting of children. For example, the children of the poor in poor countries, due to food insecurity, are typically several inches shorter than the children of the urban middles classes in the same country at the same age. People who in many, or even most, years are food secure, but who become food insecure in specific years of unusually unfavorable weather or civil strife, are said to be victims of transitory food insecurity.

A. The Numbers and Geographic Locations of the Food Insecure

In round numbers, about 700 million people are in a state of chronic food insecurity in this the last decade of the 20th century. Food insecurity is endemic in South Asia where on the order of one-third to one-half of the population are in a food insecure state and comprise roughly half of the food insecure of the world (Table I). About one-fifth of the world's food insecure are in Africa, where the proportion of the population in food insecurity is similar to that of South Asia. However, food insecurity either has been declining or is in an incipient state of decline in South Asia, while it has been increasing in Africa. Thus, within a decade there may well be more people in chronic food insecurity in Africa than in Asia. Another 10% of the food insecure are in China, primarily in the low production potential areas. The proportion of the total population in a food insecure state is about half that of South Asia. The remaining fifth of the food insecure are largely scattered in Latin America, North Africa, and the Middle East.

In addition to the 700 million people in chronic food insecurity, an additional 300 million people are close enough to the margin of chronic food insecurity that fluctuations in weather cause them to move back and forth across that line. Thus, we may speak of the total number of people in food insecurity as about one billion.

TABLE I

Geographic Distribution of Poverty and Consequent Food Insecurity, 1990[a]

Region	Total	Urban	Rural	Agricultural potential High	Agricultural potential Low
		(millions of people)			
Africa	137	14	123	62(50)[c]	61(50)
South Asia	350	70	280	140(50)	140(75)
East Asia	31	5	26	6(25)	20(75)
Latin America	72	29	43	11(25)	32(75)
Near East	34	10	24	8(33)	16(67)
China	76	0[b]	76	25(33)	51(67)
Total	700	128	572	252	320

Source: Mellor, J. W. (1990). Ending hunger: An implementable program for self-reliant growth. *In* "The World Food Crisis: Food Security in Comparative Perspective" (J. I. Hans Bakker, ed.). Canadian Scholars Press, Canada.
[a] The distribution by rural and urban classification is based on a survey of country poverty studies. All poverty in China grouped under rural poverty. There is little evidence of malnutrition in urban areas. The classification into agricultural potential is based on unpublished work by Sumiter Broca at IFPRI.
[b] Assumed to zero, a reasonable assumption when migration is regulated.
[c] Numbers in parentheses are percentage of rural population.

With such massive dimensions to food insecurity, it seems unlikely that the more well-to-do people in the relatively prosperous countries would, year-after-year, provide the transfer payments to lift so many people to food security on a long-term basis. The obverse is that the solution to the food insecurity problem must come from bringing the mass of the food insecure into the development process. Incomes must be raised through broad processes of development, based on agricultural growth and the stimulus to nonagricultural growth that comes from rising farm incomes. The key to those processes is improved agricultural technology arising from modern agricultural research systems.

The centrality of broad participation in economic growth to food security is explicitly recognized by the World Bank, the Food and Agricultural Organization of the United Nations, and the International Fund for Agricultural Development. Several of the bilateral foreign assistance agencies have also done position papers that recognize this relationship between growth and food security. With that perception, the effort to reduce food insecurity largely takes the form of broad development efforts rather than specific food security projects. [*See* INTERNATIONAL AGRICULTURAL RESEARCH.]

It should be clear that food insecurity and poverty are two sides of the same coin. People who are not poor allocate their income in such a manner as to be food secure. They may, of course, not do so very efficiently, and they may suffer some malnutrition from a poor allocation of their food budget. But they do have adequate calories for an active and healthy life. The food insecure are those who have inadequate income to command adequate quantities of food.

There has been some controversy as to whether food insecurity is a problem of inadequate supplies of food or inadequate income for commanding the food. As we will see later, this is an unproductive and diverting argument. Of course, the poor, being poor, do not have the purchasing power to obtain adequate food. However, it is the processes of increasing agricultural production and various direct and indirect effects of increased agricultural production which provide the increased incomes and purchasing power that lift the poor to food security.

B. The Rural Nature of Food Insecurity

The poor are primarily in rural areas. In Africa, roughly 90% of those who are so poor as to be food insecure are located in rural areas; in Asia, the proportion is about 80%; and in Latin America, with much higher incomes and more differentiated economies, the proportion of the poor in rural areas is much lower but still on the order of 60% (Table I). Many of the urban food insecure have fled the countryside because of endemic food insecurity. Thus, the basic solution to food insecurity lies in the rural areas of the poor countries. [See RURAL DEVELOPMENT, INTERNATIONAL.]

The distribution of the poor within rural areas relates to the level of development and instructs us as to the strategy for providing food security. In the very poorest countries, the poor are located with greater density in the rural areas with substantial agricultural production potential (Table I). Examples are the densely populated, but agriculturally rich areas of the Gangetic and Brahmaputra basins of South Asia, the volcanic soils of Java, and the upland farming areas of western Kenya. In each case, both the overall rural population density and the density of the food insecure poor are very high.

Reducing poverty and increasing food security is a straightforward process in such agricultural, technology-responsive areas. Not only does accelerated growth in agricultural production create many more jobs directly in agricultural production, but also the expenditure of higher agricultural incomes creates

substantial growth in employment, in the expanding provision of nonagricultural goods and services. The high rural population densities reduce the cost per capita of provision of the physical infrastructure of all-weather roads, electrification, and telephones which are so essential to rapid growth in rural nonagricultural employment. Thus, we find that in middle-income developing countries, the poor are virtually not to be found in the good agricultural areas and instead are found largely concentrated in the poorer agricultural areas. In those countries, development has lifted people in the more productive areas out of the absolute poverty which brings food insecurity. Thus, in higher income Thailand, there is essentially no poverty or food insecurity on the rich soils of the Central Plain. Such poverty is largely concentrated in the much poorer areas of the Northeast. In contrast in the poor countries of India and Bangladesh, we find a substantial proportion, perhaps on the order of 60–70%, of the food insecure concentrated in the rich alluvial areas of the major river systems and in the coastal areas.

We can draw a conclusion, which we will expand upon in later sections, that in the poor countries it makes sense to concentrate first on lifting people out of poverty and into food security in the richer agricultural areas. When those easier problems have been solved, one can then move to the more intractable problems of dealing with those on the poorer soil areas.

C. Children and Women

Children, in particular, and to a lesser extent women as well, are disproportionately represented among the absolute poor and the food insecure. The disproportionate representation of women arises partly from the general problem of maintaining adequate incomes in single-family headed homes but also from discrimination against women, particularly as societies modernize and as women are restrained from taking full advantage of the modern institutions such as credit, and purchased inputs, which play such an important role in lifting people out of rural poverty.

Children are disproportionately represented amongst the food insecure because the poor tend to have larger numbers of children than the more well to do and because large numbers of dependents bring greater poverty, at least in the short run. The problem of food insecure children has two faces. First, there is the extraordinary humanitarian problem of small defenseless people facing chronic hunger with its debilitating effect on their physical and mental development. The other face is the creation of a new generation of people who are vulnerable to ill-health, and have not experienced the mental development which should occur with increased schooling.

III. The Conceptual Framework for Increased Food Security

Solution to the massive problem of food insecurity requires a combination of market-oriented development activities, a public safety net involving redistribution of income, and a complex mix of public and individual action. The complexity is simplified by Mellor's Food Security Pyramid, depicted in Fig. 1.

The current dimensions of food security are depicted by the broad base of the pyramid, representing the 750 million people in chronic food deficit and the 300 million who occasionally become food deficit in periods of unfavorable weather or other natural disaster. The aspiration of a food secure future is represented by lateral and vertical contraction of the pyramid to the point of the pyramid at which time food insecurity has been eliminated.

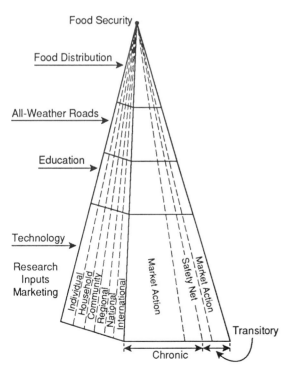

FIGURE 1   Food security pyramid.

The front face of the pyramid depicts, in horizontal bands, the actions to achieve food security. The vertical dimension comprises two segments representing chronic and transitory food insecurity. Each of those is further divided into the components to be treated by accelerated growth achieved through the operation of private enterprise and free markets in cooperation with complementary public activities and the components requiring direct public action to provide a safety net of income transfers. The side faces of the pyramid designate the continuum of action from the international arena through various levels of national organizations, both public and private, reaching the ultimate objective of the family and the individual child, woman and man within the family.

Because of human disability and misfortune, it is unlikely that the ultimate objective of contracting the pyramid to the point of universal food security will be achieved entirely by market processes. Hence, specific public programs will continue to be necessary. But the objective of moving close to that point on the basis of development and growth, supplemented by public income transfers is attainable. The remainder of this article treats the range of approaches needed to achieve that objective.

IV. Actions to Achieve Food Security

The numbers of the food insecure are so large that growth must be the primary instrument of food security. Thus, the bulk of the width of the pyramid, for both chronic and transitory food insecurity, comprises market-oriented growth activities. Those activities are much larger in total than what is depicted on the food security pyramid. The pyramid only includes the specific orientation of those efforts toward food security. Thus, as the pyramid compresses, the size of those activities specifically oriented toward food security may decline, while the general activity increases. Within the context of market-oriented growth, specific government programs will provide income transfers to reduce food insecurity.

Many types of effort contribute to increased food security. Some efforts have a direct effect while others, no less important in their impact, are indirect. Classes of such effort are depicted as horizontal bands on the pyramid with those having the most direct effect near the top of the pyramid and those having the most indirect effect near the base. Each of those activities is pursued through international and national collectivities, as well as by family and individual effort, and so they slice across the pyramid in each direction.

A. Chronic Food Insecurity

1. Markets and Growth

A development strategy that accelerates growth in the agricultural sector is key to radical reduction in poverty and hence in food insecurity. Thus, in India, the five states with the fastest growth rates of the agricultural sector reduced the proportion of the rural population in absolute poverty by over half in the 20-year period, 1963–1983. That was a period marked by similar weather at the beginning and the end of the period and hence, the trend is not biased by differences in weather. The states that did poorly in agricultural growth actually experienced an increase in the proportion of their rural population in poverty. Countries that have done well in agricultural development, such as Indonesia, Thailand, Malaysia, and Taiwan, have all experienced radical decline in absolute poverty and hence in food insecurity in parallel with the agricultural growth.

The food security pyramid draws attention not only to the importance of a broad process of agricultural growth, but also for the need to see that the process plays its role in reducing food insecurity. Thus, each activity needs to be monitored from that point of view. Does the food distribution system work effectively in areas where the poor are concentrated? Is intervention needed to ensure competition, low cost, and wide access? Are all-weather roads introduced in all food insecure areas? Does education include not only basic skills but nutrition education to improve allocation of resources for the poor to achieve food security? Is the agricultural technology system adequately oriented to the crops and livestock important to food security because of their importance in consumption or in generating income for the poor?

2. The Food Distribution System

It is the food distribution system which is, of course, closest and therefore most direct in bringing food security to the poor and innately insecure. An effective food distribution system will be largely operated in the private sector. The scale economies are not large, and the advantages of competition are great.

The primary role of government in the food distribution system is to ensure competition in the private sector. Of course, the better the system of physical infrastructure, education, and technology, the more competitive will be the private sector.

The public sector also has a role in dealing with the problems of market failure and, more important, victimization by the market. The latter is perhaps best made clear by pointing out how the market allocates a reduction in food supplies. It does so through price and the relevant income elasticities of demand. When the supply is reduced due to poor weather or other forces, prices go up. How much they go up is a function of the elasticities which reflect the resistance of a particular income class to reduce their consumption in the face of a decrease in supplies and rising prices.

The resistance of the consumer to reduced food consumption is a function of how high is the income of the consumer. In countries with very substantial populations of poor people, prices only have to rise a small amount in order to bring supply and demand into balance. That is because very poor people spend the bulk of their income on food and so a price increase brings about a drastic reduction in real income and hence a reduction in purchases. We can reflect this in the income elasticities and make relevant calculations.

Those calculations show that in a very poor country where the bottom 20–40% of the population has barely enough income to provide the minimum calories for a healthy active life, with a decrease in national food supply, the lower 20% in the income distribution reduce their food consumption by 10 times as much as do the top 5% of the income distribution. With higher prices the poor simply cannot afford as much food as before. That is, those who are hungry have to reduce consumption greatly, while those who are not hungry reduce their consumption very little when supplies decline. We consider that inequitable and all societies attempt to take action to prevent the working of markets under those circumstances.

Thus, we find in the case of transitory food insecurity, that markets do not meet societies' objectives and there must be interference. That interference, however, may involve simply taking supplies from public stock and putting them on the market to reduce price increases, or using foreign exchange to purchase internationally traded commodities to have the same effect.

3. All-Weather Roads

Without all-weather roads, food security is a function of local food production–consumption balances. Whereas food production in a small region may fluctuate as much as 50% from one year to another, and in virtually all regions is subject to at least 5–10% fluctuation, the total production of food in the world rarely fluctuates as much as 5% from one year to another. Bad weather in one place is balanced by good weather elsewhere. Thus, maintaining stable supplies and prices of food is much easier with an integrated global market. Provision of transport and other infrastructure to fully integrate markets globally is an important form of food security investment. It is also a key element in rural development.

In Asia, typically one-third of the rural population is not served by all-weather roads. In Africa, typically 90% of the rural population is not served by all-weather roads. Building roads in developing countries is a very labor-intensive process and thus road construction provides a further benefit to food security by increasing the purchasing power of the poor. In this context, food aid can be an effective means of increasing both chronic and transitory food security.

4. Education

Although the relation between education and food security is much less direct than for all-weather roads and the food distribution system, it is nevertheless important. Education is a critical element for the relief of chronic food insecurity through its effect on development.

Over time, knowledge which is so essential to progress, becomes more and more complex, requiring higher and higher levels of education. This is particularly true if environmental damage is to be avoided.

Education is also important in dealing with chronic food insecurity in the long run, because of its close relationship to family planning and population control. Thus, including women in education is particularly important. Reinforcing the need for education of women is the increased potential to improve the effect of higher incomes on food consumption and health. At very low incomes the choices for food expenditure are very limited. Rising incomes increase those choices and hence increase the return to education and particularly the education of women.

5. Technology and the Environment

The basis for increased incomes in all economies has been primarily through technological improvement. The way we increase incomes is not by increasing the supply of the factors of production so much as by making those factors of production more effective. Thus, technological change and its corollaries of research, increased input intensity, and improvement of marketing channels are crucial to the development route to increased food security.

Measures to ensure that the poorest and most food insecure benefit from improved technology start with research emphasizing commodities and conditions which are particularly important to the poor. There may also be an emphasis on increasing the productivity of land and capital which the poor have little command of, and with less emphasis on increasing labor productivity through use of more land and capital.

It is notable that improved technology requires capital and will tend to be less accessible to the poor because of the higher cost and greater risks in providing them with credit. Thus, a food security program will emphasize giving the poor access to improved technologies by opening to them the input distribution systems, the marketing systems, and in particular the credit systems.

Modern yield increasing technology has generally had favorable effects on the environment. The most important favorable effect arises from raising productivity of the better land to make it unnecessary for the poor to push out on the extensive margin of food production. The most striking examples of such destructive pushing back of the margins for arable food crop production lie in the humid tropical forests and the semi-arid grasslands. In each case the environmentally sound agriculture is based on perennial crops (grasses in the one case and trees in the other). Poverty pushes the poor to switch to arable, annual crops with consequent exposure of fragile soils to the destruction of sunlight, water, and wind, thereby accelerating their breakdown and erosion.

The higher productivity associated with improved technology also increases the availability of nonfarm jobs through the expenditure of the higher incomes of farmers and makes food less expensive to the poor who move off marginal lands, letting them revert to more appropriate uses, and move to nonfarm jobs. These favorable effects of modern yield increasing technology are rescuing large areas of fragile lands even as agricultural production concentrates on the more robust lands.

The increased intensity of high yield agriculture requires a high level of education of farmers, and extensive public support systems if the environmental advantages are not to be partially nullified by pollution. In poor agriculture, it is degradation of soils through erosion and depletion that represents the major environmental hazard. In high-income countries, it is pollution that moves to the forefront. However, no farmer wants to pollute. Chemicals are applied to benefit plants and those that leach into groundwater or are otherwise environmentally destructive do not benefit anyone. The farmer requires support of soil testing, so he or she applies the amount of chemicals needed, and research to advise on the timing of the application to maximize the effect on crops and minimize the unfavorable effects on the environment. This requires expanded public soil testing, research, and extension as well as the education of farmers. It may also require legislation to enforce needed environmental practices. But, even in the face of these problems of modern agriculture no mistake should be made in preference for the much more destructive systems of poor people facing poverty and population growth on resources that are not meant for arable agriculture and which can be displaced only by modern science and its application.

6. Safety Net and Income Transfers

Each of the slices of the pyramid has scope for special expenditure to ensure access of the poor. Through misfortune, some people will always lack the capability to provide self-sustaining food security to themselves. The extent to which that is the case will form a gradation, which offers scope for programs that range from developmental to redistributive. For example, food distribution programs can provide free food to the poor and destitute; education programs can include school lunch programs which help bring children to school and relieve food insecurity directly; and road-building programs can employ the food insecure and pay them with either food or cash for purchasing food, depending on circumstance.

B. Transitory Food Insecurity

1. Markets and Development

Treatment of even transitory food insecurity can, with adequate planning, have a developmental aspect. The private sector can be facilitated in providing distributional services. Plans can be made to tool up public works projects that build roads and school lunch programs can be enlarged. On-going developmental programs provide the basic administrative structure to respond to short-term emergencies and should be designed to fulfill that purpose.

2. Safety Net and Transfers

Transitory food insecurity also has a clear safety net or distributional aspect. In time of agricultural failure, large-scale distribution of both income and food may be necessary to meet the needs of destitute people.

V. Public Action and the Individual

The ultimate objective of food security lies with the family and the individual within the family. Each of the slices of the pyramid has an international, a national, a local governmental, a private organization, and a family and individual aspect. In each case, the program must be carried through to the individual with emphasis on conforming to the specific needs of individual children, women, and men.

A. International

International programs of food security are important because of the lesser fluctuations in global food production relative to those of small regions. It is expensive to ensure food security through stocks in small regions or nations. Because the weather is highly random, in any one area there can be substantial sequences of good or bad weather, and the consequent size of required food security stocks is immense. However, by the very nature of the randomness of weather, it is unlikely that poor weather will be general, throughout the world, at any one time. Thus, poor weather in one place is balanced by good weather elsewhere. Shipment of food from areas of good crop to areas of poor crop is a less expensive substitute for storage, to convey food from good years to poor years.

Thus, there is much to be said for dealing with the food insecurity problem at the international level with finances rather than stocks. However, poor countries suffer from problems similar to those of poor people—they have difficulty in saving and providing for difficult future circumstances. If poor countries can be guaranteed finances for importing food, they can bid that food away from the richer people who will respond by reducing their livestock consumption and hence the heavy drain of cereals into livestock feed.

In the 1980s, the International Monetary Fund set up the IMF Cereal Facility to fulfill this need. Unfortunately, there was not sufficient understanding of the special nature of food as a commodity, and hence the need for a specialized facility. Consequently the IMF Cereal Facility was substantially integrated with other foreign exchange mechanisms. The result of that and other restrictions was that it was not frequently used, and eventually became redundant. An important and efficient instrument of international contribution to food security was thereby lost.

The World Food Program, as a major international agency, is able to provide physical supplies of food in times of emergency. It also uses food aid to deal with chronic food insecurity, while at the same time furthering the development process, particularly through the Food for Works Program. This program provides food as partial compensation to those who help to build roads. It is notable that a number of bilateral donors of food aid, particularly the United States, use financing for their food aid as a means of dealing with important transitory problems and may be looked upon as part of the international system for food security.

Because of the importance of financing and the fungibility of finances, the World Bank has played an important role in food security. When countries experience sudden financial crisis, the World Bank can emphasize quick dispersing loans which in effect provide ready foreign exchange for importing food under those circumstance.

One of the objectives of the international trade negotiations of the 1990s is to reduce the production of surplus agricultural commodities in the high-income countries. One result will be reduction in the size of food stocks that high-income countries provide to developing countries, through administration of their national policies. That, in turn, will increase the instability of international prices and the supplies of food available on a concessionary basis to poor countries. In that context, increased attention needs to be given to international mechanisms for protecting poor people in poor countries from fluctuations in food availability and supplies.

B. National

National governments are crucial to reducing food insecurity. National stocking policy must ensure supplies until a transitory food insecurity situation is properly diagnosed, orders placed for food abroad, and time provided for the food to arrive. The less developed a country and the poorer its informational and transportation system, the larger those stocks must be. Some countries need as much as a 4-month supply. But for countries with more sophisticated physical and institutional systems for food security, a month or two would be adequate.

Food security requires a national food price policy. That is because it is efficient to turn to international supplies at times of transitory food insecurity. It is defending a price level derived from national policy which provides the operating rules as to when food should be imported, stocks built, and stocks depleted.

And of course, national governments are very important to agricultural development. Because farming is most efficiently carried out on small units, governments play an important role in providing research for improved technology, helping farmers organize various activities and providing physical and institutional infrastructure, including rural roads and schools.

C. Local Government

Local government is the most effective means by which international and national programs are linked to the family and individual. Small areas differ in many respects relevant to food security, such as food habits and the quality of the food distribution system. The more highly developed local government is, the more food security efforts can be fine tuned to the local situation. Nongovernmental organizations also play an important and crucial role in fine tuning of food security programs. They can organize the poor to represent their interests, and they can stand as an intermediary between poor groups and various levels of national and international governments.

D. Family and Individual

The family unit is the final objective of food security. It is noted that sometimes food is inequitably distributed within the family. However, such inequity is almost always a product of poverty. As incomes rise, the inequity of allocations within the family decline.

The family may maintain stocks of both cash for purchasing food and actual physical stocks of grain. However, the poorer the family, the smaller are such stocks. Indeed, it is the hoarding action of the more well-to-do which tightens food supplies in times of scarcity and increases the burden on the poor. Poorly developed information systems and poor infrastructure compound the problem. Thus, food security for the poor in poor countries requires public stocks and the capacity for public intervention in food markets.

VI. Population Growth and per Capita Food Availability

When Japan entered the initial period of accelerated economic growth in the late 19th century, an agricultural growth rate of around 2% per year allowed per capita agricultural output to grow at over 1% per year. That growth rate made an important contribution not only to increasing food security but also to supporting rapid growth of the nonagricultural sector and the eventual transformation of the economy to its current modern, wealthy, industrialized status.

Modern medicine has sharply reduced death rates even among very poor populations. A combination of less radical scientific advance in birth control and more complex social processes has left birth rates at high levels. Thus, population growth rates in modern developing countries are three times the levels in 19th century Japan. Agriculture must grow at some 4% per year to make as large a contribution to achieving food security and to overall economic growth as was achieved in Japan.

Fortunately, the application of modern science, reinforced by the benefits of trade, allows a catching up growth rate of 4% or so in the initially backward agriculture of developing countries. But such rates cannot be maintained indefinitely. Eventually population growth rates must be brought down.

Economic growth itself brings education, change in values regarding investment in education of children, and how early children commence adult work, all of which help reduce birth rates. But general education, integration into the larger society through improved communications, and provision of desired information about birth control speed that process. Knowledge and efficiency are increasing in all the components of birth rate reduction and so each succeeding generation of fast growth countries brings its population growth rates down more rapidly the preceding generation.

However, a few countries in Asia and most countries in Africa are lagging in these processes, are experiencing unprecedented rates of population growth, and must give special attention to the social, economic, and technical processes involved in reducing birth rates. Otherwise an intolerable burden is placed on agricultural growth alone to bring food security. Although economic growth and reduction of birth rates are highly complementary and go hand in hand, it is still notable that a percentage point reduction in the population growth rate is as valuable as a percentage point addition to the agricultural growth rate in eliminating hunger and achieving food security.

VII. Progression and Phases toward Food Security

The global task of universal food security can be achieved by the early decades of the 21st century. To do so will require concerted action and attention. In understanding global progress toward food security, it is useful to define three quite different phases. The phases differ in their central tendency, but represent a continuum of change.

A. Phase I

In Phase I, countries are very poor, the level of per capita production of food is well below that needed for an adequate diet, and the level of effective demand (that is the food which people can afford to buy) is roughly the same as the amount which is produced because producing food is the principal source of income. There is little trade. On the order of half the population is food insecure. Nowadays, population growth in this phase is rapid, increasing the food security and hunger problem, since modern development is not yet occurring and therefore food production is growing very slowly.

B. Phase II

In Phase II, technological improvement occurs at an increasing rate in the agricultural sector, and there begins to be acceleration in the production of food. If the economic processes are working well, the increased incomes from the food production will be substantially spent by the food producers, either to purchase that food itself (that is to retain it on the farm and to consume it) or to purchase relatively labor-intensively produced goods and services from the local community. The latter increases the incomes of the landless and hence their purchasing power for additional food. Because the nonagricultural sector is initially small, we can show mathematically that in the first part of Phase II there will be modest decline in food prices and quite possibly the supply will increase somewhat more rapidly than the effective demand, creating some exportable surplus. It is important that population growth rates begin the decline.

As the development process gets under way, a second part of Phase II emerges with rising real food prices or rising imports of food. The rate of growth of food production will further accelerate and there will be a better working process for increasing incomes in the nonagricultural sector, at first substantially stimulated by growth in agricultural incomes and then growing on the basis of its own income generation. The effect is growth in the effective demand for food which is considerably more rapid than the growth in supply, resulting in rapidly increasing imports. This supply–demand balance is very heavily driven by the rapid increase in the consumption of livestock commodities and hence much of the import of food will be for livestock feed. Again, it is essential that the processes for reducing birth rates be well under way in this phase.

We note this phenomenon particularly markedly in Taiwan, which went from being a modest net exporter of food in the early 1950s to becoming a massive importer of food in the 1970s and subsequently, with livestock feed driving those imports. During that period, the growth rate of the agricultural sector was rapid.

Unfavorable macro-economic policies (e.g., an over-valued exchange rate; allocation of the nations capital to low employment industries in the capital city) may intercept the favorable multipliers from the agricultural sector. The Philippines is an example. For a considerable period in the 1960s, 1970s, and 1980s, the agricultural growth rate was rapid, but growth in nonagricultural employment was slow, the real wage rate declined, and effective demand for food grew less rapidly than the supply. But that is not the normal set of relationships under more favorable macro-policy regimes. In fact the Philippines is the lone example of agricultural growth not driving non-agricultural growth.

We can make some profound statements about food security in the context of these growth phases. Most importantly, the production of food per capita grows rapidly as we move into Phase II . That increases food security by allowing people to consume more per capita than before, and thus they are able to sustain a substantial temporary drop in per capita supplies due to bad weather without reducing their consumption below the earlier levels. At the very least, they have improved their food security.

We note further that as livestock consumption increases, there is a further source of stability in consumption of food by humans. If there is a shortage of food, an increase in grain prices squeezes the margins of livestock producers who will then increase their marketings of livestock. That has two effects: an immediate increase in livestock supplies and hence consumption; and less feed consumption by livestock. Since livestock consume from 3 to 10 calories for each calorie produced, the increase in supplies for human consumption is large.

C. Phase III

In Phase III, institutionalized technological change continues to provide a significant growth rate in food production, but growth in per capita food consumption levels off. People's desire for additional food has been largely satiated and they are food secure. Even though the production growth rate may decline somewhat during this period, it still increases significantly faster than consumption, generating surpluses.

Now, when so much of the Third World is entering Phase II of food security, it is fortunate indeed that we have a substantial proportion of the world's population in Phase III, generating food surpluses. However, the world needs to show more intelligence in seeing that these food supplies effectively facilitate the development of poor countries that provides the long run guarantee of food security.

The major burden on global food supplies will come as massive countries, such as the collectivity in South Asia and China, move clearly into the second part of Phase II of food security. Supply–demand projections for India show that in 10 years of rapid income growth; net imports of cereals will increase to about 10 million tons. Those imports will be primarily in the form of coarse grains, reflecting the rapid growth in livestock consumption and feeding which is just commencing.

The tremendous growth in demand for livestock feed does not occur immediately with the onset of economic growth. The base of livestock consumption is initially small so even a high percentage growth rate still does not have a significant aggregate effect. In addition, livestock feed in early stages of growth comes largely from waste and by-products. However, the supply of those commodities is relatively inelastic. As the base of livestock consumption increases, the by-products supply is soon fully utilized. Then, when the base of livestock consumption is large, by-product feeds are fully utilized, and rapid growth in income continues, explosive growth in the use of cereals for feed is reflected in rapidly increasing imports.

The phases of food security are paralleled by phases of population growth. In the early phase, population growth has traditionally been modest with death rates a little lower than birth rates. As development occurs, the death rates come down sharply, providing explosive increase in population. Modern medicine is pushing this explosive growth in population in Phase II. In the next phase, birth rates begin to decelerate and the decline in death rates slackens, and the two begin to close in, slowing the rate of population growth.

1. Food Security in Phase III

In Phase III, countries return to self-sufficiency or even increase exports of the basic food staples such as wheat and rice that are directly used for human consumption. There may be, depending on the agricultural resource base, substantial import of horticultural commodities and either livestock products or the feed for producing livestock products. Ensuring the certainty of such a high-level diet for high population density, high-income countries requires earning foreign exchange to purchase food from abroad as needed. Supplies of food are produced in sufficiently politically and ecologically, diverse regions that food security is virtually entirely a matter of having the economic strength to be able to export goods in payment for food. With food security ensured by trade policy the concern for domestic agriculture changes from issues of agriculture's role in economic growth and food security to issues of farm incomes, rural life style and indeed the life style of the nation, and environmental concerns including its health and esthetic aspects.

2. Environmental Issues in Phase III

Because food security is assured in Phase III by a combination of domestic production and trade, and because environmental problems have increased by the very nature of development, environmental issues receive a different weight compared to the food insecure phases of development. It becomes economically sound to err on the side of control of pesticides and fertilizer use in order to preserve human health and the groundwater table. In addition, with diets satiated, consumption rising little or not at all, and technology increasing the productivity of agricultural resources it makes economic sense to take some of those benefits by withdrawing resources from agricultural in favor of environmentally sound practices. In some countries, that may well proceed to the point of requiring increased imports of food. The latter can be financed because of the high overall level of productivity in the economy.

VIII. Policy Requisites for Global Food Security

The vision presented of achieving virtually universal food security over the next few decades requires sensible policy. That policy has six elements.

First, all developing countries must pursue vigorous technological change in their agricultural sectors through research and its application and bring all people into an exchange economy through good rural infrastructure and universal education at least through the secondary school level. Foreign technical and financial assistance can greatly speed those processes.

Second, technical, social, and economic policies need to be pursued to bring down high rates of population growth.

Third, an international mechanism is needed to help the poorer countries finance food flows to ensure against transitory food insecurity.

Fourth, open-trading regimes are essential. They facilitate increased incomes to developing countries as they specialize in commodities to which their resources are best suited.

Fifth, as we approach global food security, we can attach increased weight to approaches to agriculture which may increase the cost of production but preserve and enhance the physical and esthetic qualities of the environment.

Sixth, as each nation approaches a state of food security it must pursue policies which maintain flexibility to adjust agriculture to stagnating demand in the face of continued technological improvement.

The greatest dangers to the hope of universal food security are (1) that the developing countries will not give the centrality to agricultural development that is essential to broadly participatory economic development, and (2) that the developed countries will not use their food surpluses to foster the short-term transfers and the long-term increase in rural infrastructure and education that can be accelerated by the thoughtful use of food aid.

Thus, with sensible policy at the national and international levels, we can obtain virtually complete food security over the next few decades. With judicious international policy, providing foreign assistance for both long-run development of the poor countries and short-run utilization of the surplus food of developed countries, we could achieve a close approximation of global food security within a decade. That is a grand prospect. In the course of only a few hundred years the whole world will have moved from a state of virtually universal food insecurity to a state of virtually universal food security.

Bibliography

Alamgir, M., and Poonan, A. (1991). "Providing Food Security for All," IFAD Studies in Rural Poverty #1. New York Univ. Press, New York.

Echer, C. K., and Staatz, J. M. (eds.) (1984). "Agricultural Development in the Third World." Johns Hopkins Univ. Press, Baltimore.

Foster, P. (1992). "The World Hunger Problem: Tackling the Causes of Undernutrition in the Third World." Lynn Rienner, Boulder, CO.

Maxwell, S. (1990). Food security in developing countries. *IDS Bull.* **21**(3).

Mellor, J. W., and Gavin, S. (1987). Famine: Causes, preventions, and relief. *Science* **235,** 539–545.

Mellor, J. W. (1990). Ending hunger: An implementable program for self-reliant growth. *In* "The World Food Crisis: Food Security in Comparative Perspective." (J. I. Hans Bakker, ed). Canadian Scholars' Press, Canada.

Mellor, J. W. (1988). Global food balances and food security. "World Development," (S. Kumar and M. Lipton, eds). Vol. 16(9), pp. 997–1011.

Reardon, T., and Matlon, P. (1989). Seasonal food insecurity and vulnerability in drought-affected areas of Burkina Faso. *In* "Causes and Implications of Seasonal Variability in Household Food Security" (D. Sahn, ed). The John Hopkins Univ. Press, Baltimore.

Sen, A. (1982). "Poverty and Famines. An Essay on Entitlement and Deprivation." Oxford Univ. Press, for ILO, Oxford.

World Bank (1986). "Poverty and Hunger." International Bank for Reconstruction and Development, Washington, DC.

APPENDIX A
United States Colleges and Universities Offering Academic Programs in Agriculture

Alabama

ALABAMA AGRICULTURAL & MECHANICAL UNIVERSITY
School of Agriculture and Home Economics
Normal, AL 25762
(205) 851-5783

AUBURN UNIVERSITY
College of Agriculture
Auburn, AL 36849-5401
(205) 844-2345

TUSKEGEE UNIVERSITY
School of Agriculture and Home Economics
Tuskegee, AL 36088
(205) 727-8327 or 727-8157

Alaska

UNIVERSITY OF ALASKA, FAIRBANKS
School of Agriculture and Land Resources Management
172 AHRB
Fairbanks, AK 99775-0100
(907) 474-7083

Arizona

ARIZONA STATE UNIVERSITY
School of Agribusiness and Environmental Resources
Tempe, AZ 85287-3306
(602) 965-3585

NORTHERN ARIZONA UNIVERSITY
School of Forestry
P. O. Box 15018
Flagstaff, AZ 86011
(602) 523-6638

UNIVERSITY OF ARIZONA
College of Agriculture
Tuscon, AZ 85721
(602) 621-3613

Arkansas

ARKANSAS STATE UNIVERSITY
College of Agriculture
P. O. Box 1080
State University, AR 72467
(501) 972-2085

ARKANSAS TECH UNIVERSITY
Department of Agriculture
Russellville, AR 72801
(501) 968-0625

SOUTHERN ARKANSAS UNIVERSITY
Department of Agriculture
P. O. Box 1343 SAU
Magnolia, AR 71753
(501) 235-4341

UNIVERSITY OF ARKANSAS
College of Agriculture and Home Economics
Fayetteville, AR 72701
(501) 575-2252

UNIVERSITY OF ARKANSAS, MONTICELLO
Agriculture
P. O. Box 3508
Monticello, AR 71656-3508
(501) 460-1033 or 543-8132

UNIVERSITY OF ARKANSAS, PINE BLUFF
School of Agriculture and Home Economics
Pine Bluff, AR 71601
(501) 543-8131 or 543-8132

California

CALIFORNIA STATE POLYTECHNIC UNIVERSITY
College of Agriculture
San Luis Obispo, CA 93407
(805) 756-2161

CALIFORNIA STATE POLYTECHNIC UNIVERSITY
College of Agriculture
3801 W. Temple Avenue

Encyclopedia of Agricultural Science, Volume 4   Copyright © 1994 by Academic Press, Inc.   All rights of reproduction in any form reserved.

Pomona, CA 91768
(909) 869-2204

CALIFORNIA STATE UNIVERSITY, CHICO
School of Agriculture and Human Environmental
Sciences
317 Plumas Hall
Chico, CA 95929-0440

CALIFORNIA STATE UNIVERSITY, FRESNO
School of Agricultural Sciences and Technology
Fresno, CA 93740-0079
(209) 278-2061

UNIVERSITY OF CALIFORNIA, BERKELEY
College of Natural Resources
101 Giannini Hall
Berkeley, CA 94720
(415) 642-0542

UNIVERSITY OF CALIFORNIA, DAVIS
College of Agricultural and Environmental Sciences
228 Mrak Hall
Davis, CA 95616-8571
(916) 752-6971

UNIVERSITY OF CALIFORNIA, RIVERSIDE
College of Natural and Agricultural Sciences
Riverside, CA 92521
(909) 787-7289

Colorado

COLORADO STATE UNIVERSITY
College of Agricultural Sciences
Fort Collins, CO 80523
(303) 491-6274

Connecticut

UNIVERSITY OF CONNECTICUT
College of Agriculture and Natural Resources
Storrs, CT 06269
(203) 486-2919 or 486-2920

Delaware

DELAWARE STATE COLLEGE
Department of Agriculture and Natural Resources
Dover, DE 19901
(302) 739-4929

UNIVERSITY OF DELAWARE
College of Agricultural Sciences
Newark, DE 19717-1303
(302) 831-2508

Florida

FLORIDA A & M UNIVERSITY
College of Engineering Sciences, Technology, and
Agriculture
Tallahassee, FL 32307
(904) 599-3383

UNIVERSITY OF FLORIDA
College of Agriculture
Gainesville, FL 32611
(904) 392-1961

Georgia

THE FORT VALLEY STATE COLLEGE
School of Agriculture, Home Economics, and Allied
Programs
Fort Valley, GA 31030
(912) 825-6344

UNIVERSITY OF GEORGIA
College of Agricultural and Environmental Sciences
Athens, GA 30602
(706) 542-1611

Guam

UNIVERSITY OF GUAM
College of Agriculture and Life Sciences
UOG Station
Mangilao, Guam 96923
(671) 734-2506

Hawaii

UNIVERSITY OF HAWAII
College of Tropical and Human Resources
3050 Maile Way
Honolulu, HI 96822
(808) 956-6997

Idaho

UNIVERSITY OF IDAHO
College of Agriculture
Iddings Agricultural Sciences Building
Moscow, ID 83843
(208) 885-6446

Illinois

ILLINOIS STATE UNIVERSITY
Department of Agriculture

Normal, IL 61761
(309) 438-5654

SOUTHERN ILLINOIS UNIVERSITY
College of Agriculture
Carbondale, IL 62901
(618) 453-2469

WESTERN ILLINOIS UNIVERSITY
Applied Sciences/ Agriculture Department
503 Currens Hall
Macomb, IL 61455
(309) 298-1080

UNIVERSITY OF ILLINOIS
College of Agriculture
1301 West Gregory Drive
Urbana, IL 61801
(217) 333-3380

Indiana

PURDUE UNIVERSITY
School of Agriculture
1140 Agricultural Administration Building
West Lafayette, IN 47907-1140
(317) 494-8472

Iowa

IOWA STATE UNIVERSITY
College of Agriculture
Ames, IA 50011
(515) 294-6614

Kansas

FORT HAYS STATE UNIVERSITY
College of Agriculture
600 Park Street
Hays, KS 67601
(913) 628-4364

KANSAS STATE UNIVERSITY
College of Agriculture
Manhattan, KS 66506-4015
(913) 532-6151

Kentucky

EASTERN KENTUCKY UNIVERSITY
Department of Agriculture
Richmond, KY 40475-3110
(606) 622-2228

UNIVERSITY OF KENTUCKY
College of Agriculture
Lexington, KY 40546
(606) 257-3468

MOREHEAD STATE UNIVERSITY
Department of Agriculture and Natural Resources
UPO 702
Morehead, KY 40351
(502) 762-6930

MURRAY STATE UNIVERSITY
Department of Agriculture
Murray, KY 42071
(502) 762-6930

WESTERN KENTUCKY UNIVERSITY
Department of Agriculture
Bowling Green, KY 42101
(502) 745-3151

Louisiana

LOUISIANA STATE UNIVERSITY
College of Agriculture
Baton Rouge, LA 70803
(504) 388-2362

LOUISIANA TECH UNIVERSITY
Agricultural Sciences, Technology and Education
Ruston, LA 71272
(318) 257-3275

McNEESE STATE UNIVERSITY
Department of Agriculture
Lake Charles, LA 70601
(318) 475-5691

NICHOLLS STATE UNIVERSITY
Department of Agriculture
Thibodaux, LA 70310
(504) 488-4870

NORTHEAST LOUISIANA UNIVERSITY
Department of Agriculture
Monroe, LA 71209-0510
(318) 342-1766

NORTHWESTERN STATE UNIVERSITY
Cooperative Programs and Agriculture
Natchitoches, LA 71497
(318) 357-4565

SOUTHEASTERN LOUISIANA UNIVERSITY
College of Arts and Sciences
S.L.V. Box 469
Hammond, LA 70402
(504) 549-2050

SOUTHERN UNIVERSITY & AGRICULTURAL AND
MECHANICAL COLLEGE
College of Agriculture and Home Economics

Southern Branch Post Office
Baton Rouge, LA 70813
(504) 771-3660

UNIVERSITY OF SOUTHWESTERN LOUISIANA
College of Applied Life Sciences
Box 44492
Lafayette, LA 70504
(318) 231-6643

Maine

UNIVERSITY OF MAINE
College of Natural Resources, Forestry and Agriculture
Orono, ME 04469
(207) 581-3206

Maryland

UNIVERSITY OF MARYLAND
College of Agriculture
College Park, MD 20742
(301) 405-2078

UNIVERSITY OF MARYLAND, EASTERN SHORE
School of Agricultural Sciences
Princess Anne, MD 21853
(410) 651-6075

Massachusetts

UNIVERSITY OF MASSACHUSETTS
College of Food and Natural Resources
Stockbridge Hall
Amherst, MA 01003
(413) 545-4204

Michigan

MICHIGAN STATE UNIVERSITY
College of Agricultural and Natural Resources
East Lansing, MI 48824-1039
(517) 355-0234

LAKE SUPERIOR STATE UNIVERSITY
Biology and Chemistry Department
Sault Ste. Marie, MI 49783
(906) 632-6841

Minnesota

SOUTHWEST STATE UNIVERSITY
Department of Agriculture
Marshall, MN 56258
(507) 537-6223

UNIVERSITY OF MINNESOTA
College of Agriculture
277 Coffey Hall
1420 Eckles Avenue
St. Paul, MN 55108
(612) 624-4212

Mississippi

ALCORN STATE UNIVERSITY
Division of Agriculture Research and Applied Science
P. O. Box 750
Lorman, MS 39096
(601) 877-6523

MISSISSIPPI STATE UNIVERSITY
College of Agriculture and Home Economics
Mississippi State, MS 39762
(601) 325-8579

Missouri

CENTRAL MISSOURI STATE UNIVERSITY
Department of Agriculture
Grinstead 137
Warrenburg, MO 64039
(816) 543-4240

LINCOLN UNIVERSITY
Department of Agriculture, Natural Resources and Home Economics
Jefferson City, MO 65101
(314) 681-6120

MISSOURI WESTERN STATE COLLEGE
4525 Downs Drive
St. Joseph, MO 64507
(816) 271-4405

NORTHEAST MISSOURI STATE UNIVERSITY
Department of Agriculture
156 Barnett Hall
Kirksville, MO 63501
(816) 785-4111

NORTHWEST MISSOURI STATE UNIVERSITY
Department of Agriculture
800 University Avenue
Maryville, MO 64468-6001

SOUTHEAST MISSOURI STATE UNIVERSITY
Department of Agriculture
109 Magell Hall
Cape Girardeau, MO 63701
(314) 651-2106

SOUTHWEST MISSOURI STATE UNIVERSITY
Department of Agriculture

901 South National
Springfield, MO 65602
(417) 836-5638

UNIVERSITY OF MISSOURI
College of Agriculture
Columbia, MO 65211
(314) 882-3846

Montana

MONTANA STATE UNIVERSITY
College of Agriculture
Bozeman, MT 59717
(406) 994-5744

Nebraska

UNIVERSITY OF NEBRASKA, KEARNEY
Department of Economics/ Agri-Business and Technology
School of Business and Technology
West Center Building
Kearney, NE 68849
(308) 234-8530

UNIVERSITY OF NEBRASKA, LINCOLN
College of Agricultural Sciences and Natural Resources
Lincoln, NE 68583-0702
(402) 472-2201

Nevada

UNIVERSITY OF NEVADA
College of Agriculture
Reno, NV 89557-0004
(702) 784-1095

New Hampshire

UNIVERSITY OF NEW HAMPSHIRE
College of Life Sciences and Agriculture
Taylor Hall
Durham, NH 03824
(603) 862-1451

New Jersey

RUTGERS STATE UNIVERSITY
Cook College
New Brunswick, NJ 08903-0231
(908) 932-9465 or 932-9024

New Mexico

NEW MEXICO STATE UNIVERSITY
College of Agriculture and Home Economics

Las Cruces, NM 88003
(505) 646-1807

EASTERN NEW MEXICO STATE UNIVERSITY
Department of Agriculture
Station #1 ENMU
Portales, NM 88130
(505) 562-2517

New York

STATE UNIVERSITY OF NEW YORK, COBBLESKILL
Division of Agricultural and Natural Resources
Cobbleskill, NY 12034
(518) 234-5323

CORNELL UNIVERSITY
College of Agriculture and Life Sciences
Ithaca, NY 14853
(607) 255-3081

North Carolina

NORTH CAROLINA AGRICULTURAL AND TECHNICAL STATE UNIVERSITY
School of Agriculture
Greensboro, NC 27411
(919) 334-7979 or 334-7665

NORTH CAROLINA STATE UNIVERSITY
College of Agriculture and Life Sciences
Campus Box 7642
Raleigh, NC 27695-7642
(919) 515-2614

North Dakota

NORTH DAKOTA STATE UNIVERSITY
College of Agriculture
Box 5435
State University Station
Fargo, ND 58105
(701) 237-7654

Ohio

OHIO STATE UNIVERSITY
College of Agriculture
Room 100
2120 Fyffe Road
Columbus, OH 43210
(614) 292-6891 or 292-5490

Oklahoma

CAMERON UNIVERSITY
Department of Agriculture

Lawton, OK 73501
(405) 581-2275

LANGSTON UNIVERSITY
Department of Agriculture
Langston, OK 73050
(405) 466-2231, ext. 3365

NORTHWESTERN OKLAHOMA STATE UNIVERSITY
Agriculture Department
Alva, OK 73717
(405) 327-1700

OKLAHOMA STATE UNIVERSITY
Division of Agricultural Sciences and Natural Resources
Stillwater, OK 74078
(405) 744-5395

PANHANDLE STATE UNIVERSITY
Agriculture
Box 430
Goodwell, OK 73939
(405) 349-2611, ext. 262

Oregon

OREGON STATE UNIVERSITY
College of Agricultural Sciences
Corvallis, OR 97331-2202
(503) 737-2211

Pennsylvania

PENNSYLVANIA STATE UNIVERSITY
College of Agricultural Sciences
University Park, PA 16802
(814) 865-2541

Puerto Rico

UNIVERSITY OF PUERTO RICO
College of Agricultural Sciences
Mayaguez Campus
Mayaguez, PR 00708
(809) 265-3850 or 832-4040 ext. 2181

Rhode Island

UNIVERSITY OF RHODE ISLAND
College of Resource Development
Kingston, RI 02881-0804
(401) 792-2474

South Carolina

CLEMSON UNIVERSITY
College of Agricultural Sciences
Room 102, Barre Hall
Box 340303
Clemson, SC 29634-0303
(803) 656-3013

South Dakota

SOUTH DAKOTA STATE UNIVERSITY
College of Agriculture and Biological Sciences
Brookings, SD 57006
(605) 688-5133

Tennessee

AUSTIN PEAY STATE UNIVERSITY
Department of Agriculture
APSU Box 4607
Clarksville, TN 37044
(615) 648-7267

MIDDLE TENNESSEE STATE UNIVERSITY
Department of Agribusiness and Agriscience
Murfreesboro, TN 37132
(615) 898-2523

TENNESSEE STATE UNIVERSITY
School of Agriculture and Home Economics
Nashville, TN 37203
(615) 320-3718

TENNESSEE TECHNOLOGICAL UNIVERSITY
College of Agriculture and Home Economics
Box 5165
Cookeville, TN 38505
(615) 372-3019

UNIVERSITY OF TENNESEE
College of Agriculture Sciences and Natural Resources
Knoxville, TN 37901
(615) 974-7303

UNIVERSITY OF TENNESSEE, MARTIN
School of Agriculture Sciences and Home Economics
Martin, TN 38238
(901) 587-7010

Texas

ANGELO STATE UNIVERSITY
Agriculture
P. O. Box 10888
San Angelo, TX 76909
(915) 942-2027

EAST TEXAS STATE UNIVERSITY
Department of Agricultural Sciences
Commerce, TX 75429-3011
(903) 886-5350

PRAIRIE VIEW A & M UNIVERSITY
Department of Agriculture
P. O. Box 486
Prairie View, TX 77446-486
(409) 857-2812

PRAIRIE VIEW A & M UNIVERSITY, KINGSVILLE
College of Agriculture and Home Economics
Campus Box 156
Kingsville, TX 78363
(512) 595-3712

SAM HOUSTON STATE UNIVERSITY
Division of Agricultural Sciences and Vocational Education
P. O. Box 2088
Huntsville, TX 77340-2088
(409) 294-1214

SOUTHWEST TEXAS STATE UNIVERSITY
Applied Arts and Technology
Department of Agriculture
601 University Avenue
San Marcos, TX 78666-4616
(512) 245-2130

STEVEN F. AUSTIN STATE UNIVERSITY
Department of Agriculture
P. O. Box 13000, SFA Station
Nacogdoches, TX 75962
(409) 568-3705

SUL ROSS STATE UNIVERSITY
Center of Range Animal Science
P. O. Box C-110
Alpine, TX 79832
(915) 837-8200

TARLETON STATE UNIVERSITY
College of Agriculture and Technology
Box T1119 Tarleton Station
Stephenville, TX 76401
(817) 968-9227

TEXAS A & M UNIVERSITY
College of Agriculture and Life Sciences
College Station, TX 77843-2142
(409) 845-3716

TEXAS TECH UNIVERSITY
College of Agricultural Sciences and Natural Resources
Box 42123
Lubbock, TX 79409-2123
(806) 742-2808

WEST TEXAS A & M UNIVERSITY
Division of Agriculture
WTAMU Box 998

Canyon, TX 79016-0001
(806) 656-2550 ext. 2556

Utah

UTAH STATE UNIVERSITY
College of Agriculture
Logan, UT 84322-4800
(801) 750-2267

Vermont

UNIVERSITY OF VERMONT
College of Agriculture and Life Sciences
Burlington, VT 05405
(802) 656-2981

Virgin Islands

UNIVERSITY OF THE VIRGIN ISLANDS
St. Croix, USVI 00850
(809) 776-9200

Virginia

VIRGINIA POLYTECHNIC INSTITUTE AND STATE UNIVERSITY
College of Agriculture and Life Sciences
Blacksburg, VA 24061-0334
(703) 231-6503

VIRGINIA STATE UNIVERSITY
School of Agriculture and Applied Sciences
Campus Box 4070
Petersburg, VA 23803
(804) 524-5631

Washington

WASHINGTON STATE UNIVERSITY
College of Agriculture and Home Economics
Pullman, WA 99164-6242
(509) 335-4562

West Virginia

WEST VIRGINIA UNIVERSITY
College of Agriculture and Forestry
Morgantown, WV 26506-6108
(304) 293-2691

Wisconsin

UNIVERSITY OF WISCONSIN, PLATTEVILLE
College of Agriculture
1 University Plaza
Platteville, WI 53818
(608) 342-1393

UNIVERSITY OF WISCONSIN, RIVER FALLS
College of Agriculture
210 Ag Science Building
River Falls, WI 54022
(715) 425-3535

UNIVERSITY OF WISCONSIN
College of Agricultural and Life Sciences
Madison, WI 53706
(608) 262-3003

Wyoming

UNIVERSITY OF WYOMING
College of Agriculture
University Station, P. O. Box 3354
Laramie, WY 82071
(307) 766-4133

Washington DC

AGENCY FOR INTERNATIONAL DEVELOPMENT R & D CENTER
(BIFADEC)
Room 900 SA-38, Department of State

Washington, DC 20523
(703) 816-0291

AMERICAN ASSOCIATION OF STATE COLLEGES AND UNIVERSITIES
Suite 700, Dupont Circle, N.W.
Washington, DC 20036-1192
(202) 293-7070 ext. 3232

COUNCIL FOR AGRICULTURAL RESEARCH, DC EXTENSION AND TEACHING (CARET)
Washington, DC 20250

NATIONAL ASSOCIATION OF STATE UNIVERSITIES AND LAND GRANT COLLEGES (NASULGC)
Suite 710, One Dupont Circle N.W.
Washington, DC 20036-1191
(202) 778-0822

SCIENCE AND EDUCATION, CSRS, USDA
Higher Education Programs

Policy and Evaluation Management Staff
Room 350A, Administration Building
14th and Independence Avenue, S.W.
Washington, DC 20250-2200
(202) 720-7854

Grant Programs Staff
Room 310-E, Aerospace Center
14th and Independence Avenue, S.W.
Washington, DC 20250-2200
(202) 401-1790

UNIVERSITY OF THE DISTRICT OF COLUMBIA
College of Life Sciences
Washington, DC 20008
(202) 282-7386

APPENDIX B
United Nations Agricultural and Other Related Organizations

Centro Internacional de Agricultura Tropical (CIAT)
Apartado Aereo 6713
Cali, Columbia
(57-23) 675050

Center for International Forestry Research (CIFOR)
Jalan Gunung Batu 5
Bogor 16001, Indonesia
Mailing Address:
P. O. Box 6596
JKPWB Jakarta 10065
Indonesia
62 (251) 31-9423, 32-4032, 31-4581, or 32-6458

Centro Internacional de Mejoramiento de Maiz y Trigo (CIMMYT)
Lisboa 27
P. O. Box 6-641
06600 Mexico, D. F. Mexico
(52-5) 726-9091 or (52-595) 421-00

Centro Internacional de la Papa (CIP)
Apartado 5969
Lima
Peru
(51-14) 366920

Consultative Group on International Agricultural Research (CGIAR)
The World Bank
1818 H Street, NW
Washington, DC 20433
United States
(1-202) 473-8951

Food and Agricultural Organization of the United Nations (FAO)
Via Delle Terme di Caracalla
00100 Rome Italy
(39-6) 52251

International Atomic Energy Agency (IAEA)
Wagramerstrasse 5
A-1400 Vienna
Austria
(43-1) 23600

International Center for Agricultural Research in the Dry Areas (ICARDA)
P. O. Box 5466
Aleppo
Syrian Arab Republic
(963-21) 225012, 225112, or 234890

International Center for Living Aquatic Resources Management (ICLARM)
MC P. O. Box 2631, Makati Central Post Office
0718 Makati
Metro Manila
Philippines
(63-2) 817-5255 or 817-5163

International Centre for Research in Agroforestry (ICRAF)
United Nations Avenue
P. O. Box 30677
Nairobi, Kenya
(254-2) 521450

International Crops Research Institute for the Semi-Arid Tropics (ICRISAT)
Patancheru P.O.
Andhra Pradesh 502 324
India
(91-40) 224016

International Food Policy Research Institute (IFPRI)
1200 17th Street, NW
Washington, DC 20036-3006
(1-202) 862-5600

International Fund for Agricultural Development (IFAD)
Via del Serafico 107
00142 Rome
Italy
(39-6) 54591

International Irrigation Management Institute (IIMI)
127 Sunil Mawatha
Pelawatte via Colombo
Sri Lanka

Mailing Address:
P. O. Box 2075
Colombo, Sri Lanka
(94-1) 867404

INTERNATIONAL INSTITUTE OF TROPICAL AGRICULTURE
(IITA)
PMB 5320
Ibadan
Nigeria
(234-22) 400300-318
International Mailing Address:
IITA, Ibadan
Nigeria
c/o L. W. Lambourn & Company
Carolyn House
26 Dingwall Road
Croydon CR9 3EE
United Kingdom
(44-81) 686-9031

INTERNATIONAL LABOR ORGANIZATION (ILO)
4 route des Morillons
CH-1211 Geneva 22
Switzerland
(41-22) 7996111

INTERNATIONAL LIVESTOCK CENTRE FOR AFRICA
(ILCA)
P. O. Box 5689
Addis Ababa
Ethiopia
(251-1) 613215

INTERNATIONAL LABORATORY FOR RESEARCH ON ANIMAL
DISEASES (ILRAD)
P. O. Box 30709
Nairobi
Kenya
(254-2) 632311

INTERNATIONAL NETWORK FOR THE IMPROVEMENT OF
BANANA AND PLANTAIN (INIBAP)
Parc Scientifique Agropolis - Bât 7
Bd de la Lironde
34980 Montferrier-sur-Lez
France
(33) 67611302
Mailing Address:
Parc Scientifique Agropolis
34397 Montpellier Cedex 5
France

INTERNATIONAL PLANT GENETIC RESOURCES INSTITUTE
(IPGRI)
c/o Food and Agriculture Organization of the United
Nations
Via delle Sette Chiese 142

00145 Rome
Italy
(39-6) 518921

INTERNATIONAL RICE RESEARCH INSTITUTE (IRRI)
P. O. Box 933
Manila
Philippines
(63-2) 818-1926 or 812-7686

INTERNATIONAL SERVICE FOR NATIONAL AGRICULTURAL
RESEARCH (ISNAR)
Laan van Nieuw Oost Indië 133
2593 BM The Hague
The Netherlands
(31-70) 3496100
Mailing Address:
P. O. Box 93375
2509 AJ The Hague
The Netherlands

UNITED NATIONS DEVELOPMENT PROGRAM (UNDP)
1 United Nations Plaza
New York, NY 10017
United States
(1-212) 906-5856

UNITED NATIONS EDUCATIONAL, SCIENTIFIC, AND
CULTURAL ORGANIZATION (UNESCO)
7, place de Fontenoy
75700 Paris
France
(33-1) 45681000

UNITED NATIONS ENVIRONMENT PROGRAMME (UNEP)
P. O. Box 30552
Nairobi
Kenya
(254-2) 333930

UNITED NATIONS INSTITUTE FOR TRAINING AND RESEARCH
(UNITAR)
801 United Nations Plaza
New York, NY 10017
United States
(1-212) 963-8637

UNITED NATIONS UNIVERSITY (UNU)
Toho Seimei Building
15-1 Shibuya 2-chome
Tokyo 150
Japan
(81-3) 499-2811

WEST AFRICA RICE DEVELOPMENT ASSOCIATION
(WARDA)
01 B. P. 2551, Bouake 01
Côte d'Ivoire
(225) 632396, 633242, or 634514

WORLD FOOD COUNCIL (WFC)
Via Delle Terme di Caracalla
00100 Rome
Italy
(39-6) 52257971

WORLD FOOD PROGRAMME (WFP)
Via Cristoforo Colombo, 426
00145 Rome

Italy
(39-6) 52257971

WORLD INTELLECTUAL PROPERTY ORGANIZATION
(WIPO)
34 chemin des Colombettes
1211 Geneva 20
Switzerland
(41-22) 7309111

CONTRIBUTORS

Marc D. Abrams TEMPERATE HARDWOODS
School of Forest Resources, Pennsylvania State University, University Park, Pennsylvania 16802

Perry L. Adkisson PEST MANAGEMENT, CULTURAL CONTROL
Department of Entomology, Texas A&M University, College Station, Texas 77843

George N. Agrios PLANT PATHOLOGY
Department of Plant Pathology, University of Florida, Gainesville, Florida 32611

James L. Ahlrichs SOIL, ACID
Department of Agronomy, Purdue University, West Lafayette, Indiana 47907

R. Michael Akers LACTATION
Department of Dairy Science, Virginia Polytechnic Institute and State University, Blacksburg, Virginia 24061

Louis D. Albright STRUCTURES
Department of Agricultural and Biological Engineering, Cornell University, Ithaca, New York 14850

David M. Alm PLANT ECOLOGY
Photosynthesis Research Unit, USDA-Agricultural Research Service, Urbana, Illinois 61801

Miguel A. Altieri RURAL DEVELOPMENT, INTERNATIONAL; SUSTAINABLE AGRICULTURE
Laboratory of Biological Control, and Department of Natural Science, Policy, and Management, University of California, Berkeley, Albany, California 94706

A. Amoozegar SOIL DRAINAGE
Department of Soil Science, North Carolina State University, Raleigh, North Carolina 27695

Madhu Aneja COCOA
Department of Plant Science, Rutgers University, New Brunswick, New Jersey 08903

Rudi Appels PLANT GENETIC ENHANCEMENT
Division of Plant Industry, CSIRO, Canberra ACT 2601, Australia

Tetsuo Asakura SILK PRODUCTION AND PROCESSING
Department of Biotechnology, Faculty of Technology, Tokyo University of Agriculture and Technology, Koganei, Tokyo 184, Japan

K. H. Asay RANGELAND GRASS IMPROVEMENT
USDA-Agricultural Research Service, Utah State University, Logan, Utah 84322

David Atkinson ORCHARD MANAGEMENT: SOIL ENVIRONMENT AND RESOURCES
The Scottish Agricultural College, Edinburgh EH9 3JG, Scotland

P. S. Baenziger WHEAT BREEDING AND GENETICS
Department of Agronomy, University of Nebraska, Lincoln, Lincoln, Nebraska 68583

James A. Bailey WILDLIFE MANAGEMENT
Department of Fishery and Wildlife Biology, Colorado State University, Fort Collins, Colorado 80524, *and* New Mexico Department of Game and Fish, Santa Fe, New Mexico 87504

John Baldwin PEANUTS
College of Agriculture, University of Georgia Cooperative Extension Service, Tifton, Georgia 31793

Donald M. Ball FORAGES
Department of Agronomy and Soils, Auburn University, Auburn, Alabama 36849

Moshe Bar-Joseph CITRUS FRUITS
Department of Postharvest Science, Agricultural Research Organization, The Volcani Center, Bet Dagan 50250, Israel

Hugh Barrett RANGELAND WATERSHED MANAGEMENT
Bureau of Land Management, Oregon and Washington, Portland, Oregon 97208

Philip J. Bauer COTTON CROP PRODUCTION
Soil, Water, and Plant Research Center, USDA-Agricultural Research Service, Coastal Plains, Florence, South Carolina 29502

Dwayne Beck CORN CROP PRODUCTION
Dakota Lakes Research Center, South Dakota State University, Pierre, South Dakota 57501

Gregorio B. Begonia PLANT ECOLOGY
Jackson State University, Jackson, Mississippi 39217

Donald C. Beitz FATS AND CHOLESTEROL, ROLE IN HUMAN NUTRITION
Departments of Animal Science and Biochemistry-Biophysics, Iowa State University, Ames, Iowa 50011

Shimshon Ben-Yehoshua CITRUS FRUITS
Department of Postharvest Science, Agricultural Research Organization, The Volcani Center, Bet Dagan 50250, Israel

Peter Berck PRODUCTION ECONOMICS
Department of Agricultural and Research Economics, University of California, Berkeley, Berkeley, California 94720

David B. Berkowitz TRANSGENIC ANIMALS
Office of Small Business, Scientific, and Trade Affairs, Food and Drug Administration, Rockville, Maryland 20857

Louise A. Berner DAIRY PROCESSING AND PRODUCTS
San Luis Obispo, California 93401

Richard H. Bernsten INTERNATIONAL AGRICULTURAL RESEARCH
Department of Agricultural Economics, Michigan State University, East Lansing, Michigan 48824

David A. Bessler PRICES
Department of Agricultural Economics, Texas A&M University, College Station, Texas 77843

Nyle C. Brady CONSULTATIVE GROUP ON INTERNATIONAL AGRICULTURAL RESEARCH
United Nations Development Program and World Bank, Washington, D.C. 20006

C. K. Bragg COTTON PROCESSING AND UTILIZATION
Cotton Quality Research Station, USDA-Agricultural Research Service, South Atlantic Area, Clemson, South Carolina 29631

Aaron L. Brody FOOD PACKAGING
Rubbright•Brody, Inc., Devon, Pennsylvania 19333

C. R. Brown POTATO
USDA-Agricultural Research Service, Prosser, Washington 99350

Steven T. Buccola COOPERATIVES
Agriculture and Resource Economics, Oregon State University, Corvallis, Oregon 97331

Henry Buist LAND USE PLANNING IN AGRICULTURE
Land and Capital Assets Branch, USDA-Economic Research Service, Washington, D.C. 20005

S. W. Buol SOIL GENESIS, MORPHOLOGY, AND CLASSIFICATION
Department of Soil Science, North Carolina State University, Raleigh, North Carolina 27695

David W. Burger PLANT PROPAGATION
Department of Environmental Horticulture, University of California, Davis, Davis, California 95616

Frederick H. Buttel RURAL SOCIOLOGY
Department of Rural Sociology, University of Wisconsin—Madison, Madison, Wisconsin 53706

John S. Caldwell FARMING SYSTEMS
Department of Horticulture, Virginia Polytechnic Institute and State University, Blacksburg, Virginia 24061

William C. Capman PLANT ECOLOGY
University of Illinois, Urbana, Illinois 61801

Robert G. Cassens MEAT PROCESSING
Department of Meat and Animal Science, University of Wisconsin—Madison, Madison, Wisconsin 53706

H. Marc Cathey FLORICULTURE
American Horticultural Society, Alexandria, Virginia 22306

Te-Tzu Chang PLANT GENETIC RESOURCE CONSERVATION AND UTILIZATION
Tamshui, Taipei Hsien, Taiwan-251

L. Davis Clements BIOMASS
Department of Chemical Engineering, University of Nebraska, Lincoln, Lincoln, Nebraska 68508

T. S. Colvin SOIL MANAGEMENT
National Soil Tilth Laboratory, USDA-Agricultural Research Service, Ames, Iowa 50011

Ashton Keith Cowan PLANT STRESS
Botanical Laboratories, Rhodes University, Grahamstown 6140, South Africa

Jacques Crabbe DORMANCY
Agricultural Faculty of Gembloux and Free University of Brussels, B-5030 Brussels, Belgium

D. L. Critten HORTICULTURAL GREENHOUSE ENGINEERING
Silsoe Research Institute, Wrest Park, Silsoe, Bedford MK45 4HS, England

David W. Cudney OAT
Department of Botany and Plant Sciences, University of California, Riverside, Riverside, California 92521

L. V. Cundiff ANIMAL BREEDING AND GENETICS
U.S. Meat Animal Research Center, USDA-Agricultural Research Service, Clay Center, Nebraska 68933

James R. Daniel CARBOHYDRATES, ROLE IN HUMAN NUTRITION
Foods and Nutrition Department, Purdue University, West Lafayette, Indiana 47907

A. K. Datta FOOD PROCESS ENGINEERING: HEAT AND MASS TRANSFER; FOOD PROCESS ENGINEERING: THERMODYNAMIC AND TRANSPORT PROPERTIES
Department of Agricultural and Biological Engineering, Cornell University, Ithaca, New York 14853

P. Michael Davidson FOOD PRESERVATIVES
Food Research Center, Department of Food Science and Toxicology, University of Idaho, Moscow, Idaho 83843

Prakash M. Dey PLANT BIOCHEMISTRY
Department of Biochemistry, Royal Holloway and Bedford, New College, University of London, Surrey TW20 OEX, England

G. E. Dickerson ANIMAL BREEDING AND GENETICS
U.S. Meat Animal Research Center, USDA-Agricultural Research Service, University of Nebraska, Lincoln, Lincoln, Nebraska 68508

Michael H. Dickson CABBAGE AND COLE CROPS
New York State Agricultural Experiment Station, Department of Horticulture Sciences, Cornell University, Geneva, New York 14456

David C. Dixon PLANT CYTOLOGY, MODERN TECHNIQUES
USDA-Agricultural Research Service, New Orleans, Louisiana 70179

A. Johannes Dolman TROPICAL RAIN FORESTS: HYDROLOGY AND CLIMATE
DLO-Winand Staring Center, NL-6700-AC Wageningen, The Netherlands

H. E. Dregne DESERTIFICATION OF DRYLANDS
International Center for Arid and Semiarid Land Studies, Texas Tech University, Lubbock, Texas 79409

Stephen O. Duke WEED SCIENCE
Southern Weed Science Laboratory, USDA-Agricultural Research Service, Stoneville, Mississippi 38776

Paul N. Ellinger FINANCE
Department of Agricultural Economics, Texas A&M University, College Station, Texas 77843

Clyde L. Elmore OAT
Department of Botany, University of California, Davis, Davis, California 95616

George Fedak BARLEY
Plant Research Centre, Agriculture and Agri-Food Canada, Central Experimental Farm, Ottawa, Ontario, Canada K1A OC6

Owen Fennema FOOD CHEMISTRY
Department of Food Science, University of Wisconsin—Madison, Madison, Wisconsin 53706

David C. Ferree ORCHARD MANAGEMENT SYSTEMS
Department of Horticulture, Ohio State University, Wooster, Ohio 44691

Richard F. Fisher FOREST ECOLOGY
Department of Forest Science, Texas A&M University, College Station, Texas 77843

Eric L. Flamm PLANT BIOTECHNOLOGY: FOOD SAFETY AND ENVIRONMENTAL ISSUES
International Policy Staff, Office of Policy, Food and Drug Administration, Rockville, Maryland 20857

Cornelia Butler Flora WOMEN IN AGRICULTURE
North Central Regional Center for Rural Development, Iowa State University, Ames, Iowa 50011

Robert H. Foote EMBRYO TRANSFER IN DOMESTIC ANIMALS
Department of Animal Science, Cornell University, Ithaca, New York 14853

Chester L. Foy PEST MANAGEMENT, CHEMICAL CONTROL
Department of Plant Pathology, Physiology, and Weed Science, Virginia Polytechnic Institute and State University, Blacksburg, Virginia 24061

Raymond E. Frisbie INTEGRATED PEST MANAGEMENT
Department of Entomology, Texas A&M University, College Station, Texas 77843

John H. C. Gash TROPICAL RAIN FORESTS: HYDROLOGY AND CLIMATE
Institute of Hydrology, Wallingford OX10 8BB, England

W. Gensler MEASUREMENT OF MICRO-OXYGEN SUPPLY AND DEMAND
Agricultural Electronics Corporation, Tucson, Arizona 85703

Thomas L. German PLANT VIROLOGY
Department of Plant Pathology, University of Wisconsin—Madison, Madison, Wisconsin 53706

Mario Giampietro ENERGY UTILIZATION
Istituto Nazionale della Nutrizione, Rome, Italy, and Department of Entomology, Cornell University, Ithaca, New York 14853

Thomas Gianfagna COCOA
Department of Plant Science, Rutgers University, New Brunswick, New Jersey 08903

Eliezer E. Goldschmidt CITRUS FRUITS
The Kennedy-Leigh Centre for Horticultural Research, The Hebrew University of Jerusalem, Rehovet 76100, Israel

Robert M. Goodman PLANT VIROLOGY
Department of Plant Pathology, University of Wisconsin—Madison, Madison, Wisconsin 53706

Barbara L. Goulart BERRIES
Department of Horticulture, Pennsylvania State University, University Park, Pennsylvania 16802

Donna L. Graham COOPERATIVE EXTENSION SYSTEM
Cooperative Extension Service, University of Arkansas, Fayetteville, Arkansas 72701

V. Gustafson WHEAT BREEDING AND GENETICS
Department of Agronomy, University of Nebraska, Lincoln, Lincoln, Nebraska 68583

Arnel R. Hallauer CORN GENETICS AND BREEDING
Department of Agronomy, Iowa State University, Ames, Iowa 50011

Timothy M. Hammonds FOOD MARKETING SYSTEMS
Food Marketing Institute, Washington, D.C. 20006

Heinz Häni SOIL POLLUTION
Swiss Federal Research Station for Agricultural Chemistry and Hygiene of Environment, CH 3097 Liebefeld-Berne, Switzerland

Linda H. Hardesty RANGELAND WATERSHED MANAGEMENT
Department of Natural Research Sciences, Washington State University, Pullman, Washington 99164

Richard H. Hart RANGELAND
High Plains Grasslands Research Station, USDA-Agricultural Research Service, Cheyenne, Wyoming 82009

Kriton K. Hatzios HERBICIDES AND HERBICIDE RESISTANCE
Department of Plant Pathology, Physiology, and Weed Science, Virginia Polytechnic Institute and State University, Blacksburg, Virginia 24061

Geoffrey Hawtin PLANT GENETIC RESOURCES
International Plant Genetic Resources Institute, 00145 Rome, Italy

Walter W. Heck AIR POLLUTION: PLANT GROWTH AND PRODUCTIVITY
USDA-Agricultural Research Service, and Department of Botany, North Carolina State University, Raleigh, North Carolina 27606

Ralph E. Heimlich WETLANDS AND RIPARIAN AREAS: ECONOMICS AND POLICY
Resources and Technology Division, USDA-Economic Research Service, Washington, D.C. 20005

Don J. Heinz SUGARCANE
Experiment Station, Hawaiian Sugar Planters' Association, Aiea, Hawaii 96701

James C. Heird HORSE INDUSTRY: TRENDS, OPPORTUNITIES, AND ISSUES
College of Agricultural Sciences, Colorado State University, Fort Collins, Colorado 80523

R. K. Heitschmidt RANGELAND ECOLOGY
Fort Keogh Livestock and Range Research Laboratory, USDA-Agricultural Research Service, Miles City, Montana 59301

Gloria Helfand PRODUCTION ECONOMICS
Department of Agricultural Economics, University of California, Davis, Davis, California 95616

John D. Hesketh PLANT ECOLOGY
Photosynthesis Research Unit, USDA-Agricultural Research Service, Urbana, Illinois 61801

F. Jackson Hills[1] SUGARBEET
Department of Agronomy and Range Science, University of California, Davis, Davis, California 95616

Khidir W. Hilu EVOLUTION OF DOMESTICATED PLANTS
Department of Biology, Virginia Polytechnic Institute and State University, Blacksburg, Virginia 24061

Graeme Hobson POSTHARVEST PHYSIOLOGY
Horticulture Research International, Littlehampton, West Sussex BN17 6LP, England

Heikki M. T. Hokkanen PEST MANAGEMENT, BIOLOGICAL CONTROL
Faculty of Agriculture and Forestry, Department of Applied Zoology, FIN-00014 University of Helsinki, Finland

J. L. Holechek RANGELAND GRAZING
Department of Animal and Range Sciences, New Mexico State University, Las Cruces, New Mexico 88003

Don Holt AGRICULTURAL EXPERIMENT STATIONS
Illinois Agricultural Experiment Station, and College of Agriculture, University of Illinois, Urbana, Illinois 61801

Roger Hoopingarner APICULTURE
Department of Entomology, Michigan State University, East Lansing, Michigan 48824

Carl S. Hoveland FORAGES
Department of Crop and Soil Sciences, University of Georgia, Athens, Georgia 30601

John A. Howard HETEROSIS
Plant Breeding Division, Pioneer Hi-Bred International, Johnston, Iowa 50131

Terry A. Howell IRRIGATION ENGINEERING, EVAPOTRANSPIRATION
Conservation and Production Research Laboratory, USDA-Agricultural Research Service, Bushland, Texas 79012

Natalie L. Hubbard MELONS: BIOCHEMICAL AND PHYSIOLOGICAL CONTROL OF SUGAR ACCUMULATION
Agricultural Products, E. I. DuPont, Wilmington, Delaware 19880

S. E. Hughs COTTON PROCESSING AND UTILIZATION
Southwestern Cotton Ginning Research Laboratory, USDA-Agricultural Research Service, Southern Plains Area, Mesilla Park, New Mexico 88047

David W. Hysert BREWING TECHNOLOGY
John I. Haas, Inc., Yakima, Washington 98901

W. Michael Ingledew BREWING TECHNOLOGY
Applied Microbiology and Food Science, University of Saskatchewan, Saskatoon, Saskatchewan, Canada S7N OWO

Yoshinori Itokawa MINERALS, ROLE IN HUMAN NUTRITION
Department of Environmental Medicine, Graduate School of Medicine, Kyoto University, Kyoto 606-01, Japan

Ronald S. Jackson VITICULTURE
Department of Botany, Brandon University, Brandon, Manitoba, Canada R7A 6A9

Brian G. Jamieson BIOTECHNOLOGY AND BIOLOGICAL SCIENCES RESEARCH COUNCIL, UNITED KINGDOM
Biotechnology and Biological Sciences Research Council, Swindon SN2 1UH, England

Harry W. Janes TOMATO PRODUCTION IN PROTECTED CULTIVATION
Department of Horticulture and Forestry, Rutgers University, New Brunswick, New Jersey 08903

[1] Deceased.

Digvir S. Jayas FOOD DEHYDRATION
Department of Agricultural Engineering, University of Manitoba, Winnipeg, Manitoba, Canada R3T 5V6

Charles S. Johnson TOBACCO
Virginia Polytechnic Institute and State University, Blackstone, Virginia 23824

Dale W. Johnson NITROGEN CYCLING
Desert Research Institute, Reno, Nevada 89506, and Environmental and Resource Sciences, University of Nevada, Reno, Nevada 89512

Glenn L. Johnson INTERNATIONAL AGRICULTURAL RESEARCH
Department of Agricultural Economics, Michigan State University, East Lansing, Michigan 48824

G. V. Johnson SOIL FERTILITY
Oklahoma State University, Stillwater, Oklahoma 74078

James E. Johnson CHRISTMAS TREE PRODUCTION
College of Forestry and Wildlife Resources, Virginia Polytechnic Institute and State University, Blacksburg, Virginia 24061

Lawrence A. Johnson CORN PROCESSING AND UTILIZATION
Center for Crops Utilization Research, Iowa State University, Ames, Iowa 50011

John Patrick Jordon U.S. DEPARTMENT OF AGRICULTURE: A NATIONAL SYSTEM OF AGRICULTURAL RESEARCH
USDA-Cooperative State Research Service, Washington, D. C. 20250

Stephen Kaffka SUGARBEET
Department of Agronomy and Range Science, University of California, Davis, Davis, California 95616

David L. Kaplan SILK PRODUCTION AND PROCESSING
Biotechnology Division, U.S. Army Natick Research and Development Center, Natick, Massachusetts 01760

D. L. Karlen SOIL MANAGEMENT
National Soil Tilth Laboratory, USDA-Agricultural Research Service, Ames, Iowa 50011

Gurdev S. Khush RICE GENETICS AND BREEDING
International Rice Research Institute, 1099 Manila, Philippines

Donald M. Kinsman ANIMAL BY-PRODUCTS FROM SLAUGHTER
Department of Animal Science, University of Connecticut, Storrs, Connecticut 06269

M. B. Kirkham SOIL-WATER RELATIONSHIPS
Evapotranspiration Laboratory, Department of Agronomy, Kansas State University, Manhattan, Kansas 66506

David A. Knauft CULTIVAR DEVELOPMENT
Department of Crop Sciences, North Carolina State University, Raleigh, North Carolina 27695

Travis J. Knight FATS AND CHOLESTEROL, ROLE IN HUMAN NUTRITION
Departments of Animal Science and Biochemistry/Biophysics, Iowa State University, Ames, Iowa 50011

E. Gordon Kruse IRRIGATION ENGINEERING: FARM PRACTICES, METHODS, AND SYSTEMS
USDA-Agricultural Research Service, Colorado State University, Fort Collins, Colorado 80523

Daniel E. Kugler BIOMASS
USDA-Cooperative State Research Service (CSRS), Washington, D. C. 20250

William E. Kunkle FEEDS AND FEEDING
Department of Animal Science, University of Florida, Gainesville, Florida 32611

S. E. Kunz LIVESTOCK PESTS
Knipling-Bushland U.S. Livestock, Insects Laboratory, USDA-Agricultural Research Service, Kerrville, Texas 78028

Kenji Kurata MICROCLIMATE
Department of Agricultural Engineering, University of Tokyo, Tokyo 113, Japan

Garry D. Lacefield FORAGES
Department of Agronomy, University of Kentucky, Lexington, Kentucky 40506

Evans S. Lagudah PLANT GENETIC ENHANCEMENT
Division of Plant Industry, CSIRO, Canberra ACT 2601, Australia

Rattan Lal SOIL AND WATER MANAGEMENT AND CONSERVATION
Department of Agronomy, Ohio State University, Columbus, Ohio 43210

William A. Laycock RANGELAND CONDITION AND TREND
Department of Range Management, University of Wyoming, Laramie, Wyoming 82071

Stephen G. Leonard RANGELAND SOILS
USDI-Bureau of Land Management, Reno, Nevada 89520

Patricia Brazeel Lewis U.S. DEPARTMENT OF AGRICULTURE: A NATIONAL SYSTEM OF AGRICULTURAL RESEARCH
New Jersey Agricultural Experiment Station, Rutgers University, New Brunswick, New Jersey 08903

K. A. Leymaster ANIMAL BREEDING AND GENETICS
U.S. Meat Animal Research Center, USDA-Agricultural Research Service, Clay Center, Nebraska 68933

Michael Lilburn POULTRY PRODUCTION
Department of Poultry Science, Ohio State University, Wooster, Ohio 44691

David A. Lins U.S. FARMS: CHANGING SIZE AND STRUCTURE
Department of Agricultural Economics, University of Illinois at Urbana-Champaign, Urbana, Illinois 61801

H. Alan Love QUANTITATIVE METHODS IN AGRICULTURAL ECONOMICS
Department of Agricultural Economics, Texas A&M University, College Station, Texas 77843

Bor S. Luh RICE PROCESSING AND UTILIZATION
Department of Food Science and Technology, University of California, Davis, Davis, California 95616

C. J. Lupton WOOL AND MOHAIR PRODUCTION AND PROCESSING
Wool and Mohair Research Laboratory, Texas Agricultural Experiment Station, Texas A&M University, San Angelo, Texas 76901

Gerald J. Lynch CROP SUBSIDIES
Department of Economics, Purdue University, West Lafayette, Indiana 47907

David R. MacKenzie U.S. DEPARTMENT OF AGRICULTURE: A NATIONAL SYSTEM OF AGRICULTURAL RESEARCH
USDA-Cooperative State Research Service, Washington, D.C. 20250

David Major CORN CROP PRODUCTION
Agriculture Canada Research Station, Lethbridge, Alberta, Canada T1J 4B1

George C. Martin DECIDUOUS FRUIT TREES
Department of Pomology, University of California, Davis, Davis, California 95616

Bruce A. McCarl QUANTITATIVE METHODS IN AGRICULTURAL ECONOMICS
Department of Agricultural Economics, Texas A&M University, College Station, Texas 77843

J. David McCracken EDUCATION: UNDERGRADUATE AND GRADUATE UNIVERSITY
Department of Agricultural Education, Ohio State University, Columbus, Ohio 43210

William W. McFee SOIL, ACID
Department of Agronomy, Purdue University, West Lafayette, Indiana 47907

John J. McGlone ANIMAL BEHAVIOR (ETHOLOGY)
Department of Animal Science, Texas Tech University, Lubbock, Texas 79409

Michael McKenry NEMATICIDES
Kearny Agricultural Center, University of California, Riverside, Parlier, California 93648

James I. McNitt RABBIT PRODUCTION
Department of Animal Science, Southern University and A&M College, Baton Rouge, Louisiana 70813

John W. Mellor WORLD HUNGER AND FOOD SECURITY
John Mellor Associates, Inc., Washington, D.C. 20004

Christopher Menzel TROPICAL AND SUBTROPICAL FRUIT
Queensland Department of Primary Industries, Nambour, Queensland 4560, Australia

F. R. Miller SORGHUM
Sorghum Breeding Soil and Crop Sciences, Texas A&M University, College Station, Texas 77843

Joseph E. Miller AIR POLLUTION: PLANT GROWTH AND PRODUCTIVITY
USDA-Agricultural Research Service, and Crop Science Department, North Carolina State University, Raleigh, North Carolina 27606

Raymond W. Miller SOIL TESTING FOR PLANT GROWTH AND SOIL FERTILITY
Department of Plants, Soils, and Biometerology, Utah State University, Logan, Utah 84322

Thomas A. Miller INSECT PHYSIOLOGY
Department of Entomology, University of California, Riverside, Riverside, California 92521

David Mills NATURAL RUBBER PRODUCTION IN ARID AND SEMIARID ZONES
The Institutes for Applied Research, Ben-Gurion University of the Negev, Beer-Sheva 84110, Israel

Gary E. Moore EDUCATION: CHILDREN AND YOUTH
Department of Occupational Education, North Carolina State University, Raleigh, North Carolina 27695

Paul H. Moore SUGARCANE
USDA-Agricultural Research Service, and Experiment Station, Hawaiian Sugar Planters' Association, Aiea, Hawaii 96701

B. Moreno-Sevilla WHEAT BREEDING AND GENETICS
Department of Agronomy, University of Nebraska, Lincoln, Lincoln, Nebraska 68583

William E. Muir GRAIN, FEED, AND CROP STORAGE
Department of Agricultural Engineering, University of Manitoba, Winnipeg, Manitoba, Canada R3T 5V6

M. A. Mulders SOIL AND LAND USE SURVEYS
Remote Sensing Unit—Soil Inventory Land Evaluation, Department of Soil Science and Geology, Agricultural University, 6700 AA, Wageningen, The Netherlands

William J. Murdoch ANIMAL REPRODUCTION, AN OVERVIEW OF THE REPRODUCTIVE SYSTEM; ANIMAL REPRODUCTION, MALE; ANIMAL REPRODUCTION, NONPREGNANT FEMALE; ANIMAL REPRODUCTION, PREGNANCY
Department of Animal Science, University of Wyoming, Laramie, Wyoming 82071

P. K. Ramachandran Nair AGROFORESTRY
Department of Forestry, University of Florida, Gainesville, Florida 32611

P. M. Nair FOOD IRRADIATION
Food Technology and Enzyme Engineering Division, Bhabha Atomic Research Center, Bombay 400 085, India

Terril A. Nell ENVIRONMENTAL HORTICULTURE
Department of Environmental Horticulture, University of Florida, Gainesville, Florida 32611

L. Oberthur WHEAT BREEDING AND GENETICS
Department of Agronomy, University of Nebraska, Lincoln, Lincoln, Nebraska 68583

Stephen K. O'Hair ROOT AND TUBER CROPS
Institute of Food and Agricultural Sciences, University of Florida, Homestead, Florida 33031

Pascal A. Oltenacu DAIRY CATTLE PRODUCTION
Department of Animal Sciences, Cornell University, Ithaca, New York 14853

Donald R. Ort PHOTOSYNTHESIS
Photosynthesis Research Unit, USDA-Agricultural Research Service, and Department of Plant Biology and Agronomy, University of Illinois, Urbana, Illinois 61801

David A. Orwig TEMPERATE HARDWOODS
School of Forest Resources, Pennsylvania State University, University Park, Pennsylvania 16802

Robert V. Osgood SUGARCANE
Experiment Station, Hawaiian Sugar Planters' Association, Aiea, Hawaii 96701

Edgar A. Ott ANIMAL NUTRITION, NONRUMINANT
Animal Science Department, University of Florida, Gainesville, Florida 32611

F. N. Owens ANIMAL NUTRITION, RUMINANT
Department of Animal Science, Oklahoma State University, Stillwater, Oklahoma 74078

T. B. Parkin SOIL MANAGEMENT
National Soil Tilth Laboratory, USDA-Agricultural Research Service, Ames, Iowa 50011

R. Anne Pearson DRAFT ANIMAL POWER
Centre for Tropical Veterinary Medicine, University of Edinburgh, Midlothian EH25 9RG, Scotland

Marjorie P. Penfield FOOD COMPOSITION
Food Technology and Science Department, University of Tennessee, Knoxville, Tennessee 37901

John B. Penson, Jr. FINANCE
Department of Agricultural Economics, Texas A&M University, College Station, Texas 77843

Gary E. Pepper SOYBEAN PRODUCTION
Agronomy Department, University of Illinois, Urbana, Urbana, Illinois 61801

H. H. Perkins, Jr. COTTON PROCESSING AND UTILIZATION
Cotton Quality Research Station, USDA-Agricultural Research Service, South Atlantic Area, Clemson, South Carolina 29631

Tilden Wayne Perry ANIMAL NUTRITION, PRINCIPLES
Department of Animal Nutrition, Purdue University, Van Buren, Arkansas 72956

Peter A. Peterson TRANSPOSABLE ELEMENTS IN PLANTS
Agronomy Department, Iowa State University, Ames, Iowa 50010

D. Mason Pharr MELONS: BIOCHEMICAL AND PHYSIOLOGICAL CONTROL OF SUGAR ACCUMULATION
Department of Horticultural Science, North Carolina State University, Raleigh, North Carolina 27695

Randall K. Phebus FOOD MICROBIOLOGY
Department of Animal Sciences and Industry, Kansas State University, Manhattan, Kansas 66506

Rex D. Pieper RANGELAND MANAGEMENT AND PLANNING
Department of Range Science, New Mexico State University, Las Cruces, New Mexico 88003

David Pimentel ENERGY UTILIZATION
Department of Entomology, Cornell University, Ithaca, New York 14853

W. D. Pitman TROPICAL GRASSLANDS; TROPICAL PASTURE DEVELOPMENT
Agricultural Research Center, Institute of Food and Agricultural Science, University of Florida, Ona, Florida 33865

Leo C. Polopolus LABOR
Food and Resource Economics Department, University of Florida, Gainesville, Florida 32611

Y. Pomeranz WHEAT PROCESSING AND UTILIZATION
Department of Food Science and Human Nutrition, Washington State University, Pullman, Washington 99164

Wilson G. Pond SWINE PRODUCTION
USDA-Agricultural Research Service, Children's Nutrition Research Center, Baylor College of Medicine, Houston, Texas 77030

K. Qi ANIMAL NUTRITION, RUMINANT
Agricultural Research and Extension Center, Texas A&M University, San Angelo, Texas 76901

Nancy N. Ragsdale FUNGICIDES
USDA-National Agricultural Pesticide Impact Assessment Program (NAPIAP), Washington, D.C. 20250

M. A. Rao FOOD PROCESS ENGINEERING: STORAGE AND TRANSPORT OF FLUID FOODS IN PLANTS; FOOD PROCESS ENGINEERING: THERMODYNAMIC AND TRANSPORT PROPERTIES
Department of Food Science and Technology, Cornell University, Geneva, New York 14456

W. R. Raun SOIL FERTILITY
Department of Agronomy, Oklahoma State University, Stillwater, Oklahoma 74078

Gordon C. Rausser GOVERNMENT AGRICULTURAL POLICY, UNITED STATES
Department of Agriculture and Resource Economics, University of California, Berkeley, Berkeley, California 94720

T. David Reed TOBACCO
Virginia Polytechnic Institute and State University, Blackstone, Virginia 23824

George Rehm FERTILIZER MANAGEMENT AND TECHNOLOGY
Soil Science Department, University of Minnesota, St. Paul, Minnesota 55108

J. P. Riley WATER: CONTROL AND USE
Department of Civil/Environmental Engineering, Utah State University, Logan, Utah 84322

Joe T. Ritchie IRRIGATION IN HUMID REGIONS
Department of Crop and Soil Sciences, Michigan State University, East Lansing, Michigan 48824

William F. Ritter WASTE MANAGEMENT ENGINEERING
Agriculture Engineering Department, University of Delaware, Newark, Delaware 19717

Joseph C. Roetheli BIOMASS
USDA-Alternative Agricultural Research and Commercialization Center (AARC), Washington, D.C. 20250

Lloyd W. Rooney SORGHUM
Department of Soil and Crop Science, Cereal Quality Laboratory, Texas A&M University, College Station, Texas 77843

Franklin E. Rosales BANANAS
International Banana and Plantain Program, Fundación Hondureña de Investigación Agrícola (F.H.I.A.), Honduras, Central America

Frank B. Salisbury PLANT PHYSIOLOGY
Department of Plants, Soils, and Biochemistry, College of Agriculture, Utah State University, Logan, Utah 84322

Alan R. Sams POULTRY PROCESSING AND PRODUCTS
Department of Poultry Science, Texas A&M University, College Station, Texas 77843

Colin G. Scanes POULTRY PRODUCTION
Department of Animal Science, Rutgers University, New Brunswick, New Jersey 08903

Andrew Schmitz TARIFFS AND TRADE
Department of Agricultural and Resource Economics, University of California, Berkeley, Berkeley, California 94720

Troy G. Schmitz TARIFFS AND TRADE
Department of Agricultural and Resource Economics, University of California, Berkeley, Berkeley, California 94720

G. Edward Schuh MACROECONOMICS OF WORLD AGRICULTURE
Humphrey Institute of Public Affairs, University of Minnesota, Minneapolis, Minnesota 55455

Robert W. Seagull PLANT CYTOLOGY, MODERN TECHNIQUES; PLANT CYTOSKELETON
Department of Biology, Hofstra University, Hempsted, New York 11550

H. M. Selim SOIL, CHEMICALS: MOVEMENT AND RETENTION
Agronomy Department, Louisiana State University, Baton Rouge, Louisiana 70803

Carl E. Shafer PRICES
Department of Agricultural Economics, Texas A&M University, College Station, Texas 77843

Arun Sharma FOOD IRRADIATION
Biochemistry and Food Technology Division, Bhabha Atomic Research Center, Bombay, 400 085, India

Roger H. Shaw METEOROLOGY
University of California, Davis, Davis, California 95616

Robert C. Shearman TURFGRASSES
Department of Horticulture, University of Nebraska, Lincoln, Lincoln, Nebraska 68583

Maurice Shelton GOAT PRODUCTION
Agricultural Research and Extension Center, Texas A&M University, San Angelo, Texas 76901

John L. Sherwood PLANT VIROLOGY
Oklahoma State University, Stillwater, Oklahoma 74078

Sun F. Shih WATER RESOURCES
Agricultural Engineering Department, University of Florida, Gainesville, Florida 32611

G. Steven Sibbett EDIBLE TREE NUTS, WALNUTS
University of California Cooperative Extension, Farm Advisor, Tulare County, Visalia, California 93291

C. L. Simpson COTTON PROCESSING AND UTILIZATION
Cotton Quality Research Station, USDA-Agricultural Research Service, South Atlantic Area, Clemson, South Carolina 29631

J. Thomas Sims ANIMAL WASTE MANAGEMENT
Department of Plant and Soil Sciences, University of Delaware, Newark, Delaware 19717

David M. Smith SILVICULTURE
School of Forestry and Environmental Studies, Yale University, Hamden, Connecticut 06517

G. M. Smith FOOD BIOCHEMISTRY: LIPIDS, CARBOHYDRATES, AND NUCLEIC ACIDS; FOOD BIOCHEMISTRY: PIGMENTS, FLAVORS, AROMAS, AND STABILITY; FOOD BIOCHEMISTRY: PROTEINS, ENZYMES, AND ENZYME INHIBITORS
Department of Food Science and Technology, University of California, Davis, Davis, California 95616

Mary Ann Lila Smith PLANT TISSUE CULTURE
Plant Sciences Laboratory, University of Illinois, Urbana, Illinois 61801

Kenneth A. Sorensen ENTOMOLOGY, HORTICULTURAL
Department of Entomology, North Carolina State University, Raleigh, North Carolina 27695

Donald L. Sparks Soil Chemistry
Department of Plant and Soil Science, University of Delaware, Newark, Delaware 19717

William J. Stadelman Egg Production, Processing, and Products
Department of Food Science, Purdue University, West Lafayette, Indiana 47907

George J. Staidl Rangeland Soils
USDA-Soil Conservation Service, Lincoln, Nebraska 68508

Ole H. V. Stalheim Animal Diseases
Department of Microbiology, Immunology, and Preventive Medicine, Iowa State University, Ames, Iowa 50010

Vernon M. Stern Pest Management, Cultural Control
Department of Entomology, University of California, Riverside, Riverside, California 92521

B. A. Stewart Dryland Farming
Dryland Agriculture Institute, West Texas A&M University, Canyon, Texas 79016

James Stubbendieck Rangeland Plants
Department of Agronomy, University of Nebraska, Lincoln, Lincoln, Nebraska 68508

R. W. Sutherst Entomology, Veterinary
CSIRO Division of Entomology, University of Queensland, Brisbane, Queensland 4072, Australia

Rony Swennen Bananas
Laboratory of Tropical Crop Husbandry, Catholic University of Leuven (K. U. Leuven), B-3001 Heverlee, Belgium

Ann M. Swinker Horse Industry: Trends, Opportunities, and Issues
College of Agricultural Sciences, Colorado State University, Fort Collins, Colorado 80523

Robert E. Taylor Beef Cattle Production
Department of Animal Sciences, Colorado State University, Fort Collins, Colorado 80523

S. L. Taylor Soil Fertility
Department of Agronomy, Oklahoma State University, Stillwater, Oklahoma 74078

Steve L. Taylor Food Toxicology
Department of Food Science and Technology, University of Nebraska, Lincoln, Nebraska 68583

Arthur A. Teixeira Thermal Processing: Canning and Pasteurization
Agricultural Engineering Department, Institute of Food and Agricultural Science, University of Florida, Gainesville, Florida 32611

Paul B. Thompson Ethics
Departments of Philosophy and Agricultural Economics, Texas A&M University, College Station, Texas 77843

Phillip S. Tong Dairy Processing and Products
Dairy Products Technology Center, California Polytechnic State University, San Luis Obispo, California 93407

Paul W. Unger Tillage Systems
Conservation and Production Laboratory, USDA-Agricultural Research Service, Bushland, Texas 79012

J. P. van Buijtenen Forest Tree, Genetic Improvement
Department of Forest Science, Texas Agricultural Experimental Station, Texas A&M University, College Station, Texas 77843

L. D. Van Vleck Animal Breeding and Genetics
U.S. Meat Animal Research Center, USDA-Agricultural Research Service, University of Nebraska, Lincoln, Nebraska 68508

Mark A. Varner Computer Applications in Agriculture
Department of Animal Sciences, University of Maryland, College Park, Maryland 20742

Marlow Vesterby Land Use Planning in Agriculture
Land and Capital Assets Branch, USDA-Economic Research Service, Washington, D.C. 20005

W. R. Walker Water: Control and Use
Biological and Irrigation Engineering, Utah State University, Logan, Utah 84322

Bruce L. Welch Rangeland Shrubs
Intermountain Research Station, USDA-Forest Service, Shrub Laboratory, Provo, Utah 84606

Roy L. Whistler Carbohydrates, Role in Human Nutrition
Department of Biochemistry, Purdue University, West Lafayette, Indiana 47907

J. R. Whitaker Food Biochemistry: Lipids, Carbohydrates, and Nucleic Acids; Food Biochemistry: Pigments, Flavors, Aromas, and Stability; Food Biochemistry: Proteins, Enzymes, and Enzyme Inhibitors
Department of Food Science and Technology, University of California, Davis, Davis, California 95616

James R. Wilcox Soybean Genetics and Breeding
Crop Production and Pathology Research, USDA-Agricultural Research Service, Agronomy Department, Purdue University, West Lafayette, Indiana 47907

Jerrold E. Winandy Wood Properties
Forest Products Laboratory, USDA-Forest Service, Madison, Wisconsin 53705

A. G. Wollum II Soil Microbiology
Department of Soil Science, North Carolina State University, Raleigh, North Carolina 27695

Bruce W. Wood EDIBLE TREE NUTS: PECAN AND OTHER HICKORIES
Fruit and Tree Research Station, USDA-Agricultural Research Service, Byron, Georgia 31008

Marylynn V. Yates GROUND WATER
University of California, Riverside, Riverside, California 92521

Scott R. Yates GROUND WATER
U.S. Salinity Laboratory, USDA-Agricultural Research Service, Riverside, California 92521

Y. Yen WHEAT BREEDING AND GENETICS
Department of Agronomy, University of Nebraska, Lincoln, Lincoln, Nebraska 68583

Yu Yongming TEA
Tea Research Institute, Chinese Academy of Agricultural Sciences, Hangzhou, Zhejiang 310008, The People's Republic of China

L. D. Young ANIMAL BREEDING AND GENETICS
U.S. Meat Animal Research Center, USDA-Agricultural Research Service, Clay Center, Nebraska 68933

Nevin Dale Young PLANT GENE MAPPING
Department of Plant Pathology, University of Minnesota, St. Paul, Minnesota 55108

Kenneth Ziegler POPCORN
Agronomy Department, Iowa State University, Ames, Iowa 50011

Chen Zongmao TEA
Tea Research Institute, Chinese Academy of Agricultural Sciences, Hangzhou, Zhejiang 310008, The People's Republic of China

SUBJECT INDEX

A

Abscisic acid
  biochemical characterization, **3**:210
  biosynthesis, **3**:210
  cocoa, **1**:380
  physiological roles, **3**:210, **3**:342–343
  plant stress response, **3**:364
Absolute humidity, defined, **3**:43
Absorption processes
  applications in food industry, **2**:383
  light during photosynthesis, **3**:189–190
Abundance, in forest ecosystems, **2**:430–431
Acanthocephalan infections, **1**:82
Acarapis woodi, **1**:213
Accessory glands, male reproductive system,
  1:153–155
Accidents, in grain bulks, **2**:485
Accounting
  computer-aided, **1**:390–391
  for crop and livestock producers, **2**:194–195
Acesulfane K
  as food sweetener, **2**:237
  structure, **2**:237
Acetates, antimicrobial actions, **2**:346
Acetic acid, structure, **2**:346
Acetolactate synthase, herbicide inhibitors,
  2:508
Acidity
  raw milk, **1**:561
  soil, *see* Soils, acid
Acidosis, ruminant, **1**:134
Acid phosphatase, heterotic effects, **2**:517
Acid rain, effects on soil pH, **4**:34, **4**:136
Acids, as food flavors, **2**:241–242
Acid soil, *see* Soils, acid
Acifluorfen
  chemical structure, **2**:506
  mechanism of action, **2**:506
Acreage allotments, **1**:527
Acreage Conservation Reserve (ACR) land,
  1:530
Acrodermatitis enteropathica, **3**:66
Acrosomal reaction, **1**:174–175
Actin
  isotypes, **3**:252
  in microfilaments, **3**:252–254
Activated sludge systems, for wastes, **4**:462
Activity coefficent, of food, **2**:382

Additives, feed, for ruminants, **1**:133
Additives, food, *see also* Food preservatives
  functions, **2**:281–282
  types, **2**:281–282
Additivity assumption, in linear programming, **3**:478
Adenosine triphosphate, formation during
  photosynthesis, **3**:192
Adiabatic lapse rate
  dry, **3**:43
  moist, **3**:44
Adiabatic processes, atmospheric, **3**:43
Adipokinetic hormone, insect, **2**:554
Adjuvants, herbicide, **4**:491
Adsorption processes
  applications in food industry, **2**:383
  oxygen on *in situ* electrodes in plant tissue,
    3:11–12
Advection fog, defined, **3**:46
Advection processes, in groundwater, **2**:495
Aedes mosquitoes, **2**:663
Aeration, soils, **4**:143–144
Aereoplasts, functions, **3**:12
Aerial photography
  land-cover mapping, **4**:42
  multispectral, for soil/land-use surveys, **4**:41
Aerobic digestion, sludge, **4**:463–464
Aflatoxin
  carcinogenicity, **2**:400
  in feed concentrates, **2**:176
  gamma radiation effects on spores, **2**:299
  regulation, **2**:323
  toxicity, **2**:323
Africanized bee, **1**:214
African yam bean, **3**:642
Agar, biochemistry, **2**:225, **2**:228
Agaropectin, biochemistry, **2**:225
Agarose, biochemistry, **2**:225
Agglomeration, nonfat dry milk, **1**:573
Aggradation, in rangeland watersheds, **3**:601
Aggregation, protein in foods, **2**:270
Agitation, thermal processing with, **2**:360
Agricultural Adjustment Act of 1933, **1**:527, **2**:467
Agricultural and Food Research Council (UK),
  1:304–305
Agricultural Credit Act of 1987, **2**:196–197
Agricultural drainage
  conventional ground-survey methods, **4**:481
  and groundwater quality, **2**:497

Irrigation water
 application efficiency, **2:**609
 controlled drainage, **2:**606–607
 as energy input into crop production, **2:**72–73
 herbicide applications in, **4:**490
 pollution problems, **4:**468–469
 salinity effects, **2:**608
 sodicity effects, **2:**608
 and soil cracking/swelling, **2:**608
 uses, **4:**469
 and water logging, **1:**589
Isonicotinic acid
 mechanism of action, **2:**450
 uses, **2:**450
Isophthalonitrile, fungitoxicity, **2:**447–448
Isoprene, structure, **2:**220
Isoxaben
 chemical structure, **2:**509
 mechanism of action, **2:**509
Isozyme markers, rice genes, **3:**609–610
Itai-itai disease, **3:**71
Itch mites (*Sarcoptes scabiei*)
 damage to livestock, **2:**666
 life cycle, **2:**666
 swine, **2:**659, **4:**262
IVF-ET, *see In vitro* fertilization-embryo transfer
Ixodidae, *see* Ticks

J

Jacob's Straight-Line method, for groundwater,
 2:492
Japanese beetle, biocontrol agents, **3:**161
Jenike's flow function, for powders, **2:**378–379
Jerusalem artichoke, **3:**641
Jicama, **3:**641
John Innes Centre for Plant Science Research (BBSRC),
 1:306, **1:**311
Johnston's organ, insect, **2:**558
Jorquette formation, cocoa, **1:**380
Juice, citrus, chemical composition, **1:**363
Juvenile hormone, **2:**554–555, **2:**567

K

Kales
 characteristics, **1:**329
 diseases of, **1:**332–333
 insect damage to, **1:**333–334
Kanamycin resistance
 risk factors, **3:**222
 spread of, **3:**222
Kefir, **1:**566
Kentucky bluegrass, **2:**101, *see also* Turfgrasses
 characteristics, **4:**414–415
Kernel, corn, *see* Corn
Keshan disease, **3:**69

Ketosis
 causes, **1:**111
 ruminant, **1:**134
Kidney
 by-products from, **1:**67
 disease states, role of dietary fat and cholesterol,
  2:151–152
Kidney beans, lectins in, **2:**400
Kikuyugrass, *see also* Turfgrasses
 characteristics, **4:**417
Kinetin, synthesis and characterization, **3:**209
Knitting technology
 cotton fabrics, **1:**520–522
 wool and mohair fabrics, **4:**587
Knots, in wood, **4:**551
Knowledge-based systems
 availability, **1:**393
 for cotton production, **1:**393–394
 for dairy cattle, **1:**394
 defined, **1:**389
 remote sensing integration, **1:**401
Knudsen diffusion, **2:**391
Konjak, **3:**640
Koppen climate classification, **4:**479
Korean lawngrass, *see also* Turfgrasses
 characteristics, **4:**416
Krebs cycle, in plants, **3:**204, **3:**340
Kudzu, **3:**641

L

Labor, *see also* Farm workers; Food workers
 collective bargaining, **2:**629–630
 contract, **2:**627–628
 division by gender, worldwide, **4:**544–545
 health and safety issues, **3:**175
 hired, **2:**623–624
 international migratory flows, **3:**7
 locational adjustments of production, **2:**625–626
 migrant, **2:**624
 National Labor Relations Act, **2:**629
 productivity, **2:**625, **4:**433
 seasonality, **2:**623, **2:**630–631
 unpaid family, **2:**623–624
 Wagner Act of 1935, **2:**629
Labor (parturition)
 sheep model, **1:**181–182
 stages, **1:**181
Laboratories, *see also* Agricultural research
 federal, non-USDA, **4:**424
 private, **4:**424
 university-affiliated, **4:**423–424
 USDA-affiliated, **4:**423–424
Laboratory animals
 diseases affecting, **1:**87
 embryo transfer techniques, **2:**60
α-Lactalbumin, in milk, **2:**639

INDEX OF RELATED TITLES

A

Agricultural Experiment Stations
Cooperative Extension System; Education: Undergraduate and Graduate University; USDA: A National System of Agricultural Research

Agroforestry
Farming Systems; Forest Ecology; Land Use Planning in Agriculture; Silviculture; Soil and Water Management and Conservation; Sustainable Agriculture

Air Pollution: Plant Growth and Productivity
Photosynthesis

Animal Behavior (Ethology)
Animal Breeding and Genetics; Animal Nutrition, Nonruminant; Animal Nutrition, Principles; Animal Nutrition, Ruminant; Animal Reproduction, An Overview of the Reproductive System; Animal Reproduction, Male; Animal Reproduction, Nonpregnant Female; Animal Reproduction, Pregnancy; Feeds and Feeding

Animal Breeding and Genetics
Beef Cattle Production; Dairy Cattle Production; Egg Production, Processing, and Products; Horse Industry: Trends, Opportunities, and Issues; Poultry Production; Swine Production

Animal By-Products from Slaughter
Animal Waste Management; Meat Processing; Waste Management Engineering; Wool and Mohair Production and Processing

Animal Diseases
Animal Behavior (Ethology)

Animal Nutrition, Nonruminant
Animal Nutrition, Principles; Animal Nutrition, Ruminant; Feeds and Feeding; Poultry Production; Rabbit Production; Swine Production

Animal Nutrition, Principles
Animal Nutrition, Nonruminant; Animal Nutrition, Ruminant; Feeds and Feeding; Photosynthesis

Animal Nutrition, Ruminant
Animal Nutrition, Nonruminant; Animal Nutrition, Principles; Animal Waste Management; Feeds and Feeding; Waste Management Engineering

Animal Reproduction, An Overview of the Reproductive System
Animal Reproduction, Male; Animal Reproduction, Nonpregnant Female; Animal Reproduction, Pregnancy

Animal Reproduction, Male
Animal Reproduction, An Overview of the Reproductive System; Animal Reproduction, Nonpregnant Female; Animal Reproduction, Pregnancy

Animal Reproduction, Nonpregnant Female
Animal Reproduction, An Overview of the Reproductive System; Animal Reproduction, Male; Animal Reproduction, Pregnancy

Animal Reproduction, Pregnancy
Animal Behavior (Ethology); Animal Reproduction, An Overview of the Reproductive System; Animal Reproduction, Male; Animal Reproduction, Nonpregnant Female; Embryo Transfer in Domestic Animals; Lactation

Animal Waste Management
Fertilizer Management and Technology; Ground Water; Poultry Production; Soil Pollution; Waste Management Engineering

Apiculture
Deciduous Fruit Trees; Orchard Management Systems

B

Bananas
Citrus Fruits; Fertilizer Management Technology; Herbicides and Herbicide Resistance; Nematicides; Plant Pathology; Plant Tissue Culture; Viticulture; Weed Science

Barley
Animal Nutrition, Nonruminant; Animal Nutrition, Principles; Animal Nutrition, Ruminant; Brewing Technology; Feeds and Feeding; Fungicides; Plant Gene Mapping; Plant Genetic Enhancement; Plant Genetic Resource Conservation and Utilization; Plant Genetic Resources; Plant Pathology; Plant Tissue Culture; Plant Virology; Poultry Production; Transposable Elements in Plants; Wheat Breeding and Genetics

Beef Cattle Production
Animal Breeding and Genetics; Animal By-Products from Slaughter; Dairy Cattle Production; Feeds and Feeding; Meat Processing

Berries
Irrigation Engineering: Farm Practices, Methods, and Systems; Pest Management, Chemical Control; Pest Management, Cultural Control

mal Reproduction, Pregnancy; Dairy Processing and Products; Feeds and Feeding

Dairy Processing and Products

Dairy Cattle Production; Fats and Cholesterol, Role in Human Nutrition; Food Biochemistry: Lipids, Carbohydrates, and Nucleic Acids; Food Biochemistry: Proteins, Enzymes, and Enzyme Inhibitors; Food Microbiology; Thermal Processing: Canning and Pasteurization

Deciduous Fruit Trees

Berries; Dormancy; Edible Tree Nuts: Pecan and Other Hickories; Edible Tree Nuts, Walnuts; Food Marketing Systems; Integrated Pest Management; Irrigation Engineering: Farm Practices, Methods, and Systems; Orchard Management: Soil Environment and Resources; Orchard Management Systems; Pest Management, Biological Control; Pest Management, Chemical Control; Plant Propagation; Postharvest Physiology; Prices; Water: Control and Use

Desertification of Drylands

Ground Water; Rangeland; Rangeland Condition and Trend; Rangeland Ecology; Rangeland Grazing; Rangeland Management and Planning; Rangeland Plants; Rangeland Shrubs; Soil and Water Management and Conservation; Soil Pollution; Water Resources

Dormancy

Photosynthesis; Plant Biochemistry; Plant Physiology; Root and Tuber Crops

Draft Animal Power

Animal By-Products from Slaughter; Animal Diseases; Animal Nutrition, Principles; Beef Cattle Production; Dairy Cattle Production; Feeds and Feeding; Labor

Dryland Farming

Desertification of Drylands; Fertilizer Management and Technology; Irrigation Engineering, Evapotranspiration; Irrigation Engineering: Farm Practices, Methods, and Systems; Meteorology; Nitrogen Cycling; Soil and Water Management and Conservation; Soil, Chemicals: Movement and Retention; Soil Fertility; Soil Genesis, Morphology, and Classification; Soil Management; Soil–Water Relationships; Tillage Systems; Water: Control and Use

E

Edible Tree Nuts: Pecan and Other Hickories

Entomology, Horticultural; Fungicides; Irrigation Engineering: Farm Practices, Methods, and Systems; Orchard Management: Soil Environment and Resources; Orchard Management Systems; Pest Management, Biological Control; Pest Management, Chemical Control; Pest Management, Cultural Control; Plant Pathology

Edible Tree Nuts, Walnuts

Edible Tree Nuts: Pecan and Other Hickories

Education: Children and Youth

Cooperative Extension Service; Education: Undergraduate and Graduate University; Women in Agriculture

Education: Undergraduate and Graduate University

Agricultural Experiment Stations; Cooperative Extension Service; Education: Children and Youth; Ethics; Rural Sociology; Women in Agriculture

Egg Production, Processing, and Products

Animal Nutrition, Nonruminant; Feeds and Feeding; Poultry Processing and Products: Poultry Production

Embryo Transfer in Domestic Animals

Animal Reproduction, Nonpregnant Female; Animal Reproduction, Pregnancy; Ethics; Transgenic Animals

Energy Utilization

Biomass; Corn Production; Fertilizer Management and Technology; Herbicides and Herbicide Resistance; Irrigation Engineering: Farm Practices, Methods, and Systems; Labor; Pest Management, Chemical Control; Production Economics; Quantitative Methods in Agricultural Economics; World Hunger and Food Security

Entomology, Horticultural

Integrated Pest Management; Plant Biotechnology: Food Safety and Environmental Issues; Plant Pathology; Plant Virology; Sustainable Agriculture

Entomology, Veterinary

Animal Diseases; Insect Physiology; Integrated Pest Management; Pest Management, Biological Control; Pest Management, Chemical Control; Pest Management, Cultural Control; Sustainable Agriculture

Environmental Horticulture

Floriculture; Horticultural Greenhouse Engineering; Integrated Pest Management; Pest Management, Biological Control; Plant Propagation; Plant Tissue Culture; Turfgrasses

Ethics

Dairy Cattle Production; Plant Biotechnology: Food Safety and Environmental Issues; Transgenic Animals

Evolution of Domesticated Plants

Cultivar Development; Dormancy; International Agricultural Research; Photosynthesis; Plant Genetic Enhancement; Plant Genetic Resource Conservation and Utilization; Plant Genetic Resources; Plant Physiology; Weed Science

F

Farming Systems

Cooperative Extension System; International Agricultural Research; Rural Sociology; Women in Agriculture

Fungicides
Pest Management, Chemical Control; Plant Pathology

G

Goat Production
Animal Breeding and Genetics; Animal By-Products from Slaughter; Dairy Processing and Products; Wool and Mohair Production and Processing

Government Agricultural Policy, United States
Agricultural Experiment Stations; Cooperative Extension System; Crop Subsidies; Education: Undergraduate and Graduate University; International Agricultural Policy; Macroeconomics of World Agriculture; Prices; Tariffs and Trade; USDA: A National System of Agricultural Research

Grain, Feed, and Crop Storage
Food Dehydration; Structures

Ground Water
Pest Management, Chemical Control; Water: Control and Use; Water Resources

H

Herbicides and Herbicide Resistance
Photosynthesis; Plant Physiology; Weed Science

Heterosis
Corn Genetics and Breeding; Photosynthesis; Plant Gene Mapping; Plant Genetic Enhancement; Plant Physiology

Horse Industry: Trends, Opportunities, and Issues
Feeds and Feeding

Horticultural Greenhouse Engineering
Photosynthesis; Structures; Tomato Production in Protected Cultivation

I

Insect Physiology
Entomology, Horticultural; Entomology, Veterinary

Integrated Pest Management
Cooperative Extension Service; Cultivar Development; Fertilizer Management and Technology; Fungicides; Herbicides and Herbicide Resistance; Nematicides; Pest Management, Biological Control; Pest Management, Chemical Control; Pest Management, Cultural Control; Plant Pathology; Tillage Systems

International Agricultural Research
Agricultural Experiment Stations; Consultative Group on International Agricultural Research; Cooperative Extension Service; Education: Undergraduate and Graduate University; USDA: A National System of Agricultural Research

Irrigation Engineering, Evapotranspiration
Irrigation Engineering: Farm Practices, Methods, and Systems; Water: Control and Use

Irrigation Engineering: Farm Practice
Irrigation Engineering, Evapotranspiration; Irrigation in Humid Regions; Soil Drainage; Soil–Water Relationships; Water: Control and Use; Water Resources

Irrigation in Humid Regions
Fertilizer Management and Technology; Ground Water; Irrigation Engineering, Evapotranspiration; Irrigation Engineering: Farm Practices, Methods, and Systems; Soil Drainage; Water: Control and Use; Water Resources

L

Labor
Farming Systems; Production Economics

Lactation
Animal Nutrition, Nonruminant; Animal Nutrition, Ruminant; Animal Reproduction, Nonpregnant Female; Animal Reproduction, Pregnancy; Transgenic Animals

Land Use Planning in Agriculture
Government Agricultural Policy, United States; Rangeland Management and Planning; Rural Sociology; U.S. Farms: Changing Size and Structure

Livestock Pests
Animal Diseases; Animal Waste Management; Beef Cattle Production; Dairy Cattle Production; Goat Production; Integrated Pest Management; Pest Management, Biological Control; Pest Management, Chemical Control; Pest Management, Cultural Control; Swine Production; Wool and Mohair Production and Processing

M

Macroeconomics of World Agriculture
Finance; Labor; Prices; Production Economics; Tariffs and Trade

Measurement of Micro-oxygen Supply and Demand
Plant Physiology

Meat Processing
Beef Cattle Production; Food Irradiation; Food Microbiology; Food Packaging; Food Preservatives; Food Toxicology; Poultry Production; Swine Production

Melons: Biochemical and Physiological Control of Sugar Accumulation
Bananas; Photosynthesis; Plant Biochemistry; Plant Genetic Enhancement; Plant Physiology

Meteorology
Microclimate; Water Resources

Rangeland Grazing; Rangeland Management and Planning; Rangeland Plants; Wildlife Management

Rangeland Soils
Rangeland; Rangeland Condition and Trend; Rangeland Grazing; Rangeland Management and Planning; Rangeland Plants; Rangeland Shrubs; Soil and Land Use Surveys; Soil, Chemicals: Movement and Retention; Soil Chemistry; Soil Genesis, Morphology, and Classification; Soil Microbiology

Rangeland Watershed Management
Desertification of Drylands; Ground Water; Rangeland; Rangeland Condition and Trend; Rangeland Ecology; Rangeland Grazing; Rangeland Management and Planning; Rangeland Plants; Rangeland Shrubs; Rangeland Soils; Soil Drainage; Soil–Water Relationships; Wetlands and Riparian Areas: Economics and Policy

Rice Genetics and Breeding
Cultivar Development; Plant Gene Mapping; Plant Genetic Enhancement; Plant Genetic Resource Conservation and Utilization; Plant Genetic Resources; Rice Processing and Utilization

Rice Processing and Utilization
Food Packaging; Rice Genetics and Breeding; Thermal Processing: Canning and Pasteurization

Root and Tuber Crops
Consultative Group for International Agricultural Research; Dormancy; Grain, Feed, and Crop Storage; Plant Propagation; Plant Tissue Culture; Postharvest Physiology; Potato

Rural Development, International
Farming Systems; International Agricultural Research; Sustainable Agriculture; World Hunger and Food Security

Rural Sociology
Cooperative Extension System; Education: Undergraduate and Graduate University; Sustainable Agriculture; U.S. Farms: Changing Size and Structure

S

Silk Production and Processing
Insect Physiology

Silviculture
Forest Ecology; Forest Tree, Genetic Improvement; Pest Management, Biological Control

Soil, Acid
Nitrogen Cycling; Soil, Chemicals: Movement and Retention; Soil Chemistry; Soil Fertility; Soil Genesis, Morphology, and Classification; Soil Management; Soil Microbiology; Soil Pollution; Soil Testing for Plant Growth and Soil Fertility

Soil and Land Use Surveys
Land Use Planning in Agriculture; Soil and Water Management and Conservation; Soil Genesis, Morphology, and Classification; Soil Testing

Soil and Water Management and Conservation
Irrigation Engineering: Farm Practices, Methods, and Systems; Soil Drainage; Soil Management; Soil Pollution; Soil–Water Relationships; Tillage Systems; Water: Control and Use; Water Resources

Soil, Chemicals: Movement and Retention
Fertilizer Management and Technology; Ground Water; Nitrogen Cycling; Pest Management, Chemical Control; Soil, Acid; Soil Chemistry; Soil Genesis, Morphology, and Classification; Soil Microbiology; Soil Pollution; Soil–Water Relationships

Soil Chemistry
Soil, Acid; Soil, Chemicals: Movement and Retention; Soil Genesis, Morphology, and Classification; Soil Pollution

Soil Drainage
Ground Water; Irrigation Engineering: Farm Practices, Methods, and Systems; Soil Fertility; Soil–Water Relationships; Water: Control and Use; Water Resources

Soil Fertility
Fertilizer Management and Technology; Nitrogen Cycling; Soil, Chemicals: Movement and Retention; Soil Chemistry; Soil Genesis, Morphology, and Classification; Soil Microbiology; Soil Testing for Plant Growth and Soil Fertility

Soil Genesis, Morphology, and Classification
Soil and Land Use Surveys; Soil, Chemicals: Movement and Retention; Soil Chemistry; Soil Drainage; Soil Microbiology; Soil Testing for Plant Growth and Soil Fertility; Soil–Water Relationships

Soil Management
Fertilizer Management and Technology; Herbicides and Herbicide Resistance; Nitrogen Cycling; Soil, Acid; Soil Fertility; Soil Genesis, Morphology, and Classification; Soil Microbiology; Soil Testing; Tillage Systems

Soil Microbiology
Nitrogen Cycling; Pest Management, Biological Control; Soil Chemistry; Soil Genesis, Morphology, and Classification; Soil Testing for Plant Growth and Soil Fertility; Soil–Water Relationships

Soil Pollution
Air Pollution: Plant Growth and Productivity; Soil, Acid; Soil, Chemicals: Movement and Retention; Soil Chemistry; Soil Fertility; Soil Microbiology; Soil–Water Relationships

Soil Testing for Plant Growth and Soil Fertility
Fertilizer Management and Technology; Nitrogen Cycling; Soil, Acid; Soil, Chemicals: Movement and Retention; Soil Chemistry; Soil Drainage; Soil Fertility; Soil Genesis, Morphology, and Classification; Soil Management; Soil Microbiology; Soil Pollution; Soil–Water Relationships

ment, Biological Control; Pest Management, Chemical Control; Pest Management, Cultural Control; Plant Propagation; Water: Control and Use

W

Waste Management Engineering

Animal Waste Management; Dairy Processing and Products; Meat Processing

Water: Control and Use

Dryland Farming; Ground Water; Irrigation Engineering: Farm Practices, Methods, and Systems; Water Resources

Water Resources

Ground Water; Irrigation Engineering, Evapotranspiration; Irrigation Engineering: Farm Practices, Methods, and Systems; Land Use Planning in Agriculture; Meteorology; Soil and Land Use Surveys; Soil Drainage; Soil–Water Relationships; Wetlands and Riparian Areas: Economics and Policy

Weed Science

Air Pollution: Plant Growth and Productivity; Herbicides and Herbicide Resistance; Integrated Pest Management; Pest Management, Biological Control; Pest Management, Chemical Control; Pest Management, Cultural Control; Plant Biotechnology: Food Safety and Environmental Issues

Wetlands and Riparian Areas: Economics and Policy

Prices

Wheat Breeding and Genetics

Cultivar Development; Evolution of Domesticated Plants; Plant Gene Mapping; Plant Genetic Enhancement; Plant Genetic Resource Conservation and Utilization; Plant Genetic Resources; Transposable Elements in Plants; Wheat Processing and Utilization

Wheat Processing and Utilization

Food Biochemistry: Proteins, Enzymes, and Enzyme Inhibitors; Wheat Genetics and Breeding

Wildlife Management

Forest Ecology; Rangeland Management and Planning; Silviculture

Women in Agriculture

Labor; Sustainable Agriculture

Wood Properties

Forest Tree, Genetic Improvement

Wool and Mohair Production and Processing

Animal Breeding and Genetics; Animal Diseases; Animal Nutrition, Ruminant; Feeds and Feeding; Goat Production

World Hunger and Food Security

International Agricultural Research; Rural Development, International

86094

ISBN 0-12-226674-9

90065

9 780122 266744

T2-DLO-811

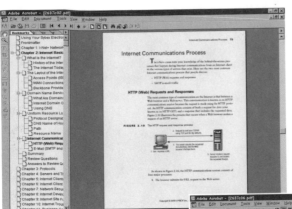

Search the i-Net+ Study Guide ebook in PDF

- Access the entire *i-Net+ Study Guide*, complete with figures and tables, in electronic format.

- Use Adobe Acrobat Reader (included on the CD-ROM) to view the electronic book.

- Search chapters to find information on any topic in seconds.

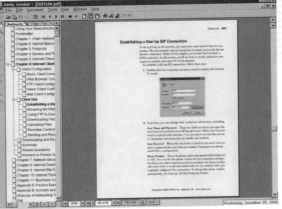

Sybex MCSE Study Guide Sampler

- Preview chapters in PDF from the best-selling line of MCSE study guides from Sybex. From the core requirements to the most popular electives, you'll see why Sybex MCSE study guides have become the self-study method of choice for hundreds of thousands seeking certification.

Praise for David Groth's Study Guides

[The *A+ Complete Study Guide*] is a great place to start your studies. I found this book to be very well laid out for beginners and advanced techs alike. It was easy to read and understand and did a great job of keeping the information in your head (the chapter quizzes and study CD were great tools). I am now A+ Certified ... and I would not have done it without this book! The book led me from knowing nothing but the basics to a solid fundamental knowledge of all exam objectives. I highly recommend this as your first study platform.

From Amazon.com
A reader from Saratoga, WY

Detailed and interesting book. I found [the *A+ Complete Study Guide*] to be very informative. It is very clear and concise. It's an awesome reference, and it's more along the lines for people who are actually interested in computers....It gives all kinds of cool, historical information on OSes and hardware. It does cover everything you need to know. All in all, this is a very educational book, and it covers a lot more than it's cracked up to.

From Amazon.com
Taylor Street, from Westwood, CA

Great job on the [*Network+ Study Guide*]! I found your study guide to be a valuable addition to my library, regardless of whether or not I decide to take the Network+ exam. The focus on practical applications and scenarios is greatly appreciated....My thanks for a job well done. Keep up the good work, folks.

Tom Harrington
Cisco Router/Switch Configuration Support Specialist

If you buy [the *Network+ Study Guide*], you'll have ... [a] large headstart towards passing your Network+ exam. You'll find detailed coverage of every exam objective here, from network topologies to leading network operating systems, clients, directory services, and more. You'll also review everything the examiners demand that you know about TCP/IP, routing, high-availability networks, disaster recovery, Ethernet, fiber optics, remote access, and network security.

Bill Camarda
barnesandnoble.com Editor

i-Net+ Exam Objectives

OBJECTIVE	CHAPTER
i-Net Basics	
Describe a URL, its functions and components, different types of URLs, and use of the appropriate type of URL to access a given type of server.	2
Identify the issues that affect Internet site functionality (e.g., performance, security, and reliability).	9
Describe the concept of caching and its implications.	9
Describe different types of search indexes—static index/site map, keyword index, full-text index.	9
i-Net Clients	
Describe the infrastructure needed to support an Internet client.	5
Describe the use of Web browsers and various clients (e.g., FTP clients, Telnet clients, e-mail clients, all-in-one clients/universal clients) within a given context of use.	6
Explain the issues to consider when configuring the desktop.	6
Describe MIME types and their components.	6
Identify problems related to legacy clients (e.g., TCP/IP sockets and their implication on the operating system).	10
Explain the function of patches and updates to client software and associated problems.	10
Describe the advantages and disadvantages of using a cookie and how to set cookies.	6
Development	
Define programming-related terms as they relate to Internet applications development.	8
Describe the differences between popular client-side and server-side programming languages.	8
Describe the differences between a relational database and a non-relational database.	8
Identify when to integrate a database with a Web site and the technologies used to connect the two.	8
Demonstrate the ability to create HTML pages.	8
Identify popular multimedia extensions or plug-ins.	8
Describe the uses and benefits of various multimedia file formats.	8
Describe the process of pre-launch site/application functionality testing.	10

OBJECTIVE	CHAPTER
Networking and Infrastructure	
Describe the core components of the current Internet infrastructure and how they relate to each other.	2
Identify problems with Internet connectivity from source to destination for various types of servers.	2
Describe Internet domain names and DNS.	2
Describe the nature, purpose, and operational essentials of TCP/IP.	3
Describe the purpose of remote access protocols.	3
Describe how various protocols or services apply to the function of a mail system, Web system, and file transfer system.	3
Describe when to use various diagnostic tools for identifying and resolving Internet problems.	10
Describe hardware and software connection devices and their uses.	1
Describe various types of Internet bandwidth technologies (link types).	1
Describe the purpose of various servers—what they are, their functionality, and features.	4
i-Net Security	
Define the following Internet security concepts: access control, encryption, auditing and authentication, and provide appropriate types of technologies currently available for each.	7
Describe VPN and what it does.	7
Describe various types of suspicious activities.	7
Describe access security features for an Internet server (e.g., e-mail server, Web server).	7
Describe the purpose of antivirus software and when to use it.	7
Describe the differences between the following as they relate to security requirements: Intranet, Extranet, and Internet.	7
Business Concepts	
Explain the issues involved in copyrighting, trademarking, and licensing.	11
Identify the issues related to working in a global environment.	11
Define the following Web-related mechanisms for audience development (i.e., attracting and retaining an audience): Push technology and Pull technology.	11
Describe the differences between the following from a business standpoint: Intranet, Extranet, and Internet.	11
Define e-commerce terms and concepts.	11

 NOTE Exam objectives are subject to change at any time without prior notice and at CompTIA's sole discretion. Please visit CompTIA's Web site (www.comptia.org) for the most current listing of exam objectives.

i-Net+ Study Guide

i-Net+™ Study Guide

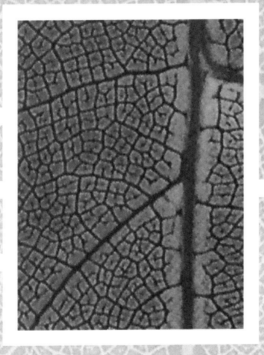

David Groth
with David Wall
and Michael de Beer

San Francisco • Paris • Düsseldorf • Soest • London

Associate Publisher: Neil Edde
Contracts and Licensing Manager: Kristine O'Callaghan
Acquisitions & Developmental Editor: Linda Lee
Editor: Judy Flynn
Project Editor: Rebecca Rider
Technical Editors: Robert Gradante, Donald Fuller
Book Designer: Bill Gibson
Graphic Illustrator: Tony Jonick
Electronic Publishing Specialist: Bill Gibson
Project Team Leader: Leslie Higbee
Proofreader: Molly Glover
Indexer: Nancy Guenther
CD Coordinator: Kara Schwarz
CD Technicians: Keith McNeil, Ginger Warner
Cover Designer: Archer Design
Cover Photographer: The Image Bank

SYBEX, Network Press, and the Network Press logo are a registered trademarks of SYBEX Inc.

Screen reproductions produced with Collage Complete.
Collage Complete is a trademark of Inner Media Inc.

Screen reproductions produced with FullShot 99. FullShot 99 © 1991-1999 Inbit Incorporated. All rights reserved.
FullShot is a trademark of Inbit Incorporated.

The CD Interface music is from GIRA Sound AURIA Music Library © GIRA Sound 1996.

Netscape Communications, the Netscape Communications logo, Netscape, and Netscape Navigator are trademarks of Netscape Communications Corporation.

Netscape Communications Corporation has not authorized, sponsored, endorsed, or approved this publication and is not responsible for its content. Netscape and the Netscape Communications Corporate Logos are trademarks and trade names of Netscape Communications Corporation. All other product names and/or logos are trademarks of their respective owners.

Internet screen shot(s) using Microsoft Internet Explorer 5 reprinted by permission from Microsoft Corporation.

The i-Net+ Certification program is an industry-wide, vendor-neutral program developed and sponsored by the Computing Technology Industry Association (CompTIA). Sybex is an independent entity from CompTIA, and not affiliated with CompTIA in any manner. Neither CompTIA nor Sybex warrants that use of this publication will ensure passing the relevant exam.

Network+, A+ Certification, and i-Net+ are trademarks of CompTIA in the United States and/or other countries. The i-Net+ Certification program logo is a registered trademark of CompTIA. All rights reserved.

TRADEMARKS: SYBEX has attempted throughout this book to distinguish proprietary trademarks from descriptive terms by following the capitalization style used by the manufacturer.

The author and publisher have made their best efforts to prepare this book, and the content is based upon final release software whenever possible. Portions of the manuscript may be based upon pre-release versions supplied by software manufacturer(s). The author and the publisher make no representation or warranties of any kind with regard to the completeness or accuracy of the contents herein and accept no liability of any kind including but not limited to performance, merchantability, fitness for any particular purpose, or any losses or damages of any kind caused or alleged to be caused directly or indirectly from this book.

Photographs and illustrations used in this book have been downloaded from publicly accessible file archives and are used in this book for news reportage purposes only to demonstrate the variety of graphics resources available via electronic access. Text and images available over the Internet may be subject to copyright and other rights owned by third parties. Online availability of text and images does not imply that they may be reused without the permission of rights holders, although the Copyright Act does permit certain unauthorized reuse as fair use under 17 U.S.C. Section 107.

Copyright © 2000 SYBEX Inc., 1151 Marina Village Parkway, Alameda, CA 94501. World rights reserved. No part of this publication may be stored in a retrieval system, transmitted, or reproduced in any way, including but not limited to photocopy, photograph, magnetic or other record, without the prior agreement and written permission of the publisher.

Library of Congress Card Number: 99-69307

ISBN: 0-7821-2637-5

Manufactured in the United States of America

10 9 8 7 6 5 4 3 2 1

Software License Agreement: Terms and Conditions

The media and/or any online materials accompanying this book that are available now or in the future contain programs and/or text files (the "Software") to be used in connection with the book. SYBEX hereby grants to you a license to use the Software, subject to the terms that follow. Your purchase, acceptance, or use of the Software will constitute your acceptance of such terms.

The Software compilation is the property of SYBEX unless otherwise indicated and is protected by copyright to SYBEX or other copyright owner(s) as indicated in the media files (the "Owner(s)"). You are hereby granted a single-user license to use the Software for your personal, noncommercial use only. You may not reproduce, sell, distribute, publish, circulate, or commercially exploit the Software, or any portion thereof, without the written consent of SYBEX and the specific copyright owner(s) of any component software included on this media.

In the event that the Software or components include specific license requirements or end-user agreements, statements of condition, disclaimers, limitations or warranties ("End-User License"), those End-User Licenses supersede the terms and conditions herein as to that particular Software component. Your purchase, acceptance, or use of the Software will constitute your acceptance of such End-User Licenses.

By purchase, use or acceptance of the Software you further agree to comply with all export laws and regulations of the United States as such laws and regulations may exist from time to time.

Software Support

Components of the supplemental Software and any offers associated with them may be supported by the specific Owner(s) of that material but they are not supported by SYBEX. Information regarding any available support may be obtained from the Owner(s) using the information provided in the appropriate read.me files or listed elsewhere on the media.

Should the manufacturer(s) or other Owner(s) cease to offer support or decline to honor any offer, SYBEX bears no responsibility. This notice concerning support for the Software is provided for your information only. SYBEX is not the agent or principal of the Owner(s), and SYBEX is in no way responsible for providing any support for the Software, nor is it liable or responsible for any support provided, or not provided, by the Owner(s).

Warranty

SYBEX warrants the enclosed media to be free of physical defects for a period of ninety (90) days after purchase. The Software is not available from SYBEX in any other form or media than that enclosed herein or posted to www.sybex.com. If you discover a defect in the media during this warranty period, you may obtain a replacement of identical format at no charge by sending the defective media, postage prepaid, with proof of purchase to:

SYBEX Inc.
Customer Service Department
1151 Marina Village Parkway
Alameda, CA 94501
(510) 523-8233
Fax: (510) 523-2373
e-mail: info@sybex.com
WEB: HTTP://WWW.SYBEX.COM

After the 90-day period, you can obtain replacement media of identical format by sending us the defective disk, proof of purchase, and a check or money order for $10, payable to SYBEX.

Disclaimer

SYBEX makes no warranty or representation, either expressed or implied, with respect to the Software or its contents, quality, performance, merchantability, or fitness for a particular purpose. In no event will SYBEX, its distributors, or dealers be liable to you or any other party for direct, indirect, special, incidental, consequential, or other damages arising out of the use of or inability to use the Software or its contents even if advised of the possibility of such damage. In the event that the Software includes an online update feature, SYBEX further disclaims any obligation to provide this feature for any specific duration other than the initial posting.

The exclusion of implied warranties is not permitted by some states. Therefore, the above exclusion may not apply to you. This warranty provides you with specific legal rights; there may be other rights that you may have that vary from state to state. The pricing of the book with the Software by SYBEX reflects the allocation of risk and limitations on liability contained in this agreement of Terms and Conditions.

Shareware Distribution

This Software may contain various programs that are distributed as shareware. Copyright laws apply to both shareware and ordinary commercial software, and the copyright Owner(s) retains all rights. If you try a shareware program and continue using it, you are expected to register it. Individual programs differ on details of trial periods, registration, and payment. Please observe the requirements stated in appropriate files.

Copy Protection

The Software in whole or in part may or may not be copy-protected or encrypted. However, in all cases, reselling or redistributing these files without authorization is expressly forbidden except as specifically provided for by the Owner(s) therein.

For my wife and daughter, without whom I could not write.

—*David Groth*

Acknowledgments

It takes many people to put a book together and this book is no exception. First, I would like to thank my coauthors, David Wall and Michael de Beer. They should be proud of the work they have done here. Thanks also to my technical editors, Robert Gradante and Don Fuller. They were responsible for making sure the information in this book is technically accurate and as up-to-date as possible.

This book would not have existed if not for the efforts of Linda Lee, this book's developmental and acquisitions editor at Sybex. Thank you for putting up with all my phone calls and e-mails! Additionally, thanks go out to Rebecca Rider for her work as project editor and Judy Flynn for turning my collection of chicken-scratchings into a cohesive, useful study guide. The production department at Sybex also deserves my thanks. Thanks to Bill Gibson, electronic publishing specialist, for making this book look the way it does; to Leslie Higbee, production team leader, for making the production end of things run so smoothly; and to Molly Glover, proofreader, for her time reading every word.

I would also like to acknowledge my wife, family, and friends. My wife, Linda, tirelessly wrote and edited the appendices as well as kept me on the right track. She was a real trooper because she did it while taking care of our new daughter, Alison. Thanks to Alison, too, for being fussy when I needed a break (or when she thought I needed a break) or cute when I needed a laugh. Thank you to my family and friends who understood when I couldn't do something because I had to work on the book. I really appreciate that.

Finally, I thank you, the reader, for purchasing this book. I know that it has all the information in it to help you pass the test. If you have questions about the i-Net+ exam or this book, feel free to e-mail me at `dgroth@corpcomm.net`. All three of us worked very hard on this book to make it the best i-Net+ study guide available. I hope you agree that it is.
—*David Groth*

I'd like to thank the Sybex team for their support, especially Linda Lee, my acquisitions and developmental editor, for her insightful suggestions and guidance. Also, thanks goes to my coworkers at IGC, especially Steve Fram, Scott Weikart, and Marci Lockwood, who have all provided me with opportunities to deepen my understanding of the Internet.
—*Michael de Beer*

I would like to thank the hard-working staff at Sybex. Linda Lee, Judy Flynn, and Rebecca Rider provided editorial guidance, while Robert Gradante and Donald Fuller did a great technical edit. Bill Gibson did super layout and design work, while Leslie Higbee and Molly Glover put many hours of work into making this project flow smoothly. I also want to thank my family and friends, particularly Adam Bergman and Joy Kinsey, for their kindness and support.

—*David Wall*

Contents at a Glance

Table of Contents

Introduction

If you are like the rest of the networking community, you've probably taken certification exams. Becoming certified is one of the best things you can do for your career in the computer or networking field. It proves that you are knowledgeable in the area in which you are certified.

In this book, you'll find out what the i-Net+ exam is all about. Each chapter covers part of the exam, and at the end of each chapter, there are review questions to help you prepare for the exam.

What Is the i-Net+ Certification?

i-Net+ is a certification developed by the Computing Technology Industry Association (CompTIA). This organization exists to provide resources and education for the computer and technology community. This is the same body that developed the A+ and Network+ exams for computer and networking technicians. In 1997, members of CompTIA convened to develop a new certification that tests skills for Internet professionals. To ensure industry-wide support, it is sponsored by many IT industry leaders, including:

- Association of Internet Professionals
- IBM
- Microsoft
- Novell

The i-Net+ exam was designed to test the skills of Internet professionals who are responsible for implementing and maintaining Internet, intranet, and extranet infrastructure and services as well as development of related applications.

The exam tests areas of Internet technologies such as the TCP/IP protocol, the various types of servers, and the concepts of Internet design and implementation, such as which items are required for an easy-to-read Web site and the prerequisites for its installation. In addition, it covers troubleshooting concepts and various how-tos.

Why Become i-Net+ Certified?

As this book is being written, the i-Net+ certification is brand-new. But i-Net+ is the next certification in a line of CompTIA certifications, starting with A+ certification and Network+ certification. Because CompTIA is a well-respected developer of industry vendor-neutral certifications, getting i-Net+ certified indicates that you are competent in the specific areas tested by the exam.

Two major benefits are associated with becoming i-Net+ certified:

- Proof of professional achievement
- Opportunity for advancement

Proof of Professional Achievement

Networking professionals are competing these days to see who can get the most certifications. And technicians want the i-Net+ certification because it is broad, covering the entire field of Internet-related technical knowledge, rather than only development or security, for example. Thus, it can be a challenge to prepare for the i-Net+ exam. Passing the exam, however, certifies that you have achieved a certain level of knowledge about vendor-independent Internet-related subjects.

Opportunity for Advancement

We all like to get ahead in our careers. With advancement comes more responsibility, to be sure, but usually it means more money and greater opportunities. In the information technology area, this can usually be accomplished by obtaining multiple technology certifications, including i-Net+.

i-Net+, because of its wide-reaching industry support, is recognized as a baseline of Internet and networking information. Some companies will specify that i-Net+ certification will result in a pay raise at review time. And some companies will specify that i-Net+ certification, in conjunction with A+ Certification, is required as a condition of employment before an employee's next review.

How to Become i-Net+ Certified

The simplest way to find out how to become i-Net+ certified is to take the exam. It is administered by Sylvan Prometric, with which most of you are familiar if you have taken any other computer certification exams. It is administered by computer. To register to take the exam, call Sylvan (not the testing center) at 877-803-6867 and tell them you want to take the i-Net+ exam. You must pay for the exam at registration time with a major credit card (for example, Visa or MasterCard). The cost is $135 for CompTIA members and $185 for non-members. Special incentive pricing may be in effect when you take the exam—check CompTIA's Web site for details.

You can also register on the Internet through Sylvan Prometric at www.sylvanprometric.com or www.2test.com.

The exam itself consists of approximately 75 questions. You have 1 hour and 30 minutes for the test. At the end of the exam, your score report will be displayed on screen and printed so that you have a hard copy.

Who Should Buy This Book?

If you are one of the many people who want to pass the i-Net+ exam, you should buy this book and use it to study for the exam. The i-Net+ exam is designed for Internet professionals with six months of experience in a variety of entry-level, Internet-related technical job functions. This book was written with one goal in mind: to prepare you to pass the i-Net+ exam by describing in detail the concepts on which you'll be tested.

How to Use This Book and CD

This book includes several features that will make studying for the i-Net+ exam easier. First, at the beginning of the book (right after this introduction, in fact) is an assessment test you can use to check your readiness for the actual exam. Take this test before you start reading the book. It will help you to determine the areas you may need to "brush up" on. You can then focus on those areas while reading the book. The answers to this test appear on a separate page after the last question. Each answer also includes an explanation and a note telling you in which chapter this material appears.

In addition, there are review questions at the end of each chapter. As you finish each chapter, answer the questions and then check your answers, which will appear on the page after the last question. If you answered any question(s) incorrectly, you'll know that you may need some additional study in that particular area of the exam. You can go back and reread the section in the chapter that deals with each question you got wrong to ensure that you "know your stuff."

Appendix A includes a practice exam. Take this exam when you have finished reading all the chapters and answering all the review questions and you feel you are ready for the i-Net+ exam. Take the practice exam as if you were actually taking the i-Net+ exam (i.e., without any reference material). The answers to the practice exam can be found at the end of the test on the last page of Appendix A. If you get more than 90 percent of the answers correct, you're ready to go ahead and take the real exam.

On the CD-ROM that is included with this book, there are several "extras" you can use to bolster your exam "readiness":

Electronic "flashcards"   You can use these 150 flashcard-style questions to review your knowledge of i-Net+ concepts on your PC. Additionally, you can download the questions into your Palm device (if you own one) for reviewing anywhere, anytime, without a PC!

Test engine   This portion of the CD-ROM includes all of the questions that appear in the text of this book: the assessment questions at the end of this introduction, the chapter review questions, and the Practice Exam questions from Appendix A. In addition, it includes a set of bonus questions that only appear on the CD-ROM. The book questions will appear similarly to the way they did in the book, and they will also be randomized. This random test will allow you to pick a certain number of questions and will simulate an actual exam. Combined, these test engine elements will allow you to test your readiness for the "real" i-Net+ exam.

Full text of the book   If you are going to travel but still need to study for the i-Net+ exam, and you have a laptop with a CD-ROM drive, you can take this entire book with you on the CD-ROM. The book is in PDF (Adobe Acrobat) format so it can be read easily on any computer.

Conventions Used in This Book

To understand the way this book is put together, you must learn about a few of the special conventions we used. Following are some of the items you will commonly see.

Italicized words indicate new terms. After each italicized term, you will find a definition.

Lines formatted in `this font` refer to the output of a program. You will usually see several of these lines together indicating what the output of a text-based program usually looks like. This font is also used in Web addresses.

Tips will be formatted like so. A tip is a special piece of information that can make either your work or your test-taking experience easier.

Notes are formatted with this symbol and this box. When you see a note, it usually indicates some special circumstance to make note of. Notes usually include information that is somewhat out of the ordinary and relates to the exam.

Warnings are found within the text whenever there is a technical situation that arises that may cause damage to a component or cause a system failure of some kind. Additionally, warnings are placed in the text to call particular attention to a potentially dangerous situation.

Sidebars

This special formatting indicates a sidebar. *Sidebars* are entire paragraphs of information that, although related to the topic being discussed, aren't actually on the exam. They are just what their name suggests: a sidebar discussion.

Keep a watchful eye out for these special items within the text as you read.

Exam Objectives

The i-Net+ exam objectives were developed by a group of Internet industry professionals through the use of an industry-wide job task analysis. CompTIA asked groups of Internet professionals to fill out a survey rating the skills they felt were important in their jobs. The results were grouped into objectives for the exam. This section includes the outline of the exam objectives for the i-Net+ exam and the weight of each objective category.

The objectives and weighting percentages given in this section can change at any time. Check CompTIA's Web site at www.comptia.org for a list of the most current objectives.

i-Net Basics (10%)

1.1 Describe a URL, its functions and components, different types of URLs, and use of the appropriate type of URL to access a given type of server. Content may include the following:

- Protocol
- Address
- Port

1.2 Identify the issues that affect Internet site functionality (e.g., performance, security, and reliability). Content may include the following:

- Bandwidth
- Internet connection points
- Audience access
- Internet Service Provider (ISP)
- Connection types
- Corrupt files
- Files taking too long to load
- Inability to open files
- Resolution of graphics

1.3 Describe the concept of caching and its implications. Content may include the following:

- Server caching

- Client caching

- Proxy caching

- Cleaning out client-side cache

- Server may cache information as well

- Web page update settings in browsers

1.4 Describe different types of search indexes—static index/site map, keyword index, full-text index. Examples could include the following:

- Searching your site

- Searching content

- Indexing your site for a search

i-Net Clients (20%)

2.1 Describe the infrastructure needed to support an Internet client. Content could include the following:

- TCP/IP stack

- Operating system

- Network connection

- Web browser

- E-mail

- Hardware platform (PC, handheld device, WebTV, Internet phone)

2.2 Describe the use of Web browsers and various clients (e.g., FTP clients, Telnet clients, e-mail clients, all-in-one clients/universal clients) within a given context of use. Examples of context could include the following:

- When you would use each

- The basic commands you would use (e.g., put and get) with each client (e.g., FTP, Telnet)

2.3 Explain the issues to consider when configuring the desktop. Content could include the following:

- TCP/IP configuration (NetBIOS name server such as WINS, DNS, default gateway, subnet mask)

- Host file configuration

- DHCP versus static IP

- Configuring browser (proxy configuration, client-side caching)

2.4 Describe MIME types and their components. Content could include the following:

- Whether a client can understand various e-mail types (MIME, HTML, uuencode)

- The need to define MIME file types for special download procedures such as unusual documents or graphic formats

2.5 Identify problems related to legacy clients (e.g., TCP/IP sockets and their implication on the operating system). Content could include the following:

- Checking revision date, manufacturer/vendor

- Troubleshooting and performance issues

- Compatibility issues

- Version of the Web browser

2.6 Explain the function of patches and updates to client software and associated problems. Content could include the following:

- Desktop security

- Virus protection

- Encryption levels

- Web browsers

- E-mail clients

2.7 Describe the advantages and disadvantages of using a cookie and how to set cookies. Content could include the following:

- Setting a cookie without the knowledge of the user

- Automatically accepting cookies versus query

- Remembering everything the user has done
- Security and privacy implications

Development (20%)

3.1 Define programming-related terms as they relate to Internet applications development. Content could include the following:

- API
- CGI
- SQL
- SAPI
- DLL—dynamic linking and static linking
- Client and server-side scripting

3.2 Describe the differences between popular client-side and server-side programming languages. Examples could include the following:

- Java
- JavaScript
- Perl
- C
- C++
- Visual Basic
- VBScript
- JScript
- XML
- VRML
- ASP

Content could include the following:

- When to use the languages
- When they are executed

3.3 Describe the differences between a relational database and a non-relational database.

3.4 Identify when to integrate a database with a Web site and the technologies used to connect the two.

3.5 Demonstrate the ability to create HTML pages. Content could include the following:

- HTML document structure
- Coding simple tables, headings, forms
- Compatibility between different browsers
- Difference between text editors and GUI editors
- Importance of creating cross-browser coding in your HTML

3.6 Identify popular multimedia extensions or plug-ins. Examples could include the following:

- QTVR (QuickTime VR)
- Flash
- Shockwave
- RealPlayer
- Windows Media Player

3.7 Describe the uses and benefits of various multimedia file formats. Examples could include the following:

- GIF
- GIF89a
- JPEG
- PNG
- PDF
- RTF
- TIFF
- PostScript

- EPS
- BMP
- MOV
- MPEG
- AVI
- BinHex
- Streaming media
- Non-streaming media

3.8 Describe the process of pre-launch site/application functionality testing. Content could including the following:

- Checking hot links
- Testing different browsers
- Testing to ensure it does not corrupt your e-commerce site
- Load testing
- Access to the site
- Testing with various speed connections

Networking (25%)

4.1 Describe the core components of the current Internet infrastructure and how they relate to each other. Content may include the following:

- Network access points
- Backbone

4.2 Identify problems with Internet connectivity from source to destination for various types of servers. Examples could include the following:

- E-mail
- Slow server
- Web site

4.3 Describe Internet domain names and DNS. Content could include the following:

- DNS entry types
- Hierarchical structure
- Role of root domain server
- Top level or original domains—edu, com, mil, net, gov, org
- Country level domains—UK

4.4 Describe the nature, purpose, and operational essentials of TCP/IP. Content could include the following:

- What addresses are and their classifications (A, B, C, D)
- Determining which ones are valid and which ones are not (subnet masks)
- Public versus private IP addresses

4.5 Describe the purpose of remote access protocols. Content could include the following:

- SLIP
- PPP
- PPTP
- Point-to-point/multipoint

4.6 Describe how various protocols or services apply to the function of a mail system, Web system, and file transfer system. Content could include the following:

- POP3
- SMTP
- HTTP
- FTP
- NNTP (news servers)
- TCP/IP

- LDAP
- LPR
- TELNET
- Gopher

4.7 Describe when to use various diagnostic tools for identifying and resolving Internet problems. Content could include the following:

- Ping
- winipcfg
- ipconfig
- ARP
- Trace Routing Utility
- Network Analyzer
- netstat

4.8 Describe hardware and software connection devices and their uses. Content could include the following:

- Network interface card
- Various types of modems including analog, ISDN, DSL, and cable
- Modem setup and commands
- Adapter
- Bridge
- Internet-in-a-box
- Cache-in-a-box
- Hub
- Router
- Switch
- Gateway
- NOS
- Firewall

4.9 Describe various types of Internet bandwidth technologies (link types). Content could include the following:

- T1/E1
- T3/E3
- Frame Relay
- X.25
- ATM
- DSL

4.10 Describe the purpose of various servers—what they are, their functionality, and features. Content could include the following:

- Proxy
- Mail
- Mirrored
- Cache
- List
- Web (HTTP)
- News
- Certificate
- Directory (LDAP)
- E-commerce
- Telnet
- FTP

i-Net Security (15%)

5.1 Define the following Internet security concepts: access control, encryption, auditing and authentication, and provide appropriate types of technologies currently available for each. Examples could include the following:

- Access control: Access Control List, firewall, packet filters, proxy

- Authentication: Certificates, digital signatures, nonrepudiation

- Encryption: public and private keys, Secure SocketsLayer (SSL), S/MIME, digital signatures, global versus country-specific encryption standards

- Auditing: Intrusion detection utilities, log files, auditing logs

- SET (Secure Electronic Transactions)

5.2 Describe VPN and what it does. Content could include the following:

- VPN in encrypted communications

- Connecting two different company sites via an Internet VPN (extranet)

- Connecting a remote user to a site

5.3 Describe various types of suspicious activities. Examples could include the following:

- Multiple login failures

- Denial of service attacks

- Mail flooding/spam

- Ping floods

- SYN floods

5.4 Describe access security features for an Internet server (e.g., e-mail server, Web server). Examples could include the following:

- User name and password

- File level

- Certificate

- File-level access: read, write, no access

5.5 Describe the purpose of antivirus software and when to use it. Content could include the following:

- Browser/client

- Server

5.6 Describe the differences between the following as they relate to security requirements:

- Intranet

- Extranet

- Internet

Business Concepts (10%)

6.1 Explain the issues involved in copyrighting, trademarking, and licensing. Content could include the following:

- How to license copyright materials

- Scope of your copyright

- How to copyright your material anywhere

- Consequences of not being aware of copyright issues and not following copyright restrictions

6.2 Identify the issues related to working in a global environment. Content could include the following:

- Working in a multivendor environment with different currencies, etc.

- International issues—shipping, supply chain

- Multilingual or multicharacter issues (Unicode)

- Legal and regulatory issues

6.3 Define the following Web-related mechanisms for audience development (i.e., attracting and retaining an audience):

- Push technology

- Pull technology

6.4 Describe the differences between the following from a business standpoint:

- Intranet

- Extranet

- Internet

6.5 Define e-commerce terms and concepts. Content could include the following:

- EDI
- Business to business
- Business to consumer
- Internet commerce
- Merchant systems
- Online cataloging
- Relationship management
- Customer self-service
- Internet marketing

How to Contact the Authors

If you have any questions while you are reading this book, feel free to contact any of the authors. David Groth can be reached via e-mail (the best way to reach him) at `dgroth@corpcomm.net`. Michael de Beer can be reached at `madebeer@igc.org`, and David Wall can be reached at `david@davidwall.com`.

Test-Taking Tips

The i-Net+ exam is a new standard (as this book is being written) and should gain wide acceptance among Internet professionals. Remember a few things when taking your test:

- Get a good night's sleep the night before.
- Take your time on each question. Don't rush it.
- Arrive at the testing center a few minutes early so that you can review your notes.
- Answer all questions, even if you don't know the answer. (Unanswered questions are considered wrong.)

- If you don't know the answer to a question, mark it and come back to it later.

- Read each question twice and make sure you understand it.

Good luck on your i-Net+ exam and in your future in the Internet industry.

Assessment Test

1. How does a certificate differ from a public key?

    A. A certificate is itself encrypted.

    B. A certificate is necessarily issued by an independent authority.

    C. A certificate has a time limit.

    D. A certificate does not change over time.

2. What is *not* true about installing an update?

    A. It can corrupt your system.

    B. It can close important security holes in your desktop security.

    C. Updates must be installed in every case.

    D. It can provide added functionality.

3. Which is true of full-text reverse indexes?

    A. They really shine for sites that update infrequently.

    B. They are primarily governed by ROBOTS.TXT spider rules.

    C. They speed queries.

    D. They provide concept-based functionality.

4. Copyright law provides protection for software but allows for
_____ .

    A. Limited use

    B. Educational use

    C. Nonprofit use

    D. Fair use

5. The test server is a Pentium-100 with 500MB of RAM running Apache on Linux. Each child of the Web server uses 5MB of RAM. The server has a dedicated T1 line and serves an unlimited number of clients that download its 100K static pages at 10 K/s. Given this test server, at what rate of incoming requests will the Web server start increasing its queue length?

   A. 2

   B. 6

   C. 11

   D. 16

6. Which networking component requests resources from a server?

   A. Workstation

   B. Server

   C. Router

   D. Firewall

7. What is Microsoft's modular software architecture called?

   A. Object-orientation

   B. C++

   C. The Microsoft Foundation Classes (MFC)

   D. The Component Object Model (COM)

8. Which component of a Web browser contains all the menus for the program?

   A. Button bar

   B. Menu bar

   C. Status Bar

   D. Activity indicator

9. One difference between patent and copyright is _____ .

    A. Patent protection is available only in the United States.

    B. There is no implicit patent; you must apply for and be granted one.

    C. Two independent inventors of a product or process may both enjoy patents on it.

    D. Copyright does not allow for corporate ownership.

10. What do HTTP response codes in the 4*xx* range mean?

    A. There has been a server error.

    B. There has been a client error.

    C. The request has been redirected.

    D. Everything went as planned.

11. During an SMTP communications session, which command does the sender use to indicate to the server that it is ready to send the body of the message?

    A. PUT

    B. rcpt to

    C. body

    D. HELO

12. Of the people who view a banner ad, the percentage that follow its link to an advertiser's site is called _____ .

    A. The clickthrough rate

    B. The passthrough rate

    C. The yield

    D. The drawing power

13. How many host IP addresses are available with the CIDR designation /21?

    A. 128

    B. 1,024

    C. 2,046

    D. 9,128

14. What is *not* true about installing an update?

    A. It can corrupt your system.

    B. It can close important security holes in your desktop security.

    C. Updates must be installed in every case.

    D. It can provide added functionality.

15. True or false. Telnet servers are somewhat of a security risk.

    A. True

    B. False

16. True or False. X.25 is a WAN transmission method.

    A. True

    B. False

17. Virtual shopping cart services are a function of which type of HTTP server?

    A. Internet

    B. Intranet

    C. FTP

    D. E-commerce

18. If someone claims she got an error message on your site, what is the first thing you should do?

   A. Ask her to try again and give you the exact error message.

   B. Look in the access log for verification that she went to your server.

   C. Check to see if the server is up.

   D. Ask remote staff to check the firewall connectivity.

19. True or False. You must have a PC in order to browse the Internet?

   A. True

   B. False

20. Which part of the URL `http://www.novell.com/index.html` is the actual DNS name of the server being accessed?

   A. `http://`

   B. `www.novell.com`

   C. `index.html`

   D. `novell`

21. What is the program that interprets Java programs called?

   A. The Java Interpreter

   B. The Java Compiler

   C. The Java Virtual Machine

   D. The Java Grinder

22. True or False. You can use Telnet to access the console of a Unix host?

   A. True

   B. False

23. When browsing the Internet with a Web browser, what is the text that links you to another page on the Web called?

   A. Hypertext

   B. Hyperlink

   C. Hyperactive

   D. Hyperbole

24. True or False. Before assigning any IP address, you must apply for a registered IP address from either the IANA or your ISP.

   A. True

   B. False.

25. Which of the following is *not* needed before transfering a file from an FTP server using an FTP client?

   A. FTP Server name

   B. DNS MX record

   C. username

   D. password

26. Dynamic packet filtering relies upon _____ .

   A. Blocking certain kinds of traffic, like ICQ transmissions

   B. Requiring packets inbound from the Internet to pass through a firewall

   C. Tracking open TCP/IP connections and only allowing the packets related to those transmissions to pass through in sequence

   D. Detecting multiple login attempts

27. What is the default subnet mask for a Class B address?

    A. 255.255.0.0

    B. 0.0.0.0

    C. 255.255.255.0

    D. 255.0.0.0

28. Access control measures limit the damage that can be done by an attacker. How do they do this?

    A. By making brute force attacks more difficult

    B. By imposing an extra layer of password protection

    C. By encrypting stored data en masse

    D. By giving users of a computer access only to those resources they need to access in order to do their jobs

29. What should people doing quality control on a Web site look for?

    A. Pages that look ugly and don't work visually

    B. Conformity with the storyboard

    C. Anything on their checklist

    D. Functionality errors only

30. A tunneling protocol is used to facilitate _____ .

    A. Secure e-commerce

    B. Firewalls

    C. Dial-up Internet connections

    D. Virtual private networks (VPNs)

31. The process of establishing a relationship between two tables in a relational database is called doing a _____ .

    A. Link

    B. Join

    C. Pivot

    D. Combo

32. Which two network utilities are the most similar?

    A. Ping and winipcfg

    B. ARP and tracert

    C. Ping and tracert

    D. Ping and ARP

33. QUALCOMM Eudora is an example of a _____ client.

    A. Mail

    B. Web

    C. FTP

    D. Telnet

34. A database management system (DBMS) is primarily responsible for what?

    A. Storing data in a database and handling queries sent to it

    B. Backing up a database

    C. Integrating a database with the Internet

    D. Providing Perl support

35. When planning the content of a Web site, it is most important to
_____ .

    A. Use the latest technologies so the site won't need to get reinvented soon.

    B. Only use technologies that won't be roadblocks for potential users.

    C. Follow the local policy, based on the goals of the site and the audience profile.

    D. Choose technology the development team enjoys and is good at.

36. An object is likely to be in a cache if _____ .

    A. The object was requested a long time ago.

    B. The object is fresh; it was requested just before the cache was last cleared.

    C. The object has high value because it has never before been requested.

    D. The object has been requested recently.

37. Licensing always allows for _____ .

    A. One party's use of another party's copyrighted material under certain terms

    B. A payment of money to the copyright holder

    C. A limited period of use

    D. Mandatory review of the terms by a judge

38. If you want to buy your sister either black high heels or purple tennis shoes, which query will be most useful?

    A. A full-text search for "black high heels or purple tennis shoes"

    B. A keyword search for "black high heels or purple tennis shoes"

    C. A full-text search for (black and "high heels") or (purple and "tennis shoes")

    D. A keyword search for "high heels or sneakers"

39. What do HTTP response codes in the 4*xx* range mean?

    A. There has been a server error.

    B. There has been a client error.

    C. The request has been redirected.

    D. Everything went as planned.

40. Which Internet access link technology is a point-to-point link that sends digital signals over the standard POTS phone lines installed in most homes, is inexpensive, but is not widely available in all areas as yet?

    A. Frame Relay

    B. T1

    C. DSL

    D. ATM

41. A company that receives income from products it sells to foreign nationals is _____ .

    A. Not liable for taxes on the income in its home country

    B. Usually responsible for paying duties on services provided over the Internet

    C. Liable for taxes on the income in its home country

    D. Usually eligible for special tax benefits

42. _____ servers allow Internet clients to search for people along with their addresses and phone numbers.

    A. Proxy

    B. FTP

    C. NNTP

    D. LDAP

43. Which T-series Internet bandwidth technology has a maximum throughput of 1.544Mbps?

   A. T1

   B. T2

   C. T3

   D. T4

44. Which FTP command produces the output "Type set to A"?

   A. put

   B. ascii

   C. get

   D. ls

45. True or False. The POP3 protocol is used to send e-mail between Internet e-mail servers.

   A. True

   B. False

46. Netscape's server-side scripting language, LiveScript, is similar to
_____ .

   A. VBScript.

   B. JavaScript.

   C. Perl.

   D. Java.

47. Access Control Lists (ACLs) are built into routers. They serve to
_____ .

   A. Define who may access a system

   B. Support the operations of a proxy server

   C. Prevent SYN floods

   D. Determine which machines may send packets in which direction over the router

Answers to Assessment Test

1. C. A certificate guarantees that someone is who he or she claims to be but guarantees its validity for only a certain time period. For more information on certificates, see Chapter 7.

2. C. Updates have both benefits and risks. The cost and benefit need to be weighed, so installing an upgrade is not required. For more information on patches and updates, see Chapter 10.

3. C. The table mapping words to files allows direct lookups on where a word is used. For more information about searching and indexing, see Chapter 9.

4. D. The doctrine of fair use describes circumstances in which someone may use copyrighted material without explicit permission. For more information of fair use, see Chapter 11.

5. C. If there are 100 processes, and each finishes serving a request every 10 seconds, 10 requests a second will be fulfilled. At 11 requests a second, one request is added to the queue every second. For more information about planning server capacity and performance, see Chapter 9.

6. A. Of all the components listed, workstations are the only ones to request resources (e.g., files, information). For more information on servers, see Chapter 1.

7. D. The Component Object Model (COM) allows for modularity in Windows code. For more on COM, see Chapter 8.

8. B. The menu bar is the only component of a Web browser that contains the menus for the program. The button bar contains all the control buttons for browsing, the status bar shows the status of the browsing session, and the activity indicator shows that Internet activity is occurring. For more information on Web browser components, see Chapter 5.

9. B. You must apply for and be granted a patent in order to be able to defend an invention from infringement. For more information on patents, see Chapter 11.

10. B. The client could be asking for a file that is forbidden or does not exist. For more on HTTP response codes, see Chapter 10.

11. C. PUT is used for HTTP requests, `rcpt to` indicates the message recipient, and `HELO` starts the communications session. For more information on the SMTP communications process, refer to Chapter 2.

12. A. The percentage of ad viewers that choose to visit the underlying site is called the clickthrough rate. For more information on the clickthrough rate, see Chapter 11.

13. C. /21 indicates that there are 21 bits used for the network address of an IP address and that there are 11 bits left over for host addresses, corresponding to a decimal number of 2,048 (subtract 2 for addresses with all 0s and all 1s, leaving 2,046). For more information on CIDR, see Chapter 3.

14. C. Updates have both benefits and risks. The cost and benefit need to be weighed, so installing an upgrade is not required. For more information on patches and updates, see Chapter 10.

15. A. Because you are giving a user from the Internet access to the server console, the user could theoretically run unauthorized programs. For more information on Telnet servers, see Chapter 4.

16. B. Actually, X.25 is an access method and assumes that a path from sender to receiver exists. For more information on X.25, see Chapter 1.

17. D. E-commerce servers provide virtual shopping cart services to help customers shop online. For more information on e-commerce servers, see Chapter 4.

18. A. You need to find out exactly what she claims to be experiencing before you can test the problem. For more information on troubleshooting, see Chapter 10.

19. B. False. It is also possible to use an Internet appliance. See Chapter 5 for more on Internet appliances.

20. B. A is the protocol, C is the name of the resource being accessed, and D doesn't represent a specific part of a URL. For more information on URLs, refer to Chapter 2.

21. C. The Java Virtual Machine (JVM) interprets Java programs. For more on Java, see Chapter 8.

22. A. True. The primary function of Telnet is to access the console of a Unix host. For more information on Telnet, see Chapter 5.

23. B. A Hyperlink is a line of text that, when clicked, will take you to another page. For more information on hyperlinks, see Chapter 6.

24. B. You don't have to apply for a registered IP address if your network isn't connected to the Internet. For more information on registered IP addresses, refer to Chapter 3.

25. B. For more information on FTP client, see Chapter 6.

26. C. Dynamic packet filtering keeps track of open connections and prevents people from breaking in while transmissions are in progress. For more information on dynamic packet filtering, see Chapter 7.

27. A. 255.255.255.0 is for a Class C address, and 255.0.0.0 is for a Class A address. For more information on default masks, see Chapter 3.

28. D. Access control measures limit the resources available to individual users, meaning that even if they get into the system, they can only do a certain degree of damage. For more information on access control measures, see Chapter 7.

29. B and C. Each site should establish a testing methodology, including a list of bugs to check for. For more information about testing a site before rolling it out to the public, see Chapter 10.

30. D. Tunneling protocols encapsulate VPN data in Internet packets, using encryption to keep it secure. For more information on tunneling protocols, see Chapter 7.

31. B. To establish a relationship between two tables in a relational database is to do a join. For more on relational databases, see Chapter 8.

32. C. Ping and tracert both send packets to a destination host. Ping is used primarily to see if the host will respond. You could use tracert for a similar job, but it is better suited to seeing the path to a host. For more information on troubleshooting utilities, see Chapter 10.

33. A. Eudora is one of the many Internet mail clients available. It doesn't perform any other of the functions listed. For more information on mail clients, see Chapter 5.

34. A. Though DBMSes may do the other tasks listed, their primary job is to store data and allow users to access it. For more on DBMSes, see Chapter 8.

35. C. Although all enjoy some truth, B is most likely to lead to a successful Web site. For more information about planning which content types to use on a Web site, see Chapter 9.

36. D. The object has been put into the cache by a recent request. Because it is recent, it is likely it hasn't expired in the cache or been pushed out by other cached content. For more information about caching, see Chapter 9.

37. A. Licensing is one party's use of another party's copyrighted material under certain terms, which may or may not be granted in exchange for payment.

38. C. The full-text search will look through the details of more pages. The search terms will not find purple high heels or black tennis shoes. For more information on searching, see Chapter 9.

39. B. The client could be asking for a file that is forbidden or does not exist. For more on HTTP response codes, see Chapter 10.

40. C. Of the answers listed, only DSL is inexpensive and not widely available in all areas. For more information on Internet access link technologies, see Chapter 1.

41. C. The income you receive from foreign customers is taxable income like any other. For more information on this subject, see Chapter 11.

42. D. Of all the types listed, only LDAP servers (such as www.switchboard.com) facilitate searching for people and their phone numbers. For more information on directory servers, see Chapter 4.

43. A. T1 is 1.544Mbps, T3 is 44.736Mbps, and T2 and T4 are actually valid T-series connections, but they aren't widely used and discussed in Internet circles. For more information on T-series Internet bandwidth technologies, see Chapter 1.

44. B. The `ascii` command changes the file type to A and thus produces the specified output. The others all produce different outputs. For more information on FTP use, see Chapter 6.

45. B. SMTP is used for this purpose. For more information on POP3 and SMTP, refer to Chapter 2.

46. B. LiveScript sometimes is called "server-side JavaScript." For more on scripting languages, see Chapter 8.

47. D. ACLs determine which machines can send packets to what machines over a router. An ACL might allow local machines to send packets out to the Internet but allow inbound traffic only in response to a request. For more information on Access Control Lists, see Chapter 7.

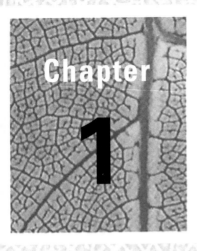

i-Net+ Networking Basics

---

i-NET+ EXAM OBJECTIVES COVERED IN THIS CHAPTER:

✓ **Describe hardware and software connection devices and their uses. Content could include the following:**

- Network interface card
- Various types of modems including analog, ISDN, DSL, and cable
- Modem setup and commands
- Adapter
- Bridge
- Internet-in-a-box
- Cache-in-a-box
- Hub
- Router
- Switch
- Gateway
- NOS
- Firewall

✓ **Describe various types of Internet bandwidth technologies (link types). Content could include the following:**

- T1/E1
- T3/E3
- Frame Relay
- X.25
- ATM
- DSL

By most accounts, the Internet is a big network. It contains many of the same components as any corporate network. To that end, before discussing the Internet, it is helpful to understand some of the basic components and concepts of a network. Many of the concepts involved in understanding networks will cross over to understanding the inner workings of the Internet. This chapter will introduce you to some of the more common networking topics you must understand when working with Internet technologies. Some of those topics include definitions of servers and protocols, hardware and software connection devices, and the various bandwidth technologies used to connect Internet sites to one another. This chapter will introduce you to these and other networking components and concepts so that you may have a better understanding of the Internet's underpinnings.

What Is a Network?

In the computer world, the term *network* describes two or more connected computers that can share a resource such as data, a printer, an Internet connection, applications, or a combination of these. Today, networks can be classified into two main types:

- Local area network (LAN)

- Wide area network (WAN)

The type used depends on the number of computers (and people) who need access, the geographical and physical layout of the enterprise, and of course, financial resources. In this section, we'll discuss each type and describe the situation that is most appropriate for its use.

Local Area Network (LAN)

By definition, a *local area network*, or LAN, is limited to a specific area, usually an office, and cannot extend beyond the boundaries of a single building. The first LANs were limited to a range (from a central point to the most distant computer) of 185 meters (about 600 feet) and to no more than 30 computers. Today's technology allows a larger LAN, but practical administration limitations require dividing it into small, logical areas called *workgroups*. A workgroup is a collection of individuals who share the same files and databases over the LAN, such as, for example, the sales department. Figure 1.1 shows an example of a LAN and its workgroups.

FIGURE 1.1   A sample LAN

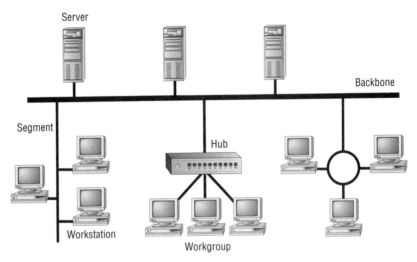

Theoretically, a LAN could connect a maximum of 1,024 computers at a maximum distance of 900 meters (around 2,700 feet, assuming thinnet cable is used). These figures are based on using one area of the network for the majority of network traffic (in what is known as a *backbone* configuration), other network areas (called *segments*) connecting workstations to the main cabling portion using special devices to extend the overall range of the network, and finally, very light network traffic. If you use a different type of cabling, these maximums decrease to 30 computers, with the most distant computer connected at a maximum of 100 meters (about 300 feet) from a central point.

Cabling Topologies

As shown in Figure 1.1, network cabling can be laid out in many different ways. The specific way network cables are arranged is known as the *cabling topology*. There are four main types: bus, star, ring, and mesh. A *bus* topology connects all computers to a single cable. In a bus topology, the network cable run starts at one computer and goes to the next, then to the next, and so on. A *star* topology, on the other hand, has cable runs from each device on the network to a central device (known as a hub). Although not very common, *ring* topologies connect each computer to two others to form a ring. Finally, a *mesh* topology connects every computer directly to every other computer. In mathematical terms, if there were *n* computers, there would be $n(n-1)/2$ cables in a mesh topology.

Wide Area Network (WAN)

Chances are, you are an experienced WAN user and didn't know it. If you have ever connected to the Internet, you have used the largest WAN on the planet. A *wide area network*, or WAN, is any network that crosses metropolitan, regional, or national boundaries. Most networking professionals define a WAN as any network that uses routers and public network links. The Internet fits both definitions.

WANs differ from LANs in the following ways:

- WANs cover greater distances.

- WAN speeds are slower.

- LANs are limited in size and scope; WANs are not.

- WANs can be connected on demand or can be permanently connected. LANs have permanent connections between stations.

- WANs can use public or private network transports. LANs primarily use private network transports.

The Internet is actually a specific type of WAN. It is a collection of networks that are interconnected and is therefore technically an *internetwork*. (*Internet* is short for the word *internetwork*.)

A WAN can be centralized or distributed. A *centralized WAN* consists of a central computer (at a central site) to which other computers and dumb terminals connect. The Internet, on the other hand, consists of many interconnected computers in many locations. Thus, it is a *distributed WAN*.

Network Hardware Components

Networks are made up of many entities, both hardware and software. Each hardware device on the network has a different function to perform. In this section, you will learn about some of these devices and the specific functions they perform.

Understanding Workstations

In the classic sense, a workstation is a powerful computer used for drafting or other math-intensive applications. The term is also applied to a computer that has multiple *central processing units (CPUs)* that are available to users. In the network environment, the term *workstation* normally refers to any computer connected to the network and used by a user to do work.

It is important to distinguish between workstations and clients. A client is any network entity that can request resources of the network; a workstation is a computer that can request resources. Workstations can be clients, but not all clients are workstations. For example, a printer can request resources from the network, but it is a client, not a workstation.

Understanding Servers

In the truest sense, a server does exactly what its name implies: it provides resources to the clients on the network ("serves" them, in other words). Servers are typically powerful computers that run the software that controls and maintains the network. This software is known as the *network operating system*, which you will learn about later in this chapter.

Servers are often specialized for a single purpose. This is not to say that a single server can't do many jobs, but more often than not, you'll get better performance if you dedicate a server to a single task. Here are some examples of servers that are dedicated to a single task:

File server   Holds and distributes files.

Print server   Controls and manages one or more printers for the network.

Proxy server   Performs a function on behalf of other computers. Proxy means "on behalf of."

Application server   Hosts a network application.

Web server   Holds and delivers Web pages and other Web content and uses the Hypertext Transfer Protocol (HTTP) to deliver them.

Mail server   Hosts and delivers e-mail. It is the electronic equivalent of a post office.

Fax server   Sends and receives faxes (via a special fax board) for the entire network without the need for paper.

Remote access server   Hosts modems for inbound requests to connect to the network. Remote access servers provide remote users (working at home or on the road) with a connection to the network.

Telephony server   Functions as a "smart" answering machine for the network. It can also perform call center and call routing functions.

Notice that each server type's name consists of the type of service the server provides (remote access, for example) followed by the word *server*, which, as you remember, means to serve.

Regardless of the specific role(s) each server plays, they all (should) have the following in common:

- Hardware and/or software for data integrity (such as backup hardware and software)

- The ability to support a large number of clients

Physical resources, such as hard drive space and memory, must be greater in a server than in a workstation because the server needs to provide services to many clients. Also, a server should be located in a physically secure area. Figure 1.2 shows a sample network that includes both workstations and servers. Note that there are more workstations than servers because a few servers can serve network resources to hundreds of users simultaneously.

WARNING   If the physical access to a server is not controlled, you don't have security. Use this guideline: if anybody can touch it, it isn't secure. The value of the company data far exceeds the investment in computer hardware and software.

FIGURE 1.2 A sample network including servers and workstations

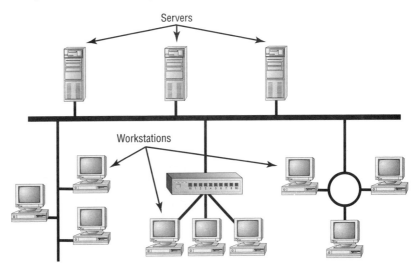

 Specific types of Internet servers will be discussed in more detail in Chapter 4.

The Network Interface Card (NIC)

The *network interface card (NIC)*, as its name suggests, is the device in your computer that connects (interfaces) your computer to the network. This device provides the physical, electrical, and electronic connections to the network media. It is responsible for converting the information your computer needs to send to the network into the special electrical signals for the type of network technology your network uses. Also occasionally called a *network adapter*, a NIC is either an expansion card (the most popular implementation) or built into the motherboard of the computer. Figure 1.3 shows a sample NIC.

FIGURE 1.3 A sample NIC

In most cases, a NIC must be added to the computer. It is usually installed into some kind of *expansion slot* on the computer's motherboard. In some notebook computers, NIC adapters can be connected to the printer port or through a built-in PC card slot.

In order to be used on a network, the NIC must have at least one protocol bound to it within the operating system. *Binding* a protocol means to logically associate a particular protocol with that instance of a NIC within an operating system so that the OS can communicate with the rest of the network using that protocol.

The important thing to remember when buying a NIC for your computer is to buy one that not only matches the bus type in your computer, but also matches the type of network you have. It sounds rather obvious, but you can't get a Token Ring card to communicate on an Ethernet network, no matter how hard you try. It just won't work because a Token Ring NIC wasn't designed to work on an Ethernet network. The electrical signals are in a completely different format.

One other thing to remember about NIC cards: All NIC cards contain a "burned-in" address (sometimes known as the hardware address, or MAC address) from the manufacturer. This address is used at the header of a packet to identify a node on the network. This address, in most NICs, cannot be changed.

Network Cables

Although it is possible to use several forms of wireless networking, such as radio and infrared, most networks communicate via some sort of cable. Although the i-Net+ exam doesn't test you on cabling technologies, it is important that we at least make an attempt to discuss network cabling because, without cabling, the network has no pathway to transmit data. In this section, we'll look at three types of cables commonly found in LANs:

- Coaxial
- Twisted-pair
- Fiber-optic

Coaxial Cable

Coaxial cable (or coax) contains a center conductor made of copper and surrounded by a plastic jacket, with a braided shield over the jacket (as shown in Figure 1.4). A plastic such as either PVC or Teflon covers this metal shield. The Teflon-type covering is frequently referred to as a *plenum-rated* coating. That simply means that the coating does not produce toxic gas when burned and is rated for use in air plenums that carry breathable air. This type of cable is more expensive but may be mandated by electrical code whenever cable is hidden in walls or ceilings.

FIGURE 1.4 Construction of a coaxial cable

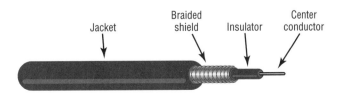

Plenum rating applies to all types of cabling.

Coaxial cable is available in different specifications that are rated according to the *RG* Type system. Different cables have different specifications and, therefore, different RG grading designations (according to the U.S. military specification MIL-C-17). Distance and cost are considerations when selecting coax cable. The thicker the copper, the farther a signal can travel—and with that comes higher costs and a less-flexible cable.

There are two main categories of coaxial cable, Thick Ethernet (or *thicknet*) and Thin Ethernet (or *thinnet*). The primary difference between the two is the diameter of the cable and the distance they can carry a signal in a single segment. Thinnet coaxial can carry a signal 185 meters in a single segment, and thicknet can carry a signal 500 meters in a single segment. Thicknet cable has approximately the same diameter as a small garden hose and is difficult to bend. Thinnet cable, on the other hand, has approximately the same diameter as a pencil, is much more flexible, and thus easier to install. Of the two, thinnet is much more common in newer installations.

The main consideration with the installation of coaxial cable is the phenomenon of signal bounce. With coaxial cable, the signal travels up and down the entire length of the wire. When the signal reaches the end of the wire, the electrical change from copper to air prevents the conversation from simply falling out the end. So the signal bounces back down the wire it just traversed. This creates an echo, just as if you were yelling into a canyon. These additional signals on the wire make communication impossible. To prevent this, you must place a *terminator* on each end of the wire to absorb the unwanted echo.

Proper termination requires that one terminator be connected to a ground. Connecting both terminators to a ground can create a *ground loop*, which can produce all kinds of bizarre, ghostlike activity, for example, a network share that appears and disappears.

Coaxial cable primarily uses BNC connectors. BNC has many definitions in the computer world. Some think British Naval Connector, citing its origins. Others would say Bayonet Nut Connector, after its function. Still others would say Bayonet Neill Concelman, after its authors. Suffice it to say, it's just easier to call it a BNC connector and know that it's used on 10Base-2 Ethernet connections to RG-58 cable.

Twisted-Pair Cable

Twisted-pair cable consists of multiple, individually insulated wires that are twisted together in pairs. Sometimes a metallic shield is placed around the twisted pairs, hence the name *shielded twisted-pair (STP)*. (You might see this type of cabling in Token Ring installations.) More commonly, you see cable with no outer shielding, called *unshielded twisted-pair (UTP)*. UTP is commonly used in 10BaseT, star-wired networks.

The wires in twisted-pair cable are twisted to minimize electromagnetic interference. When electromagnetic signals are conducted on copper wires that are in close proximity (such as inside a cable), some electromagnetic interference occurs. In cabling parlance, this interference is called *crosstalk*. Twisting two wires together as a pair minimizes such interference and also provides some protection against interference from outside sources. This cable type is the most common today. It is popular for several reasons:

- It's cheaper than other types of cabling.

- It's easy to work with.

- It permits transmission rates considered impossible 10 years ago.

UTP cable, the more common type of twisted-pair cable, is rated in the following categories:

Category 1   Two twisted-pair (4 wires). Voice grade (not rated for data communications). This is the oldest category of UTP and it is frequently referred to as *POTS*, or *Plain Old Telephone Service*. Before 1983, this was the standard cable used throughout the North American telephone system. POTS cable still exists in parts of the Public Switched Telephone Network (PSTN).

Category 2   Four twisted-pair (8 wires). Suitable for up to 4Mbps.

Category 3   Four twisted-pair (8 wires), with three twists per foot. Acceptable for 10Mbps. A popular cable choice for a long time.

Category 4   Four twisted-pair (8 wires) and rated for 16Mbps.

Category 5   Four twisted-pair (8 wires) and rated for 100Mbps.

Category 6   Four twisted-pair (8 wires) and rated for 1000Mbps. (Became a standard in December 1998.)

Frequently, you will hear *Category* shortened to *Cat*. Today, any cable that you install should be a minimum of Cat 5. We say "a minimum" because some cable is now certified to carry a bandwidth signal of 350MHz or beyond. This allows unshielded twisted-pair cables to reach a speed of 1Gbps, which is fast enough to carry broadcast-quality video over a network.

UTP cables use RJ (Registered Jack) connectors rather than BNC connectors. The connector used with UTP cable is called RJ-45, which is similar to the RJ-11 connector used on most telephone cables, except RJ-45 is larger. The RJ-11 has 4 wires, or 2 pair, and the network connector RJ-45 has 4 pair, or 8 wires.

Signaling Methods

How much of a cable's available bandwidth (overall capacity, such as 10Mbps) is used by each signal depends on whether the signaling method is baseband or broadband. Baseband uses the entire bandwidth of the cable for each signal (using one channel). It is typically used with digital signaling.

In broadband, multiple signals can be transmitted on the same cable simultaneously by means of frequency division multiplexing (FDM). *Multiplexing* is dividing a single medium into multiple channels. With FDM, the cable's bandwidth is divided into separate channels (or frequencies), and multiple signals can traverse the cable on these frequencies simultaneously. FDM is typically used for analog transmissions. Another method, time division multiplexing (TDM), can also be used to further divide each individual FDM frequency into individual time slots. Additionally, TDM can be used on baseband systems.

Fiber-Optic Cable

If your data runs are measured in kilometers, or if you have gigabits of data to move each second, fiber-optic is your cable of choice because copper cannot reach more than 500 meters (around 1600 feet—that's six football fields to you and me) without electronics regenerating the signal. Additionally, fiber-optic is the only cabling technology that can support the high data transfer speeds that the backbone of the Internet requires. You may also want to opt for fiber-optic cable if an installation requires high security because it does not create a readable magnetic field. The most common use of fiber-optic cable these days is for high-speed telephone lines.

Ethernet running at 10Mbps over fiber-optic cable is normally designated 10BaseF; the 100Mbps version of this implementation is 100BaseFX.

Although fiber-optic cable may sound like the solution to many problems, it has pros and cons just as the other cable types.

The pros are as follows:

- It's completely immune to EMI or RFI.

- It can transmit up to 4 kilometers.

Here are the cons:

- It's difficult to install.

- It requires a bigger investment in installation and materials.

Fiber-optic technology was initially very expensive and difficult to work with, but it is now being installed in more and more places. Some companies with high bandwidth requirements plan to bring fiber-optic speeds to the desktop.

The Hub

After the NIC, a hub is probably the next most common device found on networks today. A *hub* (also called a *concentrator*) serves as a central connection point for several network devices. At its basic level, a hub simply repeats everything it receives on one port to all the other ports on the hub, thus providing a communication pathway for all stations connected to it. Figure 1.5 shows an example of a hub.

FIGURE 1.5 A standard hub

Hubs are found on every twisted-pair Ethernet network, including those found at ISPs. Hubs are used to connect multiple network devices together. ISPs may have several Internet servers connected to a hub, which is in turn connected to the ISP's Internet connection, allowing the servers to communicate with each other as well as with the Internet.

There are many classifications of hubs, but two of the most important are active and passive:

- An active hub is electrically powered and actually amplifies and cleans up the signal it receives, thus doubling the effective segment distance limitation for the specific topology (for example, extending an Ethernet segment another 100 meters).

- A passive hub typically is unpowered and makes only physical, electrical connections. Normally, the maximum segment distance of a particular topology is shortened because the hub takes some power away from the signal strength in order to do its job.

The Switch

In the past few years, the *switching hub* has received a lot of attention as a replacement for the standard hub. The switching hub is more intelligent than a standard hub in that it can actually understand some of the traffic that passes through it. A switching hub (or *switch* for short) listens to all the stations connected to it and records their network cards' hardware addresses (see Figure 1.6). Then, when one station on a switch wants to send data to a station on the same switch, the data gets sent directly from the sender to the receiver. This is different from the way hubs operate. Hubs, if you will remember, don't care what stations are connected and simply repeat anything they receive on one port out to all the other ports. Because of this difference, there is much less overhead on the transmissions and the full bandwidth of the network can be used between sender and receiver.

Switches have received a lot of attention because of this ability. If a server and several workstations were connected to the same 100Mbps Ethernet switch, each workstation would need a dedicated 100Mbps channel to the server, and there would never be any collisions.

FIGURE 1.6   A switch builds a table of all addresses of all connected stations.

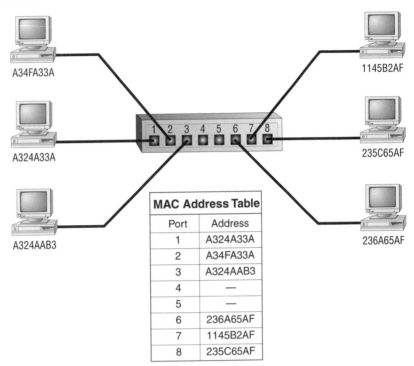

MAC Address Table	
Port	Address
1	A324A33A
2	A34FA33A
3	A324AAB3
4	—
5	—
6	236A65AF
7	1145B2AF
8	235C65AF

The Bridge

A bridge is a network device, operating at the Data Link layer of the Open Systems Interconnection (OSI) model, that logically separates a single network into two segments but lets the two segments appear to be one network to connected workstations. The primary use for a bridge is to keep traffic meant for stations on one side on that side of the bridge and not let it pass to the other side. For example, if you have a group of workstations that constantly exchange data on the same network segment as a group of workstations that don't use the network much, the busy group will slow down the performance of the network for the other users. If you put in a bridge to separate the two groups, only traffic destined for a workstation on the other side of the bridge will pass to the other side. All other traffic stays local. Figure 1.7 shows a network before and after bridging. Notice how the network has been divided into two segments; traffic generated on one side of a bridge will never cross the bridge unless a transmission has a destination address on the opposite side of the bridge.

FIGURE 1.7 A sample network before and after bridging

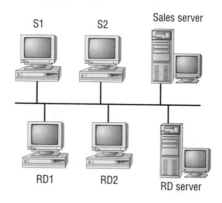

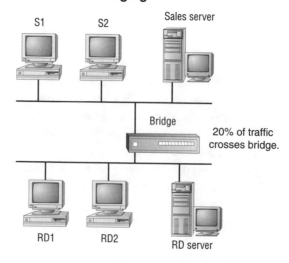

The Router

Routers play a major part in the Internet. As a matter of fact, the structure of the Internet is made up of two major items: routers and phone connections (phone connections are discussed later in this chapter). A *router* is a network device that connects multiple, often dissimilar, network segments into an internetwork. The router, once connected, can make intelligent decisions about how best to get network data to its destination based on network performance data that it gathers from the network itself. Because the router is somewhat intelligent, it is much more complex and thus more expensive than other types of network connectivity devices.

Router Ports

A router is not much to look at. Most routers have metal cases and are roughly 19 inches wide, approximately 14 inches deep, and anywhere from 1.5 inches high to 2 feet high with the more complex models. A typical router has multiple *ports*, or connection points, so that it can connect to all kinds of different network segments and route traffic between them. But at the bare minimum, most routers have at least three ports, and each has a different use.

Each port connects to a different device. For example, the most common port found on a router (there may be many of these ports) is a high-speed serial port (usually labeled something like WAN 0 or Serial 0). This port usually connects to either a modem bank or a WAN connection device like a Channel Service Unit /Data Service Unit (CSU/DSU), which is used to connect a router to a T1 phone line, discussed later in this chapter.

The second type of port is the port that connects the router to the LAN. It is usually an Ethernet port that you would connect to a hub so that the router could communicate with the rest of the LAN. It is usually labeled something like LAN 0 or Eth0 (for an Ethernet router).

The third type of port that some routers have is what is called an *out-of-band management port*. This port is a serial port (that most often uses an RJ-45 connector) that you connect to a terminal or PC running terminal software so you can configure the router. Some routers forgo this port in favor of in-band management, meaning that you run the management software on a PC connected to the network and configure the router over the network. Some routers have one or the other, but many high-end routers have both to allow you the most flexibility in configuration.

Figure 1.8 shows an example of a router and some of the most common items found on routers today. Note that the router shown in Figure 1.8 has two serial ports, a LAN port, and an out-of-band management port.

FIGURE 1.8 A sample router

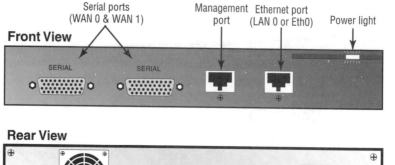

Router Use on the Internet

As mentioned, the Internet is a web of interconnected routers. An ISP's LAN is connected to a router, which is connected by some kind of leased telephone connection to the router at the ISP's ISP (called an *upstream provider*). That ISP is connected to another ISP, and so on. Routers are also capable of providing multiple, redundant links between two routers. If one connection fails, the router will send all traffic over the other connection.

In addition to providing LAN-to-Internet connectivity, a router can provide a way for dial-up clients to connect to the Internet. When you connect your home computer to the Internet via a modem, your modem is dialing another modem attached to a router of some kind. The router then routes the requests from the connected computer to the Internet and routes the associated responses back to the original requesting computer.

Figure 1.9 shows a sample router with two serial ports and one LAN port and how it might be used in an ISP. Note what devices are connected to each port. Note that the modems that customers will dial in to and the WAN connections are connected to a router's serial port (because they are serial devices) and the LAN port connects to the rest of the LAN.

FIGURE 1.9   A sample router and how it might be used in an ISP

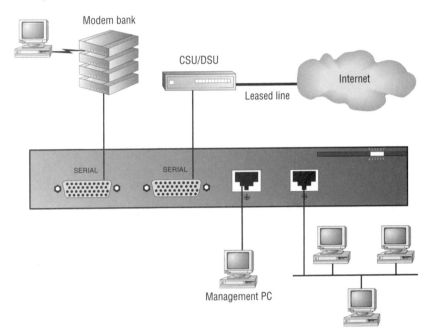

The Firewall

Networks that are connected to the Internet are subject to possible attacks from outside malicious entities located elsewhere on the Internet. To protect a network against attacks, a device called a firewall is employed. *Firewalls* reside between a company's LAN and the Internet and monitor all traffic going into and out of the network. Any suspicious or unwanted activity is monitored and, if necessary, quelled. Firewalls are usually combinations of hardware and software with multiple NICs (one for the Internet side, another for the LAN side, and possibly a third for a DMZ, discussed in a moment). Some firewalls are stand-alone hardware devices; others consist of special software that turns the server computer on which it runs into a firewall. Both types can be generalized as firewalls. The major difference between the two is that the latter may run a commercially available NOS, like NT, NetWare, or Unix, whereas the former is running its own highly specialized operating system.

Most firewalls in use today implement a feature called a *demilitarized zone (DMZ)*, which is a network segment that is neither public nor local, but halfway between. People outside your network primarily access your Web servers, FTP servers, and mail-relay servers. Because hackers tend to go after these servers first, place them in the DMZ. A standard DMZ setup has three network cards in the firewall computer. The first goes to the Internet. The second goes to the network segment where the aforementioned servers are located, the DMZ. The third connects to your intranet.

When hackers break into the DMZ, they can see only public information. If they break into a server, they are breaking into a server that holds only public information. Thus, the entire corporate network is not compromised. In addition, no e-mail messages are vulnerable; only the relay server can be accessed. All actual messages are stored and viewed on e-mail servers inside the network. As you can see in Figure 1.10, the e-mail router, the FTP server, and the Web server are all in the DMZ, and all critical servers are inside the firewall.

FIGURE 1.10   A firewall with a DMZ

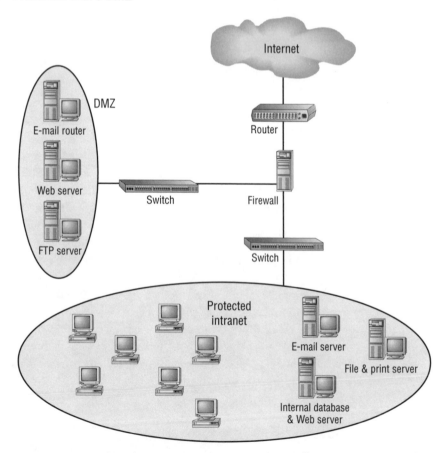

The Modem

The device most commonly used to connect computers over a public analog phone line is a *modem* (a contraction of *mod*ulator/*dem*odulator). A modem changes digital signals from the computer into analog signals that can be transmitted over phone lines and other analog media. On the receiving end, the modem changes the analog signals back to digital signals.

Modems change the digital ones and zeros into analog signals. The pattern of these analog signals encodes the data for transmission to the receiving computer. The receiving modem then takes the analog signals and turns them back into ones and zeros. Using this method, which is slower than completely digital transmissions, data can travel over longer distances with fewer errors.

A modem can be either internal or external. The key difference between the two is the amount of configuration required. You must configure internal modems with an IRQ and an I/O address as well as a virtual COM port address to ensure that they function properly. External modems simply hook to a serial port and don't require nearly as much configuration.

In addition to being either internal or external, some modems can connect either by using the telephone system or through your local cable TV cable. Analog telephone modems are the most common, but in larger metropolitan areas, cable modems are becoming more popular because they offer higher speed at a lower price. This is attractive because people will always pay less for more bandwidth.

For information on how to set up and configure a modem, see Chapter 6.

Internet Gateways

There are a couple of definitions for the term *gateway*. A gateway, in the classical sense, is any combination of hardware and software that translates one protocol or technology into another. The best example of this is an e-mail gateway. There are different types of e-mail systems, including Simple Mail Transfer Protocol (SMTP), Exchange, GroupWise, and others. When you want to connect a proprietary e-mail system (like MS Exchange or Novell GroupWise) to the Internet, you will need to use an e-mail gateway that translates the native e-mail system's mail into Internet (SMTP) mail format. When a message is sent to the Internet, the mail system will send it first to the e-mail gateway, which will translate the mail to SMTP format and then send it on to the Internet. Figure 1.11 shows how an e-mail gateway is used. Notice how the e-mail message is translated from GroupWise format to SMTP format.

FIGURE   1.11   Example of how gateways work

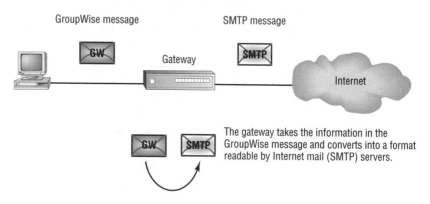

The other popular definition of a gateway is used when configuring the TCP/IP protocol (discussed in Chapter 3) on a network. In TCP/IP parlance, a gateway is another name for a router. When setting up TCP/IP on a workstation, you may have to configure a default gateway. A default gateway is the router your workstation will send all TCP/IP traffic to when the workstation can't determine the destination IP address.

A router is acting as a gateway in the sense of protocol conversion as well. For example, if your Ethernet 10BaseT network is connected to the Internet over a packet-switched Frame Relay line, you send an Ethernet packet to the router, which then encapsulates the Ethernet packet into a format the Frame Relay data link can understand. In this sense, a router does act as a gateway, performing the conversion of the Ethernet protocol to the packet-switching protocol. That is why the first routers were called gateways, and the "default gateway" configuration for IP clients has remained.

Network Software Components

In addition to all the hardware components, networks use some software components to tie together the functions of the different hardware components. Each software component has a different function on the network. In this section, you will learn about some of the software often found on a network. The most important network software components that you'll learn about include:

- Network operating system (NOS)

- Protocols

Each software component runs on a computer and provides the network with some service.

Network Operating System (NOS)

Every network today uses some form of software to manage the resources of the network. This software runs on the servers and is called a *network operating system* (or NOS, for short). NOSes are, first and foremost, computer operating systems, which means they manage and control the functions of the computer they are running on. NOSes are more complex than computer operating systems because they manage and control the functions of the network as well. A NOS gives a network its "soul" because each NOS works a bit differently. Different NOSes will need to be administered differently.

The three most popular network operating systems that you will need to know about are:

- Microsoft Windows NT/Windows 2000

- Novell NetWare

- Unix

In the following sections, you will learn background information on each NOS, its current version, its applicability to the Internet/its strength as a NOS for an Internet server, and its system requirements.

Microsoft Windows NT

There has been a buzz in the computer industry as of late about Windows NT, produced by Microsoft Corporation. Everyone's asking, "Should I be installing it?" With the same graphical interface as other versions of Windows and simple administration possible from the server console, it is a force to be reckoned with. Microsoft has put its significant marketing muscle behind it, and Windows NT has become a viable alternative in the network operating system market, previously dominated by Novell NetWare and the various flavors of Unix.

As this book is being written, Windows NT 4 is the current version of Windows NT, but Windows 2000 is scheduled to be released very soon (and may have been released by the time you are reading this book). Windows 2000 is the next generation of Windows and is designed to eventually replace both Windows 95/98 and Windows NT. Windows 2000 is the biggest release of Windows to date and has the most features, including a new directory service and Plug-and-Play support.

For more information on Windows NT, visit Microsoft's Web site at www.microsoft.com.

Microsoft's Windows NT Server has become the predominant general-purpose server for the industry. Its versatility and familiar graphical user interface (it's the same as Windows 95/98 in NT 4 and 2000) belie its complexity. Using TCP/IP and other protocols, Windows NT can communicate and be integrated with NetWare and Unix servers. Additionally, it is the preferred NOS for the intranet and Internet services of small companies because it's easy to set up and manage for Internet services. Again, this ease comes from the familiarity people have with the client OS, Windows 95/98. Also, Internet services can be installed during NOS setup with a few mouse-clicks and a minimal amount of configuration. The only downside to Windows NT is that it's sometimes unstable and it has much larger hardware requirements than the other NOSes discussed in this chapter (as listed in Table 1.1).

TABLE 1.1 Windows NT Server 4 Hardware Requirements

Hardware	Minimum	Recommended
Processor	Intel 80486 or higher (I386 architecture) or a supported RISC processor (MIPS R4x00, Alpha AXP, or PowerPC)	Pentium 90MHz or higher (the faster the better)
Display	VGA	SVGA
Hard disk space	120MB free	300MB free
Memory	16MB	32MB or greater
Network card	At least one that matches the topology of your network	At least one that matches the topology of your network
CD-ROM	None	8x or greater
Mouse	Required	Required

Novell NetWare

NetWare, made by Novell, Inc., was the first NOS developed specifically for use with PC networks. It was introduced in the late '80s and quickly became the software people chose to run their networks. NetWare is one of the more powerful network operating systems on the market today. It is almost infinitely scalable and has support for multiple client platforms. Although most companies larger than a few hundred stations are running NetWare, this NOS enjoys success in many different types of networks.

Currently, NetWare is at version 5 and includes workstation management support, Internet connectivity, Web proxy, and native TCP/IP protocol support, as well as continued support for its award-winning directory service, Novell Directory Services (NDS).

As an Internet and intranet NOS, NetWare sees use in large networks for secure intranets. In our tests, with similarly configured servers, NetWare had the best Web server performance over NT and Unix (using the included Netscape Enterprise Server for NetWare). Plus, its Web page security is integrated with Novell's directory service (NDS). Hardware requirements are listed in Table 1.2.

For more information on NetWare, check out Novell, Inc.'s Web site at
www.novell.com/.

TABLE 1.2 NetWare 5 Hardware Requirements and Recommendations

Hardware	Minimum	Recommended
Processor	Pentium	Pentium 90MHz or faster.
Display	VGA	SVGA.
Hard disk space	500MB	1GB or more.
Memory	32MB	128MB or more.
Network card	At least one	As many as required.
CD-ROM	Required	8x or greater.
Mouse	Not required	Recommended if using graphical interface. PS/2 style is the best choice.

Unix

Of the network operating systems other than Windows NT and NetWare,
the various forms of Unix are probably the most popular. It is also among the
oldest of the network operating systems. Bell Labs developed Unix, in part,
in 1969—*in part* because there are now so many iterations, commonly called
flavors, of Unix that it is almost a completely different operating system.

Although the basic architecture of all flavors is the same (32-bit kernel,
command-line based, capable of having a graphical interface, as in X Windows), the subtle details of each make one flavor better than another in a
particular situation.

Unix flavors incorporate a kernel, which constitutes the core of the operating system. The kernel can access hardware and communicate with various types of user interfaces. The two most popular user interfaces are the

command-line interface (called a *shell*) and the graphical interface (X Windows). The Unix kernel is similar to the core operating system components of Windows NT and NetWare. In Unix, the kernel is typically simple and, therefore, powerful. Additionally, the kernel can be recompiled to include support for more devices. As a matter of fact, some flavors include the source code so that you can create your own flavor of Unix.

As an Internet platform, Unix has many advantages, mainly because the Internet was first and foremost a Unix-based network. Many services available for the Internet (like Usenet news) work best on the Unix platform because these technologies were first developed on Unix. Additionally, Unix is powerful enough to scale to service hundreds of thousands of Web requests per second. Many of the most popular Web sites run on Unix.

Each flavor of Unix has widely varied hardware requirements. Some flavors can run on any processor/hardware combination. Others can only run on certain combinations. As an example, hardware requirements for the common PC-based Unix flavor Red Hat Linux 6 are covered in Table 1.3. If you need to install any flavor of Unix onto a computer, check the software's packaging or documentation for its respective hardware requirements.

Unix hardware requirements vary from vendor to vendor. As such, they are not currently tested for in the exam.

TABLE 1.3 Red Hat 6 Linux Hardware Requirements

Hardware	Minimum	Recommended
Processor	Intel 80486 or higher (I386 architecture), 680x0, or a supported RISC processor (MIPS, AP1000+, Alpha AXP, SPARC, or PowerPC)	Pentium 90MHz or higher (the faster the better)
Display	VGA	SVGA
Hard disk space	500MB free	1GB free

TABLE 1.3 Red Hat 6 Linux Hardware Requirements *(continued)*

Hardware	Minimum	Recommended
Memory	16MB	32MB or greater
Network card	None	At least one that matches the topology of your network

Protocols

All network entities must communicate to gain the benefits of being networked. In order to communicate, each device on the network must understand the same basic rules of that communication. For example, each node must understand a common "language" and the types of "words" to use. Not to imply that computers speak English, but they do need a set of rules to communicate. These rules are called *protocols*. Multiple protocols operating together are called a *protocol suite*. Finally, a software implementation of a protocol is called a *protocol stack*.

There is really only one protocol suite used on the Internet, the Transmission Control Protocol/Internet Protocol (TCP/IP) suite. It was developed at approximately the same time the Internet was developed. When it was being designed, its designers wanted a protocol that could reconfigure itself around possible breaks in the communication channel. Today, TCP/IP is almost ubiquitous because almost every operating system includes a TCP/IP protocol stack so that the operating system can communicate with the Internet. That feature, along with its relatively decent performance, makes TCP/IP a very popular protocol. We'll discuss TCP/IP in more in detail in Chapter 3.

Other Protocols

In addition to TCP/IP, there are other protocols available for use on LANs. The protocol suite Internetwork Packet eXchange/Sequenced Packet eXchange (IPX/SPX), developed by Novell for use with NetWare, is probably the second most popular protocol. It is used with both NetWare and Windows NT and is a popular choice because of its ease of configuration. Some other protocol suites you may encounter are the NetBIOS Enhanced User Interface (NetBEUI), DEC Networking (DECNet), and Systems Network Architecture (SNA) protocols, but these see much more limited use in LANs today when compared to TCP/IP and IPX/SPX.

Combination Components

Some network devices don't fit well into any category. They perform several special Internet access and performance functions without any kind of standard NOS. These devices are optimized such that they do one particular operation and do it very efficiently and very quickly. The following are two examples of combination components:

- Internet-in-a-box

- Cache-in-a-box

In the following sections, you will learn about the various combination components available; a basic description of how each one works and common applications for each one are included.

Internet-in-a-Box

With its exponential growth in the last few years, many more people are getting on the Internet and it is becoming less convenient to access it with a modem. Any company that has a network already in place can theoretically give everyone on that network Internet access by directly connecting the LAN to the Internet using a router and some kind of dedicated point-to-point or public switched connection (discussed later). The need for a faster (greater than 56Kbps), multiuser connection at an inexpensive price has arisen.

To fill this need, some router and Internet access companies (like Bay, Cisco, and 3Com) have developed "Internet-in-a-box" devices that provide Internet access to an entire network over a single Internet connection. These devices are typically "black boxes" that have a single phone line connection and a single network connection. Installation is very simple. Hook the LAN to the LAN port, hook a phone line to the phone port, and configure the box using an included configuration software package. Obviously, there is a little more to it than that, but it is still very simple. Once configured, the device will provide Internet access for everyone connected to the network.

These boxes are available with a variety of connection methods, including regular phone modem, ISDN, DSL, and T1 connections. However, most only include one connection method and can only support a limited number of users (usually fewer than 20). Any more than that would require a true router with a CSU/DSU or modem combination that can support higher throughput and a larger number of users. Figure 1.12 shows a network configured with one of these devices. The Internet-in-a-box provides a single point of access to the Internet for this network.

FIGURE 1.12 Internet connection with an Internet-in-a-box device

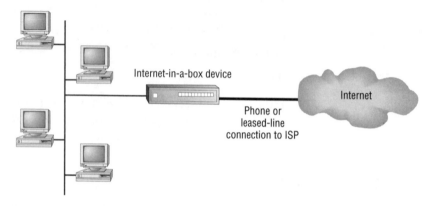

Cache-in-a-Box

One other "in-a-box" technology that is catching on is "cache-in-a-box." A cache-in-a-box is a "black box" that you plug into your network to increase Internet surfing by caching portions of frequently accessed Web sites. Internet caching systems are used to increase Internet access performance. These "preconfigured caching systems" are just hardwired versions of caching servers. Caching servers work by keeping track of every Web site that is visited and caching portions of them. The next time someone on the same network visits that same Web site, the response to the request for that Web page comes from the cache located on the local network, not from the actual Internet Web server that is hosting it. The performance benefit is realized because the cached entries are delivered at LAN speeds (10–100Mbps) and are coming from a local server (not one that is located across several routed links). Figure 1.13 illustrates this process.

FIGURE 1.13 Internet requests with and without caching

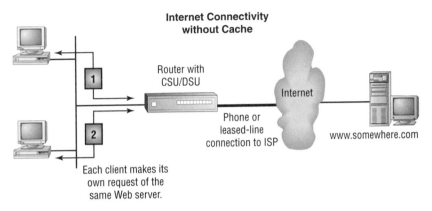

Internet Connectivity without Cache

Router with CSU/DSU

Internet

Phone or leased-line connection to ISP

www.somewhere.com

Each client makes its own request of the same Web server.

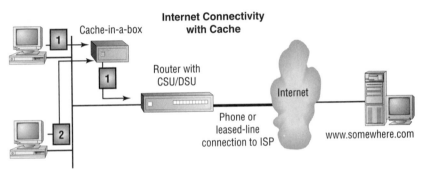

Internet Connectivity with Cache

Cache-in-a-box

Router with CSU/DSU

Internet

Phone or leased-line connection to ISP

www.somewhere.com

All stations send their Web requests to the cache machine. The first request for a Web page causes the cache to retrieve it. Subsequent requests for the the same page are fulfilled by the cache, so there is no need to retrieve it from the Internet.

Refer to Chapter 9 for information on caching implementations.

This technology has become so important and popular that some vendors are selling preconfigured cache boxes. Again, the benefit to these caches is performance and ease of setup. Basically, you plug the cache box into your network, give it a TCP/IP address, configure it using the included software, and configure all Web clients to use it. Generally speaking, these "caches-in-a-box" include high-powered processors and are designed to dedicate all their resources to caching Internet content.

Compaq's ICS (based on Novell's Internet Caching System) is one example of a cache-in-the-box.

Local Area Network Link Types

Local area networks (LANs) have many ways of delivering data from point A to point B. These "link types" include specifications that dictate how the stations will transmit their data, how the data will travel on the network, and how much data can be transmitted. The majority of networks installed today (including the ones at ISPs) use these link types. There are two popular LAN link types you will see on almost every network:

- Ethernet

- Token Ring

Most servers and workstations connect using one of these link types.

Ethernet

Ethernet, the *most* popular network specification, was originally the brain-child of Xerox Corporation. Introduced in 1976, it quickly became the network of choice for small LANs. The Unix market was the first to embrace this easy-to-install network.

Ethernet uses the CSMA/CD (Carrier Sense Multiple Access with Collision Detection) media access method, which means that only one workstation can send data across the network at a time. It functions much like the old party line telephone systems used in rural areas. If you wanted to use the telephone, you picked up the line and listened to see if anyone was already using it. If you heard someone on the line, you didn't try to dial or speak; you simply hung up and waited a while before you picked up the phone to listen again.

If you picked up the phone and heard a dial tone, you knew the line was free. You and your phone system operated by *carrier sense*. You sensed the dial tone or carrier, and if it was present, you used the phone. *Multiple access* means that more than one party shared the line. *Collision detection* means that if two people picked up the phone at the same time and dialed, they would "collide" and both would need to hang up the phone and try again. The first one back on the free line gains control and is able to make a call.

In the case of Ethernet, workstations send signals (frames) across the network. When a collision takes place, the workstations transmitting the frames stop transmitting and wait for a random period of time before retransmitting. Using the rules of this model, the workstations must *contend* for the opportunity to transmit across the network. For this reason, Ethernet is referred to as a *contention-based* system.

Current implementations of Ethernet allow for connection speeds of either 10 or 100Mbps. There are, however, standards being developed for Gigabit Ethernet (one thousand megabits per second).

Token Ring

Token Ring was developed by IBM as a robust, highly reliable network. It is more complex than Ethernet because it has self-healing properties. Token Ring is an IEEE 802.5 standard whose topology is physically a star but logically a ring. Workstations connect to the bus by means of individual cables that connect to a multistation access unit (MSAU) or controlled-access unit (CAU). MSAUs and CAUs are similar to Ethernet hubs in that they exist at the center of the star, but they are for Token Ring networks. The difference between an MSAU and a CAU is that an MSAU is a passive device that has no power plug and no intelligence, whereas a CAU has intelligence and a power plug. A CAU can perform physical network management operations.

The original Token Ring cards were 4Mbps. These were later replaced by 16Mbps cards. The 16Mbps cards are manufactured to work at 4Mbps (for compatibility), but the 4Mbps cards only run at 4Mbps. The 4Mbps version will allow only one token on the ring at a time. The 16Mbps version will allow a card to retransmit a new free token immediately after the last bit of a frame. The term for this is *early token release*.

WARNING   When configuring a Token Ring network, you must remember that all Token Ring cards must be set to either 4Mbps or 16Mbps. You cannot mix the speeds on the same segment.

In a Token Ring, although the cards attach like a star to the MSAU or CAU, they function logically in a ring. A *free token* (a small frame with a special format) is passed around the ring in one consistent direction. A node receives the token from its *nearest active upstream neighbor (NAUN)* and passes it to its *nearest active downstream neighbor (NADN)*. If a station receives a free token, it knows that it can attach data and send it on down the ring. This is called *media access*. Each station is given an equal chance to have the token and take control in order to pass data.

Each station in the ring receives the data from the busy token and repeats the data, exactly as it received it, on to the next active downstream neighbor on the ring. The addressed station (the station the data is intended for) keeps the data and passes it on up to its upper-layer protocols. It then switches 2 bits of the frame before it retransmits the information back on to the ring to indicate that it received the data. The data is sent repeatedly until it reaches the source workstation, and then the process begins again.

Each station in the ring basically acts as a repeater. The data is received and retransmitted by each node on the network until it has gone full circle. This is something like the party game called Rumor or Telephone, in which one person whispers something into one player's ear, who in turn whispers it into someone else's ear, and so on until it has gone full circle. The only difference is that, in the party game, when the person who initiated the message receives it back, it has usually undergone substantial permutations. When the originating node on the network receives the message, it is normally intact except that 2 bits have been flipped to show that the message made it to its intended destination.

Token Ring computers act as repeaters, in contrast to computers in an Ethernet network, where they are passive and therefore not relied on to pass data. This is why Token Ring networks can experience periods of latency when a computer fails and Ethernet networks will not. Also, the token-passing access method will not have collisions because only one token is on the cable at one time; Ethernet networks with CSMA/CD do have collisions.

Internet Bandwidth Link Types

An *Internet bandwidth technology* (or *link*) is the communications pathway between the various LANs that make up the Internet. These links are typically specific types of analog or digital telephone lines that carry data for a corporate WAN and for the Internet. They are leased from the telephone companies that serve the cities at the ends of the link. Hence, these WAN links are often called *leased lines*.

In addition to connecting networks together, the same WAN link technologies are also used to connect entire networks to the Internet and to provide the Internet with its structure by connecting multiple ISPs together. Wide area network links are commonly grouped into two main types:

- Point-to-point
- Public switched networks

Point-to-Point WAN Connections

Point-to-point WAN connections are WAN links that exist directly between two locations. Point-to-point connections are typically used for WAN connections between a central office and a branch office or from these locations to an ISP for Internet connectivity. These connections come in a variety of connection speeds. The main advantage of point-to-point connections to the Internet is that there is only one "hop" between the two locations, thus much less latency in each transmission, which means more data can be transmitted. The main downside is that these connections are often more expensive than their switched counterparts.

There are seven main point-to-point WAN connections in use today:

- DDS/56Kbps
- T1/E1
- T3/E3
- Asynchronous Transfer Mode (ATM)
- Integrated Services Digital Network (ISDN)
- Digital Subscriber Line (DSL)
- Synchronous Optical Network (SONET)

Each connection type differs primarily in the data throughput rates offered and in the cost. In this section, you will learn about the most popular point-to-point WAN (and Internet) connection types.

DDS/56Kbps

The Dataphone Digital Service (DDS) line from AT&T is a dedicated, point-to-point connection with throughput anywhere from 2400bps to 56Kbps. The 56Kbps digital connection is the most common, and this type of line has since obtained the moniker *56K line*. This type of line is used most often for small office connections to the central office. Some small companies may use this for their connection to their ISP for an Internet connection.

If a phone company other than AT&T provides this service, the line is known as a Digital Data Service line. The abbreviation is still DDS, however.

T1/E1

A *T1* is a 1.544Mbps digital connection that is typically carried over two pair of UTP wires. This 1.544Mbps connection is divided into 24 discrete, 64Kbps channels (called DS0 channels). Each channel can carry either voice or data. In the POTS world, T1 lines are used to bundle analog phone conversations over great distances, using much less wiring than would be needed if each pair carried only one call. This splitting into channels allows a company to combine voice and data over one T1 connection. You can also order a fractional T1 channel that uses fewer than the 24 channels of a full T1. An E1 is the same style channel, but it is a European standard and is made up of 32 64Kbps channels for a total throughput of 2.048Mbps.

A T1 connection is used very often to connect a medium-size company (50 to 250 workstations) to the Internet. It is usually cost prohibitive to have a T1/E1 connection for any company smaller than that, and it doesn't have the bandwidth that larger companies would require for high-speed WAN connections. Smaller ISPs that mainly provide residential dial-up connections may only have a T1 connection.

T3/E3

A T3 line and a T1 connection work similarly, but a T3 line carries a whopping 44.736Mbps. This is equivalent to 28 T1 channels (or a total of 672 DS0 channels). E3 is a similar technology for Europe that uses 480 channels for a total bandwidth of 34.368Mbps. Currently these services require fiber-optic cable or microwave technology. Many local ISPs have T3 connections to the major ISPs, such as SprintNet, AT&T, and MCI. Also, very large, multinational companies use T3 connections to send voice and data between their major regional offices.

Asynchronous Transfer Mode (ATM)

Of the link types we have discussed so far, Asynchronous Transfer Mode (ATM) is one link type that is used on both LANs and WANs. ATM uses cell-switching technology, which means that it works by dividing all data to be transmitted into special 53-byte packets called *cells* and sending them over a switched, permanent virtual circuit. Because all the packets are the same length, and because they are very small, ATM is a highly efficient, and very fast, set of WAN standards. It can support transmissions of voice and video in addition to data at speeds of from 1.5 to 2488Mbps. Additionally, ATM supports the ability to reserve bandwidth to ensure Quality of Service (QoS) so that voice and data transmissions won't interfere with each other. Several Internet backbone ISPs use ATM to move massive amounts of Internet data quickly.

ISDN

ISDN is a digital, point-to-point network capable of maximum transmission speeds of about 1.4Mbps, although speeds of 128Kbps are more common. Because it is capable of much higher data rates, at a fairly low cost, ISDN is becoming a viable remote Internet connection method, especially for those who work out of their homes and require high-speed Internet access but can't afford a T1 or higher. ISDN uses the same UTP wiring as your residential or business telephone wiring (also known as Plain Old Telephone Service, or POTS), but it can transmit data at much higher speeds. That's where the similarity ends, though. What makes ISDN different from a regular POTS line is how it uses the copper wiring. Instead of carrying an analog (voice) signal, it carries digital signals. This is the source of several differences.

A computer connects to an ISDN line via an ISDN terminal adapter (often incorrectly referred to as an ISDN modem). An ISDN terminal adapter is not a modem because it does not convert a digital signal to an analog signal; ISDN signals are digital.

A typical ISDN line has two types of channels. The first type of channel is called a *Bearer,* or *B,* channel, which can carry 64Kbps of data. A typical ISDN line has two B channels. One channel can be used for a voice call while the other is being used for data transmissions, and this occurs on one pair of copper wire. The second type of channel is used for call setup and link management and is known as the *Signal,* or *D,* channel (also referred to as the Delta channel). This third channel has only 16Kbps of bandwidth.

In many cases, to maximize throughput, the two Bearer channels are combined into one data connection for a total bandwidth of 128Kbps. This is known as *bonding* or *inverse multiplexing*. This still leaves the Delta channel free for signaling purposes. In rare cases, you may see user data such as e-mail on the D line. This was introduced as an additional feature of ISDN, but it hasn't caught on.

ISDN has three main advantages:

- Fast connection.

- Higher bandwidth than POTS. Bonding yields 128KB bandwidth.

- No conversion from digital to analog.

ISDN does have a few disadvantages:

- It's more expensive than POTS.

- Specialized equipment is required at the phone company and at the remote computer.

- Not all ISDN equipment can connect to each other.

DSL

Digital Subscriber Line (DSL) is a hot topic for home Internet access because it is relatively cheap (less than $100/month in most areas), fast (greater than 128Kbps), and available in most major cities in the United States. xDSL is a general category of copper access technologies that is becoming popular because it uses regular, POTS phone wires to transmit digital signals and is extremely inexpensive compared with the other digital communications methods. xDSL implementations cost hundreds instead of the thousands of dollars that you would pay for a dedicated, digital point-to-point link (such as a T1). They include Digital Subscriber Line (DSL), High Data Rate Digital Subscriber Line (HDSL), Single Line Digital Subscriber Line (SDSL), Very High Data Rate Digital Subscriber Line (VDSL), and Asymmetric Digital Subscriber Line (ADSL), which is currently the most popular. It is beyond the scope of this book to cover all the DSL types. Ask your local telephone company which method they provide.

ADSL is winning the race because it focuses on providing reasonably fast upstream transmission speeds (up to 640Kbps) and very fast downstream transmission speeds (up to 9Mbps). This makes downloading graphics, audio, video, or data files from any remote computer very fast. The majority of Web traffic, for example, is downstream. The best part is that ADSL works on a single phone line without losing the ability to use it for voice calls. This is accomplished with what is called a *splitter*, which enables the use of multiple frequencies on the POTS line.

As with ISDN, communicating via xDSL requires an interface to the PC. All xDSL configurations require a modem, called an *endpoint*, and a NIC. Often the modem and NIC are on a single expansion card.

SONET

Some of the fastest WAN connections are those employed in the Synchronous Optical Network (SONET). SONET is a high-speed, fiber-optic system that provides a standard method for transmitting digital signals over a fiber-optic network. Multiple transmission types (i.e., 64Kbs channels, T1/E1 channels) can be multiplexed together to provide SONET speeds.

SONET is able to achieve maximum transmission speeds of up to 2.488 gigabits per second. It does so by using a fixed frame size of 810 bytes. This fixed frame size makes transmissions very efficient, and thus they can carry more data.

SONET speeds are rated as channels. They are designated with an OC (Optical Character) number. The OC lines are designated OC-1 through OC-768. OC-1 channels communicate at 51.84Mbps, OC-3 channels communicate at 155.52Mbps, and OC-768 channels communicate at 40Gbps.

Public Switched Network WAN Connections

The other type of WAN link most commonly in use is the public switched network WAN connection. These connections use the telephone company's analog switched network to carry digital transmissions. Your network traffic is combined with other network traffic from other companies. Essentially, you are sharing the bandwidth with all other companies. The upside to this type of WAN connection is that it is cheaper than point-to-point connections, but because you share the bandwidth with other traffic, it isn't necessarily as efficient.

Let's take a brief look at some of the public switched network connections that companies use to connect to the Internet, including:

- Public Switched Telephone Network (PSTN)

- X.25

- Frame Relay

Public Switched Telephone Network (PSTN)

Almost everyone outside the phone companies themselves refers to PSTN (Public Switched Telephone Network) as POTS (Plain Old Telephone Service). This is the wiring system that runs from most people's houses to the rest of the world. It is the most popular method for connecting to the Internet because of its low cost, ease of installation, and simplicity. The majority of the houses in the U.S. that have Internet connections connect to their ISP via PSTN and a modem.

The phone company runs a UTP (unshielded twisted-pair) cable (called the *local loop*) from your location (called the *demarcation* point or *demarc*, for short) to a phone company building called the *Central Office*. All the pairs from all the local loop cables that are distributed throughout a small regional area come together at a central point, similar to a patch panel in a UTP-based LAN.

This centralized point has a piece of equipment called a *switch* attached. The switch functions almost exactly like the switches we mentioned earlier, in that a communications session, once initiated when the phone number of the receiver is dialed, exists until the conversation is closed. The switch can then close the connection. On one side of the switch is the neighborhood wiring. On the other side are lines that may connect to another switch or to a local set of wiring. The number of lines on the other side of the switch depends on the usage of that particular exchange. Figure 1.14 shows a PSTN system that utilizes these components.

FIGURE 1.14 A local PSTN (POTS) network

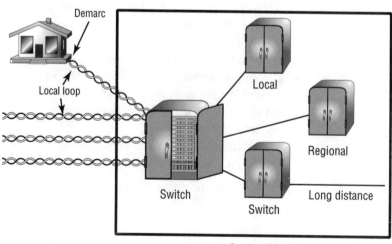

Central Office

Use caution when working with bare phone wires because they may carry a current. In POTS, the phone company uses a battery to supply power to the line, which is sometimes referred to as *self-powered*. It isn't truly self-powered; the power comes from the phone system.

POTS has many advantages, including:

- It is inexpensive to set up. Almost every home in the United States has or can have a telephone connection.

- There are no LAN cabling costs.

- Connections are available in many countries throughout the world.

POTS is the most popular remote access connection method for the Internet because only two disadvantages are associated with it: limited bandwidth and thus a limited maximum data transfer rate. At most, 64Kbps data transmissions are possible, though rarely achieved by anyone connecting from home to the Internet.

X.25

X.25 was developed by the International Telecommunications Union (ITU) in 1974 as a standard interface for WAN packet switching. It does *not* specify anything about the actual data transmission, however. It only makes specifications about the access to the WAN and just assumes that a route from sender to receiver exists. The original X.25 specification supported transmission speeds of up to 64Kbps, but the 1992 revision supports transmission speeds of up to 2Mbps. It is currently one of the most widely used WAN interfaces.

Frame Relay

Similar to X.25, *Frame Relay* is a WAN technology in which packets are transmitted by switching. Packet switching involves breaking messages into chunks at the sending router. Each packet can be sent over any number of routes on its way to its destination. The packets are then reassembled in the correct order at the receiver. Because the exact path is unknown, a cloud is used when creating a diagram to illustrate how data travels throughout the service. Figure 1.15 shows a Frame Relay WAN connecting smaller LANs.

FIGURE 1.15 A typical frame relay configuration

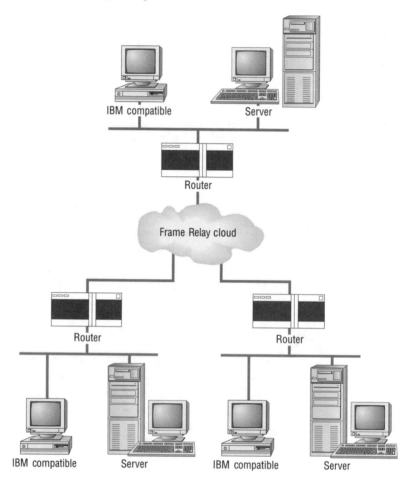

Frame Relay uses permanent virtual circuits (PVCs). PVCs allow virtual data communications circuits between sender and receiver over a packet-switched network. This ensures that all data that enters a Frame Relay cloud at one side comes out at the other over a similar connection.

The beauty of using a shared network is that sometimes you can get much better throughput than you are paying for. When signing up for one of these connections, you specify and pay for a Committed Information Rate (CIR), or in other words, a minimum bandwidth. If the total traffic on the shared network is light, you may get much faster throughput without paying for it. Frame Relay begins at the CIR speed and can reach as much as 1.544Mbps, the equivalent of a T1 line, which was discussed earlier.

However, the major downside to Frame Relay is that you share traffic with all other people within the Frame Relay cloud. If you aren't paying for a CIR, your performance can vary widely. Despite this disadvantage, Frame Relay is a popular Internet connection method because of its low cost.

Table 1.4 shows all these point-to-point connections and their respective performance, availability, and cost.

TABLE 1.4 Point-to-point WAN and Internet connection types

Connection	Max Throughput	U.S. Availability	Relative Cost
56K/DDS	56Kbps	Widely available	Low
T1/E1	1.544Mbps/ 2.048Mbps	Widely available	Medium
T3/E3	44.736Mbps/ 34.368Mbps	Widely available	High
ATM	2488Mbps	Moderately available	Very high
ISDN	Around 2Mbps	Moderately available	Low
DSL	Greater than 128Kbps	Available in larger cities, becoming more available in rural areas	Low
Frame Relay	1.544Mbps or slower	Widely available	Low
OC-1	51.84Mbps	Moderately available	Very, very high
OC-3	155.52Mbps	Moderately available	Very, very high
OC-48	2.488Gbps	Slim availability	Don't ask

Summary

In this chapter, you learned about some of some of the LAN and WAN networking technologies that apply to the business of the Internet. Because most networks are connected to the Internet these days, the concepts contained in this chapter will be valuable to you as an Internet professional. You learned the definitions of a LAN and a WAN as well as the differences between them. You also learned about some of the hardware components that exist on the network, including workstations, servers, NICs, network cables, hubs, switches, bridges, routers, firewalls, and modems. In addition to learning about the hardware components, you learned about some of the software components that work on the network to provide Internet (and other) services, including network operating systems (NOSes) and protocols. Then there are those components that don't fall easily into either category. Those components are known as combination components, and there are really only two components in this category on the i-Net+ exam, the Internet-in-a-box and the cache-in-a-box. Both components are "black boxes" you can add to your network without a large amount of configuration.

This chapter included a discussion about the link types that carry data from point A to point B on a network. LAN link types include Ethernet and Token Ring. Ethernet is the most common LAN link type. WAN link types include DDS/56Kbps, T1/E1, T3/E3, ATM, ISDN, DSL, and Frame Relay. The WAN link types can be used for connecting to the Internet and vary in speed and link cost.

You also learned about many different kinds of hardware and software connection technologies. The following list includes the most important ones to know for the i-Net+ exam:

Network interface card   Also called a network adapter or NIC, this device provides a computer with its electrical and physical connection to a network.

Various types of modems, including analog, ISDN, DSL, and cable   A modem is a device that converts the digital signals your computer uses into analog signals that can be transmitted over longer distances (typically over house phone lines). Modems can be either internal or external. Of the two types, internal modems are cheaper but require more configuration. External modems are more expensive but typically have status displays that can aid in connection troubleshooting.

Bridge   A bridge is a hardware connection device that connects two network segments into a single network. It can also divide a single network into two network segments while at the same time maintaining a unified network. Network traffic that originates on one side of a bridge for a destination on the same segment will never cross the bridge. A bridge will only pass traffic that originates on one side and is destined for a station on the other side.

Hub   This network device connects all network devices together on a twisted-pair Ethernet network. It repeats all signals it receives on one port to all other ports. This device is the central device in a star topology Ethernet network.

Router   A router is the device that connects multiple network segments into an internetwork. Routers are intelligent devices that are responsible for making routing decisions about the best path for data packets to take when traveling through an internetwork. Routers are used in ISPs to connect modem users to the Internet in addition to connecting the ISP's LAN to the Internet.

Switch   A switching hub (or *switch* for short) is a network connectivity device that listens to all the stations connected to it and records their network card's hardware addresses. Then, when one station on a switch wants to send data to a station on the same switch, the data gets sent directly from the sender to the receiver. The full bandwidth of the network can be used between sender and receiver.

Gateway   A gateway is any combination of hardware and software that translates one protocol or technology into another. The most common use of gateways on the Internet is for e-mail. *Gateway* is also another name for a router.

Network operating system   A Network Operating System (NOS) is the software that controls and manages both the server and the network. The most popular NOSes include Novell NetWare, Microsoft Windows NT, and Unix.

  - NetWare is a PC-based NOS—and the first PC-based NOS for LANs. It is a high-performance NOS with low hardware requirements

- Windows NT is an easy-to-use NOS that implements the Windows "look and feel." It is a great NOS for Internet content hosting

- Unix is the oldest NOS that is available for many hardware platforms. Linux is a PC-based flavor of Unix that has become popular as an Internet server NOS.

Firewall   Firewalls reside between a company's LAN and the Internet and monitor all traffic going into and out of the network. Any suspicious or unwanted activity is monitored and quelled, if necessary.

Internet-in-a-box   This technology allows small networks to be connected to the Internet simply. The Internet-in-a-box device has one connection that connects to the LAN and another that connects to a phone line or other Internet connection type. The box can then be configured using special software and will allow all users on the LAN access to the Internet without having to do a lot of configuration of routers, CSU/DSUs, and so on.

Cache-in-a-box   This is a "black box" that you plug into your network to increase Internet Web surfing performance by caching portions of frequently accessed Web sites. You simply plug it into your network and configure the browsers on your network to use it. Some cache boxes don't require Web browser configuration and cache all Internet traffic.

Internet link technologies   These are the links between LANs and the Internet or used as WAN connections. They are typically lines leased from the local telephone companies. Each type differs based on its speed, availability, and relative cost.

Review Questions

1. Which network hardware device connects dissimilar network topologies into an internetwork?

   A. Hub

   B. Bridge

   C. Switch

   D. Router

2. Which Internet bandwidth technology is the primary technology used on the Internet backbone?

   A. Token Ring

   B. Ethernet

   C. X.25 ✗ It's just a WAN Access Technology

   D. ATM

3. Which of the following is a standard interface for Frame Relay?

   A. X.25

   B. ISDN

   C. T1

   D. xDSL

4. Which network hardware device is required for the computer in order to connect it to a network?

   A. Bridge

   B. NIC

   C. Router

   D. Firewall

5. Which network hardware device protects a LAN against malicious attacks from the Internet?

   A. Bridge

   B. Switch

   C. NIC

   D. Firewall

6. Which of the following is the fastest possible Internet communications technology?

   A. Ethernet

   B. ATM

   C. T1

   D. T3

7. A T3 connection has a maximum bandwidth of _____ Mbps?

   A. 1.544

   B. 2.048

   C. 34.368

   D. 44.736

8. An E1 connection has a maximum bandwidth of _____ Mbps?

   A. 1.544

   B. 2.048

   C. 34.368

   D. 44.736

9. Of the following, which Internet connection type for home users is taking off and offers fairly high speed (>128Kbps) for a fairly reasonable price?

A. DSL

B. ISDN

C. Frame Relay

D. ATM

10. A T1 WAN connection has a maximum speed of _____ Mbps.

A. 1.544

B. 2.048

C. 34.368

D. 44.736

11. Which protocol is the Internet based on?

A. IPX/SPX

B. NetBEUI

C. TCP/IP

D. DECNet

12. Which network hardware device is used to segment a single network into multiple segments?

A. Hub

B. Firewall

C. NIC

D. Bridge

13. Which component of the network is responsible for providing network services to the rest of the network?

    A. Server

    B. Bridge

    C. Workstation

    D. NIC

14. What is the most widely available Internet connection method in the United States?

    A. ISDN

    B. DSL

    C. POTS

    D. X.25

15. Which network hardware device will increase your Web browsing performance?

    A. Firewall

    B. Cache

    C. Bridge

    D. Router

16. Which NOS is the oldest NOS currently in use?

    A. Unix

    B. NetWare

    C. Windows NT

    D. OS/2

17. A _____ is used in firewalls to provide a safe area for public data that is not part of the public or private networks.

    A. Firewall

    B. Internet-in-a-box

    C. DMZ

    D. Router

18. Based on speed and cost, which Internet bandwidth link type would be the best choice for a small ISP serving 100 dial-up users?

    A. 56K/DDS

    B. T1

    C. T3

    D. ATM

19. Which NOS was developed, in part, by Bell Labs and currently has several hundred different "flavors"?

    A. OS/2

    B. Windows NT

    C. NetWare

    D. Unix

20. Which network connectivity device translates one protocol or technology into another and is used to connect dissimilar network technologies?

    A. Firewall

    B. Hub

    C. Gateway

    D. DSL

Answers to Review Questions

1. **D.** Hubs, bridges, and switches connect only the same network topologies. Routers are the only devices that connect different topologies (e.g., Ethernet to Token Ring).

2. **D.** Although Token Ring and Ethernet are found in ISPs, ATM is the primary WAN technology used on the Internet backbone. X.25 is only a WAN access technology.

3. **A.** ISDN, T1, and xDSL are all Internet bandwidth technologies, whereas X.25 is the interface for Frame Relay.

4. **B.** The other devices (bridge, router, and firewall) are all different network connectivity devices, but you absolutely must have a NIC installed in a computer in order to connect the computer to a network.

5. **D.** Bridges, switches, and routers are all simply network connectivity devices. Some routers can perform packet filtering, but firewalls are designed specifically to protect a network against malicious activity from the Internet.

6. **B.** ATM has maximum speeds of 2488Mbps. Ethernet has a maximum transmission speed of 100Mbps. T1 lines are 1.544Mbps, and T3s are 44.736Mbps.

7. **D.** A T1 connection has a maximum transmission speed of 1.544Mbps. The 2.048 is E1 speed, 34.368 is E3 speed, and 44.736 is T3 speed.

8. **B.** An E1 connection communicates at 2.048Mbps. T1 connections are 1.544Mbps, E3 connections are 34.368Mbps, and T3 connections are 44.736

9. **A.** Frame Relay and ATM normally aren't for home users (unless you happen to be Bill Gates ☺). ISDN is more expensive than DSL and offers more bandwidth.

10. **A.** T1 connections have a maximum speed of 1.544Mbps. B is for E1, C is for E3, and D is for T3.

11. **C.** TCP/IP is the only protocol allowed on the Internet and was developed about the same time as the Internet.

12. D. A bridge is the only device of those listed that is used to segment a network. Hubs and NICs are only connection devices and don't divide a network. Firewalls perform security checks on network traffic but don't do any segmenting.

13. A. A server provides network services to the rest of the network. Bridges, workstations, and NICs do not. Bridges segment a network, workstations request the resources a server provides, and NICs allow a workstation to get access to a network.

14. C. Almost every home in the United States already has a PSTN (POTS) phone line. ISDN and DSL have limited availability in major metropolitan areas. X.25 isn't available in every home without additional cost.

15. B. Of the devices listed, a cache is the only device that can increase a network's Web browsing performance. All the others can actually introduce delay into Internet communications.

16. A. Although NetWare, NT, and OS/2 have been in use for some time, Unix is, in fact, the oldest.

17. C. The demilitarized zone (DMZ) is the network segment connected to a firewall where public data is placed so that it is available to both public and private networks. A, B, and D are incorrect because they are all examples of other Internet hardware and software technologies.

18. B. Because the maximum connection speed of today's modems is 56Kbps and the ISP is serving a maximum of 100 users, the maximum throughput needed is 100×56, or 5600Kbps (5.6Mbps). A 56K/DDS link would be too slow and a T3 or ATM connection would be way too fast (and probably way too expensive for a small ISP). A T1 (at 1.544Mbps) would be slower than the throughput number figured above, but it is extremely unlikely that all 100 users would be on at the same time. Plus, you can buy multiple T1s for the cost of a single T3.

19. D. The only one of these listed that was developed in any part by Bell Labs is Unix. The others were all developed by other companies, like IBM (OS/2), Novell (NetWare), and Microsoft (NT).

20. C. A gateway is the only device listed here that can connect dissimilar network technologies and perform protocol and technology translation. Firewalls and hubs are network connectivity devices, but they can't do protocol translation. DSL is actually an Internet link type.

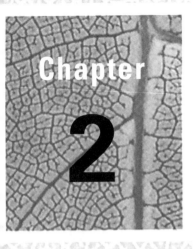

Internet Basics

i-NET+ OBJECTIVES COVERED IN THIS CHAPTER:

✓ **Describe a URL, its functions and components, different types of URLs, and use of the appropriate type of URL to access a given type of server. Content may include the following:**

- Protocol
- Address
- Port

✓ **Describe the core components of the current Internet infrastructure and how they relate to each other. Content may include the following:**

- Network access points
- Backbone

✓ **Identify problems with Internet connectivity from source to destination for various types of servers. Examples could include the following:**

- E-mail
- Slow server
- Web site

✓ **Describe Internet domain names and DNS. Content could include the following:**

- DNS entry types
- Hierarchical structure
- Role of root domain server
- Top level or original domains—edu, com, mil, net, gov, org
- Country level domains—UK

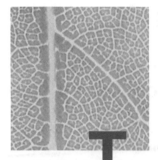

he Internet is a very complex entity. To understand the topics found in later chapters in this book, you must first understand the underlying layout and technologies of the Internet so that you have a common reference point for those discussions. In this chapter, you will learn the following:

- What the Internet is

- Internet layout

- Domain Name Services (DNS)

- Uniform Resource Locators (URLs)

- Internet communications process

Throughout this chapter, you will also learn the terminology of the devices and processes used on the Internet. Let's begin the discussion of these topics with the definition of the Internet.

What Is the Internet?

The simplest definition of the *Internet* is that it is a collection of local area networks connected together by high-speed public WAN connections. Servers on these LANs provide information to the rest of the Internet in the form of documents, images, and multimedia content. The information delivered by these servers is generally called *Internet content*. For a small fee, anyone with a computer and a modem can access the Internet and get access to this content. Figure 2.1 shows a graphical representation of the Internet.

Notice how individual users and LANs connect to Internet Service Providers (ISPs), which in turn can connect to other ISPs that connect to backbone ISPs. Backbone ISPs are ISPs with very high-speed connections between them (several hundred megabits per second). You will learn about ISPs in the sections to follow.

FIGURE 2.1 A graphical representation of the Internet

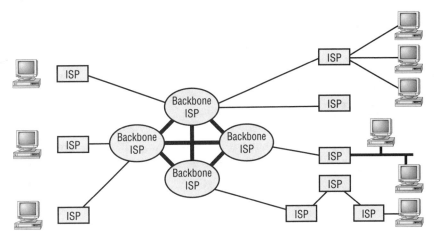

History of the Internet

The Internet started out as a project of the U.S. government's Defense Advanced Research Projects Agency (DARPA) in 1973. They wanted to design a network that could reconfigure itself around breaks and faults in case one of its nodes were taken out during a war. The architects of this network, called ARPAnet, took this into consideration and developed a suite of protocols (called TCP/IP) and a network that could do just that.

For more detailed information on TCP/IP, see Chapter 3.

Another network was developed in 1980 to connect IBM mainframes in university data centers. This network was called BITnet, and it allowed universities to communicate with one another, thus facilitating collaboration among professors at those universities with the first, primitive e-mail system.

In 1983, the Internet Architecture Board (IAB) was formed to guide the development of the TCP/IP protocol suite (the protocol used on the Internet) and to provide research data for the Internet. The IAB consists of two organizations, the Internet Engineering Task Force (IETF) and the Internet Research Task Force (IRTF). The IETF is responsible for the ongoing development of the TCP/IP protocol. When a new TCP/IP protocol is proposed, the IETF issues a Request for Comments (RFC) that details the specifications of the new protocol and how it is to be used. The IRTF, on the other hand, is responsible for researching new Internet technologies and their possible implications on the Internet as a whole.

RFCs can be found at www.ietf.org on the Internet.

In 1986, the National Science Foundation (NSF) developed NSFnet as a backbone for the now-emerging Internet. It would connect the old ARPAnet, BITnet, and a bunch of other networks together to form the Internet. At this point, the Internet became very far reaching and very powerful as thousands of people who were now connected to it could all communicate and collaborate.

The Internet Today

Since the days of the NSFnet, ARPAnet, BITnet, and all the others, Internet use has grown exponentially. No longer do only geeks and professors know about it; it has become a part of popular culture. Every television commercial ends with the company name and the address of the company's Web site so you can visit it and get even more information. One measure of a company's success is how many hits the company's Web site gets per day.

It is estimated that in September 1999, there were more than 201 million people worldwide on the Internet, and that number is estimated to double by 2001. Currently, more than 75 percent of all metropolitan areas in the United States have Internet access. Basically, any household that has a phone line can get access to the Internet (with either a local or a long distance phone call). With each passing year, Internet access technologies allow faster access to the Internet. Home access speeds are available from 33.6Kbps (modems) to 512Kbps (ISDN and DSL access). At these speeds, Internet content can include streaming audio and video.

The Layout of the Internet

Even though the Internet is a constantly evolving entity, its areas can be broken down into several basic classifications:

- Access points (ISPs)
- WAN connections
- Backbone providers

Each classification deals with a particular section of the Internet, as shown in Figure 2.2. Notice how the Internet areas connect to each other and what types of connections are used between them.

FIGURE 2.2   Layout of the Internet

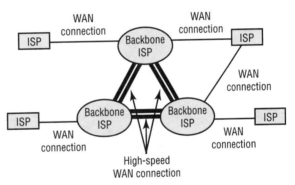

In the following sections, you will learn the details of each Internet area and the responsibilities each area has within the Internet. You will also learn which areas end users interact with and the different types of ISPs.

Access Points (ISPs)

As previously mentioned, anyone can get access to the information found on the Internet, but first they must be connected to the Internet. The Internet has often been called the "Information Superhighway." I'd actually describe it as an "Internet Tollway." To get the benefits of the "highway," you have to pay to get on. Thus, in order to get on the Internet, you have to pay the people who have set up access points to it (similar to the on-ramps of the toll high-ways). These access points are called Internet Service Providers (ISPs). An ISP has a very high-speed connection (usually capable of transmitting several megabits per second) to the Internet. The ISP then sells slower (several kilobits per second) dial-up or dedicated connections.

ISPs usually have a high-speed LAN, with a large, complex router to con-nect the LAN to the Internet. Then, on the ISP's "backbone" (as shown in Figure 2.3) are the ISP's mail, news, and Web servers, as well as the routers that provide dial-up and dedicated leased-line access to the Internet for the ISP's customers. Additionally, some ISPs sell "space" on their backbone to companies so that those companies can place their Web servers directly on the ISP's backbone for the best possible performance. This practice is called *server hosting*. In Figure 2.3, notice where the ISP's backbone is and what items connect to it within an ISP. Also notice that the backbone connects to a router that, in turn, connects the ISP to its own ISP.

FIGURE 2.3 A typical ISP setup

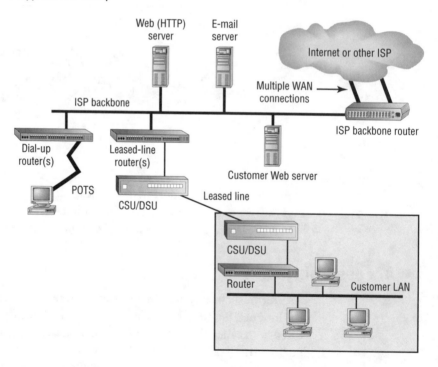

ISPs can be found in every major city in the U.S. and in almost every rural area. In Europe and the Asian countries, ISPs can be found in the larger cities. However, the Internet's reach is expanding more and more every day. Very soon it will be possible to get Internet access anywhere on (or off) Earth.

To find an ISP in your area, you can look in the Yellow Pages under "Internet providers," or, if you can get to a machine connected to the Internet, check out The List of ISPs at `http://thelist.internet.com`.

WAN Connections

If the Internet were a living entity, the ISPs would be its appendages and the WAN connections would be the arterial connections between them. A wide area network (WAN) connection is a special phone line that is leased from the local telephone company and used to carry data between two LANs. For our discussion, WAN connections connect two ISPs to provide the Internet with its structure.

WAN connection speeds range from 9600bps to hundreds of megabits per second (Mbps). These WAN connections were covered in detail in Chapter 1, but to summarize, Table 2.1 illustrates some WAN technologies and their associated speeds.

TABLE 2.1 Common WAN Connection Technologies

WAN Connection	Common Speed(s)
DDS	56Kbps
Frame Relay	56Kbps–1.544Kbps
T1	1.544Kbps
T3	44.736Mbps
ISDN	128Kbps–2Mbps
ATM	155Mbps

For more information on WAN technologies and their speeds, refer to *The Network Press Encyclopedia of Networking* by Werner Feibel (Sybex, 2000).

Backbone Providers

Although the Internet is essentially a network of ISPs, there are a few select ISPs that connect to each other with high-speed WAN connections to provide the Internet with a "backbone." These ISPs are known as *backbone providers* (as shown earlier in Figure 2.2) and connect to each other at speeds from 100Mbps to 1Gbps. The *Internet backbone* is the set of high-speed WAN connections, servers, and ISPs that provide the structure for the Internet.

Many ISPs claim to be backbone providers, but this is usually a marketing gimmick and means that they connect directly to an actual backbone provider but are not actually part of the Internet backbone. Most backbone providers are divisions of telephone companies and are called *Network Access Points (NAPs)*. Sprint and Pacific Bell are examples of NAPs. Originally, there were four major NAPs that connected the Internet. Since that time, several new NAPs have been added, like ICS and Worldcom.

Internet2: The Next Generation

The current Internet has seen many advancements, but there are even more Internet technologies are waiting to be developed, technologies such as IPv6, Quality of Service (QoS), Telemedicine, video multicasting, and many others. A number of them will improve collaboration abilities and directly benefit higher education (as did the technologies of the current Internet). For this reason, a consortium of higher education institutions have gotten together and formed the University Corporation for Advanced Internet Development (UCAID). One of UCAID's projects is *Internet2* (*I2*), the collection of next-generation Internet applications and technologies being developed for use with the Internet infrastructure in use today. Internet2 is not its own network, as some people incorrectly assume. It is only the name given to the ongoing research of these technologies and their possible applications. Just as the current Internet technologies have their roots in the collaboration efforts of education, it is the hope of the UCAID that the work done with Internet2 will increase the Internet's usability. For more information, visit UCAID at www.ucaid.edu.

Domain Name Services (DNS)

Domain Name Services (DNS) is a network service that associates alphanumeric host names with the TCP/IP address of a particular Internet host. When surfing the Web, you could refer to a host by its IP address (for example, 201.35.124.12), but it is more common to use a DNS host name (`www.sybex.com`). Internet host names are used because they are easier to remember than long, dotted-decimal IP addresses. In this section, you will learn what a domain is, how domains are organized within DNS, and the specifics of how to use DNS.

What Are Domains?

Host names are typically the name of a device that has a specific IP address, and on the Internet, they are part of what is known as a *fully qualified domain name*. A fully qualified domain name consists of a host name and a domain name.

Although you have a Social Security number and can remember it when you need it, life would be difficult if you had to remember the Social Security numbers of all your friends and associates. You might be able to remember the Social Security numbers of as many as 10 friends and relatives, but after that things would get a bit difficult. Likewise, it's easier to remember www `.microsoft.com` than it is to remember 198.105.232.6.

The process of finding the host name for any given IP address is known as *name resolution*, which can be performed in several ways, and we'll look at all of them in the next few sections. But first you need to understand Internet domains and how they are organized.

Internet Domain Organization

On the Internet, domains are arranged in a hierarchical tree structure. There are seven top-level domains currently in use:

com A commercial organization. Most companies will end up as part of this domain.

edu An educational establishment, such as a university.

gov A branch of the U.S. government.

int An international organization, such as NATO or the United Nations.

mil A branch of the U.S. military.

net A network organization.

org A nonprofit organization.

WARNING Unfortunately, the word *domain* is used in several ways, depending on the context. When the topic is the Internet, a domain refers to a collection of network host computers.

U.S. Domains

Your local ISP is probably a member of the net domain, and your company is probably part of the com domain. The gov and mil domains are reserved strictly for use by the government and the military within the United States. The com domain is by far the largest, followed by the edu domain, and well over 130 countries are represented on the Internet.

New U.S. Domains

Because the com domain is so popular, almost every company has a Web address that ends with .com. Additionally, there are no divisions in any of the domains, especially the com domain. For these reasons, the Internet Assigned Numbers Authority (IANA) has come up with some new top-level domains to further segment the U.S. Internet DNS space, for example:

firm Designed for naming businesses or firms

shop Domain for online shopping centers

web Domain for Web sites relating to information about the WWW

info Domain used for Web sites that provide some useful information to a community (like a community billboard)

arts Domain for cultural and entertainment organizations

rec Domain for completely recreational Web sites

nom Domain for an individual person's name

International Domains

In other parts of the world, the final part of a domain name represents the country in which the server is located: ca for Canada, jp for Japan, uk for Great Britain, and ru for Russia, for example. Figure 2.4 shows an example of the layout of the Internet DNS hierarchy. Notice how the com, edu, and international domains are all at the same level.

FIGURE 2.4   Internet DNS domain hierarchy

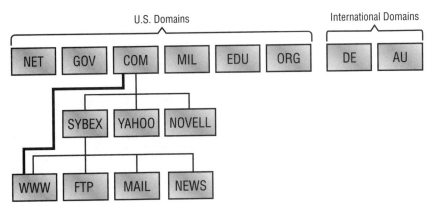

If you want to contact someone within one of these domains by e-mail, you just add that person's e-mail name to his domain name, separated by an at sign (@). For example, if you want to e-mail the president of the United States, send your e-mail to this address:

`President@whitehouse.gov`

InterNIC assigns all Internet domain names and makes sure no names are duplicated. Names are assigned on a first-come, first-served basis, but if you try to register a name that infringes on someone else's registered trademark, your use of that name will be rescinded if the trademark holder objects.

Now that we have detailed how Internet domain names work and where they came from, we can return to our discussion of name-resolution methods.

Using DNS

The abbreviation *DNS* stands for *Domain Name Services.* You use DNS to translate host names and domain names to IP addresses, and vice versa, by means of a standardized lookup table that the network administrator defines and configures. The system works just like a giant telephone directory.

Suppose you are using your browser to surf the Web and you enter the URL `http://www.microsoft.com` to go to the Microsoft home page. Your Web browser then asks the TCP/IP protocol to ask the DNS server for the IP address of `www.microsoft.com`. When your Web browser receives this address, it connects to the Microsoft Web server and downloads the home page. DNS is an essential part of any TCP/IP network, simplifying the task of remembering addresses; all you have to do is simply remember the host name and domain name.

The DNS tables that are used to resolve the host name to an IP address are composed of records. Each record is composed of a host name, a record type, and an address. There are several record types, including the address record, the mail exchange record, and the CNAME record.

The *address record*, commonly known as the *A record*, directly maps a host name to an IP address. The example below shows the address record for a host called `mail` in the `company.com` domain:

```
mail.company.com.      IN    A      204.176.47.9
```

The *mail exchange* (MX) record points to the mail exchanger for a particular host. DNS is structured so that you can actually specify several mail exchangers for one host. This feature provides a higher probability that e-mail will actually arrive at its intended destination. The mail exchangers are listed in order in the record, with a priority code that indicates the order in which the mail exchangers should be accessed by other mail delivery systems.

If the first priority doesn't respond in a given amount of time, the mail delivery system tries the second one, and so on. Here are some sample mail exchange records:

```
host.company.com.      IN    MX     10 mail.company.com.
host.company.com.      IN    MX     20 mail2.company.com.
host.company.com.      IN    MX     30 mail3.company.com.
```

In this example, if the first mail exchanger, `mail.company.com`, does not respond, the second one, `mail2.company.com`, is tried, and so on.

The *CNAME record*, or canonical name record, is also commonly known as the *alias record* and allows hosts to have more than one name. For example, your Web server has the host name www, and you want that machine also to have the name ftp so that users can easily FTP in to manage Web pages. You can accomplish this with a CNAME record. Assuming you already have an address record established for the host name www, a CNAME record adding ftp as a host name would look something like this:

```
www.company.com.      IN    A       204.176.47.2
ftp.company.com.      IN    CNAME   www.company.com.
```

When you put all these record types together in a file, its called a DNS table, and it might look like this:

```
mail.company.com.     IN    A       204.176.47.9
mail2.company.com.    IN    A       204.176.47.21
mail3.company.com.    IN    A       204.176.47.89
host.company.com.     IN    MX      10 mail.company.com.
host.company.com.     IN    MX      20 mail2.company.com
host.company.com.     IN    MX      30 mail3.company.com.
www.company.com.      IN    A       204.176.47.2
ftp.company.com.      IN    CNAME   www.company.com.
```

You can establish other types of records for specific purposes, but we won't go into those in this book. DNS can become very complex very quickly, and entire books are dedicated to the DNS system.

Obtaining Your Own Domain Name

It seems like you can't watch a television commercial these days without seeing at the bottom of the screen a domain name that matches the company name (for example, pizzahut.com for Pizza Hut, ibm.com for IBM, etc.). You may wonder how these names are obtained. It is easy and almost anyone can do it. It costs around $100.00 for a single domain name. The steps are as follows:

1. Choose a domain name (e.g., bobsroom.com).

> 2. Using your Web browser, go to www.networksolutions.com/ and use their search engine to see if the domain name you want has been taken. If the name you want is available, proceed to step 3. If not, go back to step 1 and start over.
>
> 3. Use Network Solution's Web interface to fill out your contact information as well as the hosting information for the domain. "Hosting" a domain name means that a server has been configured to tell the rest of the Internet where your domain's servers are. Your ISP can host your new domain name (providing you make arrangements beforehand) or, for a fee, Network Solutions will host it.
>
> 4. Complete the form and wait for confirmation of your domain name.
>
> That's it!

Uniform Resource Locators (URLs)

Everyone who has ever used the World Wide Web (WWW) has more than likely used a Uniform Resource Locator (URL). A URL is a standard way of referring to an Internet resource when making Internet connections and requests. You will primarily use URLs in Web clients (like Navigator and Internet Explorer) and other Internet utilities. A URL consists of several components, including:

- Protocol designation
- DNS name of host
- Path
- Resource name

For all intents and purposes, a URL is an address that tells a utility where to go on the Internet to get a resource and what protocol to use when retrieving it.

Figure 2.5 shows an example of a URL. Notice that there are different parts of the URL.

FIGURE 2.5   A sample URL

http://www.sybex.com/test/index.html

Protocol Designation

The first part of a URL that we are going to discuss is the leftmost portion (immediately to the left of the ://, as shown in Figure 2.6), the protocol designation. The *protocol designation* tells the utility you are using (in most cases, an Internet browser like Internet Explorer or Navigator) what protocol to use when connecting. Some of the most popular protocols found in URLs include:

- HTTP
- FTP
- FILE
- TELNET

FIGURE 2.6   The protocol portion of a URL

Protocol

http://www.sybex.com/test/index.html

HTTP

The HTTP protocol designation portion of a URL stands for Hypertext Transfer Protocol, which is the transport protocol used for Web content on the Internet. By placing the http:// at the start of the URL, you are indicating to the Web browser that you are making a request of a Web server and that you want to use the HTTP protocol to request and deliver the information.

This is the default protocol designation for most Web browsers. When you enter an address without a protocol designation (e.g., www.yahoo.com) into the Go To or Address line of the Web browser, the Web browser will default to the HTTP protocol designation.

FTP

The FTP protocol designation indicates that the browser will use the File Transfer Protocol (FTP) to transfer files between the specified FTP server and the workstation. When you add ftp:// to the beginning of the URL, the browser will act as an FTP client and will be able to download and upload files using the FTPprotocol designation.

TELNET

The TELNET protocol designation indicates that the Web browser will try to connect to the specified host using the TCP/IP Terminal Emulation protocol (TELNET). TELNET allows a user to enter commands on a host without actually typing the commands on the host's keyboard.

When you specify a URL using telnet://, the browser will actually open another program to provide the actual Telnet functions because an Internet browser doesn't have the ability to send TELNET commands. The TELNET protocol designation tells the browser to open up the Telnet client.

FILE

The FILE protocol designation is a special one. It actually doesn't tell the browser what protocol to use, but rather it tells the browser to go and get a file stored either locally on the computer or over a LAN. Typically, this protocol designation would look something like this:

```
FILE://E:\studeweb\Page.htm
```

The browser would then display the selected file (if possible).

The FILE protocol syntax might look slightly different in different browsers.

DNS Name of Host

The next part of a URL is the DNS name of host (as shown in Figure 2.7). This name is the actual DNS name of the host you are connecting to. Refer back to the discussion of DNS earlier in the chapter for an explanation of DNS. A DNS host name for a Web server is most often something like *aaa.something.xxx*, where *aaa* is the local host name (www, ftp, etc.), *something* is the domain name, and *xxx* is a .com, .edu, .net, or other domain extension.

FIGURE 2.7   The DNS name of host in a URL

   A TCP/IP address can be used in place of the DNS name of host in a URL.

Path

The path portion of a URL (Figure 2.8) indicates the path on the host where the requested resource can be found. This path is relative to the hosting directory on the Internet server. For example, the URL www.yahoo.com/homes/fargo points to the /homes/fargo directory under the Web software directory on the www.yahoo.com Web server.

FIGURE 2.8   The path portion of a URL

   It is important to note that the path portion of a URL can either be short (one directory) or long (more than one directory).

What the Heck Is a Tilde?

Sometimes you will see a URL listed like http://www.*somewhere*.com/ ˜dgroth/. Everything in that URL makes sense except the tilde (~) character. This character has a special purpose. In Web servers that provide Web hosting for multiple users' home pages, the ~ indicates to the Web server to get the Web pages from the specified user's (in our example, dgroth) home directory on that server. Whenever you sign up with an ISP, you are given a user account, a password, and a home directory on a Web server. You can then set up your own home page by placing the HTML files in your home directory (or in a special subdirectory under your home directory). When this method is used, the Web pages are kept relatively secure from other users, but the Web server can still access them.

Resource Name

The last part of a URL (shown in Figure 2.9) is the actual name of the resource you are requesting from the server specified in the URL. For most Web URLs, this name will be the name of an HTML file that is stored on a Web server and that you want to download and display on your computer.

FIGURE 2.9 The resource name within a URL

There are some URLs that have the name and location of a program here, for example:

http://search.yahoo.com/bin/search?p=Books

This URL is an example of a search performed at www.yahoo.com. In this case, the resource you are requesting is the script program called search, and the search parameter "books" is being passed to the script to perform a search for books. The key to identifying that this is a script is that there is no .html ending on the resource you are requesting and that there is a question mark after the name of the resource along with some search parameters.

Internet Communications Process

The i-Net+ exam tests your knowledge of the behind-the-scenes processes that happen during Internet communications from an Internet client to the various types of servers that exist. Here are the two most common Internet communications process that people discuss:

- HTTP (Web) requests and responses
- SMTP (e-mail) traffic

HTTP (Web) Requests and Responses

The most common type of communication on the Internet is that between a Web browser and a Web server. This communication is known as an *HTTP communications session* because the request is made using the HTTP protocol. An HTTP communication consists of both a request for data (also known as an HTTP GET) and a response that includes the requested data. Figure 2.10 illustrates the process that occurs when a Web browser makes a request of an HTTP server.

FIGURE 2.10 The HTTP request and response process

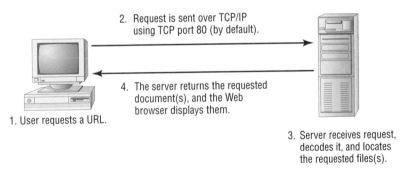

2. Request is sent over TCP/IP using TCP port 80 (by default).

4. The server returns the requested document(s), and the Web browser displays them.

1. User requests a URL.

3. Server receives request, decodes it, and locates the requested files(s).

As shown in Figure 2.10, the HTTP communications session consists of four major processes:

1. The browser submits the URL request to the Web server.

2. The browser communicates via TCP/IP and TCP port 80 to the Web server.

3. The Web server receives the request, decodes it, and locates the requested documents.

4. The server returns the requested documents and the Web browser displays them.

Let's take a brief look at each step.

Step 1: The Browser Request

There are two entities involved in any HTTP Web request: the client and the server. The client is most often a Web browser, although other Internet utilities are starting to use HTTP as a request method. The server component is almost always a Web (HTTP) server.

With a Web browser, you make a request of a Web server by entering a URL in the address line and pressing Enter or by clicking a hypertext link in an HTML document. This process initiates a request to the Web server. The request looks something like this:

```
GET http://www.accn.com/index.html HTTP/1.0
```

The GET portion of this request is known as the *HTTP request method*. This can be one of several different options. Some options for the request method are detailed in Table 2.2.

TABLE 2.2 HTTP Request Method Options

Request Method	Explanation
GET	Primary method of retrieving data from a Web server. This method requests a certain document or file from a Web server.
PUT	A method by which a client can upload a file to a Web server.
HEAD	A method that instructs an HTTP server to return only header information about a requested resource, not the actual resource itself.

Step 2: Browser Communication

Because HTTP is part of the TCP/IP protocol suite, it uses part of the TCP/IP protocol suite as a transport method. Specifically, HTTP uses the Transmission Control Protocol (TCP) as its main transport protocol. When a Web browser makes an HTTP request of a Web server, HTTP uses TCP port 80 during its communications. A TCP port identifies which TCP/IP process on the server machine the request is destined for. TCP port 80 is the default port address that specifies that the request is destined for an HTTP server process. Other port addresses can be used, but both client and server must be set up specifically to use them.

TCP/IP and its protocols are covered in more detail in Chapter 3.

In addition, HTTP requests include information like what (HTML document or multimedia content) is being requested as well as what version of HTTP is being used (HTTP 1.0 in most cases).

Step 3: Web Server Receives Request

The third step in the communications process is when the Web server receives the HTTP request and processes it. During this step, the Web server decodes the request and tries to determine exactly what the browser is asking for. Once the browser has determined what the request is, it locates the file(s) asked for in the request and proceeds to the next step, returning the requested information to the client.

Step 4: The Requested Document Is Returned

Once the server has found the requested information, it can send it back to the client that requested it. The server sends the data back using TCP or its "cousin," User Datagram Protocol (UDP). Which protocol is used depends on the type of content being sent. Most HTML documents are sent back using the TCP protocol.

E-Mail (SMTP and POP3)

E-mail, like the Web, is almost everywhere these days. All corporate business cards now have e-mail addresses on them. Communications have been enhanced to the point where large amounts of information can be conveyed almost instantaneously as well as efficiently.

E-mail is just a logical, digital version of the U.S. postal system. Digital messages are sent from a computer on one end to a recipient computer. But the message doesn't go directly from sender to recipient; instead, it passes through several computers on its way to its destination. Internet e-mail is a store-and-forward messaging system, which means the message sits in one location (stored) until a server process moves it to the next location (forwarded). This process repeats until the message arrives at its destination. Figure 2.11 shows a sample Internet mail setup.

FIGURE 2.11   An Internet mail setup

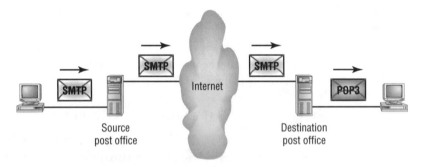

Internet e-mail consists of two major components:

- Simple Mail Transfer Protocol (SMTP)

- Post Office Protocol 3 (POP3)

Let's discuss each protocol and how they work together within the Internet to provide the Internet with its messaging system.

Simple Mail Transfer Protocol (SMTP)

The Simple Mail Transfer Protocol, as its name suggests, is the TCP/IP suite protocol used to transfer mail between Internet hosts. SMTP is most commonly used between mail clients and mail servers as well as between mail servers.

Like HTTP, SMTP uses TCP. SMTP initiates communications on TCP port 25. All SMTP conversations (either between client and server or between servers) work basically the same way. The sender opens a connection on TCP port 25, and the recipient responds that it is ready by sending back its name, address, and SMTP mail program version. The mail-sending process can then begin. During this process, SMTP uses special SMTP commands to send the mail. Each command has a special function within the SMTP communications process. To illustrate some of the most common STMP commands, let's examine a simple SMTP communication:

```
220 mail.somewhere.net ESMTP Sendmail 8.9.3/8.9.3;
Tue, 3 Aug 1999 08:52:14 -0500 (CDT)
HELO corpcomm.net
250 ns1.corpcomm.net Hello fgo1-a9.corpcomm.net
      [209.74.93.19], pleased to meet you
mail from:dgroth@corpcomm.net
250 dgroth@corpcomm.net... Sender ok
rcpt to:llee@sybex.com
250 llee@sybex.com... Recipient ok
data
354 Enter mail, end with "." on a line by itself
Test
Please ignore this message.
David G.

.

250 IAA22065 Message accepted for delivery
```

The first line (the line starting with 220) is the line that the SMTP server responds with, indicating that it is ready to start the conversation. As previously mentioned, this line includes the version of the SMTP service the recipient is running (in this case, Sendmail). The next line (starting with HELO) indicates what domain the sending computer is from. The receiving computer will then verify that the sending computer is actually at the domain it says it is from. This particular feature is fairly new. It was implemented to prevent unauthorized users from using an SMTP mail server to send mail without permission.

Once the receiving computer has verified that it is who it says it is, the sender then uses the mail from command to indicate who sent the mail. The e-mail address that appears after the mail from command is the address that appears in the From line in the header of the sent e-mail. The rcpt to: line tells the receiving computer who the mail's intended recipient is. This line specifies the e-mail address that appears on the To line of an e-mail.

The last part of this conversation begins with the `data` command, which indicates to the receiving computer that what follows is the actual body of the e-mail. After the `data` command, the sending system sends all the data that is part of that e-mail. To signify the end of the data, the sending computer sends a . on a line by itself.

The final line indicates that the mail was sent successfully.

POP3

When an e-mail gets sent over the Internet, it uses SMTP until it reaches the mail server at its destination. The e-mail then is stored on the mail server until the client is ready to download it. From there, Post Office Protocol 3 (POP3) is the protocol used to download the mail from the server to the mail client.

Most Internet e-mail clients today use SMTP for sending e-mail and the POP3 protocol for downloading received mail.

For more information on POP3, see RFC 1081, which can be found at www.cis.ohio-state.edu/htbin/rfc/rfc1081.html.

Summary

In this chapter, you learned the basics of the Internet, including such concepts as the following:

What the Internet is The Internet is a collection of local area networks connected together by high-speed public WAN connections. Also, the Internet consists of servers that store Internet content (HTML, graphics, etc.) until it is requested by a client.

Internet layout The Internet is completely interconnected. Access points (ISPs) connect to each other using high-speed public telephone lines (WAN connections). Those ISPs then connect to Internet backbone (the highest-speed WAN connections, several gigabits per second).

Domain Name Services (DNS)   DNS is the service used to translate user-friendly host names into their respective IP addresses. Domain suffixes fall into two categories: U.S. domains (such as com, org, and edu) and international domains (named after their two-letter country code, like .jp for Japan and .de for Germany).

Uniform Resource Locator (URL)   A URL is the universal way of referring to an Internet resource. They consist of a protocol designation (http:// or ftp://), followed by the DNS name of the host being accessed, then ending with the path of the resource being accessed.

Internet communications process   The last topic you learned about is the process that happens "behind the scenes" for both Web (HTTP) requests and Internet e-mail (SMTP and POP3) requests. Basically, both processes use a request-response mechanism. The client makes a request; the server processes the request and sends back a response.

Review Questions

1. Which protocol is used between a Web server and a Web browser when HTML documents are downloaded during a Web browsing session?

   A. HTML

   B. HTTP

   C. FTP

   D. TELNET

2. What does URL stand for?

   A. Universal Residence Location

   B. Uniform Resource Locator

   C. Universal Reaction Language

   D. Uniform Residence Language

3. What TCP port do HTTP requests use by default?

   A. 80

   B. 25

   C. 13

   D. 8

4. What TCP port do SMTP requests use by default?

   A. 13

   B. 21

   C. 25

   D. 80

5. Which TCP/IP suite protocol is primarily used to download Internet e-mail from an e-mail server?

A. SMTP

B. HTTP

C. HTML

D. POP3

6. Which TCP/IP service resolves host names into IP addresses and vice versa?

A. HTTP

B. DNS

C. POP3

D. SMTP

7. Which command during an SMTP communications session indicates the actual e-mail recipient to the receiving computer?

A. rcpt to

B. data

C. helo

D. mail to

8. Which items are sent by the receiving server to the sending entity during an SMTP communications session?

A. IP address of receiving server

B. DNS name of receiving server

C. Name and version of receiving server

D. Name and version of sending entity

9. Which part of the URL http://www.novell.com/index.html indicates the protocol that should be used to retrieve the Web document?

    A. www

    B. http://

    C. index.html

    D. www.novell.com

10. Which protocol(s) can be used to download files from an Internet server?

    A. HTTP

    B. TELNET

    C. FTP

    D. FILE

11. To which component of the Internet can individual users buy modem connections so that they can get on the Internet?

    A. Backbone ISP

    B. Access point ISP

    C. WAN connection

12. Which part of the URL http://www.novell.com/index.html indicates the actual resource being requested by the Web browser?

    A. http://

    B. www.novell.com

    C. index.html

    D. .com

13. Which HTTP request method allows a browser to indicate that it wants a specific file?

  A. GET

  B. PUT

  C. HOLD

  D. HEAD

14. Which HTTP request method allows a browser to upload a file to a Web server?

  A. GET

  B. PUT

  C. HOLD

  D. HEAD

15. Which DNS root-level domain is classified for schools, colleges, and other educational institutions?

  A. sch

  B. col

  C. edu

  D. com

16. Which DNS root-level domain is classified for commercial entities?

  A. com

  B. edu

  C. org

  D. gov

17. Which part of the SMTP communications session indicates the e-mail address of the sender?

A. rcpt to

B. HELO

C. data

D. mail from

18. You can send e-mail, but you can't receive it. Which protocol is most likely to blame?

A. POP3

B. SMTP

C. LDAP

D. TCP

19. Which HTTP request method allows a browser to request only the header of a document?

A. GET

B. PUT

C. HOLD

D. HEAD

20. Which protocol designation in a URL is used for viewing a file from the local hard disk in a Web browser?

A. disk://

B. file://

C. http://

D. C://

Answers to Review Questions

1. B. HTTP is the protocol used for this process. Although FTP can be used for downloads, it is generally not used during the Web browsing session to download HTML files to the browser. HTML and TEL-NET are invalid answers.

2. B. In Internet parlance, URL is short for Uniform Resource Locator.

3. A. HTTP is used on TCP port 80 (by default). Port 25 is used for SMTP and ports 13 and 8 are for other uses not discussed in this chapter.

4. C. SMTP uses TCP port 25, HTTP uses port 80, FTP uses port 21, and TCP port 13 is used for a special purpose called Daytime (not discussed in this chapter).

5. D. POP3 is the protocol used to download mail from an e-mail server. SMTP is used to send (upload) mail to an e-mail server. HTTP and HTML generally do not get involved in the client-server e-mail process.

6. B. Domain Name Services (DNS) resolves host names into IP addresses (and vice versa). HTTP is used for Web requests, and POP3 and SMTP are used for receiving and sending e-mail.

7. A. `data` designates the body of the message, `helo` starts the communication session. `mail to` is not an actual command.

8. A, C. The only items that are sent during an SMTP communications session are the IP address of the receiving server and the name and version of the receiving server.

9. B. All the other parts are part of either the DNS host name or the path to the resource being requested.

10. A, C. Both HTTP and FTP can be used to download files from an Internet server. TELNET is used to control a Unix host remotely, and FILE tells the browser to go and get a file stored either locally on the computer or over a LAN.

11. B. Backbone ISPs and WAN connections form the main structure of the Internet. Generally speaking, it is prohibitively expensive to get either a connection to a backbone ISP or your own WAN connection.

12. C. `http://` is the protocol designation, `www.novell.com` is the host being accessed, and `.com` is the top-level domain of the host being accessed.

13. A. PUT is used to send a request to a Web server.

14. B. PUT is used for uploading files, HEAD is used to retrieve only the header information, and HOLD is not a valid answer.

15. C. edu is used for educational institutions, com is for commercial companies, and the other two don't exist.

16. A. edu is used for educational institutions, org is generally for non-profit organizations, and gov is for government institutions.

17. D. `rcpt to` indicates the recipient, HELO starts the communications session, and `data` indicates the body of the message.

18. A. POP3 is used to download new mail from an e-mail server. SMTP is used for sending Internet e-mail. LDAP is used for directory queries, and TCP is a transport protocol.

19. D. GET is for retrieving the entire body, PUT is for uploading files, and HOLD doesn't exist.

20. B. `http://` is for retrieving documents from a Web browser; `disk://` and `C://` aren't valid protocol designations.

Chapter 3

Protocols

i-NET+ EXAM OBJECTIVES COVERED IN THIS CHAPTER:

✓ **Describe the nature, purpose, and operational essentials of TCP/IP. Content could include the following:**

- What addresses are and their classifications (A, B, C, D)
- Determining which ones are valid and which ones are not (subnet masks)
- Public versus private IP addresses

✓ **Describe the purpose of remote access protocols. Content could include the following:**

- SLIP
- PPP
- PPTP
- Point-to-point/multipoint

✓ **Describe how various protocols or services apply to the function of a mail system, Web system, and file transfer system. Content could include the following:**

- POP3
- SMTP
- HTTP
- FTP
- NNTP (news servers)
- TCP/IP
- LDAP
- LPR
- TELNET
- Gopher

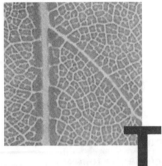

This chapter is about the protocols in use on the Internet. A *protocol* is nothing more than a set of rules that govern a particular operation. The Internet has many protocols, but the ones you're interested in are those having to do with network communications. Network communications take place using network communications protocols. A *network communications protocol* is a set of rules that govern network communications. If two computers are going to communicate, they both must be using the same protocol.

The Internet uses many different protocols (most of which are a subset of the TCP/IP protocol suite, which is discussed below). Each protocol governs a specific function (like e-mail, Web browsing, and file transfer). In this chapter, you will learn about protocols, their functions, and which protocols are used on the Internet.

The TCP/IP Protocol Suite

The Transmission Control Protocol/Internet Protocol (TCP/IP) suite is a collection, or *suite*, of protocols that operate together to provide data transport services for the Internet. The TCP/IP protocol suite is the only protocol suite used on the Internet. Because TCP/IP is so central to working with the Internet and with intranets, we'll discuss it in detail, and then we'll discuss some of the protocols that make up the TCP/IP protocol suite. We'll start with some background on TCP/IP and how it came about and then describe the technical goals defined by the original designers.

A Brief History of TCP/IP

The TCP/IP protocol was first proposed in 1973, but it was not until 1983 that a standardized version was developed and adopted for wide area use. In that same year, TCP/IP became the official transport mechanism for all connections to ARPAnet, a forerunner of the Internet.

Much of the original work on TCP/IP was done at the University of California, Berkeley, where computer scientists were also working on the Berkeley version of Unix (which eventually grew into the Berkeley Software Distribution [BSD] series of Unix releases). TCP/IP was added to the BSD releases, which in turn was made available to universities and other institutions for the cost of a distribution tape. Thus, TCP/IP began to spread in the academic world, laying the foundation for today's explosive growth of the Internet, and of intranets as well.

During this time, the TCP/IP family continued to evolve and add new members. One of the most important aspects of this growth was the continuing development of the certification and testing program carried out by the U.S. government to ensure that the published standards, which were free, were met. Publication ensured that the developers did not change anything or add any features specific to their own needs. This open approach has continued to the present day; use of the TCP/IP family of protocols virtually guarantees a trouble-free connection between many hardware and software platforms.

TCP/IP Design Goals

When the U.S. Department of Defense began to define the TCP/IP network protocols, their design goals included the following:

- It had to be independent of all hardware and software manufacturers. Even today, this is fundamentally why TCP/IP makes such good sense in the corporate world; it is not tied to IBM, Novell, Microsoft, DEC, or any other specific company.

- It had to have good built-in failure recovery. Because TCP/IP was originally a military proposal, the protocol had to be able to continue operating even if large parts of the network suddenly disappeared from view, say after an enemy attack.

- It had to handle high error rates and still provide completely reliable end-to-end service.

- It had to be efficient with a low data overhead. The majority of data packets using the IP protocol have a simple, 20-byte header, which means better performance when compared with other networks. A simple protocol translates directly into faster transmissions, giving more efficient service.

- It had to allow the addition of new networks without any service disruptions.

As a result, TCP/IP was developed with each component performing unique and vital functions that allowed all the problems involved in moving data between machines over networks to be solved in an elegant and efficient way. The popularity that the TCP/IP family of protocols enjoys today did not arise just because the protocols were there or even because the U.S. government mandated their use. They are popular because they are robust, solid protocols that solve many of the most difficult networking problems and do so elegantly and efficiently.

Let's now examine the two major components of the TCP/IP protocol suite, the Transmission Control Protocol and the Internet Protocol, as well as their makeup and functions.

Benefits of Using TCP/IP Rather Than Other Networking Protocols for the Internet

There are several reasons why TCP/IP was chosen as the primary protocol for the Internet:

- TCP/IP is a widely published open standard and is completely independent of any hardware or software manufacturer. Of all the protocols in use today, it is the most ubiquitous and, because of its widespread availability, is a natural choice for the Internet.

- TCP/IP can send data between different computer systems running completely different operating systems, from small PCs all the way to mainframes and everything in between.

- TCP/IP is separated from the underlying hardware and will run over Ethernet, Token Ring, or X.25 networks and even over dial-up telephone lines. Because of this feature, the Internet can use many different types of physical media, including phone lines and network links.

- TCP/IP is a routable protocol, which means it can send datagrams over a specific route, thus reducing traffic on other parts of the network.

- TCP/IP has reliable and efficient data-delivery mechanisms. This is a major advantage on the Internet when links constantly go up and down.

- TCP/IP uses a common addressing scheme. Therefore, any system can address any other system, even in a network as large as the Internet. (This addressing scheme will be covered in "Understanding IP Addressing" later in this chapter.)

The Transmission Control Protocol

The Transmission Control Protocol (TCP) serves to ensure reliable, verifiable data exchange between hosts on a network. TCP breaks data into pieces, wrapping it with the information needed to route it to its destination, and reassembling the pieces at the receiving end of the communications link. The wrapped and bundled pieces are called *datagrams*. TCP puts on the datagram a header that provides the information needed to get the data to its destination. The most important information in the header includes the source and destination port numbers, a sequence number for the datagram, and a checksum. Because it can ensure delivery, TCP is known as a *connection-oriented protocol*.

The *source port number* and the *destination port number* allow the data to be sent back and forth to the correct process running on each computer. The *sequence number* allows the datagrams to be rebuilt in the correct order in the receiving computer, and the *checksum* allows the protocol to check whether the data sent is the same as the data received. It does this by first totaling the contents of a datagram and inserting that number in the header. This is when IP enters the picture. Once the header is in the datagram, TCP passes the datagram to IP to be routed to its destination. The receiving computer then performs the same calculation, and if the two calculations do not match, an error occurred somewhere along the line and the datagram is resent.

Figure 3.1 shows the layout of the datagram with the TCP header in place.

FIGURE 3.1   A datagram with its TCP header

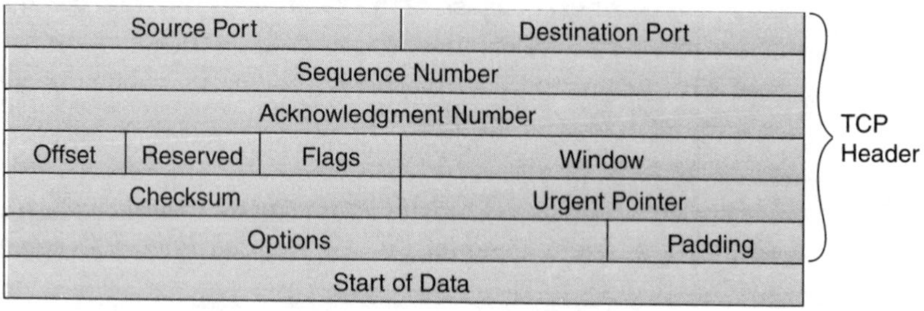

Source Port			Destination Port		
Sequence Number					
Acknowledgment Number					
Offset	Reserved	Flags	Window		
Checksum			Urgent Pointer		
Options				Padding	
Start of Data					

TCP Header

In addition to the source and destination port numbers, the sequence number, and the checksum, a TCP header contains the following information:

Acknowledgment Number   Indicates that the data was received successfully. If the datagram is damaged in transit, the receiver throws the data away and does not send an acknowledgment back to the sender. After a predefined time-out expires, the sender retransmits data for which no acknowledgment was received.

Offset   Specifies the length of the header.

Reserved   Variables set aside for future use.

Flags   Indicates that this packet is the end of the data or that the data is urgent.

Window   Provides a way to increase packet size, which improves efficiency in data transfers.

Urgent Pointer   Gives the location of urgent data.

Options   A set of variables reserved for future use or for special options as defined by the user of the protocol.

Padding   Ensures that the header ends on a 32-bit boundary.

The data in the packet immediately follows this header information.

> ### A Summary of TCP Communications
>
> You must remember a few things specifically about TCP communications:
>
> - Flow control allows two systems to cooperate in datagram transmission to prevent overflows and lost packets.
>
> - Acknowledgment lets the sender know that the recipient has received the information.
>
> - Sequencing ensures that packets arrive in the proper order.
>
> - Checksums allow easy detection of lost or corrupted packets.
>
> - Retransmission of lost or corrupted packets is managed in a timely way.

The Internet Protocol

The network routing and addressing portion of TCP/IP is called Internet Protocol. This protocol is what actually moves the data from point A to point B, in a process that is called *routing*.

IP is referred to as *connectionless*; that is, it does not swap control information (or handshaking information) before establishing an end-to-end connection and starting a transmission. The Internet Protocol must rely on TCP to determine that the data arrived successfully at its destination and to retransmit the data if it did not. IP's only job is to route the data to its destination. In this effort, IP inserts its own header in the datagram once it is received from TCP. The main contents of the IP header are the source and destination addresses, the protocol number, and a checksum.

You may sometimes hear IP described as unreliable because it contains only minimal error detection or recovery code.

Without the header provided by IP, intermediate routers between the source and destination, commonly called *gateways*, would not be able to determine where to route the datagram. Figure 3.2 shows the layout of the datagram with the TCP and IP headers in place.

FIGURE 3.2 A datagram with TCP and IP headers

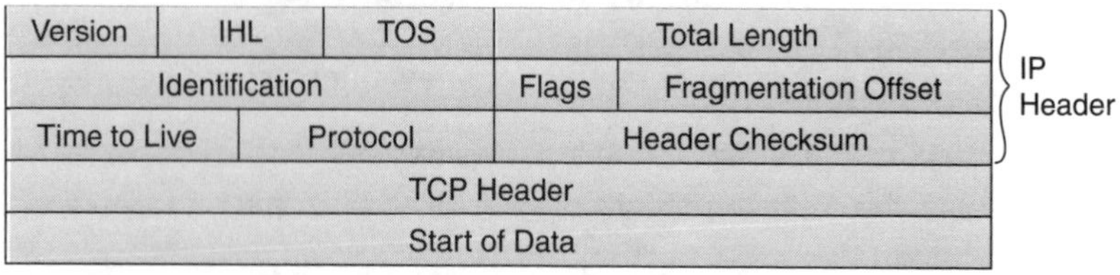

Version	IHL	TOS	Total Length	
Identification			Flags	Fragmentation Offset
Time to Live		Protocol	Header Checksum	
TCP Header				
Start of Data				

IP Header

Take a look at the fields in the IP header:

Version   Defines the IP version number. Version 4 is the current standard, and values of 5 or 6 indicate that special protocols are being used.

IHL (Internet Header Length)   Defines the length of the header information. The header length can vary; the default header is five 32-bit words, and the sixth word is optional.

TOS (Type of Service)   Indicates the kind or priority of the required service.

Total Length   Specifies the total length of the datagram, which can be a minimum of 576 bytes and a maximum of 65,536 bytes.

Identification   Provides information that the receiving system can use to reassemble fragmented datagrams.

Flags   The first flag bit specifies that the datagram should not be fragmented and must therefore travel over subnetworks that can handle the size without fragmenting it; the second flag bit indicates that the datagram is the last of a fragmented packet.

Fragmentation Offset   Indicates the original position of the data and is used during reassembly.

Time to Live   Originally, the time in seconds that the datagram could be in transit; if this time was exceeded, the datagram was considered lost. Now interpreted as a *hop count* and usually set to the default value 32 (for 32 hops), this number is decreased by each router through which the packet passes.

Protocol   Identifies the protocol type, allowing the use of non-TCP/IP protocols. A value of 6 indicates TCP, and a value of 17 indicates User Datagram Protocol (UDP).

Header Checksum   An error-checking value that is recalculated at each stopover point; necessary because certain fields change.

TCP Header   The header added by the TCP part of the protocol suite.

The data in the packet immediately follows this header information.

Gateways and Routing

As we mentioned, routing is the process of getting your data from point A to point B. Routing datagrams is similar to driving a car. Before you drive off to your destination, you determine which roads you will take to get there. And along the way, you sometimes have to change your mind and alter your route.

The IP portion of the TCP/IP protocol inserts its header in the datagram, but before the datagram can begin its journey, IP determines whether it knows the destination. If it does, IP sends the datagram on its way. If it doesn't know and can't find out, IP sends the datagram to the host's default gateway.

Each host on a TCP/IP network has a default gateway, an off-ramp for datagrams not destined for the local network. They're going somewhere else, and the gateway's job is to forward them to that destination if it knows where it is. Each gateway has a defined set of routing tables that tell the gateway the route to specific destinations.

Because gateways don't know the location of every IP address, they have their own gateways that act just like any TCP/IP host. In the event that the first gateway doesn't know the way to the destination, it forwards the datagram to its own gateway. This forwarding, or routing, continues until the datagram reaches its destination. The entire path to the destination is known as the *route*.

Datagrams intended for the same destination may actually take different routes to get there. Many variables determine the route. For example, overloaded gateways may not respond in a timely manner or may simply refuse to route traffic and time out. That time-out causes the sending gateway to seek an alternate route for the datagram.

Routes can be predefined and made static, and alternate routes can be predefined, providing a maximum probability that your datagrams travel via the shortest and fastest route.

Ports and Sockets Explained

On a TCP/IP network, data travels from a port on the sending computer to a port on the receiving computer. A *port* is an address that identifies the application associated with the data. The *source port number* identifies the application that sent the data, and the *destination port number* identifies the application that receives the data. All ports are assigned unique 16-bit numbers in the range 0 through 32,767.

Today, the very existence of ports and their numbers is more or less transparent to the users of the network because many ports are standardized. Thus, a remote computer can know which port it should connect to for a specific service. For example, all servers that offer Telnet services do so on port 23, and Web servers normally run on port 80. This means that when you dial up the Internet to connect to a Web server, you automatically connect to port 80, and when you use Telnet, you automatically connect to port 23. The TCP/IP protocol uses a modifiable lookup table to determine the correct port for the data type. Table 3.1 lists some of the well-known port numbers for common protocols.

TABLE 3.1   Well-Known Port Numbers for Common Protocols

Number	Protocol
21	File Transfer Protocol (FTP)
23	Telnet
25	Simple Mail Transfer Protocol (SMTP)
70	Gopher
79	Finger
80	Hypertext Transfer Protocol (HTTP)
110	Post Office Protocol 3 (POP3)
119	Network News Transfer Protocol (NNTP)

In multiuser systems, a program can define a port on-the-fly if more than one user requires access to the same service at the same time. Such a port is known as a *dynamically allocated* port and is assigned only when needed, for example, when two remote computers dial in to a third computer and simultaneously request Telnet services on that system.

The combination of an IP address (more on IP addresses in a moment) and a port number is known as a *socket*. A socket identifies a single network process in terms of the entire Internet. You may hear or see the words *socket* and *port* used as if they were interchangeable terms, but they are not. Two sockets, one on the sending system and one on the receiving host, are needed to define a connection for connection-oriented protocols, such as TCP.

Sockets were first developed as a part of the BSD Unix system kernel, in which they allow processes that are not running at the same time or on the same system to exchange information. You can read data from or write data to a socket just as you can with a file. Socket pairs are bidirectional so that either process can send data to the other.

Understanding IP Addressing

As you saw in "The Internet Protocol" earlier in this chapter, IP moves data between computer systems in the form of a datagram, and each datagram is delivered to the destination port number that is contained in the datagram header. This destination port number, or address, is a standard 16-bit number that contains enough information to identify the receiving network as well as the specific host on that network for which the datagram is intended.

In this section, we'll go over what IP addresses are, why they are so necessary, and how they are used in TCP/IP networking. But first, we need to clear up a possible source of confusion—Ethernet addresses and IP addresses.

Ethernet Addresses Explained

You may remember that in an earlier section we mentioned that TCP/IP is independent of the underlying network hardware. If you are running on an Ethernet-based network, be careful not to confuse the Ethernet hardware address and the IP address required by TCP/IP.

Each Ethernet network card (and any other NIC, for that matter) has its own unique hardware address, known as the media access control (MAC) address. This hardware address is predefined and preprogrammed on the NIC by the manufacturer of the board as a unique 48-bit number.

The first three parts of this address are called the OUI (Organizationally Unique Identifier) and are assigned by the Institute of Electrical and Electronics Engineers (IEEE). Manufacturers purchase OUIs in blocks and then assign the last three parts of the MAC address, making each assignment unique. Remember, the Ethernet address is predetermined and is hard-coded onto the NIC. A MAC address is a Data Link layer address used in the header of an Ethernet frame. An IP address is a Network layer address. IP addresses are very different; let's take a look.

IP Addresses Explained

TCP/IP requires that each computer on a TCP/IP network have its own unique IP address. An *IP address* is a 32-bit number, usually represented as a four-part number with each of the four parts separated by a period or decimal point. You may also hear this method of representation called *dotted decimal* or *quad decimal*. In the IP address, each individual byte, or *octet* as it is sometimes called, can have a usable value in the range 1 through 255.

The term *octet* is the Internet community's own term for an 8-bit byte, and it came into common use because some of the early computers attached to the Internet had bytes of more than 8 bits; some of DEC's early systems had bytes of 18 bits.

The way these addresses are used varies according to the class of the network, so all you can say with certainty is that the 32-bit IP address is divided in some way to create an address for the network and an address for each host. In general, though, the higher-order bits of the address make up the network part of the address, and the rest constitutes the host part of the address. In addition, the host part of the address can be divided further to allow for a *subnetwork address*. We'll be looking at all this in more detail in the "IP Address Classifications" and "Understanding Subnets" sections later in this discussion.

Some host addresses are reserved for special use. For example, in all network addresses, host numbers cannot be all 0s or all 255s. An IP host address with all host bits set to 0 identifies the network itself; so 52.0.0.0 refers to network 52. An IP address with all host bits set to 255 is known as a *broadcast address*. The broadcast address for network 204.176 is 204.176.255.255. A datagram sent to this address is automatically sent to every individual host on the 204.176 network.

When addressing nodes, you can never give a host an address where the host portion of the IP address is all zeros or all ones.

InterNIC (Internet Network Information Center) assigns and regulates IP addresses on the Internet; you can get one directly from InterNIC, or you can ask your Internet Service Provider (ISP) to secure an IP address on your behalf. Another strategy is to obtain your address from InterNIC and only use it internally until you are ready to connect to the Internet.

Intranets and Private IP Addresses

If you are setting up an intranet and you don't want to connect to the outside world through the Internet, you don't need to register with InterNIC the IP addresses you use on your intranet. These IP addresses are called *private* IP address because they are only valid on the local intranet. Registering your addresses with InterNIC simply ensures that the addresses you propose to use are unique over the entire Internet. These addresses are known as *public* IP addresses because they are known and valid across the entire Internet. If you never connect to the Internet, there's no reason to worry about whether your private addresses are redundant with a computer that *isn't* on your network.

IP Address Classifications

The current TCP/IP addressing scheme version is known as IP version 4, or IPv4 (there is a new revision that hasn't been universally accepted yet, called IPv6, but you'll learn about that later in this chapter). In the 32-bit IPv4 address, the number of bits used to identify the network and the host vary according to the network class of the address. You'll need to know that the several classes are as follows:

- Class A is used for very large networks only. The high-order bit in a Class A network is always 0, which leaves 7 bits available to define

127 networks. The remaining 24 bits of the address allow each Class A network to hold as many as 16,777,216 hosts. Examples of Class A networks include General Electric, IBM, Hewlett-Packard, Apple, Xerox, DEC, Columbia University, and MIT. All the possible Class A networks are in use, and no more are available.

- Class B is used for medium-sized networks. The two high-order bits are always 10, and the remaining bits are used to define 16,384 networks, each with as many as 65,534 hosts attached. Examples of Class B networks include Microsoft and Exxon. All the Class B networks are in use, and no more of them are available either.

- Class C is for smaller networks. The three high-order bits are always 110, and the remaining bits are used to define 2,097,152 networks, but each network can have a maximum of only 254 hosts. Class C networks are still available from some ISPs.

- Class D is a special multicast address and cannot be used for networks. The four high-order bits are always 1110, and the remaining 28 bits allow access to more than 268 million possible addresses.

- Class E is reserved for experimental purposes. The first four bits in the address are always 1111.

Figure 3.3 illustrates the relationships among these classes and shows how the bits are allocated by InterNIC.

FIGURE 3.3 The IP address structure

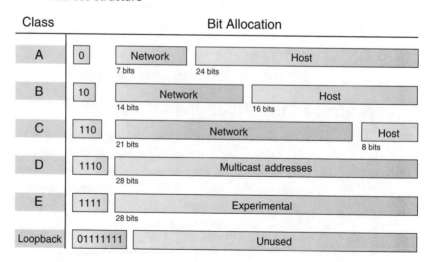

Because the bits used to identify the class are combined with the bits that define the network address, you can draw the following conclusions from the size of the first octet, or byte, of the address:

- A value of 126 or less indicates a Class A address. The first octet is the network number; the next three, the host address.

- A value of exactly 127 is reserved as a loopback test address. If you send a message to 127.0.0.1, it should get back to you unless something is wrong with your computer. Using this number as a special test address has the unfortunate effect of wasting more than 24 million possible IP addresses.

- A value of 128 through 191 is a Class B address. The first two octets are the network number, and the last two are the host address.

- A value of 192 through 223 is a Class C address. The first three octets are the network address, and the last octet is the host address.

- A value greater than 223 indicates a reserved address.

Another special address is 192.168.*xxx.xxx*, an address specified in RFC 1918 as being available for anyone who wants to use IP addressing on a private network but does not want to connect to the Internet. If you fall into this category, you can use this address without the risk of compromising someone else's registered network address. RFC 1918 also reserves the 10.*xxx.xxx.xxx* networks and the 172.16.*xxx.xxx* through 172.32.*xxx.xxx* networks.

IPv4 vs. IPv6: The Next Generation

With the explosive growth of the Internet, very few public IP addresses are left. There are no Class A addresses left; few, if any, Class Bs; and the Class C addresses that are available are strictly regulated. We are experiencing this shortage of public IP addresses mainly because the current IP addressing scheme, IP version 4 (IPv4 for short), uses a 32-bit addressing scheme that allows for around 17 million node addresses. Because of this shortage of IP addresses, a new version of IP, designated IPv6, has been specified. It uses a 128-bit addressing scheme that will allow for more than 70 octillion (70 followed by 27 zeros). That's enough for each person on earth to have more than a million IP addresses. Should be enough, don't you think? As this book was being written (Fall 1999), IPv6 had still not received widespread use.

Understanding Subnets

The current IP addressing scheme provides a flexible solution to the task of addressing thousands of networks, but it is not without problems. The original designers did not envision the Internet growing as large as it has; at that time, a 32-bit address seemed so large that they quickly divided it into different classes of networks to facilitate routing rather than reserving more bits to manage the growth in network addresses. (Who ever thought we would need a PC with more than 640KB of memory?) To solve this problem, and to create a large number of new network addresses, another way of dividing the 32-bit address, called *subnetting*, was developed.

An IP subnet modifies the IP address by using host address bits as additional network address bits. In other words, the dividing line between the network address and the host address is moved to the right, creating additional networks but reducing the number of hosts that can belong to each network.

When IP networks are subnetted, they can be routed independently, which allows a much better use of address space and available bandwidth. To subnet an IP network, you define a bit mask known as a *subnet mask*, in which a bit pattern cancels out unwanted bits so that only the bits of interest remain.

Working out subnet masks is one of the most complex tasks in network administration and is not for the faint of heart. If your network consists of a single segment (in other words, there are no routers on your network), you will not have to use this type of subnetting, but if you have two or more segments (or subnets), you will have to make some sort of provision for distributing IP addresses appropriately. You can do just that by using a subnet mask.

The subnet mask is similar in structure to an IP address in that it has four parts, or octets, but now it defines three elements (network, subnet, and host) rather than two (network and host). It works a bit like a template that, when superimposed on top of the IP address, indicates which bits in the IP address identify the network and which bits identify the host. If a bit is on in the mask, that equivalent bit in the address is interpreted as a network bit. If a bit is off in the mask, the bit is part of the host address. The 32-bit value is then converted to dotted-decimal notation. In general, you will only use one subnet mask on your network.

A subnet is only known and understood locally; to the rest of the Internet, the address is still interpreted as a standard IP address. Table 3.2 shows how this all works for the most commonly used standard IP address classes.

TABLE 3.2 Default Subnet Masks for Standard IP Address Classes

Class	Subnet Mask Bit Pattern	Subnet Mask
A	11111111 00000000 00000000 00000000	255.0.0.0
B	11111111 11111111 00000000 00000000	255.255.0.0
C	11111111 11111111 11111111 00000000	255.255.255.0

Routers then use the subnet mask to extract the network portion of the address so that they can send the data packets along the proper route on the network.

Because all the Class A and Class B networks are taken, you are most likely to encounter subnet-related issues when working with a Class C network. In the next section, we'll describe in detail how to subnet a Class C network.

The Advantages of Subnetting

Although subnetting is complex, it does have some advantages:

- It reduces the size of routing tables.

- It minimizes network traffic.

- It isolates networks from others.

- It maximizes performance.

- It optimizes IP address space.

- It enhances the ability to secure a network.

How to Subnet a Class C Network

You can subnet any class IP address, but the most common practice today is to subnet a Class C IP address block, so we'll discuss that process here. How do you find out the values you can use for a Class C network subnet mask? Remember from the previous discussion that InterNIC defines the leftmost three octets in the address, leaving you with the rightmost octet for your own network addresses? If your network consists of a single segment, you have the following subnet mask:

11111111 11111111 11111111 00000000

When expressed as a decimal number, your address is as follows:

255.255.255.0

Because all of your addresses must match these leftmost 24 bits, you can do what you like with the last 8 bits, given a couple of exceptions that we'll look at in a moment.

You might decide to divide your network into two equally sized segments, say with the numbers 1 through 127 as the first subnet (00000001 through 01111111 in binary) and the numbers 128 through 255 as the second subnet (10000000 through 11111111 in binary). Now the number inside the subnets can vary only in the last seven places, and the subnet mask becomes:

255.255.255.128

In binary this is:

11111111.11111111.11111111.10000000

Use the Windows Calculator in scientific mode (choose View ➤ Scientific) to look at binary-to-decimal and decimal-to-binary conversions. Click the Bin (binary) button, and then type the bit pattern that you want to convert. Click the Dec (decimal) button to display its decimal value; you can also go the other way and display a decimal number in binary form.

Now let's get back to the exceptions we mentioned. The network number is the first number in each range, so the first subnet's network number is X.Y.Z.0, and the second's is X.Y.Z.128 (X, Y, and Z are the octets assigned by InterNIC). The default router address or default gateway is the second number in each range, X.Y.Z.1 and X.Y.Z.129, and the broadcast address is the last address, or X.Y.Z.127 and X.Y.Z.255. You can use all the other addresses within the range as you see fit on your network.

Table 3.3 describes how you can divide a Class C network into four equally sized subnets with a subnet mask of 255.255.255.192. This gives you 61 IP addresses on each subnet once you have accounted for the network, router, and broadcast default addresses.

TABLE 3.3 Class C Network Divided into Four Subnets

Network Number	Router Address	Broadcast Address
X.Y.Z.0	X.Y.Z.1	X.Y.Z.63
X.Y.Z.64	X.Y.Z.65	X.Y.Z.127
X.Y.Z.128	X.Y.Z.129	X.Y.Z.191
X.Y.Z.192	X.Y.Z.193	X.Y.Z.255

Table 3.4 describes how you can divide a Class C network into eight equally sized subnets with a subnet mask of 255.255.255.224. This gives you 29 IP addresses on each subnet once you have accounted for the network, router, and broadcast default addresses.

TABLE 3.4 Class C Network Divided into Eight Subnets

Network Number	Router Address	Broadcast Address
X.Y.Z.0	X.Y.Z.1	X.Y.Z.31
X.Y.Z.32	X.Y.Z.33	X.Y.Z.63
X.Y.Z.64	X.Y.Z.65	X.Y.Z.95
X.Y.Z.96	X.Y.Z.97	X.Y.Z.127
X.Y.Z.128	X.Y.Z.129	X.Y.Z.159

TABLE 3.4 Class C Network Divided into Eight Subnets *(continued)*

Network Number	Router Address	Broadcast Address
X.Y.Z.160	X.Y.Z.161	X.Y.Z.191
X.Y.Z.192	X.Y.Z.193	X.Y.Z.223
X.Y.Z.224	X.Y.Z.225	X.Y.Z.255

Classless Inter-Domain Routing (CIDR)

InterNIC no longer gives out addresses under the Class A, B, or C designations. Instead, it uses a method called Classless Inter-Domain Routing (CIDR), usually pronounced "cider." CIDR networks are described as "slash x" networks; the x represents the number of bits in the IP address range that InterNIC controls. This allows InterNIC to define networks that fall between the old classifications and means that you can get a range of addresses much better suited to your needs than in times past. In CIDR terms, a network classified as a Class C network under the old scheme becomes a slash 24 network because InterNIC controls the leftmost 24 bits and you control the rightmost 8 bits. Table 3.5 shows some example slash x network types.

TABLE 3.5 Example CIDR Network Types

InterNIC Network Type	Subnet Mask	Approximate Number of IP Addresses
slash 8	255.0.0.0	16,000,000
slash 12	255.240.0.0	1,000,000
slash 16	255.255.0.0	65,536
slash 20	255.255.240.0	4,096
slash 21	255.255.248.0	2,048
slash 22	255.255.252.0	1,024

TABLE 3.5 Example CIDR Network Types *(continued)*

InterNIC Network Type	Subnet Mask	Approximate Number of IP Addresses
slash 23	255.255.254.0	512
slash 24	255.255.255.0	256
slash 25	255.255.255.128	128
slash 26	255.255.255.192	64
slash 27	255.255.255.224	32
slash 28	255.255.255.248	16
slash 29	255.255.255.248	8
slash 30	255.255.255.254	4

TCP/IP Remote Access Protocols

The most common way of accessing the Internet for the majority of the people connected is to use some kind of remote access protocol. A *remote access protocol* manages the connection between a remote computer and a remote access server. Each remote access protocol allows a remote computer to access a remote network in some fashion. In the case of Internet connections, the remote network is the Internet and the remote access protocols allow the remote computer to submit requests and receive data from the Internet.

Three primary remote access protocols are in use today:

- Serial Line Internet Protocol (SLIP)

- Point-to-Point Protocol (PPP)

- Point-to-Point Tunneling Protocol (PPTP)

Serial Line Internet Protocol (SLIP)

In 1984, students at the University of California, Berkeley, developed SLIP for Unix as a way to transmit TCP/IP over serial connections (such as modem connections over POTS). SLIP operates at both the Physical and Data Link layers of the OSI model. Today, SLIP is found in many network operating systems in addition to Unix. It is being used less frequently with each passing year, though, because it lacks features when compared with other protocols. Although a low overhead is associated with using SLIP and you can use it to transport TCP/IP over serial connections, it does no error checking, packet addressing can only be used on serial connections, and it does not support encrypted password methods. SLIP is used today primarily to connect a workstation to the Internet or to another network running TCP/IP.

Setting up SLIP for a remote connection requires a SLIP account on the host machine and usually a batch file or a script on the workstation. When SLIP is used to log in to a remote machine, a terminal mode must be configured after login to the remote site so that the script can enter each parameter. If you don't use a script, you will have to establish the connection and then open a terminal window to log in to the remote access server manually.

WARNING   It is difficult to create a batch file that correctly configures SLIP. Our advice is to avoid SLIP when possible and use PPP instead.

Point-to-Point Protocol (PPP)

PPP is used to implement TCP/IP over point-to-point connections (for example, serial and parallel connections). It is most commonly used for remote connections to ISPs and LANs.

PPP uses the Link Control Protocol (LCP) to communicate between a PPP client and a host. LCP tests the link between a client and a PPP host and specifies PPP client configuration. PPP can support several network protocols, and, because it features error checking and flow control and can run over many types of physical media, PPP has almost completely replaced SLIP. In addition, PPP can automatically configure TCP/IP and other protocol parameters. On the downside, high overhead is associated with using PPP, and it is not compatible with some older configurations.

From the technician's standpoint, PPP is easy to configure. Once you connect to a router using PPP, the router assigns all other TCP/IP parameters. This is typically done with DHCP (Dynamic Host Configuration Protocol). Within the TCP/IP protocol stack, DHCP is the protocol that is used to assign TCP/IP addressing information, including host IP address, subnet mask, and DNS (Domain Name Services) configuration. This information can be assigned over a LAN connection or a dial-up connection. When you connect to an ISP, you are most likely getting your IP address from a DHCP server.

Point-to-Point Tunneling Protocol (PPTP)

PPTP is the Microsoft-created sibling to PPP. It is used to create virtual connections across the Internet using TCP/IP and PPP so that two networks can use the Internet as their WAN link yet retain private network security. PPTP is both simple and secure.

To use PPTP, set up a PPP session between the client and server, typically over the Internet. Once the session is established, create a second dial-up session that uses PPTP to dial through the existing PPP session. The PPTP session tunnels through the existing PPP connection, creating a secure session. In this way, you can use the Internet to create a secure session between the client and the server. Also called a virtual private network, this type of connection is very inexpensive when compared with a direct connection.

PPTP is a good idea for network administrators who want to connect several LANs but don't want to pay for dedicated leased lines. But, as with any network technology, there can be disadvantages, including the following:

- PPTP is not available on all types of servers.

- PPTP is not a fully accepted standard.

- PPTP is more difficult to set up than PPP.

- Tunneling can reduce throughput.

You can implement PPTP in two ways. First, you can set up a server to act as the gateway to the Internet and to do all the tunneling. The workstations will run normally without any additional configuration. You would usually use this method to connect entire networks. Figure 3.4 shows two networks connected using PPTP. Notice how the TCP/IP packets are tunneled through an intermediate TCP/IP network (in this case, the Internet).

FIGURE 3.4 A PPTP implementation connecting two LANs over the Internet

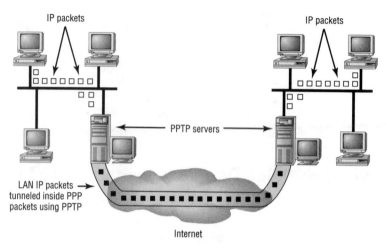

The second way to use PPTP is to configure a single, remote workstation to connect to a corporate network over the Internet. The workstation is configured to connect to the Internet via an ISP, and the VPN client is configured with the address of the VPN remote access server. The VPN then exists between the VPN client and VPN server. PPTP is often used to provide VPN functions to connect remote workstations to corporate LANs when a workstation must communicate with a corporate network over a dial-up PPP link through an ISP and the link must be secure. An example of this configuration is shown in Figure 3.5.

FIGURE 3.5 A workstation is connected to a corporate LAN over the Internet using PPTP

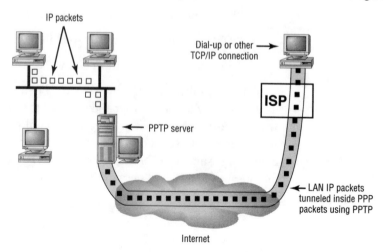

Windows 98 and Windows NT 4 include this functionality. You must add it to Windows 95.

Layer 2 Tunneling Protocol (L2TP): The Next-Generation Tunneling Protocol

PPTP has been around for awhile as part of Windows NT's Internet offerings. With the advent of the Secure IP (IPSec) technology (a method of encrypting IP traffic), a new tunneling protocol has been suggested to the IETF (in RFC 2661). This new technology (known as the Layer 2 Tunneling Protocol) uses PPP to tunnel across an intermediate IP network. It takes the best features of the two most common tunneling protocols—PPTP from Microsoft and L2F from Cisco—and merges them into a single tunneling protocol.

Other Internet Protocols

In addition to TCP and IP, the TCP/IP protocol suite has provisions for several different protocols that each have a different function. The i-Net+ exam will test your basic knowledge of these protocols. The other TCP/IP protocols include (but are not limited to):

- HTTP
- FTP
- POP3
- SMTP
- NNTP
- LPR
- LDAP
- TELNET
- Gopher

Many of these protocols are covered in more detail in other chapters, but in the following sections, you'll gain a basic understanding of what each protocol does.

Hypertext Transfer Protocol (HTTP)

The Hypertext Transfer Protocol (HTTP) is the command and control protocol used to manage communications between a Web browser and a Web server. When you access a Web page on the Internet or on a corporate intranet, you see a mixture of text, graphics, and links to other documents or other Internet resources. HTTP is the protocol that initiates the transport of each of the components of a Web page.

For more info on the HTTP communications process, see Chapter 2. Also, the HTTP server is covered in Chapter 4, and the HTTP client is covered in both Chapters 5 and 6.

File Transfer Protocol (FTP)

The File Transfer Protocol is a TCP/IP protocol that provides a mechanism for single or multiple file transfers between computer systems; FTP is also the name of the client software used to access the FTP server running on the remote host. The FTP package provides all the tools needed to look at files and directories, change to other directories, and transfer text and binary files from one system to another. File Transfer Protocol uses TCP through port 21 to actually move the files. We'll look at how to transfer files using FTP in detail in Chapter 6.

Simple Mail Transfer Protocol (SMTP)

The Simple Mail Transfer Protocol (SMTP) is the protocol responsible for moving messages from one e-mail server to another. It is also the protocol used to send e-mail from a client to an e-mail server. The e-mail servers run either Post Office Protocol (POP3) or Internet Mail Access Protocol (IMAP) to distribute e-mail messages to users. All e-mail servers that send e-mail to the Internet must be using TCP/IP and an e-mail program that can send e-mail using SMTP.

The SMTP communications process is covered in more detail in Chapter 2. Also, SMTP servers are discussed in Chapter 4 and SMTP clients are discussed in more detail in Chapters 5 and 6.

Post Office Protocol 3 (POP3)

POP3 is the protocol used to download mail from an Internet (SMTP) mail server. POP3 servers provide a storage mechanism for incoming mail. When a client connects to a POP3 server, all the messages addressed to that client are downloaded; messages cannot be downloaded selectively. Once the messages are downloaded, the user can delete or modify messages without further interaction with the server. In some locations, POP3 is being replaced by another standard, Internet Mail Access Protocol (IMAP).

Network News Transfer Protocol (NNTP)

This is the protocol used to transport Internet news (also called Usenet news) between news servers. It is also the protocol used to transport these news articles between news servers and news clients. This protocol is often confused with the Network Time Protocol (NTP), which serves a different purpose.

Line Printer (LPR) Protocol

This protocol is used primarily on Unix systems, although Windows NT uses it as well. It is the protocol used to send commands to network printers over TCP/IP. Its name suggests it works only for line printers (also called dot-matrix printers). That's mainly because, when it was being developed, the majority of the printers in use were line printers.

Lightweight Directory Access Protocol (LDAP)

This protocol is seeing increased use as network directories see increased use. The Lightweight Directory Access Protocol is the protocol used to make simple requests of a network directory (like NDS, X.500, or Active Directory). LDAP requests can consist of requests for names, locations, and other information like phone numbers and e-mail addresses. Many Web browsers (including Navigator and Internet Explorer) contain LDAP clients so they can request information from directory servers.

TELNET

This protocol is a terminal emulation protocol that allows a workstation to perform a remote logon to another host over the network. It is used primarily to allow users at workstations to access a Unix server and run commands just as if they were sitting at the server's console.

Gopher

Gopher is a text-based utility that was used in the early years of the Internet to search for data and news. It would present selections in a hierarchical format. Gopher was developed from work done at the University of Minnesota; their mascot was the gopher, so they named this technology Gopher. It was the best way to search for information before the Web came along and made everything "friendly."

Figure 3.6 shows how some of the components we've been discussing fit together within the TCP/IP protocol suite. The top layers are the various Internet server applications. Notice that the top layers rely on different bottom layers for transport and other functions.

FIGURE 3.6 The components in a TCP/IP block diagram

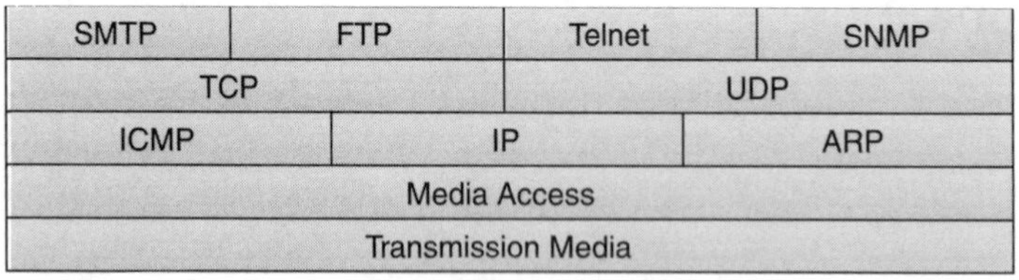

SMTP	FTP	Telnet	SNMP
TCP		UDP	
ICMP	IP		ARP
Media Access			
Transmission Media			

Summary

The TCP/IP protocol suite is the protocol used for all communications on the Internet. In this chapter, you learned about the following concepts:

The nature, purpose, and operational essentials of TCP/IP   You learned that the Transmission Control Protocol/Internet Protocol (TCP/IP) protocol suite is the primary protocol suite in use on the Internet. Stations that use TCP/IP are assigned (either manually or automatically) a 32-bit, dotted-decimal number called an IP address. It is represented as four three-digit numbers, like so: *xxx.xxx.xxx.xxx*, where each digit can be any number from 0 to 255.

Classes of IP addresses   IP addresses are characterized by their class. Table 3.6 details the classes of IP addresses based on the range of the first octet.

TABLE 3.6   IP Address Classes, Address Ranges, and Default Subnet Masks

Class	First Octet Address Range	Default Mask
A	0–126	255.0.0.0
B	128–191	255.255.0.0
C	192–223	255.255.255.0

Remote access protocols   You learned the details of the three most popular remote access TCP/IP protocols: SLIP, PPP, and PPTP. SLIP is the most primitive with the fewest features. PPP is the most often used remote access protocol because it supports protocols other than TCP/IP and it supports error checking and flow control. Finally, PPTP is the protocol used to provide VPN services over TCP/IP.

Various protocols that make up the TCP/IP protocol suite   The TCP/IP protocol suite is made up of many different individual protocols, each with a different purpose and use. Table 3.7 outlines each protocol and its function.

TABLE 3.7 TCP/IP Suite Protocols

Protocol	Function/Use
HTTP	Transporting requests for Internet content from browsers to Web servers and transporting content back to requesting browser
FTP	Transferring files
SMTP	Sending e-mail
TELNET	Terminal emulation
NNTP	Transporting Internet news between client and server
LPR	TCP/IP printing
LDAP	Internet directory queries
Gopher	Searching Internet data in a hierarchical format

Review Questions

1. What is the default subnet mask for a Class C IP address?

   A. 255.0.0.0

   B. 255.255.0.0

   C. 255.255.255.0

   D. 255.255.255.255

2. Which TCP/IP suite protocol is used to transfer text and multimedia content between a Web browser and a Web server?

   A. SMTP

   B. HTTP

   C. POP3

   D. LDAP

3. The subnet mask 255.255.255.0 corresponds to what CIDR designation?

   A. /8

   B. /24

   C. /29

   D. /30

4. Which TCP/IP suite protocol is used for reliable, point-to-point TCP/IP remote access connections?

   A. PPP

   B. PPTP

   C. CIDR

   D. TCP

5. If you were given an IP address of 176.58.24.1 for your machine, but no subnet mask, what subnet mask could you use by default?

   A. 255.0.0.0

   B. 255.255.0.0

   C. 255.255.255.0

   D. 255.255.255.255

6. Which of the following addresses is an invalid TCP/IP address to assign to a host?

   A. 204.67.129.1

   B. 7.21.1.1

   C. 170.200.1.1

   D. 191.260.42.1

7. Which TCP/IP protocol(s) can be used for Internet mail?

   A. LDAP

   B. SMTP

   C. NNTP

   D. FTP

8. Which subnet mask corresponds to a CIDR designation of /8?

   A. 255.0.0.0

   B. 255.240.0.0

   C. 255.255.0.0

   D. 255.255.240.0

9. Which remote access technology allows secure TCP/IP network connections over the Internet?

A. PPP

B. SLIP

C. SMTP

D. PPTP

10. Which of the following TCP/IP addresses are considered broadcast addresses?

A. 201.123.45.255 *broadcast*

B. 34.1.0.0

C. 107.28.94.1

D. 79.0.0.0 *refer to a specific network*

11. What is the default TCP port number for a POP3 connection?

A. 21

B. 25

C. 80

D. 110

12. Which protocol is used for Internet directory queries?

A. SMTP

B. LDAP

C. POP3

D. NNTP

13. What is the default subnet mask for the IP address 18.204.37.112?

 A. 255.0.0.0

 B. 255.255.0.0

 C. 255.255.255.0

 D. 255.255.255.255

14. Which TCP/IP protocol is used for sending print jobs to TCP/IP printers?

 A. POP3

 B. SMTP

 C. LPR

 D. NNTP

15. Which of the following addresses could you assign to an Internet host?

 A. 192.168.10.2   *reserved for Intranet*

 B. 208.34.109.255

 C. 67.22.22.22

 D. 255.12.37.109

16. What is the default subnet mask for a Class B IP address?

 A. 255.255.0.0

 B. 0.0.0.255

 C. 255.255.255.0

 D. 255.0.0.0

17. If your ISP gave you a TCP/IP address of 204.153.129.0/24, what subnet mask would you use?

    A. 255.255.0.0

    B. 255.255.255.0

    C. 255.0.0.0

    D. 0.0.0.0

18. What is the TCP/IP protocol used for sending and receiving Internet news?

    A. FTP

    B. HTTP

    C. LDAP

    D. NNTP

19. Which TCP/IP protocol is the primary protocol used to transfer text and binary files on the Internet?

    A. SMTP

    B. FTP

    C. LDAP

    D. LPR

20. Which TCP/IP protocol is used to search Internet text and news for information?

    A. SMTP

    B. Gopher

    C. Telnet

    D. FTP

Answers to Review Questions

1. C. 255.0.0.0 is Class A, 255.255.0.0 is Class B, and 255.255.255.255 is a broadcast address.

2. B. SMTP is used for sending e-mail, POP3 is used for downloading e-mail, and LDAP is used for directory queries.

3. B. A designation of /24 means the leftmost 24 bits refer to the network portion of a TCP/IP address and the rightmost 8 bits (the remainder) are used to assign host addresses. The leftmost 24 bits out of 32 bits corresponds to a subnet mask of 255.255.255.0.

4. A. Of all the answers listed, PPP is the only remote access protocol used for reliable, TCP/IP, point-to-point communications.

5. B. Because the IP address begins with 176, your address would be a Class B address. The default subnet mask for a Class B address is 255.255.0.0.

6. D. The largest number you can use in a TCP/IP address is 255. 260 is larger than 255, so it is invalid.

7. B. LDAP is used for Internet directory queries, NNTP is used for Internet news, and FTP is used for file transfer.

8. A. A CIDR designation of /8 means that the leftmost 8 bits of an address refer to the network portion. This would correspond to a subnet mask of 255.0.0.0

9. D. PPTP is used for secure communications over the Internet. PPP and SLIP are primarily used for point-to-point communications, and SMTP is used for sending e-mail.

10. A. 201.123.45.255 is the only broadcast address because all host bits are set to 1 (255 in decimal). 107.28.94.1 is a valid IP address, and 34.1.0.0 and 79.0.0.0 are IP addresses that refer to a specific network.

11. D. 110 is used for POP3 communications. Port 21 is used for FTP communications, 25 is used for SMTP, and 80 is used for HTTP.

12. B. SMTP is used for sending Internet e-mail, POP3 is used to download Internet e-mail, and NNTP is used to send and receive Internet news.

13. A. 18.204.37.112 is a Class A address. 255.0.0.0 is the default subnet mask for a Class A address. 255.255.0.0 is for a Class B, 255.255.255.0 is for a Class C, and 255.255.255.255 is a reserved address.

14. C. POP3 is used for downloading mail, SMTP is the protocol for sending mail, and NNTP is used for sending and receiving Internet news.

15. C. 208.34.109.255 and 255.12.37.109 are reserved addresses for broadcasts. 192.168.10.2 is a reserved address for intranets and cannot be routed on the Internet.

16. A. Of the answers listed, 255.255.0.0 is the default subnet mask for a Class B IP address.

17. B. A /24 CIDR designation is equivalent to a standard Class C address with a default subnet mask of 255.255.255.0.

18. D. FTP is used for uploading and downloading files, HTTP is the protocol used for transferring HTML documents and images from a Web server, and LDAP is used for making directory queries.

19. B. SMTP is used for sending Internet e-mail, LDAP is used to make Internet directory queries, and LPR is used to send print jobs to TCP/IP printers.

20. B. Gopher is the protocol used to search the Internet for text and news. SMTP is used for sending Internet mail, Telnet is used for remotely accessing a Unix host, and FTP is used for downloading and uploading files.

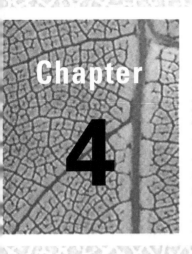

Chapter

4

Servers and Their Functions

i-NET+ EXAM OBJECTIVES COVERED IN THIS CHAPTER:

✓ Describe the purpose of various servers—what they are, their functionality, and features. Content could include the following:

- Proxy
- Mail
- Mirrored
- Cache
- List
- Web (HTTP)
- News
- Certificate
- Directory (LDAP)
- E-commerce
- TELNET
- FTP

The Internet is made up of four items: servers, clients, content, and protocols. Basically, the servers store the Internet content until a client, like a Web browser, requests it. The server then delivers the content to the client that requested it. If you'll remember, this process was covered in more detail in Chapter 2, and protocols were discussed in Chapter 3. Clients will be discussed in Chapter 5, and HTML will be discussed in Chapter 8, so this chapter will focus on a detailed discussion of the different types of servers that can be found on the Internet. You'll learn how they work and how they are most commonly used, and we'll include some common examples of each.

Web (HTTP) Servers

Web servers make up a specific class of servers that use a special program or service to provide HTML and other Internet content to clients via TCP/IP. Web servers get their name from the World Wide Web (WWW), which is a network of servers that provide Internet content from a server back end to a graphical client (also known as a browser). Actually, *Web server* is somewhat of a misnomer because all servers that serve up some kind of graphical content to a Web browser using the Hypertext Transfer Protocol (HTTP) are generically called Web servers. Although, more specifically, they should be called HTTP servers because that's really what they are. Only HTTP servers that are on the WWW should be called Web servers. For the purpose of this discussion, unless otherwise noted, an HTTP server and a Web server are the same thing.

Because the i-Net+ exam focuses more on Web servers than it does other types of servers, they will receive the most coverage in this chapter.

How Web (HTTP) Servers Work

Web servers are actually fairly simple compared to some other types of specialized servers (e.g., database servers). First of all, Web servers run a specialized program or service called an *HTTP daemon* (pronounced "dee-mon" or "day-mon," depending on whom you ask). This process is really what makes a Web server a Web server. The daemon runs as a process within the NOS and is responsible for responding to all requests from a Web browser. These responses include negotiation for an HTTP connection and the actual delivery of files. HTTP daemons are made by several different companies and for several different NOS platforms. The different brand names are covered in "Examples of Web Server Software" later in this chapter.

In addition to HTTP daemons, Web servers may have capabilities for running scripts. A script is simply a small program that the server executes when a particular action is requested on a Web page. For example, some Web pages have forms that you can fill out to send information to the owner of the Web site. Most often, a script will gather the information from the form, compress it into a readable message, then e-mail it to a predetermined e-mail address. Scripts will be covered in more detail in Chapter 8.

Basically, an HTTP server works something like this: The HTTP daemon sits idle until it receives a request from a Web browser. When the daemon receives a request, it decodes it, locates the requested document, file, or script, and returns the requested information to the requesting Web browser.

For more information on the specifics of HTTP, see RFC 2068 at www.ietf.org.

Uses for Web Servers

Even though Web servers are relatively simple in how they operate, they are used for a variety of applications. The Web's greatest power is its ability to deliver all kinds of information in an easy-to-use, consistent manner.

Because Web browsers are fairly ubiquitous on computers these days, and so many employees have access to them, many companies are trying to leverage their investment in a Web server by using it to deliver a variety of information, including:

- Company information
- Public advertisements
- Technical information
- Stock quotes
- Classified ads
- Statistical data

Web servers can deliver all this information quickly and easily. Many software developers have realized this, and as such, more and more software programs (primarily office suite applications) give the user the ability to save data to HTML format so that it can be viewed using a Web browser.

Web servers can be classified into three major categories, based on their use and the type of data they deliver:

- Internet servers
- Intranet servers
- E-commerce server

In the following sections, you'll learn about each type of Web server and the differences between them.

Internet Servers

Everyone that has ever "surfed the Web" has accessed an Internet Web server. An *Internet Web server* is just a Web server that serves *public* HTML and other content to all clients on the Internet. Public content is information that is published to the Internet for everyone to read. Content might include the following:

- Company location and contact information
- Product catalogs
- Stock quotes

Mainly, what differentiates an Internet Web server from other types of Web servers is that an Internet Web server serves public content over the Internet. You could say that it serves public content over a public medium (the Internet).

Additionally, Internet servers are usually supported by high-powered hardware to make it possible for a large amount of people to visit a site and retrieve public company and product information. This translates into company revenue because the more powerful the Web server's hardware, the more simultaneous connections the server can support, and thus, more people can be simultaneously looking at a company's Web site.

For an example of an Internet server, check out www.sybex.com and note all the public information.

Intranet Servers

Intranet servers are HTTP servers that are located on a company's LAN and serve information only to employees of that company or other users who have been given authority to view it. Intranet servers serve private company information and content and usually require that the user requesting the information log in with a username and password. Private content includes information you wouldn't want a competitor to have access to, including:

- Company policy manual
- Company memos
- Company news (not for general release)
- Human resources information
- Corporate e-mail
- Corporate phone directory

Intranet servers generally serve this private content over a private medium, the LAN. All users on the LAN access this Web server and this information using their Web browsers from a machine located inside the company firewall.

In some cases, a company will use some kind of secure authentication method to make private information available over the Internet. Then, however, the Web server would be called an *extranet server* (which isn't on the i-Net+ exam).

When the term *intranet* was first introduced, most people thought is was a misspelling of *Internet*. But companies soon saw that it was valuable to have a standard way of accessing company information. Rather than using several different programs to disseminate information (for example, Word processing, spreadsheet, and e-mail programs), they could place the information in a central repository (the intranet server), and it could be accessed using a standard program (the Web browser) that everyone already knew how to use.

In smaller companies with limited budgets, the company Internet server doubles as an intranet server. In larger companies, the Internet server and intranet server are usually two different machines and are most often located on two different areas of the network.

If you work for a company that has an intranet Web server, you know what kind of information is available. In this case, we can't give you a URL because the information on most intranets is private!

E-Commerce Servers

E-commerce is a relatively new term coined by industry analysts. It is the exchange of money and goods just as commerce is, but with e-commerce, the Internet is the exchange medium. A great number of consumers are gravitating toward making more and more of their purchases via the Internet. This trend is occurring because most companies who sell over the Internet can provide their products in a one- or two-day time frame and at a much lower cost than those selling through more traditional retail methods. This appeals to people with an "instant gratification" purchase mentality. For example, suppose you needed an Ethernet print server for your laser printer. You check with a few local vendors, but no one has it in stock, and you would have had to wait four to five days for it to be ordered. You can order it through an online vendor and receive it the next day. If you have a problem with it, you can call the company's customer service line and receive the replacement the next day. In an era where "retail customer service" is an oxymoron, e-commerce is proving to be profitable for many companies.

To provide e-commerce, a company needs to implement an e-commerce server. An *e-commerce server* is basically an Internet Web server that provides e-commerce services through Web server scripts or programs. Some of the e-commerce services commonly found on an e-commerce server include:

Catalog search service   A search service allows a prospective customer to search a "virtual catalog" of the products being sold on the Web site. The customer simply types some words or a part number in a form and clicks a button to start the search. The catalog search service returns items that match the search and displays them in a list. The customer can then select the item she wants to view or perform a different search.

Virtual shopping cart services   A potential Web customer can select items one at a time, and the shopping cart service remembers each item as if it were in a "virtual shopping cart." When the customer is done shopping, he clicks a Check Out button (or something similar). The server then tallies up all the items and displays a list in invoice format, along with a subtotal, taxes (if applicable), and shipping costs. The customer can modify his virtual shopping cart by removing items, adding additional items, and choosing appropriate shipping methods. When the customer is satisfied, he chooses an Accept button. The customer is then asked to provide personal (address, phone, and e-mail, usually) and payment information, and the order is processed. This service is the heart of the e-commerce server.

credit card authentication   Many payment options are available over the Internet, including C.O.D., check, cashier's check, and credit cards. However, using a credit card is the most efficient method of payment; money is transferred more quickly, and thus, the order is processed quickly. Customers can pay for their products immediately, and their order is processed immediately without human intervention. Credit card authentication is usually performed with a script that runs alongside all the other e-commerce services on a Web server. When a customer wants to pay with a credit card, she enters the card number and expiration date along with the order amount on a secure Web page. This information is submitted to the Web server over a secure connection. The Web server then sends the card information to the credit card authentication service, which acts like the little credit card machines in a common retail store. The authentication service contacts (either via a dial-up connection or via the Internet) the appropriate credit card company's server and indicates that the customer wants to make a purchase for a certain amount. The credit card company then returns either a rejection or a confirmation with an authorization number. The Web server's credit card authentication service returns that information to both the company's accounts receivable database and the user's Web browser. These programs also indicate to the shopping cart service that the purchase was successful and the order can be initiated.

E-mail order verification   Once the order has been placed, the e-commerce server (usually the virtual shopping cart program) will display the complete order in a Web browser window along with an order number so that the order can be tracked. The user can print this information for his records. To ensure that the user gets the information, a copy is sent to the e-mail address specified when the user entered his personal information. Most e-commerce Web sites will not let you place an order unless you enter at least your name, phone number, and e-mail address (along with appropriate payment information).

For secure orders, some e-commerce sites may use certificate servers (discussed in the sidebar "Secure Connections Using Certificate Authorities") to prove customers' identities.

E-commerce Web sites are currently a hot trend. To make money to offset the cost of putting up their Web site, some companies will sell items even if the primary purpose of the site is to disseminate information.

For examples of e-commerce Web sites, check out www.amazon.com and www.warehouse.com.

Secure Connections Using Certificate Authorities

More and more Internet sales transactions are taking place. The number of sales increases exponentially every day, so it stands to reason that there are people who make it their business to intercept sales communications and (criminally) use the information they gain to their advantage. It is therefore necessary to provide a method for private, secure communications. Today, this is done on the Internet with either secure transmissions using Secure Sockets Layer (SSL) or public key/private key cryptography using digital certificates and certificate servers. Web sites that use SSL have addresses that begin with `https://`.

Certificates, on the other hand, allow both the client and the server to prove their identity by presenting a digital version of an identity card. Using a special key, this digital identity card (called a digital certificate) is "signed" by a server that both the sender and receiver trust. The server is known as a *certificate authority* (also called a certificate server). The certificate server uses information from the requester and other third parties (like credit card companies) to verify the identify of the requester and to create the digital certificate. A server that provides e-commerce through the use of certificate authorities or other third-party security is known as a *Commercially Secured Server (CSS)*.

Examples of Web Server Software

Since the growth of the Internet exploded, there have been a multitude of Web server platforms available. The most common software available for a NOS is currently an HTTP daemon (Web server) of some type. Web server software comes in many different types and interfaces. Each type differs in the platforms it supports and the way it is administered. To prepare you for the i-Net+ exam, this section will cover a few of the most commonly used HTTP daemons, including:

- HTTPd
- IIS
- Apache

We'll discuss the features of each type of HTTP daemon and the platforms each supports.

NCSA HTTPd

The first HTTP daemon was developed by the National Center for Super-computing Applications (NCSA) at the University of Illinois at Urbana-Champaign. It is known as HTTPd (short for HTTP daemon) and is the HTTP daemon that most other Web daemons are based on. HTTPd is free; you can download it from the NCSA Web site along with all documentation and source code. It was developed for use on Unix systems and is available for use on most Unix platforms.

For more information on HTTPd, visit www.ncsa.uiuc.edu or www.cern.ch.

Microsoft IIS

When Microsoft finally realized the value of the Internet, they hastily threw together an HTTP daemon for their Windows NT operating system. This daemon is known as Microsoft Internet Information Server (IIS). Over time, it has developed into a robust HTTP server platform. The two main advantages of IIS are its cost and ease of use. IIS comes free with Windows NT and with some service packs. IIS version 2 comes free with NT Server 4 (IIS 2 is upgraded to version 3 with service pack 2 or later), and IIS version 4 is available free of charge on the NT Option Pack CD. As this book is being written, all versions of IIS are free of charge. The most current version of IIS, IIS 5, is included in Windows 2000 Server. Additionally, it is extremely easy to configure this Web server because the administration program is fully graphical and Windows based. The graphical utility used to administer IIS is known as the Microsoft Internet Service Manager (ISM), and it's used to administer all of the Microsoft Internet services running on the same NT server as the ISM. Most first-time administrators configure IIS without a great deal of training or knowledge of the inner workings of Windows NT.

Unfortunately, these advantages don't come without a price. IIS only runs on Windows NT. That's fine if all you have are Windows NT servers, but if you want to run IIS and you don't have an NT server on your network, you must install one.

For more information on IIS, check out www.microsoft.com/backoffice/.

Apache

As this book is being written, the Linux operating system is gaining popularity in the corporate network as a Web server platform. The main reason for this is the Apache Web server. Supposedly, Apache got its name because it is "a patchy" version of the NCSA HTTPd. In reality, Apache is based on the NCSA HTTPd, but it has been rewritten and has had features added so that it is now its own HTTP daemon. According to a recent survey (www.netcraft.com/Survey/), Apache is the most commonly used Web server.

Apache was developed first for the Linux operating system. But, because the source code for Apache is freely available, Apache versions can be found for many other NOSes, including most versions of Unix as well as Windows NT and OS/2.

Apache's main advantage is that it is a freely available, stable, HTTP daemon. The downside is that it can be relatively difficult for the average administrator to configure, especially if he isn't familiar with the administration of Unix daemons.

For more information about Apache, check out www.apache.org.

"Mirrored" Web Sites

A *Web site mirror* is an exact copy of a Web site that is located at a different domain name. Web sites are mirrored for a variety of reasons. Occasionally, a Web site is extremely popular, and the Web server hosting the site can't keep up with all the traffic. So the owner places copies of the Web site in different geographic areas so that people in those areas can access the mirror instead of the actual site. For example, Yahoo.com is probably one of the biggest search engines in use today. It has mirrors in many countries, and it is usually faster for people to obtain information from their "local" mirror than to go to the main site.

Popular FTP sites are mirrored as well. This is done so that popular files are available for download from multiple locations, thus spreading the load across multiple servers.

FTP Servers

An FTP server is any server that provides files to clients using the FTP protocol (a subset of the TCP/IP protocol suite, as discussed in Chapter 3). An FTP server is usually the next server that a company will set up once their Web server is installed and operational. HTTP and FTP are complimentary technologies. When you visit a computer company Web site and look for technical support information, there will often be an area where you can download support files (for example, patches, documentation, and so on). As a matter of fact, many Web software companies have FTP server software that compliments their HTTP server nicely. For example, when you install Microsoft's IIS, you have the option of installing the IIS FTP server as well.

In this section, you'll learn how an FTP server works and some uses for them. We'll also give you some examples of FTP servers.

How FTP Servers Work

FTP servers are similar in function to HTTP servers in that FTP servers also use a daemon (called an FTP daemon) to respond to client requests. FTP servers are a bit more complex than HTTP servers, however. Whereas HTTP daemons respond to a very limited set of commands, FTP daemons respond to a wide array of commands. These commands will be covered in more detail in Chapter 5.

FTP daemons run on a server and wait until they receive a request for an FTP connection from an FTP client. The FTP daemon then responds to the client and asks the user to log in. The user sends a username and password to tell the server who is requesting the file. Because most Internet sites don't need to regulate who can download files, many sites allow Anonymous or FTP as a username and will accept any text as the password. Anonymous users are generally not allowed to upload or delete files, but they can download files.

Once the user logs in, she can request a file. When the FTP daemon receives this request, it sends the requested file back to the requesting client.

The FTP process will be covered in more detail in Chapter 5, where FTP clients are discussed.

Uses for FTP Servers

As already stated, FTP servers are typically used for supplemental file delivery from a company's Web site. They are more flexible than Web servers for file delivery because they allow files to be uploaded as well as downloaded and at the same time maintain security.

The biggest use of FTP servers on both the Internet and intranets is for archival file storage and delivery. For example, there are many Web sites on the Internet that store shareware and make it available for anyone to download. These "software warehouses" store many gigabytes of software and usually have a Web interface that allows people to get descriptions of the software they're looking for and then click a link to download the file. An example of this type of FTP site is `ftp.cdrom.com`, which hosts thousands of files and can be searched via the Web site.

Examples of FTP Servers

Just as with HTTP servers, there are myriad FTP daemons. Some come free with the NOS (as in the case of FTPd), whereas others must be purchased. The two most popular FTP daemons are the Unix daemon, FTPd, and Microsoft's IIS. Here, you'll learn the differences between the two and the platforms they run on.

FTPd

The FTP Daemon (FTPd) is the FTP daemon used on most Unix-based servers. As is the case with the other Unix-based daemons (like HTTPd and Telnet), it was the first FTP daemon platform developed. The majority of software companies that make FTP daemon software base it on FTPd. Most versions of Unix include a version of FTPd for free.

IIS

Microsoft has included an FTP server in Internet Information Server (IIS). When you install IIS onto a Windows NT machine, you have the option of installing the FTP server component of IIS. During the installation, the IIS installation program asks you which directory you want to "publish" to the Internet so that people can download files. Once it's installed, people on the Internet will be able to download files from the specified directory.

IIS has the benefit of being the easiest FTP server to install and administer. The same administration program used to administer the HTTP server component of IIS (Microsoft Internet Service Manager) is also used to administer the FTP daemon portion.

News (NNTP) Servers

Most ISPs today have at least one news server to allow their subscribers access to Internet news articles. *News servers* are those Internet servers that store and distribute Usenet news articles using the Network News Transfer Protocol (NNTP). As discussed in Chapter 3, NNTP is one of the protocols in the TCP/IP protocol suite. The following sections will discuss the details of NNTP servers, including how they work, some common uses, and some examples.

How News (NNTP) Servers Work

Just like the other Internet servers, news servers use a daemon to respond to requests and to deliver news messages. NNTP clients communicate with the NNTP daemon to send and receive news articles. These news articles are simply text messages that are organized by subject into categories (called *newsgroups*). For example, there is a newsgroup called `alt.autos.studebaker`. The messages contained in this newsgroup pertain primarily to Studebaker automobiles. When you want to post a message to the Internet about Studebakers, you send the message to your local news server and designate that it belongs in the `alt.autos.studebaker` newsgroup. Then, those with similar interests can look at the `alt.autos.studebaker` newsgroup, see your message, and respond. They can respond by either posting a message back to the newsgroup or e-mailing you directly.

The individual newsgroups are stored in directories on the news server. When a client first connects to the news server, it requests a list of all newsgroups stored on the server. The server responds with a complete list of the names of all the newsgroups it stores. This can take a while because, typically, thousands of individual newsgroups exist (a typical ISP lists over 50,000). Once the client chooses a newsgroup to view, it sends a request to the news server to retrieve all the headers (that is, the Subject line, the To line, and the From line) of the messages in the newsgroup. You might be asking, "Why not download all of the message?" Well, you may not want to read every message, so it downloads only the headers so you can decide which message(s) you want to read. Then, when you click a particular message in the client, the client requests the remainder of the message. The server then locates the full message body and returns it to the client.

In addition to allowing clients to read messages, NNTP servers will send out messages that they receive, either from clients or from other servers. NNTP servers can be configured to send all their messages to other NNTP servers. Additionally, the servers that "push" news messages can also receive messages. In this way, messages that get posted to one news server will be propagated throughout the Internet. Because of this distribution mechanism, newsgroups are among the most powerful collaboration tools on the Internet.

Uses for News Servers

News servers have two main uses; both of them have to do with providing an area for discussions to take place. First, as described earlier, newsgroups provide an area for discussions to take place on the Internet. Users from all over the world can discuss their favorite topics (like Studebakers) just as if they were talking in the same room.

Second, newsgroups provide a discussion area for LAN (*not* Internet) users only. Users within a company can discuss company issues in a secure environment without having to meet face-to-face. You can do this by implementing a news server on your LAN without allowing it to communicate with Internet news servers. The advantage is the same as it is for Internet news servers: collaboration among several people without face-to-face contact. This use is not as common as the Internet variety, but it is useful and it is done.

Examples of News Servers

There are several Internet news daemons available, but the majority of them are available for Unix only. There are very few news daemons for NT, NetWare, or other platforms, mainly because NNTP is a bit more complex and difficult to configure. In addition, because of the performance and hardware support required to host 50,000+ newsgroups and upload and download all those messages, the NOS that scales the best for this application is Unix.

Don't get us wrong. News daemons do exist for other platforms besides Unix, but most ISPs run their news daemon on a Unix box.

The most common news daemon is the Internet News Daemon (INND, also referred to as simply INN). Versions of it are available for free download from the Internet for most versions of Unix, including Solaris, AIX, SVR4, and BSD. Originally written by Rich Salz, INND development was taken over in 1996 by the Internet Software Consortium (ISC, a group of people dedicated to developing free, open source Internet software). INND is a stable news server with many features, including:

- Binary message support
- Scalability
- Technical support contracts available (not bad for freeware)

As this book is being written, INND version 2.2.1 has just been released and is available for FTP download from the ISC. Their Web site is at www.isc.org, where you can find more detailed information on INND.

Mail (SMTP) Servers

Apart from Web servers, Internet mail (SMTP) servers are the second most-installed servers that companies will implement when setting up their Internet presence. An SMTP mail server will allow all the users within a company to send and receive e-mail across the Internet using the Simple Mail Transfer Protocol (SMTP). As you most likely know, e-mail servers allow people to communicate quickly, efficiently, and cheaply. It's no wonder they're popular.

How Mail (SMTP) Servers Work

As other types of Internet servers do, SMTP servers use a daemon to perform all operations. The daemon waits until someone wants to send mail to it. Once an entity makes a TCP connection to the SMTP daemon using TCP port 25, the daemon responds and indicates its readiness to receive the mail.

The sender then tells the SMTP daemon who the mail is from and who it's for and sends the body of the message. Once the body of the message is sent, the daemon verifies the integrity of the message and makes sure it is being sent to a valid address. The daemon will then perform a DNS lookup to find the IP address of the mail host for the recipient's domain (for example, if you're sending mail to bob@somewhere.com, the daemon tries to find the mail host for the somewhere.com domain). If the DNS server reports that no such host exists, the entire message is returned to the sender indicating that it was "undeliverable."

If the DNS query finds the IP address of the recipient's domain's SMTP mail server, the sending SMTP daemon will open a connection to the destination mail server and try to send the message. If it can't, the sending daemon will hold it in its "waiting to send" queue and try again at some later time (exactly when is a configurable parameter). If it can't deliver it after a specified amount of time has passed (another configurable parameter), it will return it to the sender with a message saying that the message was undeliverable after multiple retries.

When the message arrives at the destination daemon, the destination daemon will deliver it to the appropriate directory where the message will wait until it is read by the end user (either using a terminal client, like Pine, or through a POP3 client, discussed in Chapter 5).

Uses for Mail Servers

Obviously, the main use for mail servers is to send and receive e-mail. However, within that general definition, mail servers can play many different roles. First of all, a mail server can be a host mail server for an ISP. That means all the mail for the users on that ISP gets sent to and is stored on that mail server.

Also, mail servers can perform a function known as *SMTP relaying*. *SMTP relay servers* are servers that perform SMTP relaying by simply forwarding e-mail that is coming from any SMTP client or server to a destination SMTP server. They are used when a client can't send e-mail directly to its destination on the Internet.

Finally, some mail servers are used as e-mail list servers. *List servers* are servers that facilitate discussion among various people using e-mail to communicate. List servers are e-mail servers that use special add-on software configured with a special e-mail address (something like majordomo@domain .com) and a list of the e-mail addresses of the people who want to participate in the discussion. Any e-mail sent to the list server's e-mail address gets forwarded to all e-mail addresses in the list. The forwarded message contains the list server's e-mail address as the "reply to" address so that, when any member of the list replies to a message, the reply gets sent to all others on the list.

Using list servers is a great way to communicate ideas to a large amount of people, but it's also a great way to overload your mail server.

Examples of SMTP Mail Servers

The most commonly used SMTP daemon (and, therefore, probably the best example) is the Unix SMTP daemon, Sendmail. Sendmail is freely available over the Internet for most versions of Unix, including SVR4, BSD, Solaris, and Linux. Other SMTP mail servers are available for Unix and other NOS platforms, but Sendmail is the most popular and the one used by most ISPs. It was the first SMTP daemon developed, and most current SMTP daemons are based on the technology found in Sendmail.

Sendmail information and file download can be found at www.sendmail.org.

Sendmail is very complex. It requires extensive configuration to function properly. Because of its complexity, many books have been written on the configuration of the Sendmail daemon, so we won't devote a great deal of time to it here.

SMTP Gateways

You may be asking, "Well, my company doesn't use Sendmail; we use ___ ___ (fill in the blank with any commercial e-mail product), but my company's e-mail software can e-mail to and from the Internet just fine. What's up?" Commercial e-mail software like Microsoft's Exchange and Novell's GroupWise can also connect to the Internet and be mail servers, but they are primarily designed to be LAN e-mail servers only. To provide SMTP functionality, both require an add-on *SMTP gateway* to allow them to communicate with the Internet. However, once an SMTP gateway is installed, these two e-mail packages can do everything described in this section, including acting as a mail relay host (although this is configurable).

Proxy Servers

A proxy server is one of several solutions to the problems associated with connecting your intranet or corporate network to the Internet. A *proxy server* is a program that handles traffic to external host systems on behalf of the client software running on the protected network. This means that clients access the Internet through the proxy server. It's a bit like those one-way mirrors—you can see out of it, but a potential intruder cannot see in.

Another mechanism used to monitor and control traffic between the Internet and an internal network is a *firewall*. Although the functions performed by proxy servers and firewalls are related and are starting to appear in combination products, we'll talk about the proxy server functions here, and you will find more information on firewalls in Chapter 7.

Many proxy servers can cache documents, which is particularly useful if a number of clients request the same document independently; the client request is filled more quickly, and Internet traffic is reduced. Caching can be of the following types:

Active caching   The proxy server uses periods of low activity to go out and retrieve documents it thinks will be requested by clients in the near future.

Passive caching   The proxy server waits for a client to make a request, retrieves the document, and then decides whether to cache it.

Some documents, such as those from a paid subscription service or those requiring specific authentication, cannot be cached.

How Proxy Servers Work

A proxy server sits between a user on your network and a server out on the Internet. Instead of communicating with each other directly, each talks to the proxy (in other words, to a "stand-in"). From the user's point of view, the proxy server presents the illusion that the user is dealing with a genuine

Internet server. To the real server on the Internet, the proxy server gives the illusion that the real server is dealing directly with the user on the internal network. So depending on which way you are facing, a proxy server can be both a client and a server. The point to remember here is that the user is never in direct contact with the Internet server, as Figure 4.1 illustrates.

FIGURE 4.1 How a proxy server works

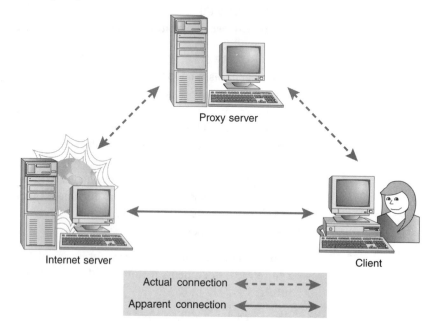

However, the proxy server doesn't just forward requests from your users to the Internet and back. Because it examines and makes decisions about the requests that it processes, it can control what your users can do. Depending on the details of your security policy, client requests can be approved and forwarded, or they can be denied. Rather than requiring that the same restrictions be enforced for all users, many advanced proxy server packages can offer different capabilities to different users.

There are two types of proxies: Winsock proxies and HTTP proxies. Winsock proxies make any kind of TCP/IP request (including FTP, HTTP, etc.) on behalf of client stations. Winsock proxies require a special piece of software on the client station. These proxies also allow TCP/IP requests to be made at the workstation using any protocol. You don't have to have TCP/IP installed or configured on the workstation to use a Winsock proxy. Most proxies fall into this category. HTTP proxies, on the other hand, simply make Web requests on behalf of a Web browser. Both types are often implemented on networks.

WARNING   A proxy server can only be effective if it is the *only* connection between an internal network and the Internet. As soon as you allow another connection that does not go through a proxy server, your network is at risk.

Uses for Proxy Servers

Proxy servers are commonly found on networks that are connected to the Internet. Because proxies examine every packet going between the Internet and the stations on the LAN, they make great firewalls. Many proxy servers have the capability to configure "allowed traffic types." This may slow down performance, but for companies without the resources to implement a separate firewall, a proxy with this capability may be the best choice.

If the proxy server does caching, it can improve Internet "surfing" and download performance. Many companies will implement a proxy to increase total Internet performance if they only have a 56Kbps connection to the Internet (like a slow Frame Relay, ISDN, or dial-up connection). In our company, we have a 56Kbps modem connected to an NT server and Microsoft Proxy Server installed. With all browsers on our home network configured to use the proxy, all the computers on the network can surf the Internet with pretty good performance (and only use one phone line and, thus, one Internet connection).

Examples of Proxy Servers

Because of the popularity of proxy servers, many software companies are selling proxy server software. There are even a few proxy servers available for free download. Here, you'll learn about two examples of proxy servers: Microsoft Proxy Server and the proxy server component of the Apache Web server. You'll learn the differences between the two and the platforms they support.

Microsoft Proxy Server

One of the most popular proxy servers is Microsoft Proxy Server (usually abbreviated MS Proxy Server). Its popularity is due to its dependence on the Windows NT platform. Currently at version 2, MS Proxy Server is available only for Windows NT systems. Because many companies have chosen Windows NT for their Internet server platform, the advantage here is that you don't have to learn another NOS.

Another of MS Proxy Server's features is its ease of administration. Just like the Microsoft FTP and HTTP server, you can use the Microsoft Internet Service Manager to administer the properties of MS Proxy Server. Once you have learned how to use the Internet Service Manager to administer one Internet service, it's simply a matter of learning the specifics for each particular service. You don't need to learn how to use a different administration tool for each service. Additionally, because most MS Proxy Server properties are configured correctly during installation, you should rarely have to do much administration after installation.

Unlike many of the components discussed in this chapter, MS Proxy Server isn't free; it must be purchased either from Microsoft or a distributor of Microsoft products. However, as this book is being written, you can buy MS Proxy Server for $995.00 retail (you should be able to find it at a reduced price through software clearing houses and warehouse stores). You can download a free trial version from Microsoft's Web site at www.microsoft.com, but it will expire and be nonfunctional after 90 days.

MS Proxy Server is a great proxy server if you have Windows NT already installed, although it may not make financial sense to put in a Windows NT server if you don't already have one.

More information on Microsoft Proxy Server can be found at the proxy portion of the Microsoft Web site at www.microsoft.com/proxy/.

Apache

The freeware Apache HTTP server discussed earlier includes a proxy server module so that the server running the Apache HTTP daemon can also be a proxy server. This functionality is possible with versions only after version 1.2. Because Apache is mainly available for Unix, its caching server has the same NOS requirement.

Apache costs less than MS Proxy Server (it's free), and because, by most people's account, Unix is a higher-performance operating system, Apache will have better performance as a proxy server as well. It should be noted, however, that different combinations of hardware and software can produce different performance results. Keeping this in mind, although there are exceptions, it is generally accepted that a Unix-based HTTP or Winsock proxy is faster than an NT-based one.

Directory Servers

The buzzword in the information technology business these days is *directory*. A directory, as it applies to networking, is a centralized repository of network resource information. This information can be used for network management purposes or other useful applications. A network directory contains information such as what kind of users, servers, printers, and so on exist on a network. Each item (usually called an *object*) and its associated properties (for example, phone number, department, address, etc.) can be searched through a standard query language. For example, if you had a network of 250 people and you wanted to e-mail someone but didn't know her e-mail address, you could use a program to query the directory and find the e-mail address.

Directories have been around for years. Only recently have they been popular with the Internet crowd. The biggest use for directories on the Internet is repositories of personal information. A directory server is a server that stores directory information and makes it available to the Internet for searches. A great example of a directory server is Switchboard (`www.switchboard.com`). With it, you can look for anyone or any business. To look for people, for example, all you need to know is their last name (although you may want to supply the server with more information).

There are many public directory servers on the Internet and each one is slightly different. For this reason, a standard request and access protocol was developed. This protocol is the Lightweight Directory Access Protocol (LDAP), and it is used to provide a common access method for the myriad of directories that exist. Additionally, there is a standard method of organizing and naming entries in these directories. This standard is known as the X.500 directory naming scheme, and many Internet directories conform to this naming standard.

It is important to note that LDAP is not a directory, but a directory access method. There is no such thing as an LDAP directory. A more plausible moniker would be an LDAP-compliant directory service.

For more information on LDAP, refer to the University of Michigan's (the developers of LDAP) Web site, www.umich.edu/~dirsvcs/ldap/doc/. More information on X.500 can be found at www.nexor.com/info/directory.htm.

How Directory (LDAP) Servers Work

Most public directory servers use two daemons to provide directory services to the network and to the Internet. The first daemon (which has different names depending on the directory service used) is responsible for managing the directory itself. A directory is, for the most part, a large, relational database that requires maintenance to stay current. This first daemon indexes the entire directory so searches can be performed. It also responds to directory calls in its own (non-LDAP) query language and protocol. The second daemon is used to provide LDAP access to the directory. The LDAP daemon waits until an LDAP query is received. The LDAP daemon formats the query in the directory's native query language and passes the query on to the directory service daemon. The directory service daemon retrieves the requested information and passes it back to the LDAP daemon, which in turn returns the information to the requesting client.

Uses for Directory Servers

As previously mentioned, directory servers on the Internet are primarily used to look up information about people. On servers like those at www.four11 .com and www.whowhere.com, you can search for addresses, phone numbers, and e-mail addresses of people you know using only part of their name for the query. For example, if you had a friend in high school that you lost touch with over the years and you know his name and the state you think he lives in, you could go to one of these directory servers and type in the information you know. The directory server would return the pertinent contact information for the people who match the query. Of course, there's no guarantee that your old high school friend will be among those listed, but the chances are pretty good.

Some companies use directory servers on their intranet as a company telephone directory. Rather than referring to a paper book or list of hundreds of names and telephone numbers, employees can type their requests into an LDAP client of some kind and query their company's directory server to find the phone number (and other information) of any other employee. The advantage to the company is that it saves paper and is much more efficient.

Examples of Directory Servers

The best example of a directory server is any server running Novell Directory Services (NDS), the default directory service for Novell NetWare versions 4.*x* and above. NDS LDAP functionality is provided by an additional module (LDAP Services for NDS) that can be downloaded from Novell's software download Web site (`www.novell.com/download/`) for free. NDS is the most widely used directory service, and it is also the most flexible.

For Internet servers, there are a number of choices, each with different advantages for different applications. But one of the most common LDAP servers in use is the Netscape Directory Server. It is available for many platforms, including various flavors of Unix and Windows NT. It's popular because many people use the Netscape Enterprise server as their main Internet or intranet Web server, or they use the Netscape Web browser and they are already familiar with the administration of Netscape's products.

To see some actual implementations of directory servers, check out www
.four11.com, www.whowhere.com, www.switchboard.com, and www.infospace
.com. These servers use a Web interface to a public directory of people and
their addresses and telephone numbers.

Telnet Servers

A *Telnet server* is any server that uses the Telnet daemon and protocol to allow a user to access the console of a machine over a TCP/IP network as though she were sitting at the console. In the context of Internet sites, there are very few dedicated Telnet servers. Most Internet users prefer to receive their information in the graphical Web browser. Plus, allowing any user on the Internet access to a server's console is a large security breach!

In the following sections, you'll learn how Telnet servers work. We'll also give you the most common examples of Telnet servers.

How Telnet Servers Work

Servers that can be accessed via Telnet are usually running some form of a Telnet daemon. The Telnet daemon runs on the Unix server and waits for Telnet connections. When you telnet in to a Unix box, you run a Telnet client and connect to the Telnet daemon over a TCP/IP connection. When you type on the keyboard, each keystroke is sent from the client to the Telnet daemon. The Telnet daemon sends the keystroke on to the Unix kernel, just as if you were sitting at the Unix server's console typing the commands. The Unix kernel then returns the display of the character that was typed to the Telnet daemon, which in turn sends it back to the Telnet client, where it is displayed on the screen.

Each keystroke is displayed in this manner. As mentioned, the Unix server doesn't know whether a client is "telnetted in" or is sitting at the keyboard of the Unix server.

Telnet is primarily a feature of Unix machines, although third-party utilities allow telnetting into any machine that has a text interface and can run a Telnet daemon.

Uses for Telnet Servers

There are two primary uses for a Telnet server. The first is to allow remote administration of any server running the Telnet daemon. If the server running the Telnet daemon is connected to the Internet, an administrator could use a Telnet client to connect to the server and perform various administrative tasks like adding users, deleting users, running programs, and shutting down the system.

The other use is to provide LAN and Internet users access to text-based Unix applications through a Telnet client. In this application, a client can connect to a Unix server and run the application as though she were sitting at the machine. This use is not very popular because this approach opens up the server to potential security threats. Potential hackers would have access to the server's console—not a very desirable situation.

Examples of Telnet Servers

Because the great majority of Telnet servers are Unix-based servers, it's no surprise that the most popular Telnet daemon is the Unix Telnet daemon, TELNETd. When you install any brand of Unix, the installation program will install several Unix components, and the Telnet daemon is almost always included. This service will automatically be started when Unix boots, and you will be able to telnet in to the server from any client on the network.

Summary

In this chapter, you learned about all the different kinds of Internet servers in use today (and covered on the i-Net+ exam), as well as how they work and their common use(s). The chapter also included some examples of each type of server. All these Internet servers use some kind of daemon (a network service that runs on the server and waits for a connection from a client of some kind). Table 4.1 lists the various types of servers and the names of the most common daemons for each.

TABLE 4.1   Internet Servers and Their Daemons

Server	Common Daemon Name(s)
Web (HTTP) server	NCSA HTTPd, Microsoft IIS
FTP server	NCSA FTPd, Microsoft IIS, Apache
News (NNTP) server	INND
Mail (SMTP) server	Sendmail
Proxy server	Microsoft Proxy Server, Apache

TABLE 4.1 Internet Servers and Their Daemons *(continued)*

Server	Common Daemon Name(s)
Directory (LDAP) server	NDS with LDAP Services for NDS, Netscape Directory Service
Telnet server	TELNETd

There are a few key points you should remember about each type of server:

HTTP servers   HTTP servers are the most popular type of server on the Internet. They are most commonly used for delivering documents and other content to Web browsers using the Hypertext Transfer Protocol (HTTP). Additionally, they are used to provide e-commerce services (buying products and services over the Internet).

FTP servers   FTP servers allow people to download files over the Internet. Often, these servers are used in conjunction with HTTP servers so that users can use the Web to search for the files and then use FTP to download them.

News servers   News servers provide an area for discussions to take place over the Internet. They store and forward news messages and deliver them using the Network News Transfer Protocol (NNTP). News messages are organized by topic into discussion groups called newsgroups.

Mail (SMTP) servers   Mail servers provide messaging services over the Internet by storing and forwarding Internet e-mail messages. When forwarding messages, Internet mail servers use the Simple Mail Transfer Protocol (SMTP).

Proxy servers   Proxy servers provide Internet services on behalf of their clients. Clients make requests to an Internet server, but the request goes to the proxy server first. The proxy server then makes the request on behalf of the requesting client. The response comes back to the proxy server, which returns it to the requesting client. To increase performance, proxy servers can also cache the responses; then, the next time a Web browser makes a similar request, the proxy responds at a much faster speed than the requested server would.

Directory servers Directory servers provide directory information to requesting clients using the Lightweight Directory Access Protocol (LDAP). Directory servers can provide names, e-mail addresses, phone numbers, and location information to requesting clients.

Telnet servers Telnet servers are most often Unix machines and run a Telnet daemon, which allows clients to access the console as if they were using the keyboard of the Telnet server itself.

Table 4.2 lists the URLs of some Web sites that offer examples of some of the types of servers discussed in this chapter. You could also visit your ISP's home page for a list of some of these servers it may have.

TABLE 4.2 Some Examples of Common Servers

Type of server	Address
Web (HTTP)	http://www.sybex.com
FTP	FTP://ftp.cdrom.com
News (NNTP)	http://www.dejanews.com
Mail (SMTP)	http://www.hotmail.com
Directory	http://www.switchboard.com

Review Questions

1. Which protocol is used by Internet mail servers for delivering Internet mail?

   A. HTTP

   C. SMTP

   B. FTP

   D. NNTP

2. Which of the following is an example of an HTTP server?

   A. IIS

   B. Sendmail

   C. TELNETd

   D. INN

3. Which server, when implemented, would allow you to perform searches for information on people and their e-mail addresses?

   A. Directory server

   B. FTP server

   C. Mail server

   D. Telnet server

4. Which protocol is used by Internet Web servers to deliver content to Web browsers?

   A. FTP

   B. HTTP

   C. LDAP

   D. NNTP

5. Which Internet server(s) can function in more than one capacity (i.e., serve more than one type of client)?

   A. IIS

   B. Apache

   C. INN

   D. SMTP

6. Which Internet server can increase the performance of Web surfing?

   A. Proxy server

   B. HTTP server

   C. FTP server

   D. SMTP server

7. Which HTTP server(s) is/are available for free download from the Internet?

   A. NDS

   B. FTPd

   C. Apache

   D. INN

8. Which protocol is most often used for file transfer?

   A. SMTP

   B. LDAP

   C. NNTP

   D. FTP

9. In order to be an e-commerce server, a Web server must offer what service(s)?

    A. File transfer

    B. credit card authentication

    C. Virtual shopping cart services

    D. Directory queries

10. Which FTP daemon is available for Unix?

    A. IIS

    B. FTPd

    C. INN

    D. LDAP

11. Telnet daemons are installed by default on which NOS platform(s)?

    A. NetWare

    B. Windows NT

    C. Unix

    D. OS/2

12. Apache is an example of which kind of Internet server?

    A. HTTP

    B. FTP

    C. News

    D. SMTP

13. What TCP/IP protocol is used to access directory servers?

    A. NNTP

    B. FTP

    C. SMTP

    D. LDAP

14. What is the default TCP/IP suite protocol used to communicate between Internet news servers?

    A. NNTP

    B. FTP

    C. SMTP

    D. LDAP

15. Which of the following is an example of a Unix Internet news daemon?

    A. FTPd

    B. INN

    C. IIS

    D. HTTPd

16. What is the name of the utility used to administer IIS?

    A. Services Manager

    B. Internet Service Manger

    C. Internet Information Server Manager

    D. Services Control Panel

17. Which of the following Internet servers does *not* run on Windows NT?

    A. IIS

    B. INN

    C. Apache

    D. Microsoft Proxy Server

18. A _____ is an SMTP server that sends any e-mails it receives to a list of e-mail recipients, thus forming a kind of "discussion group."

    A. List server

    B. E-commerce server

    C. News server

    D. Web server

19. Novell's NDS can be used as a _____ server.

    A. Web

    B. FTP

    C. Directory

    D. News

20. A _____ server is a type of Internet server that is used for e-commerce and facilitates secure transactions.

    A. FTP

    B. Certificate

    C. Directory

    D. Telnet

Answers to Review Questions

1. C. SMTP is the only protocol used by Internet mail servers to deliver mail. The other protocols are used for different Internet services.

2. A. The other daemons listed are used for other Internet services.

3. A. None of the other servers can perform this kind of search.

4. B. The Hypertext Transfer Protocol (HTTP) is used to deliver content from Web servers to Web browsers. FTP is used to transfer files, LDAP is for directory access, and NNTP is used by news servers.

5. A, B. IIS has components for HTTP, FTP, and proxy serving. Apache has components for HTTP and proxy serving. INN is for Internet news and SMTP is for Internet mail.

6. A. Proxy servers can cache the responses to Internet requests and provide them (at a much faster rate) to other clients when they make the same request.

7. C. Of all the answers listed, Apache is the only Web server and, consequently, the correct answer. NDS is a directory server, FTPd is an FTP server, and INN is a news server.

8. D. Although SMTP and NNTP might be used to transfer files as attachments to messages, FTP is the protocol used to directly transfer files from server to client.

9. B, C. These two services are the key services that, apart from content, make a regular HTTP server into an e-commerce server. File transfer and directory queries are functions of other types of servers.

10. B. Of those listed, FTPd is the only FTP daemon available for Unix.

11. C. Unix is the only platform that currently installs a Telnet daemon *by default*. The other NOSes listed may have Telnet capability, but it is an add-on feature.

12. A. Apache is a free HTTP server.

13. D. LDAP is the protocol used to access directory servers over the Internet. NNTP is used for Internet news, FTP is used for file transfer, and SMTP is used for e-mail.

14. A. NNTP is the TCP/IP protocol used to deliver Internet news. LDAP is the protocol used to access directory servers over the Internet, FTP is used for file transfer, and SMTP is used for e-mail.

15. B. The Internet News Daemon (INN) is the only daemon listed that can provide access to Internet news. FTPd is for FTP; HTTPd and IIS are for Web services.

16. B. The Microsoft Internet Service Manager is used to administer IIS and all its components.

17. B. The Internet News Daemon is only available for Unix (although attempts are being made to recompile it for Windows NT).

18. A. List servers are the only servers that perform this function.

19. C. Novell Directory Services (NDS), when used only with LDAP Services for NDS, can be used as a directory server. NDS is a directory service and cannot be used as a Web, FTP, or news server.

20. B. Certificate servers are used in conjunction with e-commerce servers to ensure that both sender and receiver in an e-commerce transaction are who they say they are.

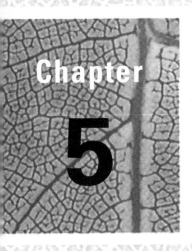

Chapter

5

Internet Clients

i-NET+ EXAM OBJECTIVES COVERED IN THIS CHAPTER:

✓ **Describe the infrastructure needed to support an Internet client. Content could include the following:**

- TCP/IP stack
- Operating system
- Network connection
- Web browser
- E-mail
- Hardware platform (PC, handheld device, WebTV, Internet phone)

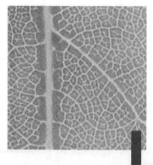

In Chapter 4, you learned about all the different types of servers that can be found on the Internet, how they work, and what they are used for, and you looked at some examples of each type of server. You'll remember from earlier chapters that the server is only one half of the client-server equation. You've learned about the server portion of the equation; now it's time to learn about the other half: Internet clients.

Of the Internet components, Internet clients are the most visible. An *Internet client* is the combination of hardware and software that allows a user to interact with servers on the Internet. The Internet client formats server requests, sends the requests to the server, and displays the results when they are received from the server.

In this chapter, you'll learn about the most common clients used on the Internet and the requirements for using them.

Internet Client Requirements

In order to use a client to make requests of the Internet, you must have a few items in place. These items make it possible for you to run the client application and use it for Internet requests:

- Hardware

- Operating system

- TCP/IP

- Internet connection

Without these items, you won't be able to use the Internet at all. Agreed—some of them are pretty obvious, but you should at least know that they are required. In this section, you will learn what items are required to run a client and use it to connect to the Internet.

Hardware

Hardware is any computer item that you can touch. Internet clients do require some type(s) of hardware in order to run. The following sections will discuss all of the hardware issues relating to Internet clients, including the following:

- Hardware requirements
- Internet client hardware platforms
- Connection hardware

You'll learn the impact each item has on Internet client use.

Hardware Requirements

Each client software package has its own hardware requirements, usually listed on the side of the box or on the manufacturer's Web site. If the hardware requirements aren't met, the software either won't run at all or will run poorly. The following list includes some of the hardware requirements you'll come across for client software:

Minimum processor speed Specifies the slowest possible processor (CPU) the client will run on. Although the software will run if the processor in your PC is the same as this value, to realize the best possible performance, it is commonly recommended that you have a processor in your computer that is newer (faster) than the specified processor.

Minimum RAM Specifies the minimum amount of memory (RAM) you must have installed in your PC for the client software to run correctly. The specification is usually given in megabytes (MB). However, for best performance, make sure the RAM configuration in your computer *exceeds* this requirement.

Hard disk space required Signifies how much disk space (megabytes, or MB) the client will require in order to be installed on your system. This number is usually pretty accurate, but it's never a bad idea to have a bit more than the requirement.

Because many software companies are realizing that software won't run well at the "minimum" requirements, some are now releasing "suggested" configurations. When at all possible, ensure that your computer is at the suggested hardware level rather than the minimum.

Internet Client Hardware Platforms

Internet clients have to run on some type of electronic hardware device. These devices fall into one of two categories, each with its own merits and disadvantages. We'll describe two of the platforms: the personal computer (PC) and the Internet appliance.

Personal Computer

Many homes have personal computers today. A personal computer (PC) is the most common Internet client hardware platform—mainly because it is so flexible. In addition to supporting Internet clients, a PC can be used to play games and use productivity applications (like a word processor or a spreadsheet program). Therefore, a PC's main advantage is its flexibility. Its main disadvantage is its cost, which is, however, continuing to drop. In fact, nowadays, it's possible to buy a PC for less than $1,000 for the entire system, including a printer.

Internet Appliance

Those that can't (or won't) buy a PC for their home may instead have an Internet appliance like Microsoft's WebTV. An *Internet appliance* is a device that you connect to your television and to a phone line to provide Internet access without a computer. Internet appliances usually come with a wireless keyboard so you can type information into forms and search engines. If your main reason for owning a PC is to search the Web, an Internet appliance may be a better choice. However, there are a few drawbacks:

- It has limited upgradability.

- You are required to sign up with the Internet appliance manufacturer's Internet Service Provider (ISP).

- There is little support for JavaScript or other client-side scripting technologies.

- It can't be used for other applications (for example, word processing).

- You can't install third-party utilities on it. If it's not built in to the "box," the box probably can't run it.

Other Devices

These days, many devices can be used as Internet hardware platforms, including cellular phones, Internet phones, and handheld PCs. Many different hardware devices are being created to allow different ways of accessing the Internet.

Connection Hardware

The other item of hardware you must consider when setting up an Internet client is the connection hardware. Connection hardware is the device(s) you use to connect your computer to your ISP. If you are connecting to the Internet via a regular phone line, you'll need a modem. As discussed in Chapter 1, a modem is a device that converts the digital signals (electrical impulses) from your computer into analog signals (tones) that can be transmitted over the telephone. When these signals reach the other end, the receiving modem converts the analog signals back to digital signals so the computer can understand what's being transmitted. Most computers you buy today come with a modem and Internet connection software already installed.

If you are connecting your computer to a LAN that is already connected to the Internet, you must install a device known as a network interface card (NIC) in order to get your PC on the Internet. As discussed in Chapter 1, the NIC converts the signals from your computer into a format the network can understand. The network administrator has already installed the hardware (i.e., routers, CSU/DSUs, and so on) that are required to connect the LAN to the Internet, so the NIC just connects your PC to the LAN and, thus, to the Internet.

Operating System (OS)

In addition to having a computer of some sort, you must have an operating system installed on your computer so the computer knows how to run applications and do "useful" things (like browsing the Internet). An operating system controls and manages all the functions of the computer on which it is installed. Additionally, it provides the interface between the user and the computer and its applications.

For the i-Net+ exam, you must know that the computer you are using to connect to the Internet must have an operating system installed on it (you can't use the computer without an OS). Furthermore, you must understand that for any Internet clients you install, your computer must be running the required OS version or the client won't install properly (or at all). For example, if you are installing a Web browser and the OS requirements say, "For Windows 95/98," that means this client only runs on the Windows 95 or Windows 98 operating system. If you try to install it on a Macintosh, it won't work (it actually won't even install).

TCP/IP Protocol Stack

Another requirement that all Internet clients have in common is that the TCP/IP protocol must be installed and running. The TCP/IP protocol stack is one of several protocol stacks. A *protocol stack* is a collection, or suite, of protocols that work together. As discussed in Chapter 3, the Internet is based on the Transmission Control Protocol/Internet Protocol (TCP/IP) suite of protocols. If the TCP/IP protocol is not installed and configured correctly, the Internet clients will be unable to send data to and receive data from the Internet. Thankfully, most operating systems (including Windows 95, 98, and NT and the MacOS) include TCP/IP support.

The software that provides TCP/IP support for Windows applications is known as WINSOCK.DLL. You may hear about commercial TCP/IP software that requires "Winsock compliance." This just means that the software will use the Winsock DLL to connect to the Internet. Most (if not all) Windows Internet clients are Winsock clients.

Internet Connection

This requirement for an Internet client almost goes without saying. If you're going to use an Internet client, you must have a connection to the Internet. There is one exception, however. If you have your own intranet and you're going to use your Internet clients as clients for your intranet, then you don't need an Internet connection. Many companies that do this also have an Internet connection because it is a valuable tool to offer employees.

The type of Internet connection you should have varies depending on your Internet needs. If you are in charge of connecting your company to the Internet and you have hundreds of computers that need access, you may want a leased-line connection of some kind between your network and your ISP. If you are setting up your computer to connect to the Internet from home, it may only be feasible to have a slower-speed (and thus, cheaper) connection to the Internet like a Plain Old Telephone Service (POTS) dial-up, Integrated Services Digital Network (ISDN), or Digital Subscriber Line (xDSL) connection.

Chapter 1 details the different types of Internet connections and their merits.

Types of Internet Clients

Just as there are many types of Internet content servers, there are many different types of Internet clients. For the most part, each client allows access to a different type of server. In this section, you'll learn about the different types of Internet clients and what they are used for, and we'll give you at least one example of each type of client.

Web Browser

When most people think of the Internet, they think of a graphical environment with lots of pictures, audio, and text. It wouldn't be possible to display this content from Web servers without the Web client (more commonly called a *Web browser*). A Web browser is an application that you use to submit requests for Internet content (i.e., Web pages, graphics, and so on) to a Web server using the Hypertext Transfer Protocol (HTTP). The Web browser also displays the responses to those requests on the screen.

Before we give you some examples of Web browsers, we'll discuss some of the components Web browsers have in common.

Web Browser Components

Although there are a few different Web browsers available, they all share a similar "look." Because Web browsers today are based, in some way, on the work done by the National Center for Supercomputing Applications (NCSA), they all have at least a few items in common (as shown in Figure 5.1):

Browser window   This is the main part of the Web browser, where the text and graphics of a Web page are displayed.

Location bar   The location bar is the component that displays the location of the Web page currently showing in the browser window. If you type the address of a Web site into this area and press Enter, the Web browser locates the Web site and displays its home page.

Menu bar   As its name implies, this is the part of the browser that contains the menus. Click a word and a menu appears with choices that control the way you use the Web browser.

Button bar   This bar contains buttons that help you navigate within the WWW. The buttons are normally user-friendly and usually perform the operation indicated by their label (for example, the Back button takes you back to the page that was displayed before the current page).

Activity indicator   In most Web browsers, this indicator will be animated when a user has made a request and is waiting for the requested Web page or Internet content to display.

Status bar   At the bottom of the browser window, there is an area called the status bar (see Figure 5.1). It shows what's happening during the request-response sequence of a Web browsing session. It will show whether the site has responded and the progress of the response to the original request (usually with an indication of the percentage downloaded).

FIGURE 5.1   Components of a typical browser

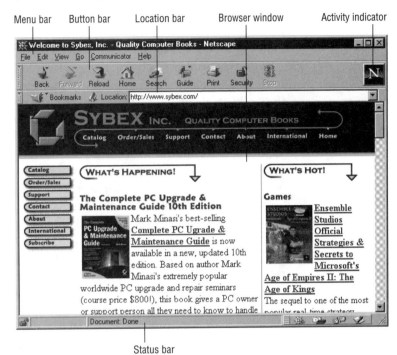

Menu bar   Button bar   Location bar   Browser window   Activity indicator

Status bar

Examples of Web Browsers

In the early days of the World Wide Web, there was only one Web browser, NCSA Mosaic. It was a very basic Web browser in that it could only display HTML text and GIF-formatted graphics. It was a free browser that you could download from the NCSA (although development rights were later sold to Spyglass). As the Internet grew, so did the number of browsers available. Every browser could display basic HTML and GIF graphics, but some could display the newer graphic format, JPEG (Joint Photographic Experts Group). Problems emerged when a Web site designed for one browser couldn't be displayed in another. Out of this chaos, two clear leaders emerged: Netscape Navigator and Microsoft Internet Explorer, both in some way based on NCSA Mosaic.

Netscape Navigator

Netscape Navigator was the first browser (apart from NCSA Mosaic) to gain widespread commercial acceptance. Navigator is extremely similar in both appearance and function to Mosaic. This is because it was developed by some of the members who originally developed NCSA Mosaic, including Marc Andreessen. In 1994, Marc left NCSA and, together with James Clark (formerly of Silicon Graphics), started Netscape Communications Corporation. Their first major product was a "Mosaic-killer" called Netscape Navigator, nicknamed Mozilla (after the name of an animated dragon that appeared in the activity indicator).

One of the features that made Netscape Navigator more popular than Mosaic was its support for document streaming. That is, Netscape Navigator would display items as it would receive them rather than waiting until it received all the items on a page before displaying them (as Mosaic did).

Figure 5.2 shows an example of what Netscape Navigator looks like (actually part of Communicator version 4). Notice the large N in the upper-right corner of the browser window (the activity indicator). This indicator is one characteristic that can help you identify which browser you are using. Also, when you are sending and receiving data on the Internet, the N will be animated with stars moving in the background.

Currently, Netscape Navigator has been incorporated into a full Internet communications suite known as Netscape Communicator. Communicator includes the standard Navigator component as well as components for reading and composing e-mail, reading and composing Internet news, and a collaboration tool.

For information on Netscape Navigator, check out www.netscape.com.

FIGURE 5.2 The Netscape Navigator browser

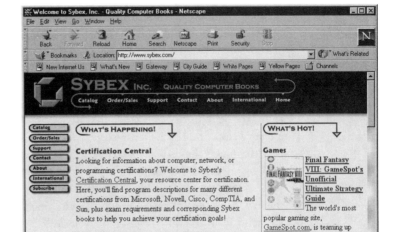

Microsoft Internet Explorer

Microsoft was late to the "Internet game." They were too busy working on their operating system and application platforms to worry about this "passing fad" called the Internet. But once they saw how popular the Netscape browser was, they had to have a piece of the market (actually, they wanted all of it). So, to quickly get their Internet market share, Microsoft now includes their Internet Explorer browser for free in all versions of their operating system, and it is difficult to remove (which was the source of the Microsoft/Department of Justice antitrust case). It is also available for free download from the Internet.

If you are interested, information on the Microsoft antitrust case can be found at www.findlaw.com/01topics/01antitrust/microsoft.html or www.microsoft.com/freedomtoinnovate/default.htm.

Because they were late to the party, Microsoft had to put together a browser in a hurry. What they ultimately did was purchase the licensing rights to the majority of the original Mosaic code from Spyglass, then added a few tweaks and released it as Internet Explorer 1. While Netscape Navigator dominated the browser market, Microsoft was going to make up for lost time by releasing a modification to Windows 95 called the Windows 95 Plus Pack. This software package included a few neat utilities, some games, and the new browser, Internet Explorer (nicknamed IE). Additionally, Microsoft included IE in the OEM release of Windows 95 and NT for distribution to computer manufacturers.

Figure 5.3 shows the Microsoft Internet Explorer window (version 5). Again, the distinguishing feature of this browser is the activity indicator. Note that it is now a Windows icon rather than a big N.

FIGURE 5.3 The Internet Explorer browser

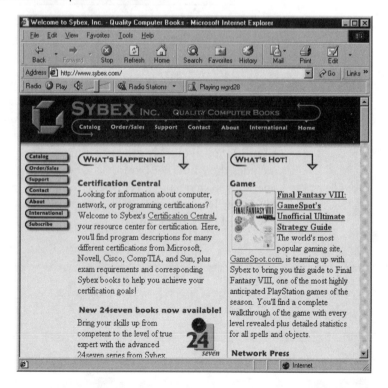

FTP Program

As mentioned in earlier chapters, FTP utilities are used to upload and download files to and from FTP servers. Unlike Web browsers, there are many different types of FTP clients. Some clients use text commands on a command line to transfer files. Other FTP clients display directories and files in a graphical interface and use mouse-clicks and menu commands to perform the file transfer functions.

There are three main FTP utilities in use today:

- Unix FTP

- Windows 95/98 FTP

- Web browsers

In this section, you'll get a general overview of the types of FTP clients in use today and how they look. In Chapter 6, you'll learn how to use an FTP client to upload and download files.

Unix FTP

The first FTP utility that was ever used was the Unix FTP utility. It's a pretty simple program. The user starts the program by typing **FTP** at a Unix command prompt. Once the program begins, a command line appears that usually looks something like this:

```
FTP>
```

At the command line, the user types commands to tell the FTP program which file to get, where to get it, and how to get it. Table 5.1 lists some of the popular commands you might use when you're using the Unix command-line FTP utility to download or upload a file. How you use these commands to transfer files is covered in "Using FTP to Download and Upload Files" in Chapter 6. Also, Figure 5.4 shows a command-line FTP utility in use.

TABLE 5.1   Unix FTP Commands

Command	Syntax	Description
open	open *<address>*	Opens an FTP session with an FTP server (for example, open ftp.sybex.com).

TABLE 5.1 Unix FTP Commands *(continued)*

Command	Syntax	Description
ls	ls	Used to list all the files and directories in the current directory (similar to the MS-DOS DIR command).
cd	cd *<dirname>*	Used to change the current directory. Used almost exactly like the MS-DOS CD command.
get	get *<filename>*	Specifies the name of the file on the remote host to download and then begins to download the specified file to the local computer.
mget	mget *<wildcards>*	Specifies multiple files (through the use of a filter) to download and starts downloading them one at a time.
put	put *<filename>*	Specifies the name of the file on the local computer to upload and then begins to upload the file to the remote computer.
mput	mput *<wildcards>*	Specifies multiple files (through the use of a filter) to upload to the remote computer and then starts to upload them one at a time.
binary	binary	Sets the transfer mode for files to binary. This must be set in order to transfer binary files (any file that is not composed of ASCII text) correctly.
ascii	ascii	Sets the transfer mode for files to ASCII text mode for transferring HTML and other ASCII text documents.
hash	hash	Toggles the printing of hash marks for each 8K downloaded.

TABLE 5.1 Unix FTP Commands *(continued)*

Command	Syntax	Description
prompt	prompt	Toggles prompting between each file upload or download using the mput or mget commands, respectively.
quit	quit	Ends the current FTP session and closes the FTP program.

FIGURE 5.4 A Unix FTP utility in use

```
$ ftp
ftp> open ftp.corpcomm.net
Connected to ns2.corpcomm.net.
220 ns2 FTP server (SunOS 5.6) ready.
Name (ftp.corpcomm.net:dgroth): anonymous
331 Guest login ok, send ident as password.
Password:
230 Guest login ok, access restrictions apply.
ftp> ls
200 PORT command successful.
150 ASCII data connection for /bin/ls (199.165.217.101,45865) (0 bytes).
0bin
abs-usa
bin
dev
etc
pub
usr
226 ASCII Transfer complete.
40 bytes received in 0.075 seconds (0.52 Kbytes/s)
ftp> cd pub
250 CWD command successful.
ftp> █
```

Windows 95/98/NT FTP

Every release of Windows since (and including) Windows 95 has included a command-line FTP program that almost exactly duplicates the Unix FTP utility. The commands and their uses are the same. Additionally, the "look and feel" is almost identical (as shown in Figure 5.5).

FIGURE 5.5 The Windows command-line FTP utility

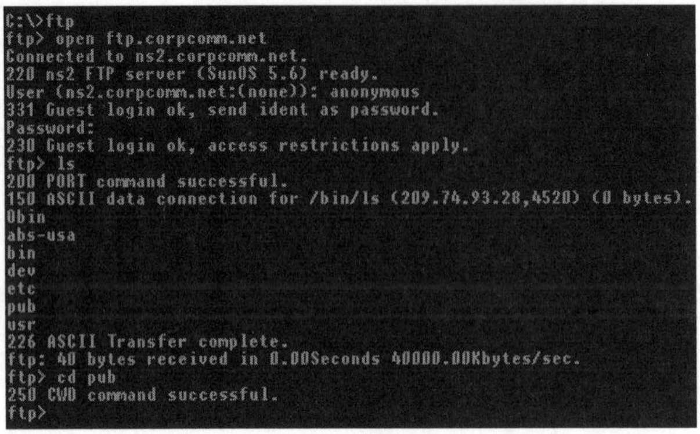

```
C:\>ftp
ftp> open ftp.corpcomm.net
Connected to ns2.corpcomm.net.
220 ns2 FTP server (SunOS 5.6) ready.
User (ns2.corpcomm.net:(none)): anonymous
331 Guest login ok, send ident as password.
Password:
230 Guest login ok, access restrictions apply.
ftp> ls
200 PORT command successful.
150 ASCII data connection for /bin/ls (209.74.93.28,4520) (0 bytes).
Obin
abs-usa
bin
dev
etc
pub
usr
226 ASCII Transfer complete.
ftp: 40 bytes received in 0.00Seconds 40000.00Kbytes/sec.
ftp> cd pub
250 CWD command successful.
ftp>
```

You can start the Windows FTP utility one of two ways. You can run the Windows Command Prompt (Start ➤ Programs ➤ MS-DOS or Start ➤ Programs ➤ Command Prompt) and type **FTP** to start the FTP utility. You could also start it by choosing Start ➤ Run, typing **FTP**, and clicking OK. Once it starts, it will work almost exactly the same as its Unix counterpart. The main difference is that, in the Windows version, local path names are shown in DOS format instead of Unix format.

Graphical FTP Utilities

Although FTP was historically a command-line utility, many companies have made graphical interfaces to make the process of transferring files to and from the Internet easier. Of the FTP utilities available for purchase or download, graphic FTP utilities are the most popular. Figure 5.6 shows an example of one such FTP utility, WS_FTP by Ipswitch Software. Rather than using complex command-line commands, graphical FTP utilities such as these represent both the local and host systems on the screen and use buttons and icons for some of the commands you can perform. For example, remember the binary FTP command that changed the transfer mode to binary. Notice in Figure 5.6 that the graphic utility has a radio button for that function.

FIGURE 5.6 An example of a graphic FTP utility (WS_FTP)

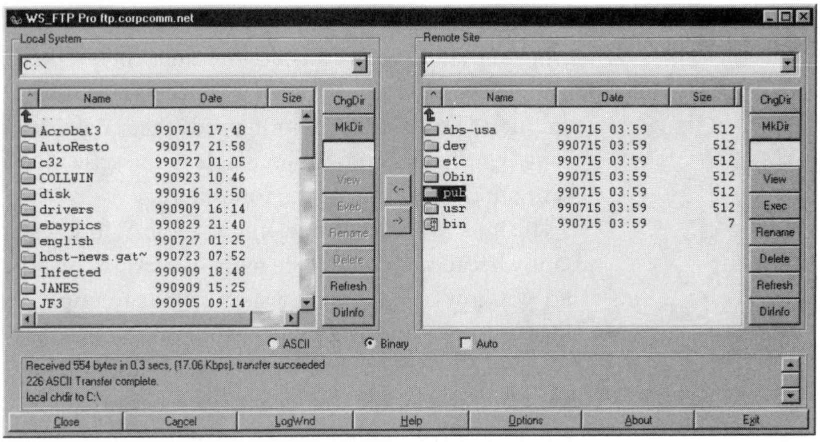

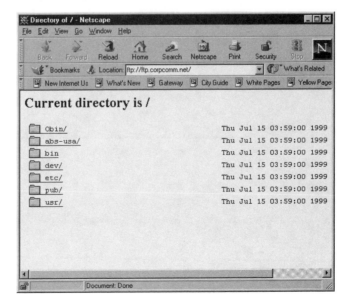

A graphical FTP utility that you have used but may not know it is your Web browser. Most Web browsers (including Netscape Navigator and Microsoft Internet Explorer) support transferring files using the FTP protocol. If you access an FTP server with a Web browser (either by typing in an FTP URL or clicking a link that leads to an FTP server), the browser will display the files in a list and allow you to navigate the FTP server's directory structure as well as download the file by clicking it. Figure 5.7 shows what Netscape Navigator looks like during a typical FTP transaction.

FIGURE 5.7 Using Netscape Navigator as an FTP client

Terminal (Telnet) Client

Telnet clients allow you enter commands on a Unix server without actually sitting at that server's console. A Telnet client takes the keystrokes from the client's keyboard and sends them to the Telnet daemon running on the Unix computer. The Telnet daemon sends the screen displays back to the Telnet client. The Telnet client then displays the screen updates within the Telnet client window on the client computer.

The most popular Telnet client is the Windows 95/98/NT Telnet client, mainly because it comes free with all versions of Windows since (and including) Windows 95. Figure 5.8 shows what a sample Telnet session would look like using the Windows Telnet program. Notice that the first thing you must do when telnetting in to a Unix server is log in. This is a function of the Unix server and not of the Telnet program because Unix requires you to log in before you do anything else. The Telnet program just displays the login and lets you log in as though you were sitting at the console.

FIGURE 5.8   The Windows Telnet client

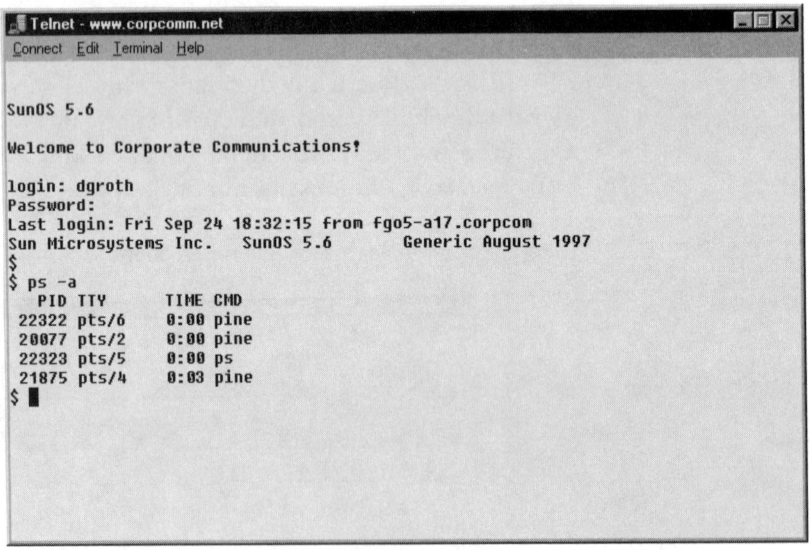

```
Telnet - www.corpcomm.net
Connect  Edit  Terminal  Help


SunOS 5.6

Welcome to Corporate Communications!

login: dgroth
Password:
Last login: Fri Sep 24 18:32:15 from fgo5-a17.corpcom
Sun Microsystems Inc.   SunOS 5.6      Generic August 1997
$
$ ps -a
   PID TTY       TIME CMD
 22322 pts/6     0:00 pine
 20077 pts/2     0:00 pine
 22323 pts/5     0:00 ps
 21875 pts/4     0:03 pine
$
```

News Client

News clients (also called newsreaders) allow you to read and post Internet news messages from an Internet news server using the NNTP protocol. Using the news client, you can view a list of all the newsgroups that exist on a specified news server. If you like a particular newsgroup (`alt.autos .studebaker`, for example), you can configure your news client to show you all the headers (subject lines) of all the messages in that newsgroup. Then, if a particular message looks interesting, you can click that message to read it and, if you wish, to respond to it.

Figure 5.9 shows one example of a newsreader: Microsoft Outlook Newsreader (it comes free with Microsoft Internet Explorer or Microsoft Outlook). As you can see, this client's screen is divided into four main areas. Across the top of the window are the menu and navigation bars. Below that, along the left side of the window, is the list of news servers and newsgroups you are subscribed to on those servers. To the right of that, in the top pane, is the list of headers of all the messages for the newsgroup that is selected in the left pane. If you click one of these headers, the client downloads the message to your machine and displays the contents of the message in the message display pane (the largest portion of this client, immediately to the right of the newsgroup list).

FIGURE 5.9 Microsoft Outlook Newsreader

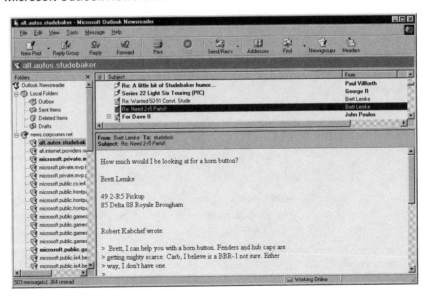

Most news clients work in a similar fashion. They may not all look exactly the same, but there will be a list of news servers along with the list of newsgroups you subscribe to on each server, and there will be a window with a list of the headers of the messages for each newsgroup and a window where you can view the body of the message.

Some other examples of newsreaders include Netscape News and Free Agent. Again, like Microsoft Outlook Newsreader, they will function similarly.

E-Mail Client

Internet e-mail clients are those software programs used to send and receive e-mail and communicate with SMTP servers. E-mail clients send mail using the SMTP protocol. They also download e-mail from SMTP servers using the POP3 protocol. E-mail clients are the second most-popular Internet client software installed on computers today (as you might imagine, Web browsers are the most popular).

E-mail clients typically include a couple of standard features:

Inbox   The Inbox is a location where all incoming mail resides. Typically, new mail in the Inbox has some kind of designation to differentiate it from mail that hasn't been read. Some software packages use an unopened envelope icon next to the message to indicate a new message and an opened envelope to indicate a message that has been read.

Outbox   The Outbox is a folder where all messages go as soon as you hit the Send button. The messages stay in this folder until they are sent to the server. This feature allows you to see what items are waiting to be sent. The main reason this feature exists is for people who send a lot of e-mail and may want to make a last-minute change after they click Send. However, once the message has been sent to the mail server, it disappears from this folder and can no longer be edited.

Sent items   This feature is a folder that keeps a duplicate copy of all messages that have been sent. When you send a message, a copy gets sent to the SMTP server and another copy gets placed into this folder. The Sent items folder allows you to keep track of what you have sent and to whom.

Address book   No e-mail program would be complete without an address book. This feature is a small database of the e-mail addresses of all the people you frequently send e-mail to. You can either type a person's e-mail address in every time you send e-mail to him or simply select his name from the address book. The program will read the selected person's e-mail address from the address book and put it in the To line of the new e-mail message, which is much more efficient.

There are two major examples of e-mail clients in use today: Microsoft Outlook and Netscape Messenger. A version of each is available with the associated manufacturer's Web browser product (Internet Explorer and Navigator, respectively). In this section, we'll briefly cover these two popular e-mail clients and explain what their interfaces look like. Configuration and use will follow in the next chapter.

Microsoft Outlook

Microsoft Outlook is one of the most popular e-mail clients for several reasons. First, it is included with the Microsoft Office 97 and Office 2000 office productivity suites, so it is readily available on many computers. Also, it is easy to use because many people are familiar with the Microsoft Office suite of products and it has a similar interface, so using it is second nature. Finally, it includes many other features besides e-mail, including a powerful contact management feature and an integrated calendar and task list.

Figure 5.10 shows the screen of Outlook 98. There are a few things to note about this graphic. The bar on the left of the screen is known as the Outlook bar, and it contains icons for your Inbox (where mail is received and stored until you move it to another folder), your Contacts folder (basically, a very powerful address book), your Calendar, and other folders. To the right of that is the display of whatever folder happens to be selected in the Outlook bar (in this case, the Inbox). If you select a different folder on the left, a different window will display on the right. Above these two windows are the menu bar and button bar. Items on these two bars are used to perform the various functions in Outlook, like creating new mail, checking for new mail, replying to mail, and organizing mail, to name a few. We'll cover how to use Outlook to send and receive mail in the next chapter.

FIGURE 5.10 Microsoft Outlook window

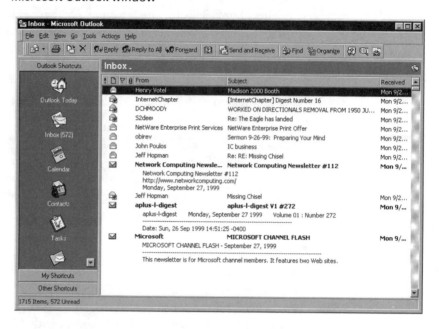

Netscape Messenger

Unlike Microsoft Outlook, Netscape Messenger (also called Netscape Mail in older versions of Netscape) is just a mail program, although the folks at Netscape may not like us for saying so. It does include a basic address book and the ability to read HTML embedded in the body of an e-mail message. Plus, it is available for free download along with Netscape Navigator.

Figure 5.11 shows what Netscape Messenger looks like. Notice that the layout of Netscape Messenger is somewhat similar to the layout of Outlook Newsreader. The list of messages (i.e., the Inbox) is at the top of the screen, and the selected message is viewed in a pane below that. Additionally, Netscape Messenger can display messages in HTML format. Apart from those items, Netscape Messenger is pretty similar to most other mail programs in functionality.

FIGURE 5.11   Netscape Messenger

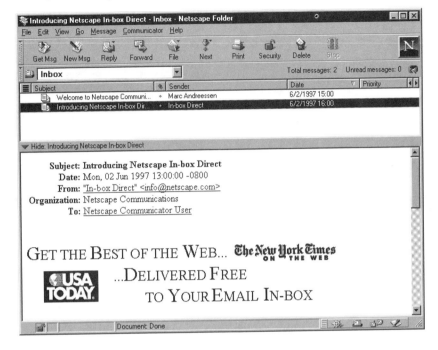

QUALCOMM Eudora

No discussion of e-mail products would be complete without a discussion of the most popular shareware, Eudora, made by QUALCOMM. There are actually two separate versions of Eudora, Eudora Pro and Eudora Light. The Eudora Pro product is a full-featured, powerful, commercial version that you can buy. Eudora Light is a stripped-down (although it still maintains many advanced features) version of Eudora Pro and is available for download for free from the QUALCOMM Web site (`eudora.qualcomm.com`).

As you can see in Figure 5.12, Eudora looks similar to the other Internet mail clients (especially Outlook). You can select a folder on the left and view its contents in the window on the right. Individual messages are listed, and you can view their contents by double-clicking them.

FIGURE 5.12 QUALCOMM's Eudora

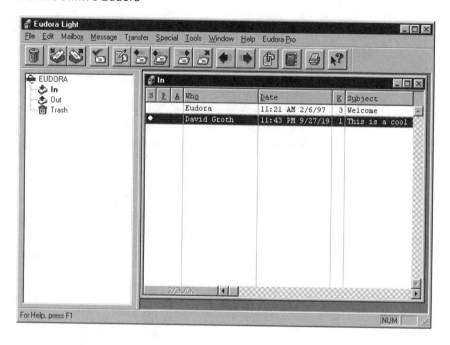

Summary

In this chapter, you learned about the infrastructure needed to support an Internet client. The items needed to support an Internet client include not only hardware but software as well. There are five main items:

Hardware platform To get on the Internet, you need to use a hardware device of some kind. You can use either a PC or an Internet appliance. A PC is the most common choice, but more and more you'll find people using Internet appliances (like the WebTV device) to surf the Internet. Internet appliances are inexpensive, but they can only perform certain Internet tasks (like browsing the Web and sending and receiving e-mail). If you use a PC, you may need additional hardware (for example, a modem or NIC) to support your connection to the Internet.

Operating system   Every hardware platform must have an operating system. This isn't so much an Internet requirement as simply a requirement of the hardware. If you want to do anything on a computer or appliance, you must have an operating system installed. Windows 95/98 is the most common Internet client operating system.

Network connection   This requirement means you must have a connection to the Internet in some form. Whether you use a modem in your PC or your entire network is connected to the Internet, you must have some kind of connection to an ISP to support your Internet clients.

Web browser   A Web browser is the Internet client that creates HTTP requests and displays the Internet content it receives. It is the tool used to view all the content on the World Wide Web (WWW). The two most popular browsers in use today are Netscape Navigator and Microsoft Internet Explorer. They both are based on the Mosaic Web browser developed at the National Center for Supercomputing Applications (NCSA) at the University of Illinois at Urbana-Champaign, so they are similar in appearance and function. The main difference in their appearance is the activity indicator. IE has a Windows icon and Navigator has an animated N.

E-mail   An e-mail client is an Internet client that can send and receive e-mail using the SMTP and POP3 (or IMAP) TCP/IP protocols, respectively. The two most popular Internet e-mail clients in use today are Netscape Messenger (also called Netscape Mail) and Microsoft Outlook.

Review Questions

1. Which item is *not* required in order to use a Web browser to browse the Internet?

   A. TCP/IP address

   B. Internet connection

   C. Some kind of hardware (PC or other) Internet device

   D. FTP client

2. Which component of a Web browser indicates activity when animated?

   A. Menu bar

   B. Button bar

   C. Activity indicator

   D. Status bar

3. Which Internet client(s) can be used to transfer files from an FTP server?

   A. FTP client

   B. Web browser

   C. Mail client

   D. Internet news client

4. Which Internet client(s) can be used to send, receive, and read SMTP mail?

   A. FTP client

   B. Web browser

   C. Mail client

   D. Internet news client

5. Which Internet client(s) can be used to read Internet news?

   A. FTP client

   B. Web browser

   C. Mail client

   D. Internet news client

6. Which FTP command is used to download a single file?

   A. get

   B. mget

   C. put

   D. mput

7. What should your FTP client be set to in order to successfully download an EXE file?

   A. ls

   B. binary

   C. exe

   D. ascii

8. Suppose you need to set up someone to use the Internet, but she doesn't have a great deal of money to spend on a computer. What device could you install so she could still send and receive e-mail?

   A. Modem

   B. Telephone

   C. PC

   D. Internet appliance

9. What protocol must be installed in order for Internet clients to function?

    A. IPX/SPX

    B. NetBEUI

    C. TCP/IP

    D. HTTP

10. Which feature of an e-mail client allows you to keep track of the e-mail addresses of the people you commonly send e-mail to?

    A. Send and Receive

    B. Inbox

    C. Outbox

    D. Address book

11. Which network hardware device connects a computer to an ISP and the Internet via a standard phone line?

    A. PC

    B. Modem

    C. Internet appliance

    D. Processor

12. Which protocol(s) can the Microsoft Outlook e-mail client use to send and receive e-mail over the Internet?

    A. IPX/SPX

    B. POP3

    C. SMTP

    D. FTP

13. Which Internet client allows you to perform Unix commands on another computer just as if you were sitting at the console?

   A. Web client

   B. FTP client

   C. Internet news client

   D. Telnet client

14. Internet news clients run on which protocol?

   A. FTP

   B. HTTP

   C. NNTP

   D. POP3

15. Which Internet client(s) allows you to view Internet HTML and multimedia content?

   A. FTP client

   B. Web client

   C. Mail client

   D. News client

16. What is the name of Netscape's Internet e-mail program?

   A. E-Mail

   B. Outlook

   C. Messenger

   D. Navigator

17. Internet Explorer is an example of what type of Internet client?

    A. Internet news client

    B. Internet e-mail

    C. FTP client

    D. Web browser

18. Microsoft Outlook is an example of what type of Internet client?

    A. Internet mail client

    B. FTP client

    C. Telnet client

    D. Web browser

19. Which component of a Web browser shows what, exactly, is happening during the request-response sequence of a Web browsing session?

    A. Status bar

    B. Button bar

    C. Menu bar

    D. Activity indicator

20. A(n) _____ is the combination of hardware and software combined in one package that allows a user to interact with servers on the Internet without using a PC.

    A. Web browser

    B. Modem

    C. Internet appliance

    D. Operating system

Answers to Review Questions

1. D. Answers A, B, and C are all required before you can use a Web browser. You do not need an FTP client to browse the Web.

2. C. The activity indicator animates when the Web browser is either sending or receiving data.

3. A and B. Both an FTP client and a Web browser can be used to transfer files from an FTP server. Mail clients and news clients are used to view text messages from other users.

4. C. Of the clients listed, an Internet mail client is the only one that can be used to send and receive SMTP mail.

5. D. Of the clients listed, the Internet news client is the only one that can read Internet news.

6. A. Although `mget` can also be used to download files, it is used for multiple files, not for single files. The `put` and `mput` commands are used to upload files.

7. B. The `ls` command is used to list files, the `ascii` command sets the ASCII mode for text files only. The `exe` command isn't a real command.

8. D. The Internet appliance is the best choice because it can be used to access the Internet but it doesn't cost as much as a PC. A modem and a telephone won't work without a PC, and a PC would be too expensive for this person.

9. C. All Internet clients require that the TCP/IP protocol be installed before they will function. The other protocols listed perform different functions, but generally speaking, they are not *required* by *all* Internet clients.

10. D. The address book allows you to keep track of people and their e-mail addresses. You can send e-mail to them by selecting their name rather than having to type in their e-mail address every time.

11. B. A modem connects a computer to the Internet via a standard phone line. An Internet appliance can connect to the Internet, but it won't connect a computer to the Internet. A PC and a computer are the same thing, and a processor is part of a PC, so both A and D would be incorrect.

12. B and C. POP3 and SMTP are protocols used by Outlook to download and upload mail, respectively. IPX/SPX is a transport protocol used on LANs, and FTP is the file transfer protocol used to upload and download files from an FTP server.

13. D. Of the clients listed, the only one that allows you to perform Unix commands as if you were sitting at the console of the computer is a Telnet client.

14. C. The Network News Transfer Protocol is used to download Internet news from news servers. FTP, HTTP, and POP3 are protocols used for other Internet clients.

15. B. A Web client is the client primarily used to view HTML and Internet content, although it is possible for some mail and news clients.

16. C. Messenger is the Internet e-mail component of Netscape Communicator. Outlook is the only other e-mail program listed, and it's Microsoft's Internet e-mail program.

17. D. Internet Explorer is Microsoft's Web browser product. Although it can transfer files with the FTP protocol, it is primarily a Web browser. It is not a news client, e-mail client, or FTP client.

18. A. Microsoft Outlook is used to send, receive, and read Internet e-mail. It cannot perform any functions of the other three clients listed.

19. A. The status bar at the bottom-left corner of the Web browser window shows exactly what is taking place during the session. Although the activity indicator does show activity, it doesn't show *exactly* what is going on. The menu bar and the button bar don't show any activity, but rather they allow the user to perform actions within the browser.

20. C. An Internet appliance is the device that's a combination of hardware and software that allows a user to surf the Web without the need for a PC. A modem is only a piece of hardware, and a Web browser and an operating system are both software.

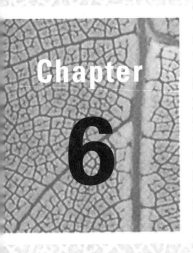

Chapter

6

Internet Client Configuration and Use

i-NET+ EXAM OBJECTIVES COVERED IN THIS CHAPTER:

✓ **Describe the use of Web browsers and various clients (e.g., FTP clients, Telnet clients, e-mail clients, all-in-one clients/universal clients) within a given context of use. Examples of context could include the following:**

- When you would use each
- The basic commands you would use (e.g., put and get) with each client (e.g., FTP, Telnet)

✓ **Explain the issues to consider when configuring the desktop. Content could include the following:**

- TCP/IP configuration (NetBIOS name server such as WINS, DNS, default gateway, subnet mask)
- Host file configuration
- DHCP versus static IP
- Configuring browser (proxy configuration, client-side caching)

✓ **Describe MIME types and their components. Content could include the following:**

- Whether a client can understand various e-mail types (MIME, HTML, uuencode)
- The need to define MIME file types for special download procedures such as unusual documents or graphic formats

✓ **Describe the advantages and disadvantages of using a cookie and how to set cookies. Content could include the following:**

- Setting a cookie without the knowledge of the user
- Automatically accepting cookies versus query
- Remembering everything the user has done
- Security and privacy implications

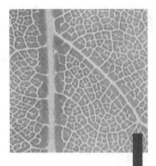

In Chapter 5, you learned about the different types of clients that exist and the requirements for using them. In this chapter, you'll learn how to configure and use each of these clients. The topics covered include both client PC and client software configuration as well as the steps you need to take to use the most popular Internet clients.

Now that you understand the basic look and features of each type of Internet client, you must learn how to configure and use them. Notice, however, that we will not be covering the installation of clients. If you are taking the i-Net+ exam, you should already know how to install software. Most software installations are similar (i.e., run SETUP.EXE, click Next a bunch of times, fill out the appropriate information when prompted, click Finish to finish the setup), so we won't devote space to them here.

Client Configuration

When client software is installed, it doesn't always work immediately. Most client software requires some kind of configuration before it will work correctly. In the following sections, you'll learn the basic steps needed to configure at least one of each type of Internet client discussed in the preceding chapter. In addition, you'll learn how to properly configure a client computer for use as an Internet client.

Basic Client Computer Configuration

Before configuring each Internet client software package, you must configure the computer running the software to support it. Although there are many client platforms, for the i-Net+ exam, you will only have to know how to configure Windows 95/98 clients, so we will cover only those in this section. Take note, however, that in the "real world," it is to your advantage to know about the many different client platforms available (including Windows 95/98, Windows NT, Linux, MacOS, OS/2, and so on) and how to configure each to connect to the Internet.

There are several items you must configure on a client computer so that it can support Internet clients:

- TCP/IP addresses

- Name resolution

- Dial-up connection

The first two are configured using the properties of the TCP/IP protocol in the Network Control Panel. To start configuring any of these items, you first must ensure that TCP/IP has been installed on the client. You can double-check that it has been installed by following these steps:

1. Open the Network Control Panel (found in Start ➤ Settings ➤ Control Panel in Windows 95/98) and see if TCP/IP is listed (as shown in the following screen shot).

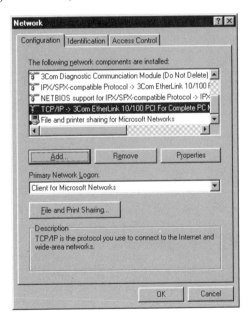

2. If TCP/IP isn't listed, click Add, and the Select Network Component Type dialog box appears.

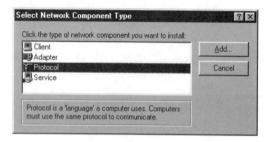

3. Select Protocol from the list of components and click Add. Once you do, the Select Network Protocol window appears and you can pick the manufacturer and the appropriate protocol. For TCP/IP, select Microsoft from the list on the left and TCP/IP from the list on the right. Click OK to install the protocol.

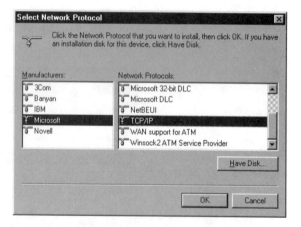

Once the TCP/IP protocol is installed, you can proceed to configure its properties, starting with the TCP/IP addresses.

TCP/IP Addresses

In addition to requiring a TCP/IP stack, an Internet client computer must be configured with a few special TCP/IP addresses:

- Client TCP/IP address

- Subnet mask

- Default gateway

You can begin the configuration of these addresses by following these steps:

1. Choose Start ➢ Settings ➢ Control Panel and double-click the Network Control Panel.

2. To view the properties of TCP/IP from this window, select TCP/IP by clicking it, then click the Properties button. This will bring up the window shown in the following screen shot. Here, you can enter or change all TCP/IP-related properties contained on the various pages within this window. You will learn what all of these items mean, and how to configure them, in the sections that follow.

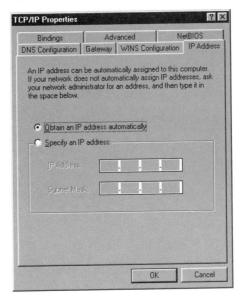

Client TCP/IP Address

The first address that needs to be configured is the address you must assign to the client PC so it can send and receive data on the Internet. This address is known as the *client IP address*. As discussed in Chapter 3, it is a 12-digit, dotted decimal number that uniquely identifies the client PC on the Internet.

All clients that will send and receive data on the Internet must have a client IP address.

Client IP addresses are assigned from the IP Address tab of the TCP/IP protocol Properties window. You can assign them either manually or automatically. To assign an address manually, select the Specify an IP Address radio button and type in the IP address you want to assign (as shown in Figure 6.1). You must ensure that the address you enter follows the IP addressing conventions (which were discussed in Chapter 3).

FIGURE 6.1   Assigning an IP address manually

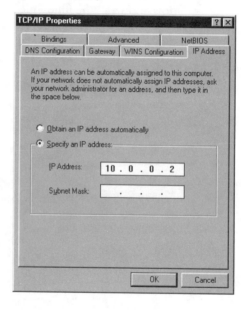

To assign an IP address to a client PC automatically, select the Obtain an IP Address Automatically radio button on the IP Address tab of the TCP/IP Properties window and let the PC obtain its own IP address information from a Dynamic Host Configuration Protocol (DHCP) server. This is the default setting. If TCP/IP is installed on the client PC and this option is enabled, the client PC will query a DHCP server for its TCP/IP address. If you set up a DHCP server on your network, you can give all your client computers (at least the ones with a TCP/IP stack that supports DHCP) IP address information automatically.

DHCP servers can assign to clients information other than TCP/IP addresses, such as subnet masks, default gateways, DNS information, and WINS server information.

The process by which a client PC requests its IP address begins when the client PC boots up. The TCP/IP stack has been configured to obtain its IP address automatically, so it sends out a broadcast on the local network segment, basically saying, "I need an IP address." Any DHCP servers on the network segment will respond by saying, "I've got one for you." The DHCP server will then assign an IP address (and any other pertinent information) to that client PC. This process is illustrated in Figure 6.2.

FIGURE 6.2   A DHCP server assigning an address

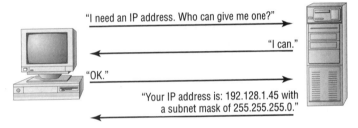

The decision on whether or not to statically address your computer or use DHCP is going to be based on the type of network you have. If you are using a connection to the Internet through an ISP, the majority of the time, you will be using DHCP to get an address. If you are unsure, check with your ISP or network administrator. Also, many ISPs automatically install and configure these network settings on a PC as part of the installation of their software (for example, if you use AT&T WorldNet to access the Internet, when you install the WorldNet CD, it automatically configures the network settings).

If you want to check your TCP/IP configuration, use the winipcfg program. To start this program, choose Start ≻ Run, type in **winipcfg**, and click OK. The utility that appears will allow you to view your entire TCP/IP configuration.

Subnet Mask

If you selected Specify an IP Address and entered an IP address manually at the TCP/IP configuration screen, you must also enter the correct subnet mask (in the specified field) for the IP address you enter or the client won't be able to communicate properly. However, if you selected Obtain an IP Address Automatically, the subnet mask will be specified by the DHCP server. For a detailed explanation of subnet masks, refer back to Chapter 3.

Default Gateway

The default gateway is the address of the router to which the client will send all TCP/IP traffic that is not addressed to a specific station on the local network. The default gateway address should be entered on any client PC that is attached to a network that is connected to the Internet via a router. The address of the default gateway is another piece of configuration information that can be distributed using a DHCP server.

Name Resolution

In addition to specifying the IP addresses for the client, you must specify how the client will resolve host names into IP addresses and vice versa. If you'll remember from Chapter 2, *host names* are logical, alphanumeric names given to computers to identify them on a network without using cryptic sequences of numbers that a user would have to remember to access that host. Host names make accessing TCP/IP hosts more "friendly" because it is easier to remember www.sybex.com than it is to remember 10.45.89.129 (at least for most people).

There are three ways to configure name resolution on a client PC:

- HOSTS file configuration

- Domain Name Services (DNS)

- Windows Internet Name Service (WINS)

DNS has been covered in previous chapters, but in this chapter, we will discuss where to find the other name resolution methods and how to configure them properly.

HOSTS File Configuration

The HOSTS file configuration is a name given to any file (usually named HOSTS.TXT or simply HOSTS, or something along those lines) that performs host name to IP address mapping. It must be manually edited by the user to add different hosts. For example, if you have a network with five PCs on it, each with its own name and HOSTS file configuration, and then you add a sixth PC, you would have to edit the HOSTS file on each PC and add the new host name of the new PC in order to refer to that new PC by its host name from any PC on the network.

This file exists in various locations on different PCs. On Windows PCs, it can generally be found in the Windows directory (usually C:\WINDOWS) or in the Windows NT directory in C:\WINNT\SYSTEM32\DRIVERS\ETC and is named HOSTS.SAM. Figure 6.3 shows a sample HOSTS.SAM file from a Windows 98 PC. This happens to be a hosts file from a PC on a home network. Notice that there are only two entries: 127.0.0.1 is mapped to the local PC (localhost), and the IP address 10.0.0.2 is mapped to the host name S1. This PC will translate the host name S1 back to the IP address 10.0.0.2.

FIGURE 6.3 A sample HOSTS.SAM file from a Windows 98 PC

```
# Copyright (c) 1998 Microsoft Corp.
#
# This is a sample HOSTS file used by Microsoft TCP/IP stack for Windows98
#
# This file contains the mappings of IP addresses to host names. Each
# entry should be kept on an individual line. The IP address should
# be placed in the first column followed by the corresponding host name.
# The IP address and the host name should be separated by at least one
# space.
#
# Additionally, comments (such as these) may be inserted on individual
# lines or following the machine name denoted by a '#' symbol.
#
# For example:
#
#    102.54.94.97    rhino.acme.com    # source server
#    38.25.63.10     x.acme.com        # x client host

127.0.0.1      localhost
10.0.0.2       S1
```

What happens, though, when a second server, S2 (with an IP address of 10.0.0.3), is added to the network? You must edit this HOSTS file (and all the HOSTS files on client PCs on the network) to include the information for the new server. In our example, then, you must start up a text editor (for example, MS-DOS EDIT.COM or Windows Notepad) and open the HOSTS .SAM file. Then, at the end of the file, insert an entry with the IP address of the new server (10.0.0.3) followed by a tab or a few spaces and then the host name you want to assign to that IP address (in this case, S2). Save the file and reboot the computer. After the reboot, the computer will be able to access server S2 by name. Figure 6.4 shows the edited HOSTS.SAM file with the new entry. Notice that the new entry follows the pattern of the other entries.

FIGURE 6.4 Updated HOSTS.SAM file

```
# Copyright (c) 1998 Microsoft Corp.
#
# This is a sample HOSTS file used by Microsoft TCP/IP stack for Windows98
#
# This file contains the mappings of IP addresses to host names. Each
# entry should be kept on an individual line. The IP address should
# be placed in the first column followed by the corresponding host name.
# The IP address and the host name should be separated by at least one
# space.
#
# Additionally, comments (such as these) may be inserted on individual
# lines or following the machine name denoted by a '#' symbol.
#
# For example:
#
#    102.54.94.97    rhino.acme.com      # source server
#    38.25.63.10     x.acme.com          # x client host

127.0.0.1       localhost
10.0.0.2        S1
10.0.0.3        S2
```

You only have to edit HOSTS files if you are using them as your method of name resolution. If you are using one of the other methods (i.e., DNS or WINS), you don't have to edit any HOSTS files; simply make the change at the DNS or WINS server.

Domain Name Services (DNS)

The functions of Domain Name Services (DNS) were discussed in earlier chapters, but in this chapter, you'll learn how to configure a client PC to make DNS requests. If you are using DNS (and not HOSTS files) to resolve host names to IP addresses and vice versa, you must tell your client PC's TCP/IP stack the IP address of a DNS server to use to resolve these names.

To start configuring DNS on a Windows 95/98 PC, use the following steps:

1. Open the Network Control Panel (as discussed earlier).

2. Open the TCP/IP Properties window (as discussed earlier).

3. Click the DNS Configuration tab. From this screen, you can configure the IP address of the DNS server(s) that your client PC should use to resolve DNS names to IP addresses.

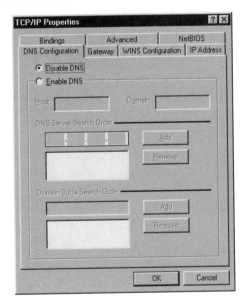

4. To configure DNS resolution on this Windows 95/98 client PC, you must first enable DNS resolution by clicking the radio button labeled Enable DNS.

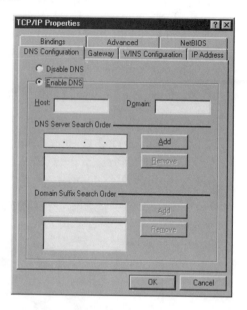

5. Once you click the Enable DNS radio button, the bottom half of the property page will brighten and allow you to enter values for DNS configuration. There are four areas that you can configure on this tab:

Host   This field allows you to set the actual host name of the Windows 95/98 PC. The default name for this field is the actual name of the PC. This name is usually specified during the installation of Windows. Windows will, by default, make the name of your computer, as seen in the identification tab of the Network Control Panel applet, the same as your host name. It is recommended you keep these the same.

Domain   In this field, enter the Internet DNS domain name that represents this entire network.

DNS Server Search Order   This field is the most important field on this tab. This is where you specify the IP addresses of the DNS server(s) for the domain specified in the Domain field. More than one server IP address can be specified. If more than one IP address is specified, the client will query the DNS servers in order (from top to bottom).

Domain Suffix Search Order If you type a host name in a Web browser and leave out the somewhere.com domain name, the entries in this field will be appended to the host name and the client will try to make DNS queries with the new name. For example, suppose you type just "snoopy" in the address line of a Web browser; that isn't a DNS domain name, so the Windows TCP/IP stack will try to resolve the name by appending whatever domain names are in this list. If somewhere.com is in this list, the TCP/IP stack will append somewhere.com to snoopy and try to resolve snoopy.somewhere.com into an IP address.

6. At a minimum, to configure DNS on a Windows 95/98 client, you must enter a host name, a domain name, and at least one DNS server IP address. Simply type in the values in the appropriate fields. For the DNS server IP address, you must first type the IP address of the DNS server in the appropriate field, then click the Add button.

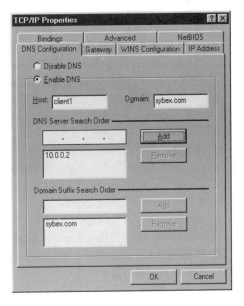

7. Once you have entered the appropriate values, you can click OK to close the TCP/IP Properties window and then click OK to close the Network Control Panel. Windows will ask you to reboot the client PC. Once rebooted, the client PC will be able to access hosts by DNS name as well as by TCP/IP addresses.

The i-Net+ exam doesn't cover the details of setting up a DNS server, and thus it is outside the scope of this book. For an excellent reference on DNS servers and their setup, check out *DNS and BIND* from O'Reilly & Associates.

Windows Internet Name Service (WINS)

The Windows Internet Name Service is a name resolution service commonly found on Windows NT networks that are using TCP/IP. WINS is used in conjunction with TCP/IP and maps NetBIOS names to IP addresses. For example, suppose you have a print server on your LAN that you have come to know as PrintServer1. In the past, to print to that server, you needed only to remember its name and to select that name from a list. However, TCP/IP is a completely different protocol and doesn't understand NetBIOS names; therefore, it has no way of knowing the location of that server or its address. That's where WINS comes in.

Each time you access a network resource on a Windows NT network using TCP/IP, your system needs to know the host name or IP address. If WINS is installed, you can continue using the NetBIOS names that you have previously used to access the resources because WINS provides the cross-reference from name to address for you.

Configuring WINS name resolution is also done through the TCP/IP Properties window. There is a tab, WINS Configuration, on the TCP/IP Properties window that allows you to configure the addresses of WINS servers (shown in Figure 6.5). These addresses are stored with the configuration, and TCP/IP uses them to query for NetBIOS host names and addresses when necessary. WINS is similar to DNS in that it cross-references host names to addresses; however, as we mentioned earlier, WINS references NetBIOS names to IP addresses, and DNS references TCP/IP host names to IP address. To view the NetBIOS name of your Microsoft computer, go to the identification tab of the Network Control Panel.

FIGURE 6.5 The WINS Configuration tab of the TCP/IP Properties window

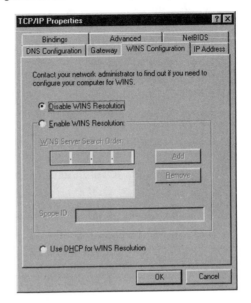

Another major difference between WINS and DNS is that WINS builds its own reference tables dynamically and you have to configure DNS manually. When a workstation running TCP/IP is booted and attached to the network, it uses the WINS address settings in the TCP/IP configuration to communicate with the WINS server. The workstation gives the WINS server various pieces of information about itself, such as the NetBIOS host name, the actual username logged on to the workstation, and the workstation's IP address. WINS stores this information for use on the network and periodically refreshes it to maintain accuracy.

Microsoft, however, has developed a new DNS record that allows the DNS server to work in perfect harmony with a WINS server. The Microsoft DNS Server software currently ships with Windows NT. Here's how it works. When a DNS query returns a WINS record, the DNS server then asks the WINS server for the host name address. Thus, you need not build complex DNS tables to establish and configure name resolution on your server; Microsoft DNS relies entirely on WINS to tell it the addresses it needs to resolve. And because WINS builds its tables automatically, you don't have to edit the DNS tables when addresses change; WINS takes care of this for you.

You can use both WINS and DNS on your network, or you can use one without the other. Your choice is determined by whether your network is connected to the Internet and whether your host addresses are dynamically assigned. When you are connected to the Internet, you must use DNS to resolve host names and addresses because TCP/IP depends on DNS service for address resolution.

WINS is disabled by default (as shown previously in Figure 6.5). To configure WINS, follow these steps:

1. First select one of the radio buttons shown, either Enable WINS Resolution or Use DHCP for WINS Resolution. If you select Use DHCP for WINS Resolution, the client PC will get its WINS server information from a DHCP server, along with its IP address information.

2. If you select Enable WINS Resolution as shown in the following screen shot, you can manually specify which WINS server(s) to use for NetBIOS host name to TCP/IP address resolution.

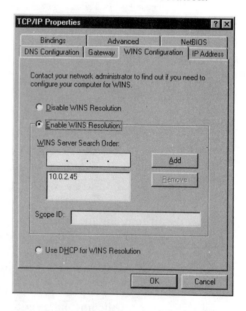

3. When you choose Enable WINS Resolution, configuration is much the same as it is with DNS configuration. Simply enter the IP addresses of the WINS servers, one at a time, and click Add to add them to the list of WINS servers.

4. When you're finished entering the IP addresses, click OK to close the TCP/IP Properties window. Then click OK to save the changes and close the Network Control Panel. Windows will ask you to reboot.

5. After the reboot, the client PC will be able to perform WINS resolution.

We didn't discuss the Scope ID field in this book because it is not often used. However, for your information, it is used to "group" NetBIOS entities together. All entities on a network with the same Scope ID value can send NetBIOS data (e.g., share lists and domain information) to one another. If you enter a scope ID of 12, this station can only communicate with other NetBIOS entities that have their scope ID set to 12. Most often, this field is left blank so that all computers can communicate with all other NetBIOS entities without restriction.

Configuring a Dial-Up Connection

The most popular way to connect a client PC to the Internet is with a standard phone line and a modem (what is known as a *dial-up* Internet connection). Because a dial-up Internet connection is the most popular way of connecting clients to the Internet, the i-Net+ exam will test your knowledge of configuring a computer to make this type of connection.

To connect your Windows 95/98 computer to the Internet over a regular modem connection, you must have a few items in place, including:

- A modem
- Windows Dial-Up Networking (DUN) software
- A valid access account with an ISP
- A configured Dial-Up Networking connection

In the following sections, we'll cover each item in more detail. Once you get your client connected, you can install a Web browser or another client and communicate with the Internet.

Modem

In order to have a dial-up connection, you must have one critical piece of hardware installed on your computer: a modem. As mentioned in Chapter 1, a modem converts the digital signals that your computer uses into analog signals that can be sent over telephone lines. Dial-up connections can use either an internal or external modem.

When installing a modem into a Windows 95/98 machine, you must have the correct Windows 95/98 driver for the modem. A modem driver is the software component that manages and controls the modem. Without the correct driver installed, the dial-up connection software would not be able to communicate with the modem and thus would not be able to dial up to the ISP.

Drivers include several embedded strings of characters called *modem initialization commands*, which are the commands sent to the modem by the communications program to "initialize" it. These commands tell the modem things like how many rings to wait before answering, how long to wait between detecting the last keystroke and disconnecting, and the speed at which to communicate.

For a while, each manufacturer had its own set of commands, and every communications program had to have settings for every particular kind of modem available. In particular, every program had commands for the Hayes line of modems (mainly because Hayes made good modems and their command language was fairly easy to program). Eventually, other modem manufacturers began using the "Hayes-compatible" command set. This set of modem-initialization commands became known as the Hayes command set. It is also known as the "AT command set" because each Hayes modem command started with the letters *AT* (presumably calling the modem to *AT*tention).

Each AT command does something different. The letters *AT* by themselves (when issued as a command) will ask the modem if it's ready to receive commands. If it returns "ok," that means that the modem is ready to communicate. If you receive "error," it means there is an internal modem problem that may need to be resolved before communication can take place.

Table 6.1 details some of the most common modem commands. Notice that we've included a couple of extra commands that aren't AT commands.

These items are characters used to affect how the phone number is dialed (including pauses and turning off call-waiting).

TABLE 6.1 Common Modem Initialization Commands

Command	Function	Usage
AT	Tells the modem that what follows the letters *AT* is a command that should be interpreted	Used to precede most commands.
ATDT *nnnnnnn*	Dials the number *nnnnnnn* as a tone-dialed number	Used to dial the number of another modem if the phone line is set up for tone dialing.
ATDP *nnnnnnn*	Dials the number *nnnnnnn* as a pulse-dialed number	Used to dial the number of another modem if the phone line is set up for rotary dialing.
ATA	Answers an incoming call manually	Places the line off-hook and starts to negotiate communication with the modem on the other end.
ATH0 (or +++ and then ATH0)	Tells the modem to hang up immediately	Places the line on-hook and stops communication. (Note: The 0 in this command is a zero.)
AT&F	Resets modem to factory default settings	This command works as the initialization string when others don't. If you have problems with modems hanging up in the middle of a session or failing to establish connections, use this string by itself to initialize the modem.
ATZ	Resets modem to power-up defaults	Almost as good as AT&F, but may not work if power-up defaults have been changed with S-registers.
ATS0-*n*	Waits *n* rings before answering a call	Sets the default number of rings that the modem will detect before taking the modem off-hook and negotiating a connection. (Note: The 0 in this command is a zero.)

TABLE 6.1 Common Modem Initialization Commands *(continued)*

Command	Function	Usage
ATS6-*n*	Waits *n* seconds for a dial tone before dialing	If the phone line is slow to give a dial tone, you may have to set this register to a number higher than 2.
comma (,)	Pauses briefly	When placed in a string of AT commands, the comma will cause a pause to occur: Used to separate the number for an outside line (many businesses use 9 to connect to an outside line) and the real phone number (e.g., 9, 555-1234).
*70 or 1170	Turns off call-waiting	The "click" you hear when you have call-waiting (a feature offered by the phone company) will interrupt modem communication and cause the connection to be lost. To disable call-waiting for a modem call, place these commands in the dialing string like so: *70, 555-1234. Call-waiting will resume after the call is terminated.

Dial-Up Networking Software

If you are going to connect your computer to the Internet via a modem and telephone line, aside from configuring the various aspects of the TCP/IP protocol, you will have to configure a Dial-Up Networking connection on Windows 95. The Windows Dial-up Networking software is used to connect Windows 95/98 to various networked systems and is included as part of Windows 95/98. It is not installed by default unless you have a modem installed in the computer when Windows 95/98 is being installed. It is also installed whenever you install a modem in the computer. Bottom line: you cannot connect your Windows 95/98 PC to an ISP (and thus, to the Internet) unless the Windows 95/98 Dial-Up Networking software is installed.

ISP Account

In addition to the software and hardware components involved in a dial-up connection, you must have a valid access account with an ISP. An ISP account includes a username and password you can use to gain access to the ISP's servers and to the Internet. ISPs charge a small fee (typically anywhere from $10–$30 per month) for access to the Internet through a modem connection.

When you do get an ISP account, they will give you a "configuration sheet" that contains all the information you will need to configure your Dial-Up Networking connection. Some ISPs have a preconfigured software installation disk with all this information already entered. In that case, all you need to do is install the software and your client PC will be configured. If your ISP doesn't have a sheet or a disk like this, you can make a "cheat sheet" by asking them a few questions and writing down the answers:

- What is the dial-up phone number?

- What is my username and password?

- What are the DNS names of your e-mail servers (outgoing and incoming)?

- What are the IP addresses or DNS names?

- What is the DNS name of your news server?

The answers to these questions will be needed in the next section, where you need to create a Dial-Up Networking connection (the last three will be used in sections that follow, where you configure the other clients, including Web browsers).

Dial-Up Networking Connection

The final component of a dial-up connection is a Dial-Up Networking connection script. This script is an icon that represents a collection of preconfigured settings for dialing up to a specific ISP. This Dial-Up Networking script is a function of Windows 95/98 Dial-Up Networking and includes settings like ISP phone number, ISP TCP/IP settings, username and password, and connection name.

To create a Dial-Up Networking connection on a Windows 95/98 client, follow these steps:

1. First ensure that all the previously listed items are in place (i.e., modem, dial-up networking software, and an ISP account).

2. To start the process, have your information sheet from your ISP (or your "cheat sheet") handy and open the Dial-Up Networking folder. You can access this folder either by opening My Computer or by choosing

Start ➤ Programs ➤ Accessories ➤ Dial-Up Networking in Windows 95 (Start ➤ Programs ➤ Accessories ➤ Communications ➤ Dial-Up Networking in Windows 98). This folder normally lists any Dial-Up Networking connections you have already configured, but you haven't configured one yet, so it should be blank.

3. Once you have this window open, you can start to configure a new connection by double-clicking the Make New Connection icon.

4. In the first screen (the following screen shot is from Windows 98), there are two fields. The first asks you to give a name to this connection (the default is My Connection). You should type in the name of your ISP or some name that indicates to you that this is a Dial-Up Networking connection to your ISP. In this sample case, we'll use TestISP. The second field asks you which modem this connection should use. This field has a drop-down list that includes more than one modem (if more than one modem is installed). The default for this field is the first modem that's installed. In this case, the only modem that's installed is a 56K U.S. Robotics and it's already selected, so you don't have to do anything with this field unless you have another modem installed and

you want to use that modem. Once you have finished entering the connection name and selecting a modem, click the Next button.

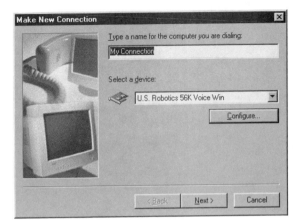

You can click the Cancel button at any point during this process to cancel the configuration of this connection.

The Configure button displayed in the first screen allows you to configure the modem settings, like modem speaker volume, modem connection speed, and manual dialing capabilities. Most often, the defaults for the modem only need to be changed with the more troublesome connections. You will also have a chance to configure these options later after the connection has been made.

5. The next screen is where you'll enter the phone number of the ISP's modem bank. The Area Code field should default to your area code (you should have entered it when you installed the modem). If not, you can change it on this screen. In the Telephone Number field, you should enter the telephone number given to you by the ISP for the ISP's modem bank. You can also choose the dialing prefix for long distance numbers by selecting your country from the drop-down list labeled

Country or Region Code. But you shouldn't have to select anything because hopefully your ISP is a local phone call!

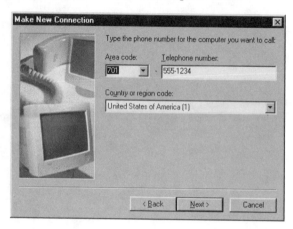

6. When you have finished entering the phone number for the ISP's modem bank, click Next to bring you to the next screen. At this screen, the Make New Connection Wizard tells you that you have successfully created a new connection.

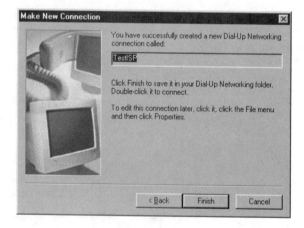

7. Click the Finish button to finish creating the connection. You will now have a new icon in the Dial-Up Networking folder.

Using this method, you are accepting all TCP/IP defaults. The default TCP/IP configuration is for the client PC to use the Point-to-Point Protocol (PPP) for dial-up and to get all TCP/IP addresses (including modem IP address, default gateway, and DNS server addresses) from the machine your client dials in to. This is the configuration that 95 percent of all ISPs use, so it will be included on the i-Net+ exam.

Web Browser Configuration

Web browsers are pretty simple. As soon as you install one, you can use it. There are only a few items that need to be configured on a Web browser, and these items are configured just to make it easier to use, faster, or more flexible. In the following sections, you'll learn how to configure each item listed below on a Web browser.

- Accessing Preferences

- Setting the home page

- Setting MIME types

- Handling cookies

- Setting local caching preferences

- Configuring proxy settings

We'll cover both popular Web browsers: Netscape Navigator (version 4.5) and Microsoft Internet Explorer (version 5).

Netscape Navigator

Netscape Navigator version 4.5 is configured through the Preferences menu option, which can be accessed through the Edit menu in the main window of Navigator. This will bring up the Preferences window shown in Figure 6.6. As you can see, there are several pages of preferences that you can set. The categories of preferences that you can change are listed on the left. Click the + sign next to a category to expand it so you can see its subcategories. Notice in Figure 6.6 that some of the categories have already been expanded. Additionally, when you want to view the individual preferences within each category and subcategory, simply click a category or subcategory in the left-hand pane. The specified collection of preferences will appear in the window on the right.

FIGURE 6.6   The Navigator Preferences window

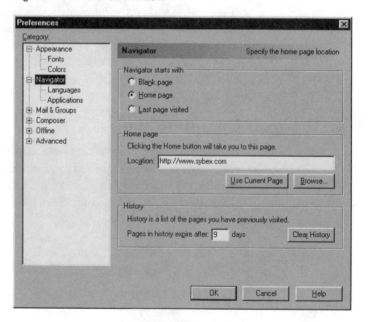

Setting the Home Page

The first preference that most people change as soon as they install their Web browser is the home page. A *home page* (in this context) is the first Web page that is displayed when you start up the browser and the Web page that is displayed when you hit the Home button in your browser. Typically, the default home page is either the Web page of the browser manufacturer (in the case of Navigator, Netscape's home page is home.netscape.com), the Web page of your ISP (in our case, www.corpcomm.net), or some kind of search engine (like www.yahoo.com). Thankfully, you can change it to any Web page you want.

You can change the home page from the Preferences window. To do so, follow these steps:

1. Open the Navigator browser.

2. Open the Preferences window by choosing Edit ➢ Preferences. The first category that comes up is, by default, the Navigator category.

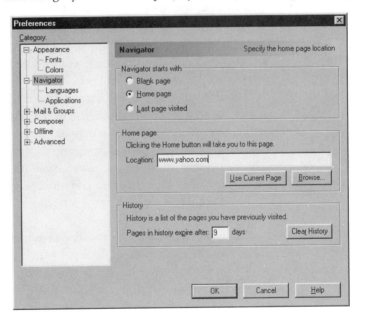

3. It is in this category that you can change the home page. Simply type the new home page address in the field labeled Location in the section with the heading Home Page. Or, if your browser is displaying the Web page you want to use as your home page, simply click the button labeled Use Current Page. Navigator will place the address of the current Web page in this field for you.

4. You can choose to start Navigator with an HTML page stored on your local hard drive. Simply click the Browse button and navigate to the HTML page you want to use as your home page. Then, when Navigator starts, it will open this HTML file from your hard drive and display it.

You can also start Navigator with either a blank page or the last page you visited instead of a specific Web page. Simply select the appropriate radio button in the Navigator Starts With section for the option you want.

Setting MIME Types

MIME is short for Multipurpose Internet Mail Extension. The purpose of MIME is to allow files other than text files to be transmitted via e-mail (and HTTP). The first purpose of MIME was to allow binary attachments to e-mails without the need to encode the binary attachment into text (using a process known as uuencoding). With MIME-compliant e-mail, attachments are encoded and decoded automatically during transmission and reception. Most e-mail servers and clients in use today use MIME to send attachments.

MIME applies to Web browsers because the Web browser is an extensible entity. As new content gets introduced (i.e., video, multimedia content), you can tell the Web browser exactly what the new content is and how to deal with it using a MIME type identification. Usually a browser deals with a new type of content by opening a helper application to open and view the content. The MIME type defines a certain application (either the Web browser or an external program) to handle the display for a certain type of Internet content.

In many cases, when you install a helper application, the Web browser is automatically configured to open the helper application when the selected type of content is downloaded. For example, if you install the RealAudio Web browser plug-in from RealNetworks, Inc. (www.real.com), it will automatically configure the MIME type for streaming audio (MIME type AUDIO with a subtype of x-pn-realaudio-plugin) so that, whenever you click a link for a RealAudio broadcast, the Web browser will open the broadcast in the RealPlayer.

Ninety-five percent of the time, you won't have to configure the MIME types. This will be handled automatically by the Web browser plug-in installation. The only time you will ever have to change MIME types for a Web browser is when two helper applications want to take over responsibility for the same MIME type. For that reason, you must know how to configure MIME types manually when necessary.

For Netscape Navigator, you can view and edit the MIME types that are configured by following these steps:

1. Open the Preferences window and select the Applications subcategory of the Navigator category. From this subcategory, you can view all the MIME types and their associated helper applications.

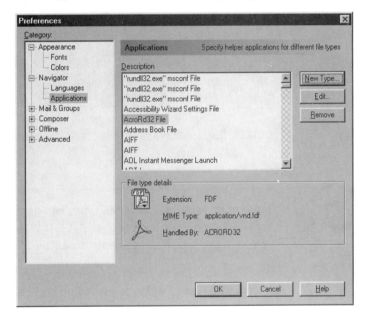

2. If by some chance you should need to manually add a MIME type and helper application to Navigator, you can do so by clicking New Type. This will bring up the New Type window. In this window, there are four fields that must be filled out or Navigator won't bring up the correct application:

Description of Type   This is a brief description of what this particular MIME type is for. If you look back at the preceding screen shot, you'll see several examples in the Description box.

File Extension   This field is used to specify what file extensions are to be associated with this MIME type. When Navigator opens a file with one of these extensions, it will open it with the application listed in the Application to Use field.

MIME Type This field specifies the actual MIME type definition.

Application to Use This field should display the path and executable name for the application that should be used to open a file with this MIME type. You can either type in the path to the executable or select the program using the Browse button.

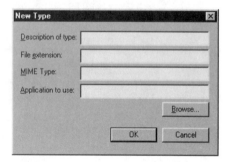

3. Once you have filled out these four fields, click OK to save the new MIME type.

More information about MIME types can be found at either www.1tsw.se/ knbase/internet/mime.htp or in RFCs 1341, 1521, and 1522 at www.cis .ohio-state.edu/hypertext/information/rfc.html.

Using Cookies

In the Internet press lately, there has been a lot of talk about cookies. Good or bad, ethical or not, this mysterious Web feature, which sounds like it should be on a plate rather than in a Web browser, is a special text message given to a Web browser by a Web server. The browser stores this message on the local hard disk (Navigator stores the cookies in a file called COOKIES .TXT). The next time someone using that Web browser on that computer visits the same Web server, the Web browser sends this message back to the Web server (which created it). Cookies are used to provide customized Web sites for users. The Web server asks the user to fill out a form and records the information in the cookie. Then, when the user returns, the Web browser sends the cookie to the Web server and returns the information. The Web server then knows who is surfing because of the information contained in the cookie, and thus the Web server can create a custom Web page for that user.

The problem with cookies is that this process can happen without the user's intervention. This poses a security problem because a cookie can contain sensitive information (such as name and address) that can be sent without the user's knowledge. Thankfully, you can configure the browser to notify you about any cookies it receives, as well as their contents.

You must configure the way Navigator handles cookies through the Advanced category of the Preferences window (shown in Figure 6.7). In this window, you have four options for how Navigator will handle cookies:

Accept All Cookies   This setting will allow Navigator to accept all cookies, no matter where they're coming from or going to. This is the least secure setting, but it gives the user the most flexibility.

Accept Only Cookies That Get Sent Back to the Originating Server
This setting is the best compromise between security and flexibility. With this setting active, the browser will only exchange a cookie with the server that sent it. It will never send a cookie created at one site to a server at another.

Disable Cookies   This setting disables cookies altogether. No cookies will be sent or received. This is the most secure setting, but some Web sites won't work correctly because they require the use of cookies to function properly.

Warn Me Before Accepting a Cookie   This setting can be used in conjunction with any of the other settings. With this setting active, if a cookie is sent or received, a message will be displayed whenever it needs to be used. This setting, when activated, will help indicate to you which sites are using cookies.

Once you are finished configuring how Navigator will respond to cookies, click OK to save the settings.

FIGURE 6.7 Configuring how Navigator deals with cookies

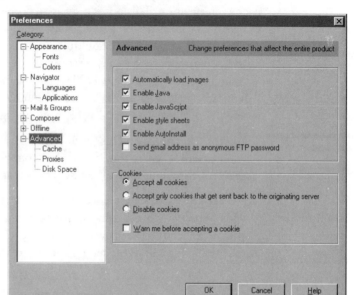

Setting Local Caching Preferences

All Web browsers have a local cache. The local cache is a storage location in both memory and on the hard disk that stores a local copy of all images and HTML documents from Web sites the user visits. When a user goes to the same Web site twice in the same session, the Web browser can retrieve the document either from memory or from the local hard disk, which is much faster than downloading it again from a Web server over a modem connection.

You can set the sizes of the memory and disk cache for the local cache to obtain better performance. This is done through the Cache subcategory of the Advanced category in the Navigator Preferences window (as shown in Figure 6.8). This screen shows you the sizes at which these two caches are currently set (1024KB for the memory cache and 7680KB for the disk cache—the default settings). You can increase the sizes of one or both to increase your Web browsing performance by simply typing in a new number next to the appropriate cache and clicking OK. Also, you can specify the local directory where Navigator will store the cached figures and HTML documents in the field labeled Disk Cache Folder. To change the folder where Navigator stores these documents and images, click the Choose Folder button, navigate to the folder where you want these items to reside (hopefully somewhere that has a lot of disk space), and click OK.

FIGURE 6.8 Setting the Navigator local cache preferences

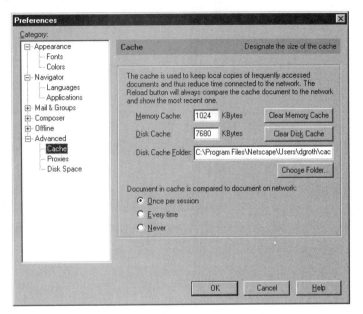

Proxy Configuration

If you'll remember from Chapter 4, a proxy server increases an entire network's Internet performance by responding to Internet requests on behalf of the various Internet clients. A Web browser must be configured to use a proxy cache server. Navigator is no exception.

Just like the other Navigator preferences, proxy cache setup is done through the Preferences window. To add or change proxy cache settings, expand the Advanced category and select the Proxies subcategory. This will display the preferences fields shown in Figure 6.9 (with similar settings). From this window, you can configure Navigator to use a proxy server.

FIGURE 6.9 Netscape Navigator proxy configuration

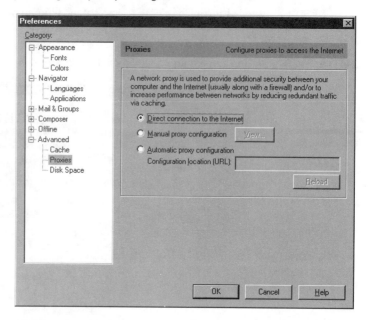

There are three options for proxy configuration:

Direct Connection to the Internet When this proxy setting is checked, the Web browser will not use a proxy. This proxy setting is the default setting for Navigator.

Manual Proxy Configuration With this setting selected, you must manually configure the proxy settings. To configure the actual settings, click the View button. This will bring up a screen similar to the one shown in Figure 6.10. Type in the address of each proxy server you want to configure and the port that it operates on in the fields provided. Click OK to close the proxy viewing window and save the proxy configuration. Then click OK to close the Preferences window.

FIGURE   6.10   Viewing the manual proxy configuration screen for Netscape Navigator

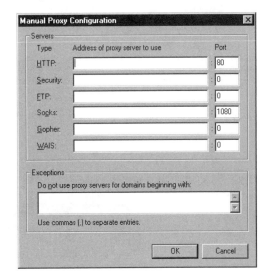

Automatic Proxy Configuration   The manual configuration of proxies is somewhat complex for the novice user. To make configuration easier, Navigator supports the automatic configuration of proxy information via a special configuration URL. To make Navigator configure its own proxy information, simply select this option, and in the field labeled Configuration Location (URL), enter the URL that the proxy server uses to store the proxy server configuration. This URL is generated during the installation of the proxy server software. Once you have entered the URL, click Reload to download the configuration to the browser.

Once you have configured the proxy settings, click OK to save the configuration and close the Preferences window. After configuring the proxies for Navigator, you should notice a marked increase in your Web surfing performance.

Microsoft Internet Explorer

The other Web browser that is used just as commonly as Netscape Navigator is Microsoft Internet Explorer. To that end, the i-Net+ exam will test your knowledge of the Web browsing settings of Internet Explorer (or IE, for short). In the previous sections, you learned how to configure certain Web browsing preferences for Netscape Navigator. In this section, you'll learn how to set the exact same settings for Internet Explorer version 5 (the current version at the time this book was written).

You learned how to access and view the preferences for Navigator. With IE, the Web browser is integrated into the Windows 95/98 interface, so configuration is handled through a control panel. Microsoft has consolidated all Internet settings into the Internet Control Panel (as shown in Figure 6.11). The Internet Control Panel can be opened by choosing Start ➤ Settings ➤ Control Panel and double-clicking the Internet Control Panel. As you can see, this control panel has several tabs, one for each category of settings.

FIGURE 6.11 The Internet Control Panel

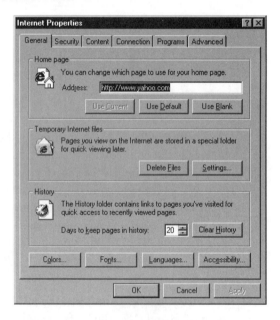

Setting the Home Page

Many people want to set the home page for their browser so the browser always starts on the same page. The home page is set from the General tab of the Internet Control Panel (as shown in Figure 6.11). Simply type the address of the home page you want to use in the field labeled Address in the Home Page section. If you want to use a blank page as your home page, click the Use Blank button. On the other hand, if Internet Explorer is running and the page you want to use as your home page is already displayed, you can click Use Current, and Internet Explorer will place the address of the current Web page in the Address field for you. When you have finished configuring the home page, click OK to accept the configuration.

Setting MIME Types

Internet Explorer handles MIME types a bit differently. Because of IE's integration with Windows 95/98, IE leaves the MIME type handling to the Windows 95/98 operating system. Configuring MIME types is a function of Windows Explorer. Additionally, Internet Explorer is intelligent enough that, when you try to view a file type for which IE doesn't have a MIME type configured, IE will try to download the appropriate helper application automatically.

If you have to manually create a MIME type, you can do so through Windows Explorer. Open the Windows Explorer program (Start ➢ Programs ➢ Windows Explorer). Once it's open, choose Options from the View menu. In the Options window, choose the File Types tab. This will present a screen similar to the one in Figure 6.12. From this screen, you can add or edit a new MIME type or associate an existing MIME type with a helper application. The addition works exactly the same as it does under Navigator's preferences.

FIGURE 6.12 Adding and editing MIME Types for Internet Explorer

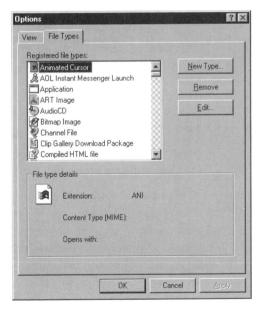

Cookie Handling

Choosing how Internet Explorer handles cookies is extremely similar to choosing how Navigator handles them. The only difference is that IE uses the Internet Control Panel to manage its settings. To set the cookie options for IE, open the Internet Control Panel, select the Advanced tab, scroll down to the Security section, and find the Cookies subsection (as shown in Figure 6.13).

FIGURE 6.13   Configuring cookie settings for Internet Explorer

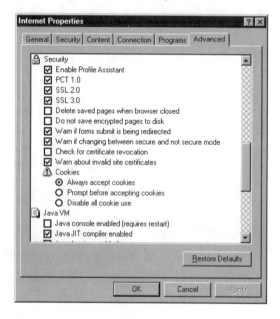

As you can see, there are three options that control how Internet Explorer handles cookies. You can only choose one option in this subcategory:

Always Accept Cookies   With this option enabled, IE will always accept cookies from any Web site.

Prompt Before Accepting Cookies   With this option enabled, IE will always ask you before accepting any cookies from any Web server. Before each cookie is accepted or rejected, a window will pop up asking you if you want to accept or reject the cookie. If you accept it, the cookie will be saved and surfing will continue as normal. If you reject it, you may receive an error or just not be able to access that Web site.

Disable All Cookie Use   With this setting enabled, IE will never accept a cookie from any Web server.

Remember, just as with Navigator, you must balance usability with security. Choose your cookie settings appropriately.

Setting Local Caching Preferences

For the local cache within IE, only the disk cache is configurable. You can set the local disk cache preferences through the General tab of the Internet Control Panel. Once there, click the Settings button in the Temporary Internet Files section of the General tab (as shown earlier in Figure 6.11) to bring up the Settings window (shown in Figure 6.14). The section you should be interested in (for the i-Net+ exam) is the Temporary Internet Files Folder section. Within this section, you can change the amount of disk space being used to cache HTML documents and images. To increase the amount of disk space being used, click and drag the slider to the right. To reduce it, drag the slider to the left. You can also change the location of the temporary files (indicated by the notation "Current folder") by clicking the Move Folder button and specifying a new location.

FIGURE 6.14   Temporary files settings window

When you finish making changes to the local caching preferences, click OK to save them.

Proxy Configuration

The final item you must configure is the proxy configuration. To access the proxy configuration for IE, open the Internet Control Panel and click the Connection tab (as shown in Figure 6.15). Within the Proxy Server section, you can specify the IP address of the proxy server you use for HTTP requests. To do so, you must first check the Access the Internet Using a Proxy Server check box. Then you can specify the address and port number of the proxy server to use.

FIGURE 6.15 The Connection tab of the Internet Control Panel

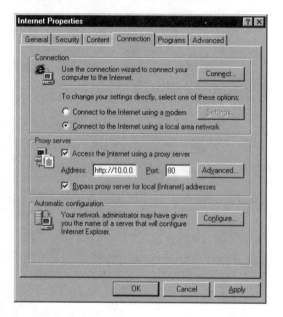

If you need to configure more than just an HTTP proxy, you can click the Advanced tab and specify addresses for each type of server (as shown in Figure 6.16). You could also specify one address and use that same proxy server for all entities by checking the Use the Same Proxy Server for All Protocols check box.

FIGURE 6.16 Advanced configuration of proxy servers

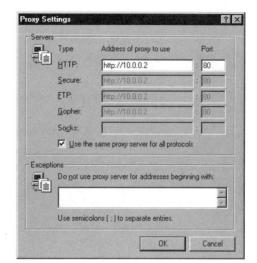

FTP Client Configuration

Unlike Web browsers, FTP clients require very little configuration apart from installation. The only item that might need to be configured in a graphical client is the list of the FTP sites that you are transferring. In this chapter and for the i-Net+ exam, however, you will only need to know how to use the command-line FTP client, which doesn't require configuration.

News Client Configuration

Internet news clients require a bit of configuration in order to function properly. You must set them up to view the newsgroups of a particular news server. Additionally, you must choose which newsgroups you want to consistently check. This process is known as *subscribing* to a newsgroup; you must subscribe to read the same newsgroup(s) every time you start the news client.

In this section, you'll learn how to configure these two settings for the Microsoft Outlook 98 Newsreader.

Microsoft provides a version of the Outlook 98 Newsreader with Internet Explorer 4 and above. This newsreader is called Outlook Express and can be configured in much the same way as the Outlook 98 Newsreader.

News Server

The news server setting for all news clients is the DNS name of the Internet news server that the news client will download news messages from and send messages to. Most ISPs these days have their own news server to provide Internet news articles to their subscribers at no charge.

To configure the Microsoft Outlook 98 Newsreader, follow these steps:

1. Start the newsreader and select Accounts from the Tools menu. This will display the Internet Accounts window. Click the News tab at the top of the window. This is the screen used to add accounts to Outlook 98 Newsreader.

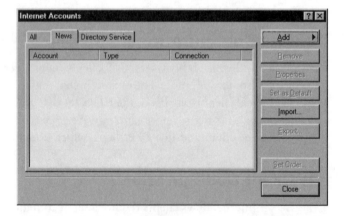

2. To add a new account, click the Add button. This will present a menu to the side giving you the choice of adding either a news account or a directory service account. Choose News.

3. Once you have indicated you want to create a news account, Outlook 98 Newsreader will begin the Internet Connection Wizard by displaying a screen similar to the one shown here. In the first screen,

enter your name as you'd like it to appear when you post a message. Click Next to continue.

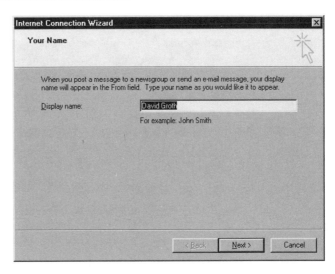

4. In the next screen, you must enter your e-mail address. This will allow people to respond to you via e-mail by clicking the Reply button rather than posting a reply to the newsgroup (which they can still do, but e-mail is quicker). Enter your e-mail address in the field provided.

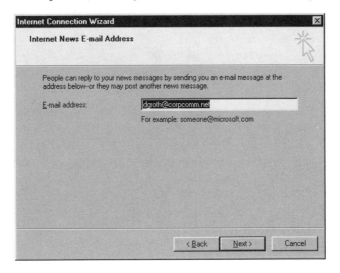

Junk e-mail is called spam (also known as Unsolicited Commercial E-Mail, or UCE). If you want to take steps against receiving spam, you can enter an e-mail address that has several invalid characters in it. For example, the e-mail address dgroth@corpcomm.net might be entered as dNgOrSoPtAhM@corpcomm.net or dgrothNOSPAM@corpcomm.net. Then a line could be placed at the bottom of each message this user posts to explain how to send mail to him so that it arrives correctly (just remove the characters *NOSPAM* from the address). This prevents e-mail harvesters from harvesting an e-mail address from a newsgroup. If they try to send e-mail to the "NOSPAM" address, the e-mail will be rejected. A human would have to edit the e-mail address to send mail to this user.

5. Once you have entered your e-mail address correctly, click the Next button to display the Internet News Server Name screen. This is the screen where you enter either the IP address or the DNS name of the Internet news (NNTP) server. You can get this information from the configuration sheet your ISP gives you or from the information you gathered in "ISP Account" earlier in this chapter. Enter the name or IP address of the NNTP server in the field provided.

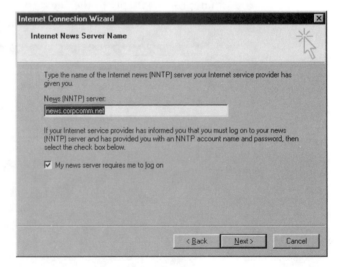

If your news server requires you to log on (ask your ISP; some do nowadays), click the My News Server Requires Me to Log On check box. When you click the Next button, you will be taken to a screen that will ask for the username and password to use when logging on.

6. When you are finished entering your news server address, click the Next button. Assuming you didn't check the My News Server Requires Me to Log On check box, a screen appears that is basically saying, "Hey. You're finished."

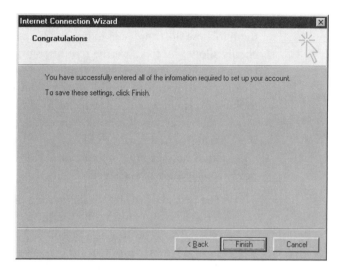

7. Click the Finish button to finish the setup of the Internet news server for the Outlook 98 Newsreader. The Internet Accounts screen appears with the new news account. Click Close to exit the Accounts window.

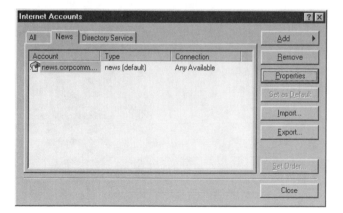

Newsgroup Subscription

The other configuration task with any newsreader is configuring your newsgroup subscription list. This is a listing of newsgroups that you constantly monitor and that the news client should keep track of. There are thousands of newsgroups (a news server can have over 53,000), so scrolling through them to view the same ones every day would be inefficient. Therefore, news clients allow you to subscribe to a newsgroup, just as you would subscribe to a magazine or newspaper. When you subscribe, you configure your news client with shortcuts to commonly read newsgroups so you don't have to go looking for them when you want to read them.

Most newsreaders (Outlook Newsreader is no exception) won't let you read articles of newsgroups unless you subscribe to them. If you want to check out a newsgroup, you can subscribe temporarily. To subscribe to a newsgroup, follow these steps:

1. The first step is to view a list of the available newsgroups on your news server. To do so using the Outlook 98 Newsreader, either click the Newsgroups button on the button bar at the top of the screen or choose Newsgroups from the Tools menu. This will normally display the list of newsgroups to which you're subscribed, but the first time, it will automatically download the entire newsgroup list. This can take 10 to 15 minutes or longer, depending on your connection speed. As the newsgroups are downloading, a window will display how many newsgroups have been downloaded.

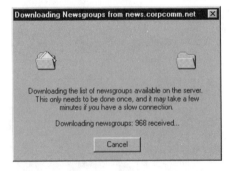

2. Once you have downloaded the entire newsgroup list, the Newsgroup Subscriptions window will appear with the list of newsgroups.

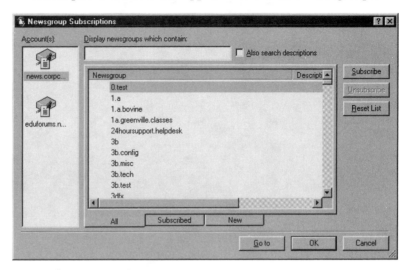

3. To locate a particular newsgroup (`alt.autos.studebaker`, for example), simply type its name into the Display Newsgroups Which Contain field. As you type, the list will get shorter. Notice in the following screen shot that, even though only "alt.autos.s" has been typed, the list in the window is now a very short list. If one more letter (*t*) is added, the only newsgroup that would appear in the list is `alt.autos.studebaker`, as shown in the next screen shot.

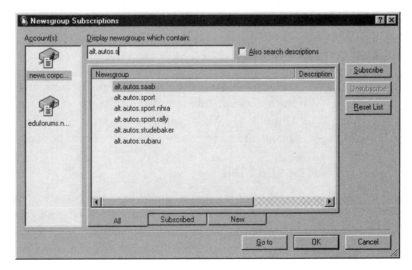

4. To subscribe, simply highlight the newsgroup you to want to subscribe to and click the Subscribe button. An icon will appear next to
it indicating that you have subscribed to it. Additionally, the subscribed newsgroup(s) will now appear on the Subscribed tab, just
below the current window and in the leftmost pane of the main window (refer back to Figure 5.9 in the preceding chapter).

5. When you are finished subscribing to newsgroups, click OK to save
your subscriptions. You will then be able to view messages from the
newsgroups you have subscribed to. This will be covered later in this
chapter.

Mail Client Configuration

Mail clients are also relatively simply to configure. In this section, you'll
learn the steps necessary to configure both Netscape Mail and Microsoft
Outlook 98. We'll explain how to configure your e-mail address and the
incoming and outgoing e-mail servers for both products.

Netscape Mail

Netscape Mail is configured from the Navigator Preferences window. The
preferences for Netscape Mail are all located in the Mail and Groups category. Therefore, to configure Netscape Mail for use as a mail client, you
must first open the Navigator Preferences window and expand the Mail and
Groups category to view the subcategories, as shown in Figure 6.17.

You can also access this screen from Netscape Mail by selecting Preferences from the Edit menu. This method will bring you directly to the Mail and Groups category.

FIGURE 6.17   Opening the Mail and Groups category in Navigator Preferences

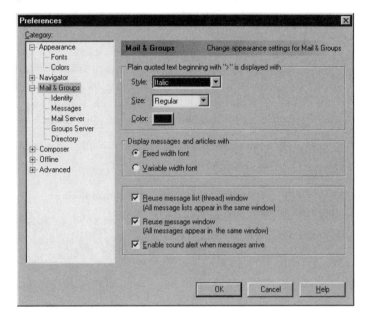

Configuring E-Mail Addresses

The first task in configuring e-mail for Netscape Mail is to configure your identity—information that will appear in the header of the e-mail messages you send to other people and information Netscape Mail needs to know to retrieve messages other people send to you. To do this, you must first open the Mail and Groups category and select the Identity subcategory (as shown in Figure 6.18). In this screen, you can enter several items, including:

Your Name   Obviously, this is the field where you enter your name.

E-Mail Address   This is the field where you enter the e-mail address you want to appear on the From line of your messages when you send them. Type your e-mail address into this field in the format `someone@somewhere.net`. If you're not sure of your e-mail address, ask your ISP.

Reply-To Address   When someone replies to a message from you, this address will appear in the To line of the reply. Fill in this field only if you send messages from one address and receive them at another. Normally, you would leave this field blank and the Reply To address will be the same as the From address.

Organization   In this field, specify a company name (presumably the company you work for). The company name is not always used in Internet communications, so this field is usually left blank.

Signature File   A *signature* is usually a short text message appended to the end of all of your e-mail messages. When this field is filled in with the path and filename of a text file that contains the signature message (you can do this by clicking the Choose button and selecting a text file that contains the signature), Netscape Mail will append the contents of the signature file to the end of every new message you send.

Once you have entered your e-mail addresses and identity information, click OK to save the changes.

FIGURE 6.18   Setting your identity in Netscape Mail

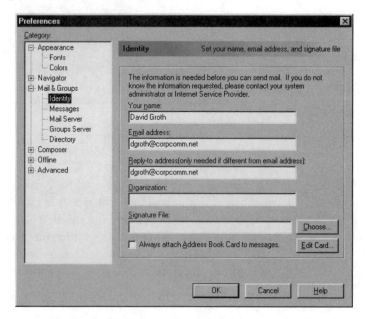

Incoming and Outgoing Mail Server

In addition to specifying your e-mail addresses and identity, you must specify how Netscape Mail should send e-mail and to what servers. This is done by specifying both an incoming (POP3 or IMAP server) and an outgoing (SMTP) server.

The information for both servers is added in the Mail Server subcategory of the Mail and Groups category (as shown in Figure 6.19). You must enter the following information in order to send and receive e-mail from Netscape Mail:

Mail Server User Name   Enter the username that you use to log on to the mail server when you are downloading your mail using either POP3 or IMAP. Netscape Mail will prompt you for a password when you first try to download your mail. If you don't know your username, you can obtain it from your ISP.

Outgoing Mail (SMTP) Server   This field is for the IP address or DNS name of the SMTP mail server to which all outgoing e-mail from Netscape Mail will be sent. The address of this server can be obtained from your ISP. The server name is usually a DNS name that typically starts with either *Mail* or *SMTP*.

Incoming Mail Server   Enter the IP address or DNS name of the mail server that is storing your mail until your mail client can download it using either the POP3 or IMAP mail protocols. This server is typically the same server as the outgoing mail server and thus will have the same address (as is the case in Figure 6.19). But larger ISPs may have multiple mail servers. When in doubt, ask your ISP what this address should be.

Mail Server Type   This set of check boxes determines which protocol Netscape Mail will use to communicate with the mail server to download mail. IMAP is a relatively new protocol, so the majority of Internet mail servers are still using POP3 to download mail to clients. When in doubt, ask your ISP.

When you are finished configuring these options, click OK to save them.

FIGURE 6.19 The Mail Server tab in Netscape Mail

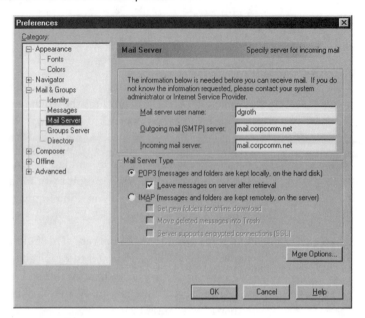

MS Outlook

When configuring Microsoft Outlook to send and receive mail, you'll basically deal with the same options you configure for Netscape Mail. With Microsoft Outlook, you'll access the settings through the Control Panel. Choose Start ➢ Settings ➢ Control Panel and double-click the Mail icon to display the Internet Accounts window, shown in Figure 6.20. From this screen, you can configure all of the Internet mail options for Outlook, including e-mail addresses and mail servers.

FIGURE 6.20 The Internet Accounts window

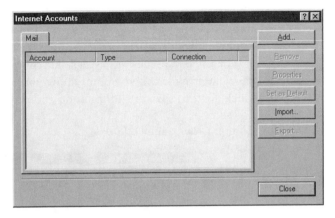

Just as with the Outlook 98 Newsreader, Outlook 98 uses this screen to enter the Internet mail account settings.

To enter any kind of Internet mail settings, you must first create a new Internet mail account. To do so, click the Add button in the Internet Accounts window. The Internet Connection Wizard will begin (Figure 6.21). You'll notice that this screen is similar to the first screen of the Internet Connection Wizard you used to configure the newsreader account earlier. The process is basically the same for both programs. Go ahead and enter your name in the field provided. This is the name that will be displayed in the From line of any e-mail messages you send.

FIGURE 6.21 Entering your name in the Internet Connection Wizard

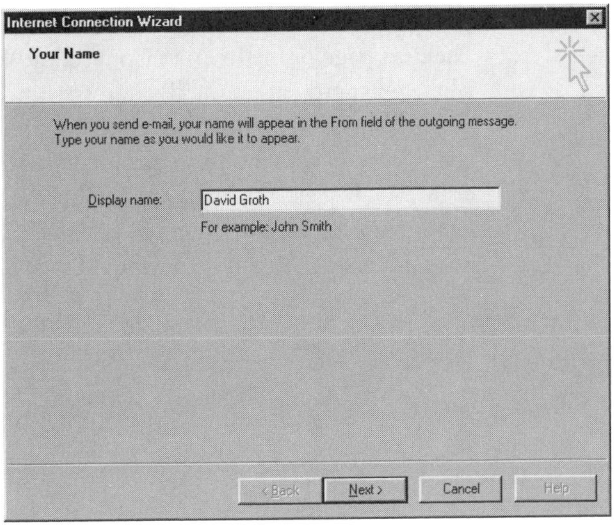

E-Mail Addresses

Once you have entered your name, click the Next button to save the name and move on. The next screen, shown in Figure 6.22, allows you to enter your e-mail address (the one that appears along with your name on the From line of any e-mail messages you send). Simply type your e-mail address into the field provided. If you don't know your e-mail address, ask your ISP. Click Next to save the information and proceed to the next page.

FIGURE 6.22 Entering your e-mail address

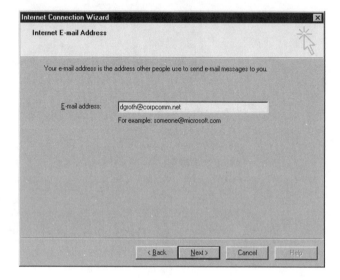

Incoming and Outgoing Mail Servers

The next page of the Internet Connection Wizard (shown in Figure 6.23) is where you enter either the IP addresses or DNS names of both the incoming and outgoing Internet mail servers. Also, there is a drop-down list that allows you to choose which type of incoming mail server you are using (either POP3 or IMAP). Just as with Netscape Mail, these fields could be filled with the same server name or two different server names. Check with your ISP to determine what addresses or names you should type into these fields.

FIGURE 6.23   Entering mail server information

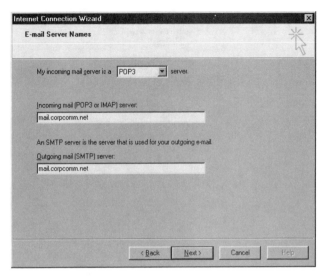

Click Next to accept those settings and move on. The next screen (Figure 6.24) requires that you enter the username and password the client must use when downloading mail from a POP3 or IMAP server. This information should have been given to you when you signed on with your ISP. Enter the correct username and password in the fields provided. Check the Remember Password check box to ensure that Outlook won't ask you for your e-mail password each time you check your mail. Leave this check box blank if you want to be prompted for your password every time Outlook downloads your mail.

FIGURE 6.24 Entering your username and password for the mail server

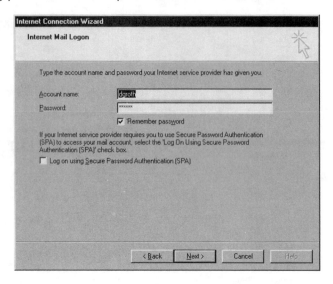

Click Next to continue. In the next screen (Figure 6.25), you'll specify how you want Outlook to connect to the Internet to send and receive mail. There are three options:

Connect Using My Phone Line   With this option selected, whenever Outlook has mail to send, it will dial the Internet automatically, send the mail and download any waiting mail, then disconnect. If you choose this option, Outlook will present you with another screen in which to choose a DUN connection to use to dial the Internet (which means you have to have one configured beforehand).

Connect Using My Local Area Network (LAN)   Selecting this option means that Outlook will connect to the Internet using a LAN adapter and the TCP/IP protocol. Use this option if your client PC is connected to a network and the network is connected to the Internet.

I Will Establish My Internet Connection Manually   Selecting this option means that Outlook will rely on the user to make the Internet connection before performing any e-mail operations.

Click Next to save the option you've selected and continue.

FIGURE 6.25   Selecting the type of Internet connection

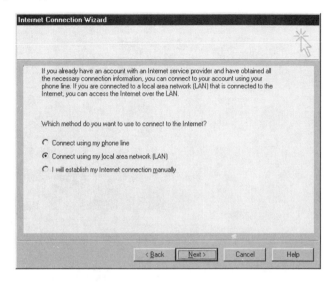

The final step in the configuration of the Outlook mail account is to simply click Finish on the final screen (shown in Figure 6.26) to save the configuration. You will then be returned to the Internet Accounts window (Figure 6.27), where the mail account you just configured will appear.

FIGURE 6.26   The final Internet Connection Wizard screen

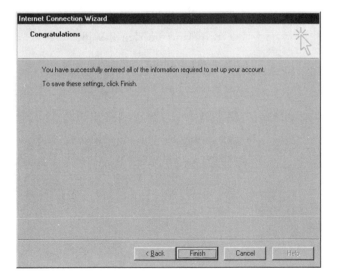

FIGURE 6.27   Internet Accounts window showing a configured mail account

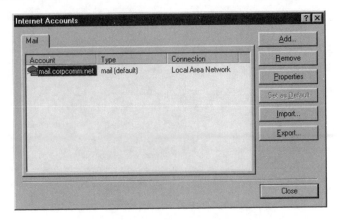

Client Use

Now that you know which clients exist and how to configure them, it is important to know how to use them. In this section, we'll review the most commonly used functions of each type of Internet client discussed in this chapter. The following client uses are covered in this section:

- Establishing a dial-up ISP connection

- Browsing the World Wide Web

- Downloading and uploading files with FTP

- Sending and receiving mail

- Downloading and reading news

For all client use, you must first establish an Internet connection, so we'll cover that procedure first.

Establishing a Dial-Up ISP Connection

To do anything on the Internet, you must have some kind of Internet connection. The most popular type of connection for home users is the dial-up Internet connection. Earlier in this chapter, you learned how to create a DUN connection. In this section, you'll see how to use the connection you created to connect your client PC to the Internet.

To establish a dial-up ISP connection, follow these steps:

1. Double-click the connection you have created to display the Connect To screen.

2. From here, you can change basic connection information, including:

   User Name and Password   These two fields are where you enter the username and password your ISP has given you. Notice that the password is replaced with asterisks (*) as you type so no one else can see it. Usernames and passwords are usually case sensitive.

   Save Password   When this check box is checked, you won't have to enter a password the next time you connect. Usernames are always saved with a configuration.

   Phone Number   This is the phone number the modem will actually try to dial. You can edit this phone number for this connection attempt, but if you close this connection and try to reconnect, the phone number will revert back to its default number (the one you entered when you originally configured this connection). To change this phone number permanently, you must use the Dial Properties button.

Dial From If you have set up multiple dialing locations (for example, Home, Work), the Dial From drop-down list box will allow you to choose which location information will be used for this connection attempt.

Dial Properties This button allows you to enter a configuration page where you can set up things like disabling call-waiting, what number(s) you dial to access an outside line, the current area code, and what number(s) you must dial for long distance.

3. Once you have entered all your (correct) information, click the Connect button to start the connection process. The Connecting To window will appear, and if you have configured your modem correctly, you should hear the modem initiate the call and start dialing. Assuming the phone number was entered correctly, you'll hear a ring or two, and then you'll hear the modem connect and emit a screeching noise. That noise is the ISP's modem attempting to communicate and negotiate the details of a modem connection (like speed, bit rate, etc.).

4. When your modem and the ISP's modem have "talked" for a bit, the screeching will cease, and the Connecting To window will indicate that it is verifying your username and password. At this point, your PC is sending the username and password you've entered in the Connect To screen and waiting for approval from the ISP's dial-up server.

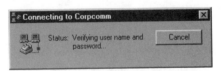

5. Once the ISP's dial-up server has approved the password, the Connecting To window closes and an icon appears in the system tray (on the right on the bar at the bottom of the screen). This icon consists of

two connected computers. The icons blink with green lights as data is
being sent or received.

DUN icon

6. If you right-click this icon, a menu will appear from which you can
   either disconnect from the ISP or view the status window. The status
   window gives you information about the status of the dial-up connection, including:

   - Connection speed (Connected At)

   - How long you've been connected (Duration)

   - Bytes Received

   - Bytes Sent

From this status window you can also click Disconnect to disconnect
your client from the ISP.

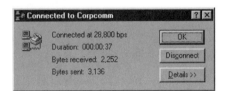

Browsing the Web

Everyone reading this book has more than likely browsed the Web. So, as
you know, browsing the Web is visiting Web sites and displaying them in a
Web browser. The Web browser is now a software component commonly
found on all computers sold today. There are many different brands and
manufacturers, but as discussed in the preceding chapter, most Web browsers are based on the NCSA Mosaic browser. Because they share the same lin-
eage, most Web browsers use the same tools to browse the Web.

In the following sections, we'll cover the standard way to browse the
Web. The process is generic and really isn't specific to one browser. We'll use
the Netscape Navigator browser for this discussion and will make exceptions where necessary.

Starting the Browser

Your Web browsing session starts when you open the browser. Choose Start ➤ Programs ➤ Netscape Communicator ➤ Netscape Navigator to open the Netscape Navigator window (shown in Figure 6.28). When you're browsing the Web, this is really the only screen you will use.

FIGURE 6.28 Netscape Navigator browsing window

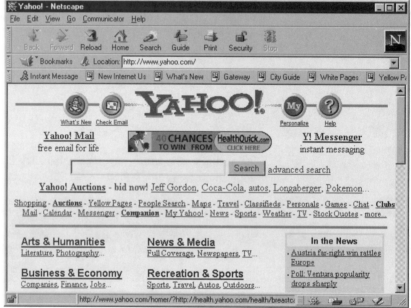

Copyright ©1999 Yahoo! Inc. All rights reserved.

Hyperlinks

As soon as you start the browser, it will go to the page configured as its home page (as discussed earlier in this chapter). Many users specify a home page with a search engine. To go to a another Web page, you can simply click any hyperlink (or *link* for short). A *hyperlink* is a special piece of HTML code that references another Web page on the Internet. Typically, a hyperlink looks like a piece of underlined text (usually a different color than the surrounding text). Each Web page usually contains a couple of links to other pages. Those pages contain links to other pages, and so on to create the network of connections that is the World Wide Web.

You can tell that an item is a hyperlink when you move your mouse pointer over it. Generally speaking, when you move the pointer over a hyperlink, the pointer changes to a hand with an outstretched index finger. You can then click the finger on the hyperlink to go to the next page.

Netscape Navigator displays the text of the Web page first and then loads the pictures (as shown in Figure 6.29). This is an advantage to users with slower modem connections because they can click through the text hyperlinks and navigate to different pages without waiting for all the pictures to load. If you want to stop the images from loading, you can click the Stop button (which is typically an icon that looks like a stop sign). The page will display as it looked the moment you clicked Stop.

If you decide you want to display the images, you can either right-click the images and choose View Image or click the Reload button.

FIGURE 6.29 Waiting for images to load in Navigator

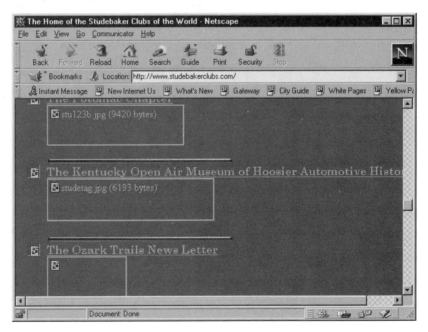

To continue browsing, just click hyperlinks on the current page or choose items from your Bookmark menu. Your Bookmark menu contains shortcuts to pages you've visited and want to visit again. To add a bookmark, choose Bookmarks ➤ Add Bookmark when the page you want to bookmark is displayed in the browser. If you want to go back to the page you visited before the page currently displaying, you can click the Back button (which typically has a left-pointing arrow on it).

Search Engines

Using hyperlinks to browse the Web is a pretty serendipitous method of finding information. If you know the address of a Web server, you can go directly to its Web site by typing the "http://" address in the Location field and pressing the Enter key. Additionally, you could use a search engine. *Search engines* are Web sites that contain the indexed text of millions of Web sites in a searchable database. Users can search these databases for any word, and the search engine will return a list of all the addresses of Web pages that contain that word anywhere on the page. Search engines generally work pretty well. However, you may not always find the information you are looking for. Or the search engine may return so many Web page addresses that it's confusing. For example, if you were looking for general information about the history of the Ford Mustang automobile and you searched for the word *Mustang*, you might get pages on both the car and the horse. You can refine your search by adding more words, such as *car* or *automobile*.

To perform a search, go to a search engine, type in the words you are searching for, and click the Search or Go button. The search engine will return a list of Web page addresses. Figure 6.30 shows the results from a sample search on the words *Ford Mustang*. Notice that the results are a list of text strings, each one a hyperlink to a Web page.

Some common search engines include Yahoo! (the example given in the text) at www.yahoo.com/, AltaVista at www.altavista.digital.com/, Infoseek at www.infoseek.com/, and DogPile at www.dogpile.com/.

FIGURE 6.30   Sample results for a search on Ford Mustang

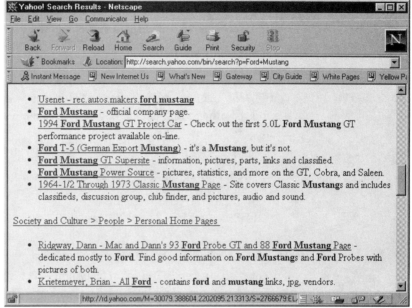

Copyright ©1999 Yahoo! Inc. All rights reserved.

Using FTP to Download and Upload Files

In recent years, FTP has become a truly cross-platform protocol for file transfer. Because Internet (and, thus, TCP/IP) use has skyrocketed, almost every client (and server) platform has implemented FTP. Windows 95/98 and NT are no exception. Both of their TCP/IP stacks come with a command-line FTP utility (as a matter of fact, they're basically the same utility).

Starting the FTP Utility

To start the FTP utility, type **FTP** at a command prompt. The result is an FTP command prompt:

```
FTP>
```

From this command prompt, you can upload and download files, as well as change the way FTP operates. To display a list of all the commands you can use at the FTP command prompt, type **help** and press Enter. To get help on a specific command, type **help**, a space, and then the name of the command.

The first step, really, in starting an FTP session is to determine the address of the FTP site and start the FTP utility. The FTP site typically has the same name as the Web site, except the first three characters are *FTP* instead of *WWW*. For example, Novell, Inc.'s Web site is www.novell.com. Its FTP site, on the other hand, is ftp.novell.com. We'll use this FTP site as an example for the rest of this section.

First, start the FTP utility as discussed earlier, and then follow these steps:

1. At the FTP command prompt, type **open**, a space, and the name of the FTP server. For example:

   FTP> open ftp.novell.com

You can also start an FTP session by typing **FTP**, a space, and the address of the FTP server (for example, **FTP ftp.novell.com**). This allows you to start the FTP utility and open a connection in one step.

If the FTP server is available and running, you will receive a response welcoming you to the server and asking you for a username, like so:

```
ftp> open ftp.novell.com
Connected to ftp.novell.com.
220 nemesis FTP server (Version wu-2.4.2-academ
  [BETA-14](4)
Tue Oct 14 17:57:04
MDT 1997) ready.
User (ftp.novell.com:(none)):
```

2. Enter a valid username, and press Enter.

Most Internet Web servers that allow just about anyone to download files allow the username *anonymous*. Remember to type the username exactly and to double-check as you enter it because usernames are case-sensitive. In addition to anonymous, you can use the username *ftp* to gain access to a public FTP server. They are both anonymous usernames. Again, remember that FTP (and Unix) usernames are case sensitive.

3. Enter your password, and press Enter.

If you are accessing a private FTP server, the administrator gave you your username and password. If you are accessing a public FTP server with a username such as anonymous, you can use your e-mail address as the password.

You don't have to enter your entire e-mail address to log in with anonymous. Most FTP server software doesn't verify the e-mail address, just that it is, in fact, an e-mail address. To do this, it checks for an @ sign and two words separated by a period. Just enter a very short e-mail address to bypass the password (like u@me.com). This is especially helpful if you have a long e-mail address. It's also more secure if you don't want lots of junk e-mail.

If you enter the wrong username and/or password, the server will tell you so by displaying the following and leaving you at the FTP command prompt:

```
530 Login Incorrect
Login failed.
```

You must now start over with the login process. If you are successful, the FTP server will welcome you and drop you back at the FTP command prompt. You're now ready to start uploading or downloading files.

Downloading Files

After you log in to the FTP server, you navigate to the directory that contains the files you want. Thankfully, the FTP command-line interface is similar to the DOS command-line interface. This is no surprise because DOS is based on Unix, and FTP is a Unix utility. Table 5.1 in the preceding chapter lists and describes the common navigation commands for FTP. Remember, these are also case sensitive.

You won't have to use these command-line commands if you are using a graphical utility. The graphical utility will most likely have buttons or icons to represent these commands.

After you navigate to the directory and find the file you want to download, you must set the parameters for the type of file. Files come in two types:

- ASCII, which contains text

- Binary, which is all other files

If you set FTP to the wrong type, the file you download will contain gibberish. When in doubt, set FTP to download files as binary files.

To set the file type to ASCII, type **ascii** at the FTP command prompt. FTP will respond by telling you that the file type has been set to A (ASCII), like so:

```
FTP> ascii
Type set to A
```

To set the file type to binary, type **binary** at the FTP command prompt. FTP will respond by telling you that the file type has been set to I (binary), like so:

```
FTP> binary
Type set to I
```

To download the file, you use the **get** command, like so:

```
FTP> get scrsav.exe
200 PORT command successful.
150 Opening BINARY mode data connection for 'scrsav.exe'
(567018 bytes).
```

The file will start downloading to your hard drive. Unfortunately, the FTP utility doesn't give you any indication of the progress of the transfer. When the file is done downloading, the FTP utility will display the following message and return you to the FTP command prompt:

```
226 Transfer complete.
567018 bytes received in 116.27 seconds (4.88 Kbytes/sec)
```

You can download multiple files using the mget command. Simply type **mget**, a space, and then a wildcard that specifies the files you want to get. For example, to download all the text files in a directory, type **mget *.txt**.

Uploading Files

To upload a file to an FTP server, you must have rights on that server. These rights are assigned on a directory-by-directory basis. To upload a file, log in and then follow these steps:

1. At the FTP command prompt, type **lcd** to navigate to the directory on the local machine where the file resides.

2. Type **cd** to navigate to the destination directory.

3. Set the file type to ASCII or binary.

4. Use the put command to upload the file.

The syntax of the put command is as follows:

```
FTP> put <local file> <destination file>
```

For example, if you want to upload a file that is called 1.txt on the local server, but you want it to be called my.txt on the destination server, use the following command:

```
FTP> put 1.txt my.txt
```

You'll see the following response:

```
200 PORT command successful.
150 Opening BINARY mode data connection for collwin.zip
226 Transfer complete.
743622 bytes sent in 0.55 seconds (1352.04 Kbytes/sec)
```

You can upload multiple files using the mput command. Simply type **mput**, a space, and then a wildcard that specifies the files. For example, to upload all the text files in a directory, type **mput *.txt**.

When you're finished with the FTP utility, simply type **quit** to return to the command prompt.

Remotely Controlling a Unix Host

A Unix host is controlled with the Telnet client. Windows 95/98 comes with a Telnet client, and the i-Net+ exam will test you on your knowledge of using it.

If you already use a Unix host, using a Unix host via a Telnet client is not hard. You must first run the Telnet client. Unlike some programs, the Telnet client isn't found in the Programs submenu under the Start menu (unless someone has added it manually). To start the Windows 95/98 Telnet client, choose Start ➤ Run and type in **telnet**. The Windows Telnet program will appear (as shown in Figure 6.31).

FIGURE 6.31   Opening the Windows 95/98 Telnet program

Before you can connect to a Unix host via Telnet, you should set the Telnet terminal preferences so that Telnet displays characters properly. These preferences can be accessed through the Preferences menu item on the Terminal menu. Once selected, this menu item will bring up the window shown in Figure 6.32. From this window, you can set the following preferences:

Local Echo   Some Unix programs will not send back keystrokes that are initiated at the local terminal. For this reason, the local option exists. When Local Echo is selected, Telnet will display a copy of any keystroke on the local screen. You may want to disable this option unless an application needs it. If you don't, you may see a duplicate of every character you type.

Blinking Cursor   This option, when checked, causes the terminal cursor to blink in a steady on-off pattern.

Block Cursor   This option controls the appearance of the terminal cursor. When Block Cursor is checked, the cursor will be a solid block as big as one character. When the option is unchecked, the cursor will be an underscore (_).

VT100 Arrows   This option controls how the arrow keys on your keyboard work. When the option is checked, the Telnet client will send the codes so that the arrow keys work like they do on an actual VT100 terminal.

Buffer Size   This field specifies how many screen lines the Telnet client will keep in memory so you can scroll back and see what you've done.

Emulation   This setting has two options: VT-52 or VT-100/ANSI. Click the radio button for the type of terminal emulation your Unix box requires. If you don't know, try one. If it doesn't work, try the other. If neither work, you may need to get a more flexible Telnet program.

Fonts   This button brings you to a screen where you can change the font (type style), size, and color of the text being displayed.

Background Color   This button allows you to pick the background color of the Telnet window. The default color is white, but you can change it to any color you prefer.

If you change your background color, make sure you don't change it to the same color as the text font; if you do, you won't be able to see the text being displayed.

FIGURE 6.32 Setting terminal preferences in Telnet

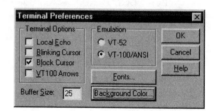

Once you have set the terminal emulation preferences, you can initiate the connection with the Unix host by choosing Remote System from the Connect menu. This will bring up the window shown in Figure 6.33, which allows you to specify which host you are connecting to and how to connect. From this window, you can specify three different items to control how Telnet will connect to the host:

Host Name   This field is where you can specify the DNS name or IP address of the host you want to connect to. You can simply type in an address, or because Telnet keeps track of all the previous hosts you have connected to, you can select one from the drop-down list.

Port   This field allows you to use Telnet to connect to any other TCP port (Telnet uses the Telnet port, TCP port 23, by default). You can use Telnet to check the responsiveness of any service that responds to TCP port requests by typing the address of the host you want to connect to in the Host Name field and the appropriate port number in the Port field. (You can also select the port from the drop-down list provided.)

TermType   If your Telnet host daemon responds to the TermType setting (check your documentation to be sure), you can specify what terminal commands to use from this field. Select the appropriate setting from the drop-down list to configure this setting.

Once you're finished changing the settings, click Connect to connect to the remote host.

FIGURE 6.33 Telnet connection settings

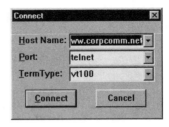

When you're connected, you can do anything you could do if you were sitting in front of that machine. Telnet will transmit the keystrokes to the server and return screen updates. When you are finished, click the Disconnect option on the Connect menu. You can connect to a new address using the procedure just outlined, or you can choose Exit from the Connect menu to exit the Telnet program.

Sending and Receiving E-Mail

Everyone with access to the Internet has sent e-mail at some point or another. It is the preferred method of communication on the Internet. Internet e-mail has become so popular that it is now considered part of popular culture. It is common to see e-mail addresses in addition to addresses and phone numbers in newspapers and on business cards.

There are many clients that can be used to send and receive e-mail, but this chapter will only cover the aspects of sending and receiving mail for two of them: Netscape Mail (Messenger) and Microsoft Outlook.

Netscape Messenger

When sending and receiving mail with Netscape Messenger, you must first run the Netscape Mail program. The program can be found under Start ➤ Programs ➤ Netscape Communicator ➤ Netscape Messenger. Once you start the program, you will see a window similar to the one in Figure 6.34. Within this window, you can do all client functions, including sending and receiving mail.

FIGURE 6.34   The main window of Netscape Messenger

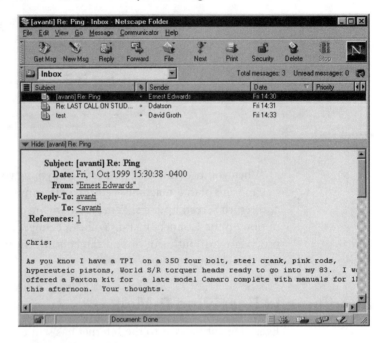

To send a new e-mail, follow these steps:

1. You must first create an e-mail message. To do so, click the New Msg button on the button bar. This will cause a new message window to appear.

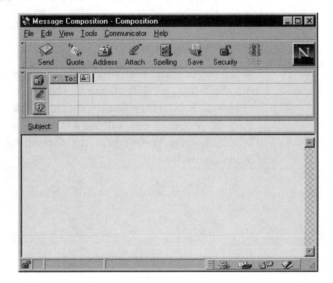

2. From this window, type in the e-mail address of the person you are sending the mail to. In the message shown in the following screen shot, the recipient is `Devarim@earthlink.net`. You can type in more than one recipient e-mail address; just press Enter and enter the next address on the next line.

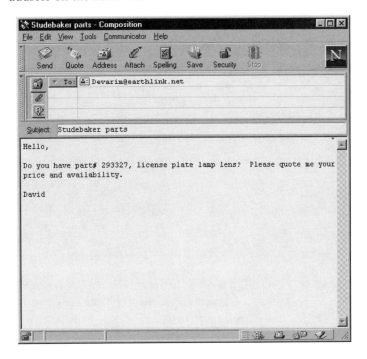

3. Make sure you type a subject in the Subject line so the recipient knows what the message is about. Then type in your message in the large white area below the Subject line.

Always enter a subject so the recipient can tell what the message is about without having to read the whole message. Also, keep the message short and to the point. It's excruciatingly painful to read a three-page essay on the fact that you need more "sticky" notes! Finally, don't attempt sarcasm in an e-mail message. It doesn't work. "You stink" comes across as "You stink!"

4. To send the message you have composed, simply click the Send button. The message will be sent immediately. A window indicating the status of the sending process will appear. If the send is successful, a message indicating that the mail was sent successfully will appear in this window.

Mail is received pretty much automatically. Every few minutes (the interval is configurable), Netscape Messenger will contact the mail server and determine if there is any mail to download to the mail client. If mail is waiting, the mail client will automatically download it to the client using the POP3 (or IMAP) protocol and display the *message headers* (the Subject and From lines) of any new messages. Figure 6.35 shows the Inbox of a sample Netscape Messenger client. Notice the difference between a new message and messages that have been read. For new messages, the font is darker (boldfaced) than the font for the messages that have been read.

 If you want to force Netscape Messenger to "go and get the mail," you can do so by clicking the Get Msg button.

FIGURE   6.35   Receiving a new e-mail message

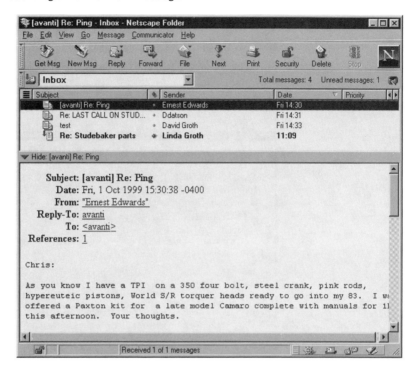

To read the message you have received, simply click the new, boldfaced message you want to read. The text of the message will appear in the bottom of the Messenger window (as shown in Figure 6.36). You can read any message by simply clicking it. There are a few options for what to do with the message once you have read it. You can keep it in your Inbox or you can delete it by clicking the Delete button on the button bar; when you delete a message, it will disappear from your Inbox. You can also reply to the original sender by clicking the Reply button, typing a reply, and clicking Send, just as you would send a new message. Finally, you can forward the message to someone else by clicking the Forward button, typing the e-mail address of the person you want to forward the message to in the To line, and clicking Send.

FIGURE 6.36 Reading a new message

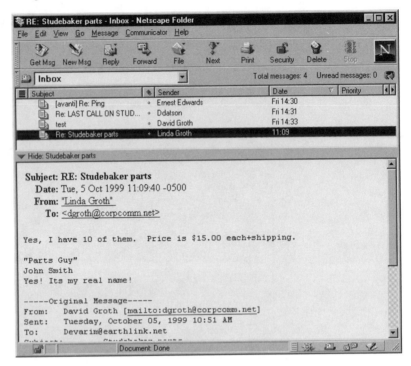

 For more information on using Netscape Messenger, check out Netscape's support page at help.netscape.com.

Microsoft Outlook

Microsoft Outlook (a part of the Microsoft Office suite) and Netscape Messenger are similar when it comes to sending and receiving mail. To send or receive mail with Outlook, you must first start the Outlook program by choosing Start ➤ Programs ➤ Microsoft Outlook. This will display the screen shown in Figure 6.37. From this window, you will do all of the mail operations.

FIGURE 6.37   Microsoft Outlook main screen

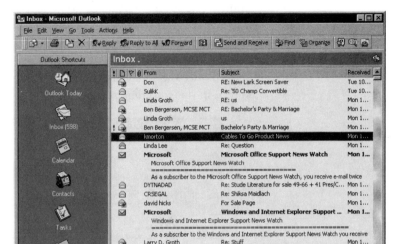

To send a new mail message, follow theses steps:

1. From the main window, click File ➢ New ➢ Mail Message. The new, blank message will display in its own window.

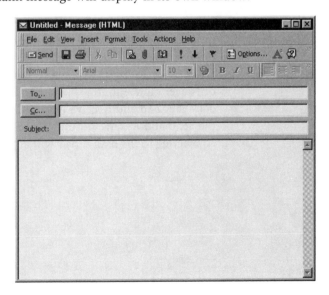

2. Just as in Netscape Messenger, you must type the recipient's e-mail address in the To line. You can type in multiple e-mail addresses, but you must separate them with a colon. Then you must type a subject in the Subject field, and the body of the message goes into the large, white message area. A completed message is shown in the following screen shot. Notice the similarity to the Netscape Messenger mail messages shown in the preceding section.

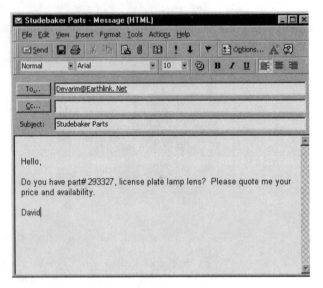

3. Click the Send button to send the message. This process will cause the message to be transferred to the *Outbox* (a folder where items waiting to be sent reside). To complete the send process, you can wait until Outlook performs an automatic "Send and Receive" cycle (which it does every few minutes—a configurable amount of time) or you can click the Send and Receive button on the main screen. If you do click the Send and Receive button, a window indicating that Outlook is connecting to the mail server will appear; then Outlook will display a

progress bar indicating how many messages it has sent and how many messages are left to send.

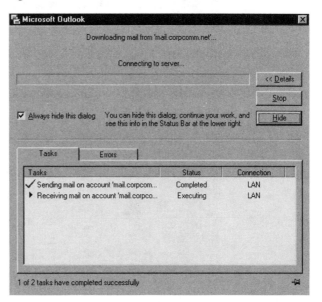

Receiving a message, as with Netscape Messenger, is somewhat automatic. Again, you can either wait for the "Send and Receive" cycle or click the Send and Receive button to have Outlook query the mail server to see if there is any mail to download. If there is, Outlook will download the mail using either the POP3 or IMAP protocol. When a new message arrives, as in Netscape Messenger, the mail will appear in the Inbox boldfaced. Outlook, however, will display an icon of an envelope next to the message. Messages that have been read will have an open envelope next to them (as shown in Figure 6.38). Notice also that Outlook displays the first few lines of all new messages so that you can decide if you want to read them. You can read the entire message by double-clicking it to bring up the message in its own window (as in Figure 6.39). From here, you can read the entire body of the message and close the window when you're finished. You can also reply to or forward the message from this screen by clicking the Reply or Forward button. If you want to delete this message, select the message in the main screen and click the button with the icon of a trash can on it on the main screen.

FIGURE 6.38 Receiving a new message

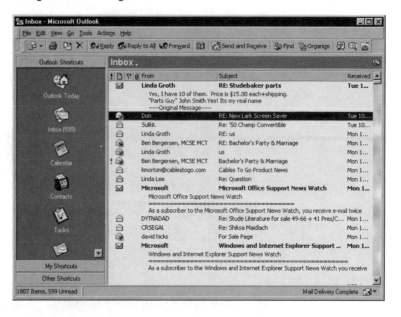

FIGURE 6.39 Reading a new message

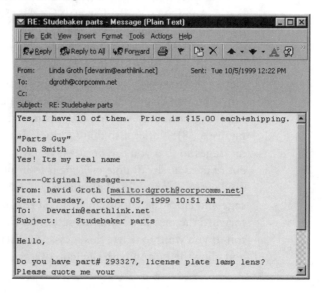

Downloading and Reading News

Reading news is very much like reading e-mail. As a matter of fact, if you use Microsoft Outlook for your e-mail and Microsoft Outlook Newsreader as your Internet news client, the process is almost exactly the same.

To start reading news, you must first configure the newsreader and subscribe to at least one newsgroup. To start the Outlook Newsreader, choose Start ➢ Programs ➢ Microsoft Outlook Newsreader. This will display the screen shown in Figure 6.40.

FIGURE 6.40 Microsoft Outlook Newsreader

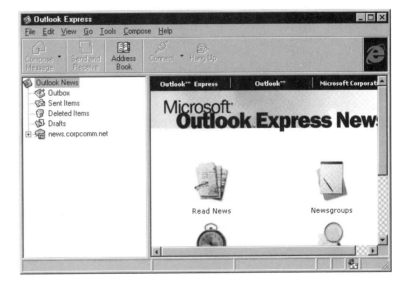

On the left side of the screen is a list of the news servers you have configured for the client. To view a list of the newsgroups you have subscribed to on a particular news server, click the + next to the news server. This will expand the list of newsgroups, as shown in Figure 6.41.

FIGURE 6.41 Displaying the list of newsgroups on a particular server

To download and view a particular newsgroup, click the name of the newsgroup you want to view. This will tell the Outlook Newsreader to contact the news server, download all the headers for all the messages in the selected newsgroup, and display the list of headers in the window on the upper right (as shown in Figure 6.42). The Outlook Newsreader downloads only the header of each message mainly for efficiency. Some messages can be very large, and downloading several hundred messages at a time could take forever. You'd spend more time downloading messages than reading them.

FIGURE 6.42 Displaying the headers downloaded for a particular newsgroup

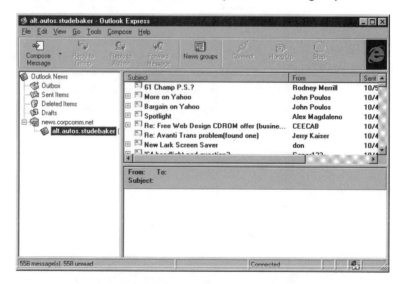

To view the body of a particular news message, you only need to click that message. The text of the message will appear in the window below the list of headers (as shown in Figure 6.43). Similar to Outlook, when you read a message, it changes from boldfaced to regular type.

FIGURE 6.43 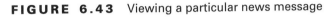 Viewing a particular news message

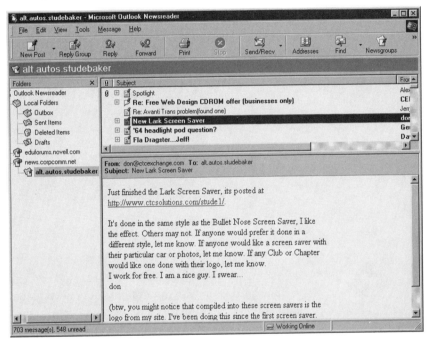

If you want to post your own message, click the New Post icon and fill out the New Post form (as shown in Figure 6.44) with the subject of the post and the information you wish to share. Make sure you post information that is relevant to the newsgroup or you may get some nasty e-mail messages telling you to pay attention to the topic. When you're ready, click Post to post the message.

FIGURE 6.44 Posting a new message

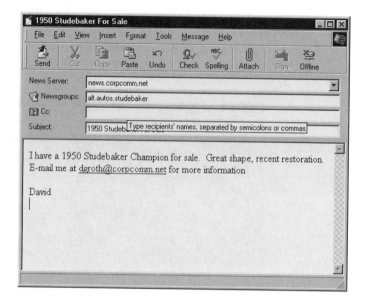

Remember that your e-mail address is posted every time you post a message to a newsgroup unless you configure your newsreader to send a bogus e-mail address when you post. You do *not* send your e-mail address when you just read news articles.

Summary

In this chapter, you learned about the types of clients that exist as well as their requirements, configuration, and use. The important concepts covered in this chapter include the following:

Client types The chapter included some examples of each type of client, including Web browsers (Netscape Navigator and Internet Explorer), Internet News (Microsoft Outlook Newsreader), and Internet e-mail (Netscape Mail and Microsoft Outlook).

Client configuration   You learned which items you must configure in order for each client to function properly. Some clients (like Web browsers) must be configured by entering all settings manually, field-by-field, into a preferences screen. Others (like the Microsoft e-mail and newsreaders) will guide you through the configuration process with a configuration wizard. Still others (like the command-line FTP program) require little, if any, configuration.

Client use   You also learned how to use each client, including browsing the Web with a Web browser, uploading and downloading files with an FTP client, sending and receiving e-mail messages with e-mail clients, and downloading and reading Internet news.

Review Questions

1. What is the name of the name resolution file for Windows 98?

   A. HOSTS

   B. HOSTS.TXT

   C. HOSTS.SAM

   D. HOSTS.NAM

2. Which component of the Internet indexes Web sites so they can be found by a user searching for a word or phrase?

   A. Index servers

   B. Search engines

   C. Search servers

   D. Web searchers

3. What item(s) must you configure on a Web site before browsing the Internet?

   A. Your name

   B. Your e-mail address

   C. Home page

   D. None of the above

4. Before you can use any Internet client for a dial-up connection, what must be installed/configured on the client PC?

   A. Client IP address

   B. Modem

   C. NIC

   D. Web browser

5. When configuring a dial-up connection to an ISP, what information do you need to get from your ISP before setting up the connection on your Windows 95/98 PC?

A. ISP mailing address

B. Web server name

C. ISP dial-up phone number

D. Username and password

6. Once you have started the FTP utility, what is the command used to connect to an FTP server?

A. get

B. help

C. put

D. open

7. What item(s) must you configure in an e-mail client before you can send and receive e-mail?

A. Your e-mail username and password

B. SMTP mail server DNS name

C. Mail server memory configuration

D. POP3 mail server DNS name

8. You try to telnet in to a Unix host, but every character is duplicated on screen when you type it (i.e., if you type *what*, it displays as *wwhhaatt*). What could be wrong?

A. Local Echo is enabled on the client.

B. Local Echo is disabled on the client.

C. Local Echo is enabled on the server.

D. Local Echo is disabled on the server.

9. How do you access the home page settings for Internet Explorer?

   A. Edit ➤ Preferences from main window

   B. Internet Control Panel

   C. Tools ➤ Preferences from main window

   D. IE Control Panel

10. When your Internet client PC is connected to the Internet via a router, in addition to a client IP address and a subnet mask, what other TCP/IP address must be configured in order for the client to communicate on the Internet?

    A. Default gateway

    B. SMTP server address

    C. DNS server address

    D. WINS client address

11. Which is an example of the proper syntax for uploading a file (`file.txt`) to an FTP server?

    A. `upload file.txt`

    B. `put file.txt`

    C. `move file.txt`

    D. `copy file.txt`

12. Which Web browser setting controls how a Web browser receives information and automatically downloaded content from Web sites?

    A. Cookies

    B. Security

    C. Proxy

    D. Mail server

13. What item(s) must you configure in an FTP client before you can connect to an FTP server, log in, and download files?

   A. FTP server name

   B. Client IP address

   C. All of the above

   D. None of the above

14. How do you access the home page settings for Netscape Navigator?

   A. Edit ➤ Preferences from main window

   B. Internet Control Panel

   C. Tools ➤ Preferences from main window

   D. IE Control Panel

15. Netscape Navigator is an example of what type of Internet client?

   A. Web browser

   B. FTP

   C. E-mail

   D. Internet news

16. What item(s) must be configured before you can read news with Microsoft Outlook Newsreader?

   A. Subscribe to a newsgroup

   B. Mail server DNS name

   C. News server DNS name

   D. Download newsgroup list

17. Where in Windows 95/98 do you configure the TCP/IP address of that machine?

  A. Properties of My Computer ➤ TCP/IP address

  B. Start ➤ Settings ➤ Devices ➤ Network Interface cards ➤ TCP/IP

  C. Start ➤ Settings ➤ Control Panel ➤ TCP/IP

  D. Start ➤ Settings ➤ Control Panel ➤ Network ➤ TCP/IP ➤ Properties

18. Which item(s) must be configured for a client PC to support Internet clients?

  A. TCP/IP address

  B. Internet connection

  C. Web browser

  D. DNS server IP address

19. Which modem initialization (AT) command will reset a modem back to its factory defaults?

  A. ATA

  B. ATDT

  C. AT&F

  D. ATFACT

20. When downloading files from an FTP server, which FTP command is used?

  A. download

  B. put

  C. get

  D. down

Answers to Review Questions

1. C. The only correct name resolution file listed for Windows 98 is HOSTS.SAM.

2. B. Search engines index all the words in all Web sites so that you can search for a particular Web site by searching for a word or phrase.

3. D. Although there are places to enter your name, e-mail address, and home page, you don't *have* to enter them before browsing.

4. B. Of the items listed, the only one that is required for a dial-up connection to an ISP is a modem.

5. C, D. When setting up a dial-up connection on your Windows 95/98 PC, at some point you will be asked for the dial-up phone number of the ISP and your username and password.

6. D. The open command is used to open a connection to an FTP server. The get command is used to start downloading a file, help is used to get help, and put is used to initiate a file upload.

7. A, B, D. When configuring an e-mail client, you must configure your e-mail username and password, your ISP's SMTP mail server DNS name, and the POP3 mail server DNS name.

8. A. Local Echo is a setting on the client only, and when enabled, it will duplicate on the screen all characters typed at the keyboard. It is used for those Unix hosts that don't respond properly to Telnet requests.

9. B. All settings for Internet Explorer are controlled through the Internet Control Panel.

10. A. Answers B, C, and D are often configured, but they are actually optional. The only item that is required is the default gateway.

11. B. The only correct syntax for uploading the file file.txt is put file.txt.

12. A. The Cookies setting controls how a Web browser receives cookies (special pieces of information from a Web site). It is a security setting because you may not always want to automatically receive content from a Web server. It could be malicious content.

13. D. Although you must enter the FTP server name during the connection process, there is really no configuration for an FTP client apart from installing it.

14. A. The home page settings are found in the main Preferences window, which is accessed by choosing Preferences from the Edit menu in the main Netscape Navigator browsing window.

15. A. Although it has add-on components to provide many Internet client functions, Netscape Navigator is primarily a Web browser.

16. A, C, D. When using Microsoft Outlook Newsreader, you must enter the DNS name of the news server, download the newsgroup list, and subscribe to at least one newsgroup before you can read any news.

17. D. The TCP/IP address of a machine is set through the Network Control Panel in the Properties window for the TCP/IP protocol.

18. A, B, D. Although a Web browser is a client, it is not required for a PC to support Internet clients.

19. C. ATA will tell the modem to answer, ATDT causes the modem to dial a number, and ATFACT is not an AT command.

20. C. The `get` command is used to "get" (or download) files. The `put` command is used to upload files. The other two answers aren't really FTP commands

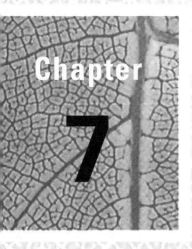

Chapter

7

Network Security

i-NET+ EXAM OBJECTIVES COVERED IN THIS CHAPTER:

✓ **Define the following Internet security concepts: access control, encryption, auditing and authentication, and provide appropriate types of technologies currently available for each. Examples could include the following:**

- Access control: Access Control List, firewall, packet filters, proxy
- Authentication: Certificates, digital signatures, nonrepudiation
- Encryption: Public and private keys, Secure Sockets Layer (SSL), S/MIME, digital signatures, global versus country-specific encryption standards
- Auditing: Intrusion detection utilities, log files, auditing logs
- SET (Secure Electronic Transactions)

✓ **Describe VPN and what it does. Content could include the following:**

- VPN in encrypted communications
- Connecting two different company sites via an Internet VPN (extranet)
- Connecting a remote user to a site

✓ **Describe various types of suspicious activities. Examples could include the following:**

- Multiple login failures
- Denial of service attacks
- Mail flooding/spam
- Ping floods
- SYN floods

✓ **Describe access security features for an Internet server (e.g., e-mail server, Web server). Examples could include the following:**

- User name and password
- File level
- Certificate
- File-level access: read, write, no access

✓ **Describe the purpose of antivirus software and when to use it. Content could include the following:**

- Browser/client
- Server

✓ **Describe the differences between the following as they relate to security requirements:**

- Intranet
- Extranet
- Internet

Computer networks are a huge blessing, making it possible for us to share databases, files, messages, and other information quickly and easily. But the blessing comes with several problems—information security chief among them.

Think about it. If you have a stand-alone computer, the only way to get access to the information on it (the only way that doesn't involve very expensive, James Bond–type bugging equipment that monitors the computer's radio frequency emissions) is to somehow sit down at that computer and operate it. On the other hand, a computer connected to a network may be accessed via its network link. It may be possible to access files and other information on the computer over that connection—indeed, there probably are legitimate reasons for doing so. But that connection can be abused, and a connection to the Internet just widens the field of potential intruders.

Author Craig Hunt makes an apt analogy in his *Network Security*, a Hewlett-Packard Job Aid published by O'Reilly & Associates. Hunt says that computers connected to the Internet are like homes and businesses and that the Internet is like the network of roads and highways. Anyone who owns property wants to protect his or her possessions, but the way to do that is not by blocking the thoroughfares—after all, they're useful for legitimate purposes as well as nefarious ones. Rather, people interested in keeping themselves and their stuff safe from intruders lock their doors, securing safe private zones from open public zones.

You'll hear a lot about the nobility of hackers and crackers. Some say that people who break into secured systems are really helping the owners of those systems in the sense that they point out problems that need to be corrected. Perhaps there's some truth to this, but others—notably John C. Dvorak of *PC Magazine*—point out that in many small towns, people leave their doors unlocked because they trust their neighbors. Clearly, if someone were to take advantage of this trust by illegally entering a house, he or she would be damaging the community and serving no useful purpose whatsoever.

This chapter aims to bring you up to speed on the issues and technologies of network security. You'll get definitions of terms you'll hear as you start to work on a global network populated by bad guys as well as good.

Security Fundamentals

The security of networked computers is all about making sure that the right people have access to the right information, and that they get it intact without anyone listening in as the information is transmitted. To accomplish those goals, you have to be sure that people are who they claim to be. You also have to have a way of dealing with security breaches while—and after—they occur, so you can figure out what is (or was) going wrong in order to correct the problem. The difference between security on a local area network (LAN) and security on the Internet is largely one of scale. The threats to security on the Internet are more numerous and more geographically distributed (and therefore harder to detect in some cases), but the motivations and techniques of attackers are largely the same on large and small networks.

In this section you will learn about the key elements of computer security:

- Authentication

- Access control

- Encryption

- Auditing

These are all vital elements to a secure Internet presence. A weakness in any of them could lead to a breach of the whole system. Let's examine them individually.

Authentication

The first step in network security is *authentication*. Authentication is the process of verifying that a person (or a piece of software, in situations where programs share information without human intervention) is who he claims to be. If we don't know who someone is, we can't be sure if he deserves access to protected computing resources. In real life, we can look at someone and ascertain if he is known and trusted, known and distrusted, or unknown. In operations that take place across networks, visual identification (usually) isn't possible and other means of identity verification need to be devised.

Password Authentication

The simplest sort of authentication is a password. Someone who wants access to a computer resource enters her username. On a very (dangerously) trusting system, a username would be all that was needed to get in. But for most systems, the logic process goes like this: "Here is a person claiming to be so-and-so. What is something only so-and-so would know, by which I can verify the claimed identity?" The answer is so-and-so's password. In theory, only so-and-so knows her password and is the only one capable of correctly entering it. So the system prompts for a password, and if the password entered matches the one the system knows to be associated with so-and-so, the person is admitted to the system.

The problem with passwords is that people are sloppy with them, and this leads to more problems. People write down their passwords (making them more easily stolen—see the beginning of the movie *WarGames* for an example of this). Other times, people choose passwords that may easily be guessed, such as the names of relatives or towns (going back to *WarGames*, Prof. Falken's choice of his son's name—Joshua—as his password was woefully dumb).

When choosing a password, select one that's not obvious. Indeed, choose one that's not even a real word in any language (sometimes, bad guys will attack a system with a dictionary program that submits thousands of words as passwords in a sort of random-guess approach—this is called a dictionary attack). One popular technique is to choose a sentence—say, "My cat Otis has two twitching ears"—and use the initial characters to make a password—McOh2te in this case. Make sure to use a mixture of uppercase letters, lowercase letters, numerals, and other characters if you can.

Key and Card Authentication

In situations in which passwords aren't enough, some systems require users to have a physical thing they must present in order to gain access. Whether it's an actual metal key to be inserted and twisted or a magnetic card, physical authentication devices increase the likelihood that the person trying to gain access is who he claims to be. The logic is that it's less likely for a password *and* a key to be stolen than just one or the other. Also, a legitimate user will know if his physical device has been lost or stolen and can report it as such. There's no way to know if your password has been stolen.

Biometric Authentication

It may sound like something out of a James Bond movie (indeed, it is), but it's becoming increasingly possible and economical to use biometric technology to authenticate users. Biometric authentication relies on the fact that all people have unique physical characteristics that may be used to absolutely distinguish them from one another. The practicalities of biometrics are still being worked out, but it's clear that there are going to be several solutions of varying accuracy and expense:

Fingerprints   Everyone has fingerprints different from those of everyone else. There are devices that scan the ridges on the tip of your index finger and compare the scanned ridges to a database of fingerprint images.

Voiceprints   Everyone has a unique voice, which a computer can describe mathematically and use as a point of comparison for authentication purposes.

Face recognition   Computers and video cameras can look at a user and compare facial dimension data—such as eye separation, mouth width, and nose size—to a database.

Retinal scanning   Similar to fingerprints, the pattern of capillaries on the inside-rear of your eyeballs is unique to you. Machines can scan this pattern and compare it to a database of images.

There are two problems with biometrics. For one thing, people change over time (both long-term and short-term). What if you have a scratchy morning voice when you first try to log on via voiceprint? What happens if you go away for the holidays, gain 10 pounds, and then try to have your computer recognize your face? What happens if you wear makeup some days and not others? These are problems that biometrics companies are working on full-time, and they've made real progress.

The other, less serious problem is a biometric impostor. It's sometimes possible to make a latex cast of someone's finger, complete with ridges, and fool a fingerprint scanner that way. This problem has been pretty much licked by modern devices, though.

Digital Signatures

Digital signatures are pieces of electronic information that serve to guarantee that an item—a document, a credit-card number, whatever—was not tampered with as it traveled over the Internet from sender to recipient. By examining a digital signature that arrives with a piece of data, you can be sure that the data has arrived in exactly the same state it was in as it left its sender's computer.

Digital signatures rely on a mathematical algorithm called a *one-way hashing algorithm*, or one-way hash. A hash takes a piece of data—the characters in an e-mail message, say—and runs it through a series of operations. The operations yield a value that is unique to the information—even slightly different pieces of the original information will yield vastly different hash results. One-way hashes are so named because you can't work them backwards. You can't look at a hash result and figure out the original data from it. This sounds a lot like public-key encryption (a means of hiding messages from prying eyes, which we'll get to soon), and indeed that process also uses a one-way hashing algorithm. In digital signatures, the hash doesn't alter the information itself. Rather, it generates a result that's based on the information.

How Digital Signatures Work

Let's walk through the process of sending a digitally signed message traveling between two parties, Al and Bert. The message might be an e-mail message, an attached document, the contents of a Web form—the details of the information don't matter.

First, Al decides that he wants to send a digitally signed message to Bert. Al generates his message in the usual way, typing it in plainly readable text. Then, Al applies a hashing algorithm to the message, generating a result. Finally, Al puts the result in a package with a statement of the hashing algorithm he used and encrypts the package (but not necessarily the message itself) with Bert's public key. The encrypted package is called the digital signature, and it's sent along with the message to Bert.

[handwritten margin note: How does Bert know the original msg Al sent.]

When Bert gets the signed message, he uses his private key to decrypt the digital signature. He then knows the hashing algorithm Al used and the results Al got when he applied that algorithm to the message. If Bert can apply the algorithm to the message he received and get the same result that Al sent, then he knows that the message was not altered as it traveled across the Internet.

Digital signatures only verify that information wasn't tampered with during transmission—they don't verify that the sender is who he claims to be. E-mail messages commonly use digital signatures. To use digital signatures, you need a digital certificate.

Digital Certificates

Certificates are proof that people (or things) are what they claim to be. Your passport is a good example of a certificate. It states some information about you—your name, your date of birth, your nationality, and so on—and associates it with a photograph of you. The idea is that someone can look at your passport, compare the photo in it with your actual appearance, and assume that, if the two match, the personal information in the passport applies to you. The other important element of a passport is that a government issues it. You can't make your own passport. Rather, you have to prove your identity through procedures established by your government. If your government is well-known and its identity-verification procedures are widely regarded as rigorous, your passport is more likely to be regarded as an accurate statement of who you are. Forging a passport is difficult because governments—particularly the well-regarded ones—use special paper, holograms, distinctive bindings, and other devices to make it hard for individuals to manufacture passports.

You can think of a *digital certificate* as the electronic analogue of a passport in an environment that's based on bits rather than on paper. Like a paper passport, a digital certificate—we'll call them *certificates* from now on—meets several criteria:

- It's unique to its owner.

- It's easy to determine whether the person presenting the certificate is in fact its owner.

- A universally recognized authority issues it.

- It's hard to forge.

How Digital Certificates Work

Say you want a certificate for the purpose of proving your identity on the Internet. The first step in acquiring one is to generate a key pair for yourself—one public key and one private key. Most Web browsers will do this for you, as will various e-mail clients and other Internet tools. You must take steps to protect your private key, either by encrypting and password-protecting it on your local machine, storing it on a smart card or other device you carry with you, or some combination of these. Your private key must remain secure.

Then, you'd take your public key and approach a *certification authority (CA)*. A certification authority is an organization that's responsible for verifying the identity of people who come to it and issuing certificates to those whose identities can be verified. Typically, you'd go to the CA's Web site and enter some information—including your public key—there. Then it's up to the CA to verify that you are who you say you are and not someone who's using your public key and personal information to gain a certificate in your name.

Often, CAs issue different kinds of certificates to entities that have proven their identities with varying degrees of rigor. An applicant might get one kind of certificate if the CA merely verifies that e-mail sent to the applicant's address is received. The applicant might get a better certificate if the personal information she provides matches some authoritative, secure database (such as a government list of Social Security numbers in the United States). She might get an even better certificate if she actually shows up at the CA's office for a fingerprint check. Different applications require different degrees of assurance that someone is who she claims to be.

Once a CA has verified the applicant's identity to the necessary degree, the CA generates a certificate for the applicant (usually one that complies with the X.509 certificate specification). The certificate includes several elements:

- A serial number
- Information about the certificate holder (name and affiliation)
- The certificate holder's public key
- Information about the CA
- The CA's digital signature
- An expiration date

Bear in mind that a certificate can be hijacked, but doing so isn't very useful unless the thief also steals the private key that corresponds to the public key incorporated into the certificate. If you send an encrypted message to someone based on the public key in his certificate, he'd be unable to read it without the corresponding private key and the game would be up.

Together with digital signatures, certificates provide the basis for *nonrepudiation technologies*. A nonrepudiation technology is any means of providing absolute proof (where *absolute* is defined as strong enough to stand up in court) that something occurred. A nonrepudiation scheme might involve a system of receipts—you send me a certified, signed message and I send you another certified, signed message that says I received what you sent. The messages don't have to be e-mail messages—they could just as well be stages in a transaction involving Web forms.

Access Control

Say you've ascertained the identity of a person trying to gain entry to your system and agreed to let him in because the authentication information matches. You can then protect your resources by restricting users—both individually and as classes—to only the information they need in order to do their jobs.

It stands to reason that a user from the engineering department has no need to look at most internal financial statements and that accountants don't need to see product drawings. *Access control* is any system that keeps people from accessing resources they don't need. If they can't access it, they can't steal it.

Access control is more complicated than it might seem at first because there's overlap among the functional units of an organization. An engineer might not deserve to know how much money his colleagues are making, but it would be wrong to bar him from all human resources information because he has a legitimate need to see data about his health insurance. The trick is figuring out who needs which information and giving them the needed access, but no more.

There are a number of methods of controlling access to critical data on a LAN or over the Internet. Among the most common methods are firewalls, proxy servers, Access Control Lists, and packet filtering. Each method is explained in more detail in the sections that follow. Each functions to secure data on an internal network and keep it from being accessed without authorization via the Internet.

Firewalls

A firewall is a computer or other network device that prevents unwelcome parties from gaining access to a secured network. Just as a conventional firewall prevents problems (such as fire) in an engine compartment from immediately spreading to the rest of a car or aircraft, a network firewall keeps the bad guys on one side of itself and the good guys (those whose information it protects) on the other. Firewalls use a variety of techniques to provide insulation from attacks. Access Control Lists (ACLs), dynamic packet filtering, and protocol switching are among the most popular techniques. We'll examine them individually now.

Access Control Lists (ACLs)

Access Control Lists (ACLs), as they apply to firewalls, are collections of rules about what resources on the secured network may be accessed by entities (people and machines) on the Internet, outside the secured network. Routers may (indeed, should) be equipped with Access Control Lists that determine how they handle requests for service. An ACL might be set up, for example, to let people on the open Internet access the Web server that contains the company's public sales information. The same ACL might prohibit anyone from outside the local network from accessing the database server that keeps track of orders.

Figure 7.1 shows how an ACL-equipped router might protect a LAN from Internet access. See how the router—acting as a firewall here—has a list of rules? Each time a packet comes through, it checks to see that its desired path is permissible according to the rules in its ACL.

FIGURE 7.1   A router with an ACL protects a private network.

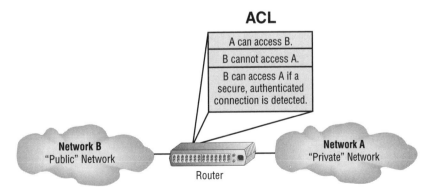

ACL

| A can access B. |
| B cannot access A. |
| B can access A if a secure, authenticated connection is detected. |

Network B
"Public" Network

Network A
"Private" Network

Router

WARNING

The problem with ACLs is that it's possible for bad guys to pretend to be using computers they're not—a practice known as IP spoofing. That's why other protective measures remain necessary.

Dynamic Packet Filtering

When two computers are engaged in communications over the Internet, they communicate by sending packets back and forth. When one of the computers is on a network that's protected by a firewall and the other is on the open Internet, the packets must pass through the firewall as they travel from one computer to the other. A firewall that keeps track of the packets traveling between two computers as part of a particular communications session is a powerful security device. The process of monitoring the packets involved in an exchange and rejecting those that don't fit is called *dynamic packet filtering*.

You see, the packets involved in a communications session are numbered, and a firewall with dynamic packet filtering features keeps track of the number of the next packet it expects to receive as part of a transaction (the number is stored in a *state list*). If a packet with another number comes along, claiming to be part of the same transaction, the firewall knows not to let it into the secured network. Figure 7.2 shows how this works. The session the firewall is keeping track of involves A (the server on the left) and B (the client on the right). When the hacker attempts to impersonate the server, the firewall protects the client by recognizing that the hacker is attempting to use nonsequential packets.

FIGURE 7.2 A firewall with dynamic packet filtering protecting a network

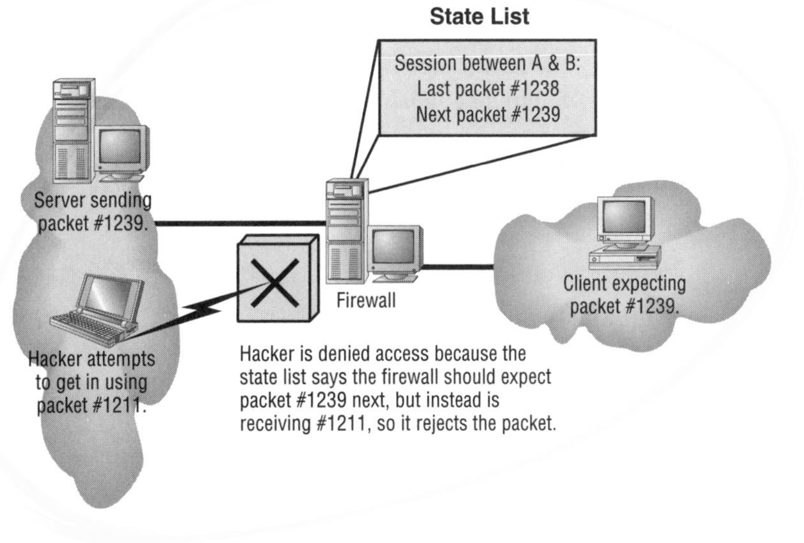

State List

Session between A & B:
Last packet #1238
Next packet #1239

Server sending
packet #1239.

Firewall

Client expecting
packet #1239.

Hacker attempts
to get in using
packet #1211.

Hacker is denied access because the
state list says the firewall should expect
packet #1239 next, but instead is
receiving #1211, so it rejects the packet.

Protocol Switching

Some Internet attacks—notably SYN floods and Ping of Death attacks—
take advantage of characteristics of the TCP/IP protocols on which the Internet operates. An easy way to stop such attacks is to base your secure networks on protocols other than TCP/IP. A TCP/IP attack won't be effective
against a secure network that's based on AppleTalk, NetBEUI, or IPX. A
firewall that provides *protocol switching* takes TCP/IP traffic from the Internet and translates it into some other protocol for transmission across the
secure network.

On the other hand, there's a lot to be said for the TCP/IP protocols as the
basis for a protected network. They're the standard network protocols for
Windows NT and Unix machines, for one thing. You can use protocol
switching to protect networks like this by means of a dead zone. A *dead zone*
is a network segment between two routers on which a non-TCP/IP network
protocol runs. TCP/IP traffic runs into one router, which translates it into
another protocol and passes it on to the other router. The second router
translates the traffic in the intermediate protocol back into TCP/IP for use on
the secured network.

Figure 7.3 shows how protocol switching works with and without a dead zone. The scheme on the left has a dead zone—the Internetwork Packet eXchange/Sequenced Packet eXchange (IPX/SPX) protocol is used between the two routers. The system on the right has no dead zone, but the whole secured network runs IPX/SPX and so is secure from TCP/IP-based attacks.

FIGURE 7.3 Protocol switching with and without a dead zone

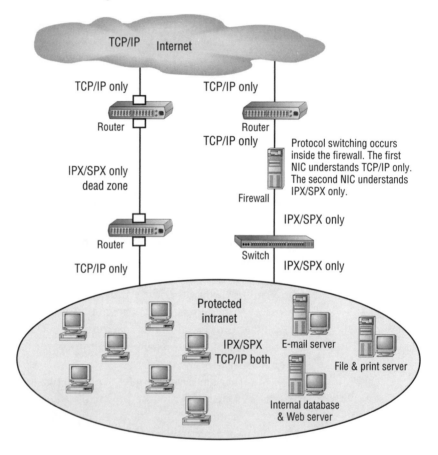

Demilitarized Zones (DMZ)

A *demilitarized zone (DMZ)* is a special network segment that's kept separate from networked resources that need to be held to a higher level of security. Resources in the DMZ—such as Web servers and Internet-accessible database servers—are meant to be accessed from the open Internet. They should be protected from attack—no one wants their Web pages altered by vandals—but they can't be as heavily defended as, say, an internal mail server or a database server that holds proprietary sales data. With the DMZ machines on one segment and the really sensitive resources on another, the DMZ can be given one level of protection and the rest of the network another, much higher, security level. Figure 7.4 shows how a DMZ fits into a firewall protection scheme. The protected intranet, on a network segment separate from the Internet servers, can be made subject to different security rules than the public and semipublic resources.

FIGURE 7.4   A firewall with Internet-accessible computers in a DMZ

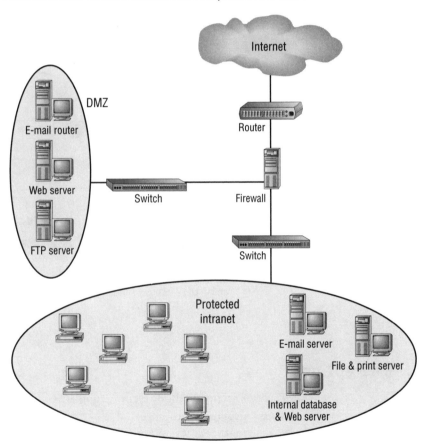

Proxy Servers

A *proxy server* is a computer that acts on behalf of the computers on a secured network when they want to access information on the public Internet. If you are on a secured network and want to access a Web site, you'd send your request to the proxy server. It would then get the information you want and, in a separate transaction, send it to you. Think of proxy servers as clerks in an old-fashioned store, where you don't pick the products off the shelves yourself but rather make requests of the clerk. Figure 7.5 shows how this works. The data traveling in each direction remains untouched, but the address header on each packet of data is changed when the packet passes the proxy server. The remote resource is unable to send packets to the client directly.

FIGURE 7.5 A proxy server assisting an Internet transaction

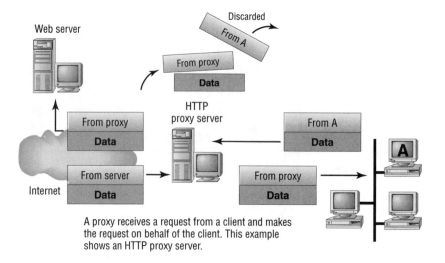

A proxy receives a request from a client and makes the request on behalf of the client. This example shows an HTTP proxy server.

Encryption

Encryption is any method of converting a readable message—known as a *cleartext* message—into unreadable *ciphertext*. Encryption is all about advanced mathematics and hashing algorithms—remember them from our earlier discussion of digital signatures? To refresh your memory, here's how encryption works.

If Ann wants to send a message to Beth over the Internet and has reason to believe that Callie will intercept the message *en route*, Ann can encrypt the message before sending it. Ann takes her cleartext message and runs it through an *encryption algorithm* (also called a *hashing algorithm*)—a sequence of mathematical procedures that alters the text and renders it unreadable. Encryption algorithms depend on keys, which we'll cover in greater depth soon. Having encrypted her text, Ann can send the ciphertext to Beth over the Internet. Beth can decrypt the message with a decryption algorithm and a particular key. If Callie intercepts the message, it doesn't matter because she doesn't have the key that Beth has.

Differences among encryption systems center on the key. Keys can be long or short, public or private. Encryption and decryption algorithms can be the same or different. On the Internet, most transactions rely on *public-key encryption*, which is a system that involves encrypting messages with one key and decrypting them with another. Encryption comes in handy for all sorts of tasks, ranging from e-mail messages to electronic commerce transactions involving credit card numbers.

Encryption relies upon mathematical functions that use a key to convert cleartext into ciphertext. The key is a string of random characters, the longer the better. Longer keys result in ciphertext that's harder to crack.

Key length is measured in bits. A 40-bit key is considered the minimum for even marginal security, whereas ciphertext created with a 128-bit key is very hard to decode.

There are two basic kinds of encryption, public-key and private-key. Private-key encryption is, under certain circumstances, theoretically unbreakable but is not well-suited to the kinds of transactions that go on on the Internet, which frequently involve people who have never met. Public-key encryption is extremely strong but theoretically breakable (though only with extraordinarily powerful computers and hundreds of years) and does not require participants in a transaction to meet. We'll explore these applications further in the following sections.

Private-Key Encryption

Private-key encryption relies upon a single, secret key. The sender uses the secret key to encrypt a message. The encrypted message is then sent to the recipient, who uses the same key to convert it back into cleartext. There's one key, and both parties to the exchange must know what it is. In order for the exchange to be secure, no one else must know what the key is.

Lots of military communications rely on private-key encryption. When there's a message to be transmitted to the missile submarine or the B-52, the base uses a specific code to encrypt it. The encrypted message then is radioed to its recipient, where someone uses the same code key (often dramatically snapped from a plastic shell) to decode the message.

The thing about private keys is that they must be synchronized—the sender and the recipient must have the same key. Further, the keys must be synchronized securely, without a spy or other bad guy getting a copy with which to decode the messages.

Private-key encryption works great for environments like the military, where keys may be synchronized between senders and recipients at (theoretically) secure locations like ports and air bases. But don't forget that moles sometimes steal private keys.

In any case, the Internet is not a military operation, and there's rarely an opportunity for senders and receivers to synchronize their keys in a secure location. The Internet demands a different solution, and so private-key encryption isn't used much on the Internet.

Public-Key Encryption

In contrast to private-key encryption schemes, sending an encrypted message by a *public-key* setup requires two keys. One key is used to encrypt the message; the other is used to convert it back into readable cleartext form.

Let's say Bill wants to send a message to Kate. To encrypt the message, Bill looks up Kate's public key—a key that's freely available and listed in a directory—and uses it to encrypt his message. He then sends the encrypted message to Kate via the open network.

It's true that anyone who wants to can snag the message along the way and also can get access to Kate's public key the same way that Bill did. But the neat thing is that Kate's public key is useful only for encrypting messages meant for her—you can't use it to decrypt messages. This is called a *one-way encryption scheme*.

To decrypt the message Bill has sent her, Kate must apply her private key. Her private key is a secret, known only to her and useful only for decoding messages encrypted with her public key. Unlike in a private-key encryption scheme, there's less chance that the private key in a public-key system will leak because there's no need to share it with anyone at all. Figure 7.6 shows how this works. In the illustration, X first sends a message to Y. That message is encrypted with Y's public key and decrypted with Y's private key. The reply message, which goes from Y to X, is encrypted with X's public key and decrypted with X's private key.

FIGURE 7.6 Public-key encryption in action

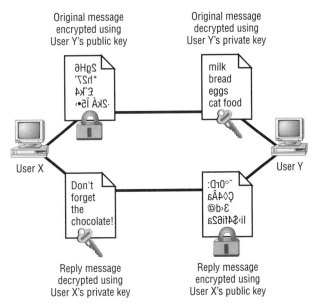

Original message encrypted using User Y's public key

Original message decrypted using User Y's private key

User X

User Y

Reply message decrypted using User X's private key

Reply message encrypted using User X's public key

Political Restrictions on Encryption

If you've ever downloaded a Web browser in the United States, you were probably offered a choice of key lengths. You could download the 40-bit version of the browser without any further questions, but you had to make a lot of statements about your citizenship and location if you wanted to have a browser that could handle 128-bit encryption.

The reason for this is legislative. The U.S. government has designated strong encryption technologies as munitions, along the lines of bombs and air-search radar units. The theory is that, if a hostile government (or an international criminal, or a terrorist group, or whatever) had strong encryption, they'd be free to communicate in secret.

Therefore, it is illegal to export from the United States encryption technologies based upon keys of more than 40 bits. If you're going to design a piece of software for use outside the United States, either do your developing outside the country's borders and use non-U.S. strong encryption technology or, if it's developed in the United States, use 40-bit encryption.

Encryption Technologies

As with any technology, there's a difference between encryption in theory and encryption in practice. Although the principles of public-key encryption apply to many different situations—such as secure electronic mail and secure credit card transactions with Web sites—the implementations of encryption differ in different circumstances. Here, we'll explore Pretty Good Privacy (PGP) and S/MIME as e-mail encryption technologies, Secure Sockets Layer (SSL) as a way of encrypting Web traffic, and Secure Electronic Transactions (SET) as a means of protecting credit card information.

Pretty Good Privacy (PGP)

Developed by mathematician Philip R. Zimmermann, Pretty Good Privacy is a multipurpose encryption scheme based on public-key architecture. PGP can use keys of various lengths, is simple to apply to many different kinds of information, and can be very powerful—so powerful Zimmerman had to fight the government in court to defend his right to distribute and make money from PGP. It was the first widely available application of public-key encryption theory for the Internet.

PGP later become the base behind a company—PGP, Inc.—that sold encryption software and technology. Network Associates eventually bought that company and now operates it as a division.

Read all about PGP at www.pgp.com.

Secure Sockets Layer (SSL)

Secure Sockets Layer (SSL) provides an encrypted link between a client computer and a server computer over a TCP/IP connection. Most frequently, it's seen as the mechanism by which Web browsers establish secure connections with Web servers for the purpose of exchanging confidential information like credit card numbers.

Here's how an SSL transaction works. A client requests a secure connection between itself and a server by requesting a particular Web page or other resource from that server. The server, which has to have a valid digital certificate in order for SSL to work, presents its certificate to the client. The client then has a reasonable level of certainty that the server is what it is supposed to be (say, that a computer presenting itself as Amazon.com's e-commerce server really belongs to Amazon.com). Once the identity of the server has been validated, the client and server use a single transaction, encrypted with a public key, to agree on a private key that's used for the rest of the transaction. Once there is a private key, the client and server can securely exchange sensitive information, such as credit card numbers.

Secure Multipurpose Internet Mail Extension (S/MIME)

Secure Multipurpose Internet Mail Extension (S/MIME) is a proposed standard for securing electronic mail. S/MIME is related to ordinary e-mail attachments, digital signatures, and public-key encryption.

A message that is to be sent in S/MIME format is typed normally, then converted to S/MIME. That process encrypts the message text using the recipient's public key and generates a digital signature for the message—see the section on digital signatures earlier in this chapter. The digital signature is attached to the message as a binary file, which is one of the problems with S/MIME—the binary attachment slows the message's progress across the Internet.

Secure Electronic Transactions (SET)

Secure Electronic Transactions (SET) is a system, developed by Visa (a credit card company) that provides a framework for secure electronic financial transactions on the Internet, particularly at the consumer level. SET relies heavily on VeriSign certificate technology to validate the legitimacy of consumers, merchants, billing consolidators, and card-issuing banks.

Digital Signatures

Digital signatures rely on encryption to guarantee that a document or other information transmitted over the Internet has not been tampered with. Refer back to the section on digital signatures for more information.

Auditing

The final key element of security is auditing. *Auditing* is a system of record keeping, which basically means that software takes notes about what it does and why and allows administrators to look at those notes (called log files) later. Log files also can be examined by software that's designed to detect problems.

A system properly equipped with security auditing features will provide its administrators with some information with which to figure out the nature of security problems that are occurring (or have occurred). A good auditing scheme will help administrators ascertain the severity of a breach by identifying which information was compromised. It also will help them track down the bad guys.

Log Files

Log files are text files that record things that happen as software operates, such as logons, file accesses, failed connection attempts, and more. Information recorded in log files might include the following:

- All login attempts, successful and failed
- All files copied
- All files deleted
- All programs launched
- All remote logins to other computers

When examining log files, look for signs of suspicious activity, such as repeated and frequent failed passwords or rejected attempts to access a particular resource. You should monitor your log files regularly, just to get a feel for what's normal. You'll be better able to recognize unusual events when you're familiar with what's usual.

Auditing Logs

Because, on a large system, such an auditing scheme might quickly generate log files of many gigabytes in size, logs typically are kept for a few days, analyzed, and deleted. When the logs are analyzed—usually automatically by an analysis program—the administrator gets an alert if suspicious activity shows up. Suspicious activity might include, for example, an extraordinary number of unsuccessful login attempts under a particular username. Log analyzers oriented toward detecting illegal entry into a system are called *intrusion detection utilities*.

Understanding Suspicious Activities and Attacks

In the game of computer security, your enemies are the people who want to break into your networked resources. To protect you network, you need to understand both what motivates these people and how they go about their dastardly business. In this section, you will learn about some of the common motivations behind attacks, the types of attacks you can expect, and the methods of attacking a network.

Attackers' Motivations

The first step in understanding network attacks is being aware of the factors that motivate such attacks. Motivations can vary depending on each situation and can run the gamut from relatively harmless entertainment to intentional destruction and monetary gain. Possibly the biggest threat to a company's network security is its own employees. Employees have the easiest access to security information. Did you ever notice that, in the movies, if a person wanted access to a company's information, she almost always got it through an employee?

Entertainment

Playing with computers is fun, and breaking into real-world resources has elements of truth and danger that games lack. In fact, people have written and tried to sell computer games in which the object is to break into a computer across a network—these games haven't done well. Real-life break-ins are much more fun.

Proving Competence

What better way to prove your skill at network trickery than by doing something another expert has set out to prevent you from doing? An attacker might think that if you have wrapped a network with security measures to the best of your ability and she is able to get around them, she is more skilled than you are. So there.

Although attacks like these are less likely to end in serious damage to your information or theft of anything of value, they may cause embarrassment when, say, your Web site is altered. Don't underestimate the attractiveness of a challenge.

Spite

Some people are just plain mean and will go to considerable lengths to trash a system for no other reason. It's hard to identify these folks ahead of time.

However, disgruntled insiders rank high among the attackers motivated by spite. An employee, miffed because she was passed over for a promotion or about to defect to a competitor, might intentionally wreak havoc with your networked resources. This is one of the main reasons to control access on networks.

Political Causes

Some folks will take on a network to promote a political cause. For example, when Congress was debating the Communications Decency Act—which the U.S. Department of Justice supported—intruders broke into the Justice Department's Web site (and posted pornographic images there) to register their opposition to the act.

The most dramatic sort of politically motivated attack is so-called "cyber warfare," in which agents of a government (or of some cause) make large-scale, coordinated attempts to disrupt the computing infrastructure of an opposing country. One example of this (although the whole story isn't yet public) is when the Pentagon accused Serbia's government of leading coordinated attacks against its computer networks during the 1999 war in the Balkans.

Monetary Gain

People who break into a network and grab the right kind of information can get rich. Whether they steal credit card information with which to make fraudulent charges or proprietary technical information they can use to defeat you in business, there's money to be made by taking information.

Types of Attack

To protect an Internet resource from problems, you have to be aware of the guises an attack can take. Malicious attacks take many forms but may generally be categorized under two categories:

- Denial of service
- Information theft and destruction

Additionally, there are viruses. Viruses can be a sort of denial of service attack when they tie up a processor or erase data, though more often they're mere nuisances that generate messages.

Let's examine each of these.

Denial of Service

A *denial of service (DOS) attack* is an attack in which the legitimate users of a computing resource are prevented from accessing it. Typically, a DOS attack relies upon overwhelming a computer or other resource with an extraordinary number of requests for its attention. Most systems will at least slow down under such conditions.

Information Theft and Destruction

Lots of attackers will attempt to damage you by stealing or destroying important information. This is called *information theft or destruction*. It may be done for profit or for any of the other reasons listed earlier.

The trouble with an information theft attack is that you may not immediately know that it's taken place. If someone breaks into your house and steals your television, you know it's gone. But if someone makes a copy of a critical file, you have no way of knowing about it unless you have an auditing program in place.

Methods of Attack

How do the bad guys gain access to protected computing resources? Their collective resourcefulness runs deep, so it's impossible to describe everything they might do. But here are some general strategies they employ to get access to the resources they want.

Social Engineering Attacks

A lot of attackers get the passwords and other information they need by simply asking for it. Often posing as someone with a legitimate need for the information (such as a technician, an accountant, or a particular user), the bad guy will call someone on the phone, explain a made-up situation, and ask for the information that's allegedly needed to fix the problem. For a long time, bad guys got free America Online accounts by posing as billing auditors and asking users for their passwords (the practice has been curtailed by an AOL education program). This, in the network security field, is called *social engineering*.

The key to defeating social engineering attacks is education. Train people to be suspicious of anyone who attempts to get information related to network access. Teach them that they should never, for any reason, reveal passwords or other security information to anyone (a legitimate administrator would never need to know an individual's password, for example).

Brute Force Attacks

Brute force attacks rely on the capacity of attacking computers to tirelessly generate different combinations of characters and feed them to defended network resources. Typically, brute force attacks are used to find passwords and break encrypted messages. A bad guy will set up a program that tries thousands of different passwords until it finds one that works or will try many different keys in his attempt to crack a message.

The thing about brute force attacks is that they rely on large amounts of computing power, and computing power costs money. Every processor cycle that's devoted to a brute force attack is a cycle that can't be used for other purposes. As the cost of these computing resources adds up, it becomes apparent that the value of the information you're attempting to steal had better exceed the money you're putting into the attack. Breaking a message encrypted with a long key might require $20,000.00 in computer time—hardly worth it for a credit card with a limit of $10,000.00.

Attacks upon Known or Detected Weaknesses

Operating systems, server software, browsers, and other programs are incredibly complex and so are certain to have flaws. Some of these flaws are of the sort that allow intruders to access the system covertly.

In the normal course of an operating system's use in a variety of installations, security problems are found. Sometimes, they pop up as a result of administrators' vigilance. Other times, it takes a break-in to make a problem known. Either way, the manufacturer of the operating system should take steps to correct the problem. Typically, the manufacturer will make a *patch* freely available. The patch is a little piece of software that plugs the security hole.

The problem occurs when there's a known bug for which a patch exists but the system administrator—out of laziness or whatever—doesn't install the patch. Then, attackers are free to exploit the hole by well-published means. To make their jobs easier, intruders use software that looks for unpatched holes in systems.

The moral: Keep up-to-date on the flaws that have been found in your operating system and always install published patches immediately.

For more information on updates and patches, see Chapter 10.

Overload Attacks

An overload attack is a form of denial of service attack. A system that's working perfectly can be made useless if an attacker presents it with so much work that it's overwhelmed. This sort of attack doesn't even require a password or other special mode of access because the resource being attacked is just being asked to do what it normally does—except it's being asked to do it a lot. Mail servers can fall victim to mail floods, for example, when they're presented with an extraordinary volume of mail to cope with.

Spam and Mail Flooding

Everyone hates spam, which is the mass broadcast of unsolicited messages to hundreds of thousands of e-mail addresses (many people hate Spam, a variety of processed meat that comes in a can, as well). Aside from annoying its recipients, spam places an undue load upon mail servers. A mail server that has to deliver the same (useless) message to each of its user accounts has to waste time getting the job done. If enough spam messages show up, a large proportion of the server's time can go toward delivering them.

Mail flooding is slightly different. It has to do with unleashing a barrage of mail on a particular user. Whether by subscribing the user to hundreds of mailing lists (the ones, meant for pilots, that distribute hourly airport wind condition reports are favorites) or by sending the user very large messages full of garbage characters, mail flooding can cause real trouble. Mail flooding also is called *mail bombing*.

Ping Floods

Ping is a special-purpose program that's supposed to be used to ascertain the "aliveness" of another computer on the network. For example, a Ping packet might be sent to your computer, which would receive the packet and acknowledge that it had done so. Normally, the amount of processing power required by a Ping transaction is negligible, but a ping flood ties up the processor with the need to respond to many, many pings in a short period of time—in effect creating a denial of service situation.

A ping flood is a barrage of pings. Under a ping flood, a computer receives many ping packets in a short period of time and must reply to them all. This can tie up the processor, the memory, and the network connection, denying legitimate users the performance they're used to receiving.

One of the most popular uses of ping floods is in online gaming. You can unleash a ping flood on an opponent's machine just as you're sneaking up on his character. When the other player detects you and attempts to defeat your attack, his machine's response is slower than usual because it's overloaded by the ping attack.

Ping of Death

It's sometimes possible to bring down a target computer by sending a Ping packet of more than 65,536 bytes in size, in excess of the maximum size allowed by the Ping specification. This is known as the Ping of Death or the Ping o' Death. Most operating systems and Ping utilities know about the Ping of Death now and have been patched to deal with it. Make sure your systems have the proper patches in place.

SYN Floods

A SYN flood attack takes advantage of a particular characteristic of the TCP/IP protocols and the operating system resources devoted to handling them. SYN floods can result in the inability of a computer to connect to other computers over the Internet. If the computer attacked with a SYN flood is a firewall, the effect can be that the network the firewall protects is isolated from the Internet.

Basically, networked operating systems have a facility for handling TCP/IP connections in the process of being made. There's a buffer for connections that are waiting for packets to come back over the network in order to complete their links. In a SYN flood, this buffer is filled to capacity by a malicious program, making it impossible for legitimate users to create any new TCP/IP connections. The computer is swamped by half-open connections. You can defeat SYN floods by implementing protocol switching on your network because SYN floods work only under TCP/IP.

You should be aware that SYN flooding requires less than 10 percent of the bandwidth going into a computer. They're an easy way to deny service without a huge volume of information passing back and forth between machines.

Identifying Security Requirements

Security requirements vary among different kinds of networks. Intranets, for example, exist for the purpose of sharing potentially secret information among people who have a right to see it. Internet sites, on the other hand, are meant to be accessed by everyone in the world and so should contain only information that's appropriate for that kind of exposure. Other kinds of networks—extranets and virtual private networks—are hybrids and so require special treatment.

This section explores the differences among the different kinds of networks and helps you identify the special security requirements of each.

In large part, an organization's security requirements depend upon the nature of the organization. If your information has inherent and obvious value—say, a list of credit card numbers—it's attractive to intruders. If your company is well-known, you're attractive to bad guys looking to earn bragging rights. But if your networks store information of limited inherent value and your organization is not well-known, your security strategy needs to be less elaborate.

Internet Security

Internet security is a balancing act. You want everyone on the open Internet to have access to your public information without any trouble at all, and you want your organization's employees to have unencumbered access to external resources on the Internet. Yet, you want to prevent attackers from vandalizing your Web site, reading your inbound and outbound e-mail, and using your employees' Internet link as a point of entry through which to attack resources you want to keep secret.

Approach the problems separately. To keep intruders from attacking your secure network through its Internet connection, put a firewall in place and isolate public and semipublic resources in a DMZ. Make sure your firewall has an ACL and performs dynamic packet filtering.

To prevent your employee's legitimate Internet activities from falling victim to thieves and spies, make sure the employees properly secure their Internet transactions. They should encrypt Internet e-mail, use digital signatures to keep tampering in check, and apply encryption to files. They should use SSL to protect exchanges with remote Internet sites.

Intranet Security

Intranets, in theory, are insulated from the Internet. Assuming that you've secured the intranet from external invasion, your concerns are with the damage an insider can do intentionally or accidentally.

A disgruntled insider can steal or trash information. To limit the damage an individual can do, compartmentalize information. Give a user access only to the portions of the intranet he needs to see in order to do his job. Make sure you have a backup program in place and that it runs frequently enough to protect your organization from costly data loss in the event of internal vandalism.

A merely careless insider might unwittingly share her password with an unauthorized user. For this reason, you should enforce rules requiring users to change their passwords every so often. You might also want to supplement password protection with smart cards or biometric measurements. Also, deploy antivirus software to prevent an intranet user from introducing a malicious program via a floppy disk, CD-ROM, or DVD.

Extranet Security

Extranets vary in their purposes, and so vary in their implementation. They are kind of like virtual private networks (VPNs)—which are covered in the next section—in that they use the open Internet for communications between geographically separate entities, but they're different because the connections between the parties are more sporadic. Extranets give certain parties access to special information over the Internet in addition to the information that's published on the Internet for the world at large.

Many organizations rely on their Web server software to secure their extranets. Each remote extranet user—each supplier, or whatever—has a directory on the Web server. Those directories are password-protected, and transactions involving their contents are secured with SSL. Databases that contain information that's internal to the organization as well as information that's to be shared across the extranet can have different rules for different users. Users with "extranet" rights can access only certain information, whereas "internal" users can access the entire set of data.

Virtual Private Network (VPN) Security

A virtual private network (VPN) is a network of computers that acts like a bunch of machines on a LAN or private WAN but that uses the Internet to provide its long-distance links between sites. Because very sensitive information travels over LANs and private WANs, security is extremely important. Lately, some new technologies have begun to emerge. *IPsec* is a variation on the IP protocol that allows for better inherent security in transmissions between IP addresses. Part of IPsec called the *Layer 2 Tunneling Protocol (L2TP)* is of particular interest to VPN developers. L2TP provides for secure connections between points on an IPsec network. A VPN user connecting to a remote site with IPsec and L2TP enjoys a high level of security.

There are two typical architectures under which VPNs exist. In one, there's a regular link between two or more fixed sites. In the other, a roaming user logs in to the VPN from various locations. Let's take a look at each architecture.

Regular Links between Fixed Sites

In the case of a fixed VPN structure, there are several locations (offices or whatever) with LANs in each location. The individual LANs need to be linked as if they're one big LAN so a person in location A can share files with someone in office B as easily as with someone who works in the next cubicle.

Traditionally, this has been made possible with dedicated private telecommunications links—leased lines and the like. Those are secure, but very expensive. In this situation, using the Internet to carry traffic between the two locations makes a lot of sense. However, the traffic has to be protected from the bad guys on the open Internet.

This is what tunneling protocols are for. A *tunneling protocol*—Microsoft's Point-to-Point Tunneling Protocol (PPTP) is one—encapsulates encrypted data in an Internet-friendly wrapper. The packets move over the Internet. When they get where they're going, the Internet wrapper is stripped off, the contents are decrypted automatically, and a virtual link—a secure one—exists.

Variable Links to Roaming Users

VPNs also need to take care of the roving salesperson who logs in to the network, usually via a slow connection, from a different place each time. These people can use tunneling protocols as well, or they can rely upon SSL and other general-purpose Internet security measures to protect the data they send and receive. They also can rely on signed and encrypted e-mail to protect data they send and receive.

Summary

In this chapter, you learned about many different kinds of network and Internet security issues. The most important ones to know for the i-Net+ exam are the following:

Authentication   The process of ascertaining that an entity (a person or a computer, typically) is who he claims to be.

Authentication technologies   Methods of authentication that include passwords, smart cards and keys, biometric checks, and digital certificates.

Digital certificates   Electronic certificates (like passports) that provide some guarantee that their holders are who they claim to be.

Certification authority(CA)   An organization that issues digital certificates after verifying applicants' identities to some degree.

Encryption   The process of rendering a message unintelligible to all parties but the sender and recipient.

Public-key encryption   Encryption that relies on the sender encoding a message with the recipient's public key and the recipient decoding that message with his own private key.

Digital signature   An electronic signature that serves as an indicator that shows whether a message was altered as it traveled from sender to recipient.

Secure Sockets Layer (SSL)   A mechanism for securing transactions between a Web browser and a Web server.

Firewall   A computer that protects a secured network from unauthorized access via the Internet.

Dynamic packet filtering   A method used by firewalls to keep track of the numbered packets that make up communications sessions and prevent attackers from breaking into the sequence.

Access Control Lists (ACLs)   A security measure firewalls may use to determine which computers may access which resources. An ACL might allow internal computers to access any external computer while allowing external computers to access only public resources on the defended network.

Protocol switching   Used by firewalls, a method that involves translation from the TCP/IP protocols to another protocol (and possibly back again) to head off TCP/IP-based attacks.

Demilitarized zone (DMZ)   A separate network segment in which resources that are meant to be public or semipublic, such as Web servers and mail distributors, can be located. The DMZ resources are subject to less strict Internet-access rules than the secure portion of the network.

Proxy server   A computer that acts on behalf of protected computers when they make requests for information from the Internet. The protected computers make requests of the proxy server, which in turn makes requests on the Internet, then passes the information back to the protected computer.

Denial of service (DOS) attacks   Attacks that involve overwhelming a resource with requests for service, preventing legitimate users from using the resource. Mail flooding is a kind of DOS attack directed at a mail server.

Ping flood   A DOS attack that overwhelms an operating system's Ping utility by querying it many times in a short time period.

SYN flood   A DOS attack that takes advantage of the TCP/IP protocol stack's willingness to wait for a connection.

For the i-Net+ exam, you should know the following about securing various kinds of networks:

- An intranet is mainly subject to internal attack and so should be defended with carefully designed user access rights. Intranets also need to be protected against viruses with screening software.

- An extranet requires that certain outsiders be able to access certain special resources. You can implement an extranet with secured directories on a Web server, SSL, and/or modifications to an ACL.

- Organizations can protect their Internet connections by isolating their Internet resources in a DMZ, placing a strict firewall between the open Internet and the secure network, using a proxy server for outbound access, and keeping an eye on system logs for suspicious activity such as multiple failed login attempts.

- A virtual private network (VPN) is a hybrid of the Internet and an intranet. The Internet connections that link the geographically distributed elements of the intranet need to be protected—typically with an encrypted protocol such as Point-to-Point Tunneling Protocol (PPTP).

Review Questions

1. A denial of service (DOS) attack aims to do the following:

   A. Steal information

   C. Prevent a particular user from accessing a resource

   C. Prevent anyone from using a resource

   D. Render all passwords invalid

2. *Biometrics* is the term applied to methods of _____ .

   A. Verifying a user's identity through assessment of his or her physical characteristics

   B. Using fingerprints as a means of security

   C. Comparing the physical traits of a machine's various users

   D. Assessing the severity of security breaches by applying algorithms that derive from genetics

3. Nonrepudiation technologies facilitate accountability by _____ .

   A. Making it harder to acquire a public key

   B. Making private keys harder to copy

   C. Making it possible to say with some certainty that a particular person or entity did something

   D. Guaranteeing that messages aren't tampered with in transit

4. A firewall prevents unauthorized access to a secured network by _____ .

   A. Banning known bad guys from the network

   B. Adding an extra layer of encryption

   C. Monitoring and controlling packet flow

   D. Maintaining a list of users' access privileges

5. Social engineering is _____ .

   A. Getting passwords and other access information through smooth talking or impersonation

   B. Organizing networks around friendships and other social relationships

   C. Keeping careful track of employees' level of disgruntlement

   D. Firing potential internal attackers immediately

6. You should never choose a password _____ .

   A. That includes hard-to-remember characters

   B. That is very long

   C. That lacks an underscore character

   D. That appears in any dictionary

7. A security patch _____ .

   A. Fixes a security problem that has been found

   B. Is a way of attacking a system

   C. Guarantees that no security weaknesses exist

   D. Is a type of firewall

8. A brute force attack _____ .

   A. Involves smashing a computer with a heavy object

   B. Involves a bunch of rapidly generated random guesses against a password, telephone number, or other security element

   C. Necessarily involves a flood of e-mail

   D. Exploits a characteristic of the TCP/IP protocol suite

9. What is the key to foiling social engineering attacks?

   A. Longer passwords

   B. Better firewalls

   C. More restrictive access controls

   D. Education

10. An attack motivated by money is worthwhile only when _____ .

    A. The value of the attack's results exceeds the cost of the attack.

    B. Credit card information is stolen.

    C. Money is transferred to an attacker's account.

    D. The attacker is a paid professional.

11. Your risk of coming under attack by thrill-seekers is higher if _____ .

    A. You post lots of Quake files

    B. Yours is a high-profile organization

    C. You keep quiet about your computing resources

    D. You use access control measures

12. What does a ping flood involve?

    A. A quirk of the SMTP protocol

    B. Exploitation of a Windows NT weakness

    C. Breaking a password

    D. Overloading a machine with ordinarily legitimate requests of a certain kind

13. A SYN flood takes advantage of _____ .

A. A characteristic of the TCP/IP protocol suite

B. A characteristic of the NNTP protocol

C. Recompiling the Linux kernel

D. The Ping utility

14. A Ping of Death can _____ .

A. Disable the Ping utility

B. Crash a computer

C. Harm an attacker's computer as well as the victim's

D. Slow down a computer for a few seconds

15. What is authentication?

A. A password challenge-and-response sequence

B. A biometrics setup

C. Any technique for guaranteeing the identity of someone or something

D. Relevant in anonymous FTP connections

16. One problem with biometrics is that _____ .

A. It's not certain that fingerprints are really unique.

B. Retinal scanning is painful.

C. People's appearances change over time.

D. Sensing equipment is extremely expensive.

17. What is encrypted text called?

  A. Codetext

  B. Spaghettitext

  C. Cryptotext

  D. Ciphertext

18. What is the advantage of authentication that uses a key or a card?

  A. Users are likely to know when their key or card has been stolen.

  B. Keys and cards are guaranteed to provide absolute security.

  C. Keys and cards are able to eliminate the need for passwords.

  D. Users' public keys may be encoded on magnetic cards.

19. Minimally secure encryption requires a key that is _____ bits long.

  A. 32

  B. 128

  C. 256

  D. 40

20. What is the problem with private-key encryption?

  A. The key must be synchronized between senders and receivers in a secure way.

  B. It's not secure.

  C. It can't support keys longer than 64 bits.

  D. It requires proprietary software.

Answers to Review Questions

1. C. A DOS attack breaks or overwhelms a resource and prevents anyone from using it. An attacker could bring about a DOS situation by disabling passwords, by the way.

2. A and B. Biometrics includes any method of recognizing a user, including face recognition, fingerprinting, voiceprinting, and retinal scanning.

3. C. Nonrepudiation makes it harder for someone to question the authenticity of a message, acknowledgment, or other piece of information that appears to have come from him.

4. C. Firewalls monitor and regulate the flow of packets in and out of a network. They may use Access Control Lists (ACLs) and dynamic packet filtering to do the job.

5. A. An alarming amount of sensitive information is given out to impostors on the telephone, just for the asking.

6. D. Bad guys sometimes try to find passwords by running through the words in a dictionary. A good password should be at least six characters long and include obscure characters.

7. A. The publisher of a piece of software will publish patches to correct flaws that have been identified and to prevent attackers from exploiting them.

8. B. Brute force attacks can take many forms, including floods of e-mail. The term most often applies to the use of an automated guessing program applied to a password.

9. D. Educating members of your organization about social engineering attacks and how they work is critical. Tell people to never give their access information to anyone—legitimate technicians won't need it.

10. A. The value of information stolen (which may or may not be directly monetary in nature) must exceed the cost of the human and computational resources devoted to the attack.

11. B. People out to gain bragging rights by breaking into a system need a system that everyone has heard of. Microsoft, the Pentagon, and TV networks are favorite targets.

12. D. In a ping flood, a machine is sent lots of "pings," which it must acknowledge to prove that it is alive. Too much pinging saps the machine's ability to process other jobs.

13. A. A SYN flood fills up a machine's buffer for keeping track of TCP/IP connections that are in the process of being made.

14. B. The Ping of Death is a super-large ping that can crash the computer it's sent to. Most operating systems have patches that protect them from these attacks.

15. C. Authentication is any technique for guaranteeing the identity of someone or something, including biometric schemes and passwords.

16. C. If users wear makeup, gain weight, lose weight, or speak with emotion, their biometric data may change.

17. D. Text to which an encryption algorithm has been applied is called ciphertext.

18. A. Nothing can provide absolute security, and keys and cards are usually used in combination with passwords. But, although passwords may be stolen without users' knowledge, keys usually can't be—at least not for long.

19. D. Keys shorter than 40 bits may be broken quickly. On the other hand, 128-bit encryption is pretty much unbreakable.

20. A. Private keys have to be synchronized in private. This is okay for certain applications, but not on the Internet in most cases.

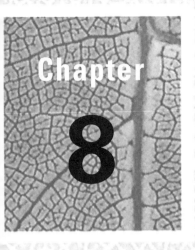

Chapter

8

Internet Development

i-NET+ EXAM OBJECTIVES COVERED IN THIS CHAPTER:

✓ **Define programming-related terms as they relate to Internet applications development. Content could include the following:**

- API
- CGI
- SQL
- SAPI
- DLL—dynamic linking and static linking
- Client- and server-side scripting

✓ **Describe the differences between popular client-side and server-side programming languages. Examples could include the following:**

- Java
- JavaScript
- Perl
- C
- C++
- Visual Basic
- VBScript
- JScript
- XML
- VRML
- ASP

✓ **Content could include the following:**

- When to use the languages
- When they are executed

✓ **Describe the differences between a relational database and a non-relational database.**

✓ **Identify when to integrate a database with a Web site and the technologies used to connect the two.**

✓ **Demonstrate the ability to create HTML pages. Content could include the following:**

- HTML document structure
- Coding simple tables, headings, forms
- Compatibility between different browsers
- Difference between text editors and GUI editors
- Importance of creating cross-browser coding in your HTML

✓ **Identify popular multimedia extensions or plug-ins. Examples could include the following:**

- QTVR (QuickTime VR)
- Flash
- Shockwave
- RealPlayer
- Windows Media Player

✓ **Describe the uses and benefits of various multimedia file formats. Examples could include the following:**

- GIF
- GIF89a
- JPEG
- PNG
- PDF
- RTF
- TIFF
- PostScript
- EPS
- BMP
- MOV
- MPEG
- AVI
- BinHex
- Streaming media
- Non-streaming media

The state of the art in Internet software development is a slippery thing. New technologies are always emerging; others fade away as they're recognized as too weak, too complicated, or too expensive. Your job as an Internet professional is to stay familiar, in a broad way, with what's new in software development. Then, when you're called upon to solve a particular problem, you should be able to consult books and Internet resources to figure out which technologies apply and how to use them. There are no authorities, only people willing to teach themselves quickly.

This chapter endeavors to introduce you to some Internet software and media development concepts that seem built to last, at least for a while. Understanding these will help you grasp the new developments as they appear.

Network Software Concepts

Sun Microsystems notes in its advertisements that "the network is the computer." Increasingly, computation has more to do with sharing information among machines than with processing it on any given machine. Clients request data from servers; servers make requests of other servers; processing jobs are shared among many machines and therefore accomplished faster. This section has to do with the design of software systems that are meant to operate in networked environments.

Client-Server Architecture

Client-server architecture describes a particular kind of relationship between two computers. It's easy to assume that a server is a big, powerful computer and that a client is an everyday personal computer, but that's not necessarily true. The server in a client-server relationship is simply a computer on which a particular resource—particular data—resides. The client is a computer that requests a copy of that information for its own use.

Clients and servers don't have to be thought of as items of hardware. They can be separate pieces of software, and indeed the two pieces of software in the equation can be running under the same processor. You can install a Web server—Apache, Personal Web Server, whatever—on your machine and request Web pages from it, using a Web browser that's running as a separate process. For this reason, you'll hear Web browsers referred to as "Web clients," just as programs like Apache are called "Web servers," independent of the hardware they run on.

When you surf the Web, you're acting as the client in a series of client-server relationships. The computers that are identified by domain names—yahoo.com, amazon.com, and so on—contain collections of data. When you request a document that's identified by a particular URL, a copy of that document is sent from the computer on which it resides (the server) to your computer (the client). Similarly, when you use your computer to send a query to a database server and receive a particular set of data in response, your machine is the client in a client-server relationship. Client-server transactions need not involve Web pages by any means. However, Web servers and Web clients illustrate many client-server concepts clearly, so we'll focus on them for the present.

Client Software

In the case of Web surfing, a Web browser is the client software in a client-server relationship. People use their Web browsers to request information from other computers. The browsers then receive the requested information and are responsible for presenting it to their users properly. The process of interpreting and presenting information is not trivial because Web pages can consist of several different kinds of data:

- Text with embedded markup information

- Special, embedded content that browsers can interpret without outside help

- Code written in a scripting language, which must be interpreted and executed

- Code written in Java or an ActiveX language

- Content that must be interpreted by a plug-in

Let's explore these different kinds of content in greater detail.

Text and Markup Languages

The simplest Web pages are just text documents—sequences of characters, formatted as American Standard Code for Information Interchange (ASCII)—with special sequences of characters inserted here and there to indicate what the text means and how it should be displayed. You're probably somewhat familiar with the most popular Web markup language—it's called Hypertext Markup Language (HTML)—and we'll cover some of its details later in this chapter. For now, just know that every Web browser incorporates an HTML interpreter that interprets the HTML tags in documents.

There are other markup languages; eXtensible Markup Language (XML) isn't as concerned with how text is displayed as with the meaning of individual passages of text. XML is one way to share database information among machines.

Native Embedded Content

In addition to their ability to interpret and display HTML-formatted text, Web browsers can display certain other kinds of data that is referred to in HTML documents. Graphics fall into this category. All Web browsers can interpret JPEG and GIF graphics; various browsers can interpret other image formats as well (Microsoft Internet Explorer, for example, can display BMP images). The pieces of software that interpret these embedded files—the *interpreters*—are inseparable parts of the Web browsers.

Scripting Languages

Sometimes, the markup tags that define Web documents include passages of code in scripting languages like JavaScript or VBScript. You can use scripting languages to provide your Web pages with a certain level of interactivity and animation. The code that makes up programs—you'll learn more about it later in this chapter—is never compiled. It always remains readable to human beings. Web browsers that are capable of running scripting-language programs interpret the code directly, without it first being compiled.

Java and ActiveX Content

Though they're kind of like graphics in the sense that they're assigned a rectangular region and interpreted separately from the HTML document in which they're embedded, Java applets and ActiveX controls deserve special mention. Java applets and ActiveX Controls are little pieces of software that occupy portions of the browser windows in which they run.

Plug-In Content

Although browsers can make sense of and display certain kinds of content natively, other kinds of files—such as those containing certain kinds of sounds, three-dimensional graphics, and other special media—fall outside the browser's built-in capabilities. The most popular browsers, however, can take *plug-ins*, which are software modules that users add to their browsers to expand their capabilities. When a browser encounters a piece of embedded media that it can't interpret natively, it checks its roster of plug-ins to see if one of them can handle the content. If so, the handling is seamless—it looks to the user as if the browser can handle the content by itself.

WARNING   The problem with plug-ins is that no one has all of them, and you're asking a lot of a user if you ask her to download and install a particular plug-in just to view your content. The basic rule is to stick to media that browsers can interpret natively. If you need to use plug-in content to get an effect you need—chemists, for example, use special file formats to display images of complex molecules in three dimensions—make sure the benefits to users are great enough to warrant the trouble of downloading and installing the plug-in.

Server Software

In the client-server equation as it applies to Web publishing, the Web server is both a piece of software (the program that doles out pages in response to client requests) and a unit of hardware (the physical machine on which the server software runs).

Popular Web server software includes:

- Apache
- Microsoft Internet Information Server (IIS)
- Netscape Enterprise Server

Each handles requests for Web pages. They may also have capacities to work with server-side scripting languages, extensions, Java servlets, and independent server-side programs that provide some sort of processing service.

Server Extensions

A *server extension* is sort of like a plug-in for Web server software. A software module that expands the capabilities of the server software itself, server extension may be published by the same company that put out the server software or by another publisher. The Microsoft FrontPage Extensions are perhaps the most popular server extensions around. They allow servers to support some of the interactive features Microsoft FrontPage lets developers embed in their pages.

Java Servlets

Java servlets are special Java programs that expand the capabilities of Web server software. Similar to server extensions, the advantage of a Java servlet is that a single, properly designed servlet will run under any operating system for which there is a Java Virtual Machine (JVM)—the same as any Java program.

Server-Side Scripting Languages

Server-side scripting languages are programming languages designed for writing code that's embedded in Web pages and interpreted before those pages are sent out to the client. Active Server Pages (ASP) and Hypertext Preprocessor (PHP), both covered later in this chapter, are two of the most popular server-side scripting languages.

Compiled Server-Side Programs and Other Servers

In addition to exercising their native capabilities and those provided by add-in servlets and extensions, Web servers may also cooperate with other kinds of server software, such as a database server. When a program written in a server-side scripting language requests data from a database server, the Web server is capable of allowing the script to access the database server and retrieve the information it needs.

Communication between Client and Server

If you're going to have software that takes advantage of client-server architecture, you must have mechanisms in place for transmitting information back and forth between the two elements in the equation.

Forms

As far as the Web is concerned, client-server communications rely upon forms in Web pages that collect information from the user. The data the user puts into those forms is then submitted (or *posted*) to the program on the server side. The form data is packaged and sent to the server in a format defined by the Common Gateway Interface (CGI) specification.

Common Gateway Interface (CGI)

The *Common Gateway Interface (CGI)* specification defines a way of packaging text data (such as the contents of a form) for transmission over a network. The CGI specification takes the contents of a form and the names of the form elements (as specified in HTML) and assembles them all into a long string of characters. That string can then be passed to a program on the server side for processing and a response. A CGI submission might tell a server-side database interface to search for something and return a results page, for example. Computers running Microsoft's Internet Information Server (IIS) support the *Internet Services Application Programming Interface (ISAPI)*, which can be used to carry out CGI-like tasks on IIS-equipped servers.

WARNING   Do not make the mistake of thinking CGI is a programming language. It is not. Although it is correct to speak of a "CGI program," such programs are referred to that way because they accept CGI data as input (as from a Web form), not because they are written in a language called CGI. There is no such language (at least, there is none of any significance).

Security

The problem with CGI is that it involves the transmission of a text string—that is by default readable to anybody who cares to intercept it—across a network. If you're using CGI to move data over the Internet, you're exposing yourself and your client-side users to security risks. You shouldn't ever enter sensitive information such as credit card data into a form for CGI transmission unless you're sure the transmission will be protected.

How are CGI submissions protected? Typically, Secure Sockets Layer (SSL) encrypts data transmitted between a client and a server. Read all about SSL and other encryption technologies in Chapter 7.

Trends in Network Computing

For many years, the trend in computing technology was toward more storage space, faster processors, more capable software, and lower prices on everything. Now it seems that, although "more, faster, and cheaper" will always be appealing, computer technology is getting to be "good enough" for many everyday applications. Personal computers spend most of their processor cycles idling, waiting for their human users to do something.

The trends in computer technology have mainly to do with *network computing*, which is computing performed by multiple computers linked together on some kind of network. Whether the collaborative computing has to do with sharing information or sharing processor power, it seems that a network often provides more computing power than its component machines could if they were acting alone. You can distinguish the two main trends in networking by determining what is shared:

- In enterprise computing, it's typically the data that's shared. One machine can access and operate upon information from another or from a central repository.

- In distributed computing, the processing work is spread over several machines.

Of course, there's some overlap, and it's not always easy to tell where processing begins and data-sharing ends. Let's explore these trends further.

Enterprise Computing

Enterprise computing has to do with sharing information among the applications with which an organization, such as a company or a unit of government, does its business. This kind of sharing can help the company realize efficiencies in its overall process of buying, making, processing, and selling goods and services and in the accounting, finance, human resources, and management infrastructures it maintains to facilitate those processes. An Enterprise Resource Planning (ERP) system, because of its purchasing features, might note that two different plants were buying the same part from different suppliers. Because of its integration with the manufacturing process, it might note that one supplier's products had far fewer defects than the other's did. The two purchasing agents at the plants might have had spotty communication without the ERP system, but the ERP system is much better able to spot situations like this and advise the buyer of the faulty parts to try the other plant's supplier.

SAP (pronounced as three distinct letters), a German company, is generally recognized as the world leader in enterprise computing. Its flagship ERP product, SAP R/3, is standard equipment among very large organizations all over the world, and SAP consultants make very good coin planning, implementing, and expanding SAP R/3 installations. The trend is beginning to trickle down to smaller companies, as well, and some pundits expect that technologies like XML will make it easier to share information among small-business software products from many publishers.

SAP has several Web sites, each of which highlights some aspect of its business. The main one, www.sap.com, will direct you to the information you need. Another site, www.mysap.com, focuses on SAP's products and services for companies somewhat smaller than enormous.

Distributed Computing

Distributed computing has to do with spreading portions of a computing job over several machines. This is not *parallel processing*, in which an operating system divides the running of some program over several CPUs, but rather a system of sharing discrete business tasks over several machines. The discrete tasks might include the following:

- Collecting data

- Managing a database that stores the data

- Analyzing the data

- Performing financial operations (such as billing) based on the data

Any given task might require work from several machines, each of which is responsible for one of the above. The load is spread, and therefore the job is completed more quickly.

JavaBeans

JavaBeans are the epitome of componentization in the Java language. It's possible to build a Bean with an elaborate feature set and considerable power, then use it as a sort of "black box" that carries out some particular duty in various software systems of which it is a part. You can distribute your Beans to others as well, either freely or, because Beans are compiled and have no visible source code, commercially. Beans have found application in Sun's own graphical user interface toolkit, as well as in other projects.

Component Object Model (COM)

The *Component Object Model (COM)* is Microsoft's answer to JavaBeans. It's a means of writing independent code modules and having them communicate with one another. The idea is that you could have a single, specialized COM module that various other pieces of software (other COM modules and non-COM programs) refer to for different reasons.

A single COM module might, for example, serve to perform queries on any specified database. One program might refer to that COM module to query an employee database; another COM module might refer to the query module for accessing a sales database. It's an economy of scale: one COM module does double duty.

Distributed Component Object Model (DCOM)

Distributed Component Object Model (DCOM) components are really no different from COM components. DCOM is a subset of COM that includes COM modules running on different machines and referring to one another across a network.

Understanding Programming Languages

A *programming language* is any system of syntax and grammar that, when used to generate sets of instructions called programs, can have an effect on the behavior of a computer. Programming languages broadly include everything from HTML to C++. Here, we'll focus on highly capable, full-featured development languages and slightly less capable (but simpler) scripting languages.

Full-Featured Development Languages

A *full-featured development language* is one that can be used to write stand-alone programs. You can use a full-featured development language to write an elaborate word processor, a Web browser, or a database front end. You could write a whole operating system with certain languages if you wanted to. Examples of such languages in the network software milieu include:

- Java
- Visual Basic
- C and C++

These are *compiled languages*. When you have written source code, you must run it through a special processor called a *compiler* that translates the human-readable source code into machine code that processors and operating systems can understand. An operating system makes its resources available to programs running under it by means of an *application programming interface (API)*.

Java fans will tell you that their language is not really compiled, and that's sort of true. When you write Java code, you must run it through a program that converts it to *bytecodes*, which are instructions that have meaning to an imaginary chip called the *Java Virtual Machine (JVM)*.

Java

The prime attraction of Java is platform neutrality—a concept that requires some background. Other programming languages, such as C++, require that programmers write different programs for different operating environments. There's one version of Microsoft Word for Windows 95, another version for Windows 3.*x*, and another version for MacOS. That's not acceptable on the Internet, where a server might have to provide the same program to many different kinds of computers—and might not be able to determine what kind of computer needed the program at a given time. Plus, it's a pain—an expensive pain—for software developers, who must multiply the effort required to write a program by the number of platforms they want to support.

The single biggest attraction of Java is that, theoretically, you can write one Java program, compile it, and expect it to run similarly under Windows 95, MacOS, Solaris, and half a dozen other operating environments—a feature called architecture neutrality. In practice, architecture neutrality doesn't work as well as many programmers would like, especially with complicated graphical programs. But it works fine with simple programs, and future versions of Java will surely have even better architecture neutrality. And, most important, other languages don't even make attempts at architecture neutrality.

Visual Basic

Microsoft Corporation designed Visual Basic as a tool for fast development of programs for its Windows operating systems. The latest versions of Visual Basic incorporate a certain amount of sensitivity to network software development, but the primary use of Visual Basic is in writing software for use under Microsoft Windows 98 and Windows NT. A large portion of the work done with Visual Basic involves the creation of user interfaces for databases.

Lately, Visual Basic has become more oriented toward network programming. You can use Visual Basic to create ActiveX controls for embedding in Web pages that will be interpreted by Microsoft Internet Explorer. You also can use Visual Basic to create Component Object Model (COM) components.

You'll find the latest Microsoft news about Visual Basic at `msdn.microsoft.com/vbasic/`.

C and C++

Widely regarded as the top of the heap as far as general-purpose programming languages are concerned, C and C++ are the standards by which most other such languages are measured. You can do *anything* with C and C++, from manipulating the pixels on a video screen individually to reading the contents of memory one bit at a time. Programs written in the C languages are fast, too.

What's the difference between C and C++? The latter is object oriented, which means (to cite one important characteristic) it supports the creation of code modules that can inherit traits from other such modules. Say you'd created a module that performed a countdown operation. If you wrote that module generically enough, you could write other modules that exploited the countdown capability in different ways. You might, for example, write one program that displayed a countdown in Roman numerals and another that used Thai numerals, both based on the same abstract underpinnings. You'll often note that C and C++ programs consist of more than one file. There's usually a primary executable, then several libraries. Windows uses dynamic link libraries (DLLs) most of the time; other platforms use static linking arrangements.

C and C++ both have large communities of developers using them, which means there's a large body of prewritten C and C++ code out there (both for sale and in the public domain). An increasing amount of the prewritten code has to do with communicating information over networks, so it's fair to say that the languages are network friendly. However, they don't support cross-platform development like Java does. If you compile a C program for MacOS, it's a MacOS program forever.

General-Purpose Scripting Languages

A scripting language is any language whose code is not compiled. Further, scripting languages rely on a *host* to interpret their programs and provide an environment for them to operate in. The host can be an operating system (most operating systems support at least one scripting language) or a stand-alone program (most programs' macro languages are examples of scripting languages).

Because they're easy to learn (relative to full-featured programming languages) and so well suited to quick-and-dirty solutions to problems, an awful lot of server site activity is coordinated by programs written in general-purpose scripting languages. Oftentimes, developers will use an operating system's native scripting language (shell scripting) or install and use a more capable (or more attractive) scripting language like Perl or Tcl.

Shell Scripting

Because of the need of users and administrators to automate miscellaneous tasks, most operating systems have a shell scripting language. A *shell scripting language* is a programming language (usually a fairly simple one) that can issue command-line instructions, manipulate files and directories, do some text management, and invoke other programs. The MS-DOS batch language (which lives on in Windows NT 4 and elsewhere) is an example of a shell scripting language.

Users of Unix variants can typically install any of several shells on their machines to provide different sets of commands and different capabilities.

These shells—csh, ksh, and bash are some examples of Unix shells—have their own shell scripting languages. Microsoft Windows 98 is the first Microsoft operating system in some time to have a decent shell scripting language. Its Windows Script Host (WSH), available as a retrofit for Windows NT 4 and slated to be standard equipment on all versions of Windows 2000, allows you to perform shell scripting tasks with JavaScript, VBScript, or any other scripting language for which someone makes available a WSH language module.

For Web developers, shell scripting languages are suitable for certain user interactivity tasks. You could use your shell scripting language to take information from a form and store it in a file or to assemble somewhat customized pages for users to view. Still, compared to Perl, shell scripting languages are usually pretty weak.

Perl

The darling of system administrators and Web developers everywhere (as well as one of the greatest triumphs of the open-source movement), Practical Extraction and Reporting Language (Perl) is like a good video game: easy to learn, but hard to master. The odds are excellent that if the task you have in mind can be accomplished at all, it can be accomplished with Perl. Server-side scripts written in Perl may not run as fast as compiled programs or exhibit the elegance of object-oriented programs, but they get the job done and usually can be written in a hurry.

Perl excels at text processing, which means it's great at picking information out of form submissions and very good at assembling custom Web pages in response to surfer requests. Its various modules—there are many—provide Perl programmers with easy access to many different environments, including all popular server-side databases. Plus, it's free. Larry Wall and a community of developers have released Perl to the public domain and continue to develop it for the public benefit. Though Web developers are mainly concerned with command-line Perl programs that interface with remote Web clients, the language also can be used in conjunction with the Tk graphical user interface (GUI) toolkit to create programs with graphical interfaces.

The best way to learn about Perl is to install it and play with it yourself. You can download the Perl tools (in source code form and in various compiled forms) from many sites, including the Comprehensive Perl Archive Network (CPAN) at `www.cpan.org/`.

Tcl

The Tool Command Language (Tcl) is a scripting language designed as a sort of glue with which to share information among applications. Pronounced "tickle," Tcl was developed by John Osterhout. Like Perl, Tcl can work with the Tk GUI toolkit to create windowed applications. You'll often hear the two referred to collectively as Tcl/Tk. Tcl isn't as big a deal for Web development as Perl and shell scripting languages.

There's a collection of Tcl FAQs on the Web at `www.tclfaq.wservice.com/ tcl-faq/`. John Osterhout started a Tcl-related company called Scriptics; its Web site is `www.scriptics.com`. You can download the Tcl development environment there.

Web-Specialized Server-Side Scripting Languages

A server-side scripting language is any language whose code is embedded in text documents and meant to be interpreted by the Web server program before it sends the documents (typically containing HTML and server-side scripting, as well) out to the client. Server-side scripts can, for example, insert the current date and time in a document, customize a document with the user's name, or insert a hit counter.

Server-side scripting languages can sometimes work with arguments, which are extra pieces of data supplied with the client's request for a document. A client might, for example, request this document:

```
results.php3
```

This is a Hypertext Preprocessor (PHP) program called `results.php3`. Presumably, this program yields output in a form the client can understand—

typically HTML. A client might also specify an argument by specifying this file:

```
results.php3?physics
```

That causes *physics* to be available to `results.php3` as the value for one of its variables. Such a system might power a search engine, for example.

Hypertext Preprocessor (PHP)

Deriving its abbreviation from its German spelling, *Hypertext Preprocessor (PHP)* is a public-domain server-side scripting language. It originally was developed for Unix systems and continues to find most of its applications under Apache servers, but a version of the language for 32-bit Microsoft Windows machines is available, too. Get the details at `www.php.net`.

Active Server Pages (ASP)

Active Server Pages (ASP) is the server-side scripting solution for Microsoft Web servers—mainly, Internet Information Server (IIS). If you're running a Windows NT server as your platform for Web content and need the versatility of server-side scripting, ASP probably is the way to go. It's based on VBScript and you can use Microsoft Visual InterDev to automate some of the development process. Get the details at `msdn.microsoft.com`.

LiveScript

LiveScript is the server-side scripting solution for Netscape Communications Corporation's Web servers. Essentially, it's a variant of JavaScript—often, you will in fact hear it called "server-side JavaScript." Get the goods on this language at `devedge.netscape.com`.

Client-Side Markup Languages

A client-side markup language is any system of adding tags (markup) to a text document to supply information about how the text should be rendered or what it means. Client-side markup languages are interpreted by the browser, so you'll sometimes see subtle variations in how different browsers interpret the same markup.

Hypertext Markup Language (HTML)

Hypertext Markup Language (HTML) is the most popular language for creating Web documents. With fundamentals that are easy to learn and high-end capabilities that satisfy many advanced publishing requirements, HTML is the workhorse of Web publishing. HTML code is not always elegant, it does not lend itself to searching (the way XML does), and different browsers will frequently interpret the same HTML document differently, but at present HTML is the standard language of Web publishing.

A basic orientation to HTML coding appears later in this chapter.

eXtensible Markup Language (XML)

While HTML describes how its surrounding text should appear in a browser window, *eXtensible Markup Language (XML)* describes what the text means. Rather than lock publishers into a universal set of tags that must be made to apply in all situations (as HTML does), XML allows users to define their own tags as needed.

The idea is that, within a given group of XML users—people in a given industry, say, or people wanting to communicate corporate financial information to shareholders—there would be a common XML specification called a *document type definition (DTD)*. One party could publish data in conformance with that DTD, and another party, having access to the same DTD, could interpret it.

Remember, XML isn't so much about the display of data. An XML document on its own, in fact, is not renderable—you have to supply style sheets and other information in order to associate the data in an XML document with cosmetic characteristics a browser could use. For this reason, XML is as much a data-interchange tool for communicating data among applications as a language for displaying data to a person.

Virtual Reality Markup Language (VRML)

Still primarily a novelty, *Virtual Reality Modeling Language (VRML)* is a way of describing three-dimensional space via tags in a text document. VRML includes means of describing shapes, relative positions, surface textures, and light sources.

Although it's technically astute, fun to play with, and the center of a considerable community on the Internet, VRML really hasn't found a killer application yet. It's a minor publishing language.

Client-Side Scripting Languages

A client-side scripting language is a scripting language whose code is interpreted on the client side of the client-server relationship. Client-side scripting code typically is embedded in HTML documents. It's not executed when the server runs the server-side code. Instead, it's run by the client computer after the download is complete. Client-side scripting languages can provide animation and interactivity (such as form prevalidation and simple calculations) without adding to the server's processing load.

There are two main client-side scripting languages:

- JavaScript and JScript (technically two languages, but very similar ones)

- VBScript

This section explores these languages.

JavaScript and JScript

JavaScript is a powerful yet fairly simple scripting language you can use to add "intelligence" and interactivity to your Web pages. With JavaScript, you can do such things as:

- Make your browser's status bar display a label when you pass your mouse pointer over a link

- Design a registration form that makes sure visitors to your site send in valid information

- Equip your pages with animated elements

JScript is Microsoft Internet Explorer's version of JavaScript. It can handle any JavaScript program...more or less. Though JScript is mostly compatible with JavaScript, Microsoft Internet Explorer doesn't interpret everything the same way Netscape's browser does. The lesson to you: test your pages with Microsoft Internet Explorer as well as Netscape Navigator.

Here's an HTML document that incorporates a simple JavaScript program, just to give you an idea of the basic syntax:

```
<HTML>
<HEAD>
<TITLE> Hello </TITLE>
</HEAD>
<BODY>
<H1>Say hello to the nice reader...</H1>
<SCRIPT LANGUAGE="JavaScript">
<!--
document.write("<P>Hello, network!")
// -->
</SCRIPT>
<H1>Very good!</H1>
</BODY>
</HTML>
```

Figure 8.1 shows what the code looks like when interpreted by a browser. Note that the document.write() statement results in text that looks like an integral part of the HTML code.

FIGURE 8.1 The results of a simple JavaScript program

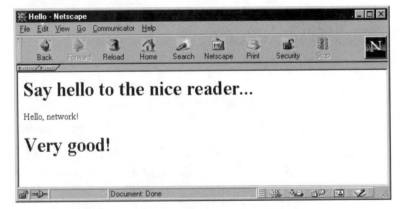

VBScript

If JavaScript borrows much of its structure and syntax from Java, VBScript borrows a great deal from Visual Basic. As Microsoft's preferred client-side scripting language, VBScript can do all sorts of automation, animation, verification, and organization jobs on the client side. If you know standard Visual Basic, you'll probably find it easy to pick up a working knowledge of VBScript. In fact, you can use your VB development environment to do many VBScript development tasks.

Here's a simple VBScript program to give you a feel for the language's appearance:

```
<HTML>
<HEAD>
<TITLE> Hello </TITLE>
</HEAD>
<BODY>
<H1>A VBScript Demonstration</H1>
    <INPUT TYPE=BUTTON VALUE="Say Hello" NAME="Hello">
<SCRIPT LANGUAGE="VBScript">
<!--
    Sub Hello_OnClick
      MsgBox "I want my i-Net+ certification!", 0,
    "VBScript Demonstration"
    End Sub
-->
</SCRIPT>
<H1>Very good!</H1>
</BODY>
</HTML>
```

Figure 8.2 shows what this code looks like in Microsoft Internet Explorer (which is the only browser, by the way, with native capacity to interpret VBScript). The subroutine executes only when the user clicks the button.

FIGURE 8.2   A simple VBScript program that spawns a dialog box

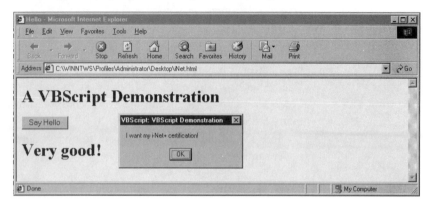

Databases

A *database* is any collection of data. A card file is a kind of database; a list of telephone numbers on a piece of paper is a database. Computer databases are essentially the same sorts of things, but with the information (and the labels identifying it) stored digitally.

Database Management Systems (DBMSes) are programs that add data to databases, extract data from them, organize the data for various applications, and generally attempt to guarantee that the database is fast, easily accessible, and secure from outsiders. *Data mining* applications attempt to analyze the data in databases and draw conclusions from it. Data mining applications at Wal-Mart Stores, Inc., for example, realized that most people who buy breakfast cereal at Wal-Mart also buy bananas during the same visit. The result of the data mining is that most Wal-Marts now stock bananas in their cereal aisles, hoping to encourage even more cereal buyers to pick up some bananas on impulse.

Non-Relational Databases

Non-relational databases (or flat-file databases) are essentially unadorned lists. A non-relational database might serve to correlate names with e-mail addresses or atomic symbols with atomic numbers. Non-relational databases play a big role in the operation of the Internet because they store the Domain Name Services (DNS) lists that associate domain names with IP addresses.

The problem with non-relational databases is that they can't keep track of sets of data with multiple relationships among the fields. Non-relational databases that are used to keep track of data with such complex relationships end up having multiple instances of each piece of data—an inefficiency that's one of the cardinal sins of database design. Relational databases are better for applications that involve complicated relationships.

Relational Databases

A relational database is a database with multiple tables, each having something in common with at least one other. Say, for example, that you work for your government's automobile-registration organization. You might have one table that correlates license plate numbers to Vehicle Identification Numbers (VINs) and another table that correlates VINs with the registered owners of the vehicles those VINs represent. Still another table might contain contact information about the people who have registered vehicles with your government.

So, if the police want to find the address of the woman who just held up the liquor store in your town, they'd go to the motor vehicle authority with the license plate number of her getaway car. The doughty database administrator there would be able to find the robber's name and address by associating the plate number with a VIN, the VIN with a name, and the name with an address. There are three tables involved, all *related* to one another by some common piece of information. This is a relational database.

Database Servers

A *database server* is any program that's responsible for maintaining one or more databases and responding to queries sent to them. Database servers combine efficient storage and access with DBMS software. All major database servers comply with the Structured Query Language (SQL) specification—more on that later—though many of them supplement standard SQL with proprietary or otherwise nonstandard extensions to the language.

In addition, a computer that's dedicated to running a database server program is called a database server.

Many companies publish database server software. They all have their fans. Some fit better into certain applications than others; some cost more than others. Evaluate the companies' offerings next to your organization's needs. Here are the big players, in alphabetical order:

- Hughes Technologies puts out mSQL, a server for small- and mid-size applications that's free for use under certain circumstances. Read about it at www.hughes.com.au/.

- Microsoft publishes Microsoft SQL Server 7, which runs best under Windows NT. Details are at www.microsoft.com/sql/.

- Oracle made its name with database servers. Its latest products are the servers of the Oracle 8I family. Details appear at www.oracle.com/database/oracle8i/.

- Sybase also has been selling database servers for years. Its latest ones compose the Adaptive Server family. Read all about them at www.sybase.com/products/databaseservers/.

- T.c.X DataKonsult improved upon mSQL and came out with MySQL, which also is free under some circumstances. The server has a Web site: www.mysql.com/.

Structured Query Language Fundamentals

Structured Query Language (SQL) is the standard language for working with relational databases. It's a complex, powerful language that's far beyond the scope of this book and the i-Net+ exam, but its fundamentals are worth a mention here.

SQL is a descriptive language, which is a kind of language different from the procedural and object-oriented languages that characterize most software development jobs. Here's an analogy. Say you went to a delicatessen to acquire a ham sandwich. If you were only able to speak in procedural languages, you'd have to tell the guy exactly what to do in order to yield the results you wanted. You'd have to say, "Cut the roll in half and place the halves side-by-side, cut side up. Spread mustard on the halves. Slice ham until you have a quarter-pound of it. Remove the ham from the slicer...." You get the idea.

With a descriptive language, you could just describe the results you want. "I want a ham sandwich on a Kaiser roll with Dijon mustard and an olive," you'd say. And then the counterman, being a skilled maker of sandwiches, delivers what you want. The process is a lot easier. In the case of databases, the database server knows how to extract information from the databases it knows about. Clients who make requests for data from the databases describe the data they want with SQL. These requests are called *queries*.

Let's take a look at an example of an SQL query:

```
SELECT firstName, lastName FROM employeeTable;
```

That query would yield a list—called a *report*—of all values in the firstName and lastName fields of every record in the employeeTable table. What if we didn't want all of them? We could try this:

```
SELECT firstName, lastName FROM employeeTable
WHERE wage > 8.5;
```

That would yield the contents of the firstName and lastName fields in every record in which the wage field contained a value greater than 8.5.

Note that queries don't have to extract data from databases. The SQL instructions that create tables, insert data into them, and establish relationships (called *joins*) among tables are called queries, too.

There's a good SQL tutorial on the Web at `w3.one.net/~jhoffman/sqltut.htm`.

HTML Fundamentals

Most Web publishing involves Hypertext Markup Language (HTML) to some degree or another. This section aims to orient you to the barest fundamentals of the language. Detailed coverage of HTML is beyond the scope of this book and the i-Net+ exam. For further information on the language and its uses, refer to a specialized tutorial or reference book.

How to Write an HTML Document

If you're going to write HTML, you need a tool for doing so. You have two options:

- A text editor for editing the HTML code directly

- A graphical editing environment that handles code generation for you

Editing Code Directly

If you understand HTML, you may find it preferable to work with the code directly. Because HTML files are just ASCII text files with special tags added, you can edit HTML code with any text editor. Which text editor you use is more a matter of preference than anything else, though some editors ship with macros and other aids that speed the HTML writing process.

Some popular text editors include:

- Wilson WindowWare's WinEdit (www.winedit.com)

- Bare Bones Software's BBEdit (www.bbedit.com/products/bbe-dit/bbedit.html)

- Fookes Software's NoteTab (www.notetab.com)

- SimpleText (ships with MacOS)

- Notepad (ships with Microsoft Windows)

- Emacs (ships with most versions of Unix)

There also are some hybrid editors on the market. These editors allow you to switch back and forth between a direct view of the code (as in a text editor) and a view of the formatted page as it would appear in a browser (as in a WYSIWYG editor, discussed next). Allaire HomeSite (available for trial download at www2.allaire.com/products/homesite/) is such a product.

Using a WYSIWYG Editor

Some people prefer not to fool with HTML code directly and would rather use a development tool that lets them see how things will look right away.

There are several popular programs in this competitive market. The top players include:

- Macromedia DreamWeaver (`www.macromedia.com/software/ dreamweaver/`)

- Microsoft FrontPage (`www.microsoft.com/frontpage/`)

- Allaire HomeSite (`www2.allaire.com/products/homesite/`)

These What-You-See-Is-What-You-Get (WYSIWYG) editors work a lot like word processing programs like Lotus Word Pro. You enter, arrange, and format text and graphics visually, allowing the software to take care of the underlying code. Sometimes, you'll hear WYSIWYG editors called graphical user interface (GUI) editors. Figure 8.3 shows a page under construction in DreamWeaver.

FIGURE 8.3 Macromedia DreamWeaver in action

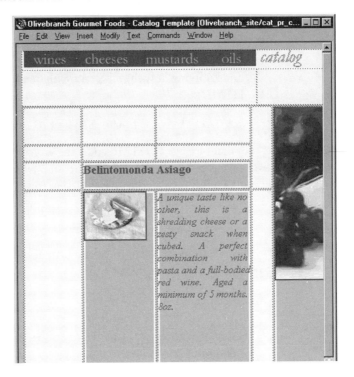

Viewing Your Code

Web browsers allow you to view the HTML code on which a Web page is based. You may want to do this if you want your own pages to include an effect you spotted on someone else's Web page, but don't want to copy code exactly without permission. Here's how to view HTML.

Under Microsoft Internet Explorer, choose View ➢ Source from the menu bar, or right-click the document and choose View Source. The latter approach is particularly handy with multiframed documents. Later versions (5) of IE also have an icon on the toolbar to enable editing with FrontPage with a single click.

Under Netscape Navigator, view the HTML by choosing View ➢ Page Source from the menu bar, or right-click the document and choose View Source.

HTML Document Structure

HTML documents are ASCII text files with special sequences of characters, called *tags*, inserted in the text the tags describe. The process of learning HTML is largely a process of learning the different tags, knowing what they do, and knowing how they interact with one another. Here's the basic syntax for HTML tags:

```
<B> Text to which the tags apply </B>
```

In that passage of HTML code, the words "Text to which the tags apply" are formatted under the rules associated with the <B>...</B> tags. Those tags, as it happens, indicate bold formatting of text, and so a browser interpreting this passage would format the words in boldface, like this:

Text to which the tags apply

Simple enough? Well, those are probably the most straightforward tags around. It gets more complex from there. But that's how tags work, in a nutshell.

HTML is not case sensitive, but it is a good idea to be consistent with your use of uppercase letters for the sake of clarity.

This section provides only the barest introduction to HTML and the things you can do with it. Any serious HTML publisher needs a full-scale tutorial and reference book on the subject—such books typically run to more than 1,000 pages.

Basic Elements

The simplest HTML document consists of a statement of the HTML specification being used (there are several), a head region, a body region, and some <HTML>...</HTML> tags that define the whole document. Here's a skeletal HTML document. It contains nothing, but a browser will open it without objection:

```
<!DOCTYPE HTML PUBLIC "-//W3C//DTD HTML 3.2 Final//EN">
<HTML>
<HEAD>
</HEAD>
<BODY>
</BODY>
</HTML>
```

This example begins with a declaration of the document type, which states that this document complies with the HTML 3.2 language specification as defined by the World Wide Web Consortium (W3C). You'll learn more about DOCTYPE statements if you decide to explore XML in depth someday. Additionally, there are three sets of tags in the example, specifically:

- <HTML>...</HTML> defines the portion of the document in HTML format—all of it.

- <HEAD>...</HEAD> defines the head segment of the document, in which some scripting code and other invisible elements will go.

- <BODY>...</ BODY> defines the body segment of the document, in which visible elements will go.

You also can add some simple elements to provide your document with some content. Here's another document:

```
<!DOCTYPE HTML PUBLIC "-//W3C//DTD HTML 3.2 Final//EN">
<HTML>
<HEAD>
```

```
<TITLE> A Very Simple HTML Document </TITLE>
</HEAD>
<BODY>
<H1> Venus and Adonis </H1>
<H2> By William Shakespeare </H2>
<P>
<BR>EVEN as the sun with purple-colour'd face
<BR>Had ta'en his last leave of the weeping morn,
<BR>Rose-cheek'd Adonis hied him to the chase;
<BR>Hunting he loved, but love he laugh'd to scorn;
<BR>Sick-thoughted Venus makes amain unto him,
<BR>And like a bold-faced suitor 'gins to woo him.
</BODY>
</HTML>
```

That's the same document, outfitted with some text and some additional tags. Here's a rundown of the added tags:

- <TITLE>...<TITLE> define the label for the browser window that's displaying this page.

- <H1>...</H1> define text as a level-one (i.e., big) heading.

- <H2>...</H2> define text as a level-two (i.e., somewhat less big) heading.

- <P> defines the beginning of a paragraph—used here to get some white space.

-
 indicates a line break

Figure 8.4 shows how the document looks when rendered by a browser.

FIGURE 8.4 A basic HTML document

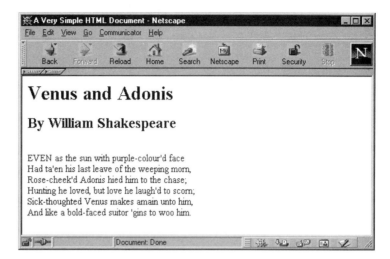

Tables

Often, you'll want to include tables in your HTML documents. For one thing, tables are handy for organizing data and highlighting the relationships among variables. They're also useful for implementing relatively complicated page layouts.

Several tags come into play in the creation of a table. Here's a summary:

- <TABLE>...</TABLE> tags surround the whole table.

- <TR>...</TR> tags surround each row of cells (think "table row").

- <TD>...</TD> tags surround the contents of each individual cell (think "table data").

In addition to using the basic tags—which are adequate to define a table by themselves—you can insert *attributes* into the tags to specify additional formatting information. The opening <TABLE> tag, for example, takes an attribute called BORDER. If you use the following syntax, you'll get a border one pixel wide between all your cells and around the table's exterior:

```
<TABLE BORDER=1>
```

Here's an HTML document that illustrates the use of table-making tags:

```
<!DOCTYPE HTML PUBLIC "-//W3C//DTD HTML 3.2 Final//EN">

<HTML>
<HEAD>
<TITLE> A Very Simple HTML Document </TITLE>
</HEAD>
<BODY>
<H1> Rainfall Values </H1>
<H3> Inches </H3>

<TABLE ALIGN="Center" BORDER="1" CELLSPACING="0"
CELLPADDING="0" WIDTH="100%">

<TR>
<TD ALIGN="center" VALIGN="middle"></TD>
<TD ALIGN="center" VALIGN="middle">May</TD>
<TD ALIGN="center" VALIGN="middle">June</TD>
<TD ALIGN="center" VALIGN="middle">July</TD>
</TR>


<TR>
<TD ALIGN="center" VALIGN="middle">Phoenix</TD>
<TD ALIGN="center" VALIGN="middle">1</TD>
<TD ALIGN="center" VALIGN="middle">2</TD>
<TD ALIGN="center" VALIGN="middle">1</TD>
</TR>


<TR>
<TD ALIGN="center" VALIGN="middle">Seattle</TD>
<TD ALIGN="center" VALIGN="middle">4</TD>
<TD ALIGN="center" VALIGN="middle">3</TD>
<TD ALIGN="center" VALIGN="middle">5</TD>
```

```
    </TR>

    </TABLE>

    </BODY>
    </HTML>
```

Figure 8.5 shows how the table looks when the HTML is rendered by a browser. Note the border called for by the BORDER attribute.

FIGURE 8.5   An HTML document that includes a table

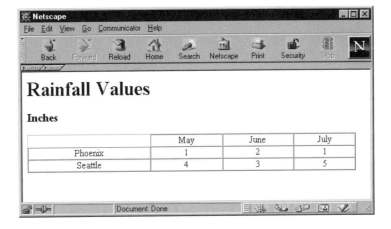

Links

To create a link from one document to another, use the <A> tag. Say you have a line of text that looks like this:

```
<P>The time has come, the walrus said,
to talk of many things
```

That's a plain line of text. You want the word *walrus* to become a link. When the user clicks *walrus*, you want her to see information about the animal. Here's the syntax for that link:

```
<P>The time has come, the <A
```

```
HREF="http://www.seaworld.org/animal%5Fbytes/walrusab.html"
>walrus</A> said, to talk of many things
```

See? The word you want to make into a link is surrounded by <A> and </A> tags. The <A> tag has an attribute, HREF, that is set to be equal to the URL to which you want the link to go.

You can use URLs other than Web addresses with the HREF tag. If you wanted a click on the link to spawn an e-mail message preaddressed for Ruth Anne Krinkelmeyer, you could use this syntax:

```
<P>The time has come, the <A HREF="mailto:ruthann@purple-
sage.com">walrus</A> said, to talk of many things
```

The mailto: prefix precedes e-mail URLs.

Forms

Most of HTML has to do with rendering words and pictures in a browser window, but the most valuable Internet transactions are those in which a server sends information to you. After all, that's how you get demographic information and credit card details.

HTML includes tags that cause user interface elements to appear in the browser window. Called *forms*, these collections of user interface elements can include text fields, check boxes, radio buttons, selection lists, and several kinds of buttons.

Detailed coverage of HTML forms is outside the domain of this book and the i-Net+ exam, but here's a simple form that incorporates two text fields, a Reset button, and a Submit button. It could be used to collect registration information about site users:

```
<!DOCTYPE HTML PUBLIC "-//W3C//DTD HTML 3.2 Final//EN">
<HTML>
<HEAD>
<TITLE> A Document With a Form </TITLE>
</HEAD>
<BODY>
<H1> Registration </H1>

<FORM NAME="registrationForm" METHOD="post"
ACTION="http://www.davidwall.com/cgi-bin/register.pl">
```

```
<P>Name:
<INPUT NAME="userName" TYPE="Text" SIZE=15>
<P>Email:
<INPUT NAME="userEmail" TYPE="Text" SIZE=25>
<P>
<INPUT NAME="submitButton" TYPE="Submit" VALUE="Submit">
<INPUT NAME="resetButton" TYPE="Reset" VALUE="Reset">
</FORM>

</BODY>
</HTML>
```

Figure 8.6 shows how this form looks when it's rendered by a browser. When the user clicks the Submit button, the contents of the form are assembled into a CGI-compliant text string and sent to the Perl program at www.davidwall.com/cgi-bin/register.pl (not a real program). That program could then process and respond to the CGI string.

FIGURE 8.6 An HTML document that includes a form

Compatibility with Different Browsers

When writing HTML, you have to be concerned with how your pages will look when interpreted by each of the many browsers that Internet surfers use. At the very least, you should verify that your pages render properly when loaded by the most recent two or three releases of each of the two major browsers—Netscape Navigator and Microsoft Internet Explorer.

Aside from testing, there are a couple of strategies you can employ when attempting to make your pages cross-browser compatible. The first is to stick with an HTML version a generation or two behind the state of the art. Browsers typically have been out for a while, and the most recent release may have come out before the announcement of the most recent HTML specification (and don't forget that many users don't run the latest browser anyway).

The second approach involves client-side scripting. You can use a client-side scripting language such as JavaScript to determine the publisher and version of the client's browser. That script's test of the page's environment can trigger the generation of different code for different browsers or cause different pages to load under different conditions.

Multimedia

*M*ultimedia is kind of a strange word. Really, it ought to apply to all means of communicating ideas from one person to another, which is what media is. But in the jargon, *multimedia* has come to refer to media other than text and still graphics. Most commonly, it's applied to sounds, moving pictures, and certain kinds of user interfaces that allow users to click buttons, choose options, and see behaviors in response. Multimedia incorporates full-motion video with interlaced sound, silent video, animation (both with sound and without), and sound information (as from a radio).

Communicating multimedia over the Internet poses special challenges. Most of the challenges have to do with the fact that multimedia presentations require lots of digital information, and the capacity for communicating data in such volume is limited.

Streaming versus Non-Streaming Media

Media files are great in that they can appeal to senses that aren't normally stimulated during Web surfing. An audio file can run in the background while a user pays attention to work; a video can communicate feelings of motion and excitement that static images cannot convey. But all this capability comes with a drawback. Media files—those containing sound, video, or both—tend to be huge. In a world that's still dominated by slow modem connections, you can't expect the members of your audience to wait patiently while a massive file dribbles in through a slow connection.

As is often the case with problems that crop up on the Internet, there's a solution to the difficulties presented by large media files and slow connectivity. Streaming media allow users to begin enjoying multimedia content before they've downloaded whole files. This section explores the differences between traditional, non-streaming multimedia and the improved, streaming variety.

Non-Streaming Media

Non-streaming media relies on the concept of files. An article of media—a sound clip, a video, whatever—is electronically encoded in some format as a file (you'll learn more about multimedia file formats shortly). The file is stored on a server. When a client makes a request for the media file, it must be transferred to the client machine completely before the client can begin playing it. The trouble with non-streaming media has to do with time. If a user wants to see a video clip and must wait for the whole thing to download before he sees anything, he's going to lose patience with the downloading process if the clip is more than a second or two long. A short clip will disappoint him otherwise. Streaming media allow for media presentations of theoretically infinite length with relatively tiny up-front download times.

Popular non-streaming media formats include:

- MOV, MPEG, and AVI videos
- WAV and AU sounds

Streaming Media

The idea behind *streaming media* is that use of the data that represents the sound, video, or whatever can begin before the entire file is downloaded. A client can request a very large audio file and begin presenting its contents after it has received only a fraction of the total file. Then, while it plays what it has received, the client continues to download more of the file.

Indeed, in many cases, "files" are sort of nebulous concepts in streaming situations. Many radio stations send their live audio feeds to streaming media servers, which dole out the stream to users as it is requested. The files in these applications are more like buffers—they contain the most recent two minutes or so of the broadcast, but newly generated material is constantly coming in and older material is being thrown away. So, a client that's playing streaming media can be receiving an ongoing transmission from some server, "tuning in" long after the stream started and "tuning out" before the server stops sending information.

Most streaming media formats implement a buffer on the client side. That is, they'll download 10 seconds or so of the stream before they begin playing it, to allow for slowdowns in the transfer rate later in the download process. If such a slowdown occurs, the player can just draw down the contents of the buffer rather than interrupt what the user hears or sees.

The two main streaming media technologies are RealPlayer, from Real-Networks, and Windows Media Player, from Microsoft. You'll find details of RealPlayer on the Web at `www.real.com/` and further information on Windows Media Player at `www.microsoft.com`.

Browser Plug-Ins

Browser plug-ins attach themselves to the base browser code and expand its capabilities to interpret data. Plug-ins are code libraries, typically written in C or C++, that most often enable the browser to display new kinds of media. When a browser encounters a media file that it can't interpret natively, it turns responsibility for that file over to the appropriate plug-in (assuming there's an appropriate one installed). Some of the most popular plug-ins include:

Macromedia Shockwave Shockwave allows publishers to embed fairly elaborate animations—with sound and some interactivity—in their Web pages. Macromedia Flash has superceded Shockwave because of its more compact files.

Macromedia Flash Like its predecessor, Shockwave, Flash provides a format for encoding animation and sound. Its files are much more svelte than those in Shockwave format. Flash files employ vector graphics, which means they're composed of mathematically defined curves rather than huge catalogs of pixel details.

RealPlayer RealPlayer handles streaming audio and video files. Please refer to the discussion of RealPlayer as part of the streaming media coverage in the preceding section.

Windows Media Player   Windows Media Player handles streaming audio and video files. Windows Media Player was also part of the streaming media coverage in the preceding section.

Apple QuickTime VR   QuickTime VR allows the user to view a 360-degree panoramic image. Often, QuickTime VR files find application in showing off building interiors and natural scenery.

File Formats

Anything you publish on the Internet must be in the form of a file. *Files* are sequences of bytes, organized into discrete units that can be managed by operating systems. Within those units, the bytes take on different patterns of organization depending upon what kind of data they represent.

Image File Formats

Still graphics take the form of nontextual, nonexecutable binary files. There are several file formats, each with strengths and weaknesses with regard to color depth, file size, and suitability to the network environment. The following are most important to the Internet:

- GIF and GIF89a
- JPEG
- PNG

GIF and GIF89a

Graphics Interchange Format (GIF) files can hold images of from two to 256 colors. The version of the GIF (pronounced either "giff" or "jiff") specification that came out in 1989 is known as GIF89a and has a couple of neat capabilities:

- Transparency
- Animation

Transparency allows pixels in the GIF file to show whatever color is behind the image—this trait is handy for creating images that have apparently irregular borders. Animated GIFs are really a series of GIFs strung together and shown in sequence. They're one way to create somewhat flickery animations that most browsers can interpret properly, without plug-ins.

GIF files also are *progressive*, meaning that the data in a given file is organized in such a way that a client can download a blocky version of the image first, then gradually refine the image's sharpness as more data comes through the pipe.

Technically, CompuServe invented GIF and could try to collect royalties from companies who use GIF technology in their software—or even people who use GIF images on their Web sites. In practice, though, GIF is in the public domain. To be on the safe side of this issue (and to correct some of GIF's technical shortcomings), the Portable Network Graphics (PNG) format has evolved as a replacement for GIF.

JPEG

Joint Photographic Experts Group (JPEG) files are distinguished by their ability to include the entire spectrum of perceptible color (16.7 million shades) without being prohibitively huge. The secret is a compression algorithm that exploits the fact that human eyes are more sensitive to subtle differences in brightness than to subtle differences in color. By simulating some color shading with brightness gradients, JPEG (pronounced "jay-peg") files can convey full color without being huge. Because its compression algorithm results in changes to the image data, the compression algorithm is said to be *lossy*. A *lossless* algorithm, in comparison, would not result in changes to the data.

JPEG files are not always progressive, though they can be. A *progressive JPEG* is one in which the information has been organized to allow progressive refinement of the image during the course of its downloading.

Arriba Soft has a detailed JPEG FAQ on its Web site. Take a look: www.arribasoft.com/lounge/library/Jpegfaq/top.html.

PNG

The Portable Network Graphics (PNG) format is a recently established image specification that provides lossless compression of 256-color images. In effect, it's a replacement for the GIF format, which isn't easy for programmers to manipulate and has always been dogged by copyright issues (see the GIF section earlier).

The most comprehensive PNG Web site is the one Greg Roelofs has put together to support his book *PNG: The Definitive Guide* (O'Reilly & Associates, 1999). The URL is www.cdrom.com/pub/png/pngbook.html. Scroll to the bottom of that page for a list of PNG links.

BMP

Windows Bitmap (BMP) files are capable of displaying 16.7 million colors—more than the human eye can distinguish. However, BMP files are notoriously large and so usually don't find their way into situations where they must be downloaded across slow networks. Web browsers can't interpret them without plug-ins anyway. As a result, BMP files are generally relegated to duty on Microsoft Windows machines.

TIFF

Tagged Image File Format (TIFF) files support 16.7 million colors as well, but they are large and natively unsupported by Web browsers. For these reasons, TIFF files usually are used in desktop publishing applications and other situations in which network communication of the image data isn't important.

EPS

Encapsulated PostScript (EPS) files are recorded in the PostScript printer language, which means it's possible to generate a PostScript file on one computer and print that file on any PostScript printer, even if the computer to which the printer is connected contains no software that understands PostScript. Web browsers don't support EPS, though, and so its application to Internet publishing is limited.

Video and Animation File Formats

Like still images, moving images may be encoded as a series of bytes in a file. There are several such file formats, each with its own characteristics. Despite their differences, all video and animation files tend to be large. If you need to put video or animation on a Web site, consider doing so with a streaming file format such as RealVideo or Windows Media Player.

QuickTime

Developed by Apple Computer, the QuickTime format supports full-motion video and animation with synchronized sound. QuickTime files usually carry a `.MOV` filename extension.

Audio Visual Interleaved

Like QuickTime, Audio Visual Interleaved (AVI) format supports full-motion video and animation with sound. Developed for the Windows environment by Microsoft, AVI files usually have `.AVI` filename extensions.

Motion Picture Experts Group

Motion Picture Experts Group (MPEG) files handle full-motion video, but the first version of the specification, MPEG-1, does not support sound. The newer MPEG-2 standard does. Developed by a consortium of telecommunications industry representatives, MPEG files carry `.MPEG` or `.MPG` filename extensions.

Compressed File Formats

Because data-transmission capacity on the Internet is limited, there's a lot to be said for making files as small as possible. If you're going to attach a Lotus Word Pro document to an e-mail message, say, you might be concerned that the file was 700KB in size. If you compressed it—converted it to a compressed file format—the size might be reduced dramatically. After transmission over the Internet, the recipient could uncompress the file—convert it back to its original format—and use it as if nothing had happened.

In addition to shrinking files for transmission, compression has the added benefit of combining multiple files into neat packages. You can combine several files into one compressed file, then convert them back to separate files during decompression. Some compression formats allow you to extract compressed files individually, as well. Here's a rundown of some popular compressed file formats.

Zip

The standard for Windows machines, Zip files allow you to combine several files into one compressed unit and extract them individually. Zip files usually have a `.ZIP` filename extension.

You can download a version of WinZip at www.winzip.com.

BinHex

The MacOS standard, the BinHex format allows you to combine several files into one compressed unit and extract them individually. BinHex files usually have an .HQX filename extension.

Tape Archive

Designed for the needs of tape backup machines connected to Unix boxes, the tape archive format strings multiple files together into a single unit but does not compress them. Tape archive files usually have a .TAR filename extension. Often, you'll see tape archive used in conjunction with Gzip, covered next. When Gzip compresses a tape archive file, the resulting file usually has a .TAR or .GZ extension.

Gzip

As Zip does for Windows files, Gzip compresses files under Unix. Gzip files usually have a .GZ filename extension. Gzip often is applied to tape archive files, as covered above.

Text and Layout File Formats

Multimedia files are great, but the fact is that most of the information that's sent over the Internet is some kind of text. There are many ways to encapsulate text in files for transmission.

ASCII Text

The granddaddy of text formats, the American Standard Code for Information Interchange (ASCII) represents an efficient way to store text (though it's not too good for representing non-Latin character sets). ASCII text files usually carry a .TXT filename extension.

Adobe Acrobat

Adobe Corporation came out with Acrobat before the Internet revolution, but the technology languished until the Web took off. Acrobat allows users on diverse platforms to view (and, in its latest version, annotate) documents that incorporate text, graphics, hyperlinks, and complex layouts. It's better than HTML because the publisher has absolute control over how her publication looks on users' machines. Acrobat files carry a .PDF filename extension.

You can download the Adobe Acrobat Reader software at www.adobe.com.

Rich Text Format

The baseline format for formatted text, Rich Text Format allows you to endow text with fairly elaborate formatting—including font information—and expect that almost any word processing program will be able to open your files. RTF files take an .RTF filename extension.

Microsoft Word

Love it or hate it, Microsoft Word is the most popular word processing application out there. It exists in Windows and MacOS versions, and many other programs can interpret the Word file format. Therefore, it's a reasonable bet that any given user will be able to open a Word document. They usually carry .DOC filename extensions.

PostScript

Designed to enable publishers to generate publications on one computer and print them on a PostScript-compatible printer somewhere else (such as at a service bureau), it's possible to encode complex, multipage documents in PostScript files and expect others to be able to view them. Acrobat files usually are better, though. PostScript files carry .PS or .EPS filename extensions.

Summary

In this chapter, you learned about Internet development. The most important facts and concepts to know for the i-Net+ exam are the following:

- A client is a piece of software that requests information from a server, which is another piece of software that supplies the information.

- There are many kinds of server software, including Web servers and database servers.

- Web clients interpret text, markup languages, native embedded content, scripting, Java, ActiveX, and plug-in content to yield a presentation to their users.

- Server extensions, Java servlets, and scripting languages may expand the capabilities of servers.

- On the Web, clients and servers often communicate with text strings in CGI format.

- Distributed computing (as with COM, DCOM, and JavaBeans software) involves spreading the computing load over several machines.

- Enterprise computing involves sharing data seamlessly among an organization's programs.

- Full-featured languages like Java, C, C++, and Visual Basic can be used to create stand-alone applications.

- Versatile scripting languages like Perl, Tcl, and various shell languages are handy for quick solutions to problems.

- Server-side scripting languages for Web publishing (such as ASP, PHP, and LiveScript) can be used to modify pages before they go out to browsers.

- Client-side markup languages like HTML and XML describe the intended appearance and meaning of the text in a document, respectively.

- Client-side scripting languages such as JavaScript and VBScript can take some load off the server.

- Non-relational databases are lists of data and are not very versatile.

- Relational databases store information more efficiently than non-relational databases.

- Database servers maintain databases and allow clients to query them.

- Structured Query Language (SQL) is the standard language of database queries.

- You can use a text editor or a WYSIWYG editor—sometimes called a graphical user interface (GUI) editor—to edit an HTML document.

- Implementing features in HTML documents is a matter of learning the proper tags.

- Cross-browser compatibility can be achieved either through use of an older HTML specification or through a test performed with a client-side scripting language.

- Streaming multimedia formats allow users to begin viewing or listening to a file before it finishes downloading.

- Plug-ins enable browsers to handle exotic multimedia formats.

- Many different file formats for text, still images, moving images, and sounds exist.

Review Questions

1. What is a *server*?

   A. An extraordinarily powerful computer

   B. A piece of software from which information is requested

   C. Software that necessarily runs on a machine other than the one running the client

   D. A program that distributes Web pages

2. What is a *client*?

   A. A Web browser

   B. A custom database interface

   C. A spreadsheet connected to a database server

   D. Any program that requests information from a server

3. Which of the following is an example of a Web server program?

   A. Microsoft Internet Explorer

   B. Netscape LiveScript

   C. Apache

   D. Kiowa

4. How does a Java servlet differ from a non-Java server extension?

   A. A given servlet will run under any operating system for which there is a Java Virtual Machine (JVM).

   B. Servlets run faster than server extensions.

   C. Servlets occupy less disk space than server extensions.

   D. Servlets do not support CGI.

5. Server-side scripting languages are which of the following?

   A. Compiled

   B. The same as client-side scripting languages

   C. Handy for doing database queries

   D. Not used much in Web publishing

6. What is the most common way of getting information from a Web surfer?

   A. An HTML form

   B. A custom application

   C. A Vulcan mind-meld

   D. ActiveX

7. What is a Common Gateway Interface (CGI)?

   A. A programming language

   B. A kind of Web server

   C. A specification for packaging data for the trip between client and server

   D. A database query language

8. You can easily secure CGI submissions with what?

   A. A password

   B. Secure Sockets Layer (SSL) encryption

   C. Java encryption

   D. PHP

9. What is the program that translates human-readable source code into machine language called?

   A. Interpreter

   B. Compiler

   C. Java Virtual Machine

   D. Object packager

10. What is one of the most attractive aspects of the Java language?

   A. The fact that an independent standards body defines it

   B. Its gentle learning curve for novices

   C. The cross-platform nature of Java programs

   D. Its integration with MacOS

11. Visual Basic is often used in the creation of what?

   A. Java applets

   B. Operating systems

   C. Perl modules

   D. ActiveX controls

12. When are the C and C++ programming languages good candidates for jobs?

   A. When it is very important to keep development time to a minimum

   B. When you need cross-platform capabilities in the program you create

   C. When you need absolute control over memory management

   D. When you need to create a database interface

13. Perl is an open-source language. What does that mean?

    A. Perl programs are not compiled.

    B. Perl programs must run in the foreground.

    C. Anyone may download and use Perl, free of charge.

    D. You must make your Perl programs available to others.

14. What is Perl extraordinarily good for?

    A. Text processing

    B. Creating windowed applications

    C. Optimizing memory usage

    D. Programs written in languages that use a non-Latin character set

15. What is Microsoft's preferred server-side scripting technology for Web publishers called?

    A. Internet Information Server (IIS)

    B. VBScript

    C. Active Server Pages (ASP)

    D. ActiveX Server Extensions (ASE)

16. What does eXtensible Markup Language (XML) describe?

    A. How documents should appear in browser windows

    B. The meaning of the information in XML documents

    C. A client-server relationship

    D. Dynamic HTML information

17. JavaScript is _____ .

    A. More or less supported in both major browsers

    B. The same as Java

    C. Exclusively a server-side language

    D. Useful only for doing image rollovers

18. Why is a relational database frequently better than a non-relational database?

    A. Non-relational databases require special software.

    B. Complex relationships among data can be represented in relational databases without multiple instances of the same data.

    C. Relational databases may be queried more speedily.

    D. Oracle supports relational databases.

19. Streaming media formats allow for slowdowns in the data stream by _____ .

    A. Dividing the available bandwidth into "normal" and "backup" segments

    B. Compressing data in the Zip format

    C. Building up a buffer of data before playback begins

    D. Storing media information in a database

20. What kind of image file supports transparency?

    A. GIF

    B. GIF89a

    C. GIF87a

    D. JPEG

Answers to Review Questions

1. B. Although a program that distributes Web pages is one kind of server and a server program may run on an extraordinarily powerful computer, a server is any program from which a client requests data.

2. D. A client is any program that requests information from a server. The other three answers are narrow examples of client software.

3. C. Apache is a popular Web server program.

4. A. Java is a cross-platform programming language, so servlets will run under almost any operating system. Non-Java server extensions are compiled for a particular environment.

5. C. You can do a database query with a server-side scripting language and incorporate the results into a document that's sent to a client.

6. A. HTML forms present the user with a variety of interface elements into which she can enter information for transmission to the server.

7. C. Common Gateway Interface (CGI) describes a way of packaging data for the trip between client and server.

8. B. Secure Sockets Layer (SSL) is the easiest way to securely transfer CGI data from the client to the server.

9. B. A compiler converts source code into machine code.

10. C. If you write a program in Java, you should be able to execute it on any computer that has a Java Virtual Machine (JVM) installed—including MacOS.

11. D. Visual Basic and its development environment make it easy to generate ActiveX controls.

12. C. Although it is possible to create database interfaces with C and C++, the languages really excel in applications in which tight control over memory and other resources is important.

13. C. Although it's polite to share your programs with others, that's not what *open source* means. Rather, the term means the language is in the public domain.

14. A. Perl has strong text-processing features, such as its ability to work with regular expressions.

15. C. You can use ASP scripts to automate page generation tasks in Microsoft environments. The system relies heavily on VBScript.

16. B. XML has to do with the meaning, not so much with the appearance, of information.

17. A. Though Microsoft Internet Explorer's implementation is called JScript, it's very similar to JavaScript and many programs run the same in both environments.

18. B. Relational databases excel at linking multiple data tables through common fields.

19. C. Streaming media applications store a few seconds' worth of data in a buffer that can be drawn down in the event of a network problem.

20. B. Files of type GIF89a can include transparent regions.

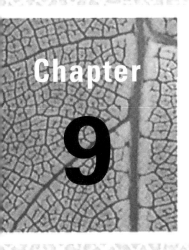

Chapter 9

Internet Site Functionality Design

---

i-NET+ EXAM OBJECTIVES COVERED IN THIS CHAPTER:

✓ **Identify the issues that affect Internet site functionality (e.g., performance, security, and reliability). Content may include the following:**

- Bandwidth
- Internet connection points
- Audience access
- Internet Service Provider (ISP)
- Connection types
- Corrupt files
- Files taking too long to load
- Inability to open files
- Resolution of graphics

✓ **Describe the concept of caching and its implications. Content may include the following:**

- Server caching
- Client caching
- Proxy caching
- Cleaning out client-side cache
- Server may cache information as well
- Web page update settings in browsers

✓ **Describe different types of search indexes—static index/site map, keyword index, full-text index. Examples could include the following:**

- Searching your site
- Searching content
- Indexing your site for a search

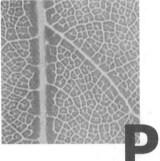

Perhaps the most important aspect of implementing and maintaining a Web site is making sure that it is accessible and usable by your audience. Regardless of how wonderful content is, if users cannot access the site in a timely and reliable way, they will go elsewhere for the information they seek. Therefore, it is important to know enough about the technologies that run the Internet that you can ensure that your site will meet the demands of its users.

In this chapter, you will learn about several critical topics that have an impact on a site's functionality and usability:

- Site functionality issues

- Technology and content-type planning

- Caching

- Site indexing

Each of these major topics contributes to the overall usability of a Web site.

Site Functionality Issues

Internet users are a fickle bunch. Technological glitches not only harm functionality, they often cost sites their reputation for usability and reliability. Everyone has given up on a Web page because it is too slow or just plain broken. What do we do if www.amazon.com/ goes down? We go to www .barnesandnoble.com/. What do we do if a site requires ActiveX and our corporate security policy is to disallow ActiveX? We go to a different site. It is important to know the most common errors users experience and why they occur.

Functionality errors manifest themselves in three ways:

- Users can't get to the site at all.

- It takes too long to download and view a page.

- The document they request is missing or appears to be broken.

In the following sections, we'll take a look at the technological factors underneath each of these errors.

Connectivity Failure

The most basic Web browser error is when a user fails to get any information from your Web server. These attempts will generate a warning message in the browser such as "Host not found" or "Request timed out." Such a warning message is shown in Figure 9.1—the user is trying to go to the Web site www.bahoozit.com, which does not exist.

FIGURE 9.1   "DNS Not Found" error message

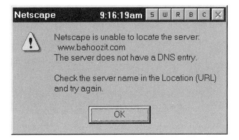

Not all error messages indicate a connectivity problem. If the server gives a dreaded "404—File not found" error, for example, your client is connecting to the server but the requested document cannot be found. If the host wasn't found or the request timed out, there was never a full-fledged connection between the client and the browser. Because connectivity errors mean that the server never gets a full connection to the client, such problems are often never logged on the server.

As explained in Chapter 2, several client queries and server responses need to succeed for a user to browse a Web page—the server's domain name needs to be resolved into an IP address, and the client needs to make a successful request to the Web server at that address. If the user can't get to a site at all, the problem could be caused by one of several factors:

- The client's network settings or DNS services are not working.

- The client's connection to the Internet is down.

- The server's hardware or software is malfunctioning or overwhelmed.

- The server's connection to the Internet is down or overwhelmed.

- Available IP network connections between client and server are over-saturated.

- The server's DNS records are corrupt or unavailable.

Determining the exact cause of failure requires some troubleshooting. For more information on troubleshooting, see Chapter 10.

Another common reason that users get an error message is that the domain name they entered is incorrect. The best way to counter this potential problem is to register a domain name that is short, descriptive of your organization, and easy to remember. If the domain name isn't unique sounding, people can forget it and try similar names. Some organizations register multiple domain names that people might think of going to. George W. Bush, for his U. S. presidential campaign, registered domains like www.gwbush.com and www.bush .com. In addition to registering a primary domain name, some organizations will register common misspellings.

Download and View Time

One common reason a user doesn't use a Web site is that it is too slow. How slow is too slow? Researchers at Yale claim that 10 seconds is the threshold of frustration. Users may wait longer than that if the information cannot readily be found elsewhere or if they are particularly interested in a site, but then again, they might not. So depending on the patience level of the audience, pages should finish loading within 10 seconds of the time a user clicks a link.

In the following sections, you'll learn:

- The different stages of a request that can eat into those 10 seconds
- How to estimate the time it takes to download a page
- How available bandwidth limits download speeds
- Examples and rules of thumb for download times

These sections will enable you to estimate whether your page is going to be too slow.

Stages of a Request

The 10 seconds a user will wait gets split up into several steps, and each step uses up a portion of that time. The major steps are as follows:

1. DNS lookup and initial connection from client to Web server occurs.
2. Request sits in the Web server queue, waiting to be serviced.
3. Server generates response to the request (gets a file, runs a script).
4. Server transmits the data to the client.
5. Client renders/displays the data.

Combined, steps 1 and 5, which are the ones most clearly out of the control of the server, generally take a second or two. The time required for steps 2 and 3 depends on the server configuration, although they can often also be reduced to less than a second (you'll learn more about this in "Planning Robust Back-End Service" later in this chapter). The bulk of the time, therefore, is spent on step 4, transmitting the data from server to client.

Step 5 can sometimes take longer than one second. Slow computers may take several seconds to parse and render HTML documents. Even fast computers can get bogged down by complex HTML code, such as nested tables.

Determining Transmission Time

Step 4 generally takes the longest amount of time, so it has the most impact on the apparent speed of the Web site. If the Web page takes too long to load, the user will leave. Therefore, it is important to be able to estimate how long a Web page will take to download for different types of users.

Transmission time is a function of how large the page is, divided by the speed at which it is downloaded. The size of the page is measured in kilobytes for the HTML, graphics, and multimedia files. The standard way to express this is as follows:

Time of Download = (Size of Page ÷ Available Bandwidth)

If a site has a 100K page, the time it will take someone to download it with a 5KB/s connection can be estimated. Using 100K for the size of the page and 5KB/s for the available bandwidth, the formula shows that it would take 20 seconds to download:

X seconds = (100 kilobytes ÷ 5 kilobytes per second) = 20 seconds

Be careful not to confuse bytes and bits. People write about file sizes and download speeds using the terms kilobytes and kilobits. Bytes are generally 8 bits. Also, kilobytes and kilobits refer to 1,024 bytes and bits respectively, not 1,000. Unfortunately, some folks, especially advertisers, represent kilobits and kilobytes with inconsistent symbols. Kilobits are referred to as K, k, kb, and Kb. Kilobytes are referred to as K, k, kB, and KB. The symbols K and k are ambiguous! When looking at a number like 14K or 14k, a good rule of thumb is that modem-like devices are generally measured in terms of kilobits per second, and file sizes are almost always measured in kilobytes. Lacking any other clues, KB is likely to be kilobytes and kb (or Kb) kilobits. When writing, choose clear notation, such as KB and kb.

Bandwidth Bottlenecks

When data is downloaded, it flows in a pipeline from the server to the server's Internet connection to the general Internet, then from the client's network connection to the client. So the available bandwidth is the speed of the slowest segment of the pipeline. In 1999 in the United States, the slowest segment is generally the client's network connection. If a U.S. browser is visiting a server in Kenya, however, the slowest segment is likely going to be the slow connection between the Kenyan and U.S. national backbones.

Theoretical and Practical Download Speeds

The goal of Web designers should be to design pages that won't take too long to download. Network connections, however, rarely perform exactly as advertised. Therefore, you should consider the following:

- Know the theoretical speed of different devices.

- Take these speeds with a grain of salt.

It is easy to determine the theoretical speed of any device. A 56Kbps modem, for example, should be able to download about 7K per second. You can determine that with this formula:

(56Kbps ÷ 8 bits per byte) = 7KB/s

Table 9.1 lists the theoretical speeds of several types of network connections.

TABLE 9.1 Network Connection Speed

Network Connection	Theoretical Speed
Modem	Up to 56Kbps
BRI ISDN	64–128Kbps
Frame Relay	56Kbps–1.544Mbps
T1	1.544Mbps
E1	2.048Mbps
E2	8.448Mbps
Cable modem	(Varies widely)
Ethernet	10Mbps (variations go up to 100 or even 1000Mbps)
OC-3	155.52Mbps

Real-world factors like initial connection times, intervening devices, and line noise slow downloads to below their advertised limits. Even with a fast server and a good ISP, a 56Kbps modem, for example, will rarely achieve that speed. 56Kbps modems operate at 33.6Kbps over analog phone lines. If an ISP has digital lines, there is a chance that their users will be able to get 56Kbps download speed, but uploads will stay at 33.6Kbps. A 14.4Kbps modem will often download at 1.5KB/s, a 28.8Kbps modem at 3KB/s, a 56Kbps modem will optimistically download at 5KB/s, and an unloaded T1 dedicated line will download at 180KB/s.

DSL and cable modem users will notice large variances in their download speeds, anywhere from 384Kbps to 10Mbps. Even DSL services that are advertised at 384Kbps frequently get download speeds of 800Kbps (100KB/s) during unloaded times and 100Kbps or slower when the DSL network is saturated. For more information on benchmarking DSL and cable modems, see the links on `home1.gte.net/awiner/`.

Example: A Page Viewers Might Abandon

Freshmeat (`www.freshmeat.net`), a popular Unix software directory, weighs in at 78K, almost all HTML. As you can see in Figure 9.2, modem users have a smaller Internet pipeline than DSL users do. It will take a 28.8K modem user about 26 seconds to download a page this size, whereas a DSL modem running at the advertised 384Kbps would receive it in about 2 seconds. Downloading this page hovers on the threshold of frustration for 56Kbs modem users—fickle users might get bored with waiting for the page and jump over to see if `linuxapps.com` is loading any quicker (at a slightly slimmer 75K).

FIGURE 9.2 Download times for `freshmeat.net`

Example: A Page Viewers Would Not Abandon

Google (www.google.com) has a highly functional search page of only 12K. As you can see in Figure 9.3, even a 14.4 modem user can download the page in less than the 10 second threshold of frustration. It is unlikely that even the impatient users would abandon the Google page in less than 8 seconds to try another search engine like www.hotbot.com (a lean 30K).

FIGURE 9.3   Download times for google.com

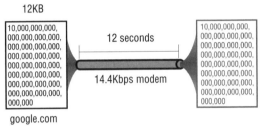

Download Times for google.com

 You can test out the probable download times of any page on the Internet with this free online tool: www2.imagiware.com.

Inability to Open or View Files

If people can't use the files on your site, they will often feel frustrated and give up. Files that cannot be opened are either corrupt or are somehow incompatible with certain software and hardware configurations. In this section, you will learn the following:

- How a browser successfully recognizes a file

- What stops a browser from opening a multimedia file

- What stops a browser from opening an HTML file

- How to identify and fix corrupt files

It is important for Web site owners to fix the broken files and mark incompatible ones with warnings as to who can and cannot use them.

Many times when someone says a file "won't open," it is because the file is simply not there. Broken links and missing files are quite common on the WWW. People move the files in their Web site around a lot, and the links to their old files are not automatically updated. See Chapter 10 on how to set up a system to counter this potential source of errors.

How a Browser Recognizes a File

Browsers sometimes fail to display a file or display it in a mangled fashion. To understand why they fail, like good doctors we need to first understand what happens with our patient when everything goes right and the browser *succeeds* in displaying a file. The technology that makes this happen is *MIME* file types.

MIME is an acronym that stands for Multipurpose Internet Mail Extension. It allows Web browsers and e-mail clients to recognize and view lots of different types of files. Servers that deliver pages tag these pages as being certain file types. Clients display these file types as best they can. Read www.whatis.com/ mime.htm for details.

In a foreign culture, even people who know the language need to be told when something is a joke. They often don't pick up the subtle clues they need to change the context of their understanding from "serious" to "joke." In a similar way, browsers need to be told explicitly what mode they should use to interpret each file. Browsers handle many different types of files. The first Web browser was designed to display only HTML. Later browsers learned to understand files from Gopher servers, FTP servers, and WWWAIS index servers. The next generation of browsers learned to display inline images like GIF and JPEG files. More recently, browsers can open Adobe Acrobat portable documents, Java applets, XML documents, and others.

When a browser downloads a file, the Web server tells the browser exactly what type of file it is. The server uses a configuration file (MIME.TYPES in

Apache and Netscape servers) to figure out what files should be marked as being which file types. As you can see in Figure 9.4, MIME.TYPES has two fields—the field on the left names a content-type. The field on the right contains all the file extensions that should trigger the Web server to mark a file as the corresponding content-type in the field on the left.

FIGURE 9.4   MIME.TYPES on the server

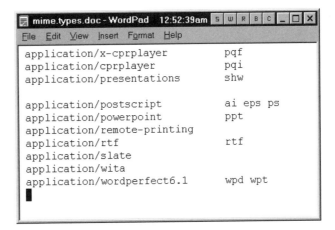

The browser uses the MIME information to decide what to do with a particular type of file. The browser could try to parse and display the file, save the file, or launch an external program to open the file. The client uses a flexible lookup table mapping "MIME-type" to "what to do." In Figure 9.4, you can see a list of different MIME types and what MIME types the browser knows belong to each extension. Figures 9.5 and 9.6 show the user configuring the exact mapping; the MIME type audio/x-pn-aiff is being mapped to run on a RealPlayer external program.

FIGURE 9.5 Configuring client MIME types

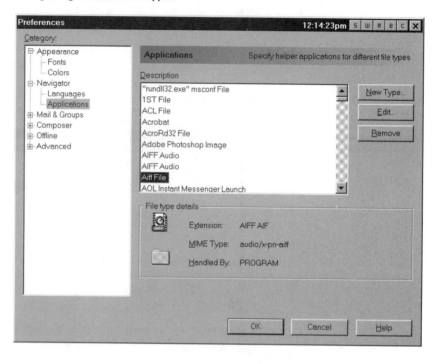

FIGURE 9.6 The Edit Type dialog box

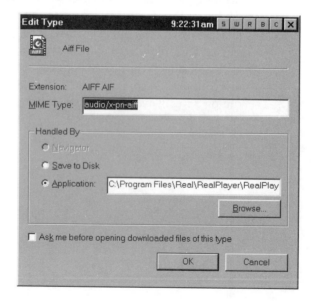

Web servers send a MIME header with each file, specifying what type of file it is. The Web site administrator maintains a lookup table on the Web server that matches file extension to *MIME-type*. If you are adding a new file type to your site, add it to this lookup table.

Missing MIME-Types and Plug-Ins

After a browser uses MIME-types to recognize a file, it may use either an external program or a "plug-in" to open nonstandard file types. *Plug-ins* are mini-programs that work within the browser and add extra functionality, such as Shockwave or VRML browsing. If the browser comes upon a MIME-type that it doesn't have in its lookup table, it may be unable to display the file. Likewise, if the MIME-type requires a plug-in, the browser may lack that plug-in and be unable to read the file.

If the browser doesn't have a plug-in or external program capable of opening the file, a file can appear unreadable to the user. The file isn't really unreadable, it is just not "openable" for that particular user. If the user had a stand-alone application or plug-in that can read the file, then the file would be readable. To assist the user, Microsoft and Netscape browsers check to see if there are any downloadable plug-ins available that can be used to view a new MIME-type.

Not all MIME-types have plug-ins for every platform. Some plug-ins only exist for Macintosh computers, others only for Windows. Therefore, users can be unable to open a special multimedia file because the plug-in needed to open that file simply does not exist for their platform.

Misconfigured MIME-Types

If the server sends the wrong MIME-type, the browser may try to use the wrong application to interpret the data. This will look to the user like a "'broken" file.

If a document is supposed to be a Microsoft Word document, but the browser tries to open it as a plain text file, MIME is probably the reason. Check that the server is sending DOC files with the MIME header application/msword and that the browser is set to use WINWORD.EXE to open files of type application/msword.

See Chapter 6 for more on configuring MIME on the client.

Malformed HTML

Browsers internally render documents with the MIME-type text/html, so users don't need any plug-ins for normal Web documents. However, even HTML can be "not viewable" when one of the following conditions exist:

- The HTML contains tags that the browser does not support.
- The page includes an incompatible Java or JavaScript program.
- There isn't enough room to properly display the HTML.

Nonstandard Tags

If the HTML uses nonstandard HTML tags, and the browser doesn't support those tags, the page can be unusable—the frame tags without the "no-frames" option is a good example of this problem. If the HTML is invalid (for example, if it is missing closing tags), the browser may not know how to render the page and just render nothing for the entire malformed item. In the case of a malformed <TABLE>...</TABLE>, the entire page could be blank.

Java and JavaScript

HTML pages now can also include client-side scripting using JavaScript and, for those who only use Microsoft Internet Explorer browsers, VBScript. They can also include small Java applications called applets. Both JavaScript and Java have different versions, and not all browsers support all versions. If a page that contains JavaScript works for the developers but fails to load properly for other users, check to see if the JavaScript is written so that it needs a recent browser.

Graphic Resolution

HTML is usually viewable on monitors of many different sizes. Paragraphs wrap to fit the available space. Some HTML tags (including <IMG> and <TABLE>) can specify absolute widths in terms of pixels. If a Web site uses a <TABLE SIZE=900 ALIGN=CENTER> tag, then a user with monitor resolution of 640x480 pixels will not be able to view most of the Web site. This can be even more destructive when the frame option is used and the ability to scroll horizontally is removed!

Computer screens generally display between 72 and 96 pixels per inch, and there are still many monitors that only display 640x480 pixels. Therefore, when scanning in pictures, keep in mind that a Web browser will convert a high-resolution image (say, 300 dots per inch) to 72 pixels per inch. This means a 3.5-inch photograph scanned in at 300 dots per inch can end up displaying at 1,050 pixels—larger than the screen of a large number of browsers.

The terms *dots per inch (dpi)* and *pixels per inch (ppi)* are often used interchangeably when discussing screen resolution. This is not technically correct, however. Dots per inch is a printer resolution, whereas pixels per inch is a screen resolution.

Not only is the image larger than the viewable area of the browser window, it also requires extra bandwidth to download the larger graphic file. Sticking to a screen resolution image (72 to 96ppi) will help keep files small enough to transmit quickly.

Corrupt Files

File corruption can also stop some files from being opened. *Corruption* means that a working file has been changed so that its application can no longer understand, or parse, the file. In the Web server environment, files are rarely corrupted. Generally, "corrupt" files are really files that aren't being opened with the right program or that have been misnamed or otherwise mangled by the user.

For example, suppose a user has a file called `BIGDIARY.DOC` and then puts this file in the compressed zip archive `ARCHIVES.ZIP`. To open `ARCHIVES.ZIP`, a user would need to have a program that could parse ZIP files. But if that user renames `ARCHIVES.ZIP` to `ARCHIVES.DOC`, Microsoft Word would claim that the file is corrupt.

The best way to fix file corruption is to try to open the original file on the original computer. If the file is not corrupted, replace the corrupted version with the uncorrupted version and try again. If you're transferring a file from one computer to another using FTP, set the FTP program to use ASCII when transferring text files (such as HTML, scripts, and files with the `.TXT` extension) and BINARY when transferring binary files (such as files with the extensions `.EXE` and `.DOC`).

Technology and Content Planning

The best way to ensure a well-functioning Web site is to plan ahead. By planning ahead, administrators can address potential problems before their customers are screaming for blood. Also, comprehensive planning leads to optimal trade-offs with factors like high functionality versus compatibility.

This section will address planning both the front end (what the users see) and the back end (what makes the site work behind the scenes). Specifically, it will consider the processes for the following:

- Planning which content types (media) to use

- Planning for what server and network resources may be needed

A well-thought-out and well-implemented plan for both the front and back end of a Web site will minimize the problems discussed in the previous sections.

Audience-Appropriate Media

A Web site's content is more than just the words in an HTML document. The content can also includes the graphics, video, and other multimedia files on your site. Some people will appreciate these glitzy multimedia effects; others will be unable or unwilling to view nonstandard or large multimedia files. Choices to either include or not include different content types will have consequences on who uses a Web site.

Keep the following in mind when choosing your content policies:

- Determine the attitude and key technical attributes of your audience.

- Given the goals of your Web site, choose a content policy tailored to your audience.

A site that follows these methods will serve its viewers in a strategic way and is therefore more likely to achieve its goals.

Audience Profiles

One simple yet beautiful strategy for building up or maintaining an audience is to use technologies that work for them. Before you can do that, though, you need to know who your audience is. In terms of what content types to use, you will especially want to consider their desires and technical capacity to use different media. This section breaks these attributes into two areas:

- Desire for multimedia content
- Client performance levels

This information should help you made informed decisions about the appropriate content and capabilities for your Web site.

Desire for Multimedia Content

It is difficult to know exactly what anyone wants without asking them directly. This section provides a rule of thumb for guessing when multimedia content would be desired. It also shows real-life examples of when such content is appropriate and presents a hypothetical example of when Shockwave multimedia would be a good idea.

The rule of thumb for multimedia content is this: does the functionality of the file directly serve the central purpose of the Web page and dramatically enhance the usability of the page? If the answer is yes, users will desire that content and may be willing to go through the effort to get to it. If the answer is no, the multimedia files will cause frustration if they delay users or ask them to modify their browsers in any way.

For example, when NASA first released pictures from Galileo at `galileo .jpl.nasa.gov/images/io/ioimages.html`, people went to the site and waited for a long time to download the pictures. Visitors to the NASA site went there especially to view the pictures, so their motivation to wait was high. But when users go to Yahoo!, they don't expect to be dazzled by a Flash graphic; they have come to find another Web site. Yahoo! keeps multimedia delays to a minimum and focuses on its functionality as a category browser. Although it's different, Yahoo! and NASA are each providing the content their viewers want.

For more on designing usable Web sites, visit dmoz.org/Computers/ Internet/WWW/Web_Usability/.

Think about who your audience is and why they come to your site. How much time are they willing to spend for multimedia content? Take, for example, Shockwave, which is a plug-in that allows users to play simple games and view animated pictures. Would your audience want to download a Shockwave plug-in in order to view your site? If you have a news site, nice pictures would be appealing, but a Shockwave game might not be compelling. But if your site provides Web-based tools for diagramming atoms, scientists would probably have enough motivation to download a plug-in. It really depends on how relevant the multimedia is to the purpose of the Web page.

Client Performance Levels

To make the best possible site, you'll need some information about the Internet abilities of your audience. Audiences have different abilities and technological needs. Their abilities and needs will depend upon factors such as network and Internet connection speed, browser type and version, and operating system.

NETWORK SPEED

The speed of a user's Internet connection affects her willingness to download big files. Users who get Internet connectivity by dialing in to an ISP with a modem have vastly slower Internet connections than those who have DSL, cable modems, or T1s. Those with especially slow network connections need text-oriented navigation and content because they may surf "images off" (meaning that they turn off the capability for their browser to display images, thus making the page load faster). Those who have fast Internet connections are more likely to want to download extras like software and music.

Web servers can record how long it takes viewers to download each file. You can use the formula outlined in "Download and View Time" earlier in this chapter to compute the average network speed of your viewers.

BROWSER VERSION

It is important to determine what browsers your visitors are using so you know what capabilities they have. Browsers come in more options than just Netscape Navigator and Microsoft Internet Explorer (IE). Each browser can implement different features, and different versions of a browser also have differing capabilities.

Although the latest browsers, like Netscape Navigator 4.7, implement cutting-edge features, using these features may break the Web site for other browsers. There are actually hundreds of different brands and versions of browsers, and they can all differ from each other in terms of their capabilities:

- The Lynx text-mode browser can't view Java applets.

- Only IE can use VBScript.

- Only recent versions of IE can display raw XML.

- Netscape Navigator 2 doesn't format text according to <STYLE> tags.

For a more complete listing of browser features, see www.browsercaps.com.

It's often easier to upgrade a browser than it is to get a faster network connection, but there are still a lot of older browsers in use. A Web server can log the browser version used by each visitor to your Web site.

Lynx is a text browser for the World Wide Web. It comes installed on most Linux machines and was widely used at universities in the early days of the WWW. It remains the browser of choice for tens of thousands of users. For more information, see lynx.browser.org/.

OPERATING SYSTEMS

People surf the Web on many flavors of Microsoft Windows, Macintosh computers, Linux and other Unix systems, BeOS boxes, Amigas, and more. Browsers often send along the name of their operating system to the Web server so it too can be logged and analyzed.

Browsers are highly cross platform, so the operating system is not usually an issue. However, if the Web site relies on special content types that need plug-ins, those plug-ins may not be available for all operating systems. Also, external plug-in programs may be limited to only a few operating systems.

EXAMPLE PERFORMANCE PROFILES

Suppose your audience consists of university computer science departments. How would you categorize their Internet capabilities and needs? Computer science labs typically have fast network connections, recent versions of Web browsers, and a mix of operating systems. If your audience consists of Windows gamers, you can't assume that they have more than a 28.8Kbps modem, but you could assume they are running Windows with a recent browser and can download a Windows-only plug-in if there was a good reason to do so.

Sites designed for these two different audiences might very well differ in the media use.

Content-Technology Policies

After gathering information about your audience, the next step is to draft a content type policy. The policy will guide the entire organization as to what content types to use on the Web site.

The goal of the content policy is to make sure the Web site can inform, entertain, and supply the target audience with the tools they want *without* putting up roadblocks. As you saw in the preceding section, different people will consider different content types a roadblock, so no policy will satisfy everyone.

An absence of policy can lead to confusion among the Web site developers and frustration among its audience, so it is worth considering the basic types of policies and how to implement one.

Types of Policies

Should the Web site use only content types that everyone is able to view? Should you use a technology if only 80 percent of your visitors have access to it? Here are four of the most common policies. These basic policies can be modified to reflect an organization's goals and culture.

CAPTIVE AUDIENCE

With a *captive audience policy*, the Web site creators create the content in the format they want to use and their audience must use only browsers that work with the content types they've chosen. Captive audience policies usually rely on the content creators having control of the browsers people have on their desktops. This is generally only the case in corporate intranets, and even then, only when there is strict control and standardization of computing resources. Where it is feasible, such a policy can lead to the full use of leading-edge money-saving technologies.

LOWEST COMMON DENOMINATOR

A *lowest common denominator policy* is the opposite of the captive audience policy—a Web site designer creates a site that is functional for almost any browser, even those with extremely low capabilities. The idea here is to create the content so it looks good on the text-only Lynx browser, and it'll work even better in everything else.

To demonstrate how a lowest common denominator policy works in practice, Figures 9.7 and 9.8 show the same Web page—a community site for Canadian activists—in both Lynx and Netscape Navigator. The site in Lynx, a text-mode browser, functions perfectly well, as you can see in Figure 9.7. Figure 9.8 shows the same content in Navigator, which offers all the Lynx features and more—including fonts, colors, and a background image.

FIGURE 9.7 The Web Networks Web site in a text-only browser

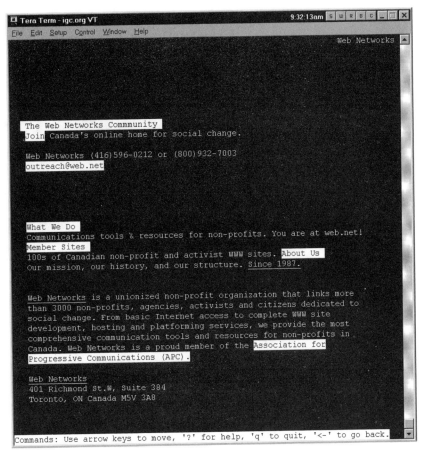

FIGURE 9.8 The Web Networks Web site in a graphical browser

There is a techno-political movement that supports the lowest common denominator approach: www.anybrowser.org/campaign/.

85% POLICY

The *85% policy* states that you should "use technologies that will reach many people, but don't let the stragglers drag functionality down for other viewers." A lot of sites don't care deeply about reaching everyone. For example, college students generally put up a home page for fun. Their home pages don't generate more fun for them if they were created so the tiny fraction of text-only browsers can view them. But a Shockwave party invitation might increase the fun considerably, so they will design the site so that the majority of the visitors will be able to visit it and take advantage of its features.

Businesses generally put up a Web site to sell something. A glitzy Web site may sell more than a plain one, even if the glitzy page is theoretically not accessible to those with slower modems.

ADAPTIVE CONTENT

Using an *adaptive content policy*, Web site developers don't necessarily have to choose between accessibility and glamour. Instead, sites can deliver advanced features to clients that can use them and deliver standard features to those who can't. This way, the whole audience is well served. Creating such a Web site, however, adds complexity and often cost.

There are two ways to create a Web site that provides high functionality to advanced clients and also gracefully provides reduced functionality:

Differential content   Servers identify which clients can use advanced features and send pages with those features only. For example, you could create a Web page that recognizes older browsers and redirects them to a portion of the site that doesn't use frames. Figure 9.9 shows a Web page in which users are asked which version of the Web site they want to visit.

Graceful degradation   Like subtle irony in the *Simpsons*, Web pages can sometimes include advanced features in a way that harmlessly passes over the heads of less-advanced browsers. This is called *graceful degradation—* if the browser can't use advanced features like frames or JavaScript, these extra features are just ignored. The benefit of the graceful degradation is that everyone can use the site as they would like to use it; in other words, "the user is always right." The cost is added complexity in maintaining multiple versions of documents or in documents that degrade well.

FIGURE 9.9   www.browsercaps.com asks what site version to use.

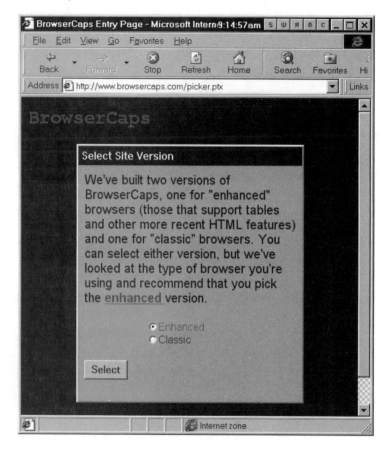

Implementing a Policy

Once you have put all that effort into researching your audience and choosing the type of policy to use, it would be a waste to ignore the policy. There are two main factors in the success of a policy:

- That it is specific
- That it is adopted and used

CONCRETE AND SPECIFIC

Content policies serve as a style guide for content creators and Web site designers. The policy should give these people specific guidelines to follow. Here are some examples of guidelines you might include:

- Limit main navigation pages to a maximum size of 80K.

- Mark links to pages that are larger than 150K.

- Do not use HTML that requires a browser more recent than Netscape 3.

Your guidelines may be more restrictive or less restrictive than these sample guidelines, but they should be as specific.

KNOWN AND ADOPTED

Many people contribute to the health of a site and play a role in creating its content. There needs to be agreement on what technologies to use. This policy might be handed down by the CEO, or it might be collaboratively developed. But it should be written down, and new employees should be trained in its use.

Planning Robust Back-End Service

Plan for the Web site back end so that it is robust and can meet the demands placed upon it by good fortune. If you don't, the consequences can be quite severe. There is an amusing television commercial that illustrates this. In a self-help group, a man says, "I just can't help get over my feeling of being stupid," and the group facilitator says, "Nobody is stupid, Bob." Bob then reports how he blew a multimillion dollar marketing campaign by not warning the server guys, and the site couldn't take the hits. The closing comment is "That is stupid Bob!" Don't be stupid like Bob ☺.

There are two ways in which the failure of the server operations brings down a site:

- Too many hits overload the server.

- A critical component dies or malfunctions.

The following sections cover strategies for minimizing these two possibilities.

Abundance Equals Performance

Web servers are often no heavier or bulkier than a simple word processor, yet they can almost magically serve up millions of documents to people all over the world. Just as mysteriously, they can bog down and serve documents slowly. The actual *performance* of a Web server depends on network speed, RAM, processor and hard-disk speed, software, and operating system. That said, there is a general theory that you can use to plan in advance how much of these resources your server(s) are going to need. In the following sections, we'll try to demystify Web server performance by providing an overview of these topics:

- Basic theory on Web server performance

- A strategy for high performance

- Finding performance blocks

The bottom line is that an overloaded server will seem slower, so it is important to always operate servers with spare capacity. Given that surges of interest can generate demand spikes, it is desirable to have plenty of spare capacity.

Even with extremely fast computers that have enough RAM, an individual request can only be fulfilled as quickly as the client can receive the response (see the section on proxy servers later in this chapter for caveats to this).

Performance Theory

Web servers are built to handle many simultaneous requests, much like a busy restaurant is designed to handle the constant flow of dining traffic. People wait in the lobby until there is a free table. Then a waiter leads them to a table and services their requests until they are done and leave. Web servers generally have 10 to 200 semi-independent processes or threads that can each fulfill one request at a time. Each process or thread is called a *child* of the Web server. Incoming requests cool their heels in a pool of unassigned requests (the lobby). When a Web server process (waiter) is unoccupied, it'll be assigned to handle a request in the pool.

The following sections use the words *threads* and *processes* because the multithreaded, multiprocess model is the most used in today's software. Apache, for example, is the most widely used Web server, and it uses threads and processes, depending on the underlying operating system. But not all Web servers rely on the multithreaded or multiprocess model. See the World Wide Web Consortium's list of servers at www.w3.org/Servers.html for more information on all different types of servers.

Mathematicians have described the properties of these pools of waiting people in *queue theory*. *Queue* is the British word for *line*. One thing that queue theory predicts is that the length of the queue is dependent on the relative size of the outgoing and incoming flows. Queue theory uses the term *utilization rate* to signify things like the number of new requests per second divided by the number of requests that can be fulfilled each second:

Utilization Rate = (Rate of New Requests ÷ Maximum Rate Fulfilled)

For example, a Web server that can finish 10 requests each second and gets 8 requests per second will have a utilization rate of .8. This Web server's queue will approach zero because there will usually be zero requests waiting in the queue. Even if there are occasionally more than 10 requests in a second, the server will quickly be able to recover and bring the queue down to zero again. If the Web server gets 11 requests a second, however, then in the long run, the queue will grow by at least 1 per second. In 10 minutes, the queue will have more than 600 waiting requests, and the queue time will be a minute. So if our example Web server goes from 8 requests to 11 requests a second, the performance degradation is massive, not incremental.

Keep Utilization Rate Low

When the utilization rate approaches 1.0, the queue will grow and the performance of the server will start to degrade. The key is to ensure that the utilization rate (even at peak times) is a lot less than 1. There are two ways to lower the utilization rate:

- Reduce the number of incoming requests.

- Increase the maximum rate of fulfilled requests.

Reducing the number of incoming requests is simple—immediately reject or discard requests after a threshold has been reached. This is often unacceptable and is used only as a safety measure to make sure overloaded Web sites don't lock up.

Therefore, it is often necessary to increase the rate of fulfilled requests. This rate is the number of children actively fulfilling requests divided by the average length of time it takes each request to be fulfilled. The equation looks like this:

Rate of Fulfilled Requests = Active Children ÷ Time per Request

Note that the equation is only accurate when both the number of active children and the time per request is fairly constant. So if a Web server generally has 20 busy children and the average request is fulfilled in 4 seconds, the Web server has a rate of about 5 requests per second. It may be possible to decrease the utilization rate by increasing the number of effective children.

Removing Blocks to High Performance

The preceding section indicated that increasing the number of effective children can increase the maximum capacity of the Web server and thereby increase the performance of the system. Increasing the number of effective child processes requires a balance of resources. The word *effective* is very important—simply increasing the number of children may actually reduce the number of effective children. If there are more waiters than tables, they'll just be stumbling into each other and fewer people will get served.

When planning your server environment, you need a balance of elements such as network bandwidth, RAM, disk I/O, and database connections. Any one of these can easily become a bottleneck. The most common limiting factor for Web servers is the lack of network bandwidth to serve people at peak times. See the sidebar "Choosing the Right Amount of Bandwidth for a Server" for more on this.

If there is plenty of bandwidth, it will certainly take experimentation to ascertain what is limiting the number of effective children. As an example of calculating the right balance, let's consider an Apache Web server, which is one of the most commonly used Web server softwares. After bandwidth, the lack of RAM is the most frequent limiting factor for Apache. Each child process will use some amount of memory (5MB of RAM, for example), and so a server with 500MB of RAM available for Web serving can only support 100 of these children. Even doubling the CPU cycles will not significantly increase the speed of a system that is RAM bound, and vice versa.

The use of a Swap file or virtual RAM is usually unacceptable for Web servers. The time it takes to swap memory to the hard disk increases the average length of time it takes each request to be fulfilled.

There are other possible constraints on the number of effective children. If the children execute computationally intensive scripts or programs, the CPU may be the bottleneck. If each process consumes some other limited resource, such as database connections or disk I/O, it can reduce the usefulness of more children.

Choosing the Right Amount of Bandwidth for a Server

The formula for determining current bandwidth needs is the maximum request rate divided by the average download speed of each request. If a Web server gets a maximum of 5 requests a second, with an average download speed of 3 K/s, then it only needs 15 K/s of bandwidth, such as a fast ISDN line. When a site is nearing its capacity, it is likely beginning to slow down, which causes users to give up, thereby reducing the bandwidth required. Adding bandwidth to a busy site reduces response time, so fewer people quit.

This means that, after increasing bandwidth, a site will often see its use jump up and needs to increase bandwidth again. The exact utilization rate at which performance is degraded depends on the network hardware and configuration. Request rates often increase in a linear fashion for a while and then sharply spike up when the site is listed in a popular magazine or search engine or when a community site has a critical mass of users.

The key is to be able to easily increase a site's capacity. How easy is it to get your ISP to add an extra T1 of bandwidth or to change ISPs? If it takes a week of lead time, it may be unacceptable to have bad performance for a week. In this case, the network planner should buy bandwidth in advance of possible marketing successes.

Redundancy Equals Reliability

Your back-end service is only as good as its weakest link. If your organization's name servers don't work, no one will be able to get to your site and it doesn't matter if your site has plenty of bandwidth.

Don't forget to ensure that network services like DNS and e-mail are also redundant. Crackers can disable or clog poorly configured servers. When DNS stops working, no one can find your site. When e-mail goes down, most organizations shut down. In addition to the security measures covered in Chapter 7, consider getting redundant mail and DNS servers so you'll be covered in case of crackers, earthquakes, or other emergencies.

It is necessary to plan what would happen if any resource suffered a breakdown and to make sure no crucial points can fail without a backup. There are two ways most organizations assure that they can recover from a malfunctioning component:

- Owning spares for the component
- Knowing someone will fix the broken component immediately

Whichever strategy or combination of strategies you use, be sure to consider the cost of the strategy against the potential cost of downtime.

Owning Spares

Servers can fail, T1s can fail, routers can fail, ISPs can fail, and Internet backbones can fail. Redundancy is the safest strategy to cope with the possibility of failure. People who adhere to the mantra of redundancy keep spare hardware for their servers, have spare servers, have multiple network connections, and even keep two generators in their basement. Buying two of everything can be expensive! For sites where downtime costs tens of thousands of dollars an hour, redundancy is a lot less expensive than downtime. Many sites compromise by standardizing on one type of processor, for example, and then keeping two spares for every 10 active computers. If they use a spare, they replace it immediately, so they always have a spare on hand.

Some companies have entire Web server spares. Several copies of the same Web site exist on different servers that are "hot" (active). These "spare" servers are queried, round-robin style, for Web requests. If one Web server goes down, the other server(s) take over for all requests without interruption. The hardest hit Web sites (e.g., Amazon.com, Yahoo!, etc.) use Web servers in this fashion.

Service Agreements

It can be burdensome to be ready to fix anything that could possibly go wrong. Organizations with money can buy their way out of this headache by arranging with other organizations to immediately fix any problems that might crop up. People can purchase an on-site service agreement for their servers and networking equipment.

Internet Connection Points and Your ISP

Even if your server is powered and has connectivity to your ISP, it could be isolated from the rest of the world if your ISP loses network connectivity.

The Internet is an interconnected set of networks. As discussed in Chapter 2, packets of information often have to cross several networks, or backbones, whenever a Web page is downloaded. These backbones are connected to each other at *Network Access Points* (*NAPs*). The largest backbones interconnect with the most other networks. Smaller regional networks often only connect with a few other networks, and so packets from them rely on hopping from network to network. If your network only has a single NAP, then all its customers are vulnerable to a fault in that NAP. So although it is good to pick an ISP that has a history of avoiding or quickly resolving problems, it is also wise to see how many NAPs they are connected to and how redundant their network connections are.

Caching

The concept of caching is increasingly being used throughout the Internet—by browsers, workgroups, ISPs, servers, and even in operating systems. *Caching* is the prudent storing of information that may be used shortly. Systems use caching to avoid asking for the same data over and over. Caching is used to speed applications and reduce expensive queries.

A dictionary definition of a cache is "a secure place of storage." In the Internet realm, a *cache* is the local and/or fast place to temporarily store information, especially information that is likely to be needed again shortly.

The effects and caveats of different types of caching are different in different technologies. The following sections start off with caching basics and then explore how caching is used in key zones of Internet technology:

- Caching basics
- Why cache?
- Caching in the browser
- Proxy servers and caching
- Reverse proxy servers

Caching interrupts the normal request-response loop described in Chapter 2. Either by accident or on purpose, this can sometimes lead to using less than the most up-to-date version of a document. After reading the following sections, you should be able to recognize both where caching is causing unexpected behavior and where it can lead to a performance gain.

Caching Basics

Caching is similar to how you look up people's phone numbers. If you want to call a friend, you'll look first in your personal phone list. It is faster to look it up there than to call 411. If you don't have your friend's information, you'll call 411 or dig out your big phone book and look up his information. After calling 411 once, you'll write down the phone number in your personal phone list so it'll be easier and faster to find it next time. Of course, this works best with information that isn't changing all the time. It won't help to have your own "private copy" of current events—by its very nature this information is usually useless when old. Likewise, if you have someone's work telephone number from 45 years ago, it isn't likely to do you much good.

In computer networking, caching takes into account many of the same considerations we use when looking up someone's phone number. Caching is generally used to save time, like a personal phone list is used to save us from hauling out dozens of huge metropolitan phone books. Also, there are rules about when to use the cache and when to go to the original source, just like we have internal guidelines about when we won't even try our outdated phone list. The biggest danger in caching is using outdated information. Many times caches will take a short query to the original document and say, "Have you changed?" If the document has changed, the whole document is retrieved. If the document has not changed, the cached copy is used. This is similar to trying someone's phone number and looking it up if the number is wrong.

Why Cache?

People use caching to save time and money. This section outlines how one organization could save big dividends by caching and demonstrates a simple mathematical formula for determining possible gains by caching.

Storing local copies of reusable information can be complicated, but it often pays big dividends. Consider an adventurous group of scientists stationed in Antarctica. These scientists share five computers and a single 64K ISDN line to the Internet. When it is his or her turn on the computer, each researcher checks a Web page with an Antarctica weather map—a 200K graphic taken straight from a Russian satellite. They use this information to decide whether it is safe for them to visit different parts of the frozen tundra that day. Without caching any information, viewing this weather map could consume a lot of bandwidth, for which the scientists pay for by the minute. If each computer is used by four scientists, the minimum amount of time it will take can be figured out as follows:

$$4 \text{ scientists} \div \text{computer} \times 5 \text{ computers} \times 200K \text{ image} = 4000K \div 5Kbps$$
$$\text{ISDN line} = 800 \text{ seconds} = 13 \text{ minutes}$$

The image only changes once a day, so if each computer cached the image for a day, then only the first scientist for each computer would download the image. As you can see in Figure 9.10, a cache can shorten a request. If the request is in the cache, it can be used directly instead of the original file. In this case, if the document exists in the cache, the browser can immediately read the file from its RAM or hard disk cache and not wait for a lengthy connection to the Internet. When the other three scientists check the page, they would see the stored copy. This alone would shorten the time from 13 minutes to 4. It could get even better—these computers could effectively share a single cache. If they did that, then the whole group would only have to download a single copy of the image, done in less than a minute, and all the scientists could use that file. Caching could reduce these scientists' connectivity charges by 92 percent—enough to buy them all earmuffs!

FIGURE 9.10   Caching shortens the loop.

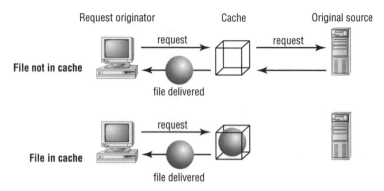

Caching Shortens the Loop

When a cache is queried, either it will find the document in the cache (called a cache "hit") or it will not (a cache miss). A false hit is when the cache returns a document that should not be used, such as an out-of-date document.

Web Caching

You saw in "Download and View Time" that downloading files is often frustrating to users with slow modems. Therefore, it should come as no surprise that most browsers are configured to do some caching, called *Web caching*, so they don't waste time unnecessarily redownloading large files.

If you go to a new page, your browser downloads the images. It also stores these images in both its memory and disk cache. The cache is a "first in, first out system"; that is, the documents in the cache that have been there the longest will be the first documents to be removed from the cache to make room for new documents. This way, the most recent items are generally cached, but the cache doesn't get bigger than the limits set in the browser. If a browser is spending a lot of time downloading images for a frequently visited Web site, check to make sure you have a big cache and that caching is turned on.

Objects in the memory cache are in the computer's RAM; objects in the disk cache are stored on the hard disk. A computer accesses its RAM much more quickly than its hard disk, although a hard disk is generally still faster than a T1 line. See lowendmac.com/tech/howfast.shtml for an interesting comparison between relative speeds of SCSI, Ethernet, and RAM.

For each request, the browser makes a decision about whether to use the cache. Because the cache might have outdated information, these rules favor not using the cache. They are applied in roughly this order:

1. If there is no cached document, get the original.

2. If the browser is set to never use a cached document, get the original.

3. If the server has flagged content as "not cacheable," get the original.

4. If the user hits the Reload button, get the original.

5. If the document was selected by using the Back button or browser history, use the cache.

6. Otherwise, compare the cached document's time to load against the original's and use the original if it is newer.

Shift+Reload also reloads all the images and other multimedia files on a page.

The browser can force the issue. Its update settings specify how often it should reload even valid cached documents. In Netscape 4.04, the Document in Cache Is Compared against Document on Network setting can be found under Edit ➤ Preferences ➤ Advanced ➤ Cache. Figure 9.11 shows how a user changes her caching preferences, in particular how big her cache is and how often the settings force her browser to reload cached images.

FIGURE 9.11 Editing caching preferences

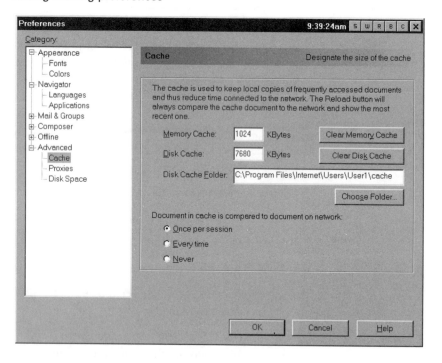

The browser can be configured as to what cached documents it will try to use. The Every Time setting eliminates caching. The Once Per Session setting is the standard setting—it will consider the documents that were cached since the browser was started. The Never setting means that the browser will always attempt to use the cache, even on pages that may have been visited a long time ago.

When to Clear the Cache

There are generally two cases when a user would want to empty the cache.

The first is if she wants see the most up-to-date version of many pages that are in her cache. She could click Reload on each page, but it may be faster to just clear the cache.

> The second reason to dump the cache is to conceal where the user has been. Even if the user exits Navigator, the disk cache is still there, containing information on which pages the user has visited.
>
> You can clear either the disk or the memory cache from Edit ➤ Preferences ➤ Advanced ➤ Cache. You can perform the same operation in Internet Explorer by going to Tools ➤ Internet Options and, on the General tab, using the controls under Temporary Internet Files.

Proxy Caching

Proxy servers are "middlemen" between Web browsers and Web servers. They are used to monitor and regulate a browser's use of the WWW and, less ominously, to act as a shared cache between the users of the proxy server. There are several different types of proxy servers:

- LAN-based proxy servers
- ISP-based proxy servers
- Regional proxy servers

Millions of users use proxy servers. Some do so to provide a shared cache in their workgroup, others as an invisible part of the ISP. In any case, proxy services should be configured to be as transparent to the user as possible.

Inktomi, `www.inktomi.com/`, is the market leader in advanced caching. On the lower end, Squid, `squid.nlanr.net/`, is a free and easy-to-use caching proxy server, available on Linux and funded by the National Science Foundation.

LAN-Based Proxy Servers

Remember those Antarctic scientists who could reduce their download time to less than a minute by effectively sharing a cache? They could do so by using a Web proxy server on their LAN. A *LAN-based proxy server* is a computer in a local area network that serves as a middleman between the other computers and the Internet. There is typically a very fast connection between computers on the LAN and a slower connection from the LAN to the rest of the Internet. Therefore, it's quicker to retrieve files cached on the LAN than it is to retrieve files on the Internet. As you can see in Figure 9.12, the scientists would enjoy a 10Mbps connection to their proxy server and only a shared 64Kbps connection to the rest of the Internet. Thus, the LAN proxy server would speed their downloads.

FIGURE 9.12 LAN proxy

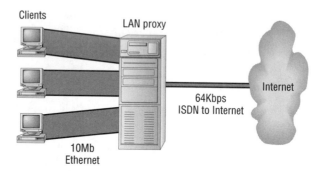

 When using a LAN proxy, set the disk cache on your browser to zero. This will save space and take advantage of proxies with a lot of RAM.

ISP Proxy Servers

Most people who use proxies do so through their ISP and never even know they are using a proxy. An ISP's dial-up customers all use the ISP's proxy server. As you can see in Figure 9.13, an ISP proxy server is similar to a LAN proxy sever except that it's not connected to the dial-up customers by a fast Internet connection. AOL, for example, has all of its dial-up customers automatically use the AOL Web proxy servers. This means that all AOL browsers connect to the AOL Web proxy servers, and the Web proxy servers connect to the rest of the Internet. The AOL servers cache a huge portion of the Internet!

FIGURE 9.13 An ISP proxy server

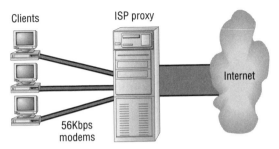

Whenever a proxy isn't located directly on the LAN, it has a mixed effect on speed. If the proxy servers are overloaded, this can increase the response time of the ISP's users. AOL proxies generally speed up the access of their dial-up customers, especially where there is poor connectivity between AOL and the target server.

If people rely on proxies for browsing, it is important that the proxies are reliable.

Regional Proxy Servers

Just as a collection of users can see performance gains by using a proxy server, a collection of proxy servers can use other servers as proxies. This way, groups of proxy servers can be nested in hierarchies. These groupings are especially useful where bandwidth is expensive or limited.

For example, as we saw with the Antarctica situation, the proxy server will be most helpful for speed if it is placed right on the LAN with the other workstations. But if all of Antarctica shared a single ISDN line to other continents, it might make sense to use a second-tier proxy server. Figure 9.14 shows a two-tier proxy system. Clients have very fast connections with the LAN proxy closest to them, but they also benefit from a regional proxy. If the first-tier (LAN) proxy server had a miss, it could analyze the request. If the request was destined for an Antarctica site, it would query that site directly, but if it was for an international server, it would forward the request to a continental proxy server.

FIGURE 9.14 A two-tier proxy system

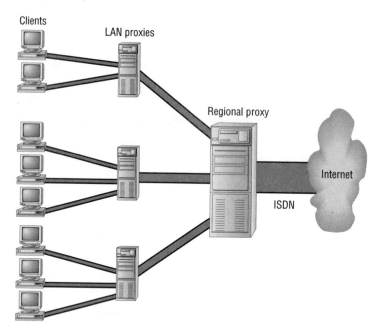

Problems with Proxy Servers

There are plenty of times that different people should not get the same file, even if they go to the same URL. If Sally views a page at my.yahoo.com, and Dave uses the same proxy as Sally and he also goes to my.yahoo.com, they don't want to get the same information. If the server at the other side isn't "aware" of proxies, it might mistake Dave for Sally.

 You can configure a proxy exclusion list for some browsers. If a proxy server is causing trouble with a particular site only, the user can add that site to the browser's proxy exclusion list. This means the browser will attempt to use the proxy for most connections but will connect directly to the sites on the proxy exclusion list.

A person's identity can be established in many ways. One way is to consider a stream of requests from a particular IP address within a certain time frame to be the same person. All requests to the Internet from a proxy server appear to come from the proxy server's IP address. If several people are using a proxy server to go to the same Web site, it is possible the Web server might mistake those people for one person. The obvious way around this is to not rely on using IP addresses as a reliable way of distinguishing between people. Proxies generally don't confuse cookies or hidden fields containing special tokens.

Caching at the Server: Reverse Proxies

Web servers use another type of caching to increase the number of clients they can serve. *Reverse proxy servers* are Web servers that act as middlemen between an organization's main Web server and the general public.

Reverse proxy servers are also known as Web server accelerators and sometimes as caching Web servers.

When Web proxies receive requests from the public, they first check their cache—if they have received the request before, they'll respond to the request directly. If they don't have a "hit" in their cache, they will query the main Web server, store the result in the cache, and then respond to the client. As you can see in Figure 9.15, there is a very fast network connection between the main server and the reverse proxy. This allows the main server to quickly respond to the proxy's requests.

FIGURE 9.15   A reverse proxy

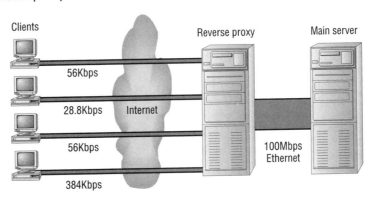

Although reverse proxies add a step to many requests, in specialized situations they can increase a server's maximum capacity and speed. In the following sections, we'll discuss when to use reverse proxies and how to calculate the benefits. After reading these sections, you will be able to recognize the potential benefit of adding a reverse proxy server between the teeming hordes and your main Web server.

When to Use Reverse Proxies

The main reason to use reverse proxies is to make economical use of server resources. It is seemingly strange that duplicating work is economical—two servers are now potentially receiving and responding to the same request, one after the other. It can be quite effective, however, because reverse proxy servers are typically much better at their specialized task: transmitting server responses while consuming as few resources as possible.

Proxy servers are most effective when used in conjunction with an application server. Most Web server processes are "heavy"—each one uses a lot of RAM by carrying around instructions on how to do all sorts of things. The Apache Web server can be built with mod_perl, for example, and then it has the full Perl interpreter built into each process. Like a tank, it uses a lot of fuel, but it's equipped to swiftly deal with any eventuality. Reverse proxies allow each type of process to specialize in what it does best—the heavy processes can run the complicated programs and the light "proxy" processes can transmit responses to browsers.

People use Apache more than any other Web server because they would rather install a little bit more RAM than use a less functional Web server. Web proxies can give you both efficient use of RAM and a highly configurable Web server.

Calculating Performance Increase

Let's apply our model of server performance to reverse proxies and see how effective they can be.

Our test server will have 600MB of RAM. The real amount of RAM each Apache process consumes varies between 1MB and 20MB, depending on configuration options and whether mod_perl is installed. For the sake of argument, let's consider a worst-case scenario and say each Apache process uses 20MB of RAM. With this limit in mind, the server can only have 30 children (600 ÷ 20 = 30). If each browser takes 10 seconds to download a request, the maximum response rate is 3 responses a second. During the 10 seconds of each response, the full power of the Perl-enabled process is typically only used for less than a second—it is effectively wasting its extra RAM by babysitting the data as it is transferred over to the client.

This is where the reverse proxy steps in. A reverse proxy server has lightweight processes, taking less than 1MB per process. If a server is configured to have 200 reverse proxy children and 20 Apache children, then the maximum response rate will go way up. The 20 Apache children can each handle a request a second. They then hand off the full request to the reverse proxy server, which slowly ekes it out over the network. The 200 reverse proxy children can also sustain a response rate of 20/s. So, for no additional server hardware, the server can suddenly handle six times as many clients.

Although the preceding example uses a single computer to host both the reverse proxy and the main server, in a high-bandwidth situation, the system architect would likely choose at least one machine to be the main server and the other to be the reverse proxy. It is also important to remember that bandwidth is more frequently a roadblock to a site's speed than lack of RAM is, and so reverse proxies are rarely needed.

Searching and Indexing

The ability to find what you're looking for should not be underestimated. Conversely, great content is useless if it is not found. If users can't find the information they want on your site, they will leave and take their business with them. Searching in the general sense is looking for information that is not readily at hand. There are a variety of search technologies that you can use to make your site easier to find and more functional:

- Basic searches

- Pre-indexed searches

- Advanced searches

- Linguistic searches

The following sections provide an overview of the different types of search features you can put on your Web site, as well as an overview of how this relates to your site being found by the large search engines.

Basic Searches

Once a user is at a site, he is probably looking for something in particular. For example, different people would use a book on nuclear fission in different ways:

- The novice would scan the chapter titles for an introduction.

- The expert would check the index for very specific terms.

Web sites are similar—people use a combination of site maps (like using a table of contents) and search pages (like looking up a term in the index) to find information on large sites.

Site Maps

A site index is like a table of contents—it gives an overview of what is available. Site maps and hierarchical indexes are useful when the amount of information available is small or when the user does not know the exact word she is looking for. Site maps help people learn about the scope of information that is available.

For example, Eric S. Raymond, one of the spokespeople for the open source movement, has scripts generate his site map from meta tags in his HTML pages (see `www.tuxedo.org/~esr/sitemap.html`). The site map has a one-sentence description of each of his pages. A user could quickly browse this site map and see what page was useful. The site `www.dmoz.org/` has an extremely high-quality, hierarchical, and browseable index.

Site maps have limited yet useful functionality. They require repeat visitors to click down through a hierarchy of information. If you know an identifying set of words, searching for pages that match those words can be a faster way to find the information you need.

Searching

On the Internet, a simple search query asks, "What documents do you have that contain this word." Then the server will return a clickable list of documents that have the searched-for word. Behind the scenes, the local search engine knows two things: the search terms and a set of documents to search. It will compare the contents of these documents against the search terms.

Very primitive search engines will compare this material by examining all the words in all the documents one-by-one for each search. This is a slow way to search. If a site has 1,000 documents (which is not unusual) and they each have 2,000 words, 2 million comparisons are performed for each search. If there is one new search every minute, the server will swiftly use up all its CPU cycles and RAM.

Search Syntax

Search syntax is the language that people use to describe what search to perform. For example, if a user searches for "apples pears", then the search engine will generally return a list of all the documents that have either the word *apples* or the word *pears* and put the documents that have both words at the top of the result list.

Different search engines use different search syntaxes, but the rules in Table 9.2 are the most common.

TABLE 9.2 Search Syntax Rules

Rule	Explanation
+word	word must exist
-word	word must not exist
word otherword	word or otherword should exist
word-otherword	word should exist, otherword must not
word AND otherword	+word +otherword

You can use parentheses to group conditions. Consider this search expression:

ice and ((man or woman) or (green and blue))

This will return pages with the words *ice man*, *ice woman*, and *ice green blue*, but it will not return pages with *ice green*.

Internet spiders don't just search documents on the local machine. They perform three phases of their search—they request files, index them, and then use the information in those files to find more files to request.

Reverse Index Searches

Searches can use the concept of caching for massive speed improvements. Most local Web site search engines index all their files once a night (usually around 2:00 A.M.) and save a list of all the words someone might want to search for and what documents are good finds for each word. Then for the rest of the day, the search engine can just look up each incoming query and compare it to this list of pregenerated results.

The indexing portion of search software stores the words and the documents that refer to those words in a file called a *reverse index*. On each line of the reverse index is a single word, and next to the word is a list of all the files that contain this word. You can often further optimize an index so that a number replaces the name of the file and is then used to look up the filename. So in this scenario, there are two files:

```
WORDS.DB
Bob: 2
Jane: 1
Summer: 1
Vacation: 1, 2
Winter: 2
```

```
FILENAMES.DB
1: JANE.LTR
2: BOB.LTR
```

If the search query is for "Bob", the search software doesn't need to search through both JANE.LTR and BOB.LTR. It can quickly scan through WORDS.DB for the word *Bob* and see that this word exists in file number 2. If the query is "Bob or Vacation", then the search would return both files as matching. Using a reverse index is much faster! Our example of 1,000 documents, each with 2,000 words, would probably have less than 16,000 unique words because people tend to reuse the same words over and over. Using a simple scanning algorithm, it takes less than 17 comparisons to find a word in a file that contains a sorted list of 16,000 unique words. Therefore, the combined search of `WORDS.DB` and `FILENAMES.DB` would require less than 30 comparisons for each word. So the indexed full-text search is more than 60,000 times faster than the 2 million comparisons required by the naïve full-text search.

Why Search Engines Find Bogus Information

Using an indexed search is a bit like having a cache—the index stands in for the real data. As with a cache, searches can find the wrong information (false hit) and can fail to find the right information (false miss). If the indexer ran on Monday and a file is deleted on Tuesday, then on Wednesday the search program will still report "hits" for the deleted file.

To compensate for this, you can reindex your data every time you change any files, which may be computationally expensive. It is also sometimes possible to do "real-time" verification on search hits and remove any false hits from the cache or mark these hits as "unavailable." Real-time verification does not work for false-negatives. The only way to eliminate false-negatives is to do an incremental update to the cache by adding the new files.

Advanced Searches

A full-text search is a great tool, but it can fail to be discerning enough to handle the enormous volume of information available on the Internet, or even on very large sites.

There are probably millions of pages on the Internet that have the word *bear* in them. Some of them use it as in "I shot the bear," some say, "You will bear the full cost of this," others in still other ways. Maybe a logger in Oregon signs all his Web pages "Bear of the North." A full-text search by itself will not be able to find the highest-quality Web pages focusing on bears. There are at least three main approaches to narrowing search results to a more manageable number:

- Use explicit meta information.

- Infer nonexplicit information.

- Consider the relationship of the search result page to other sites.

Explicit Meta Information

The first strategy is to use explicit *meta information*. Meta information is information about other information. The document's size is part of the meta information. HTML pages have <META> tags like <KEYWORDS> and <DESCRIPTION>. Indexes that only include words from these sections are more likely to return only pages that are really about bears and not pages that just use the word *bear* in an off-hand way.

Annotating pages with meta information is even more valuable when people searching use the same vocabulary as the people annotating the pages. This is a strategy library scientists have developed to a high degree.

Nonexplicit Information

The second strategy is to infer information about what is most relevant. The simplest way to do this is to just count the number of times each word is used in a document and return the documents that use the word the most number of times. This way, casual references to bears are excluded, but it doesn't require that all document authors remember to include <META> tags. Some people, of course, abuse this system by repeating words hundreds of times so their documents will show up first in search results. Many search engines are heavily optimized to avoid manipulation of this sort.

Popularity Contests

The third strategy uses the popularity of a Web page in deciding where the Web page should be placed in the search results. If the page is "popular" and matches the other search criteria, it will float to the top of the search results. In its simplest form, pages to which a lot of links lead are bumped up in search results—in a sense, other sites have voted for the usefulness of the popular site.

Google (www.google.com/) seems to be the search technology leader with weighted voting. In Google search results, votes are weighted in all sorts of ways. Google search results are determined by complex mathematical calculations, including the relative worth of each page and whether pages share similar keywords.

Linguistics

Many search engines use their understanding of the relationships between words and the meaning of words in searching and indexing. Common words like *a*, *or*, and *the* are eliminated; these are called stop words or "noise" words, and they are usually filtered from an index for efficiency because people rarely search on just those words. Words with the same base, like *run*, *ran*, and *running*, are consolidated into one word (this is called stemming). Words with multiple possible meanings are classified as having one meaning or another based on their neighboring words. When a query is run, a similar analysis is done on the search terms; documents with the same context are returned.

Some search engines have a "concept search." Words that frequently appear next to each other are considered part of the same concept. Each of these words is linked to a concept cluster (another reverse index of words and clusters). The concept search finds pages that have the concept to which the search word is linked. If the search term is in several concept clusters, an example of each cluster may be shown. If the user chooses a "more like this result" icon, the search engine will return other results that ranked highly in that cluster. It may also use other "Query by Example" criteria, such as being from the same Web site or being linked to by the same documents

Getting Noticed by Big Search Engines

Big search engine companies such as Excite, Google, and AltaVista all have massive servers indexing the Internet, and if you're lucky, they will index your site too. Because so many people use the big search engines, sites that show up on the first page in search results get a lot more hits. There are two things that you can do to try to get top billing by the large search engines like www.google.com and www.excite.com:

- Make sure the search engines know about your URL.

- Prepare your site so that it appears prominently in the result list.

To speed up this process of being noticed by the spiders, you can submit your URLs to the search engines. For example, if you go to www.excite.com/info/add_url, you can submit your URL and give some contact information as well as some meta information about the site. That will put the URL in their queue. There are a lot of search engines nowadays, and it could take a long time to fill out all their Web forms. One of the original tools to submit your link to many search engines was www.submitit.com/, which now is only partially free. To find similar, but free, services, see www.google.com/search?q=submitit+clone. Other commercial services offer the same thing but claim their human experts will personally analyze the link and help classify it in all the various schemes. See www.worldsubmit.com/meta-information for an example.

WARNING

Don't expect to be listed right away in the big search engines. They have a large queue, and therefore new pages might not be indexed for a while. Plan early by submitting the page before you are ready to launch new pages.

Even once your site has been indexed by the big search engines, few searches may wade through all the other search results to find your page. Search engines use the technologies mentioned in the previous sections to prioritize the relative values of their huge number of indexed pages. Different search engines use different combinations of explicit meta information, inferred meta information, and the popularity of a Web site.

You can prepare your site so it seems valuable by several different metrics. Some engines pay attention to how often your site is linked to, so you should ask other sites to link to yours. Other engines only pay attention to <META> tags, so make sure your Web site has descriptive <META> tags. See www.searchenginewatch.com/ for details on which search engines use which prioritization systems.

Summary

You can be sure that the exam will cover issues that affect functionality, the concepts of caching and proxy servers, and different types of searching, especially search syntax. In this chapter, you learned about many different topics. This section will help you to review the most important topics to know for the i-Net+ exam.

Here are some of the concepts you should know when developing a Web site:

- Be able to compute how long it takes to download a file.

- Understand how ISPs are directly connected to the Internet at Network Access Points.

- Have a rough understanding of the relative speeds of modems, ISDN lines, DSL, T1, OC-3, and so on.

- Understand how browsers use MIME and plug-ins to read many different file types.

- Be able to estimate and recognize when servers are getting overloaded with requests.

- Know how to do rough calculations on the capacity of a Web server and how to use these calculations in planning a Web server's resources.

Caching and proxy servers are important tools to maximize a Web site's functionality:

- Caching is useful for speeding up queries. If you want to speed up your download times, increase the size of your Web cache. If you want to always get the newest information, clear your cache, click Shift+Reload, or turn off Web caching.

- Proxy servers act as middlemen between your client and an Internet server. To your client, the proxy server is almost invisible. It normally just makes browsing faster and more secure. Thus, proxy servers tend to reduce the number of hits in Web servers' logs.

- Reverse proxies are specialized proxy servers built to speed up connections between intensive application servers and the general public.

In addition to these items, you learned about the different types of Internet searches and how they are used, including such topics as the following:

- Searching is looking up search terms in a prebuilt index.

- Different types of searches index different amounts of data.

- Full-text searches index all of the words in a file.

- Keyword searches typically only index meta information in the file.

- For the exam, you should also be able to construct both broad and specific search queries.

Review Questions

1. Users will happily wait how many seconds for a Web page to display?

   A. 10

   B. 20

   C. 40

   D. 80

2. What is usually the longest step of a server's response?

   A. The request waiting in the server's queue

   B. The server generating or looking up content for the response

   C. Transmitting the response from server to client

   D. Displaying or rendering the content

3. A user with a 28.8Kbps modem will take about how many about seconds to download a 100K file?

   A. 15

   B. 30

   C. 45

   D. 60

4. Which answer describes browser plug-ins to display special file formats?

   A. They are the mark of a hip site.

   B. They turn some users away.

   C. They are one application of MINE-encoding.

   D. A and C.

5. Some pages will display improperly unless the browser is at least a certain width. Which of the following assertions is most true?

    A. There should be a rule strictly forbidding pages to have minimums.

    B. The "standard" minimum is 800 pixels. This works with smaller resolution because GIFs are only 72dpi.

    C. There shouldn't be any rules about minimums because how the page displays depends on the expert designers.

    D. A minimum of 400 pixels works for any computer with a graphical browser and a 640x480 resolution.

6. Which answer describes a Web log analysis?

    A. It is useless to determine usage patterns because HTTP is stateless.

    B. It is useful to determine the profile of a site's actual audience.

    C. Station address information is less accurate because of proxies.

    D. B and C.

7. The test Web server is a Pentium-100 with 100MB of RAM running Apache on Linux. Each child of the Web server uses 5MB of RAM. The server has a dedicated T1 line and serves an unlimited number of clients that download its 100K static pages at 10K/s. What is the biggest limitation to the number of pages it serves a second?

    A. RAM

    B. CPU cycles

    C. Bandwidth

    D. DNS reliability

8. Which of the following statements is true?

    A. DNS is built into TCP/IP, so it is simply reliable.

    B. DNS is the responsibility of ISPs and the InterNIC.

    C. DNS is subject to failure, so it requires the same reliability audit as other servers and network services.

    D. DNS can be speeded up by having enough Web server children to handle the load.

9. Which term means the document requested exists in the cache?

    A. Win

    B. Hit

    C. Score

    D. Cast

10. Who would get the most value out of a Web proxy server on their LAN?

    A. Dull employees who visit the same pages every day

    B. Dutiful employees who browse the LAN intranet server

    C. Naughty employees who follow breaking news on remote discussion servers

    D. Remote staff who dial in to the LAN to get Internet connectivity

11. An ISP could cut their bandwidth costs by installing a Web proxy server for their dial-up customers if their customers _____ .

    A. Were scientists

    B. Visited dynamic Web pages that take a long time to generate

    C. Went to similar Web sites

    D. Favored Web sites in other countries

12. Reverse proxies are designed to do what?

A. Correct flaws in regular server software

B. Hide busy servers from slow international users

C. Conserve bandwidth

D. Use concepts of division of labor and specialization

13. Which of the following is true of caching?

A. Caching is designed to make the Internet more reliable.

B. Caching reduces the cost and latency of requests.

C. Caching is efficient because it was built with the HTTP protocol in mind.

D. Caching seems efficient, but not because of the popularity of dynamic Web sites.

14. Site indexes are _____ .

A. A holdover from Gopher

B. Based on library science

C. Only useful to experts who want to jump straight into content

D. A good overview on what is available

15. Full-text searches are most useful in which situations?

A. When the search query is strange and uncommon

B. When the number of documents to search is less than 20

C. When the content is in a database

D. When the number of documents to search grows to more than a million

16. What is *not* a search technology?

    A. Stemming

    B. Stopping

    C. Starting

    D. Query by example

17. What does the acronym MIME stands for?

    A. Multipurpose Internet Mail Extension

    B. Multiformat Internet Mail Extension

    C. Mandatory Internet Mail Exchange

    D. Multimedia Internal Memory Exchange

18. What search would find the most number of pages?

    A. Ice and cream or Sundays

    B. ice and cream and Sundays

    C. ice Sundays

    D. There isn't enough information to say.

19. What is true about HTML?

    A. It is a form of hypertext.

    B. Because it is a standard, there is no cross-browser standard for displaying HTML.

    C. HTML is generally rendered by a plug-in.

    D. HTML should be transferred via FTP in the BINARY mode.

20. A site with 10,000 documents has 5,000 terms in its index. If the site grows to 20,000 documents, which of the following statements is true?

   A. The number of terms will grow to 10,000 terms.

   B. A search that used to find 10 hits is now likely to find 20 documents.

   C. Searching will take twice as long as before.

   D. It will no longer be possible to use keywords because the total size of the index will surpass the allowed maximum size.

Answers to Review Questions

1. **A.** Although it depends on the user, research into "human factors" by universities and software companies indicates that 10 seconds is the threshold of frustration for waiting for pages to display.

2. **C.** Clients are usually on modems, which are relatively slower than most servers and the Internet.

3. **B.** To figure out how long it will take to download, use the following equation: (100 kilobytes × 8 bits/byte) ÷ (28.8kilobits/s) = 27.78, or around 30, seconds.

4. **B.** Users without needed plug-ins leave a site more often than they download a plug-in.

5. **D.** D is factually true. A and C are opinions and B is wrong (there is no one standard).

6. **D.** Logs are not 100 percent accurate, but they indicate what browser and operating system users are using. Proxies do frustrate attempts to log the exact IP address of every visitor because when a proxy is used, the address of the proxy server rather than the user's IP address is recorded.

7. **A.** The server is relatively under-powered in RAM. It can only sustain 20 children, which could only upload at their client's capacity of 10K/s, for a total bandwidth usage of 200K/s. This means that at 100-percent utilization of RAM, the bandwidth usage is only 20 percent.

8. **C.** DNS is reliable, to a point. But it does require auditing to ensure it's continued reliability.

9. **B.** If a cache has a usable stored result, it is called a hit. If it doesn't, it is a miss.

10. **A.** The graphics and static pages on these same pages will be quicker to download from the cache.

11. **C.** Proxy servers are most effective in reducing bandwidth when multiple people get the cached responses to identical requests.

12. D. Reverse proxies are designed to off-load the plodding and easy work from sophisticated Web servers to lightweight ones.

13. B. Caching is important for more than just the Internet.

14. D. Site indexes help people who don't know exactly which search words to use to search on a particular topic.

15. A. Naive full-text searches often return too many hits. Strange words eliminate false-positives.

16. C. A and B are techniques that use knowledge about what words are different versions of each other and what words are too common to be used in searching. Query by example is used to group documents by certain characteristics, such as concept clusters, host, or a series of Web sites that link to one another.

17. A. MIME was first an extension of regular Internet mail. The format of specifying content types proved popular and has been adopted by many applications, including Web browsers.

18. C. Ice Sundays is interpreted as Ice or Sundays. This is less restrictive than both A and B.

19. A. HTML allows linking between documents. B should be true, but there are multiple versions of HTML, and browsers sometimes permit nonstandard HTML.

20. B. If the new documents are similar to the old documents, it is quite possible that doubling the number of documents will result in double the number of hits for any particular query. Due to the efficiency of indexing, and the shared vocabulary of most documents, doubling the number of indexed documents will not double either the number of words or the length of a search.

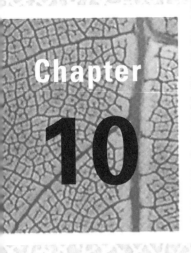

Chapter

10

Internet Troubleshooting

i-NET+ EXAM OBJECTIVES COVERED IN THIS CHAPTER:

✓ **Identify problems related to legacy clients (e.g., TCP/IP sockets and their implication on the operating system). Content could include the following:**

- Checking revision date, manufacturer/vendor
- Troubleshooting and performance issues
- Compatibility issues
- Version of the Web browser

✓ **Explain the function of patches and updates to client software and associated problems. Content could include the following:**

- Desktop security
- Virus protection
- Encryption levels
- Web browsers
- E-mail clients

✓ **Describe the process of pre-launch site/application functionality testing. Content could include the following:**

- Checking hot links
- Testing different browsers
- Testing to ensure it does not corrupt your e-commerce site
- Load testing
- Access to the site
- Testing with various speed connections

✓ **Describe when to use various diagnostic tools for identifying and resolving Internet problems. Content could include the following:**

- Ping
- winipcfg
- ipconfig
- ARP
- Trace Routing Utility
- Network Analyzer
- Netstat

Bugs and errors infest the World Wide Web—expect them to crop up on your Web site. Bugs stop people from using your Web site and can permanently damage your reputation. So, although some bugs are inevitable, it is important to reduce the number and effect of bugs that sneak into your site.

In the preceding chapter, you learned the importance of advance planning for the back and front ends of your Web site. Careful planning will reduce the number of bugs and errors that your users experience, but bug detection and fixing is an ongoing process.

In this chapter, you'll learn about important areas of troubleshooting and debugging:

- Fixing bugs before your audience sees them

- Resolving Internet problems

- Virus protection

- Software updates

- Legacy clients

A clear understanding of these topics will limit the number of bugs you inflict on your users and can lead to quicker resolution of errors that you do find.

Web Site Pre-Rollout Testing

Before you roll out a new Web site, or change an existing site, you should make sure it has as few bugs as possible. A new site is kept "private" until its launch date. When it is rolled out, everyone is allowed in to try it out. You should only make your site public once you have ironed out most of the bugs.

You probably have similar concerns for your existing sites—you don't want to make your big mistakes in public. Changes to a Web site can make the site unreadable or make Web applications return an error. Web sites are complicated and contain unexpected dependencies—so even changes to one page may break something on a different part of the site. Just as new sites are kept private until they are rolled out, changes to existing sites should be tested in a private area, and then the changes can be installed once they are verified as correct.

To "break" a Web site is to make it unusable. There are many ways to break a Web site, most of them unexpected. You might corrupt the graphic layout of a page, make a CGI script stop performing its duties, or even make the server freeze.

There are two things you need before you make your site public:

- A method for privately testing your changes
- A checklist of what problems to look for

With a method and checklist in place, you can tinker with your Web site and not be afraid that your changes will break the chairman of the board's favorite page.

Develop a Testing Methodology

If avoiding errors in your public Web site is important to you, you should use a standard *testing methodology*. A testing methodology is the set of procedures you perform each and every time you make a change. The goal is to check the validity of every page. With a written methodology, you will use the same procedure each time you check your site, reducing the possibility of missing a potential problem through carelessness, sloppy work, or ignorance.

Whether your Web site is small or large, a testing methodology decreases the likelihood that you'll seriously break it. By following a standard procedure, you're less likely to forget to check for whatever broke your site the last time you changed something. As time goes on, you can fine-tune the extent of your testing, depending on how often things break and how effective your testing is in finding errors.

In the following sections, we'll give you an example of a simple testing methodology and then discuss some components of a more advanced testing methodology—a location for testing and a storyboard to follow. Later, we'll review the different types of problems you may discover in a Web site. You can then proceed to develop a testing methodology that fits your needs.

Simple Error Checking

Different scale Web sites require different scale tests. Joe's home page probably doesn't need as much testing as Amazon.com's home page; the cost of an uncaught bug is significantly smaller for Joe than it is for Amazon.com. Joe could probably get away with a simple testing methodology like the following:

1. Download old page from public Web site.

2. Edit page on local computer.

3. View local page in browser.

4. Upload page to public Web site.

5. View public page in browser to make sure the changes show up.

These steps reduce the chance that Joe will break his home page and that the broken page will remain broken until someone e-mails Joe. For example, he'll know when he performs step 5 if his upload failed. Notice two key points about Joe's method:

- Joe used his hard drive as a private area for development.

- Joe double-checked his changes to make sure he didn't break anything.

More advanced checking builds on these two fundamental aspects of Joe's testing methodology.

Private Testing Area

One component of a good testing methodology is the use of a private testing area. Joe had this component in his methodology—he tried out changes on his hard drive. He could experiment freely without worrying that people would view his rough drafts. Although Joe might be perfectly happy using a hard drive as a development area, this won't work for all Web sites.

More complex Web sites require different types of private areas. If more than one person will be testing a Web page, it needs to be published on a private site. Once it is on a private site, the testers can collaborate on the page. Depending on your needs, there are a couple of areas where you can try out your changes:

- A private area on your main Web server
- An entirely separate test server

In the following sections, you'll see the differences between these two testing areas. You'll also learn about tools for moving your files from your testing area to the main server.

Main Web Servers

For most Web sites, the best option for a private testing area is in a private section of the main Web server. This is a common choice because it provides a more functional test environment than a stand-alone hard drive but doesn't require many additional resources. By reusing an existing server, you can also save the cost of an additional server.

You will certainly want to consider publishing your changes to a Web server if you have multiple people looking at a site or if you use pages that need to be tested on a server. By publishing to a private section of a server, you can test server functionality before releasing your site to the public. If the pages being edited use CGI scripts, for example, they can't be easily tested on a hard drive.

Staging Servers

If you find that the private version of your Web site is interfering with your main site, you may need a *staging server*. A staging server is a separate Web server on which you can put a private version of your public Web site. It has almost all the functionality of the public Web site, yet it won't interfere with the public site. Staging servers are useful because tests to it will accurately predict how changes will affect the public site, but tests that corrupt the staging server will not affect the main site.

Staging servers are particularly useful if you are experimenting with new versions of an operating system, new databases, or anything that might crash a whole server. If you ever find yourself wondering if your actions on your test site are going to crash the server, you may want to consider getting a staging server.

Quality assurance is a job function in which applications are checked to make sure they work as expected. People doing quality assurance report bugs.

Copying Files between Servers

Whatever the complexity of your testing needs, it should be fairly simple to move files between the private testing area and the main area. If it is too complicated, errors can be introduced in the transfer process. HTML editors, such as NetObjects Fusion or Microsoft FrontPage, have publish/export/save as settings that explicitly support uploading development code to multiple servers or to different areas on a single server. These HTML helpers make sure the file location tags are rewritten to accommodate multiple servers.

Figures 10.1 and 10.2 demonstrate the capabilities available in many HTML helpers. Figure 10.1 shows the Server Locations tab in the Publish Setup dialog box of NetObjects Fusion. In this dialog box, users can add, edit, or delete server locations. Notice that there are presently three server locations defined: Main Server, My Computer, and Remote Staging Server. Figure 10.2 shows the Publish Site dialog box. Here, the user can select which server to publish to, as well as whether to publish the entire site or only the changed assets. Once you set up the location of each server, it should be easy to try out and debug changes before your audience can find them.

FIGURE 10.1 Defining multiple servers

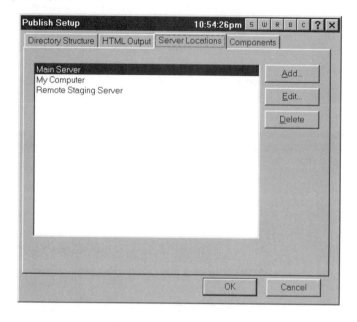

FIGURE 10.2 Publishing to a staging server

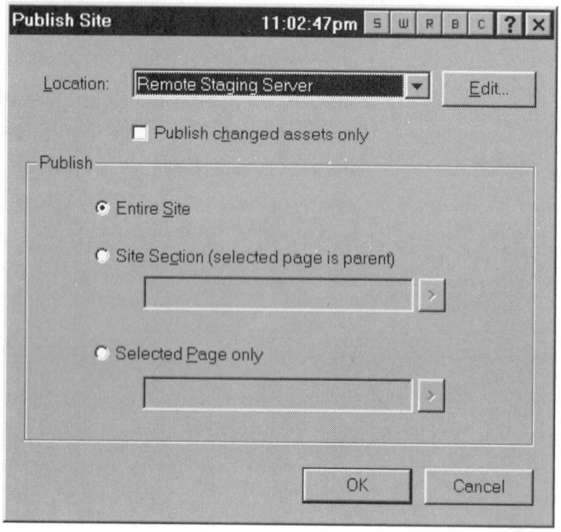

Avoid Corrupting E-Commerce Web Sites

Changes to e-commerce Web sites require special care. Bugs in e-commerce sites mean lost money, so it is especially important that these sites don't suffer from errors. E-commerce Web sites also typically rely on complex interactions between application servers, SQL databases like Microsoft SQL Server and Oracle, and legacy order-fulfillment systems. Whereas updating a normal Web site is much like releasing the new version of a book, updating an e-commerce Web site is like releasing a software upgrade. Changes in the user interface often accompany changes in the software that runs the site and talks to the database, credit card companies, and possibly an order-fulfillment system.

Private testing areas for e-commerce Web sites need to be carefully designed by the people who wrote the software for the e-commerce main site.

Use the Storyboard

Another crucial component to any testing methodology is checking to make sure the page does what it is supposed to do. When Joe double-checks the changes to his home page, he can just look at the single new page and see if the changes are correct. If you happen to have a more complex site, it is more difficult to determine if a set of pages works correctly. A common way to ensure that changes are correct is to check the new pages against a comprehensive description of how the pages should look and function. This description is often called a *storyboard*.

A storyboard is a document that describes how the pages should look and function. It lists screen-by-screen how the pages will look and how the user might interact with them. It will often separate the different elements that go into each screen: what text, graphics, animations, and application code should be on each page. Also, it charts out the relationships between the pages, especially what actions occur when users choose each option on each page.

People performing quality-assurance checks can follow each path on the storyboard (like a map) and make sure the text, graphics, and applications all behave as expected. They should make sure the new pages have all the functionality called for in the storyboard, as well as look for any bugs.

In this section, we looked at two key elements you need to have in place in order to properly test your Web site—a private location to test the pages and a storyboard to check the pages against. We haven't gone over what you should be testing—you need to decide what is important to you. The next section will serve as a pointer to some of the things you may want to put on your checklist.

What to Check

As quality control testers go through the site, they should look for everything that could appear to be a bug to the target audience. Basically, they ask the following questions:

- Do all pages exist?

- Do pages appear and function correctly?

- Do new pages cause applications to generate error messages or use the wrong logic?

- Do pages meet site policies, such as on content types and file size?

- Can the server handle the new files?

In the following sections, we'll cover each of these elements in more detail. Once all of these elements have been checked, you can safely roll out your site.

Link Checking (Checking Hot Links)

Link checking solves a common problem with Web sites: broken hot links. Broken hot links are links that return a "404—File not found" message when you follow them. The server says "File not found" because the links are to files that don't exist. Link checking is the process of ensuring that all of the files are in place. To check links, follow the site map or storyboard and click every link. If you find a broken link, report it. You should also look for paths that the storyboard or site map indicates should exist yet do not.

Nothing beats the human eye, but there are some automated tools that visit every link on the site for you and report broken links and malformed HTML. See tucows.tierranet.com/htmlval95.html for a list of Windows utilities that do this.

Storyboard and Appearance Checking

As you are checking your site, make sure it looks good and works well. Make sure the pages operate according to your plan. If each page has been detailed in a storyboard, you can check the storyboard against the actual operation of the page.

For example, the storyboard may include detailed instructions for a login page. If the storyboard calls for a login page to verify a user's password, then the page should really verify the password and take the user to either the "verified user page" or the "password incorrect page." If the login page verifies people who have not registered through to the "verified user page," then it is failing to work properly.

Verify both the appearance and functionality of the site on more than one browser. If you expect visitors who use Internet Explorer 3, Internet Explorer 4, Navigator 4, and Navigator 4.5, test the site functionality with all of these browsers. This is especially important if your site relies on client-side scripting or Java applets because they are sensitive to different browser versions. Also, as mentioned in Chapter 9, Web sites with nonstandard features like style sheets or frames might work according to the storyboard in Netscape 4 yet fail to work properly in Netscape 3.

Similarly, if the site aims at supporting clients on modems, you may want to try out the site on a modem. You can often discover which graphics or features are painfully slow when downloading at 56Kbps.

The standard screen resolution is 72 dots per inch (dpi). If pictures were scanned at 300dpi, they will appear four times as large on the screen. You can override the natural size of images by specifying the image size in your HTML document. If you manually set the image size, your browser will shrink or stretch the image to fit the required size. It is most efficient to just scan an image at 72dpi. Check out www.lib.berkeley.edu/Web/imagesizetips.html for information on image resolution.

CGI Errors and File Corruption

Moving files around can sometimes cause or expose problems with files and programs on the server. After you install your new files, you'll want to double-check that your CGI scripts and other Web applications work. You'll also want to download any updated or new binary files to make sure they haven't been corrupted.

When you test your CGI scripts, don't enter only "good" data. Enter all sorts of bogus data into the forms that run CGI scripts to see if the scripts return errors or do the wrong thing. You can be sure users will type garbage into these forms, so you might as well do it first and find out how your script will behave. Especially try the following:

- Enter nothing at all in required fields.

- Paste very long strings of text into fields meant for short answers.

- Type special characters like & ; * - $ < >.

See "Debug Server Problems" later in this chapter for some tips on debugging errors in CGI scripts.

Policy-Compliant Pages

Your site probably has a number of policies and guidelines. It's a good idea to review the pages with these policies in mind. Here are just a few of the possible types of policies you may have:

- Security policy for CGI scripts (see Chapter 8)

- Policy on size of pages or maximum download times (see Chapter 9)

- Policy on content types (see Chapter 9)

- Copyright policy (see Chapter 11)

Although it isn't good to straitjacket a site with rules, policies and guidelines can be valuable in building a knowledge base of successful practices. Your customer support engineers, for example, may have learned that your Web site gets half as many complaints when page size is kept below 50KB. This is valuable knowledge, but it will be wasted if it doesn't change the actions of the Web site designers. By crystallizing the understanding of this facet of customer behavior as a site policy, you can translate knowledge into action. It is often helpful, of course, to document the reason for the policy. Otherwise, the designers may feel unnecessarily constricted.

Server's Ability to Handle the New Files

If you are about to release either a totally new or upgraded Web site, it's possible that many more people will start coming to it. Before you install a new version of your site, determine if your servers can withstand an increase in demand. Are your pages large, or do you expect them to be wildly popular? You may want to use the suggestions in Chapter 9 about determining your bandwidth needs to see if you need to add server capacity.

Predict Server Response with Load-Testing Software

Load-testing software simulates the activity of thousands of users visiting your Web site. If you aren't sure how well your Web server will stand up to demand, you can run load-testing software to predict what will happen. See www.google.com/search?q=load+testing+website for a current list of commercial products that do load testing. Some load-testing products test a single component, like the ability of the Web server to deliver thousands of pages a minute or the ability of the database engine to run many inserts, deletes, and selects. The other type of load testing pretends to be thousands of virtual users, each taking a path through the Web site, trying out different options, and using different resources (see, for example, Portent software at www.loadtesting.com/). Both types of load testing can be useful.

Web sites that let people download software often face a dilemma here. Software vendors want to make their 2MB software package available online, but if 500 people each try to download the file, it could consume all available network resources. One way of handling this is to create a *mirror site*, which is another site that copies a portion of your site. For example, a software company may mirror documentation to sites all over the world. A user can then pick any of the mirror sites, reducing the load on any particular site. As you can see in Figure 10.3, software sites mirror their software around the world and then point people to the distributed download points. This helps them avoid bandwidth and latency problems.

FIGURE 10.3 MySQL download mirrors

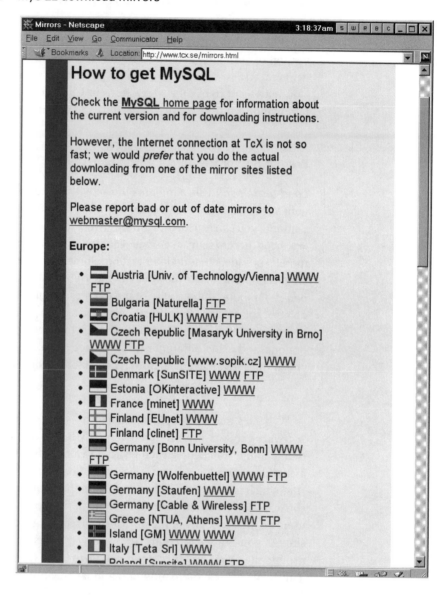

If you are unsure of whether you need to worry about the capacity of your server, keep an eye on your network and server utilization. If they are approaching 95 percent during peak usage, consider upgrading the server or adding mirrors for large static files.

Resolving Internet Problems

Despite your best efforts in checking your Web site before rolling it out, users will still find bugs in your system. Moreover, users will often mistake problems on their own computers or Internet connectivity problems for errors in your Web site. At a minimum, you'll have to be able to discern if a bug report indicates that your site is broken. Sometimes you may want to help users figure out where their problem is.

To resolve an Internet problem, you need to diagnose whether the problem is a misconfigured Web browser or one with your site. In this section, you'll learn some troubleshooting steps, including:

- How to identify the exact error that the client reports
- How to isolate the location of the error
- How to debug server problems
- How to use tools to debug connectivity problems

Users may not always describe problems they're having in terms you understand. And they may not understand the technical terms you use. For a humorous look at this problem, see the Jargon File (www.tuxedo.org/~esr/jargon/) for a funny user/sysadmin translation phrase book.

Troubleshooting Steps

When you're troubleshooting, it's helpful to follow a procedure so you don't forget important steps. You can follow CompTIA's Network+

troubleshooting model, for example, to debug your Internet problems. This model has eight steps:

1. Identify the exact issue.

2. Re-create the problem.

3. Isolate the cause.

4. Formulate a correction.

5. Implement the correction.

6. Test the solution.

7. Document the problem and the solution.

8. Give feedback.

To facilitate our discussion of the troubleshooting steps, let's assume that a user has called you, a Web site owner, to complain about not being able to connect to your Web site.

Step 1: Identify the Exact Issue

Obviously, if you can't identify a problem, you can't begin to solve it. Typically, you need to ask some questions to begin to clarify exactly what is happening; for example:

- Which parts of the Web site are you having trouble accessing?

- Is it just this particular Web site? Any Web site?

- Can you use your Web browser?

You may find out that the user has trouble accessing all of your Web site but can access any other site.

Be especially mindful of the simple stuff. It's a good idea to make sure cables are plugged in or the modem connection is up before going on to other steps.

Step 2: Re-Create the Problem

The next question to ask anyone who reports a Web site problem is "Can you show me what 'not working' looks like?" If you can reproduce the problem, you can identify the conditions under which it occurs. And if you can identify the conditions, you can start to determine the source. Unfortunately, not every problem can be reproduced. The hardest problems to solve are those that can't be reproduced but instead appear randomly and with no pattern.

Computers and networks are fickle; they can work fine for months, suddenly malfunction horribly, and then continue to work fine for several more months, never again exhibiting that particular problem. And that's why it's important to be able to reproduce the problem. If you can't reproduce the problem, you won't be able to tell if your attempted solution actually fixes it.

It is a definite advantage to be able to watch the user try to reproduce the problem. That way, you can determine whether the user is performing the operation correctly.

Step 3: Isolate the Cause

If you can reproduce the problem, your next step is to attempt to determine the cause. Drawing upon your knowledge of the Internet, Web servers, and Web clients, you might ask yourself and your user questions such as the following:

Were you ever able to do this?   If not, maybe he is trying to do something he simply cannot do.

If so, when did you become unable to do it?   If the computer was able to perform the operation and then suddenly could not, the conditions that surround this change become extremely important. You may be able to discover the cause of the problem if you know what happened immediately before the change. It is likely that the cause of the problem is related to the conditions surrounding the change.

Has anything changed since you were last able to do this?   This question can give you insight into a possible source for the problem. Most often, the thing that changed before the problem started is the source of the problem. When you ask this question of a user, the answer is typically that nothing has changed, so you might need to rephrase it. For example, did anyone add anything to your computer? Or, are you doing anything differently from the way you normally proceed?

Were any error messages displayed?   This is one of the best indicators of the cause of a problem. Error messages are designed by programmers to help them determine what aspect of a computer system is not functioning correctly.

Are other people experiencing this problem?   This is one question you must ask yourself. That way, you might be able to narrow the problem down to a specific item that may be causing the problem. Try to duplicate the problem yourself from your own workstation. If you can't duplicate the problem on another workstation, it may be related to only one user or group of users (or possibly their workstations). If more than one user is experiencing this problem, you may know this already because several people will be calling in with the same problem.

Is the problem always the same?   Generally speaking, when problems crop up, they are almost always the same problem each time they occur. But the symptoms may change ever so slightly as conditions surrounding them change. A related question is, If you do x, does the problem get better or worse? For example, you might ask a user, "If you use a different file, does the problem get better or worse?" If the symptoms become less severe, it might indicate that the problem is related to the original file being used.

These are just a few of the questions you can use to isolate the cause of the problem.

Step 4: Formulate a Correction

After you observe the problem and isolate the cause, your next step is to formulate a solution. Trust us, this gets easier with time and experience.

You must come up with at least one possible solution, even though it may not be correct. And you don't always have to come up with the solution yourself. Someone else in the group may have the answer. Also, don't forget to check online sources and vendor documentation.

You might have determined, for example, that a problem was caused by an improperly configured DNS lookup on a workstation. The correction would be to reconfigure DNS on the workstation.

Step 5: Implement the Correction

In this step, you implement your formulated correction. In our example, you would need to reconfigure DNS on the workstation.

Step 6: Test the Solution

Now that you have made the changes, you must test your solution to see if it solves the problem. In our example, you would ask the user to try to access the site again. In general terms, ask the user to repeat the operation that previously did not work. If it works, great! The problem is solved. If it doesn't, try the operation yourself.

If the problem isn't solved, you may have to go back to step 4, formulate a new correction, and redo steps 5 and 6. But it is important to make note of what worked and what didn't so that you don't make the same mistakes twice.

Step 7: Document the Problem and the Solution

It is often important to document the solution to a problem. If one person has a problem, other people are likely to have it. You definitely want to document problems and solutions so that you have the information at hand when a similar problem arises in the future. With documented solutions to documented problems, you can assemble your own database of information that you can use to troubleshoot other problems.

Step 8: Give Feedback

Of all the steps in the troubleshooting model, this is probably the most important. Give feedback to the people who need to know, especially the person experiencing the problem (so they know the problem is fixed). If a malfunctioning Web site was a cause of the problem, you should also notify the person responsible for the broken part of the site. Web site developers can use feedback to improve their own debugging process. They can learn what errors slipped through their debugging efforts and improve their pre-rollout testing methodology.

Troubleshooting Tips

These eight steps are a good overall methodology for troubleshooting. You can bolster this methodology with tips and advice from the following sections. Here's a guide for when to use the tips in the following sections during the model troubleshooting process.

Understanding Client Error Codes   The tips in this section will prove to be helpful for step 1.

Isolate the Cause of HTTP Errrors   Use these tips for steps 3 and 4.

Debug Server Problems   If you've narrowed a problem down to the server, this section will give you a tip that will help you determine the exact cause of a failed request.

Network Connectivity Utilities   This section documents when you would use different tools to test Internet connectivity. These tools can be used in both steps 3 and 6.

Understanding Client Error Codes

Step 1 of the troubleshooting methodology is to identify the exact problem. In the realm of HTTP clients and servers, you can do this by paying attention to the *error code*. If you get an error when trying to access a Web site, your browser will often report the error using a particular phrase.

See www.cnet.com/Resources/Tech/Advisers/Error/ for more information on error messages.

Let's review how error messages are generated. Web requests use the HTTP protocol. As described in Chapter 2, the client issues a request, and the server responds to the request. Along with the response, the server sends a *response code*. A response code is information about the response, generally saying whether or not the server could fulfill the request and listing any problems it had in doing so.

Error messages are only clues to the underlying problem. If trying again doesn't work, the next step will be to isolate and fix the problem. Error codes are a useful tool for fixing problems, but they only indicate the results of one person's requests. Thorough troubleshooting includes testing the extent of the problem. See "Isolate the Cause of HTTP Errrors" later in this chapter for more information on this topic.

When Web browsers give error messages, they are saying one of three things:

- I tried and failed to do something on the local computer.

- I couldn't get a clear response from the server.

- Here is the response code from the server, which I'm passing on to you.

The first two types of messages will generally show up as pop-up windows in the browser. You can see the pop-up error message "The server does not have a DNS entry" in Figure 10.4. Notice that the error message shows up in a small window floating above the main browser window.

The third type of error message will generally show up in the main browser window. You can see this type of error message in Figure 10.5. Figure 10.5 shows a "404—File not found" error message. The error code shows up in the title bar. A cryptic explanation appears in the main browser window.

FIGURE 10.4 A Netscape pop-up error message

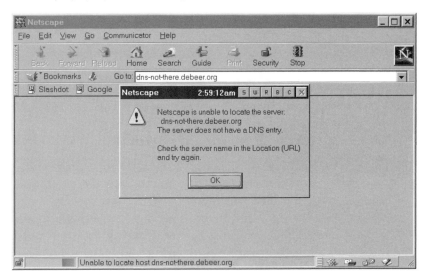

FIGURE 10.5 A Netscape online error message

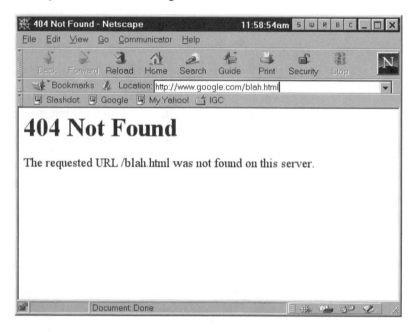

In the following sections, we'll examine in more detail these three different types of error messages and what they may indicate.

Browser Functionality Errors

Many error messages that the browser generates may have nothing to do with the Internet. If a browser recognizes that it is being asked to do something it can't do, it will report an error—for example, if it is being asked to launch a plug-in or helper that isn't installed or is installed improperly. In Figure 10.6, you can see the browser reporting its failure to open a PDF file. Unless the PDF file is corrupt, this indicates a misconfigured browser.

FIGURE 10.6 Navigator can't open Acrobat.

Similar internal error messages include "Helper application not found" and "Viewer not found." These messages will also alert the user to local problems such as her hard drive running out of disk space or her computer lacking abundant RAM to perform a task.

Connectivity Errors

All of the following messages indicate that the browser could not establish a good connection with the server:

No DNS entry   This error message indicates that the browser failed to find an IP address for the domain name. This could mean that some DNS server is either corrupt or inaccessible. If a DNS server is the problem, it could be either the DNS server that is authoritative for the domain or the client's DNS server. This error also occurs when the client has no connectivity to its own DNS server. See Chapter 2 for more on DNS.

Server not responding   The error occurs when the client can resolve an IP address for the host, but there doesn't seem to be any network connectivity between the server and the client.

Connection reset by peer   The server seems to have abruptly cancelled the connection. This could indicate a number of network connectivity problems.

Server returned an invalid or unrecognized response   The client received a response, but it didn't conform to the HTTP protocol and was probably garbled.

File contains no data   The response has an HTTP header, but no content. This probably indicates a server application error, such as a CGI script that is failing without giving a good warning message. Although it looks like a connection error, in fact it is more likely to be a server error.

WARNING   This is not a complete list of all error messages. Browsers may not use the same words for the same error. One browser might say, "No DNS entry." Another might say, "Error resolving host www.anyhost.com." They are the same basic error, but the error message will vary slightly.

Connectivity problems often go away if you try again in a minute or two. You can see Internet Explorer failing to find the DNS entry for www .google.com in Figure 10.7 and then finding the DNS entry and displaying the Web page seconds later in Figure 10.8.

FIGURE 10.7 Internet Explorer can't find the DNS entry.

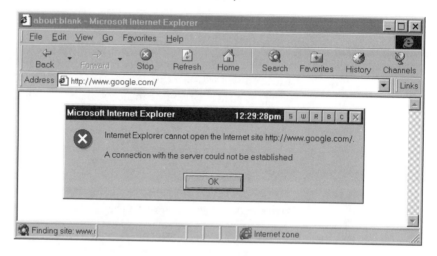

FIGURE 10.8 Internet Explorer can find the DNS entry.

If network problems persist, see "Isolate the Cause of HTTP Errrors" later in this chapter. Isolating the problem is step 3 in the Network+ trouble-shooting model.

HTTP Response Codes

Even if the browser successfully received a response to its query, the response may indicate a problem. The HTTP response codes are grouped into four sections:

- The 2*xx* codes represent success.
- The 3*xx* codes indicate that the file has been moved.
- The 4*xx* codes indicate an error, probably on the client.
- The 5*xx* codes indicate an error, probably on the server.

Here are common HTTP error codes (you can read more about all the response codes at www.w3.org/Protocols/HTTP/HTRESP.html):

400—Bad request   The request had bad syntax or it was inherently impossible to fulfill it.

401—Unauthorized   The server has not yet certified the client's request as authorized. Usually the client will immediately ask the user for a password and try again.

403—Forbidden   The request is for something forbidden. Authorization will not help.

404—Not found   The server has not found anything matching the URL given (see Figure 10.9). Usually this is because a file is missing or the user has typed in the wrong URL.

500—Internal error   The server ran into a problem. Typically, this indicates that the server tried to run a broken CGI script.

You can see the dreaded 404 error code in Figure 10.9. The client tried to look up a file, called imaginary-file.html, that didn't exist. The other common error code is 500—Internal error. Both 404 and 500 error messages can actually indicate either user error or Web site malfunction.

Some Web server software (e.g., Microsoft IIS) allows you to configure your own error messages to make a Web site more "friendly."

FIGURE 10.9 A Netscape "File not found" error

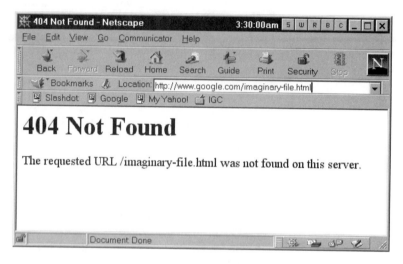

Isolate the Cause of HTTP Errors

The first part of step 3 (of the troubleshooting steps discussed earlier) is to determine where on the network an Internet problem occurs. The previous sections on network troubleshooting describe the sorts of questions to ask to determine where a problem might be happening.

Once you have asked these questions and done some preliminary testing, you should be able to say what conditions cause the bug. At this point, you should be able to determine who is experiencing the problem:

- Everyone looking at the site

- Groups of users, but not everyone

- The user experiencing problems with the Internet in general

- The user experiencing problems with just this site

- The user experiencing problems with just certain pages on this site
- Many users experiencing problems with certain pages on this site

Determining which category of symptoms applies is important for two reasons. First, it suggests a particular network component to debug. Second, it reveals the scope of the outage and thus the relative priority for fixing it. In the following sections, we'll give you some tips for formulating a correction depending on the sort of problems—it should be helpful as you consider step 4.

Keep accounts on several different networks. Then when you are trying to see if a site is really unreachable, you can try to connect to it from multiple places on the Internet. This allows you to get a better sense of where Internet connectivity problems are.

Server or Server's Network Is Down

If the problem occurs for everyone trying to look at a site, either the server is down or the target site's network connection is down. If you have access to the server, see if it is on and if it has network connectivity to the Internet (see "Network Connectivity Utilities" later in this chapter).

If a site is inaccessible to certain groups of users, it also generally indicates a connectivity problem. If the server is accessible within the firewall but not outside the firewall, check to see if network connectivity is broken between the firewall and the Internet. If a site is inaccessible only to people on certain Internet backbones, there is probably a connectivity problem between the site's Internet access provider and other backbones. In this case, the only thing you can do is report the connectivity problem to the site's Internet access provider and wait for them to fix the problem.

User Connectivity Problem

If it turns out the entire Internet is not accessible to a user, then the problem most likely lies with that user and not with any particular Web server. At this point, it is useful to determine who's responsible for the user's connectivity—usually it will be the user's ISP or his corporate IS department. Whoever helps the user will look at his network connectivity and network settings. Even though the user may be complaining to the administrator of a certain Web site, that Web site may not be relevant to the debugging effort.

Web Site Bugs

If the user gets an error message only when trying to use your site, or portions of your site, you should find out exactly what the error message is. It may indicate a bug with the pages of your site, or it may indicate that the user's browser is incompatible or misconfigured. Duplicate the user's actions and see if the page acts as it should. Refer to the storyboard if necessary.

If the page works for you but not for the reporting user, see if different browser versions or browser settings make a difference. If so, refer to your content type policy to see whether the pages need to be changed. If the page doesn't work for anyone, then there is surely a bug on the Web server, which you'll learn more about in the next section.

Debug Server Problems

If isolating a problem points to the Web server, the next step is to troubleshoot the Web server. To debug the server problem, repeat the troubleshooting steps 1 through 8, but this time, focus on the Web server.

As you troubleshoot the server problem, you should keep in mind two topics that are especially relevant to the cause of errors and the source of resolution, respectively, for many Web server problems:

File permissions   Misconfigured file permissions on the server are a common problem, so be sure to look for this information in troubleshooting step 3.

Log files   Web servers keep track of information about the requests they fulfill. You can use the log files to see what is happening with each request. This accurate information is especially helpful in troubleshooting steps 1, 3, and 6.

Bogus Bug Reports

A user might say, "The help page on how to use the calendar is gone." Perhaps this help page never existed, has never been promised, or has never been alluded to. A callous and foolish administrator might say, "There is no bug here, the user is mistaken." But the user is not just mistaken, she is just unknowingly telling you something else. For every user who files a bug report or complains, there are dozens, perhaps hundreds who just ignore their problem. So although the people who write in are unusually cranky, they are also like the sensitive canary that miners take into mines. When one of them croaks, it isn't time to ignore them; it is time to pay attention to what ails them. Maybe there *should* be a help page for the calendar!

Here's a quick review of how Web servers work so that the discussions about file permissions and log files will make more sense.

How Web Servers Fulfill Requests

A Web server responds to almost every request it receives. If it can't fulfill the request, it responds with an error message that has an error code. As it considers each request, it performs a series of tasks, which can be summarized as follows:

1. The server translates the URL to a local file on the Web server.

2. The server sees if the user is allowed to make this request.

3. The main action occurs when the server tries to gather the content needed for the request (such as reading a file or executing a script) and sends it back to the client.

4. Finally, the server logs the request as either successful or unsuccessful.

You will note that the server may fail in step 3 if the file is missing. Also, the Web server will log a request whether or not the request succeeds.

File and Directory Permissions

As you are trying to isolate the cause of Web server error, don't overlook *permission settings*. It is quite common for files to have the wrong permission settings and therefore be unreadable by the Web server.

In a multiuser operating system, file permissions allow people to keep their files private. The Web server isn't really a person, but to the computer it is just another user. If someone sets the permission on their files so the Web server can't read them, the Web server will be denied access to the files by the operating system.

In fulfilling requests, a Web server will try to gather content and send it to the client. Gathering content for HTML or graphics files consists of reading the file. Gathering content for scripts or applications consists of executing the programs and reading the output.

If the Web server tries to read a file that doesn't exist, it will fail and report a "404—File not found" error. Likewise, if the Web server tries to read a file that it does not have permission to read, or if it tries to execute a file it does not have permission to execute, the server will fail and report a "403—Forbidden" error. To fix this, simply change the permission on the file so the Web server user can access it.

Log Files

Web servers log the problems they run into so you can debug and fix the errors that caused the problems. A server stores a history of its activity, especially its success and failure at fulfilling Web requests, in *log files*. Log files can be an invaluable tool in debugging Web server problems. There are least two different log files on a Web server—the access log and the error log.

Access Log

The *access log* records each hit to the Web server. For each hit, it may record the IP address of the client, the name of the browser, the URL of the request, the date and time of the request, the status (200, 403, 404, or otherwise) of the request, and other information of that sort. The access log can be very useful in tracing the path of someone who is having trouble. You can see what requests the Web server thought were successful and which ones were not.

Error Log

The *error log* records errors, and its detailed messages can make it clear exactly what a problem is. For example, CGI scripts often fail to run for mysterious reasons. Because CGI scripts leave debugging information in the error log when they fail, you can look in the error log to figure out why your CGI script isn't working.

You can see a broken CGI script in Figure 10.10. The HTML error message is not very instructive. The error log for this failed request is more helpful—Figure 10.11 shows that when the server tried to execute broken-cgi.pl, it couldn't execute the script because of a syntax error on line 14.

FIGURE 10.10 A broken-cgi.pl Web output

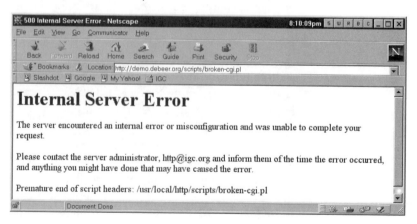

FIGURE 10.11 A broken-cgi.pl log output

See Tom Christiansen's "The Idiot's Guide to Solving Perl CGI Problems" at www.perl.com/CPAN-local/doc/FAQs/cgi/idiots-guide.html for common solutions to fixing broken CGI scripts.

Network Connectivity Utilities

As you hone your network debugging skills, your toolset should include utilities to test network connectivity. You learned that error messages like "Server not responding" indicate a connectivity problem. But to determine a problem's scope and location, you need to do further debugging.

There are many network utilities available, and each serves a particular purpose. In the following sections, you'll learn when to use various diagnostic tools for identifying and resolving Internet problems. Specifically, you'll learn about the following utilities:

- ARP
- Netstat
- Ping
- winipcfg
- ipconfig

- Trace Routing utility
- Network analyzer utilities

The i-Net+ exam only covers *when* to use these utilities, not *how* to use them. If you want to learn more about the exact syntax for these utilities, see the *Network+ Study Guide* (Sybex, 1999), which covers them in more detail.

The ARP Utility

The ARP protocol translates TCP/IP addresses to MAC (media access control) addresses that are used by local network devices such as Ethernet cards.

The ARP utility is primarily useful for resolving duplicate IP addresses. For example, a workstation receives its IP address from a DHCP (Dynamic Host Configuration Protocol) server, and it accidentally receives the same address as another workstation. When you try to ping it, you get no response. The reason you fail to get a response is that your workstation is trying to determine the MAC address of the destination computer, and it can't do so because two machines are reporting that they have the same IP address. To solve this problem, you can use the ARP utility to view your local ARP table and see which TCP/IP address is resolved to which MAC address.

netstat

Using netstat is a great way to see the TCP/IP connections (both inbound and outbound) on your machine. You can also use it to view packet statistics (similar to the MONITOR.NLM utility on a NetWare server console), such as how many packets have been sent and received, the number of errors, and so on.

When used without any options, netstat produces output similar to that in Figure 10.12, which shows all the outbound TCP/IP connections (in the case of Figure 10.12, a Web connection). The netstat utility, used without any options, is particularly useful in determining the status of outbound Web connections.

FIGURE 10.12   Output of the netstat command without any switches

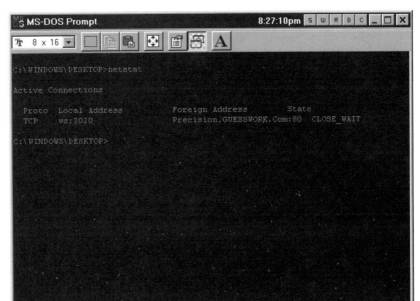

In Figure 10.12, the Proto column lists the protocol being used. Because this is a Web connection, the protocol is TCP. The Local Address column lists the source address and the source port. In this case, the source address is ws and the source port is 3020. The foreign address is the Web site Precision .GUESSWORK.Com, at the default HTTP port of 80. The state is shown to be closed—the network connection is currently finished.

The Ping Utility

Ping is the most basic TCP/IP utility and is included with most TCP/IP stacks for most platforms. Windows 95/98 and NT are no exception. In most cases, Ping is a command-line utility (although there have been some GUI implementations). You use the Ping utility for two primary purposes:

- To find out if you can reach a host
- To find out if a host is responding

You can use both Ping and tracert to see if you can reach a host. You generally will use Ping if you just want to see if the host is responding to you. If you also want to see how your packets are routed over the Internet to the host, use tracert.

The winipcfg and ipconfig Utilities

Of all the TCP/IP utilities that come with Windows 95/98 or NT, the IP configuration utilities are probably the most overlooked. These utilities display the current configuration of TCP/IP on a workstation, including the current IP address, DNS configuration, WINS configuration, and default gateway. winipcfg is the Windows 95/98 version of this utility, and ipconfig is the Windows NT version and is command-line driven.

The winipcfg utility comes in handy when you're resolving TCP/IP address conflicts and configuring a workstation. For example, if a workstation is experiencing Duplicate IP Address errors, you can run winipcfg to determine its IP address. Also, if the address was obtained from a DHCP server, you can release it and obtain a new IP address by clicking the Renew All button. You can see in Figure 10.13 that it is easy to view your basic TCP/IP information simply by running winipcfg.

FIGURE 10.13   The winipcfg utility's IP configuration dialog box

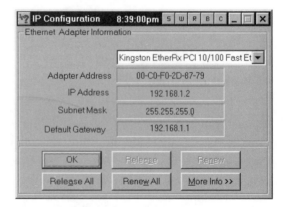

The Trace Routing (tracert) Utility

Have you ever wondered where the packets go when you send them over the Internet? The TCP/IP Trace Routing (tracert) command-line utility will show you every router interface a TCP/IP packet passes through on its way to a destination.

To use tracert, at a Windows 95/98 or NT command prompt, type **tracert,** a space, and the DNS name or IP address of the host for which you want to find the route. The tracert utility responds with a list of all the DNS names and IP addresses of the routers the packet is passing through on its way. Additionally, tracert indicates the time it takes for each attempt. Figure 10.14 shows sample tracert output from a workstation connected through an ISP (PacBell Internet, CA, in this case) to the search engine Yahoo!

FIGURE 10.14   Sample tracert output

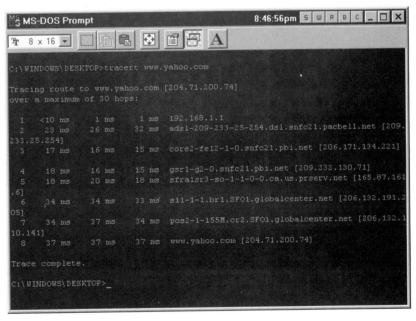

As you can see, the packet bounces through several routers before arriving at its destination. This utility is useful if you are having problems reaching a Web server on the Internet and you want to know if a WAN link is down or if the server just isn't responding.

You can use tracert to ascertain how many hops a particular host is from your workstation. This is useful in determining how fast a link should be. Usually, if a host is only a couple of hops away, access should be relatively quick.

Network Analyzer Utilities

Network analyzers, like Network Associates's NetXRay, are tools that monitor and analyze network traffic. More specifically, they listen in on all the traffic on a certain network segment and provide sophisticated reporting tools that display the traffic in both an overall and a packet-by-packet level. Network analyzers are useful for seeing what is happening at the protocol level.

If all your computer networks are switched, a network monitor can't listen in on the network conversations of other computers. Switched networks route traffic only to their recipients. If you need to analyze what is going on with a certain computer, you could add a small hub to the network, with the hub uplinking to the switch and both the target computer and the computer running the network analyzer plugged into the hub.

You can see in Figure 10.15 that an administrator can get a picture of how busy the network is—in this case, the 100Mbps Ethernet card is at less than one percent capacity. You can use network analyzers to see what computers are taking up lots of network traffic and what protocols they are using to do so. By filtering the traffic by address and protocol, you can pinpoint network trouble spots.

FIGURE 10.15 Checking network utilization

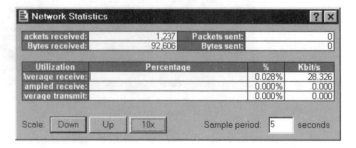

Network analyzers allow you to filter and capture packets. This is great for debugging failed network connections—you can set up a filter to look at a conversation between two computers and then examine the exact content of this conversation. You can see two conversations being captured in Figure 10.16. The first two connections show the first conversation. The workstation (192.168.1.2) and chat.excite.com (198.3.98.70) are sending small packets to each other. This is probably the Excite's PAL client checking with the server to see if any of the workstation's buddies are online. The rest of the connections signify the activity of checking Usenet newsgroups—although you can't see all of it in the figure, the workstation is resolving the IP address for news.pacbell.net and then initiating an NNTP connection to news.pacbell.net.

FIGURE 10.16 Capturing two conversations

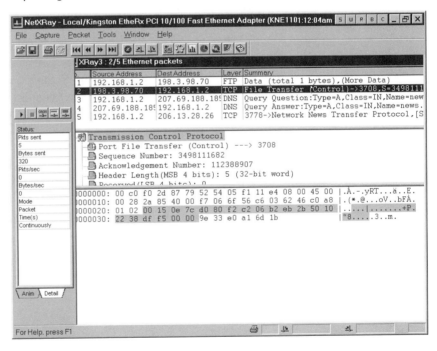

Virus Protection

One of the most frustrating things to debug is a virus that is causing havoc with your systems. A *virus* is a program that causes malicious change in your computer and makes copies of itself. Sophisticated viruses encrypt and hide themselves to thwart detection. These stealthy viruses can be tricky to detect, and unfortunately, the Internet makes it easy to transmit them from one network to another.

There are tens of thousands of viruses that your computer can catch. Known viruses are referred to as being "in the wild." Research laboratories and universities study viruses for commercial and academic purposes. These viruses are known as being "in the zoo," or not out in the wild. Every month the number of viruses in the wild increases.

Viruses can be little more than hindrances, or they can shut down an entire corporation. The types vary, but the approach to handling them does not. You need to install virus protection software on all computer equipment. This is similar to vaccinating your entire family, not just the children who are going to summer camp. Workstations, personal computers, servers, and firewalls all must have virus protection, even if they never connect to your network. They can still get viruses from floppy disks or Internet downloads.

Types of Viruses

Several types of viruses exist, but the two most popular are *macro* and *boot sector*. Each type differs slightly in the way it works and how it infects your system. Many viruses attack popular applications, such as Microsoft Word, Excel, and PowerPoint, which are easy to use and for which it is easy to create a virus. Because writing a unique virus is considered a challenge to a bored programmer, viruses are becoming more and more complex and harder to eradicate.

Macro Viruses

A macro is a script of commonly enacted commands that are used to automatically perform operations without a user's intervention. Macro viruses use the Visual Basic macro scripting language to perform malicious or mischievous functions in Microsoft Office products. Macro viruses are among the most harmless (but also the most annoying). Because macros are easy to write, macro viruses are among the most common viruses and are frequently found in Microsoft Word and PowerPoint. They affect the file you are working on. For example, you might be unable to save the file even though the Save function is working, or you might be unable to open a new document—you can only open a template. These viruses will not crash your system, but they are annoying. Cap and Cap A are examples of macro viruses.

Boot Sector Viruses

Boot sector viruses get into the master boot record. This is track one, sector one on your hard disk. No applications are supposed to reside there. At boot up, the computer checks this section to find a pointer for the operating system. If you have a multi–operating system boot between Windows 95/98, Windows NT, and Unix, this is where the pointers are stored. A boot sector virus will overwrite the boot sector, thereby making it look as if there is no pointer to your operating system. When you power up the computer, you will see a "Missing operating system" or "Hard disk not found" error message. Monkey B, Stealth, and Stealth Boot are examples of boot sector viruses.

These are only a few of the types of viruses out there. For a more complete list, see your antivirus software manufacturer's Web site, or go to Symantec's Web site at www.symantec.com/.

Updating Antivirus Components

A typical antivirus program consists of two components:

- The definition files
- The engine

The definition files list the various viruses, their type, and footprints, and they specify how to remove specific viruses. More than 100 new viruses are found in the wild each month. An antivirus program would be useless if it did not keep up with all the new viruses. The engine accesses the definition files (or database), runs the virus scans, cleans the files, and notifies the appropriate people and accounts. Eventually, viruses become so sophisticated that a new engine and new technology are needed to combat them effectively.

Heuristic scanning is a technology that allows an antivirus program to search for a virus even if there is no definition for that specific virus. The engine looks for suspicious activity that might indicate a virus. Be careful if you have this feature turned on. A heuristic scan might detect more than viruses, like a software installation (that you actually want to happen).

For an antivirus program to be effective, you must upgrade, update, and scan in a specific order:

1. Upgrade the antivirus engine.

2. Update the definition files.

3. Create an antivirus emergency boot disk.

4. Configure and run a full on-demand scan.

5. Schedule monthly full on-demand scans.

6. Configure and activate on-access scans.

7. Update the definition files monthly.

8. Make a new antivirus emergency boot disk monthly.

9. Get the latest update when fighting a virus outbreak.

10. Repeat all steps when you get a new engine.

If you think this is a lot of work, you are right. However, not doing it can mean a lot more work and a lot more trouble.

Upgrading an Antivirus Engine

A *virus engine* is the core program that runs the scanning process; virus definitions are keyed to an engine version number. For example, a 3.*x* engine will not work with 4.*x* definition files. When the manufacturer releases a new engine, consider both the cost to upgrade and the added benefits.

Before installing new or upgraded software, back up your entire computer system, including all data.

Updating Definition files

Every month, you need to update your list of known viruses—called the *virus definition files*. You can do this manually or automatically through the manufacturer's Web site. As you can see in Figure 10.17, the antivirus software goes out to a central server and grabs any new antivirus information. In this way, the antivirus folks don't get too far behind the virus writers. Antivirus updates don't seem to cause many problems, so use them!

FIGURE 10.17   AntiVirus gets LiveUpdate.

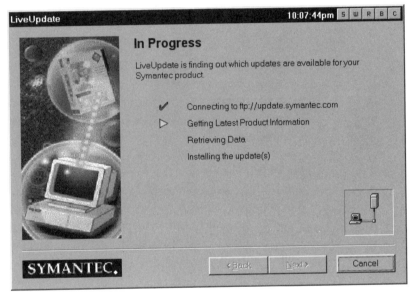

Scanning for Viruses

An antivirus scan is the process in which an antivirus program examines the computer suspected of having a virus and eradicates any viruses it finds. There are two types of antivirus scans:

- On-demand
- On-access

An *on-demand scan* searches a file, a directory, a drive, or an entire computer. An *on-access scan* checks only the files you are currently accessing. To maximize protection, you should use a combination of both types.

On-Demand Scans

An on-demand scan is a virus scan initiated by either a network administrator or a user. They can manually or automatically initiate an on-demand scan. Typically, you schedule a monthly on-demand scan, but you should also do an on-demand scan in the following situations:

- After you first install the antivirus software

- When you upgrade the antivirus software engine

- When you suspect a virus outbreak

Before you initiate an on-demand scan, be sure that you have the latest virus definitions.

When you encounter a virus, scan all potentially affected hard disks and any floppy disks that could be suspicious. Establish a cleaning station, and quarantine the infected area. The support staff will have a difficult time if a user continues to use the computer while it is infected. Ask all users in the infected area to stop using their computers. Suggest a short break. If it is lunchtime, all the better. Have one person remove all floppies from all disk drives. Perform a scan and clean at the cleaning station. For computers that are operational, update their virus definitions. For computers that are not operational or are operational but infected, boot to an antivirus emergency boot disk. Run a full scan and clean the entire system on all computers in the office space. With luck, you will be done before your users return from lunch.

On-Access Scans

An on-access scan runs in the background when you open a file or use a program. For example, an on-access scan can run when you do any of the following:

- Insert a floppy disk

- Use FTP to download a file

- Receive e-mail messages and attachments

- View a Web page

The scan slows the processing speed of other programs, but it is worth the inconvenience.

A relatively new form of malicious attack makes its way to your computer through ActiveX and Java programs (applets). These are miniature programs that run on a Web server or that you download to your local machine. Most ActiveX and Java applets are safe, but some contain viruses or snoop programs. The snoop programs allow a hacker to look at everything on your hard drive from a remote location without your knowledge. Be sure that you properly configure the on-access component of your antivirus software to check and clean for all these types of attacks.

Many programs will not install unless you disable the on-access portion of your antivirus software. This is dangerous if the program has a virus. Your safest bet is to do an on-demand scan of the software before installation. Disable on-access scanning during installation, and then reactivate it when the installation is complete.

Emergency Scans

In an *emergency scan*, only the operating system and the antivirus program are running. An emergency scan is called for after a virus has invaded your system and taken control of the machine. In this situation, insert your antivirus emergency boot disk and boot the infected computer from it. Then scan and clean the entire computer.

If you don't have your boot disk, go to another computer and create one.

Software Patches

Patches, fixes, service packs, and updates are all the same thing—free software revisions. They are intermediary solutions until a new version of the product is released. A patch may solve a particular problem, as does a security patch, or change the way your system works, as does an update. You can apply a so-called hot patch without rebooting your computer; in other cases, applying a patch requires that the server go down.

You should be aware of the reasons people use patches, the sorts of software that people patch, and the problems that buggy upgrades can cause. We'll discuss these topics in the following sections:

- What to consider when deciding if you should install a patch
- Where to get patches
- Desktop security patches
- Encryption patches
- Internet client patches

After looking through these sections, you should have a good understanding of why people use patches—especially security, encryption, and browser updates—and what sorts of problems updates can cause.

Is It Necessary?

Because patches are designed to fix problems, it would seem that you would want to download the most current patches and apply them immediately. That is not always the best thing to do. Patches can sometimes cause problems with existing, older software. Different philosophies exist regarding the application of the newest patches. The first philosophy is to keep your systems only as up-to-date as necessary to keep them running. This is the "If it ain't broke, don't fix it" approach. After all, the point of a patch is to fix your software. Why fix it if it isn't broken? The other philosophy is to keep the software as up-to-date as possible because of the additional features that a patch will sometimes provide.

You must choose the approach that is best for your situation. If you have little time to devote to chasing down and fixing problems, go with the first philosophy. If you always need the latest and greatest features, even at the expense of stability, go with the second.

Where to Get Patches

Patches are available from several locations:

- The manufacturer's Web site
- The manufacturer's CD or DVD

- The manufacturer's support subscriptions on CD or DVD
- The manufacturer's bulletin (less frequently an option)

You'll notice that, in every case, the source of the patch, regardless of the medium being used to distribute it, is the manufacturer. You cannot be sure that patches available through online magazines, other companies, and shareware Web sites are safe. Patches for the operating system are also sometimes included when you purchase a new computer.

Desktop Security

The Internet has made it easier to communicate, and unfortunately, this means it has made it easier for our computers to be monitored or sabotaged by others. Users are naturally concerned about this, and so when a new security alert goes out, many download a patch that fixes the new security problem.

RealJukebox Surreptitiously Monitors Users—A Patch in the Making

The *New York Times* reported that "RealNetworks' popular RealJukebox software for playing CD's on computers surreptitiously monitors the listening habits and certain other activities of people who use it and continually reports this information, along with the user's identity, to RealNetworks." After this was publicized, RealNetworks released a patch that would prevent this behavior. Microsoft has similar software, and it also monitors what songs people listen to, although Microsoft doesn't link this feature with forced user registration.

Some *desktop security* patches change the basic core of the operating system, such as the way it handles network logons and permissions. In Windows, this usually means changes to central DLLs and Registry information. As anyone who has upgraded a number of systems knows, change the Registry at your own risk!

At the very least, back up your configuration files before you update your core system. That way, if the new DLLs don't work, you can revert to your old system.

Encryption Levels

Encryption products use mathematical formulas to hide real information and render it useless without a secret electronic key. You rely on encryption to keep your data safe from unauthorized eyes. Those people who want to steal your data also want to be able to decrypt your information. Thus, when there are flaws in encryption software, or previous levels of security become insufficient, it is necessary for you to update your encryption software and hope your previously encrypted data isn't in the hands of your enemies.

Any encryption scheme that is untested and unpublished is probably vulnerable to being broken. Trust peer-reviewed encryption like that used in PGP (www.pgp.com/).

For example, Allaire's ColdFusion Web development system used a private encryption system to encrypt users' applications so the applications' source code could not be viewed but would still run. This encryption allowed companies to distribute their ColdFusion applications without worrying that someone would look at their raw code. However, this encryption level proved insufficient and it was cracked. Allaire is studying new encryption options, but this won't help secure all of the now-exposed commercial ColdFusion applications.

The United States regulates the strength of encryption that U.S. companies export. Netscape was only allowed to export 40-bit encryption with Navigator 4.08, but due to a changing legal environment, it can export 58-bit encryption with Communicator 4.7. International companies that use Netscape browsers will likely want the added encryption.

Web Browsers and E-Mail Clients

In the mad rush to market, software companies often release buggy software or software with missing functionality. They don't want to, but they are afraid they'll lose millions of dollars by releasing their products too late and increasing the market share of competing products. So many software companies would rather release a product, stay in business, and then release a *patch* than release a product after their competitors do. You can see just a few of the patches Microsoft deems to be critical in Figure 10.18. There are multiple security patches for Internet Explorer.

FIGURE 10.18   Critical Microsoft software patches

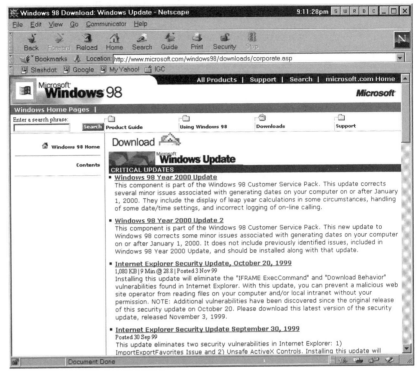

Screen shot reprinted by permission from Microsoft Corporation.

IE is not alone in security problems. Netscape has also had its fair share of security bugs and patches.

Netscape and Microsoft have both often released buggy products (with their integrated Web browsers/e-mail clients) and then released a series of patches to fix them. Typically they will add features without fixing all the potential bugs.

When upgrading your browser, you should take the same care as when you are upgrading your operating system. Back up your mail and preferences so you can go back to your old browser if the upgrade corrupts them.

After upgrading to a new client, you should be sure that all your bookmarks, mail, and preferences have been copied over to your new system. Often your ISP's technical support line can assist you with upgrading your Internet client software.

Legacy Clients

As you debug and troubleshoot Internet problems, you may come across legacy clients. *Legacy client* is a term used to describe software or hardware that is quite old. In general, there are three aspects of legacy clients that you should know for the exam:

- Compatibility issues

- Troubleshooting and performance issues

- Determining the version of a client

People use legacy software when it is more expensive to upgrade to than it is to keep using old systems. Although you may encounter whole rooms of Windows 3.11 legacy computer systems, it shouldn't concern you. If the systems weren't fairly stable, they wouldn't have lasted this long.

Compatibility Issues

Legacy software uses technology that is older than the latest trends coming out of Silicon Valley. If you want to use new software alongside your old software, you may have a *compatibility issue*, which means that different technologies may not work with each other.

In terms of the Internet, the most common legacy client is the old Windows 3.1 TCP/IP Socket system. As you learned in Chapter 2, sockets are mechanisms clients and servers use to carry on multiple conversations with each other over the TCP/IP protocol. In Windows, the operating system, through a file called WINSOCK.DLL, provides access to the TCP/IP protocol. This means that individual client programs, like Netscape, don't have to understand anything about your modem; they just talk to the operating system and the operating system talks to the modem. If your client program isn't compatible with the version of Winsock you are running, your client program won't run.

The flip side to legacy compatibility is that some programs written to use the legacy system will simply not work with newer systems.

Performance

There are two aspects of legacy performance:

Speed gain   Software has bloated over time. Many new software versions are actually slower than their predecessors. Windows 3.1, for example, runs faster than Windows 98 on some hardware. Some newer browser versions are noticeably slower than older ones.

Speed loss   Newer technologies do increase the maximum speed of networks. Newer versions of Winsock come in both 16- and 32-bit flavors, for example, whereas 3.11 Winsock systems are all 16 bit. Obviously, 32-bit processing is faster than 16-bit processing.

Before asking people to give up their legacy system, find out if it is faster than the one you want them to use.

Version Checking

Legacy software is often not compatible with newer versions of other software. Therefore, if you have legacy software, it is useful to know exactly what type of software you are running and exactly what version of other software you have installed. Then you can determine if the legacy software and the new software will work together.

Summary

Bugs are inevitable, so troubleshooting is important. The i-Net+ exam will contain questions on several aspects of troubleshooting that you learned about in this chapter. These four topics will be covered on the exam:

Pre-launch testing   Before you launch your site, you should check to make sure it is working. At its most basic, this testing should include checking to make sure all the links work and that pages load correctly. More advanced testing includes checking to make sure the pages conform to policies on download time and content type and that the servers have enough capacity to serve pages.

Diagnostic tools   You can use various diagnostic tools to identify and resolve Internet problems. For the exam, you should know when to use each tool. Use Ping, for example, when you want to see if another computer is on the network, but use tracert to map the network topology to another host.

Patches and updates   Patches and updates are software releases that fix and upgrade existing software. For the exam, you should be able to recognize update-related problems, such as e-mail not working properly after a browser has been updated.

Legacy clients   Legacy clients are old versions of software, such as the text-mode browser called lynx or Trumpet Winsock for Windows 3.11. For the exam, you should understand that, although legacy clients do have drawbacks, they serve a purpose for the people who use them.

Review Questions

1. Which utility can you use to find out how many hops it takes to get from your computer to another host on the network?

   A. Host

   B. ARP

   C. Hop

   D. tracert

2. What are network analyzers good for?

   A. Seeing if your network is up

   B. Monitoring the utilization of your network

   C. Counting the number of hops through a network

   D. Checking and modifying your Internet settings

3. What would you use winipcfg for?

   A. To see if your network is up

   B. To monitor the utilization of your network

   C. To count the number of hops through a network

   D. To check and modify your TCP/IP configuration

4. What type of Web sites should have a pre-rollout methodology?

   A. Only small sites

   B. Only medium and large sites

   C. All sites

   D. Sites where the cost of failure is high

5. What is a storyboard?

   A. A document that says what each page on the site should do

   B. A cardboard display of the site

   C. A version of the site used by graphic designers

   D. B and C

6. What is a staging server?

   A. A small server that developers use to try out ideas in private

   B. The main server that acts as a stage for the world

   C. A server that serves as a proxy between the main server and people outside the firewall

   D. A backup server in case the main server goes down

7. What method of copying files from the staging server to the main server is least likely to introduce an error?

   A. Manual FTP because it is simple and won't break

   B. Choosing Save As in your text editor (such as Notepad)

   C. An automated publishing tool such as NetObjects Fusion

   D. Symlinks

8. Human quality control is _____ .

   A. Vital to reduce the amount of bugs

   B. Wasted effort if you have automated tools

   C. A function of the salaries of your designers

   D. Vital to network connectivity

9. What is the standard screen resolution?

   A. 31 dots per inch

   B. 72 dots per inch

   C. 640 x 480

   D. 300 dots per inch

10. If you are testing CGI scripts, where would you look for syntax errors?

   A. In the access log

   B. On the console

   C. In the browser window

   D. In the error log

11. What role does load-testing software play?

   A. It extrapolates how your server will do under load.

   B. It places demands on your server and measures the effect.

   C. It examines your log files and flags peak usage.

   D. It warns you when your Web server is overloaded.

12. How can you find out what browser someone was using when he got an error message?

   A. Look in the access log.

   B. Look in the error log.

   C. Ask the user.

   D. A and C.

13. You can telnet into your Web server and change your files using command-line tools. Which of the following is generally a poor use of this method?

   A. Checking file permissions

   B. Checking scripts for syntax errors

   C. Looking at log files

   D. Editing documents

14. What can you do if you don't have enough bandwidth to distribute your software over the Internet?

   A. Nothing—send it by CD.

   B. Add extra bandwidth.

   C. Ask other sites to mirror your software.

   D. Either B or C.

15. If you try to go to a Web site and the browser gives you the message "The server *xxxx* does not have a DNS entry," what is the reason?

   A. The URL you have typed is invalid.

   B. The Web server reset the connection.

   C. Your name server couldn't resolve the IP address of the Web server.

   D. The Web site is overloaded.

16. You try to go to a Web site and the browser gives you the error "Server not responding." What is going on?

   A. The client sends off a request to the server's IP address and specified port, but the server doesn't send a response back.

   B. Your name server is nonresponsive.

   C. You have the wrong DNS information cached. Reboot your computer to clear the cache.

   D. There is an ARP conflict between IP addresses.

17. You try to go to a Web site and the browser gives you the error "File contains no data." What is the most likely culprit?

    A. The file is missing on the Web server.

    B. Your client needs to support XML.

    C. There is a CGI error.

    D. There is no connectivity between you and the server.

18. What do HTTP response codes in the *3xx* range mean?

    A. There has been a server error.

    B. There has been a client error.

    C. The request has been redirected.

    D. Everything went as planned.

19. What do HTTP response codes in the *5xx* range mean?

    A. There has been a server error.

    B. There has been a client error.

    C. The request has been redirected.

    D. Everything went as planned.

20. What authorization level does the Web server need to run CGI scripts?

    A. Read, Write, Execute

    B. Read, Write

    C. Read, Execute

    D. Write, Execute

Answers to Review Questions

1. D. tracert shows the path your TCP/IP packets take to go to another host.

2. B. Network analyzers display many things about a network segment, including how much of its bandwidth capacity has been utilized.

3. D. winipcfg will display your basic network settings and let you get a new IP address if you are using DHCP.

4. C. All sites benefit from some sort of pre-rollout methodology to find bugs. Different size sites will just use different methodologies.

5. A. Everyone can use the storyboard to see what each page should do.

6. A. People publish to a staging server to see how their changes work before publishing to the real server.

7. C. Publishing tools will rewrite URLs and check to make sure every resource is published.

8. A. Human beings see a wide range of problems, especially if they are supported with a checklist of errors to look for.

9. B. Screen resolution is generally 72 dots per inch.

10. D. Web servers generally store the full error message in the error log.

11. B. Load-testing software simulates the activity of thousands of users visiting your Web site.

12. D. The most accurate thing to do is to just ask the user. If you want to look for patterns, you can check the access log.

13. D. If you directly edit the documents that are being served to the world, there is no testing phase before the whole world can see your pages.

14. D. A lot of popular software is distributed by mirroring the download page around the world.

15. C. For whatever reason, your DNS server could not resolve the URL. This could be for a number of reasons.

16. A. If the client doesn't get a response from the server, it warns the user.

17. C. The server sent a partial response but "forgot" to send the contents of the response.

18. C. The redirect could be either permanent or temporary.

19. A. Generally, this is a CGI or application error.

20. C. Servers need to be able to read a script in order to run it, and furthermore, they need the Execute permission to be able to run any program.

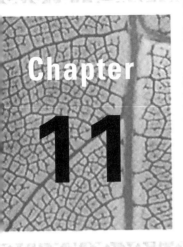

Chapter

11

Business Concepts

i-NET+ EXAM OBJECTIVES COVERED IN THIS CHAPTER:

✓ **Explain the issues involved in copyrighting, trademarking, and licensing. Content could include the following:**

- How to license copyright materials
- Scope of your copyright
- How to copyright your material anywhere
- Consequences of not being aware of copyright issues, not following copyright restrictions

✓ **Identify the issues related to working in a global environment. Content could include the following:**

- Working in a multivendor environment with different currencies, etc.
- International issues—shipping, supply chain
- Multilingual or multicharacter issues (Unicode)
- Legal and regulatory issues

✓ **Define the following Web-related mechanisms for audience development (i.e., attracting and retaining an audience):**

- Push technology
- Pull technology

✓ **Describe the differences between the following from a business standpoint:**

- Intranet
- Extranet
- Internet

✓ **Define e-commerce terms and concepts. Content could include the following:**

- EDI
- Business to business
- Business to consumer
- Internet commerce
- Merchant systems
- Online cataloging
- Relationship management
- Customer self-service
- Internet marketing

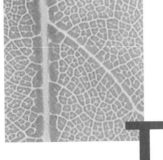

The Internet started out as the province of government agencies and academic institutions. Profit wasn't an issue then. But as the Internet extended its reach into households around the world, businesses realized the potential for Internet commerce. Today, business facilitated by the Internet is a giant industry. It continues to grow rapidly.

As an Internet professional, you have to understand the business issues that (in many cases) drive technical innovations. From copyright, to marketing, to the design of Internet storefronts, you have to know what drives the decisions. This chapter explains some of the issues.

Intellectual Property on the Network

Intellectual property denotes any intangible product of a human being, a group of human beings, or another legal entity (such as a corporation). Intellectual property law aims to protect the rights of creative people to capitalize on the things they create.

Practically speaking, intellectual property is any creative product—particularly one that has monetary value. Examples of intellectual property include the following:

- The words to "Louie, Louie"

- The text of *Hamlet*

- The cosmetic design of the iMac

- The source code for the OS/2 operating system

- The formula for making Coca-Cola
- The Nike "swoosh" logo
- The design of the Trinitron picture tube
- The tune to "Macarena"

The question of what qualifies as intellectual property is an open question—court cases come up all the time in which one party alleges that something previously unmentioned in law enjoys copyright protection. The Harley-Davidson Motorcycle Company sued Honda over its bikes' exhaust noise. Harley claimed that its bikes' noise was a distinctive feature of their design and enjoyed copyright protection. Harley lost, but this case gives an indication of the evolving nature of intellectual property law.

The computer revolution has forced many tests of intellectual property protections, many of which came about in the days when making a copy of a work of music or literature was a difficult, expensive process. Should a piece of software, which may be duplicated perfectly, instantaneously, and for negligible cost, enjoy copyright? Should Web publisher A be able to sue Web publisher B when B "frames" A's content and presents it as his own? These are open questions still in the process of being decided.

Copyright

A *copyright* is the right of an author, artist, publisher, or other legal entity to collect money from the use of words, music, performance works, items of visual art, or other creative products. Facts and short phrases cannot be copyrighted (though certain short phrases may be protected under trademark law). Copyright, in the United States, attempts to guarantee the creator several benefits:

- The right to reproduce the work and distribute the copies
- The right to revise and improve the work
- The right to perform or display the work publicly
- The right to have some assurance that the work won't be defaced or used in a way the author did not intend
- The right to receive credit for others' references to the work

A copyright depends on the ability of a person or entity that is claiming protection to prove original creation of the work in question and to prove that creation took place on a certain date. U.S. law actually allows two creators to have copyright on identical creative works, provided they arrived at their respective creations independently of one another.

There's a good copyright FAQ on the Web at `bricolage.bel-epa.com/resources/lounge/bureau/copyright/`.

A creative work whose author renounces his copyright or refuses to enforce it through infringement suits is said to be in the *public domain*. Public domain works may be used by anyone, for any purpose, without the user paying royalties or licensing fees to anyone. Other ways material may enter the public domain include the following:

- Copyright protection can lapse, as it does after some time period (usually 50 or 75 years after the author dies, depending upon when it was first created or published).

- Materials published by most governments (including that of the United States and its individual state governments) are automatically in the public domain.

Note that it is possible to sell public domain works. This is what the publishers of William Shakespeare's plays do, for example.

Getting a Copyright

On one level, it's very easy to get a copyright. If you create a work, and can prove the date on which it was created, you have a legal copyright. This is known as a common law copyright. Common law copyright protects you from the moment that you create a work. Of course, proving original creation and its date can be tricky.

If you put a copyright statement on a document, you alert the world that you claim ownership of the intellectual property contained in that document. A suitable copyright statement looks like this:

Copyright © January 1, 2000, Billy Pilgrim.

That copyright symbol is a tricky thing. The c-in-a-circle isn't part of all font packages, and it's not clear that (c) is the legal equivalent of © just because the former is easier to make with a computer. However, the spelled-out word *copyright* should be adequate.

Because text can be edited so easily, you can improve the legitimacy of the date from which you claim copyright protection by sealing your document in an envelope and mailing it to yourself. The sealed, postmarked envelope serves as stronger—but not absolute—proof that you had the intellectual property on the date you claim.

Registered Copyright

You can achieve an extra level of legal protection for a creative work by registering the work with your government's copyright office. Essentially, formal copyright registration provides a fairly unquestionable way of establishing when a work was created. The duration of copyright protection established this way varies among media. To cite one example, an author who registered a novel today would enjoy copyright protection for the remainder of her life, and her heirs could enjoy the benefits of copyright protection for 50 years after her death.

In the United States, the Copyright Office handles copyright registrations. Its Web site appears in Figure 11.1. Other governments have similar agencies. You request a registration form from the Copyright Office, fill it out, and send it in to the government with two copies of the work you're registering. You can request the necessary forms from the Copyright Office's voice-mail system at +1 202 707 9100 or get them on the Web in Adobe Acrobat format at www.loc.gov/copyright/forms/. You need particular forms for particular kinds of works. Here's a list:

Form TX   Books, manuscripts, software, and games

Form PA   Music (in written form), plus films, video recordings, scripts, and plays

Form SR   Music (recorded)

Form VA   Drawings, photos, and cartoons

Under a treaty called the Berne Convention, copyrights registered in any signatory country are valid in all others. All major countries of the world are signatories.

FIGURE 11.1 The U.S. Copyright Office Web site

Fair Use of Copyrighted Material

Copyright law recognizes that a vibrant creative community relies, in part, on artists' ability to use the creative products of others as starting points for their own creative work. Such applications of copyrighted material are known as *fair use* applications in the law.

Here are some examples of fair use:

- Cited excerpts in academic work

- Excerpts that appear in a review

- Parody and satire

- Reproductions for personal, not-for-profit use

These aren't cast in stone—the nature of fair use is constantly undergoing revision as those accused of copyright violations claim (and sometimes prove to a court) that their use was fair.

Though no precise statement of what is not fair use exists, the determining factors seem to be the size of the excerpt and the profit motive of the party using the copyrighted material. Courts tend to favor fair-use claims presented by nonprofit organizations over those put forward by organizations that have made money from their use of copyrighted material. If you're not making money (or causing the rightful copyright holder to lose money) as a result of your use of brief snippets, you're probably okay.

Licensing Copyrighted Products

If you want to use a copyrighted work in your own products—and remember, it does not matter whether the copyright is registered with a government—you must ask permission. The copyright holder is free to do three things:

- Refuse you permission to use the material

- Allow you to use the material free of charge, provided you credit the copyright holder

- Require you to pay a fee for the use of the copyrighted material

The last of the three options is called *licensing*, and it's a big part of the intellectual property business. Licensing deals take many forms and usually state explicitly what rights are being granted and what compensation will be paid for them. A writer, for example, might write a story and grant a magazine the rights to publish the story once in its North American editions. The magazine would pay a writer a fee for that right. The writer would retain the rights to sell the story again for use as part of a compilation put out by a book publisher, without consideration to the magazine. The writer would also retain, for example, the ability to license the story to a movie studio for adaptation into a screenplay.

Securing the Entire Copyright

If you're a publisher and want to secure the copyright to a work created by someone else (such as a freelance writer), you can secure the rights by either of two means. A *work-made-for-hire* agreement states that the creator of a work (the freelancer) created it because he was hired by the publisher to do so and paid accordingly (or paid something, anyway). Therefore, the publisher has the copyright and the freelancer does not.

A creator also can transfer the copyright on a work to another entity by *assignment*. Usually, assignment must involve an explicit, written statement that says the original creator is granting her copyright to someone else, such as a publisher.

Infringement Consequences

Copyright, in the United States and most developed countries, is a matter of civil law. That is, a copyright holder cannot complain to the government that someone has committed a crime by infringing upon her copyright. Rather, a copyright holder can file a civil suit alleging infringement. If the civil suit goes to trial and the infringement is found to have taken place, the defendant may be made to pay damages to the copyright holder.

In point of fact, civil suits are expensive and generally are the last resort of copyright holders who feel their rights have been infringed upon. Usually, those using copyrighted material for purposes perceived to be unfair by the copyright holders will receive stern letters from the copyright holder or his lawyer, asking that the use stop. If the perceived problem continues, the copyright holder can file suit and fight the matter in court. If an infringement is determined to have occurred, the entity using the material without permission may be judged responsible for damages and made to pay money to the copyright holder.

Trademarks

A *trademark* is much like a copyright except that trademarks apply to words, phrases, and images used to describe products and services (technically, a word, phrase, or logo that describes a service is called a *servicemark*, but the legal concepts are pretty much the same). The following are examples of trademark-protectable intellectual property:

- A company's name (e.g., Netscape Communications Corporation)

- A product's name (e.g., Diet Coke)

- A logo (e.g., the AT&T globe image)

- A graphic device (e.g., the Izod alligator)

Oppenheimer Wolff & Donnelly LLP, a law practice, has put together a neat FAQ on the topic. It's on the Web at www.owdlaw.com/intprop/trademark/faq/faq.html.

Registering a Trademark

As is the case with larger creative works protected by copyright, U.S. law provides for trademark protection on words, phrases, and devices even if they've not been formally registered with the government. You can assert a trademark or servicemark right by always printing a TM (for trademarks) or SM (for servicemarks) next to the device you want to protect.

You can establish stronger legal protection for your trademark by registering it. Governments maintain registries of trademarked intellectual property. In the United States, the U.S. Patent and Trademark Office (USPTO) maintains the list of registered trademarks. To register a trademark, you must establish that it represents a unique way of denoting a product or service and is not in use by another entity. You must also be actively using the trademark—you can't register a trademark in anticipation of applying it to a product or service you'll develop in the future (though this used to be possible). Once you have registered a trademark, you can follow it with the ® symbol to denote the registration.

You can get further information about registering a trademark at the USPTO Web site, www.uspto.gov/.

Using Trademarked Material

Trademarks run the risk of bringing about their own demise. If a trademarked word is heavily advertised and becomes synonymous with a product or service, it loses its protectability. This is why Xerox Corporation is so adamant that people not talk about "making xeroxes" or "xeroxing documents." The correct phrases, acknowledging the trademark on the Xerox name, are "making Xerox copies" and "copying documents" (as with a Xerox copier). You have to be careful to use trademarked words as adjectives, not nouns.

Generally, it's not possible to license trademarked material. The companies holding the trademarks usually are loath to share them with those selling products and services other than their own. There is protection, however, for the incidental appearance of trademarks in creative media. The producers of a movie that features a scene in Trafalgar Square—where a giant Virgin Records sign appears—probably would not infringe upon Virgin's trademark protection by showing the sign in the film as an incidental part of the scenery.

Infringement Consequences

Trademark protection is a matter of civil law, and so enforcement of trademark rights is similar to that of copyrights. Refer to the copyright section for information on legal enforcement of intellectual property.

Patents

Patent law exists to protect physical devices and processes. You might patent a cleaner-running engine for automobiles, a faster kind of memory chip, a way of making harder steel, or a chemical formula for a more flexible plastic. Essentially, patent law is the same as the law governing other kinds of intellectual property. The difference is in the nature of the creative product. In applying for a patent, you agree to make the details of your product or process available to the public in exchange for a monopoly in profiting from your invention. The monopoly is limited by time—design patents (on the appearance of a product) last 14 years in the United States, while the time limit on utility patents (on products and processes) lasts 20 years.

David Kiewit, a patent lawyer, has posted a good patent FAQ on the Web at patent-faq.com/index.htm.

Securing a Patent

Unlike other kinds of intellectual property, there are no implicit patents. You can't sue someone for patent infringement unless you have formally registered your claim with your government's patent office. Even if you and another party arrived at the same product independently, the right to sue for patent infringement goes to the party that first secures government registration.

In order to be protectable by patent, a product or process must satisfy the following three requirements.

Useful   The product or process must accomplish something desirable.

New   It must not have been patented before.

Nonobvious   The product or process must be the result of creative work, not something that would come naturally to someone skilled in the trade to which the product or process applies.

Of these, the newness and nonobviousness requirements are the hardest to prove. Novelty can by verified by a search of existing patents, which is something patent lawyers are trained to do. Expert witnesses can assert non-obviousness.

In the United States, the U.S. Patent and Trademark Office (USPTO) handles patent applications. Its Web site appears in Figure 11.2. You can apply for a patent by describing it and filing the proper paperwork with the USPTO. When the USPTO has examined your application and agrees that your idea is patentable, you are granted a patent. Between the time you file and the time you receive your patent, you can refer to your product as having "patent pending" status. Legally, the phrase means little, but it may discourage aspiring idea thieves.

You can get further information about registering a patent at the USPTO Web site, www.uspto.gov/.

FIGURE 11.2   The U.S. Patent and Trademark Office Web site

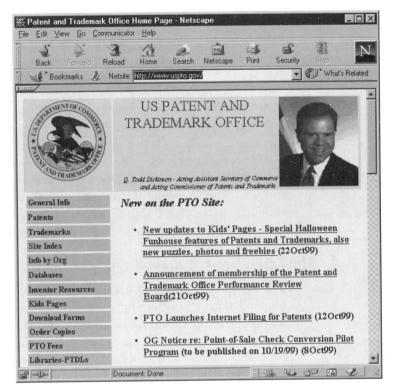

Licensing Patented Products

Companies and individuals that have secured patents on their inventions often are eager to license their patents to others. Indeed, many companies exist for the sole purpose of securing patents that may later be licensed to production companies (this business model is common in the biotechnology industries). Often, a patent license may involve a compensation system that's based on the number of products sold. At the end of each accounting period, the licensee pays the patent holder some royalty for each instance of the protected item it sold during the period.

Open Source and Public Licensing

Most of the software industry is based on companies and individuals—software publishers—writing software, compiling it, and selling the compiled binary code to consumers. The publishers invest in the people and other resources needed to create their products' source code; they then keep that source code secret. The idea is that a publisher deserves to profit from something in which it has invested money to produce.

But an alternative model has long been a part of the hobbyist and academic communities. These groups espouse the idea of writing software and making the source code public, available for anyone to examine, modify, and redistribute. Such freely distributed programs are called *open source* software. The source code of certain Unix variants has always been available to the public, and lots of Unix utilities are open source, too. But the idea hasn't started to translate into the world of Intel-standard processors until recently.

The Open Source Movement

The open source movement—an informal group of software publishers, book publishers, academic institutions, and individuals—holds the belief that software for which source code is freely available inspires innovation, whereas closed source software stifles it. Opponents of the traditional microcomputer business model and of Microsoft Corporation in particular, members of the open source movement champions free software like the Linux operating system, the Perl language, and the GNU utilities.

Public-domain software has no copyright protections at all. This means that anyone may acquire, copy, and use the software without paying a licensing fee to anyone (there's no copyright holder to which to pay such a fee). Publishers are free to charge for public-domain software, and they may get the price they ask if they package it attractively and offer extra features, such as technical support. This is the business model behind Red Hat, Caldera, and other distributors of the Linux operating system, the kernel of which is in the public domain.

The concept of *copyleft* is part of the open source movement. The idea of copyleft is that an organization (usually a not-for-profit group like the Free Software Foundation) establishes a copyright to an item of intellectual property—source code for software, usually—then distributes it, free of charge. People who use the software must agree to its licensing agreement, which specifies they may not make a profit on its distribution. The GNU utilities are covered by copyleft.

There are details of copyleft on the Free Software Foundation's Web site, at `www.gnu.ai.mit.edu/copyleft/copyleft.html`.

Using Open Source Software

You're free to use open source software for any purpose you wish without paying a licensing fee to anyone. You may modify the software to suit your particular needs, and you may redistribute the software as you wish. You can even try to sell the software if it is in the public domain. If the software is copylefted, however, you may be prohibited from making a profit on it.

The Global Marketplace

The Internet spans the planet. It has the potential to bring about truly free, worldwide markets in which the most efficient providers of goods and services have the advantage over others, unencumbered by geography and politics. It's a Utopian vision, but one that's beginning to come true. Your organization may want to get on board.

But first, we need some perspective. Fewer than three percent of the world's population have ever used the Internet in any way (a statistic that isn't so shocking when you consider that only about half the people in the world have placed a telephone call). Regardless, the community of Internet users is a great market, comprising mostly people of greater-than-average income and education.

If you're going to sell to the world over the Internet, you must be aware of what you're getting into. You have to be prepared to communicate with people who prefer many different languages. You'll have to address varying customs and courtesies. You'll also have to be sure that your company can deliver what it promises, get paid for its work, and comply with all relevant laws.

Language and Communication

Communications technologies exist for the purpose of helping people talk to one another even when separated by time and distance. You can chat with someone anywhere in the world in real time, and your Web site can sell your products while you're asleep. But the best communications tools can't help you unless you and your audience share a common human language. You have to be able to tell each other what you're thinking.

Language

English is the *lingua franca* on the Internet, probably because English-speaking Americans make up a huge proportion of the user population and Americans are notoriously reluctant to pick up other languages. Plenty of Internet resources exist in languages other than English, but it seems that two parties attempting to communicate across cultures default to English a lot of the time. New innovations, such as the *Unicode* character set that makes it easier to incorporate non-Latin characters into displayed text, are making it easier to cater to the needs of non-English speakers.

English is an awful language. It's loaded with irregularities, exceptions, special cases, and strange pronunciations. Many English-language conventions—ungendered nouns, say—are totally at odds with what's normal in other tongues. Learning English as a secondary language is devilishly hard.

So, when someone writes to you (assuming you're an English speaker) and refers to a piece of software as "him" or talks about "the weather, which one is rainful," recognize that the writer is going to considerable effort to accommodate *you*. Don't disregard a message because its English is faulty. Do your best to interpret it, politely ask for clarification when you must, and reply as you would to a grammatically perfect message.

As a Web publisher, you may decide to publish your content in multiple languages. If you do so, make sure the translations are all good—have them done by someone who speaks both languages superbly and can catch all the idioms. Don't assume that translation software is good enough—it almost never is, and it's obvious when translation has been done that way. A bad translation is worse than no translation at all in many cases.

Cultural Differences

Everyone knows how hard it is to communicate emotion in electronic mail. A person who mentions a "brilliant idea" you had may be paying you a compliment, or may be using sarcasm to mock you. The problem grows when the sender and recipient of a communication are on different cultural wavelengths.

In Brazil, it's not unusual for a man, casually wishing another man good-bye, to pat his acquaintance on the stomach. An Englishman, subjected to belly-patting for the first time, may be insulted—the same gesture in the United Kingdom might mean that the patter thought the pattee was putting on weight. In fact, it's just a friendly gesture that's meant to convey nothing more than familiarity. It's a cultural affectation that the Englishman must learn to recognize and interpret properly.

The same sort of situation can arise in e-mail. Receiving an e-mail from a business contact in Australia, an American might be put off by the Aussie's formal tone—such a stiff approach is adversarial, she might think. It's not—it's a cultural trait of many Australians to use a somewhat reserved tone in written business communications of all kinds, even e-mail.

It's not fair to generalize. There certainly are Australians who like to write casual e-mails for business and Americans who prefer a formal writing style. The point is, be slow to take offense at perceived oddities in communications from other countries. The odds are good that no hard feelings are meant and that you're coming across just as strangely.

Delivering the Goods

Sharing information is one thing, but business is based on actually providing customers with something they're willing to pay for. The process of getting goods and services to consumers is easy enough in a geographical area with a good postal service and other package-delivery resources, but it's more of a challenge when there are oceans between you and your customers. If you're doing manufacturing work overseas or importing materials, you have to be concerned about the effect of shipping issues on your supply chain. Getting paid for the things you sell can prove challenging, as well.

Order Fulfillment

Many Internet businesses, tasked with delivering physical products to customers scattered far and wide, set up distribution centers in various parts of the world. Amazon.com, for example, has one warehouse in Delaware, one in Seattle, one in the United Kingdom, and one in Germany. The relative efficiencies of different snail-mail systems and routes still mean a lot. Australians, for example, report faster shipment of books from Amazon.co.uk in England than from Amazon.com in the United States.

Getting Paid

Credit cards are magical things. If a German uses his Visa card to make a purchase in Hong Kong, the merchant gets paid in Hong Kong dollars and the German pays his bill in Euros. The banks and the credit card companies handle the currency exchange behind the scenes (at bulk interbank rates favorable to everyone) and the transaction goes as smoothly as one at the German's local grocery store.

The same holds true on the Web. An American can buy a product from a British site without problem. The merchant is paid in British pounds and the American pays his bill in U.S. dollars. Assuming there's a way to get the product from Britain to the United States, the transaction proceeds without problem. The moral: Use credit cards for cross-border transactions wherever possible.

If you can't use a credit card, you have other options.

- Wire transfers between banks

- Wire transfers of cash (e.g., American Express and Thomas Cook)

- Personal delivery of cash

- Payment in kind

These aren't really applicable to retail operations on the Web, but they're all workable for consulting relationships and other business-to-business transactions. You can try all kinds of strategies in businesses characterized by a low volume of high-value transactions.

Bear in mind that many countries regulate cash outflows (the United States, for example, requires you to report movements of sums greater than U.S. $10,000 out of the country). Bank transfers in some countries don't always go as smoothly as in others and may require some personal shepherding by a local citizen.

Obeying the Law

The legal standing of companies physically located in one country (to the extent that they have a physical location at all) while doing business in another country is still up in the air. The matter seems to be reaching the courts piecemeal. The U.S. state of Wisconsin, for example, is attempting to prosecute several Caribbean companies for alleged violations of the state's anti-gambling laws by Internet gambling sites. If the player was in Milwaukee, the server simulating a slot machine was in Jamaica, and the server's owner was in Britain, where did the gambling take place? It's a matter for the courts to decide. You have to be aware of legal and regulatory issues in all places you do business.

Criminal law aside, it's generally accepted that any organization is responsible for paying taxes on all its income wherever it is incorporated, regardless of where the money comes from. A Maryland company that receives cash from Argentina must pay state (Maryland) and federal (U.S.) taxes on that income. It's also responsible for paying whatever import duties Argentina levies on the incoming goods.

Legal and regulatory matters are always complicated, and you almost certainly pay for legal help in your own country. The logic applies even more strongly in other countries. Hire a local lawyer or other consultant. A trustworthy expert can be invaluable.

Online Marketing

It's as the old saw (so to speak) about the tree falling in the woods says: You have to have an audience in order to make a splash in Internet business. The raw numbers of people are out there, for sure, but you have to motivate enough of them to come to your site and keep returning.

The first rule of marketing is to know your target market. What kind of people do you want to attract? Once you've figured that out, try to identify things that appeal to people like that. Provide your audience with the things it likes, and make a point of advertising what's available on your site.

Advertising

You can build the best Web site in the world, but random chance and word-of-mouth will draw only so much traffic to your pages. If you want to bring people in, you have to tell them to come and why they should do so. You have several ways to advertise.

Pull and Push Technologies

A *push technology* is any system that causes information to appear on a user's screen without them having specifically requested it, at least not in the immediate sense. The most popular (and generally most effective) push technology is electronic mail. Certain Web sites offer people the opportunity to sign up for mailing lists, which then send e-mail messages containing a mixture of useful information and advertising. Less popular push technologies include PointCast and other specialty software packages for getting news onto a user's screen automatically. Push technologies contrast with *pull technologies*, which require users to specifically request information at the time they want it. Standard Web sites are examples of pull technology.

Both push and pull systems can make effective marketing tools. Push schemes keep your message in front of users, even long after they've departed your Web site. Be careful not to annoy them, though.

Paid Banner Ads

A banner ad is a rectangular graphic, usually about 500 pixels wide by 60 pixels tall, that's placed on a Web page where the people who look at that page can see it. When a surfer clicks a banner ad, he's taken to the advertiser's Web site (and usually, the fact that he got there through a banner ad is noted). Figure 11.3 shows a banner ad.

FIGURE 11.3 A banner ad

The banner-ad industry remains in its infancy. High-traffic sites, such as CNN.com, get tens of thousands of dollars for an ad placed on their pages. Other sites take payment in kind, usually in the form of reciprocal advertising. Often, a banner-ad deal will involve a combination of cash and in-kind payments.

Usually, banner-ad placement is priced in views. If you buy 10,000 views on a site, you've agreed to pay a fee in exchange for your ad being sent out to surfers, as part of a page, 10,000 times. There's no guarantee that merely showing an ad to a surfer will motivate him to *click through* to your site. You might try negotiating a banner-ad deal based on a certain number of clickthroughs—say, the site will show your ad until 500 people click it to see your site. Estimates of realistic *clickthrough rates* are generally low—one or two percent of the people shown a well-designed ad will click through to the advertiser's site.

You can get creative with search sites, specifying that your ad appear at the top of results lists when people search for particular words.

Webring Banner Ads

A *webring* is a community of sites that relate to some common interest. As a courtesy to their users, each site in the webring agrees to post banner ads for the other sites in the ring, increasing traffic to all the sites. Webrings usually are casual affairs that find application among fans of a particular musical group or participants in a specific hobby. They're not usually a popular option among commercial publishers.

Non-Web Advertising

Spending on Web advertising remains tiny in comparison to the money organizations drop on traditional media, and for good reason: Many more people listen to the radio and watch television than surf the Web. There's lots of overlap between the Web and traditional media. Hardly anyone interacts with the Web exclusively, never picking up a newspaper or watching a television show.

The trick in choosing a non-Web advertising venue is to figure out what your audience does. If you're trying to appeal to people who read books for pleasure, you might have good luck advertising on public radio and on billboards near large bookstores. If you want to attract expectant mothers, shun advertising on cocktail napkins and try distributing imprinted pens to obstetricians. Find out where your people are, and talk to them there.

Partnerships

Internet sites are loaded with *partnerships*, which are relationships between companies that can take any number of forms. On some sites, partnerships is another word for advertising relationships. On other sites, partnerships denote broader financial support of the company that's publishing the site.

On still other sites, partnerships denote vendor-customer relationships or a common parent company. Sometimes, a small company will describe a better-known company as its "partner," no matter how slender the relationship, just to get some rub-off credibility from the name recognition.

Some companies, such as Sun Microsystems, have formal rules about partnerships. A consultant that has passed certain certification tests can describe herself as a Sun partner for her consulting work.

Free Information

Although talk of the Internet as a gift economy has faded, it's easy to give information away on the global network. Indeed, Web surfers have come to expect free information in many cases and can take umbrage at organizations that are stingy with data.

In many cases, it's in an organization's interest to be free with information. If having product manuals on the Web can cut down on technical support calls from people who have lost their documentation, then the Web site saves some telephone expenses and a technician's time. The same goes for all kinds of everyday information people once routinely called in to get, often using a toll-free number and an expensive call center in the process. Such information includes the following:

- Credit card balances

- Frequent-flyer statements

- Stock quotes

- Bank statements

- Store hours and locations

Analyze your customer service calls. If the operators have stock answers to standard questions, put those answers on the Web. Everyone will be happier—and your organization will look better in the public eye.

New Marketing Challenges

With every blessing comes a curse, and there is a considerable dark side to the cheap marketing brought about by the Internet. For one thing, your organization's competitors can promote themselves as easily as your organization can. It's yet another arena for you to fight it out in your media campaigns, and indeed it's a lot easier for customers to compare competing sites side-by-side than to compare radio commercials. There are other challenges:

- Sites published by customers unhappy with your products and services
- Communications media that allow rumors to spread very quickly

"Disgruntled Customer" Sites

It's always been true that an unhappy customer tells more people about his bad feelings than does a satisfied customer. But traditionally, such customers could only share their feelings with a relatively small number of people. Now, though, it's a simple matter for a customer who feels that he's been wronged to post all sorts of vitriol on the Web. When someone searches for the name of your company or one of its products, guess what comes up in the results? Your company's page, but also the page titled "Why ABC Company is a Scourge upon the Earth." Surfers read pages like that and weigh what they say against other information they have about your company. Similarly, sites like Deja.com (`www.deja.com`) promote themselves as forums in which consumers can sound off for and against the things they buy. A bad review here can really hurt you.

Your best defense against problems like this is to provide good products and services. If you take care of your customers, positive feedback should outweigh negative comments—something potential buyers will notice.

The High-Speed Rumor Mill

Internet-enabled media like Usenet, e-mail, and chat provide customers with new, global forums for their opinions about your company and its products. True or not, information about you can circulate faster than ever before. You have two responsibilities.

First, be aware of what's being said about your organization in the Internet media. Monitor the chat rooms in which your customers gather. Check in at the Web sites that consumer groups and professional organizations maintain. Read relevant columnists' work. Participate in forums, where appropriate, to build goodwill and to establish trust so your arguments against negative comments, when they arise, are taken seriously.

Second, be prepared to counteract problems when they pop up. Recognize your products' problems; note that you want to fix them and that you take customer comments seriously. Offer to compensate the complainer with freebies, if needed.

The Business Case for Networks

Setting up a network of computers isn't cheap. Doing so requires specialized equipment (such as routers and switches), specialized services (such as dedicated telephone lines and Internet backbone services), and on-site experts (such as yourself). These things are expensive, and they're not always easy for the people who dispense money to understand. Part of your job is to explain the business cases for different kinds of networks. You have to be able to explain why they're good investments.

Internet

Your company's Internet site is its storefront for most of the world. It's always available and should be used to provide nonstop marketing and customer-service functions that would cost too much to provide otherwise.

Brochureware   Your site can contain basic information about your business—the sorts of things that would appear in a basic marketing brochure.

Self-service customer information   You can reduce the load on a customer-service department by enabling customers to help themselves.

Marketing materials   Supplementing the basics of brochureware, marketing materials enable customers to get the information they want, at the levels they want it. One customer might want general descriptions; another might want technical details.

Ordering facilities   Internet sites can generate revenue through catalogs and credit card acceptance.

Intranet

An intranet enables the people in your organization to collaborate efficiently, sharing information and files. Intranets use Internet standards, and so employees can conduct business on the intranet with the Internet tools they already know how to use. Applications might include the following:

- Messaging
- Conferencing

- Database access

- News

- Information libraries

Extranet

An extranet involves granting certain outsiders limited access to your company's internal resources. You might find it advantageous, for example, to allow a vendor to monitor your level of some raw material and automatically send you more when your supply drops to some prearranged limit. An extranet might also enable you to share information with an external service provider, such as a payroll company or a marketing house. You might implement the following technologies on an extranet:

- Shared database access

- Conferencing

Some extranets incorporate *Electronic Data Interchange (EDI)*, which is the automated sharing of information among computers. A supplier's database may automatically transfer data on shipping schedules to a customer's machine, for example.

Virtual Private Network

A virtual private network (VPN) is functionally similar to a local area network (LAN), except for the fact that some or all of the network nodes are connected by communications channels established on the open Internet. Secure networking protocols make it possible to operate a VPN with a high degree of confidence that your data remains confidential.

The business case for a VPN is strong. Your argument for a VPN should hinge on the fact that a distributed network otherwise would require a considerable investment in communications services. Here are some advantages:

Telecommunications savings Where linking geographically separated network resources required dedicated lines before, a VPN can provide the same connectivity for far less cost.

Flexibility Because there are no contracts on dedicated-line service, you can reconfigure your VPN more easily than a networked based on traditional telecommunications links.

Internet Commerce

Internet commerce is any sort of business that is facilitated by the Internet. Usually, the term applies primarily to commerce that involves a Web site of some kind.

There are as many variations to the Internet commerce tune as there are companies on the Internet, but it's fair to fit the business models into two broad categories. Business-to-consumer sites sell to individuals; business-to-business sites sell to organizations.

Business to Consumer

The best-known Internet commerce sites have to conduct business by selling goods and services to individual people. Typically, so-called business-to-consumer sites involve presenting a catalog of products, a virtual shopping cart in which surfers can store the ones they want, and a credit card acceptance facility.

Internet business-to-consumer sites offer opportunities to increase sales in ways conventional stores and paper catalogs do not. There are a couple of strategies you can try:

Cross-sell   *Cross-sell* is the process of selling the buyer of a given product accessories and other related products. You might design your e-commerce system to present the buyer of a computer printer, for example, with advertisements for toner cartridges, parallel cables, and paper trays.

Upsell   *Upsell* is the process of encouraging a buyer who thinks she wants one product to buy another, more profitable product. Upsell may involve pitching a larger package of the same stuff or a more feature-rich variant of the same model.

Amazon.com does a great job of cross-promoting its products. If you're looking at the detail page for a particular book, you see a list of other products buyers of that book have purchased. If you're looking at the detail page for a stereo amplifier, you see references to compatible speakers. Where making such pitches consistently in a bricks-and-mortar store would require a highly trained sales staff, the same pitches on the Internet require only a well-designed database.

Not all business-to-consumer operations on the Internet take the form of storefronts. Some sites (such as the Wall Street Journal, `www.wsj.com`) charge a subscription fee for access to information. Others, such as the assortment of Internet stock brokerages, provide some information (such as portfolio tracking pages) free of charge while collecting a fee on other services (such as trades).

Business to Business

While retailers like Amazon.com and eToys.com get all the headlines at present, many experts predict that the Internet marketplace for business-to-business commerce will soon overshadow the retail market by a large margin. *Business-to-business commerce* is exactly what it sounds like—businesses providing goods and services to other businesses.

Business-to-business transactions can mimic business-to-consumer commerce closely. Businesses buy paper clips, computers, motor vehicles and travel products all the time, just like individuals do. Companies like Dell Computer Corporation (`www.dell.com`) and the Internet Travel Network (`www.itn.net`) do good business selling to companies, governments, and other organizations this way.

But a greater potential may lie in providing information services to businesses. Trucking companies, for example, typically waste a lot of money moving empty trucks around because the next hauling job usually starts some distance from where the previous one ended. There's a market for a company that finds buyers for the hauling capacity that presently goes unused.

The great thing about business-to-business work is that companies often buy more of what you're selling, more frequently, than an individual consumer does. The volume of transactions might be lower, but their individual value is higher.

Summary

In this chapter, you learned about Internet business concepts. The most important facts and concepts to know for the i-Net+ exam are the following:

Intellectual property   Intellectual property laws exist to protect the rights of creators to profit from their creative works.

Copyright law protects works of literature, music, and other visual and performance arts, including software.

Copyright law is generally interpreted to allow for limited, free use of protected materials under certain circumstances. This is called *fair use*.

Trademark law protects slogans, phrases, and visual devices.

Patent law protects inventions, including devices, processes, and procedures.

The global marketplace   The Internet facilitates a global exchange of products, services, and money, which means buyers and sellers must be sensitive to language and cultural differences.

It's relatively easy to collect money from anyone in the world through the use of credit cards, but delivering physical goods can be more difficult.

Companies and individuals are liable for taxes on the income they bring in over the Internet, even from other countries.

It's often worthwhile to hire a lawyer or other consultant in a foreign country in which you want to do business, just to be sure you're complying with relevant laws.

Internet marketing   You'll have to advertise your Web site in order to draw traffic to it.

Web banner ads typically are sold based on the number of times they're exposed to surfers. You might be quoted a rate for each thousand exposures.

An instance of a surfer clicking a banner ad and being taken to the site it's promoting is called a *clickthrough*.

The frequency with which viewers of a particular ad on a particular site click through is called the *clickthrough rate*.

You may also choose to advertise your site as part of a *webring* or on media other than the Internet.

There are advantages to be realized by putting lots of free information on the Internet. Such information can reduce calls to customer support lines and provide customers with a source of help that's always available.

The Internet provides customers with an efficient way to broadcast their feelings—good and bad—about your company and its products.

The business case for networks   An Internet site can reduce the load on an organization's customer-service department and bring in cash through online sales.

An extranet can make an organization's interactions with its suppliers and subcontractors more efficient by providing them with easy, automated access to the information they need about your organization.

An intranet can provide efficient file-sharing, conferencing, and database access to the people in a building, all with familiar and easily supportable Web tools.

A virtual private network (VPN) cuts down on the expenses of the dedicated lines that were once required to connect geographically separate network nodes.

Internet commerce   A business-to-consumer site sells goods and services to individuals, usually by presenting them with a catalog, allowing them to choose items and then pay for their selections with a credit card.

A business-to-business site focuses on the needs of corporations, government agencies, and other organizations. Such sites sell the goods and information these entities need.

Review Questions

1. Copyright law applies to _____ .

   A. Software only

   B. Works of literature only

   C. Slogans and logos

   D. Software, literature, and works of graphic and performing arts

2. Copyright law prohibits _____ .

   A. All use of copyrighted material by anyone other than the copyright holder

   B. All unlicensed use of copyrighted material by anyone other than the copyright holder

   C. All but "fair use" of the copyrighted material by anyone other than the copyright holder without permission

   D. Parody of copyrighted works

3. In order to enjoy copyright protection, a work _____ .

   A. Must be registered with a government copyright agency

   B. Must be an original creation

   C. Must have an individual author

   D. Must not include excerpts of other copyrighted works

4. In the United States, what government agency registers copyrights?

   A. The Department of Justice

   B. The Patent and Trademark Office

   C. The Copyright Office

   D. The individual states

5. The process of securing formal permission, perhaps in exchange for money, to use copyrighted material is called _____ .

   A. Licensing

   B. Rights management

   C. Permissioning

   D. Copyright contracting

6. Two ways to transfer a copyright permanently from the creator of a piece of intellectual property to another party are _____ .

   A. Work-made-for-hire agreements and assignment contracts

   B. Work-made-for-hire agreements and permanent licensing

   C. Assignment contracts and licensing

   D. Reregistration and work-made-for-hire agreements

7. Trademark protection applies to _____ .

   A. Logos

   B. Words, phrases, logos, and representative devices

   C. Only words, phrases, logos, and representative devices that have been registered with the Trademark Office

   D. Advertising slogans for as-yet-unreleased products

8. The raised TM symbol denotes _____ .

   A. A registered trademark

   B. A trademark for which registration is pending

   C. Something for which trademark protection is claimed, even if registration has not yet taken place

   D. A trademark whose validity has been upheld in court

9. A notable risk assumed by companies that hold trademarks is
_____ .

   A. That the trademarked term will become part of the common
vocabulary and therefore lose its protection

   B. That a judge will disallow the validity of the trademark

   C. That another company will come out with a similar slogan or
device

   D. That the value of the trademark will fade in the public
consciousness

10. A patent secures protection for _____ .

   A. A physical product

   B. An idea for a product

   C. A software program

   D. A product or process

11. If two organizations invent the same product independently and
simultaneously, which enjoys patent protection on the product?

   A. Both

   B. Neither

   C. Whichever one applies for and receives a patent first

   D. Whichever sues the other and wins the right to apply for a patent

12. In order to qualify for patent protection, a product or process must be
_____ .

   A. Useful

   B. Unique

   C. Useful, new, and nonobvious

   D. New and nonobvious

13. Open source software in the public domain _____ .

    A. May not be sold at a profit

    B. May be modified by anyone

    C. May not be incorporated into for-profit software

    D. Must carry a copyright notice

14. The most common human language for interaction across borders on the Internet is _____ .

    A. English

    B. French

    C. Esperanto

    D. XML

15. Dealing with nonnative speakers of your language requires _____ .

    A. An eagerness to correct grammar and spelling

    B. A tendency to use elaborate colloquialisms

    C. Patience and appreciation of their efforts

    D. A total reliance on translation software

16. You might consider establishing a warehouse in another country so _____.

    A. Your tax standing in that country is clearer

    B. You can worry less about delivery times

    C. You can avoid customs duties

    D. You can apply for United Nations subsidies

17. A Web site posted by a disgruntled customer is best dealt with by
_____ .

    A. Filing a libel suit

    B. Providing honestly good products and services so the positive buzz drowns out the complaints

    C. Attacking the site covertly

    D. Slandering the publisher of the site in newsgroups

18. Placements of banner ads typically are sold in terms of _____ .

    A. Cost per hundred exposures

    B. Cost per thousand exposures

    C. Cost per hour of exposure

    D. Cost per byte

19. Lots of advertisers pay for their ads with reciprocal ad space or other non-cash commodities. Such payments are called _____ .

    A. Illegal

    B. Nontaxable

    C. Payments in kind

    D. Payment in viewer volume

20. The easiest way to handle intercurrency sales is with _____ .

    A. Wire transfers

    B. Payment in kind

    C. Interbank transfers

    D. Credit cards

Answers to Review Questions

1. D. Copyright protection applies to software, literature, and works of graphic and performing arts.

2. C. Fair use allows for academic excerpting, commentary, parody, and other applications.

3. B. Though registration of a copyrighted work with a government agency can help establish the date of its creation, it is not necessary to have copyright protection.

4. C. The United States Copyright Office handles copyright registrations.

5. A. The process of securing permission is called licensing.

6. A. Work-made-for-hire agreements and assignment contracts can transfer copyright from one holder to another.

7. B. Trademarks protect the words, phrases, logos, and representative devices that denote products and the companies that provide them.

8. C. The TM symbol denotes an unregistered trademark. The ® symbol denotes a registered trademark.

9. A. A trademarked word that becomes generic loses its protection. *Aspirin*, for example, once referred to a particular brand of painkiller.

10. D. Patents protect items (products) and processes.

11. C. In order to have patent protection, an inventor must apply for and be granted a patent by a government.

12. C. The law specifies that patentable products and ideas must be useful, new, and nonobvious.

13. B. You can sell public-domain software for a profit, or at least try to do so. You can also modify it as needed.

14. A. Because there are so many English speakers on the Internet, that language is the default for many international communications.

15. C. You have to be patient with and appreciative of people who are going to the trouble to accommodate you.

16. B. By establishing distribution centers in other countries with which you do a lot of business, you eliminate the time and expense associated with lots of international shipments.

17. B. You can't argue with the truth and expect to win.

18. B. Ad rates often are quoted in terms of some price per 1,000 exposures of the ad.

19. C. A payment in kind is any payment made with something other than cash. Such transactions are taxable.

20. D. Though their issuers collect fees, credit cards allow for easy conversion among currencies.

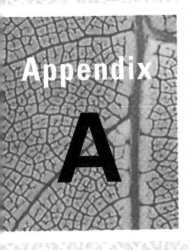

Appendix A

Practice Exam

1. People are complaining that they don't know what type of documents your site has. What would improve things?

   A. A site map

   B. A more consistent user interface

   C. Full-text search

   D. A content type policy

2. People are complaining that there are too many documents listed on your site and they can't find the documents they are looking for. What technology would best help them find the information they need?

   A. A site map

   B. A more consistent user interface

   C. Full-text search

   D. A content type policy

3. You don't want your information to be indexed by the large search engines. What can you do?

   A. Update the site infrequently.

   B. Add an entry in your ROBOTS.TXT file to ward spidering robots away.

   C. Avoid links from other sites.

   D. Move to a database-driven dynamic Web site.

4. Which is *not* a factor in a client's performance level?

   A. Network speed

   B. Browser version

   C. Color scheme

   D. Operating system

5. Secure Sockets Layer (SSL) usually is used for what?

   A. To encrypt e-mail messages

   B. To secure the flow of credit card transaction data among banks

   C. To make transactions between Web browsers and Web servers secure

   D. To encrypt usernames and passwords

6. Log files can contain information that indicates what?

   A. A stolen password

   B. A brute force attack on a password

   C. A disgruntled employee

   D. Whether bad guys are spoofing IP addresses to bypass your firewall

7. What is public-key encryption's big advantage on the Internet?

   A. There's no need to exchange keys privately.

   B. It's more secure than other forms of encryption.

   C. It's especially suitable to e-mail encryption.

   D. It makes routers' work easier.

8. One way to design a Web page for compatibility with diverse browsers is to _____ .

   A. Include a JavaScript test of the browser version

   B. Design with the latest HTML specification

   C. Not use tables

   D. Avoid streaming media

9. Multimedia content that requires clients to have plug-ins works best _____ .

   A. On public Web sites

   B. On sites with an academic focus

   C. For streaming media

   D. In environments where the work at hand absolutely requires the plug-in-enabled content

10. What is the emerging replacement for the GIF image?

    A. Tagged Image File Format (TIFF)

    B. Portable Network Graphics (PNG)

    C. Joint Photographic Experts Group (JPEG)

    D. Encapsulated PostScript (EPS)

11. The audio-video file format developed for Microsoft Windows is called _____ .

    A. QuickTime

    B. Gzip

    C. Audio Visual Interleaved (AVI)

    D. MPEG

12. What are the two most popular streaming media standards?

    A. RealPlayer and Windows Media Player

    B. RealPlayer and Audio Visual Interleaved (AVI)

    C. RealPlayer and RealPlayer G2

    D. Windows Media Player and Motion Picture Experts Group (MPEG)

13. The tape archive format usually is used in conjunction with _____ .

 A. The Zip compression format

 B. The Gzip compression format

 C. The BinHex compression format

 D. The Solaris archive format

14. Open source software that is protected by copyleft _____ .

 A. Cannot be sold for profit

 B. May not be modified

 C. Must be attributed to the Free Software Foundation

 D. Includes the Linux operating system

15. The success of a banner-ad placement is usually measured by its _____ .

 A. Cost per view

 B. Clickthrough rate

 C. User commentary

 D. Graphic design values

16. What is one business advantage of a virtual private network?

 A. The extra security it provides

 B. The reduction in telecommunications expenses

 C. The inherent ability to bring vendors onto your network

 D. The elimination of the need for an Internet site

17. What is the proper HTML syntax to use to make the copyright symbol (©) appear in an HTML page correctly?

    A. <COPYRIGHT>

    B. ©

    C. <COPY>

    D. &copy

18. What are the best types of documents to distribute using Electronic Data Interchange (EDI)?

    A. Orders and invoices

    B. Memos

    C. Reports

    D. E-mail

19. What is the best way to increase traffic to a Web site?

    A. Bulk e-mail

    B. Search engine placement

    C. Banner ads

    D. Banner ads on a search engine site

20. A Web site designed for use by a company's inside sales staff is an example of an _____ .

    A. Internet

    B. Intranet

    C. Extranet

    D. Outernet

21. When is it appropriate to use the copyright symbol (©) on a
    Web page?

    A. After copyright has been obtained

    B. During the copyright application process

    C. As soon as the Web page is displayed

    D. Whenever you feel like it

22. When designing a global Web site, which aspect is the most critical?

    A. Display language

    B. Scripting language

    C. Layout

    D. Server type

23. A network or Web site designed specifically for business-to-business
    transactions is called an _____ .

    A. Internet

    B. Extranet

    C. E-commerce

    D. Intranet

24. Online sales transactions are best protected by which technology?

    A. HTML

    B. SSL

    C. HTTP

    D. PGP

25. Why is it important to obtain permission before linking to a graphic on a third-party site (e.g., using HTML that displays a graphic or a portion of another Web page in your Web page)?

   A. It is illegal in some states.

   B. You are making a derivative work.

   C. It is a requirement of HTML.

   D. The owner of the originating Web site must do something to the server on his end to make it possible.

26. What is arguably the most common mistake people make when designing an international Web site?

   A. Using HTML coding

   B. Using graphics

   C. Using English as the primary language

   D. Using colloquialisms

27. Which type of site has the capability to reach the largest audience?

   A. Internet

   B. Extranet

   C. Intranet

   D. Outernet

28. Point-to-Point Tunneling Protocol (PPTP) is most often used for providing _____ functions between a corporate office and a branch office.

   A. Remote access

   B. VPN

   C. Internet

   D. Telephone

29. When setting up a U.S. Web site for international use, what is the highest level of encryption you can support?

   A. 40 bit

   B. 60 bit

   C. 80 bit

   D. 128 bit

30. Your Web site about classic Studebaker automobiles is not showing up when you search for "Studebaker" on your favorite Web search engine. You can improve your Web site's chances of appearing in search results through the use of _____.

   A. HTML tags

   B. JavaScript

   C. Meta tags

   D. Search forms

31. A merchant system will allow _____ on your Web site.

   A. Secure access

   B. FTP access

   C. Credit card transactions

   D. The use of usernames and passwords

32. Push technology allows users to _____ .

   A. Subscribe to information and automatically receive updates of that information

   B. Send information to other users without knowing their addresses

   C. Allow other users to access their computer's hard disk

   D. Share their files via FTP and e-mail

33. The DIR attribute in HTML 4 indicates what?

   A. Forms order

   B. List formatting

   C. Picture formatting

   D. Arrow direction

34. Which graphics format requires a plug-in to be viewed by a Web browser?

   A. GIF

   B. JPEG

   C. GIF87a

   D. TIFF

35. Which scripting language is compiled before execution?

   A. XML

   B. Java

   C. VBScript

   D. VRML

36. What is the use of the "NAME=" attribute in the <FRAME> tag within an HTML page?

   A. To assign a frame horizontal position

   B. To assign a frame vertical position

   C. To name an image frame

   D. To identify a target frame

37. Of those listed, which Web graphics format allows an image to be transparent (i.e., you can see part of the Web page through it)?

A. JPEG

B. GIF89a

C. GIF87a

D. PNG

38. If you want to use 3-D effects within a Web-based presentation, what is the best technology for the task?

A. RealPlayer

B. Shockwave

C. QuickTime VR

D. VRML

39. What should you change in the following HTML Web page code to make sure it displays properly?

```
<HTML>
<title>David's web page <title>
<P>
Welcome to my web page.  Enjoy your visit
</P>
<A href=http://www.studebakerclubs.com/roughrider/
>Click me</A>
</HTML>
```

A. Change all tags to lowercase.

B. Change all tags to lowercase and correct the <TITLE> tag.

C. Correct the <TITLE> tag.

D. Nothing.

40. In an Internet context, what does CSS stand for?

   A. Commercially Secured Server

   B. Controlled Server Side

   C. Can't Stand Stuff

   D. Controlled State Server

41. If you want to play streaming video on your Web site, which technology would you implement?

   A. RealPlayer

   B. Flash

   C. Acrobat

   D. QuickTime VR

42. METHOD, ACTION, ENCTYPE, TARGET are all attributes of which HTML tag?

   A. <TITLE>

   B. <A>

   C. <FORM>

   D. <IMAGE>

43. You want music to play in the background when a user views a particular Web page. Which is the best format for the music?

   A. AVI

   B. BGSound

   C. RealPlayer

   D. Embed

44. You want to distribute the video recording of a shareholder meeting via your company's intranet. What technology would be best suited for the task?

   A. QuickTime VR

   B. RealPlayer

   C. AVI

   D. MP3

45. What is the most efficient data store for a training calendar?

   A. ASCII text file

   B. ISAM

   C. Object-oriented

   D. ODBC

46. What HTML component dictates to a browser *exactly* how text will appear?

   A. Font

   B. Tag

   C. Image

   D. Script

47. What does CGI stand for?

   A. Common Group Interchange

   B. Commercial Gateway Interplex

   C. Common Gateway Interface

   D. Commercial Group Interface

48. What is the proper HTML tag to use to format a numbered list?

    A. <LI>

    B. <UL>

    C. <CP>

    D. <OL>

49. A client-side script is not working correctly. What is the most likely cause?

    A. The server can't parse the script.

    B. The Web client doesn't support the scripting.

    C. The HTTP connection has been lost.

    D. The OS doesn't support scripting.

50. A Web client is experiencing time-out errors when opening a socket to a Web server. You are able to use other Internet services (FTP, e-mail, and so on), but you cannot browse to any Internet Web sites. What is the most likely cause?

    A. The Web browser is not functioning correctly.

    B. The proxy server is blocking the socket.

    C. The proxy server is down.

    D. TCP/IP is not installed on the client.

51. Which technology provides an interactive 3-D environment?

    A. Java

    B. XML

    C. VRML

    D. HTML

Answers to Practice Exam

1. A. Site maps help people who don't know what is on a site learn what they can do there.

2. C. Full-text searches help people narrow the list of documents to only those that meet the search criteria.

3. B. Search engines should respect exclusions in the ROBOTS.TXT file.

4. C. Network speed, browser version, and operating system all affect the ability of a client to use the Internet.

5. C. When you send your credit card number to an online shopping site, the transmission is made secure by SSL in most cases.

6. B. A log file might show lots of unsuccessful login attempts, which indicates a brute force attack on a password.

7. A. Public-key encryption doesn't require a private, secure exchange of keys the way private-key encryption does.

8. A. You can test the browser version with JavaScript. Alternately, you can use an older, more widely supported HTML specification.

9. D. A community of users that will really benefit from seeing plug-in-enabled content will be happy to download the needed plug-in.

10. B. The emerging replacement standard is called Portable Network Graphics (PNG).

11. C. Audio Visual Interleaved (AVI) files were developed for Windows.

12. A. RealPlayer and Windows Media Player are fighting it out in the streaming media market.

13. B. Tape archive files (with a .TAR extension) are usually compressed with Gzip.

14. A. Copyleft prohibits for-profit sale of the software it protects.

15. B. The clickthrough rate is the percentage of people who view an ad and click through to its underlying Web site.

16. B. Because VPNs use the Internet for their long-distance communications, the need for expensive dedicated lines disappears.

17. D. None of the other answers will cause the symbol to display correctly.

18. A. EDI is best suited for distributing orders and invoices among companies. Memos and reports are best suited for e-mail.

19. D. Bulk e-mail is irresponsible and tends to irritate customers. Placement of a Web site address in a search engine and indiscriminate use of banner ads can be just as ineffective. Banner ads placed in the correct category of a search engine can be very effective in increasing Web traffic.

20. B. Intranets are networks designed for use by a single company's employees. The other items listed will not serve in this capacity.

21. C. A Web page is considered to be protected by copyright as soon as it is available for viewing by the public even though a federal copyright may be pending. The symbol must be displayed properly, indicating the year of publication and owner of the work.

22. A. You must choose a language or languages that can be read throughout the world.

23. B. The Internet is used for public access to information. E-commerce Web sites are used to sell items, and intranets are used for distributing information within an organization.

24. B. Secure Sockets Layer (SSL) is a method of making encrypted transactions over the Internet. Pretty Good Privacy (PGP) is, in fact, a method of encryption, but it is too slow for use in online sales transactions. The other two (HTML and HTTP) are not methods of protecting transactions.

25. B. Because you are using a portion of a copyrighted work, you are, in effect, making a derivative work and thus must have permission from the original copyright holder.

26. D. Colloquialisms are localized language derivatives. You would have to live in a specific area to understand a colloquialism. Thus, they may not make any sense to someone who doesn't live in the area from which they originated, much less in a completely different country.

27. A. Both extranet and intranet sites have a limited audience by definition. Outernet is not a viable answer.

28. B. Of the items listed, the best answer is VPN because PPTP is a protocol most often used to provide VPN functions between a corporate office and a branch office.

29. A. To comply with U.S. encryption export regulations, the highest level of encryption that can be exported is 40-bit encryption.

30. C. With meta tags, your site will be indexed in a search engine correctly. Although the other items are used in Web sites, they will not improve your site's chances of appearing in search engine results.

31. C. Merchant systems are collections of server software for Web sites that allow credit card transactions.

32. A. Push technology allows users to subscribe to a content provider and receive regular updates of the content.

33. B. The DIR attribute in HTML 4 is used for formatting a list as a directory listing.

34. D. TIFF is the only file format listed that cannot be displayed in a Web browser without a plug-in.

35. B. Of all the languages listed, Java is the only true programming language, and thus, it must be compiled before execution.

36. D. The "NAME=" attribute is used to identify a target frame for a hyperlink within a frame.

37. B. Of the image file formats listed, the GIF89a format is the only one that allows an image to be transparent.

38. B. Although QuickTime VR and VRML can be used for 3-D modeling, Shockwave is the most efficient technology for providing 3-D effects within a presentation.

39. C. The majority of HTML tag sets (including <TITLE>) must have a beginning tag (<TITLE>) and an ending (</TITLE>) tag. In the example given, the / was missing from the ending tag.

40. A. Although all answers would technically expand the abbreviation, Commercially Secured Server is the correct answer.

41. A. Of the formats listed, RealPlayer is the only streaming video format.

42. C. The attributes only correspond to the <FORM> tag.

43. D. Although each of the formats can be used for playing sound, some require plug-ins. Thus, the most efficient (and thus the best) format for playing background music would be to embed it in the HTML code.

44. B. Of all the technologies listed, RealPlayer would be the most efficient. QuickTime VR and AVI are non-streaming formats and would take too long to download. MP3 is an audio-only format.

45. A. Although all these data stores would work, an ASCII file would be the most practical and efficient because the training calendar doesn't change often.

46. B. HTML tags are used for various purposes, but the most common is to format text for display in a Web browser.

47. C. Common Gateway Interface is the proper expansion of the abbreviation CGI. The others are not valid.

48. D. <OL> stands for ordered list, the HTML tag used for a numbered list. <UL> stands for unordered list and is the HTML tag used for a list of items without numbers.

49. B. When client-side scripting doesn't work, it's usually the fault of the client (i.e., the Web browser).

50. B. Because other Internet services are functional, it's not C or D. Because a specific Internet service is not functional, the most likely cause is B.

51. C. Of those listed, the only technology that provides a fully interactive 3-D environment is the Virtual Reality Modeling Language (VRML).

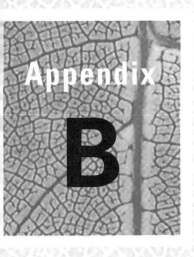

Appendix B

Acronym and Abbreviation Expansion Guide

Acronyms and abbreviations are part of the computer business. Below, you will find a list of acronyms and abbreviations that are used in the computer industry and can be found throughout this book. On the right-hand side of this list, you will find the common expansion of each.

ACL	Access Control List
ADSL	Asymmetric Digital Subscriber Line
ARPA	Advanced Research Projects Agency
ASCII	American Standard Code for Information Interchange
ASP	Active Server Pages
AVI	Audio Visual Interleaved
bash	Bourne Again Shell
BDC	backup domain controller
BNC	Bayonet Neill Concelman, Bayonet Nut Connector, or British Naval Connector
BSD	Berkeley Software Distribution
CA	certification authority
CGI	Common Gateway Interface
CIDR	Classless Inter-Domain Routing
CIR	Committed Information Rate
COM	Component Object Model
CPAN	Comprehensive Perl Archive Network
CPU	central processing unit
CSMA/CA	carrier sense multiple access with collision avoidance
CSMA/CD	carrier sense multiple access with collision detection
DARPA	Defense Advanced Research Projects Agency
DBMS	Database Management Systems

DCOM	Distributed Component Object Model
DDS	Dataphone Digital Service (also used for Digital Data Storage and Digital Data Service)
DHCP	Dynamic Host Configuration Protocol
DLL	Dynamic Link Library
DLT	digital linear tape
DMZ	demilitarized zone
DNS	Domain Name Services
DOD	Department of Defense
DOS	denial of service
dpi	dots per inch
DSL	Digital Subscriber Line
DTD	document type definition
DUN	Dial-Up Networking
DVD	digital video disc or digital versatile disk
EMI	electromagnetic interference
EPS	Encapsulated PostScript
ERP	Enterprise Resource Planning
FDM	frequency division multiplexing
FTP	File Transfer Protocol
FTPd	File Transfer Protocol Daemon
GIF	Graphics Interchange Format
GSNW	Gateway Services for NetWare
GUI	graphical user interface
HDSL	High Data Rate Digital Subscriber Line
HP	Hewlett-Packard

HTML	Hypertext Markup Language
HTTP	Hypertext Transfer Protocol
HTTPd	Hypertext Transfer Protocol Daemon
IAB	Internet Architecture Board
IBM	International Business Machines
IE	Internet Explorer
IEEE	Institute of Electrical and Electronics Engineers
IETF	Internet Engineering Task Force
IHL	Internet Header Length
IIS	Internet Information Server
INND	Internet News Daemon
IPX	Internetwork Packet eXchange
IPX/SPX	Internetwork Packet eXchange/Sequenced Packet eXchange
IRQ	interrupt request lines
IRTF	Internet Research Task Force
ISDN	Integrated Services Digital Network
ISO	International Organization for Standardization
ISP	Internet Service Provider
JPEG	Joint Photographic Experts Group
JVM	Java Virtual Machine
LAN	local area network
LCP	Link Control Protocol
LDAP	Lightweight Directory Access Protocol
MAC	media access control
MIME	Multipurpose Internet Mail Extension

MPEG	Motion Picture Experts Group
MSAU	multistation access unit
MX	mail exchange
NADN	nearest active downstream neighbor
NAUN	nearest active upstream neighbor
NCSA	National Center for Supercomputing Applications
NDS	Novell Directory Services
NetBEUI	NetBIOS Enhanced User Interface
NetBIOS	Network Basic Input Output System
NIC	network interface card
NNTP	Network News Transfer Protocol
NOS	network operating system
OEM	original equipment manufacturer
OS	operating system
OSI	Open Systems Interconnection
OUI	Organizationally Unique Identifier
PDC	primary domain controller
PGP	Pretty Good Privacy
PHP	Hypertext Preprocessor
PNG	Portable Network Graphics
POP3	Post Office Protocol version 3
POTS	Plain Old Telephone Service
ppi	pixels per inch
PPP	Point-to-Point Protocol
PPTP	Point-to-Point Tunneling Protocol
PSTN	Public Switched Telephone Network

PVC	permanent virtual circuit
QoS	Quality of Service
RAM	random access memory
RFC	Request for Comments
RFI	radio frequency interference
RIP	Routing Information Protocol
RISC	reduced instruction set computing
RJ	Registered Jack
SAM	Security Accounts Manager
SCSI	Small Computer System Interface
SDSL	Single Line Digital Subscriber Line
SET	Secure Electronic Transactions
SLIP	Serial Line Internet Protocol
SMTP	Simple Mail Transfer Protocol
SOP	standard operating procedures
SPARC	Scalable Processor ARChitecture
SPX	Sequenced Packet eXchange
SQL	Structured Query Language
SSL	Secure Sockets Layer
STP	shielded twisted-pair
Tcl	Tool Command Language
TCP	Transmission Control Protocol
TCP/IP	Transmission Control Protocol/Internet Protocol
TDM	time division multiplexing
Telnet	Terminal Emulation for Networks
TIFF	Tagged Image File Format

TM	Trademark
TOS	Type of Service
UDP	User Datagram Protocol
UID	user ID
URL	Uniform Resource Locator
USPTO	United States Patent and Trademark Office
UTP	unshielded twisted-pair
VDSL	Very High Data Rate Digital Subscriber Line
VPN	virtual private network
VRML	Virtual Reality Modeling Language
WINS	Windows Internet Name Service
WSH	Windows Script Host
WWW	World Wide Web
XML	eXtensible Markup Language

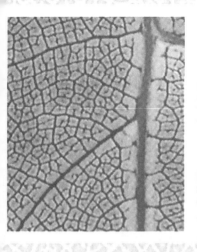

Glossary of
Networking Terms

10Base-2   An implementation of Ethernet that specifies a 10Mbps signaling rate, baseband signaling, and coaxial cable with a maximum segment length of 185 meters (approximately 607 feet).

85% policy   A Web site design policy that encourages the use of technologies that will reach many people but not let the stragglers drag functionality down for other viewers. The Web site is designed so that the majority of Internet users can view its content.

abend   Short for *ab*normal *end*. Novell's term for a server crash.

ABEND.LOG   The log file in the SYS:\SYSTEM directory on a NetWare 4.11 or later server that records all abends that have occurred on a NetWare server, including detailed information regarding the abend.

access control   Any system that keeps people from accessing resources they don't need. If they can't access it, they can't steal it.

Access Control List (ACL)   The list of rights an object has to resources in the network. Also a type of firewall. In this case, the lists reside on a router and determine which machines can use the router and in what direction.

access log   A Web server log file that indicates who has accessed which resource. The access log records the IP address of the accessing station, the time and date of the access, which file was accessed, and the protocol used to access it.

ACK   *See* acknowledgment.

acknowledgment (ACK)   A message confirming that the data packet was received. This occurs at the Transport layer of the OSI model.

ACL   *See* Access Control List.

active detection   A type of intruder detection that constantly scans the network for possible break-ins.

active monitor   Used in Token Ring networks, a process that prevents data frames from roaming the ring unchecked. If the frame passes the active monitor too many times, it is removed from the ring. Also ensures that a token is always circulating the ring.

Active Server Pages (ASP)   The server-side scripting solution for Microsoft Web servers—mainly, Internet Information Server (IIS).

adaptive content policy   A Web site design policy in which Web sites don't necessarily have to choose between accessibility and glamour. Instead, sites can deliver advanced features to clients that can use them and standard features to clients who can't use advanced features. In this way, the whole audience is well served. Writing the Web site to work in this way, however, adds complexity and often cost.

Adobe Acrobat   A file format that is used on the Internet to distribute files that contain graphics and text in a specified layout. Acrobat allows users on diverse platforms to view (and in its latest version, annotate) documents that incorporate text, graphics, hyperlinks, and complex layouts. It's better than HTML because the publisher has absolute control over how the publication looks on users' machines. Acrobat files carry a `.PDF` filename extension.

American Standard Code for Information Interchange (ASCII)   The standard code used to convert decimal numbers used during computer communications into characters, numbers, and symbols for display on screen.

antivirus   A category of software that uses various methods to eliminate viruses in a computer. It typically also protects against future infection. *See also* virus.

Application layer   Layer seven of the OSI model; the Application layer deals with how applications access the network and describes application functionality, such as file transfer, messaging, and so on.

application log   Windows NT log file, viewable in the Event Viewer, that is used to keep track of events for network services and applications.

application server   Any server that hosts a network application.

ARCNet   The Attached Resource Computer Network, which was developed by Datapoint Corporation in the late 1970s as one of the first baseband networks. It can use either a physical star topology or a bus topology.

ARP table   A table used by the ARP protocol. Contains a list of known TCP/IP addresses and their associated MAC addresses. The table is cached in memory so that ARP lookups do not have to be performed for frequently accessed TCP/IP and MAC addresses. *See also* Address Resolution Protocol; media access control; Transmission Control Protocol/Internet Protocol.

ASCII   *See* American Standard Code for Information Interchange (ASCII).

ASP   *See* Active Server Pages (ASP).

Asynchronous Transfer Mode (ATM)   A connection-oriented network architecture based on broadband ISDN technology that uses constant-size 53-byte cells instead of packets. Because cells don't change size, they are switched much faster and more efficiently than packets across a network.

AT command set   A set of modem initialization commands developed by the Hayes company for their modems, so named because each command begins with *AT*. *See also* modem initialization commands.

ATM   *See* Asynchronous Transfer Mode.

Attachment Unit Interface (AUI) port   On some NICs, a port through which the NIC can be connected to different media types by using an external transceiver.

Audio Visual Interleaved (AVI) files   A video file format that has support for full-motion video and animation with sound. Developed for the Windows environment by Microsoft, AVI files usually have .AVI filename extensions.

auditing   A system of record keeping in which special software takes notes of what is happening on a network and why and allows administrators to look at those notes (called log files) later.

authentication   The process of verifying that a person (or a piece of software, in situations where programs share information without human intervention) is who he claims to be.

AVI files   *See* Audio Visual Interleaved (AVI) files.

B channel   *See* Bearer channel.

backbone ISP   An ISP with very high-speed connections (several hundred megabits per second) to the other backbone ISPs. These connections form the "backbone" of the Internet.

backup domain controller (BDC)   Computer on a Windows NT network that has a read-only copy of the SAM database for fault-tolerance and per-formance-enhancement purposes. *See also* Security Accounts Manager.

bandwidth   In network communications, the amount of data that can be sent across a wire in a given time (usually in one second). Each communica-tion that passes along the wire decreases the amount of available bandwidth.

banner ads   A rectangular graphic, generally about 500 pixels wide by 60 pixels tall, that's placed on a Web page, usually to sell some items or services. When a surfer clicks a banner ad, he's taken to the advertiser's Web site (and usually, the fact that he got there through a banner ad is noted).

baseband   A transmission technique in which the signal uses the entire bandwidth of a transmission medium.

baseline   A category of network documentation that indicates how the net-work normally runs. It includes such information as network statistics, server utilization trends, and processor performance statistics.

Bearer channel   The channels in an ISDN line that carry data (also called the B channel). Each Bearer channel typically has a bandwidth of 64Kbps.

bindery   Flat database used in NetWare 3.*x* and earlier servers to store net-work resource information (such as user, group, and security information). Each server in the network has its own bindery database.

BinHex   The MacOS file compression standard. The BinHex format allows you to combine several files into one compressed unit and extract them indi-vidually. They usually have an `.HQX` filename extension.

biometric authentication   A type of authentication that uses fingerprints, retinal scan, voiceprints, face recognition, and other biologically unique fea-tures of humans instead of passwords for network authentication.

Bit Fiddler   A virus that changes small random bits in files.

BNC connector   Tubular connectors most commonly used with coaxial cable.

boot sector virus   A virus that overrides the boot sector, thereby making it appear as if there is no pointer to your operating system. When this happens, you will see a "Missing operating system" or "Hard disk not found" error message on power-up.

bounded medium   A network medium where the signal travels over a cable of some kind.

bridge   A network device, operating at the Data Link layer, that logically separates a single network into segments but lets the two segments appear to be one network to higher-layer protocols.

broadband   A network transmission method in which a single transmission medium is divided so that multiple signals can travel across the same medium simultaneously.

brouter   A connectivity device that will act as a router for routable protocols and act as a bridge for nonroutable protocols.

brownout   *See* power brownout.

browser   A computer program that uses the Hypertext Transfer Protocol and is used on a workstation to access hosts on the Web.

brute force attack   A type of network attack where the attacker simply uses a computer to generate random combinations of characters in the hope of stumbling onto the correct combination for a password. Brute force attacks rely on the capacity of attacking computers to tirelessly generate different combinations of characters and feed them to defended network resources.

burst mode   An addition to NCP that allows multiple date frames to be sent without waiting for an acknowledgment for the previous frame of data. *See also* NetWare Core Protocol.

business-to-business commerce   Businesses providing goods and services to other businesses.

bytecodes   The result of running Java source code through a Java compiler. This result is used within an imaginary chip called the Java Virtual Machine (JVM). *See also* Java Virtual Machine (JVM).

C   A general-purpose programming language that can be used to write programs for various platforms. The code must be specifically written for a particular platform, however.

C++   An object-oriented version of C. *See also* C.

CA   *See* certification authority.

cable   A physical transmission medium that has a central conductor of wire or fiber surrounded by a plastic jacket.

cable map   A general network documentation indicating each cable's source and destination as well as where each network cable runs.

cable tester   *See* time-domain reflectometer.

cache-in-a-box   A "black box" that you plug into your network to increase Internet surfing by caching portions of frequently accessed Web sites.

CAD program   Any program that is used during the computer-aided design (CAD) process; typically used by engineers.

captive audience policy   A type of Web content policy that by which Web site creators create the content in the format they want, their audience must use only browsers that work with these content types. Captive audience policies usually rely on the content creators also having control of the browsers people have on their desktops.

carrier sense multiple access with collision avoidance (CSMA/CA)   A media access method that sends a request to send (RTS) packet and waits to receive a clear to send (CTS) packet before sending. Once the CTS is received, the sender sends the packet of information.

carrier sense multiple access with collision detection (CSMA/CD)   A media access method that senses whether there is a signal on the wire, indicating that someone is transmitting currently. If no one else is transmitting, it attempts a transmission and listens to hear whether someone else tries to transmit at the same time. If this happens, both senders back off and don't transmit again until some random period of time has passed.

centralized WAN　A WAN with a computer that connects computers and dumb terminals to a central site. *See also* wide area network.

certificate　Proof that someone (or something) is what he or she (or it) claims to be.

certification authority　An organization that's responsible for verifying the identity of people and issuing certificates to those whose identities can be verified. Also known as a certificate authority.

CGI　*See* Common Gateway Interface.

ciphertext　Text after it has been encrypted.

CIR　*See* Committed Information Rate.

cleartext　Normal text before it is encrypted.

Client Services for NetWare (CSNW)　Software that allows Windows NT computers to access NetWare resources.

client-server network　A server-centric network in which all resources are stored on a file server; processing power is distributed among workstations and the file server.

client-side markup language　Any system of adding tags (markup) to a text document in order to supply information about how the text should be rendered in a Web browser or what it means. Client-side markup languages are interpreted by Web browsers.

clipper chip　A hardware implementation of the skipjack encryption algorithm.

coaxial cable　Often referred to as coax. A type of cable used in network wiring. Typical coaxial cable types include RG-58 and RG-62. 10Base-2 Ethernet networks use coaxial cable. Coaxial cable is usually shielded.

cold site backup system　A backup system that does not run continuously. Therefore, before you can restore data, the computer must be repaired and the software must be reloaded on the server.

collision The error condition that occurs when two stations on a CSMA/CD network transmit data (at the Data link layer) at the same time. *See also* carrier sense multiple access with collision detection.

Committed Information Rate (CIR) A commitment from your service provider stating the minimum bandwidth you will get on a Frame Relay network.

Common Gateway Interface (CGI) A specification that defines a way of packaging text data (such as the contents of a form) for transmission over a network. The CGI specification takes the contents of a form and the names of the form elements (as specified in HTML) and assembles them all into a long string of characters. That string can then be passed to a program on the server side for processing and a response.

compiler A special software program that translates the human-readable source code of a programming language into machine code that processors and operating systems can understand. Compilers are usually specific to a programming language.

Component Object Model (COM) The Microsoft "twin" to JavaBeans. It's a means of writing independent code modules and having them communicate with one another. The idea is that you could have a single, specialized COM module that various other pieces of software (other COM modules and non-COM programs) refer to for different reasons. Unlike JavaBeans, however, COM currently will work only on Windows (and some Unix) machines.

concentrator *See* hub.

connectionless protocol A transport protocol, such as UDP, that does not create a virtual connection between sending and receiving stations. *See also* User Datagram Protocol.

connection-oriented protocol A transport protocol that uses acknowledgments and responses to establish a virtual connection between sending and receiving stations. TCP is a connection-oriented protocol. *See also* Transmission Control Protocol.

CONSOLE.LOG A NetWare server log file that keeps a history of all errors and information that has been displayed on the server's console since the `CONLOG.NLM` file was loaded.

contention A media access method that allows any computer to transmit whenever it has data. Every station has an equal opportunity to transmit.

cookie A special text message given to a Web browser by a Web server. The browser stores this message on the local hard disk. The next time someone using that Web browser on that computer visits the same Web server, the Web browser sends this message back to the Web server (which created it). Cookies are used to provide customized Web sites for users.

copyleft A legal term whereby an organization (usually a not-for-profit group like the Free Software Foundation) establishes copyright to an item of intellectual property—source code for software, usually—then distributes it free of charge. People who use the software must agree to its licensing agreement, which specifies that they may not make a profit on its distribution. The GNU utilities are covered by copyleft.

copyright The right of an author, artist, publisher, or other legal entity to collect money from the use of words, music, performance works, items of visual art, or other creative products.

country codes The two-letter abbreviations for countries; used in the DNS hierarchy. *See also* Domain Name Services.

CRC *See* cyclical redundancy check.

crossover cable The troubleshooting tool used in Ethernet UTP installations to test communications between two stations, bypassing the hub. *See also* unshielded-twisted pair.

cross-sell The process of selling the buyer of a given product accessories and other related products.

CSMA/CA *See* carrier sense multiple access with collision avoidance.

CSMA/CD *See* carrier sense multiple access with collision detection.

CSNW *See* Client Services for NetWare.

cyclical redundancy check (CRC)   An error-checking method in data communications that runs a predefined formula against data before transmissions. The sending station then appends the resultant value (called a checksum) to the data and sends it. The receiving station uses the same formula on the data. If the receiving station doesn't get the same checksum result for the calculation, it considers the transmission invalid, rejects the frame, and asks for a retransmission.

Data Encryption Standard (DES)   A government standard for private key systems that has lookup table functions and fast encryption. A 64-bit private key is used. *See also* private key; public key.

Data Link layer   The second layer of the OSI model; the Data Link layer describes the logical topology of a network—the way that packets move throughout a network. It also describes the method of media access. *See also* Open Systems Interconnection.

data mining   The process by which applications attempt to analyze the data in databases and draw conclusions from it.

data packet   A unit of data sent over a network. A packet includes a header, addressing information, and the data itself. A packet is treated as a single unit as it is sent from device to device.

database   Any collection of data, usually organized in some fashion.

Database Management System (DBMS)   A program that adds data to databases, extracts data from them, organizes the data for various applications, and generally attempts to guarantee that the database is fast, easily accessible, and secure from outsiders.

database server   Any program that's responsible for maintaining one or more databases and responding to queries sent to them. This definition also refers to a type of server that runs database server software.

datagram   A unit of data smaller than a packet.

Dataphone Digital Service (DDS) line   This type of Internet bandwidth link technology from AT&T is a dedicated, point-to-point connection with throughput anywhere from 2400bps to 56Kbps. The 56Kbps digital connection is the most common, and this type of line has since obtained the moniker 56K Line. When not purchased from AT&T, this line is known as a Digital Data Service line.

DBMS   *See* Database Management System (DBMS).

DCOM   *See* Distributed Component Object Model (DCOM).

default gateway   The router that all packets are sent to when the workstation doesn't know where the destination station is or when it can't find the destination station on the local segment.

Defense Advanced Research Projects Agency (DARPA)   The government agency responsible for the creation of ARPAnet, on which the foundation for the Internet was laid.

Delta channel   A channel used for link management on an ISDN line. *See also* Integrated Services Digital Network.

demilitarized zone (DMZ)   The special area (defined by a firewall) where all public access servers are located, protected from outside attack yet available to users on both sides of the firewall.

denial of service (DOS) attack   Type of attack that prevents any users, even legitimate ones, from using the system and its resources.

DES   *See* Data Encryption Standard.

DHCP   *See* Dynamic Host Configuration Protocol.

differential backup   Backs up data that has changed since the last full backup.

digital   Any signal that has discrete values over time. A digital signal has no transition between values. It is one value in one instant (that is, a specific number, such as 1) and a different value the next (that is, a second number, such as 0).

digital certificate   Digital proof that someone is who he claims to be on the Internet.

digital signature   Pieces of electronic information that serve to guarantee that an item—a document, a credit card number, whatever—was not tampered with as it traveled over the Internet from sender to recipient. By examining a digital signature that arrives with a piece of data, you can be sure that the data has arrived in exactly the same state it was in when it left the sender's computer.

Digital Subscriber Line (DSL)   A digital WAN technology that brings high-speed digital networking to homes and businesses over POTS. There are many types, such as HDSL (High Data Rate Digital Subscriber Line) and VDSL (Very High Data Rate Digital Subscriber Line). *See also* Public Switched Telephone Network.

directory   A network database that contains a listing of all network resources, such as users, printers, groups, and so on.

directory service   A network service that provides access to a central database that contains detailed information about the resources available on a network.

disk drive subsystem   The entire set of hard disks, controllers, and software that makes up the storage component of a workstation or a server.

disk drivers   NLMs that provide NetWare with access to the disk channel. *See also* NetWare Loadable Module.

disk striping   Technology that enables writing data to multiple disks simultaneously in equal portions called stripes. These stripes maximize use by having all of the read/write heads working constantly. Different data is stored on each disk and is not automatically duplicated (this means that disk striping in and of itself does not provide fault tolerance).

distance vector   A route-discovery method in which each router, using broadcasts, tells every other router what networks and routes it knows about and the distance to them.

Distributed Component Object Model (DCOM)   A subset of COM that includes COM modules running on different machines and referring to one another across a network. *See also* Component Object Model (COM).

distributed computing   A technology where portions of a computing job are spread over several machines.

DLL   *See* Dynamic Link Library.

DMZ   *See* demilitarized zone.

DDNS   *See* Dynamic DNS.

DNS resolver   Client software used to make requests of the DNS server in order to resolve DNS host names into IP addresses. *See also* Domain Name Services; Internet Protocol.

DNS server   Any server that performs DNS host name to IP address resolution. *See also* Domain Name Services; Internet Protocol.

DNS zone   An area in the DNS hierarchy that is managed as a single unit. *See also* Domain Name Services.

document type definition (DTD)   A common XML specification that allows one party to publish data in conformance with a DTD so that another party, having access to the same DTD, can interpret the information published.

DOD Networking Model   A four-layer conceptual model describing how communications should take place between computer systems. The four layers are Process/Application, Host-to-Host, Internet, and Network Access.

domain   A group of networked Windows computers that share a single SAM database. *See also* Security Accounts Manager.

Domain Name Services (DNS)   Used in TCP/IP networks, the network service that translates host names to IP addresses. *See also* Transmission Control Protocol/Internet Protocol.

drive mapping   The process of assigning a drive letter at the client to a directory or folder on the server.

DSL   *See* Digital Subscriber Line.

D-type connector   A type of network connector that connects computer peripherals. It contains rows of pins or sockets shaped in a sideways *D*.

dumb terminal   A keyboard and monitor that send keystrokes to a central processing computer (typically a mainframe or minicomputer) and return screen displays to the monitor. The unit has no processing power of its own, hence, the moniker *dumb*.

duplexed hard drives   Two hard drives to which identical information is written simultaneously. A dedicated controller card controls each drive. Used for fault tolerance.

Dynamic DNS (DDNS)   A Windows 2000 feature that dynamically registers a DNS host name for network workstations as they are brought online. *See also* Domain Name Services.

dynamic entry   An entry made in the ARP table whenever an ARP request is made by the Windows TCP/IP stack and the MAC address is not found in the ARP table. The ARP request is broadcast on the local segment. When the MAC address of the requested IP address is found, that information is added to the ARP table. *See also* Address Resolution Protocol; Internet Protocol; media access control; Transmission Control Protocol/Internet Protocol.

Dynamic Host Configuration Protocol (DHCP)   A protocol used on a TCP/IP-based network to send client configuration data—including TCP/IP address, default gateway, subnet mask, and DNS configuration—to clients. *See also* Domain Name Services; default gateway; subnet mask; Transmission Control Protocol/Internet Protocol.

Dynamic Link Library (DLL)   Small pieces of executable Windows code that Windows programmers use so they don't have to write commonly used routines into each program.

dynamic packet filtering   The process of using a firewall to monitor the packets involved in an exchange between the Internet and a private network and rejecting those that don't match patterns for "safe" packets.

dynamic routing   The use of route discovery protocols to talk to other routers and find out what networks they are attached to. Routers that use dynamic routing send out special packets to request updates of the other routers on the network as well as to send their own updates.

dynamic state list A list that is held on a firewall and changes as communication sessions are added and deleted. Only computers that are in a current communication session are allowed to send information back and forth.

E1 An E1 is the same style channel as a T1 connection, but it is a European standard and is made up of 32 64Kbps channels for a total throughput of 2.048Mbps. *See also* T1.

E3 E3 is a bandwidth technology for Europe that uses 480 64Kbps channels for a total bandwidth of 34.368Mbps.

e-commerce The exchange of money and goods using the Internet as the exchange medium.

e-commerce server An Internet Web server that provides e-commerce services through Web server scripts or programs.

EEPROM *See* electronically erasable programmable read-only memory.

electromagnetic interference (EMI) The interference that can occur during transmissions over copper cable because of electromagnetic energy outside the cable. The result is degradation of the signal.

electronic mail (e-mail) An application that allows people to send messages via their computers on the same network or over the Internet.

electronically erasable programmable read-only memory (EEPROM) A special integrated circuit on expansion cards that allows data to be stored on the chip. If necessary, the data can be erased by a special configuration program. Typically used to store hardware configuration data for expansion cards.

electrostatic discharge (ESD) A problem that exists when two items with dissimilar static electrical charges are brought together. The static electrical charges jump to the item with fewer electrical charges, causing ESD, which can damage computer components.

emergency scan A scan used after a virus has taken control of a computer. An emergency antivirus boot disk is used.

EMI *See* electromagnetic interference.

Encapsulated PostScript (EPS) files A graphics file format where the graphic is recorded in the PostScript printer language, which means it's possible to generate a PostScript file on one computer and print it on any PostScript printer, even if the computer to which the printer is connected contains no software that understands PostScript. Web browsers don't support EPS, though, so its application to Internet publishing is limited.

encoding The process of translating data into signals that can be transmitted on a transmission medium.

encryption Any method of converting a readable message into a coded message for secure transmission over an unsecure medium (for example, the Internet).

encryption algorithm Also called a hashing algorithm. A sequence of mathematical procedures that alters the text and encrypts it, thus rendering it unreadable.

encryption key A string of alphanumeric characters used to encrypt and decrypt a message. A message cannot be encrypted or decrypted without the key.

ENS *See* Event Notification Services.

enterprise computing The process of sharing information among the applications with which an organization, such as a company or a unit of government, does its business.

EPS files *See* Encapsulated PostScript (EPS) files.

error log A type of Web server log file that logs any errors reported by the Web server.

ESD *See* electrostatic discharge.

Ethernet A shared-media network architecture. It operates at the Physical and Data Link layers of the OSI model. It uses baseband signaling over either a bus or a star topology with CSMA/CD as the media access method. The cabling used in Ethernet networks can be coax, twisted-pair, or fiber-optic. *See also* carrier sense multiple access with collision detection; Open Systems Interconnection (OSI).

Event Notification Services (ENS)   A component of Novell Directory Print Services (NDPS) broker that notifies users and administrators of network-printing events. *See also* Novell Directory Print Services.

expansion slot   A slot on the computer's bus. Expansion cards are plugged into these slots to expand the functionality of the computer (for example, if you plug in a NIC card, you can add the computer to a network). *See also* network interface card.

eXtensible Markup Language (XML)   A type of markup language that describes what the text in a browser window means. Rather than lock Web publishers into a universal set of tags that must be made to apply in all situations (as HTML does), XML allows users to define their own tags as needed.

failover server   A hot site backup system in which the failover server is connected to the primary server. A heartbeat is sent from the primary server to the backup server. If the heartbeat stops, the failover system starts and takes over. Thus, the system doesn't go down, although the primary server is not running.

fair use   Copyright law recognizes that a vibrant creative community relies, in part, on artists' ability to use the creative products of others as starting points for their own creative work. Such applications of copyrighted material are known as *fair use* applications in the law.

fault-resistant network   A network that will be up and running at least 99 percent of the time or that is down less than 8 hours a year.

fault-tolerant network   A network that can recover from minor errors.

fax server   A computer with a special fax board that sends and receives faxes without the need for paper. It delivers and receives faxes for the entire network.

FDDI   *See* Fiber Distributed Data Interface.

FDM   *See* frequency division multiplexing.

Fiber Distributed Data Interface (FDDI)   A network topology that uses fiber-optic cable as a transmission medium and dual, counter-rotating rings to provide data delivery and fault tolerance.

fiber-optic A type of network cable that uses a central glass or plastic core surrounded by a plastic coating.

fibre channel A type of server-to-storage system connection that uses fiber-optic connectors.

File and Print Services for NetWare (FPNW) A method of providing files and printers hosted by Windows NT to Novell clients. When installed and configured on a Windows NT server, this service makes a Windows NT server look like a NetWare server to Novell clients.

file server A server that specializes in holding and distributing files.

File Transfer Protocol (FTP) A TCP/IP protocol and software that permit the transfer of files between computer systems. Because FTP has been implemented on numerous types of computer systems, files can be transferred between disparate computer systems (for example, a personal computer and a minicomputer). *See also* Transmission Control Protocol/Internet Protocol.

firewall A combination of hardware and software that protects a network from attack by hackers that could gain access through public networks, including the Internet.

forms Collections of user interface elements that include text fields, check boxes, radio buttons, selection lists, and several kinds of buttons to allow a user to enter information into an HTML page.

FPNW *See* File and Print Services for NetWare.

FQDN *See* fully qualified domain name.

Frame Relay A WAN technology that uses packet switching to transmit packets over a WAN. *See also* packet switching.

frequency division multiplexing (FDM) The division of a single transmission medium into multiple channels so that multiple signals can be carried on the medium simultaneously, each using a different frequency.

FTP *See* File Transfer Protocol.

FTP proxy A server that uploads and downloads files from another server on behalf of a workstation.

full backup   A backup that copies all the data to the archive medium.

full-featured development language   A programming language that can be used to write stand-alone programs. You can use a full-featured development language to write an elaborate word processor, a Web browser, or a database front end.

fully qualified domain name (FQDN)   An address that uses both the host name (workstation name) and the domain name.

gateway   The hardware and software needed to connect two disparate network environments so that communications can occur.

Gateway Services for NetWare   Software that is installed as a service on a Windows NT server and translates requests for Windows NT resources into NetWare requests. It also translates SMB protocol requests into NCP requests. It allows multiple Windows NT clients to connect through a Windows NT server to NetWare servers using only Windows NT client software and protocols. *See also* NetWare Core Protocol; Server Message Block.

GIF   *See* Graphics Interchange Format.

global group   A type of group in Windows NT that is used in multiple-domain environments. Members from the local domain can be placed into global groups, which can be used anywhere in the network, and rights can be assigned to any resource in the network.

Gopher   A text-based utility that was used in the early years of the Internet to search for data and news. This utility would present selections in a hierarchical format. Developed from work done at the University of Minnesota. Their mascot was the gopher, so they named this technology Gopher.

Grandfather-Father-Son (GFS) backup method   A standard rotation scheme for backup tapes. Daily backups are the Son, the last full back up of the week is the Father, and the last full backup of the month is the Grandfather.

Graphics Interchange Format (GIF)   A graphics file type that specifies images that consist of from 2 to 256 colors.

ground loop   A condition that occurs when a signal cycles through a common ground connection between two devices, causing EMI interference. *See also* electromagnetic interference.

grouping   A method for organizing users (into administrator groups, printer groups, and so on, for example) that eases network administration.

Gzip   A Unix file compression utility similar to WinZip. Gzip files usually have a .GZ filename extension. Gzip is often applied to tar files to further compress them.

HAL   *See* Hardware Abstraction Layer.

HAM   *See* Host Adapter Module.

Hardware Abstraction Layer (HAL)   The layer in the Windows NT architecture that makes Windows NT platform independent. A new HAL is required to run Windows NT on a platform other than the commonly accepted choices (Intel, MIPS, Alpha).

hardware address   A Data Link layer address assigned to every NIC at the MAC sublayer. The address is in the format $xx:xx:xx:xx:xx:xx$; each xx is a two-digit hexadecimal number. *See also* network interface card; media access control.

Hardware Compatibility List (HCL)   The list of Microsoft-recommended hardware for running Windows operating system software. Hardware must be on this list to be truly compatible with Windows operating systems.

hardware loopback   Connects the transmission pins directly to the receiving pins, allowing diagnostic software to test whether a NIC can successfully transmit and receive. *See also* network interface card.

HCL   *See* Hardware Compatibility List.

header   The section of a packet where the source and destination address reside.

hop   One pass through a router. *See also* router.

host   Any network device with a TCP/IP network address. *See also* Transmission Control Protocol/Internet Protocol.

Host Adapter Module (HAM) A feature of the NetWare Peripheral Architecture that provides communication with the host adapter.

HOSTS file A file within many operating systems (including Windows 95/98 and NT and Unix) that provides manual host name to IP address resolution. The file must be edited on each client machine with a list of all host names and IP addresses on the network.

hot backup system A complete duplicate of a set of computing services stored in a server room. If the main system fails, it can take over operation without any downtime.

HTML *See* Hypertext Markup Language.

HTML forms *See* forms.

HTML tags *See* tags.

HTTP *See* Hypertext Transfer Protocol.

hub A Physical layer device that serves as a central connection point for several network devices. Also known as a concentrator, a hub repeats the signals it receives on one port to all other ports.

Hypertext Markup Language (HTML) A set of codes used to format text and graphics that will be displayed in a browser. The codes define how data will be displayed.

Hypertext Transfer Protocol (HTTP) The protocol used for communication between a Web server and a Web browser.

IBM data connector Used to connect IBM Token Ring stations using Type 1 STP cable. This connector is both male and female, so every IBM data connector can connect to any other IBM data connector. *See also* shielded twisted-pair.

ICMP *See* Internet Control Message Protocol.

IEEE *See* Institute of Electrical and Electronics Engineers.

IEEE 802.x standards The IEEE standards for LAN and MAN networking.

IEEE 802.1 LAN/MAN Management   Standard that specifies LAN/MAN network management and internetworking.

IEEE 802.2 Logical Link Control   Standard that specifies the operation of the Logical Link Control (LLC) sublayer of the Data Link layer of the OSI model. The LLC sublayer provides an interface between the MAC sublayer and the Network layer. *See also* media access control; Open Systems Interconnection.

IEEE 802.3 CSMA/CD Networking   Standard that specifies a network that uses a logical bus topology, baseband signaling, and a CSMA/CD network access method. *See also* carrier sense multiple access with collision detection.

IEEE 802.4 Token Bus   Standard that specifies a physical and logical bus topology that uses coaxial or fiber-optic cable and the token passing media access method.

IEEE 802.5 Token Ring   Specifies a logical ring, physical star, and token passing media access method based on IBM's Token Ring.

IEEE 802.6 Distributed Queue Dual Bus (DQDB) Metropolitan Area Network   Provides a definition and criteria for a DQDB metropolitan area network (MAN).

IEEE 802.7 Broadband Local Area Networks   Standard for broadband cabling technology.

IEEE 802.8 Fiber-Optic LANs and MANs   A standard containing guidelines for the use of fiber-optics on networks, which includes FDDI and Ethernet over fiber-optic cable. *See also* Fiber Distributed Data Interface; Ethernet.

IEEE 802.9 Integrated Services (IS) LAN Interface   A standard containing guidelines for the integration of voice and data over the same cable.

IEEE 802.10 LAN/MAN Security   A series of guidelines dealing with various aspects of network security.

IEEE 802.11 Wireless LAN   Defines standards for implementing wireless technologies such as infrared and spread-spectrum radio.

IEEE 802.12 Demand Priority Access Method   Defines standards that combine the concepts of Ethernet and ATM. *See also* Asynchronous Transfer Mode; Ethernet.

IETF   *See* Internet Engineering Task Force.

incremental backup   Backs up data that has changed since the last full or incremental backup.

Institute of Electrical and Electronics Engineers (IEEE)   An international organization that sets standards for various electrical and electronics issues.

Integrated Services Digital Network (ISDN)   A telecommunications standard that is used to digitally send voice, data, and video signals over the same lines.

Intel 386 (I386) architecture   Platform that includes the 386, 486, Pentium, Pentium Pro, Pentium II, and Pentium III processors.

intellectual property   A legal term that denotes any intangible product of a human being, a group of human beings, or another legal entity (such as a corporation). That product then further belongs to the individual or group that created it. It is a legal way of allowing an idea to be copyrighted.

International Organization for Standardization (ISO)   The standards organization that developed the OSI model. This model provides a guideline for how communications occur between computers.

Internet   A global network made up of a large number of individual networks interconnected through the use of public telephone lines and TCP/IP protocols. *See also* Transmission Control Protocol/Internet Protocol.

Internet Architecture Board (IAB)   The committee that oversees management of the Internet. It is made up of two subcommittees: the Internet Engineering Task Force (IETF) and the Internet Research Task Force (IRTF). *See also* Internet Engineering Task Force; Internet Research Task Force.

Internet bandwidth link   The communications pathway between the various LANs that make up the Internet.

Internet commerce   Any sort of business that is facilitated by the Internet. Usually, the term applies primarily to commerce that involves a Web site of some kind.

Internet Control Message Protocol (ICMP)   A message and management protocol for TCP/IP, primarily used for error checking. The Ping utility uses ICMP. *See also* Ping; Transmission Control Protocol/Internet Protocol.

Internet Engineering Task Force (IETF)   An international organization that works under the Internet Architecture Board to establish standards and protocols relating to the Internet. *See also* Internet Architecture Board.

Internet layer   Layer of the DOD model that corresponds to the Network layer of the OSI model. *See also* Open Systems Interconnection.

Internet Protocol (IP)   The protocol in the TCP/IP protocol suite responsible for network addressing and routing. *See also* Transmission Control Protocol/Internet Protocol.

Internet Research Task Force (IRTF)   An international organization that works under the Internet Architecture Board to research new Internet technologies. *See also* Internet Architecture Board.

Internet Service Provider (ISP)   A company that provides, usually for a fixed monthly fee, direct access to the Internet for home and business computer users.

Internet-in-a-box   Specialized devices that provide Internet access to an entire network over a single Internet connection quickly and easily.

Internetwork Packet eXchange (IPX)   A connectionless, routable network protocol based on the Xerox XNS architecture. It is the default protocol for versions of NetWare before NetWare 5. It operates at the Network layer of the OSI model and is responsible for addressing and routing packets to workstations or servers on other networks. *See also* Open Systems Interconnection; Xerox Network System.

intranet server   HTTP servers that are located on a company's LAN and serve information only to employees of that company or any other user who has been given authority to view it.

intrusion detection utilities Special software programs that detect illegal entry attempts into a system.

IP *See* Internet Protocol.

IP address An address that is used by the Internet Protocol and identifies a device's location on the network.

IP proxy A method by which all communications look as if they originated from a proxy server because the IP address of the user making a request is hidden. Also known as network address translation (NAT).

IP spoofing The method used by a hacker trying to gain access to a network by pretending his machine has the same network address as the internal network.

ipconfig A Windows NT utility used to display that machine's current configuration.

IPX *See* Internetwork Packet eXchange.

IPX network address A number that represents an entire network. All servers on the network must use the same external network number.

ISDN *See* Integrated Services Digital Network.

ISDN modem *See* ISDN terminal adapter.

ISDN terminal adapter The device used on ISDN networks to connect a local network (or single machine) to an ISDN network. It provides power to the line and translates data from the LAN or individual computer for transmission on the ISDN line. *See also* Integrated Services Digital Network.

ISP *See* Internet Service Provider.

Java A programming language developed by Sun Microsystems. Java is used to write programs that will run on any platform that has a Java Virtual Machine installed (which is 95 percent of the operating systems that exist).

Java servlets Special Java programs that run on a Web server and expand the capabilities of the Web server software.

Java Virtual Machine (JVM)   Software developed by Sun Microsystems that creates a virtual Java computer on which Java programs can run. A programmer writes a program once without having to recompile or rewrite the program for all platforms.

JavaBeans   Individual snippets of Java programming code that can be executed by themselves or as part of a larger program. It's possible to build a Bean with an elaborate feature set and considerable power and then use it as a sort of "black box" that carries out some particular duty in various software systems of which it is a part. You can distribute your Beans to others, as well, either freely or, because Beans are compiled and have no visible source code, commercially. Beans have found application in Sun's own graphical user interface toolkit, as well as in other projects.

JavaScript   A powerful yet fairly simple scripting language, based in part on the Java programming language, that you can use to add "intelligence" and interactivity to your Web pages.

joins   Relationships that connect SQL tables. *See also* Structured Query Language.

Joint Photographic Experts Group (JPEG) files   A type of graphics file format distinguished by its ability to include the entire spectrum of perceptible color (16.7 million shades) without being prohibitively huge. The secret is a compression algorithm that exploits the fact that human eyes are more sensitive to subtle differences in brightness than to subtle differences in color.

JPEG files   *See* Joint Photographic Experts Group (JPEG) files.

JScript   Microsoft Internet Explorer's version of JavaScript. It can handle any JavaScript program…more or less. Though JScript is mostly compatible with JavaScript, Microsoft Internet Explorer doesn't interpret everything the same way Netscape's browser does.

jumper   A small connector (cap or plug) that connects pins. This creates a circuit that indicates a setting to a device.

JVM   *See* Java Virtual Machine.

LAN   *See* local area network.

LAN driver   The interface between the NetWare kernel and the NIC installed in the server. Also a general category of drivers used to enable communications between an operating system and a NIC. *See also* network interface card.

Large Internet Packet (LIP)   A technology used by the IPX protocol so that IPX can use the largest possible packet size during a transmission. *See also* Internetwork Packet eXchange.

laser printer   A printer that uses a laser to form an image on a photosensitive drum. The image is then developed with toner and transferred to paper. Finally, a heated drum fuses toner particles onto the paper.

Layer 2 switch   A switching hub that operates at the Data Link layer and builds a table of the MAC addresses of all the connected stations. *See also* media access control.

Layer 3 switch   Functioning at the Network layer, a switch that performs the multiport, virtual LAN, data pipelining functions of a standard Layer 2 switch, but it can perform basic routing functions between virtual LANs.

LCP   *See* Link Control Protocol.

LDAP   *See* Lightweight Directory Access Protocol (LDAP).

licensing   Paying a fee for the use of the copyrighted material.

Lightweight Directory Access Protocol (LDAP)   The protocol used to make simple requests of a network directory (like NDS, X.500, or Active Directory). These requests are for names, locations, and other information like phone numbers and e-mail addresses. Many Web browsers (including Navigator and Internet Explorer) contain LDAP clients so they can request information from directory servers.

line conditioner   A device used to protect against power surges and spikes. Line conditioners use several electronic methods to clean all power coming into them.

Line Printer (LPR) Protocol   The TCP/IP protocol used to send commands to network printers. Its name suggests that it works only for line printers (also called dot matrix printers). That's mainly because, when it was being developed, the majority of the printers in use were line printers.

Link Control Protocol (LCP) The protocol used to establish, configure, and test the link between a client and PPP host. *See also* Point-to-Point Protocol.

link light A small light-emitting diode (LED) that is found on both the NIC and the hub. It is usually green and labeled Link or something similar. A link light indicates that the NIC and the hub are making a Data Link layer connection. *See also* hub; network interface card.

link state route discovery A route discovery method that transmits special packets (Link State Packets, or LSPs) that contain information about which networks the router is connected to.

link state routing A type of routing that broadcasts its entire routing tables only at start-up and possibly at infrequently scheduled intervals. Aside from that, the router only sends messages to other routers when changes are made to the router's routing table.

Link Support Layer (LSL) Part of the Novell client software that acts as sort of a switchboard between the Open Data-Link Interface (ODI) LAN drivers and the various transport protocols.

Linux A version of the Unix operating system, developed by Linus Torvalds. Runs on Intel-based PCs and is generally free. *See also* Unix.

LIP *See* Large Internet Packet.

LiveScript The server-side scripting solution for Netscape Communications Corporation's Web servers. Essentially, it's a variant of JavaScript. You will in fact hear it called "server-side JavaScript."

local area network (LAN) A network that is restricted to a single building, group of buildings, or even a single room. A LAN can have one or more servers.

local groups Groups created on individual servers. Rights can be assigned only to local resources.

locus destination In NetWare, indicates which component system is affected by an error message.

log file   A file that keeps a running list of all errors and notices, the time and date they occurred, and any other pertinent information.

logical bus topology   Type of topology in which the signal travels the distance of the cable and is received by all stations on the backbone. *See also* backbone.

logical link control (LLC)   A sublayer of the Data Link layer. Provides an interface between the MAC sublayer and the Network layer. *See also* media access control; topology.

logical network addressing   The addressing scheme used by protocols at the Network layer.

logical port address   A value that is used at the Transport layer to differentiate between the upper-layer services.

logical ring topology   A network topology in which all network signals travel from one station to another; they are read and forwarded by each station.

logical topology   Describes the way the information flows. The types of logical topologies are the same as the physical topologies except that the information flow specifies the type of topology.

lowest common denominator policy   A type of Web content design policy where a Web site designer creates a site that is functional for almost any browser, even those with extremely low capabilities.

LPR   *See* Line Printer (LPR) Protocol.

LSL   *See* Link Support Layer.

MAC   *See* media access control.

macro   A script of commands that can be invoked with a single keystroke.

mail bombing   *See* mail flooding.

mail flooding   Unleashing a barrage of mail on a particular user in an attempt to render the user's e-mail account useless. This is typically done by signing the user up for hundreds of e-mail mailing lists that each send out hundreds of messages daily. The resulting flood of messages makes it impossible for a user to retrieve his e-mail.

mail server   A server that hosts and delivers e-mail.

MAN   *See* metropolitan area network.

manufacturer's readme file   A file that the manufacturer includes with software to give the installer information that was too late to make it into the software manuals. It's usually a last-minute addition that includes tips on installing the software, possible incompatibilities, and any known installation problems that might have been found right before the product was shipped.

media access   The process of vying for transmission time on the network media.

media access control (MAC)   A sublayer of the Data Link layer; the MAC controls the way multiple devices use the same media channel. It controls which devices can transmit and when they can transmit.

member server   A computer that has Windows NT server installed but doesn't have a copy of the SAM database. *See also* Security Accounts Manager.

meta information   Information about other information. Often used to categorize different types of information because it is quicker than indexing the entire body of information.

meta tags   Special HTML tags used to identify an HTML page's content for search engine indexing.

metropolitan area network (MAN)   A network that encompasses an entire city or metropolitan area.

Microsoft Word   A popular word processing application created by Microsoft Corporation. It exists in Windows and MacOS versions. Word files usually carry .DOC filename extensions.

mirrored hard drive   Two drives to which the same information is written. Therefore, if one of the drives fails, the information will still be retrievable from the other drive. A single controller drive controls both drives. Used for fault tolerance.

modem   Short for *modulator/dem*odulator. A device that changes digital signals from a computer into analog signals that can be transmitted over phone lines and other analog media. On the receiving end, the modem changes the analog signals back to digital signals.

modem initialization commands   Special commands sent to the modem by the communications program to "initialize" it. These commands tell the modem things like how many rings to wait before answering, whether or not to use compression, and the speed at which to communicate.

Motion Picture Experts Group (MPEG) files   A video file format that handles full-motion video, but the first version of the specification, MPEG-1, does not support sound. The newer MPEG-2 standard does. Developed by a consortium of telecommunications industry representatives, MPEG files carry .MPEG or .MPG filename extensions.

MPEG files   *See* Motion Picture Experts Group (MPEG) files.

MSAU   *See* multistation access unit.

multimedia   A term that has come to refer to media other than text and still graphics. Multimedia normally includes full-motion video, sound, and pictures.

multiple server backup   A system in which multiple servers run continuously, each providing backup and production services at the same time. (This way, expensive servers are not sitting around as designated "backup" servers, used only when an emergency arises.) If a server fails, another just takes over without any interruption of service.

multiplexing   The process of dividing a single network medium into multiple channels.

Multipurpose Internet Mail Extension (MIME)   A feature of both e-mail and Web clients that allows nonstandard file types to be opened by the appropriate program. MIME types define which program created a file. Each client can then be configured with the name of a program to open a file with a particular MIME type.

multistation access unit (MSAU)   The central device in Token Ring networks, it acts as the connection point for all stations and facilitates the formation of the ring.

NADN   *See* nearest active downstream neighbor (NADN).

name resolution   The process of translating (resolving) logical host names to network addresses.

name-space NLM   Allows different file types to be stored and accessed on NetWare servers.

naming conventions document   Type of SOP that specifies how network entities are named. Some common items that have entries in the naming conventions document are servers, printers, user accounts, and test accounts. *See also* standard operating procedure.

NAT   Abbreviation for network address translation. *See also* IP proxy.

National Computing Security Center (NCSC)   The agency that developed the Trusted Computer System Evaluation Criteria (TCSEC) and the Trusted Network Interpretation Environmental Guideline (TNIEG).

National Security Agency (NSA)   The U.S. government agency responsible for protecting U.S. communications and producing foreign intelligence information. It was established by presidential directive in 1952 as a separately organized agency within the Department of Defense.

NAUN   *See* nearest active upstream neighbor (NAUN).

nbtstat (NetBIOS over TCP/IP statistics)   The Windows TCP/IP utility that is used to display NetBIOS over TCP/IP statistics. *See also* Network Basic Input Output System; Transmission Control Protocol/Internet Protocol.

NCP   *See* NetWare Core Protocol.

NCSC *See* National Computing Security Center.

NDPS *See* Novell Distributed Print Services.

NDS *See* Novell Directory Services.

NDS tree A logical representation of a network's resources. Resources are represented by objects in the tree. The tree is often designed after a company's functional structure. Objects can represent organizations, departments, users, servers, printers, and other resources. *See also* NetWare Directory Services.

nearest active downstream neighbor (NADN) The station in a Token Ring network immediately downstream (next in line for receiving network traffic) from the station being referenced.

nearest active upstream neighbor (NAUN) The station in a Token Ring network immediately upstream (the node from which the station being referenced received its network traffic).

NetBEUI Transport protocol that is based on the NetBIOS protocol and has datagram support and support for connectionless transmission. *See also* Network Basic Input Output System.

NetBIOS *See* Network Basic Input Output System.

netstat A utility used to determine which TCP/IP connections, inbound and outbound, the computer has. It also allows the user to view packet statistics, such has how many have been sent and received. *See also* Transmission Control Protocol/Internet Protocol.

NetWare The network operating system made by Novell.

NetWare 3.*x* The version series of NetWare that supported multiple, cross-platform clients with fairly minimal hardware requirements. It used a database called the bindery to keep track of users and groups and was administrated with several DOS, menu-based utilities (such as SYSCON, PCONSOLE, and FILER).

NetWare 4.*x* The version series of NetWare that includes NDS. *See also* Novell Directory Services.

NetWare 5.*x* The version series of NetWare that includes a multiprocessing kernel. It also includes a five-user version of Oracle 8, a relational database, and the ability to use TCP/IP in its *pure* form.

NetWare Administrator The utility used to administer NetWare versions 4.*x* and later by making changes to the NDS directory. It is the only administrative utility needed to modify NDS objects and their properties. *See also* Novell Directory Services.

NetWare Core Protocol (NCP) The upper-layer NetWare protocol that functions on top of IPX and provides NetWare resource access to workstations. *See also* Internetwork Packet eXchange.

NetWare Link State Protocol (NLSP) Protocol that gathers routing information based on the link state routing method. Its precursor is the Routing Information Protocol (RIP). NLSP is a more efficient routing protocol than RIP. *See also* link state routing.

NetWare Loadable Module (NLM) A component used to provide a NetWare server with additional services and functionality. Unneeded services can be unloaded, thus conserving memory.

Network Address Translation (NAT) *See* IP proxy.

Network Basic Input Output System (NetBIOS) A Session layer protocol that opens communication sessions for applications that want to communicate on a network.

Network File System (NFS) A protocol that enables users to access files on remote computers as if the files were local.

network interface card (NIC) Physical device that connects computers and other network equipment to the transmission medium.

Network layer Layer three of the OSI model. The Network layer is responsible for logical addressing and translating logical names into physical addresses. This layer also controls the routing of data from source to destination as well as the building and dismantling of packets. *See also* Open Systems Interconnection.

network media The physical cables that link computers in a network; also known as physical media.

Network News Transfer Protocol (NNTP)   The protocol used to transport Internet news (also called Usenet news) between news servers. It is also the protocol used to transport these news articles between news servers and news clients.

network operating system (NOS)   The software that runs on a network server and offers file, print, application, and other services to clients.

Network Support Encyclopedia (NSEPro)   *See* Novell Support Connection.

network-centric   Refers to network operating systems that use directory services that maintain information about the entire network.

newsgroup   A collection of articles pertaining to a particular subject.

newsreader   A type of Internet client used to read newsgroups on the Internet.

NFS   *See* Network File System.

NIC   *See* network interface card.

NIC diagnostics   Software utilities that verify that the NIC is functioning correctly and that test every aspect of NIC operation. *See also* network interface card.

NIC driver   *See* LAN driver.

NLM   *See* NetWare Loadable Module.

NLSP   *See* NetWare Link State Protocol.

NNTP   *See* Network News Transfer Protocol (NNTP).

nonrepudiation technologies   Any means of providing absolute proof (where *absolute* is defined as strong enough to stand up in court) that something occurred.

non-streaming media   A multimedia download method where the entire file is downloaded to the browser before the movie or sound is played. Popular non-streaming media formats include MOV, MPEG, and AVI videos as well as WAV and AU sounds.

non-unicast packet   A packet that is not sent directly from one workstation to another but instead is sent to either an entire network (broadcast) or a group of computers on the network (multicast).

NOS   *See* network operating system.

Novell Directory Services (NDS)   A NetWare service that provides access to a global, hierarchical directory database of network entities that can be centrally managed.

Novell Distributed Print Services (NDPS)   A printing system, designed by Novell, that uses NDS to install and manage printers. NDPS supports automatic network printer installation, automatic distribution of client printer drivers, and centralized printer management without the use of print queues.

Novell Support Connection   Novell's database of technical information documents, files, patches, fixes, NetWare Application Notes, Novell lab bulletins, Novell professional developer bulletins, answers to frequently asked questions, and more. The database is available from Novell and is updated quarterly.

NSA   *See* National Security Agency.

NT Directory Services (NTDS)   System of domains and trusts for a Windows NT Server network.

NTDS   *See* NT Directory Services.

ODI   *See* Open Datalink Interface (ODI).

on-access scan   An antivirus scan that is done in the background as a file or a program is opened.

on-demand scan   An antivirus scan that a network administrator or user manually or automatically schedules.

one-way encryption scheme   Any encryption method where the key used can only encrypt the data. Another key must be used to decrypt the data. Public key encryption is one example of a one-way encryption scheme.

one-way hashing algorithm   A one-way hashing algorithm used to encode data into a digital signature. Hashes take a piece of data—the characters in an e-mail message, say—and run it through a series of operations. The operations yield a value that is unique to the information—even slightly different pieces of original information will yield vastly different hash results. One-way hashes are so named because you can't work them backwards. You can't look at a hash result and figure out the original data from it.

Open Datalink Interface (ODI)   A driver specification developed by Novell that enables a single workstation to communicate transparently with several different protocol stacks by using a single NIC and a single NIC driver.

open source software   Software programs in which the source code is publicly available for anyone to examine, modify, and redistribute.

Open Systems Interconnection (OSI)   A model defined by the ISO to categorize the process of communication between computers in terms of seven layers. *See also* International Organization for Standardization.

OpenLinux   A version of the Linux network operating system developed by Caldera.

Oracle 8   Oracle's leading relational database software. A five-user copy is included with NetWare 5.*x*.

Orange Book   Layperson's term for the TCSEC. *See also* Trusted Computer System Evaluation Criteria.

OS/2 Applications (OS/2 Subsystem)   Windows NT feature that can run IBM's OS/2 applications, although the applications must use only the pure OS/2 development tools and run only in character mode. OS/2 graphical applications are not supported.

OSI   *See* Open Systems Interconnection.

overload attack   A form of denial of service attack. During an overload attack, a system that's working perfectly can be made useless if an attacker presents it with so much work that it's overwhelmed.

oversampling   Method of synchronous bit synchronization in which the receiver samples the signal at a much faster rate than the data rate. This permits the use of an encoding method that does not add clocking transitions.

over-voltage threshold   The level of over-voltage that will trip the circuit breaker in a surge protector.

packet   The basic division of data sent over a network.

packet switching   The process of breaking messages into packets at the sending router for easier transmission over a WAN.

parallel processing   Operating method by which an operating system divides the running of a program over several processors, thus providing increased performance.

passive detection   A type of intruder detection that logs all network events to a file for an administrator to view later.

password   A string of alphanumeric characters used to uniquely identify a person on a network or on the Internet.

patch   Software that fixes a problem with an existing program or operating system.

patch cable   Any cable that connects one network device to the main cable run or to a patch panel that in turn connects to the main cable run.

patch panel   A central wiring point for multiple devices on a UTP network. *See also* unshielded twisted-pair.

patent   A legal document that proves that you are the owner of a process or product you designed. When applying for a patent, you agree to make the details of your product or process available to the public in exchange for a monopoly in profiting from your invention. The monopoly is limited by time—design patents (on the appearance of a product) last 14 years in the United States, and the time limit on utility patents (on products and processes) last 20 years.

PDC   *See* primary domain controller.

peer-to-peer network   Computers that are hooked together and have no centralized authority. Each computer is equal and can act as both a server and a workstation.

Perl   *See* Practical Extraction and Reporting Language (Perl).

permanent virtual circuit (PVC)   A technology used by Frame Relay that allows virtual data communications (circuits) to be set up between sender and receiver over a packet-switched network.

PGP   *See* Pretty Good Privacy.

PHP   A server-side scripting language.

physical bus topology   A network that uses one network cable that runs from one end of the network to the other. Workstations connect at various points along this cable.

Physical layer   Layer one of the OSI model. The Physical layer controls the functional interface. *See also* Open Systems Interconnection.

physical media   *See* network media.

physical mesh topology   A network configuration that specifies a link between each and every device in the network.

physical parallel port   A port that is on the back of a computer and allows a printer to be connected with a parallel cable.

physical port   An opening that is on a network device and allows a cable of some kind to be connected. Ports allow devices to be connected to each other with cables.

physical ring topology   A network topology that is set up in a circular fashion. Data travels around the ring in one direction, and each device on the ring acts as a repeater to keep the signal strong as it travels. Each device incorporates a receiver for the incoming signal and a transmitter to send the data on to the next device in the ring. The network is dependent on the ability of the signal to travel around the ring.

physical star topology   Describes a network in which a cable runs from each network entity to a central device called a hub. The hub allows all devices to communicate as if they were directly connected. *See also* hub.

physical topology   The physical layout of a network, such as bus, star, ring, or mesh.

Ping   A TCP/IP utility used to test whether another host is reachable. An ICMP request is sent to the host, who responds with a reply if it is reachable. The request times-out if the host is not reachable.

ping flood   A barrage of ICMP packets from the TCP/IP Ping utility. Under a ping flood, a computer receives many Ping packets in a short period of time and must reply to them all. This can tie up the processor, the memory, and the network connection, denying legitimate users the performance they're used to receiving.

Ping of Death   A large ICMP packet that is sent to overflow the remote host's buffer. This usually causes the remote host to reboot or hang.

pixels per inch (ppi)   A rating of many monitors and displays. Indicates how many pixels are contained in a square inch of screen area.

Plain Old Telephone Service (POTS)   Another name for the Public Switched Telephone Network (PSTN). *See also* Public Switched Telephone Network.

plenum-rated coating   Coaxial cable coating typically made of Teflon that does not produce toxic gas when burned.

plug-ins   Software modules that users add to their browsers to expand the browser's capabilities.

PNG   *See* Portable Network Graphics (PNG).

point-to-point   Network communication in which two devices have exclusive access to a network medium. For example, a printer connected to only one workstation would be using a point-to-point connection.

Point-to-Point Protocol (PPP)   The protocol used with dial-up connections to the Internet. Its functions include error control, security, dynamic IP addressing, and support for multiple protocols.

Point-to-Point Tunneling Protocol (PPTP)   A protocol that allows the creation of virtual private networks (VPNs), which allow users to access a server on a corporate network over a secure, direct connection via the Internet. *See also* virtual private network.

polling   A media access control method that uses a central device called a controller that polls each device in turn and asks if it has data to transmit.

POP3   *See* Post Office Protocol version 3.

port   Any interface that a device can be connected to for the purpose of transmitting data, not just network data (like LPT1 for a printer or a serial port for a mouse).

Portable Network Graphics (PNG)   A graphics file format and replacement for the Graphics Interchange Format (GIF). A recently established image specification that provides lossless compression of 256-color images.

Post Office Protocol version 3 (POP3)   The protocol used to download e-mail from an SMTP e-mail server to a network client. *See also* Simple Mail Transfer Protocol.

PostScript   A page-description language designed to enable publishers to generate publications on one computer and print them on a PostScript-compatible printer somewhere else (such as at a service bureau). PostScript files carry `.PS` or `.EPS` filename extensions. *See also* Encapsulated Post-Script (EPS) files.

POTS   Acronym formed from Plain Old Telephone Service. *See* Public Switched Telephone Network.

power blackout   A total loss of power that may last for only a few seconds or as long as several hours.

power brownout   Power drops below normal levels for several seconds or longer.

power overage   Too much power is coming into the computer. *See also* power spike; power surge.

power sag   The power level drops below normal and rises to normal in less than one second.

power spike   The power level rises above normal and drops back to normal for less than a second.

power surge   The power level rises above normal and stays there for longer than a second or two.

power underage   The power level drops below the standard level. *See also* power sag.

PPP   *See* Point-to-Point Protocol.

PPTP   *See* Point-to-Point Tunneling Protocol.

Practical Extraction and Reporting Language (Perl)   A simple programming language developed by Larry Wall and used on Unix hosts and Web servers. Perl was designed specifically for processing text. Often used for processing CGI scripts.

Presentation layer   Layer six of the OSI model. The Presentation layer is responsible for formatting data exchange such as graphic commands and conversion of character sets. Also responsible for data compression, data encryption, and data stream redirection. *See also* Open Systems Interconnection.

Pretty Good Privacy (PGP)   Developed by mathematician Philip R. Zimmermann, Pretty Good Privacy is a multipurpose encryption scheme based on public-key architecture. It is a shareware implementation of RSA encryption. *See also* RSA Data Security, Inc.

primary domain controller (PDC)   An NT server that contains a master copy of the SAM database. This database contains all usernames, passwords, and Access Control Lists for a Windows NT domain. *See also* Security Accounts Manager.

print server   A centralized device that controls and manages all network printers. The print server can be hardware, software, or a combination. Some print servers are actually built in to network printer NICs. *See also* network interface card.

print services   The network services that manage and control printing on a network, allowing multiple and simultaneous access to printers.

private key   An encryption key known only by the sender and receiver.

private key encryption   A technology in which both the sender and the receiver have the same key. A single key is used to encrypt and decrypt all messages. *See also* public key.

proactive defense   A type of intruder defense that allows a person to ensure that the network is invulnerable to attack.

profile   Used in Windows NT to define the user's environment. A user's desktop colors and icons, program groups, Start menu settings, and network connections are remembered in a profile.

programming language   Any system of syntax and grammar that, when used to generate sets of instructions called programs, can have an effect on the behavior of a computer. Examples of programming languages include Java, Visual Basic, C, and C++.

protocol   A predefined set of rules that dictate how computers or devices communicate and exchange data on the network.

protocol analyzer   A software and hardware troubleshooting tool that is used to decode protocol information to try to determine the source of a network problem and to establish baselines.

proxy   A type of firewall that prevents direct communication between a client and a host by acting as an intermediary. *See also* firewall.

proxy cache server   An implementation of a Web proxy. The server receives an HTTP request from a Web browser and makes the request on behalf of the sending workstation. When the response comes, the proxy cache server caches a copy of the response locally. The next time someone makes a request for the same Web page or Internet information, the proxy cache server can fulfill the request out of the cache instead of having to retrieve the resource from the Web.

proxy server   A type of server that makes a single Internet connection and services requests on behalf of many users.

PSTN   *See* Public Switched Telephone Network.

public key encryption   A technology that uses two keys to facilitate communication, a public key and a private key. The public key is used to encrypt a message to a receiver. The private key is then used to decrypt the message. *See also* private key.

Public Switched Telephone Network (PSTN)   This is the U.S. public telephone network. It is also called the Plain Old Telephone Service (POTS).

public-domain software   Software that has no copyright protections at all. This means that anyone may acquire, copy, and use the software without paying a licensing fee to anyone (there's no copyright holder to which to pay such a fee).

public-domain work   A creative work whose author renounces her copyright or refuses to enforce it through infringement suits.

PVC   *See* permanent virtual circuit.

QoS   *See* Quality of Service.

Quality of Service (QoS)   Data prioritization at the Network layer of the OSI model. Results in guaranteed throughput rates. *See also* Open Systems Interconnection.

QuickTime   A video file format developed by Apple Computer, Inc. that supports full-motion video and animation with synchronized sound. Quick-Time files typically have the extension .MOV.

radio frequency interference (RFI)   Interference on copper cabling systems caused by radio frequencies.

RAID   *See* Redundant Array of Independent (or Inexpensive) Disks.

Red Book   Layperson's term for the TNIEG. *See also* Trusted Network Interpretation Environments Guideline.

reduced instruction set computing (RISC)   Computer architecture in which the computer executes small, general-purpose instructions very rapidly.

Redundant Array of Independent (or Inexpensive) Disks (RAID) A configuration of multiple hard disks used to provide fault tolerance should a disk fail. Different levels of RAID exist, depending on the amount and type of fault tolerance provided.

regeneration Process in which signals are read, amplified, and repeated on the network to reduce signal degradation, which results in a longer overall possible maximum segment length.

remote access server A computer, usually a server, that provides network services to remote clients. Typically, a server that has one or more modems installed to enable remote connections to the network.

repeater A Physical layer device that amplifies the signals it receives on one port and resends or repeats them on another. A repeater is used to extend the maximum length of a network segment.

report The output list that results from a SQL query.

response code Meta information about a Web server error response, generally indicating whether the server could fulfill the request and any problems it had in doing so.

RFI *See* radio frequency interference.

RG-58 The type designation for the coaxial cable used in thin Ethernet (10Base-2). It has a 50ohm impedance rating and uses BNC connectors.

RG-62 The type designation for the coaxial cable used in ARCNet networks. It has a 93ohm impedance and uses BNC connectors.

Rich Text Format The baseline file format for formatted text, Rich Text Format allows you to endow text with fairly elaborate formatting—including font information—and expect that almost any word processing program will be able to open your files. RTF files take an .RTF filename extension.

RIP *See* Router Information Protocol.

RISC *See* reduced instruction set computing.

RJ-connector   A modular connection mechanism that allows for as many as eight copper wires (four pairs). Commonly found in phone (RJ-11) or 10BaseT (RJ-45) connections.

roaming profiles   Profiles downloaded from a server at each login. When a user logs out at the end of the session, changes are made and remembered for the next time the user logs in.

router   A device that connects two or more networks and allows packets to be transmitted and received between them. A router determines the best path for data packets from source to destination.

Router Information Protocol (RIP)   A distance-vector route discovery protocol used by IP and IPX (there are different versions for each). It uses hops and ticks to determine the cost for a particular route. *See also* Internetwork Packet eXchange.

routing   A function of the Network layer that involves moving data throughout a network. Data passes through several network segments using routers that can select the path the data takes. *See also* router.

routing information table   A table that contains information about the location of other routers on the network and their distance from the current router.

RSA Data Security, Inc.   A commercial company that produces encryption software. RSA stands for Rivest, Shamir, Adleman, the founders of the company.

S/MIME   *See* Secure Multipurpose Internet Mail Extensions (S/MIME).

SAM   *See* Security Accounts Manager.

scripting language   A programming language where the program itself is not compiled and the code is simply read by an interpreter in real time. Scripting languages are used to perform various functions in Web browsers and on host systems. Macros, batch files, shell scripts, and JavaScript are all examples of scripting languages.

search engine   A special Web site on the Internet that allows users to search a database containing the content of many different Web sites to find a specific Web site or a site that contains a particular piece of information.

Secure Electronic Transactions (SET)   A system developed by Visa (a credit card company) that provides a framework for secure electronic financial transactions on the Internet, particularly at the consumer level.

Secure Hypertext Transfer Protocol (S-HTTP)   A protocol used for secure communications between a Web server and a Web browser.

Secure Multipurpose Internet Mail Extensions (S/MIME)   A proposed standard for securing electronic mail. S/MIME is related to ordinary e-mail attachments, digital signatures, and public-key encryption. The text of an e-mail is encrypted using the recipient's public key and a digital signature is generated for the message. The digital signature is attached to the message as a binary file, which is one of the problems with S/MIME—the binary attachment slows the message's progress across the Internet.

Secure Sockets Layer (SSL)   Secure Socket Layer (SSL) provides an encrypted link between a client computer and a server computer over a TCP/IP connection. Most frequently, it's seen as the mechanism by which Web browsers establish secure connections with Web servers for the purpose of exchanging confidential information like credit card numbers.

Security Accounts Manager (SAM)   A database within Windows NT that contains information about all the users and groups and their associated rights and settings within a Windows NT domain.

security log   Log file used in Windows NT to keep track of security events specified by the domain's Audit Policy.

segment   A unit of data smaller than a packet. Also a portion of a larger network (a network can consist of multiple network segments).

Sequenced Packet eXchange (SPX)   A connection-oriented protocol that is part of the IPX protocol suite. It operates at the Transport layer of the OSI model. It initiates the connection between the sender and receiver, transmits the data, and then terminates the connection. *See also* Internetwork Packet eXchange; Open Systems Interconnection.

Serial Line Internet Protocol (SLIP)   A protocol that permits the sending of IP packets over a serial connection.

server   A computer that provides resources to the clients on the network.

server configuration documents   General network documentation that includes information such as the current hardware configuration, currently installed software packages, and any installed patches.

server extension   Similar to a plug-in for Web server software, it is a software module that expands the capabilities of the server software itself. Server extensions may be published by the same company that put out the server software or by another publisher. The Microsoft FrontPage Extensions are perhaps the most popular server extensions around.

server log file   Log file that lists errors that occur on the server.

server-side scripting languages   Programming languages designed for writing code that's embedded in Web pages and interpreted by the Web server software before those pages are sent out to the client.

servicemark   A word, phrase, or logo that describes a service.

Services for Macintosh (SFM)   Software that must be installed and configured before a Macintosh can access a Windows NT server.

Session layer   Layer five of the OSI model. The Session layer determines how two computers establish, use, and end a session. Security authentication and network naming functions required for applications occur here. The Session layer establishes, maintains, and breaks dialogs between two stations. *See also* Open Systems Interconnection.

SFM   *See* Services for Macintosh.

share-level security   In a network that uses share-level security, instead of assigning rights to network resources to users, passwords are assigned to individual files or other network resources (such as printers). These passwords are then given to all users that need access to these resources. All resources are visible from anywhere in the network, and any user who knows the password for a particular network resource can make changes to it.

shell scripting language   A programming language (usually a fairly simple one) that can issue command-line instructions, manipulate files and directories, do some text management, and invoke other programs.

shielded twisted-pair   A type of cabling that includes pairs of copper conductors, twisted around each other, inside a metal or foil shield. This type of medium can support faster speeds than nonshielded wiring.

S-HTTP   *See* Secure Hypertext Transfer Protocol.

signal encoding   The process whereby a protocol at the Physical layer receives information from the upper layers and translates all the data into signals that can be transmitted on a transmission medium.

signaling   The process of transmitting data across the medium. Two types of signaling are digital and analog.

Simple Mail Transfer Protocol (SMTP)   A program that looks for mail on SMTP servers and sends it along the network to its destination at another SMTP server.

Simple Network Management Protocol (SNMP)   The management protocol within TCP/IP created for sending information about the health of the network to network management consoles.

Skipjack   An encryption algorithm that was developed as a possible replacement for Data Encryption Standard (DES) and is classified by the National Security Agency (NSA). Not much is known about this encryption algorithm except that it uses an 80-bit key.

SLIP   *See* Serial Line Internet Protocol.

SMTP   *See* Simple Mail Transfer Protocol.

SNMP   *See* Simple Network Management Protocol.

social engineering   A method of obtaining necessary security information by simply asking people who have the security information for their usernames and passwords through deception (by pretending to be someone you're not, for example).

Solaris   An operating system based on Unix that adds the following capabilities: multithreading, symmetric multiprocessing, and real-time processing. It can automatically mount remote files, and it includes utilities for configuring networks and installing software.

SOP *See* standard operating procedure.

source address The address of the station that sent a packet, usually found in the source area of a packet header.

spam Any mass-broadcast e-mail that the recipient did not specifically request.

spamming The mass broadcast of unsolicited messages to hundreds of thousands of e-mail addresses.

SPS *See* Standby Power Supply.

SPX *See* Sequenced Packet eXchange.

SQL *See* Structured Query Language.

SSL *See* Secure Sockets Layer.

standard operating procedure (SOP) Usually found in a company manual; the policies and guidelines outlining company standards and procedures.

Standby Power Supply (SPS) A power backup device that has power going directly to the protected equipment. A sensor monitors the power. When a loss is detected, the computer is switched over to the battery. Thus, a loss of power might occur (typically for less than a second).

static entry An entry that is added to a Windows ARP table manually. *See also* Address Resolution Protocol.

static routing Describes the process by which the router's routing table is updated manually by the network administrator.

streaming media A type of media download method where the sound or video can begin playing before the entire file is downloaded. A client can request a very large audio file and begin presenting its contents after it has received only a fraction of the total file.

Structured Query Language (SQL) The standard language for working with relational databases. It is a powerful programming language that is used to format requests for client-server database servers.

subdomains   A logical grouping of domains into zones.

subnet mask   A group of selected bits that identify a subnetwork within a TCP/IP network. *See also* Transmission Control Protocol/Internet Protocol.

subnetwork   A network that is part of another network. The connection is made through a gateway, bridge, or router.

surge protector   A device that contains a special electronic circuit that monitors the incoming voltage level and then trips a circuit breaker when an over-voltage reaches a certain level called the over-voltage threshold.

switching hub   A network device that listens to all the stations connected to it and records their network cards' hardware addresses. When one station on a switch wants to send data to a station on the same switch, the data gets sent directly from the sender to the receiver in a virtual "pipe" between sender and receiver.

SYN flood   A denial of service attack in which the hacker sends a barrage of SYN packets. The receiving station tries to respond to each SYN request for a connection, thereby tying up all the resources. All incoming connections are rejected until all current connections can be established.

SYSCON   The DOS menu-based utility used to administer NetWare 3.*x*.

system log   The Windows NT log file that keeps track of system-related events that occur on a computer.

T1   A 1.544Mbps digital connection that is typically carried over two pairs of UTP wires.

T3   A T3 line works similarly to a T1 connection but carries data at 44.736Mbps. This is equivalent to 28 T1 channels.

Tagged Image File Format (TIFF) files   A graphics file format that supports 16.7 million colors, but the files are large and natively unsupported by Web browsers. TIFF files are usually used in desktop publishing applications and other situations in which network communication of the image data isn't important.

tags Special sequences of characters that are inserted in the text of an HTML document and dictate what the browser should do with the text between the tags.

tar The Unix file compression utility and file format. Files that have been compressed with the tar utility typically have the extension .TAR.

Tcl *See* Tool Command Language (Tcl).

TCP *See* Transmission Control Protocol.

TCP/IP *See* Transmission Control Protocol/Internet Protocol.

TCSEC *See* Trusted Computer System Evaluation Criteria.

TDM *See* time division multiplexing.

TDR *See* time-domain reflectometer.

telephony server A computer that functions as a smart answering machine for the network. It can also perform call center and call routing functions.

Telnet A TCP/IP protocol that functions at the Application layer of the OSI model, providing terminal emulation capabilities. *See also* Open Systems Interconnection.

template A set of guidelines that you can apply to every new user account created.

terminal emulator A program that allows a PC to act as a terminal for a mainframe or a Unix system.

terminator A device that prevents a signal from bouncing off the end of the network cable, which would cause interference with other signals.

test account An account set up by an administrator to confirm the basic functionality of a newly installed application, for example. The test account has equal rights to accounts that will use the new functionality. It is important to use test accounts instead of administrator accounts to test new functionality. If an administrator account is used, problems related to user rights may not manifest themselves because administrator accounts typically have full rights to all network resources.

TFTP *See* Trivial File Transfer Protocol.

TIFF files *See* Tagged Image File Format (TIFF) files.

time division multiplexing (TDM) A method to divide individual channels in broadband communications into separate time slots, allowing more data to be carried at the same time. It is also possible to use TDM in baseband communications.

time to live (TTL) A field in IP packets that indicates how many routers the packet can still cross (hops it can still make) before it is discarded. TTL is also used in ARP tables to indicate how long an entry should remain in the table. *See also* Address Resolution Protocol.

time-domain reflectometer (TDR) A tool, also called a cable tester, that sends out a signal and measures how much time it takes to return. It is used to find short or open circuits.

Tk The graphical toolkit that works with Tcl to produce graphical applications. *See also* Tool Command Language (Tcl).

TNIEG *See* Trusted Network Interpretation Environmental Guideline.

token passing A media access method in which a token (data packet) is passed around the ring in an orderly fashion from one device to the next. A station can transmit only when it has the token. The token continues around the network until the original sender receives the token again. If the token has more data to send, the process repeats. If not, the original sender modifies the token to indicate that the token is free for anyone else to use.

Token Ring network A network based on a physical star, logical ring topology in which data is passed along the ring until it finds its intended receiver. Only one data packet can be passed along the ring at a time. If the data packet goes around the ring without being claimed, it is returned to the sender.

tone generator A small electronic device used to test network cables for breaks and other problems. It sends an electronic signal down one set of UTP wires. Used with a tone locator. *See also* unshielded twisted-pair.

tone locator   A device used to test network cables for breaks and other problems; designed to sense the signal sent by the tone generator and emit a tone when the signal is detected in a particular set of wires.

Tool Command Language (Tcl)   A scripting language designed as a sort of glue with which to share information among applications. Pronounced "tickle," Tcl was developed by John Osterhout.

topology   The physical and/or logical layout of the transmission media specified in the physical and logical layers of the OSI model. *See also* Open Systems Interconnection.

tracert   The TCP/IP trace route command-line utility that shows the user every router interface a TCP/IP packet passes through on its way to a destination. *See also* Transmission Control Protocol/Internet Protocol.

trademark   A legal term, much like a copyright, except that trademarks apply to words, phrases, and images used to describe products and services.

trailer   A section of a data packet that contains error-checking information.

transceivers   The part of any network interface that transmits and receives network signals.

transient   A high-voltage burst of current.

Transmission Control Protocol   The protocol found at the Host-to-Host layer of the DOD model. This protocol breaks data packets into segments, numbers them, and sends them in random order. The receiving computer reassembles the data so that the information is readable for the user. In the process, the sender and the receiver confirm that all data has been received; if it hasn't, it is resent. This is a connection-oriented protocol.

Transmission Control Protocol/Internet Protocol   The protocol suite developed by the DOD in conjunction with the Internet. It was designed as an internetworking protocol suite that could route information around network failures. Today it is the de facto standard for communications on the Internet.

transmission media   Physical cables and/or wireless technology across which computers are able to communicate.

transmission time   The amount of time (in seconds) it takes to download an entire Web page from a Web server to a Web browser.

Transport layer   Layer four of the OSI model. The Transport layer is responsible for checking that the data packet created in the Session layer was received error free. If necessary, it also changes the length of messages for transport up or down the remaining layers. *See also* Open Systems Interconnection.

Trivial File Transfer Protocol (TFTP)   A protocol similar to FTP that does not provide the security features of FTP. *See also* File Transfer Protocol.

Trusted Computer System Evaluation Criteria (TCSEC)   Evaluation criteria released by the NCSC in 1983. It defines the standard parameters of a trusted computer in several classes, ranked by letter and number. It is referred to as the Orange Book. *See also* National Computing Security Center.

Trusted Network Interpretation Environmental Guideline (TNIEG) Evaluation criteria released by the NCSC that defines the certification criteria for trusted networks. It is referred to as the Red Book. *See also* National Computer Security Center.

T-series connections   A series of digital connections leased from the telephone company. Each T-series connection is rated with a number based on speed. T1 and T3 are the most popular.

TTL   *See* time to live.

twisted-pair cable   A type of network transmission medium that contains pairs of color-coded, insulated copper wires that are twisted around each other. A twisted-pair cable consists of one or more twisted pairs in a common jacket.

UDP   *See* User Datagram Protocol.

Uniform Resource Locator (URL)   A URL is one way of identifying a document on the Internet. It consists of the protocol that is used to access the document and the domain name or IP address of the host that holds the document, for example, http://www.sybex.com.

uninterruptible power supply (UPS)   A natural line conditioner that uses a battery and power inverter to run the computer equipment that plugs into it. The battery charger continuously charges the battery. The battery charger is the only thing that runs off line voltage. During a power problem, the battery charger stops operating, and the equipment continues to run off of the battery.

Unix   A 32-bit, multitasking operating system developed in the 1960s for use on mainframes and minicomputers.

unshielded twisted-pair cable   Twisted-pair cable consisting of a number of twisted pairs of copper wire with a simple plastic casing. Because no shielding is used in this cable, it is very susceptible to EMI, RFI, and other types of interference. *See also* electromagnetic interference; radio frequency interference.

UPS   *See* uninterruptible power supply.

upselling   The process of encouraging a buyer who thinks she wants one product to buy another, more profitable product. Upsell may involve pitching a larger package of the same stuff or a more feature-rich variant of the same model.

URL   *See* Uniform Resource Locator.

User Datagram Protocol (UDP)   Protocol at the Host-to-Host layer of the DOD model; it corresponds to the Transport layer of the OSI model. Packets are divided into segments, given numbers, sent randomly, and put back together at the receiving end. This is a connectionless protocol. *See also* connectionless protocol; Open Systems Interconnection.

User Manager for Domains   The Windows NT utility that you use to manage all users, groups, and policies for a Windows NT domain.

user-level security   A type of network in which user accounts can read, write, change, and take ownership of files. Rights are assigned to user accounts, and each user knows only his own username and password, which makes this the preferred method for securing files.

Utility NLM   An NLM that is not a LAN driver, disk driver, name-space module, or platform support module; for example, `MONITOR.NML` or `INSTALL.NLM`. *See also* NetWare Loadable Module.

VBScript   Microsoft's preferred client-side scripting language. VBScript can do all sorts of automation, animation, verification, and organization jobs on the client side. If you know standard Visual Basic, you'll probably find it easy to pick up a working knowledge of VBScript.

version conflict   The result of new software or patches that conflict with other installed products.

virtual private network (VPN)   Using the public Internet as a backbone for a private interconnection (network) between locations.

Virtual Reality Modeling Language (VRML)   A way of describing three-dimensional space via tags in a text document. VRML includes means of describing shapes, relative positions, surface textures, and light sources.

virus   A program intended to damage a computer system. Sophisticated viruses encrypt and hide in a computer and may not appear until the user performs a certain action or until a certain date. *See also* antivirus.

virus engine   The core program that runs the virus-scanning process.

Visual Basic   A graphical programming language developed by Microsoft and used for developing programs in the Microsoft Windows environment. Programs developed in Visual Basic are easy to write, but they will only run on Windows.

volume   A logical way of organizing disk space into usable sections.

VPN   *See* virtual private network.

VRML   *See* Virtual Reality Modeling Language (VRML).

WAN   *See* wide area network.

warm site backup   An off-site backup system that has all the same systems as the primary system but not the most current data. The system is off-site to reduce the chances of both the primary and backup systems going down or being destroyed at the same time.

Web server   A server that holds and delivers Web pages and other Web content using the HTTP protocol. *See also* Hypertext Transfer Protocol.

Webring   A community of sites that relate to some common interest. As a courtesy to its users, each site in the Webring agrees to post banner ads for the other sites in the ring, increasing traffic to all the sites.

wide area network (WAN)   A network that crosses local, regional, and international boundaries.

Win16 Application (Win16 Subsystem)   A feature of Windows NT that can run almost any 16-bit Windows application, providing the application conforms to the Microsoft standards for writing Windows 3.*x* applications.

Win32 Applications (Win32 Subsystem)   A feature of Windows NT that can run 32-bit applications designed for Windows 95/98 and Windows NT.

Windows Internet Name Service (WINS)   A Windows NT service that dynamically associates the NetBIOS name of a host with its IP address. *See also* Network Basic Input Output System.

Windows NT   A network operating system developed by Microsoft that uses that same graphical interface as the desktop environment, Windows 95. Windows NT (New Technology) was designed to provide enhanced security and performance for networked computers.

Windows NT 3.51   The version of Windows NT based on the "look and feel" of Windows 3.*x*. *See also* Windows NT.

Windows NT 4   The version of Windows NT based on the "look and feel" of Windows 95/98. *See also* Windows NT.

Windows NT Service   A type of Windows program (a file with either an .EXE or a .DLL extension) that is loaded automatically by the server or manually by the administrator.

winipcfg   The IP configuration utility for Windows 95/98 that allows you to view the current TCP/IP configuration of a workstation.

WinNuke   A Windows-based attack that affects only computers running Windows NT 3.51 or 4. It is caused by the way that the Windows NT TCP/IP stack handles bad data in the TCP header. Instead of returning an error code or rejecting the bad data, it sends NT to the Blue Screen of Death (BSOD). Figuratively speaking, the attack nukes the computer.

WINS   *See* Windows Internet Name Service.

workgroup   A specific group of users or network devices organized by job function or proximity to share resources.

work-made-for-hire agreement   A method of securing copyright to a material. This agreement states that the creator of a work created it because he was hired by the publisher to do so and paid accordingly (or paid something, anyway).

World Wide Web (WWW)   A collection of HTTP servers running on the Internet. They support the use of documents formatted with HTML. *See also* Hypertext Markup Language; Hypertext Transfer Protocol.

worms   Similar to a virus. Worms, however, propagate themselves over a network. *See also* virus.

X Windows   A graphical user interface (GUI) developed for use with the various flavors of Unix.

X.25   X.25 was developed by the International Telecommunications Union (ITU) in 1974 as a standard interface for WAN packet switching. It does *not* specify anything about the actual data transmission; it is just an interface.

xDSL   A term used to collectively generalize the different categories of Digital Subscriber Lines (DSLs). *See also* Digital Subscribe Line (DSL).

XML   *See* eXtensible Markup Language.

Z.E.N.works   Workstation management software for NetWare. A light (scaled-down) version is included in NetWare 5.*x*.

ZIP files   Files compressed by the standard file compression utility for Windows machines, WinZip. This compression utility allows you to combine several files into one compressed unit and extract them individually. Zip files usually have a .ZIP filename extension.

Index

Note to Reader: In this index, **boldfaced** page numbers refer to primary discussions of the topic; *italics* page numbers refer to figures.

G

Q

U

Build Your Own Networking Reference Library

with Sybex Network Press™ books

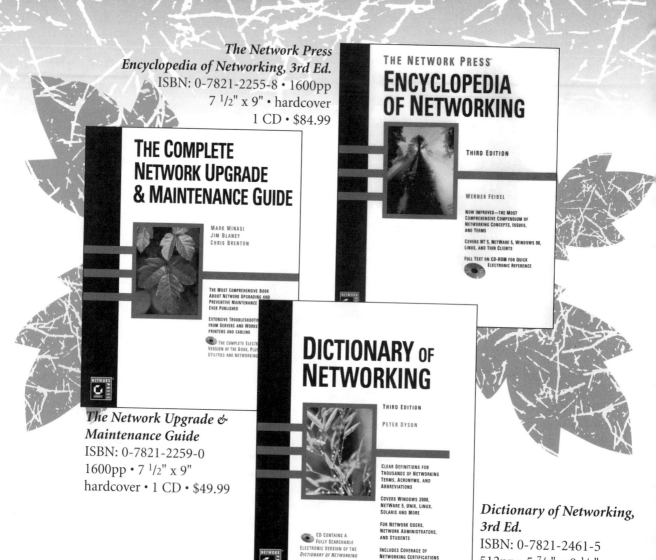

The Network Press Encyclopedia of Networking, 3rd Ed.
ISBN: 0-7821-2255-8 • 1600pp
7 1/2" x 9" • hardcover
1 CD • $84.99

THE NETWORK PRESS
ENCYCLOPEDIA OF NETWORKING

THIRD EDITION

WERNER FEIBEL

NOW IMPROVED—THE MOST COMPREHENSIVE COMPENDIUM OF NETWORKING CONCEPTS, ISSUES, AND TERMS

COVERS NT 5, NETWARE 5, WINDOWS 98, LINUX, AND THIN CLIENTS

FULL TEXT ON CD-ROM FOR QUICK ELECTRONIC REFERENCE

THE COMPLETE NETWORK UPGRADE & MAINTENANCE GUIDE

MARK MINASI
JIM BLANEY
CHRIS BRENTON

THE MOST COMPREHENSIVE BOOK ABOUT NETWORK UPGRADING AND PREVENTIVE MAINTENANCE EVER PUBLISHED

EXTENSIVE TROUBLESHOOTING FROM SERVERS AND WORKSTATIONS PRINTERS AND CABLING

THE COMPLETE ELECTRONIC VERSION OF THE BOOK, PLUS UTILITIES AND NETWORKING

The Network Upgrade & Maintenance Guide
ISBN: 0-7821-2259-0
1600pp • 7 1/2" x 9"
hardcover • 1 CD • $49.99

DICTIONARY OF NETWORKING

THIRD EDITION

PETER DYSON

CLEAR DEFINITIONS FOR THOUSANDS OF NETWORKING TERMS, ACRONYMS, AND ABBREVIATIONS

COVERS WINDOWS 2000, NETWARE 5, UNIX, LINUX, SOLARIS AND MORE

FOR NETWORK USERS, NETWORK ADMINISTRATORS, AND STUDENTS

INCLUDES COVERAGE OF NETWORKING CERTIFICATIONS

CD CONTAINS A FULLY SEARCHABLE ELECTRONIC VERSION OF THE DICTIONARY OF NETWORKING

Dictionary of Networking, 3rd Ed.
ISBN: 0-7821-2461-5
512pp • 5 7/8" x 8 1/4"
softcover • 1 CD • $29.99

Available in April 2000: *Cabling: The Complete Guide to Network Wiring*
ISBN: 0-7821-2645-6 • 960pp • 7 1/2" x 9"
hardcover • $49.99

www.sybex.com

Boost Your Career
with Certification

2nd Edition
Completely revised and updated for 1999–2000!

Detailed information on all the key computer and network certification programs, including:

- Computer hardware
- Operating systems
- Software
- Networking hardware
- Network operating systems
- Internet
- Instructor and trainer certifications

COMPUTER
AND NETWORK PROFESSIONAL'S
CERTIFICATION GUIDE

SECOND EDITION

J. SCOTT CHRISTIANSON
AND AVA FAJEN

FULLY UPDATED SECOND EDITION
INCLUDES COVERAGE OF NETWARE 5
CNA/CNE, NETWORK+, AND MORE

SELECT THE RIGHT CERTIFICATION
TO ADVANCE YOUR CAREER

COVERS THE FULL RANGE OF
COMPUTER AND NETWORKING
CERTIFICATIONS FROM MORE THAN
60 COMPANIES AND ORGANIZATIONS

UPDATED SECOND EDITION
COVERS MORE THAN 300 CERTIFICATIONS

ISBN: 0-7821-2545-X
640pp • 5 $^{7}/_{8}$ x 8 $^{1}/_{4}$ • Softcover
$19.99

Learn why to get certified,
when to get certified,
and how to get certified.

NETWORK ®
PRESS
SYBEX

www.sybex.com

SECURE YOUR NETWORK

Network Press® provides the information you need to

- Assess the security of your network
- Devise a workable security plan
- Implement effective security measures

Mastering Network Security
0-7821-2343-0 · US $59.99
704 pages · Hardcover

NT 4 Network Security
0-7821-2425-9 · US $49.99
960 pages · Hardcover

Firewalls 24seven
0-7821-2529-8 · US $34.99
496 pages · Softcover

www.sybex.com

www.24sevenbooks.com

MCSE CORE REQUIREMENT STUDY GUIDES FROM SYBEX

CDs Include:
- **Expanded test engine with adaptive testing**
- **Product simulator software**
- **Electronic flashcards for PCs and palm devices**
- **Computer based interactive instruction on key MCSE topics**

ISBN: 0-7821-2695-2
704pp • 7¹/₂" x 9" • Hardcover
$49.99

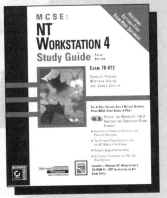

ISBN: 0-7821-2698-7
784pp • 7¹/₂" x 9" • Hardcover
$49.99

ISBN: 0-7821-2696-0
832pp • 7¹/₂" x 9" • Hardcover
$49.99

ISBN: 0-7821-2697-9
704pp • 7¹/₂" x 9" • Hardcover
$49.99

A $50.00 SAVINGS!

MCSE Core Requirements , 3rd ed.
Box Set
ISBN: 0-7821-2699-5
4 hardcover books;

Microsoft Certified
Professional
Approved Study Guide

www.sybex.com   **SYBEX**

LearnKey

STUDY GUIDES FOR THE MICROSOFT CERTIFIED SYSTEMS ENGINEER EXAMS

SYBEX BOOKS ON THE WEB

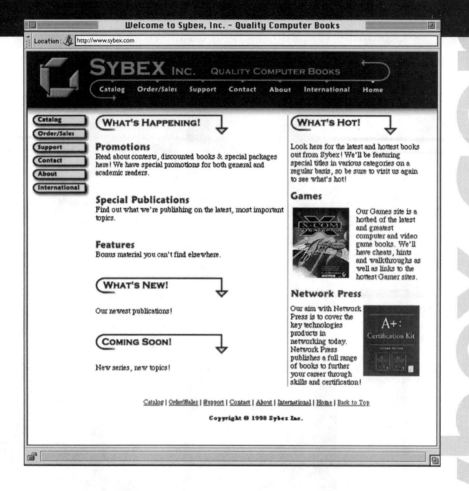

At the dynamic and informative Sybex Web site, you can:

- view our complete online catalog
- preview a book you're interested in
- access special book content

- order books online at special discount prices
- learn about Sybex

www.sybex.com

SYBEX Inc. • 1151 Marina Village Parkway, Alameda, CA 94501 • 510-523-8233

A+™ TEST PREPARATION FROM THE EXPERTS

Sybex presents the most comprehensive study guides
for CompTIA's A+ exams for PC technicians.

ISBN 0-7821-2344-9
800 pp. 7½" x 9" $49.99
Hardcover

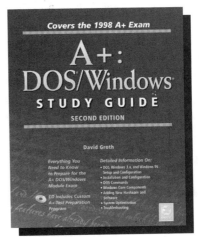

ISBN 0-7821-2351-1
688 pp. 7½" x 9" $49.99
Hardcover

ISBN 0-7821-2345-7
304 pp. 5⅞" x 8¼" $19.99
Softcover

ISBN 0-7821-2490-9
1104 pp. 7½" x 9" $49.99
Softcover

ISBN 0-7821-2346-5
304 pp. 5⅞" x 8¼" $19.99
Softcover

www.sybex.com

NETWORK+™ CERTIFICATION FROM NETWORK PRESS™

The Network+ certification from the Computing Technology Industry Association (CompTIA) is a vendor- and product-neutral exam intended to test and confirm the knowledge of networking technicians with 18–24 months experience.

Each Network+ book:

- *Provides full coverage of every CompTIA exam objective*
- *Written by experts who participated in the development of the Network+ certification program*

Study!

ISBN: 0-7821-2547-6
7.5"x 9" • 656pp • $49.99 U.S.

- Learn about networking technologies and network design concepts
- Includes hundreds of review questions
- CD includes exclusive Network Press Edge Test exam-preparation program

Practice!

ISBN: 0-7821-2548-4
7.5"x 9" • 480pp • $24.99 U.S.

- Reinforce your Network+ knowledge with detailed review questions
- Study summaries of all the information you need to know for the exam
- Gauge your test-readiness with tough practice questions

Review!

ISBN: 0-7821-2546-8
5.875"x 8.25" • 432pp • $19.99 U.S.

- Quickly learn essential information for each exam objective
- Contains detailed analysis of the key issues
- Preview the types of questions found on the exam

SYBEX®   www.sybex.com

 CompTIA.
One Industry. One Voice.

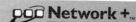 Network +™
A CompTIA Certification Program

i-Net+ Exam Objectives